SAS® for Mixed Models

Introduction and Basic Applications

Walter W. Stroup
George A. Milliken
Elizabeth A. Claassen
Russell D. Wolfinger

sas.com/books

The correct bibliographic citation for this manual is as follows: Stroup, Walter W., George A. Milliken, Elizabeth A. Claassen, and Russell D. Wolfinger . 2018. *SAS® for Mixed Models: Introduction and Basic Applications*. Cary, NC: SAS Institute Inc.

SAS® for Mixed Models: Introduction and Basic Applications

Copyright © 2018, SAS Institute Inc., Cary, NC, USA

978-1-64295-183-7 (Hardcover)
978-1-63526-135-6 (Hardcopy)
978-1-63526-154-7 (Web PDF)
978-1-63526-152-3 (epub)
978-1-63526-153-0 (mobi)

Contents

About This Book vii

Dedication and Acknowledgments xi

Chapter 1: Mixed Model Basics 1

1.1 Introduction 1

1.2 Statistical Models 2

1.3 Forms of Linear Predictors 6

1.4 Fixed and Random Effects 8

1.5 Mixed Models 9

1.6 Typical Studies and Modeling Issues That Arise 10

1.7 A Typology for Mixed Models 15

1.8 Flowcharts to Select SAS Software to Run Various Mixed Models 16

Chapter 2: Design Structure I: Single Random Effect 19

2.1 Introduction 19

2.2 Mixed Model for a Randomized Block Design 20

2.3 The MIXED and GLIMMIX Procedures to Analyze RCBD Data 23

2.4 Unbalanced Two-Way Mixed Model: Examples with Incomplete Block Design 32

2.5 Analysis with a Negative Block Variance Estimate: An Example 41

2.6 Introduction to Mixed Model Theory 44

2.7 Summary 47

Chapter 3: Mean Comparisons for Fixed Effects 49

3.1 Introduction 49

3.2 Comparison of Two Treatments 50

3.3 Comparison of Several Means: Analysis of Variance 52

3.4 Comparison of Quantitative Factors: Polynomial Regression 58

3.5 Mean Comparisons in Factorial Designs 67

3.6 Summary 99

Chapter 4: Power, Precision, and Sample Size I: Basic Concepts 101

4.1 Introduction 101

4.2 Understanding Essential Background for Mixed Model Power and Precision 102

4.3 Computing Precision and Power for CRD: An Example 104

4.4 Comparing Competing Designs I—CRD versus RCBD: An Example 108

4.5 Comparing Competing Designs II—Complete versus Incomplete Block Designs: An Example 112

4.6 Using Simulation for Precision and Power 117

4.7 Summary 129

Chapter 5: Design Structure II: Models with Multiple Random Effects 131

5.1 Introduction 131

5.2 Treatment and Experiment Structure and Associated Models 132

5.3 Inference with Factorial Treatment Designs with Various Mixed Models 146

5.4 A Split-Plot Semiconductor Experiment: An Example 150

5.5 A Brief Comment about PROC GLM 161

5.6 Type × Dose Response: An Example 162

5.7 Variance Component Estimates Equal to Zero: An Example 171

5.8 A Note on PROC GLM Compared to PROC GLIMMIX and PROC MIXED: Incomplete Blocks, Missing Data, and Spurious Non-Estimability 177

5.9 Summary 179

Chapter 6: Random Effects Models.. 181

6.1 Introduction: Descriptions of Random Effects Models 181

6.2 One-Way Random Effects Treatment Structure: Influent Example 188

6.3 A Simple Conditional Hierarchical Linear Model: An Example 196

6.4 Three-Level Nested Design Structure: An Example 202

6.5 A Two-Way Random Effects Treatment Structure to Estimate Heritability: An Example 210

6.6 Modern ANOVA with Variance Components 214

6.7 Summary 216

Chapter 7: Analysis of Covariance 217

7.1 Introduction 217

7.2 One-Way Fixed Effects Treatment Structure with Simple Linear Regression Models 218

7.3 One-Way Treatment Structure in an RCB Design Structure—Equal Slopes Model: An Example 223

7.4 One-Way Treatment Structure in an Incomplete Block Design Structure: An Example............ 237

7.5 One-Way Treatment Structure in a BIB Design Structure: An Example 246

7.6 One-Way Treatment Structure in an Unbalanced Incomplete Block Design Structure: An Example............ 254

7.7 Multilevel or Split-Plot Design with the Covariate Measured on the Large-Size Experimental Unit or Whole Plot: An Example 256

7.8 Summary 267

Chapter 8: Analysis of Repeated Measures Data... 269

8.1 Introduction 269

8.2 Mixed Model Analysis of Data from Basic Repeated Measures Design: An Example............ 272

8.3 Covariance Structures 283

8.4 PROC GLIMMIX Analysis of FEV1 Data 293

8.5 Unequally Spaced Repeated Measures: An Example 301

8.6 Summary 305

Chapter 9: Best Linear Unbiased Prediction (BLUP) and Inference on Random Effects 307

9.1 Introduction 307

9.2 Examples Motivating BLUP 308

9.3 Obtainment of BLUPs in the Breeding Random Effects Model... 311

9.4 Machine-Operator Two-Factor Mixed Model 316

9.6 Matrix Notation for BLUP 334

9.7 Summary 337

Chapter 10: Random Coefficient Models.. 339

10.1 Introduction 339

10.2 One-Way Random Effects Treatment Structure in a Completely Randomized Design Structure: An Example 342

10.3 Random Student Effects: An Example 348

10.4 Repeated Measures Growth Study: An Example 353

10.5 Prediction of the Shelf Life of a Product 364

10.6 Summary 376

Chapter 11: Generalized Linear Mixed Models for Binomial Data 377

11.1 Introduction 377

11.2 Three Examples of Generalized Linear Mixed Models for Binomial Data............................ 378

11.3 Example 1: Binomial O-Ring Data... 380

11.4 Generalized Linear Model Background 383

11.5 Example 2: Binomial Data in a Multicenter Clinical Trial.. 394

11.6 Example 3: Binary Data from a Dairy Cattle Breeding Trial 412

11.7 Summary 417

Chapter 12: Generalized Linear Mixed Models for Count Data 419

12.1 Introduction 419

12.2 Three Examples Illustrating Generalized Linear Mixed Models with Count Data 420

12.3 Overview of Modeling Considerations for Count Data..421

12.4 Example 1: Completely Random Design with Count Data 424

12.5 Example 2: Count Data from an Incomplete Block Design...429

12.6 Example 3: Linear Regression with a Discrete Count Dependent Variable.......................445

12.7 Blocked Design Revisited: What to Do When Block Variance Estimate is Negative 453

12.8 Summary..456

Chapter 13: Generalized Linear Mixed Models for Multilevel and Repeated Measures Experiments 457

13.1 Introduction 457

13.2 Two Examples Illustrating Generalized Linear Mixed Models with Complex Data 457

13.3 Example 1: Split-Plot Experiment with Count Data..458

13.4 Example 2: Repeated Measures Experiment with Binomial Data......................................473

Chapter 14: Power, Precision, and Sample Size II: General Approaches 487

14.1 Introduction 487

14.2 Split Plot Example Suggesting the Need for a Follow-Up Study 487

14.3 Precision and Power Analysis for Planning a Split-Plot Experiment..................................489

14.4 Use of Mixed Model Methods to Compare Two Proposed Designs 492

14.5 Precision and Power Analysis: A Repeated Measures Example...495

14.6 Precision and Power Analysis for Non-Gaussian Data: A Binomial Example....................501

14.7 Precision and Power: Example with Incomplete Blocks and Count Data 505

14.8 Summary..508

Chapter 15: Mixed Model Troubleshooting and Diagnostics.........................509

15.1 Introduction 509

15.2 Troubleshooting...510

15.3 Residuals 514

15.4 Influence Diagnostics 520

15.5 Two Diagnostic Plots Useful for Non-Gaussian Data 538

15.5 Summary..541

Appendix A: Linear Mixed Model Theory 543

A.1 Introduction 543

A.2 Matrix Notation..543

A.3 Formulation of the Mixed Model...544

A.4 Estimating Parameters, Predicting Random Effects 549

A.5 Statistical Properties...557

A.6 Model Selection 558

A.7 Inference and Test Statistics...559

Appendix B: Generalized Linear Mixed Model Theory 563

B.1 Introduction 563

B.2 Formulation of the Generalized Linear Model..563

B.3 Formulation of the Generalized Linear Mixed Model...566

B.4 Conditional versus Marginal Models and Inference Space 569

B.5 Integral Approximation 572

References 577

Index 585

About This Book

What Does This Book Cover?

During the past 25 years, mixed models have become an integral part of statistical methodology. Nearly all areas of application that use statistics use mixed models in some form. Mixed models are taught in graduate-level statistics courses, as well as disciplines outside traditional statistics. Mixed models are familiar to most statisticians. Nonetheless, many persons who are engaged in analyzing mixed model data have questions about the appropriate implementation of the methodology. In addition, given the rapid growth of degree programs in data science, as well as statistics, those who are new to the discipline and ready to extend their knowledge of statistical methods to mixed models need a place to start. Being an area of active research and methodological development, mixed models have ever-increasing new applications capabilities available. Those who studied the topic several years ago may not be aware of these developments and need a resource that makes these advances accessible. This edition is intended to address the needs of this diverse audience.

Like the first two editions of *SAS for Mixed Models*, this third publication presents mixed model methodology in a setting that is driven by applications. The scope is both broad and deep. Examples represent numerous areas of application and range from introductory examples to technically advanced case studies. The book is intended to be useful to as diverse an audience as possible, although persons with some knowledge of analysis of variance and regression analysis will benefit most.

The first chapter provides important definitions and categorizations and delineates mixed models from other classes of statistical models. Chapters 2 through 10 cover specific forms of mixed models and the situations in which they arise. Randomized block designs (Chapter 2) give rise to models with fixed treatment and random block effects—among the simplest mixed models. These enable us to introduce elementary mixed model concepts and operations, and to demonstrate the use of SAS mixed model procedures in this simple setting. An overview of mean comparison procedures for various treatment designs is presented in Chapter 3. The topic of "power and sample size" often means doing a power calculation for a designated design at the end of the planning process. However, power involves more than sample size—different designs with the same sample size can yield very different power characteristics. Mixed models provide a powerful methodology for comprehensive assessment of competing plausible designs. Mixed model power and precision analysis is introduced in Chapter 4. Studies with multiple levels, such as split-plot and hierarchical designs, are common in many areas of application. These give rise to models with multiple random effects. The analysis of the associated models is discussed in Chapter 5. Chapter 6 considers models in which all effects are random, and it covers variance component estimation and inference on random effects. Chapter 7 covers analysis of covariance in the mixed model setting. Repeated measures in time or space and longitudinal data give rise to mixed models in which the serial dependency among observations can be modeled directly; this is the topic of Chapter 8. Chapter 9 continues with inference on random effects, a topic begun in Chapter 6. Chapter 9 is devoted to statistical inference based on best linear unbiased prediction of random effects. This naturally leads us to random coefficient and multilevel linear models (Chapter 10).

The second edition of *SAS for Mixed Models* was published when the earliest version of the GLIMMIX procedure had just been released. Since then, new releases of PROC GLIMMIX have greatly expanded SAS capability to handle generalized linear mixed models (GLMMs), mixed models for non-Gaussian data. Although the first two editions of *SAS for Mixed Models* devoted a single chapter to GLMMs, this edition devotes three. The GLMM is introduced in Chapter 11 with binomial data. Chapter 12 introduces GLMMs for count data. Chapter 13 covers multilevel and repeated measures designs in a GLMM context.

In Chapter 14 we revisit power and precision. Chapter 4 concerns simple designs and Gaussian data only, whereas Chapter 14 considers more complex designs and non-Gaussian data. Chapter 14 showcases the full potential of GLMM-based precision and power analysis. Chapter 15 covers mixed model diagnostics based on residuals and influence analysis, as well as some trouble-shooting strategies.

Good statistical applications require a certain amount of theoretical knowledge. The more advanced the application, the more an understanding of mixed models' theoretical foundations will help. Although this book focuses on applications, theoretical developments are presented as well. Appendix A covers linear mixed model theory. Appendix B covers generalized linear mixed model theory. These appendices describe how mixed model methodology works, provide essential detail about the algorithms used by SAS mixed model software, and cover the assumptions underlying mixed model analysis. In addition to describing how mixed models work, these appendices should help readers understand why things are not working in cases (hopefully few) where problems arise.

Topics included in *SAS for Mixed Models, Second Edition*, but not appearing in this volume are as follows:

- Bayesian analysis
- spatial variability
- heterogeneous variance models
- the NLMIXED procedure
- additional case studies

The authors have reserved these topics for a planned subsequent publication.

What's New in This Edition?

SAS for Mixed Models, Second Edition, has been *the* go-to book for practitioners, students, researchers and instructors on mixed model methodology for more than a decade. PROC GLIMMIX is *the* most comprehensive and sophisticated mixed model software on the market. The current version of PROC GLIMMIX was released in 2008, two years after the publication of the second edition. This publication will be a worthy update incorporating developments over the past decade, building on the *SAS for Mixed Models* go-to status and fully taking advantage of PROC GLIMMIX capabilities.

Some topics have been rearranged to provide a more logical flow, and new examples are introduced to broaden the scope of application areas. Nearly all examples have been updated to use PROC GLIMMIX as the "one-stop shop" for linear modeling, whether fixed effect only, linear mixed models, or generalized linear mixed models. The chapters on GLMMs greatly expand on *SAS for Mixed Models, Second Edition,* as knowledge and software capability have both improved over the past decade. Expanded power and precision chapters enhance the researcher's ability to plan experiments for optimal outcomes. Statistical graphics now utilize the modern SGPLOT procedures.

Is This Book for You?

SAS for Mixed Models: Introduction and Basic Applications is useful to anyone wanting to use SAS for analysis of mixed model data. It is meant to be a comprehensive reference book for data analysts working with mixed models. It is a good supplementary text for a statistics course in mixed models, or a course in hierarchical modeling or applied Bayesian statistics. Mixed model applications have their roots in agricultural research, the behavioral sciences, and medical research—aspects of mixed model methodology arose somewhat independently in these three areas. But the same or similar methodology has proven to be useful in other subject areas, such as the pharmaceutical, natural resource, engineering, educational, and social science disciplines. We assert that almost all data sets have features of mixed models.

Not everyone will want to read the book from cover to cover. Readers who have little or no exposure to mixed models will be interested in the early chapters and can progress through later chapters as their needs require. Readers with good basic skills may want to jump into the chapters on topics of specific interest and refer to earlier material to clarify basic concepts.

To gain the most benefit from this book, ideally readers will have intermediate knowledge of SAS. More importantly, knowledge of some statistical ideas, such as multiple regression, analysis of variance, and experimental design, will ensure that the reader gains the most value from the book.

What Should You Know about the Examples?

This book includes examples for you to follow to gain hands-on experience with SAS.

Software Used to Develop the Book's Content

The software products used to develop the content for this book are as follows:

Base SAS 9.4
SAS/STAT 14.3
SAS/GRAPH 9.4

Example Code and Data

You can access the example code and data for this book by linking to its author pages at https://support.sas.com/authors.

Output and Figures

The tabular and graphical output in this book was generated with a SAS Output Delivery System style customized for optimal book print quality; therefore, your output will differ in appearance. Color versions of Figures 3.11 and 3.13 are included with the example code and data: https://support.sas.com/authors.

SAS University Edition

This book is compatible with SAS University Edition. If you are using SAS University Edition, then begin here: https://support.sas.com/ue-data .

SAS Press Wants to Hear from You

 Do you have questions about a SAS Press book that you are reading? Contact us at saspress@sas.com.

 SAS Press books are written *by* SAS Users *for* SAS Users. Please visit sas.com/books to sign up to request information on how to become a SAS Press author.

 We welcome your participation in the development of new books and your feedback on SAS Press books that you are using. Please visit sas.com/books to sign up to review a book

 Learn about new books and exclusive discounts. Sign up for our new books mailing list today at https://support.sas.com/en/books/subscribe-books.html.

 Learn more about these authors by visiting their author pages, where you can download free book excerpts, access example code and data, read the latest reviews, get updates, and more:

https://support.sas.com/en/books/authors/walter-stroup.html

https://support.sas.com/en/books/authors/george-milliken.html

https://support.sas.com/en/books/authors/elizabeth-claassen.html

https://support.sas.com/en/books/authors/russell-wolfinger.html

x

Dedication and Acknowledgments

This book is dedicated in memory of William L. Sanders (1942–2017).

Dr. Sanders was a professor of statistics at the University of Tennessee-Knoxville, where he created the Agricultural Experiment Station Statistical Consulting unit in 1972 and served as its director until 2000. He then became Director of the Educational Value-Added Assessment System (EVAAS) at SAS Institute. Bill served as Tennessee's representative to University Statisticians of Southern Experiment Stations (USSES), a multistate group formed in the 1960s.

USSES was instrumental in the original development of SAS software. In 1983, USSES initiated a project that practically revealed the power and usefulness of mixed model methodology and its widespread applicability. Bill was the project's public face and most effective advocate. The project completed its initial primary publication, "Applications of Mixed Models in Agriculture and Related Disciplines," *Southern Cooperative Series Bulletin No. 343* (1988, pp. 39–48) just as USSES had its annual meeting that year at SAS Institute headquarters in Cary, North Carolina.

The pivotal event at that meeting was a dinner at which Bill sequestered SAS CEO Dr. Jim Goodnight, keeping him there into the wee hours of morning. At breakfast the next morning, Bill looked tired but very pleased. He had persuaded Dr. Goodnight to push well beyond the GLM procedure and the VARCOMP procedure to invest seriously in developing full-fledged mixed model capabilities in SAS/STAT. A direct result was the MIXED procedure, which then branched into the suite of mixed model procedures:

- PROC NLMIXED
- PROC HPMIXED
- PROC HPLMIXED
- PROC GLIMMIX

In addition, mixed model capabilities in JMP software and the MCMC procedure were developed. His foresight and persistence came full circle when the EVAAS operation began using the computationally intensive mixed model algorithms incorporated directly into the HPMIXED procedure.

This book would have been impossible without Bill's contributions to the USSES mixed model project, and his tireless advocacy at SAS Institute. Indeed, Bill's efforts figure prominently in the development of the comprehensive mixed model capability we see in SAS today. Bill was also an important mentor to many of us involved in this project as it matured. We enjoyed countless pleasant hours in his company, and he even taught us a lesson or two on the golf course, a game at which he was quite skilled. Acknowledging our indebtedness to Bill, we dedicate this edition to him. Rest in peace, Dr. Sanders.

We extend a special thanks to the editorial staff at SAS Press. We thank Julie McAlpine Palmieri, editor-in-chief, whose persistent prodding got this project off the ground. Our editor, Jenny Jennings Foerst, had the patience of a saint, as life events kept pushing deadlines back. The attention to detail our copyeditor, John West, has shown improved the quality of this book immeasurably.

We also especially thank Oliver Schabenberger for his tireless and immense effort on the second edition of *SAS for Mixed Models*, as well as on PROC GLIMMIX, on which much of the content here is based. His vast energy and acumen have carried him into a role of exceptionally high responsibility at SAS, which has prevented him from joining as an official coauthor. Nonetheless, we know he is with us in spirit and retains a love for mixed models.

We acknowledge Ramon Littell. As a coauthor on the first two editions of the SAS for Mixed Models series, and the *SAS for Linear Models* editions that set the stage for the mixed model series, Dr. Littell has been a prominent figure in the development of linear and mixed model methodology and application since the inception of SAS.

We acknowledge Dallas E. Johnson for long-term help on complex designs and resulting mixed models analysis, as well as for helping work with PROC GLM (even before PROC MIXED) to provide appropriate analyses of difficult and messy split-plot and blocked designs. These analyses have provided key groundwork for our interpretation of the results from PROC MIXED and PROC GLIMMIX.

We acknowledge Robert A. McLean, who, as a colleague of Bill Sanders at the University of Tennessee and a key contributor to the USSES regional mixed model project, played a crucial role in the events that ultimately led to the development of PROC MIXED.

Thanks to those reviewers whose feedback on draft chapters helped refine and clarify the text.
A special shout-out goes to our colleagues from SAS—Phil Gibbs, Kathleen Kiernan, and Jill Tao—for promoting, supporting, and clarifying these methods on the front line for so many years. You guys are the best. In SAS Research and Development, John Sall, Dave DeLong, Bob Rodriguez, Randy Tobias, Maura Stokes, Chris Gotwalt, Min Zhu, John Castelloe, and Tianlin Wang have all provided wise, instrumental guidance and code on which we were able to constantly draw.

Special thanks goes also to reviewers outside SAS: Billy Bridges Jr., Alumni Distinguished Professor of Mathematical Sciences, Clemson University, and Julia L. Sharp, Associate Professor and Director of the Franklin A Graybill Statistical Laboratory, Department of Statistics, Colorado State University. These two reviewers generously contributed much painstaking commentary that helped us improve the manuscript significantly.

We could not have written this book without the support, input, and energy of many individuals, groups, and organizations. Foremost, we need to thank our families for their patience, understanding, and support. Thanks to our respective employers—the University of Nebraska, Kansas State University, and SAS—for giving us freedom to undertake this project. Thanks to mixed model researchers and statistical colleagues everywhere for shaping our thinking through their work. Much appreciation to the countless scientists, analysts, engineers, and researchers who shared their data sets and stories and allowed us to pass them along to our readers.
The widespread use and popularity of the two books that this one updates have been overwhelming and humbling. Our hearts are full of gratitude to all who have effectively leveraged and utilized these methods in ways we never dreamed possible and then provided feedback. We celebrate your successes and wish you many more as we all continue to experiment and learn. Your strong interest and demand prompted this new, expanded edition.

Finally, Elizabeth thanks the veteran members of the author team for welcoming her enthusiastically and guiding her through her first foray into book authorship. In turn, we thank her for countless hours of work pulling together many loose ends into a coherent sequence and keeping the whole author team organized and on track.

Chapter 1: Mixed Model Basics

1.1 Introduction 1
1.2 Statistical Models..2
    1.2.1 Simple Example with Two Treatments 2
    1.2.2 Model Characteristics..2
    1.2.3 Models with Subsampling..3
    1.2.4 Experimental Units 4
    1.2.5 Simple Hierarchical Design...5
1.3 Forms of Linear Predictors...6
1.4 Fixed and Random Effects...8
1.5 Mixed Models...9
1.6 Typical Studies and Modeling Issues That Arise...10
    1.6.1 Random Effects Model..10
    1.6.2 Multi-location Example 11
    1.6.3 Repeated Measures and Split-Plot Experiments 12
    1.6.4 Fixed Treatment, Random Block, Non-normal (Binomial) Data Example 13
    1.6.5 Repeated Measures with Non-normal (Count) Data...13
    1.6.6 Repeated Measures and Split Plots with Nonlinear Effects 13
1.7 A Typology for Mixed Models...15
1.8 Flowcharts to Select SAS Software to Run Various Mixed Models..16

1.1 Introduction

There is someone or something collecting data on everything that moves, grows, thinks or changes as time marches on. It is very important to have the appropriate tools to analyze the resulting data sets. But it is very important to identify the structure or structures embedded in a data set so analysts can select the appropriate tool or tools needed to extract useful information from the data set. This chapter provides guidelines to help identify data structures that require a *generalized linear mixed model* to extract necessary information. Types of data structures and types of models are discussed in the following sections.

Data sets presented in this book come from three different situations: (1) designed experiments, (2) sample surveys, and (3) observational studies. Virtually all data sets are produced by one of these three sources. The primary objectives of a study are influenced by the study's construction:

- In *designed experiments*, the primary objective might be to compare two or more drug formulations in their ability to control high blood pressure in humans. The process is to apply treatments or formulations to experimental units (persons) and then observe the response (blood pressure). In a human *clinical trial*, the experimental units are volunteer patients who meet the criteria for participating in the study. The various drug formulations are randomly assigned to patients, their responses are subsequently observed, and the formulations are compared.

- In *sample surveys*, data are collected according to a plan called a *survey design*, but treatments are not applied to units. Instead, the units, typically people, already possess certain attributes such as age or occupation. It is often of interest to measure the effect of the attributes on, or their association with, other attributes, as described by the primary objectives of the study.

- In *observational studies*, data are collected on units that are available, rather than on units chosen according to a plan. An example is a study at a veterinary clinic in which dogs entering the clinic are diagnosed according to their skin condition, and blood samples are drawn for measurement of trace elements depending on the primary objectives. Alternatively, observational studies may use data that have already been collected. For example, an ecological study may use data collected on animal populations over the past several decades in order to better understand the impact of factors such as decreasing wetland area or suburban development on animal species of interest. All studies evolve from the primary objectives the researchers want to study.

The objectives of a project, the types of resources that are available, and the constraints on what kind of data collection is possible all dictate your choice of whether to run a designed experiment, a sample survey, or an observational study. Even though the three have striking differences in the way they are carried out, they all have common features or structures leading to a common set of statistical analysis tools.

For example, the terms *factor*, *level*, and *effect* are used alike in designed experiments, sample surveys, and observational studies. In designed experiments, the treatment condition under study (e.g., from examples you decide to use) is the factor, and the specific treatments are the levels. In the observational study, the dogs' diagnosis is the factor and the specific skin conditions are the levels. In all three types of studies, each level has an effect; that is, applying a different treatment in a designed experiment has an effect on the mean blood pressure response. The different skin conditions show differences in their respective mean blood trace amounts. These concepts are defined more precisely in subsequent sections.

In this book, the term *study* refers to whatever type of project is relevant: designed experiment, sample survey, or observational study.

1.2 Statistical Models

Statistical models are mathematical descriptions of how the data conceivably can be produced. Models consist of at least two parts: (1) a formula relating the response to all explanatory variables (e.g., effects), and (2) a description of the probability distribution, or distributions, assumed to characterize random variation affecting the observed response. In addition to providing a description of how the data arose, statistical models serve as a template for how the data will be analyzed.

Although much of the focus of this book is on the "template for analysis" aspect of modeling, readers should note that when things go wrong, when implementation of a model goes off track, more often than not it is because not enough attention has been paid to "how did the data arise?"—or this aspect of modeling has been disregarded altogether. Ideally, you should be able to simulate your data using your model in conjunction with random number generators. If you can't simulate a data set like the one you have or will have is a possible red flag indicating that the modeling assumptions may have gone bad.

Writing the model as a narrative of how the data arose in terms of a formula and probability distribution requires you to translate the study design into a plausible statistical model. The clear majority of "modeling issues" are really faulty design-to-model translation issues, and they often have their roots in inadequate understanding of basic design principles. Accordingly, our discussion of statistical models begins with a review of design concepts and vocabulary and a strategy for identifying models that are reasonable given the study design that produced the data we want to analyze.

1.2.1 Simple Example with Two Treatments

To illustrate, consider the paired comparison, a design introduced in all first courses in statistics. In a designed experiment, the paired comparison takes the form of a blocked design with two treatments. The "*pairs*" are referred to as "*blocks*." Each block has two observations, one per treatment. In survey designs, the "pairs" take the form of strata or clusters. Observations in each stratum or cluster are taken on two levels of an attribute that plays a role analogous to a treatment. In observational studies, paired comparisons often take the form of matched-pair or case-control studies. That is, observations are matched retrospectively according to criteria deemed relevant to the study so that a member of each pair represents the two "treatments." For example, a pair may be as alike as possible except that one is a smoker and the other is not.

1.2.2 Model Characteristics

From a modeling perspective, these different versions of the paired comparison share the same structure. Each has three sources of variation: the pair, the treatment, and anything unique to the unit within a pair not accounted for by pair or treatment. These sources of variation hold the key to translating a study design into a plausible model. First, however, a brief excursion into what not to do, and an approach many readers may find that they will need to unlearn.

Historically, these sources of variation give rise to the model equation, where "residual" is understood to mean "anything unique to the unit within a pair not accounted for by the pair or by the treatment.":

$$\text{Observation} = \text{Overall Mean} + \text{Treatment Effect} + \text{Pair Effect} + \text{Residual}$$

This equation is a simple form of a *linear statistical model* and is a special case of what has become known as the *"general" linear model*. This approach to writing the model, called the *model equation approach*, works well when the observations can be assumed to be normally distributed *and* the design structure is simple. The "observation=model effects + residual" equation-based approach to modeling does not adapt well to modeling data from study designs with even a moderate amount of complexity, nor does it adapt well to modeling data from *any* design when normality cannot be assumed. The "general" linear model is not at all "general" by modern standards. This approach is ill-suited for some of the study designs, models, and analyses that are considered in this book.

The *linear mixed model* extends the linear statistical model to allow appropriate analyses of data from study designs more typical of modern research, analytics and data-based decision making. To specify a plausible model, start with the sources of variation, but take a different approach:

1. In the first step, you identify the unit at which the observations are taken. In study design terminology, this is called the *unit of observation.*

2. Next, write a plausible probability distribution to assume for the observations. For example, if you can assume normality, denote the observation on treatment i and pair j as y_{ij} and write the distribution as $y_{ij} \sim N(\mu_{ij}, \sigma^2)$. On the other hand, if the observations are discrete counts, it may be more plausible to assume a Poisson or negative binomial distribution, such as $y_{ij} \sim \text{Poisson}(\lambda_{ij})$.

3. Once you identify the distribution of the observations, the next step is to write an equation describing how the sources of variation in the study design affect the mean of the distribution of the observations. If you can assume normality, $\mu_{ij} = \mu + \tau_i + p_j$, where μ denotes the overall mean, τ_i denotes the treatment effect and p_j denotes the pair effect, is commonly used to describe how treatments and pairs affect the means. The right-hand side of this equation is called the *linear predictor*. This strategy for writing the statistical model is called the *probability distribution approach*. Notice that the required elements of the model are (1) the probability distribution at the unit of observation level and (2) the linear predictor. Often, there are additional required elements, depending on the study design, the distribution of the observations, and the nature of the model effects.

Once you have identified the probability distribution and the sources of variation to include in the linear predictor, there are three issues that you need to resolve before a model is ready for implementation. These are:

- What form should the linear predictor use to address the primary objectives of the study? The simplest version of this issue involves deciding if the source of variation is best modeled as a discrete effect, as in the τ_i specification above, or as a continuous effect, as in regression models. See Section 1.3 for an introduction to *regression models*.

- Which model effects are fixed and which are random? In other words, which effects arise from sampling a population and therefore must be treated as random variables with probability distributions, and which effects do not. The existence of random model effects is what distinguishes the "general" linear model from mixed models. Study designs with even a modest amount of complexity – e.g. the paired comparison – have effects that should be considered random. See Section 1.4 for an introduction to the fixed vs. random effect issue.

- What should be on the left-hand side of the equal sign in the linear predictor? For normally distributed observations, μ_{ij} is the obvious choice. For non-normally distributed observations, there are usually better choices. The non-normally distributed observations are discussed in Sections 1.3 and 1.6 and Chapters 11 through 13 on generalized linear models and generalized linear mixed models for a full presentation.

Before considering these issues, complete our study design and translation to model review to make sure you have the necessary tools for model construction and implementation. To complete this section, consider two common design formats. The first is a design with subsampling. The second is a hierarchical design, also called a *multi-level design* or a *split plot design*.

1.2.3 Models with Subsampling

First consider subsampling. The distinguishing feature of this type of design is that the unit of observation is a subset from the unit that receives the treatment. For example, suppose that a school evaluates a new curriculum by assigning one group of teachers to use the current curriculum and another group of teachers to use the new curriculum. The treatment is assigned at the teacher, or classroom, level. Suppose that the observations are test scores. These will be obtained from individual students in the class. Thus, the student is the unit of observation. In the language of design, the classroom is the *experimental unit* and the student is the *sampling unit*.

Variations on the design with subsampling include the following:

- In a clinical trial, treatments may be assigned to clinics, and measurements taken on individual patients. In this case, clinic is the experimental unit; patient is the sampling unit.

- In a retrospective study, a community may have been exposed to a toxic environmental condition or not. Measurements may come from individuals in the community. If they do, community is the experimental unit and individuals are the sampling units.

1.2.4 Experimental Units

Formally, *experimental unit* is defined as the smallest entity to which treatment levels are *independently* assigned. Emphasis on the word *independently*. Each classroom in theory can be assigned to use a different curriculum. While it is true that students are assigned a curriculum, individual students in a classroom cannot receive different curricula. Assignment to classrooms is independent; assignment to students is not. You can also think of the experimental unit as the *unit of randomization* or the unit of treatment assignment (see Chapters 4 and 5 of Milliken and Johnson, 2009, for a more detailed discussion).

While the term *experimental unit* appears to be specific to designed experiments, it is not. Survey designs and observational studies all have analogues to the experimental unit, such as the communities in the toxic exposure study. *Correctly identifying the experimental unit is perhaps the single most important pre-condition to constructing a plausible model*. With this in mind, consider the second format, the hierarchical or split plot design.

Suppose that in addition to a new curriculum, schools are also trying a new professional development program. The district assigns one group of schools to participate in the professional development program and another group of schools to serve as a control. Within each school, certain classrooms are assigned to use the current curriculum and other classrooms are assigned to use the new curriculum. Students in each classroom are given pre- and post-tests and their scores are used to measure the impact of curriculum and the professional development program. Now there are two types, or levels, of experimental unit. The unit of assignment for the professional development program is the school. The unit of assignment for curriculum is the classroom within a school. In other words, there are two sizes of experimental units; (1) the school and (2) the classroom. The sampling unit is the student within a classroom.

How do you translate these study designs into plausible models? One strategy, suggested by Stroup (2013), is to build on a suggestion due to Fisher in comments following the Yates (1935) presentation entitled *Complex Experiments*. Stroup (2013) called this strategy *What Would Fisher Do?* (WWFD), but you can also think of it as *the ANOVA table repurposed*. The strategy consists of listing the components of the study design other than treatments, then separately listing the components of the study design that are the treatments (or analogues to treatments, as is the case in many surveys and observational studies), and finally combining the two. Fisher called the components of the design other than treatments the "topographical aspect" of the design– Federer (1955) and Milliken and Johnson (2009) refer to them as the "experiment design" or "design structure." Fisher called the treatment components the "treatment aspect." Federer and Milliken and Johnson refer to them as the "treatment design" or "treatment structure."

For the subsampling design, suppose that there are 10 schools that participate in the study and two classrooms per school, one assigned to the current curriculum, the other to the new. For simplicity, suppose there are 20 students per classroom. The ANOVA strategy leads to Table 1.1.

For the Experiment Design, there are 10 schools, so there are $10 - 1$ or 9 degrees of freedom for schools. There are 2 classrooms per school so there is $2 - 1 = 1$ *df* for classrooms within each school, thus there are $10 \times 1 = 10$ *df* for classrooms nested within schools. There are 20 students per classroom so there are $20 - 1 = 19$ *df* for variability of students within each school and a total of $19 \times 2 \times 10$ *df* for variability of students within classrooms *pooled* or *nested* across schools.

For the Treatment Design, there are 2 curriculums and thus 1 *df* for comparing curriculums. The parallels consist of all *df* that are not contributed to the treatments.

Next, combine the experiment and treatment designs where school and curriculum have the same *df*. The classroom(school) term *df* are reduced by 1 as the curriculum effect is a between-classroom within-school effect. This effect is denoted as Classroom(School)|Curriculum. The variability of student within classrooms pooled across classrooms within schools has 380 *df*, which is unchanged from the Experiment Design Column.

Table 1.1: Three Steps Demonstrating the Analyses of the Experiment Design, the Choice of the Treatment Design, and the Process of Combining the Two Designs into the Final ANOVA Table

Experiment Design		Treatment Design		Combined Experiment and Treatment Designs	
Source	***df***	**Source**	***df***	**Source**	***df***
School	9	—	—	School	9
—	—	Curriculum	1	Curriculum	1
Classroom(School)	10	—	—	Classroom(School | Curriculum	10 − 1 = 9
Student(Classroom)	380	"Parallels"	398	Student (Classroom)	380
Total	**399**		**399**		**399**

The experimental design components of the study design are *school*, *classroom*, and *student*. These are put in the left-hand side of Table 1.1 under Experiment Design. The treatment design component is curriculum. Fisher used the term "parallels" mainly as a placeholder for everything but treatment in the treatment design column. The right-hand side of Table 1.1 combines the Experiment Design columns with the Treatment Design column to provide the basis for the statistical model. Notice that the Experimental Design factor, schools, and the treatment design factor, curriculum, move intact from their columns to the combined column. Also notice the placement of curriculum in the table, in the line immediately above classroom(school). This is important, because it signifies that classroom is the experimental unit with respect to the treatment factor curriculum.

In the combined column of Table 1.1, the classroom source of variation appears as "Classroom(School) | curriculum." Read this as "classroom nested within school given (or 'after accounting for the effects of') curriculum." The degrees of freedom for this effect results from subtracting the curriculum degrees of freedom from the original classroom degrees of freedom in the experiment design column. The degrees of freedom columns within each of the three major columns are not strictly necessary, but they do help individuals new to data analysis, and the degrees of freedom in the combined column provide useful checks on the degree of freedom algorithms used by mixed models software, particularly SAS.

In traditional ANOVA, it is convention to relabel the last line as "residual." This is a good habit to break. Here it is misleading, because student is *not* the experimental unit with respect to treatment, and hence the last line of the ANOVA does not measure experimental error for estimating or testing curriculum effects. For non-normal data, the word "residual" has no meaning: relabeling the last line "residual" is not only misleading, it is nonsense.

Following the steps to construct the model for the school-curriculum example, first identify the unit of observation. In this case, it is Student(Classroom). Next, write the assumed distribution of the observations. If you can assume normality, this will be

$$y_{ijk} \sim N(\mu_{ij}, \sigma^2)$$

Models for which normality cannot be assumed will be previewed in Section 1.6 and dealt with in full in Chapters 11–13. The next step is to write the linear predictor. Assuming normality, an obvious candidate for the linear predictor is

$$\mu_{ij} = \mu + s_i + \tau_j + s\tau_{ij}$$

where s_i denotes school effects, τ_j denotes curriculum effects, and $s\tau_{ij}$ denotes classroom(school)|curriculum effects.

Note that in this design, knowing the school and curriculum treatment uniquely identifies the classroom. The final step is to decide which effects should be considered as random. Any effect in the linear predictor that is the experimental unit with respect to a treatment factor must be random, so you know $s\tau_{ij}$ must be a random effect.

For further discussion about the school and curriculum effects, see Section 1.4.

1.2.5 Simple Hierarchical Design

The final example of design-to-model translation is the hierarchical design described above. As with the sub-sampling example, suppose there are 10 schools, 2 classrooms per school and 20 students per classroom. In addition, five schools are assigned to participate in the professional development program and the other five serve as the control. The resulting ANOVA table is Table 1.2.

Table 1.2: Experiment Design, Treatment Design, and Combination of the Experiment and Treatment Designs for the Hierarchical Design for Professional Development (PD) and Curriculum (C) Study

Experiment Design		Treatment Design		Combined Experiment and Treatment Designs	
Source	*df*	**Source**	*df*	**Source**	*df*
—	—	Professional Development	1	Professional Development	1
Schools	9	—	—	School|PD	9 – 1 = 8
—	—	Curriculum	1	Curriculum	1
—	—	C × PD	1	C × PD	1
Classroom(School)	10	—	—	Classroom(school) | C, PD	10 – 2 = 8
Student (Classroom)	380	"Parallels"	396	Student(Classroom) | School. C, PD	380
Total	**399**	**Total**	**399**	**Total**	**399**

The experiment design components are school, classroom, and student. The treatment design components are the two levels of professional developments crossed with the two levels of curriculums, which form a 2×2 factorial treatment structure. Place professional development of the Treatment Design in the line above school, because school is the experimental unit with respect to professional development. Place curriculum of the Treatment Design in the line above classroom, because classroom is the experimental unit with respect to curriculum. The curriculum × professional development interaction effect also goes immediately above the line for classroom, because classroom is the experimental unit for the interaction.

At this point, follow the steps as before. The unit of observation is student(classroom). Denote the observation as y_{ijk} and write its assumed distribution. Then write the linear predictor using the other sources of variation. A plausible candidate is

$$\mu + \rho_i + s(\rho)_{ij} + \tau_k + \rho\tau_{ik} + s\rho\tau_{ijk}$$

where ρ_i denotes professional development effects, and

$$s(\rho)_{ij}$$

denotes school after accounting for professional development —also known as school nested within professional development effects— τ_k denotes curriculum effects, $\rho\tau_{ik}$ denotes professional development × curriculum interaction effect, and $s\rho\tau_{ijk}$ denotes classroom(school) after accounting for professional development and curriculum effects (because classroom is uniquely identified by school, professional development and curriculum).

The effects $s(\rho)_{ij}$ and $s\rho\tau_{ijk}$ must be random effects, because they are experimental units with respect to professional development and curriculum, respectively.

In principle, as Fisher implied in his comments that motivated Stroup to develop the *WWFD ANOVA*, if you follow this process, it should be clear how to proceed with modeling any study design of arbitrary complexity. Chapters 4 and 5 of Milliken and Johnson (2009) present an equally effective alternative using a graphical approach to demonstrate a process of constructing complex models.

1.3 Forms of Linear Predictors

As a broad overview, the linear predictor has two components and serves two purposes. The first component deals with the treatment design. The treatment component follows the nature of the treatment design and the study's objectives. Examples that follow in this section clarify how this is done. The second component of the linear predictor deals with the experiment design. In general, components of the experiment design should be considered random effects. A more detailed discussion of this issue appears in Section 1.4.

We begin our discussion of the treatment component of the linear predictor with a one-way treatment design. Consider an experiment with five drugs (say, A, B, C, D, and E) applied to subjects to control blood pressure where the primary objective is to determine if there is one drug that controls blood pressure better than the other drugs. Let μ_A denote the mean blood pressure for subjects treated with drug A, and define μ_B, μ_C, μ_D, and μ_E similarly for the other drugs. Suppose that the experiment design is completely randomized and that we can assume that variation in blood pressure is normally distributed with mean μ_i for the ith drug.

The simplest linear predictor to describe how treatments affect the mean is simply to use μ_A through μ_E. That is, for the jth observation on the ith drug,

$$y_{ij} \sim N\left(\mu_i, \sigma^2\right)$$

and the linear predictor is μ_i. This is called a *means model* because the only term in the linear predictor is the treatment mean.

The mean can be further modeled in various ways. You can define the effect of drug A as α_A such that $\mu_A = \mu + \alpha_A$, where μ is defined as the intercept. This form of the linear predictor is called an *effects model* (Milliken and Johnson 2009, Chapter 6). If the distribution of y_{ij} is Gaussian, as given above, this is equivalent to the one-way *analysis of variance* (ANOVA) model $y_{Aj} = \mu + \alpha_A + e_{Aj}$.

Note that the effects model has more parameters (in this case 6, μ and the 5 α_i) than factor levels (in this case 5). Such models are said to be *over-parameterized* because there are more parameters to estimate than there are unique items of information. Such models require either placing a constraint on the solution to estimate the parameters, or using a *generalized inverse* to solve the estimating equations. The SAS linear model procedures discussed in this book all use a generalized inverse that is equivalent to constraining the last factor level, in this case α_E, to zero. An alternative, called the *sum-to-zero* or set-to-zero constraints (Milliken and Johnson (2009) Chapter 6) involves defining μ as the overall mean implying $\alpha_A = \mu_A - \mu$ and thus

$$\sum_{i=A}^{E} \alpha_i = 0$$

Its advantage is that if the number of observations per treatment is equal, it is easy to interpret. However, for designs with unequal observations per treatment, the sum-to-zero constraint becomes unwieldy, if not completely intractable, whereas alternative constraints are more generally applicable. In general, for effects models, the estimate of the mean $\mu_A = \mu + \alpha_A$ is unique and interpretable, but the individual components μ and the α_i may not be.

Another approach to defining the linear predictor, which would be appropriate if levels A through E represented amounts, for example, doses of a drug given to patients, is to use linear regression. Specifically, let X_A be the drug dose corresponding to treatment A, X_B be the drug dose corresponding to treatment B, and so forth. Then the linear predictor $\mu_i = \beta_0 + \beta_1 X_i$ could be used to describe a linear increase (or decrease) in the mean blood pressure as a function of changing dose. Assuming normality, this form of the linear predictor is equivalent to the *linear regression* model $y_i = \beta_0 + \beta_1 X_i + e$.

One important extension beyond linear statistical models involves cases in which the response variable does not have a normal distribution. For example, suppose in the drug experiment that c_i clinics are assigned at random to each drug, n_{ij} subjects are observed at the jth clinic assigned to drug i, and each subject is classified according to whether a medical event such as a stroke or heart attack has occurred or not. The resulting response variable y_{ij} can be defined as the number of subjects having the event of interest at the ij^{th} clinic, and $y_{ij} \sim \text{Binomial}(n_{ij}, \pi_i)$ where π_i denotes the probability of a subject showing improvement when treated with drug i.

While it is technically possible to fit a linear model such as $p_{ij} = \mu_i + e_{ij}$, where $p_{ij} = y_{ij}/n_{ij}$ is the sample proportion and $\mu_i = \pi_i$, there are conceptual problems with doing so. First, there is no guarantee that the estimate of π_i will be between 0 and 1. Regression models are especially prone to producing nonsense estimators. Second, any model with a *residual term e_{ij}* implicitly requires you to estimate the variance, σ^2, as a separate act from estimating the mean. However, the variance of the binomial response variable in this example is $n_{ij}\pi_i(1-\pi_i)$. Once you estimate the mean, you know the variance—there is no separate variance to estimate.

The residual term e_{ij} is superfluous. A better model might be as follows: $\pi_i = 1/(1+e^{-\eta_i})$ and either $\eta_i = \eta + \alpha_i$ or $\eta_i = \beta_0 + \beta_1 X_i$, depending on whether the effects-model or regression framework discussed above is more appropriate.

Notice that for non-normal data, you replace μ by η in the linear predictor, because the linear predictor is not an estimate of the mean. In other contexts, modeling $\pi_i = \Phi(\eta_i)$, where $\Phi(\bullet)$ is the *standard normal distribution*, $\eta_i = \eta + \alpha_i$ or $\eta_i = \beta_0 + \beta_i X_i$, may be preferable, because, for example, interpretation is better connected to the subject matter under investigation. The former are simple versions of logistic ANOVA and logistic regression models, and the latter are simple versions of probit ANOVA and regression. Both are important examples of *generalized linear models.*

Generalized linear models use a general function of a linear model to describe the expected value of the observations. Specifically, η_i is called the *link function* and the function that related the expected value to the link function, e.g. $\pi_i = 1/(1 + e^{-\eta_i})$, is called the *inverse link*. The linear predictor you equate to the link function is suggested by the design and the nature of the explanatory variables, similar to the rationale for ANOVA or regression models. The form of the link and inverse link are suggested by the probability distribution of the response variable. Note that the link function can be the linear model itself and the distribution can be normal; thus, "standard" ANOVA and regression models are in fact special cases of generalized linear models. Chapters 11 and 12 discuss mixed model forms of *generalized linear models.*

In addition to generalized linear models, another important extension involves nonlinear statistical models. These occur when the relationship between the expected value of the random variable and the treatment, explanatory, or predictor variables is nonlinear. Generalized linear models are a special case, but they require a linear model embedded within a nonlinear function of the mean. *Nonlinear models* may use any function, and may occur when the response variable has a normal distribution. For example, increasing amounts of fertilizer nitrogen (N) are applied to a crop. The observed yield can be modeled using a normal distribution—that is, $y_{ij} \sim N(\mu_i, \sigma^2)$. The expected value of y_{ij} in turn is modeled by $\mu_i = \alpha_i \exp(-\exp(\beta_i - \gamma_i X_i))$, where X_i is the ith level or amount of fertilizer N, α_i is the asymptote for the ith level of N, γ_i is the slope, and β_i/γ_i is the inflection point. This is a Gompertz function that models a nonlinear increase in yield as a function of N: the response is small to low N, then increases rapidly at higher N, then reaches a point of diminishing returns and finally an asymptote at even higher N. Mixed model forms of nonlinear models are not discussed in this book.

1.4 Fixed and Random Effects

The previous section considered models of the mean involving only an assumed distribution of the response variable and a function of the mean involving only factor effects that are treated as unknown constants. These are called *fixed effects models.* An effect is called *fixed* if the levels in the study represent all possible levels of the factor, or at least all levels about which inference is to be made. Notably, this includes regression models where the observed values of the explanatory variable cover the entire region of interest.

In the blood pressure drug experiment, the effects of the drugs are fixed if the five specific drugs are the only candidates for use and if conclusions about the experiment are restricted to those five drugs. You can examine the differences among the drugs to see which are essentially equivalent and which are better or worse than others. In terms of the model $y_{ij} = \mu + \alpha_i + e_{ij}$, the effects α_A through α_E represent the effects of a particular drug relative to the intercept μ.

The drugs means, $\mu_A = \mu + \alpha_A$, $\mu_B = \mu + \alpha_B, \dots, \mu_E = \mu + \alpha_E$, and differences among drug means, for example, $\alpha_A - \alpha_B$, represent fixed, unknown quantities. Data from the study provide estimates about the five drug means and differences among them. For example, the sample mean from drug A, $\bar{y}_{A.}$ is an estimate of the population mean μ_A.

> **Notation Note:** When data values are summed over a subscript, that subscript is replaced by a period. For example, $y_{A.}$ stands for $y_{A1} + y_{A2} + \dots + y_{An}$. A bar over the summed value denotes the sample average. For example, $\bar{y}_{A.} = n^{-1} y_{A.}$.

The difference between two sample means, such as $\bar{y}_{A.} - \bar{y}_{B.}$, is an estimate of the difference between two population means $\mu_A - \mu_B$. The variance of the estimate $\bar{y}_{A.}$ is $n^{-1}\sigma^2$ and the variance of the estimate $\bar{y}_{A.} - \bar{y}_{B.}$ is $2\sigma^2/n$. In reality, σ^2 is unknown and must be estimated. Denote the sample variance for drug A by s_A^2, the sample variance for drug B by s_B^2, and similarly for drugs C, D, and E. Each of these sample variances is an estimate of σ^2 with $n-1$ degrees of freedom. Therefore, the average of the sample variances, $s^2 = (s_A^2 + s_B^2 + \dots + s_E^2)/5$, (called the *pooled estimate of the variance*) is also an estimate of σ^2 with $5(n-1)$ degrees of freedom. You can use this estimate to calculate standard errors of the drug sample means, which can in turn be used to make inferences about the drug population means. For example, the standard error of the estimate $\bar{y}_{A.} - \bar{y}_{B.}$ is as follows:

$$\sqrt{2s^2/n}$$

The confidence interval is as follows, where t_α is the α-level, two-sided critical value of the t-distribution with $5(n-1)$ degrees of freedom:

$$(\overline{y}_{A\bullet} - \overline{y}_{B\bullet}) \pm t_\alpha \sqrt{2s^2/n}$$

Factor effects are *random* if they are used in the study to represent a sample (ideally, a *random sample*) of a larger set of potential levels. The factor effects corresponding to the larger set of levels constitute a population with a probability distribution. The last statement bears repeating because it goes to the heart of a great deal of confusion about the difference between fixed and random effects: *a factor is considered* random *if its levels plausibly represent a larger population with a probability distribution.* In the blood pressure drug experiment, the drugs would be considered random if there are actually a large number of such drugs and only five were sampled to represent the population for the study. Note that this is different from a regression or response surface design, where doses or amounts are selected deliberately to optimize the estimation of fixed regression parameters of the experimental region. Random effects represent true sampling and are assumed to have probability distributions.

Deciding whether a factor is random or fixed is not always easy and can be controversial. Blocking factors and locations illustrate this point. In agricultural experiments blocking often reflects variation in a field, such as on a slope with one block in a strip at the top of the slope, one block on a strip below it, and so forth, to the bottom of the slope. One might argue that there is nothing random about these blocks. However, an additional feature of random effects is *exchangeability*. Are the blocks used in this experiment the only blocks that could have been used, or could any representative set of blocks from the target population be substituted? Treatment levels are not exchangeable: you cannot estimate the effects of drugs *A* through *E* unless you observe drugs *A* through *E*. But you could observe them on any valid subset of the target population. Similar arguments can be made with respect to locations. Chapter 2 considers the issue of random versus fixed blocks in greater detail. Chapter 6 considers the multi-location problem.

When the effect is random, we typically assume that the distribution of the random effect has mean zero and variance σ_a^2, where the subscript a refers to the variance of the distribution of treatment effects. If the drugs are randomly selected from a population of similar drugs then the drug effects are random, where σ_a^2 denotes the variance among drug effects in the population of drugs. The linear statistical model can be written in model equation form as $y_{ij} = \mu + a_i + e_{ij}$, where μ represents the mean of all drugs in the population, not just those observed in the study. Alternatively, you could write the model in probability distribution form by giving the conditional distribution of the observations $y_{ij} \mid a_i \sim N(\mu + a_i, \sigma^2)$ and the distribution of the drug effects, $a_i \sim NI(0, \sigma_a^2)$. As noted earlier, the probability distribution form is preferred because it can be adapted for non-normal data, whereas the model equation form cannot. Note that the drug effect is denoted a_i rather than α_i as in the previous model. This book follows a frequently used convention, denoting fixed effects with Greek letters and random effects with Latin letters. Because the drugs in this study are a sample, the effects a_i are random variables with mean 0 and variance σ_a^2. The variance of y_{ij} is $\mathrm{Var}[y_{ij}] = \mathrm{Var}[\mu + a_i + e_{ij}] = \sigma_a^2 + \sigma^2$.

1.5 Mixed Models

Fixed and random effects were described in the preceding section. Models that contain both fixed and random effects are called *mixed models*. Consider the blood pressure drug experiment from the previous sections, but suppose that we are given new information about how the experiment was conducted. The *n* subjects assigned to each drug treatment were actually identified for the study in carefully matched groups of five. They were matched for criteria such that they would be expected to have similar blood pressure history and response. Within each group of five, drugs were assigned so that each of the drugs A, B, C, D, and E was randomly assigned to exactly one subject. Further assume that the *n* groups of five matched subjects each was drawn from a larger population of subjects who potentially could have been selected for the experiment. This process of grouping experimental units is a form of *blocking*. The resulting study is *a randomized complete block design* (RCBD) with fixed treatment effects and random block effects.

In model equation form, the model is $y_{ij} = \mu + \alpha_i + b_j + e_{ij}$, where $\mu, \alpha_A, ..., \alpha_E$ represent unknown fixed parameters—intercept and the five drug treatment effects, respectively—and the b_j and e_{ij} are mutually independent random variables representing blocks (matched groups of five) and error, respectively. In the preferred probability distribution form, the required elements of the model are $y_{ij} \mid b_j \sim N(\mu_{ij}, \sigma^2)$ and $\mu_{ij} = \mu + \alpha_i + b_j$. Assume that the random block effects b_j are independently and identically distributed with mean zero and variance σ_b^2. Additionally, for the model equation form, assume that the residual effects, e_{ij}, are independently and identically distributed with mean zero and variance σ^2. The variance of y_{ij}, the observation of the randomly chosen matched set j assigned to drug treatment i, is $\mathrm{Var}[y_{ij}] = \sigma_b^2 + \sigma^2$. The difference between two drug treatment means (say, drugs A and B) within the same matched group is $y_{Aj} - y_{Bj}$. It is noteworthy that the difference expressed in terms of the model equation is

$$y_{Aj} - y_{Bj} = \alpha_A - \alpha_B + e_{Aj} - e_{Bj}$$

which contains no block or matched group effect. The term b_j drops out of the equation. Thus, the variance of this difference is $2\sigma^2/n$. The difference between drug treatments can be estimated free from matched group effects. On the other hand, the mean of a single drug treatment, $\bar{y}_{A.}$ has variance $(\sigma_b^2 + \sigma^2)/n$, which *does* involve the variance among matched groups.

The randomized block design is just the beginning with mixed models. Numerous other experimental and survey designs and observational study protocols produce data for which mixed models are appropriate. Examples of mixed models include nested (or hierarchical) designs, clustered designs, split-plot experiments and repeated measures (also called longitudinal) studies. Each of these designs has its own model structure depending on how treatments or explanatory factors are associated with experimental or observational units and how the data are recorded. In nested and split-plot designs there are typically two or more sizes of experimental units. Variances and differences between means must be correctly assessed in order to make valid inferences.

Modeling variation is arguably the most powerful and important single feature of mixed models, and what sets it apart from conventional linear models. This extends beyond variance structure to include correlation among observations and, for non-normal data, the impact of distribution on how variance and covariance are characterized. In repeated measures designs, discussed in Chapter 8, measurements taken on the same unit close together in time are often more highly correlated than measurements taken further apart in time. The same principle occurs in two dimensions with spatial data. Care must be taken to build an appropriate covariance structure into the model. Otherwise, tests of hypotheses, confidence intervals, and possibly even the estimates of treatment means themselves may not be valid. The next section surveys typical mixed model issues that are addressed in this book.

1.6 Typical Studies and Modeling Issues That Arise

Mixed model issues are best illustrated by way of examples of studies in which they arise. This section previews six examples of studies that call for increasingly complex models.

1.6.1 Random Effects Model

In the first example, 20 packages of ground beef are sampled from a larger population. Three samples are taken at random from within each package. From each sample, two microbial counts are taken. Suppose you can reasonably assume that the log microbial counts follow a normal distribution. Then you can describe the data with the following linear statistical model:

$$y_{ijk} = \mu + p_i + s(p)_{ij} + e_{ijk}$$

Here, y_{ijk} denotes the kth log microbial count for the jth sample of the ith package. Because packages represent a larger population with a plausible probability distribution, you can reasonably assume that package effects, p_i, are random. Similarly, sample within package effects, $s(p)_{ij}$, and count, or error, effects, e_{ijk}, are assumed random. Thus, the p_i, $s(p)_{ij}$, and e_{ijk} effects are all random variables with means equal to zero and variances σ_p^2, σ_s^2, and σ^2, respectively. This is an example of a *random effects model*. Note that only the overall mean is a fixed effects parameter; all other model effects are random.

The modeling issues are as follows:

- How should you estimate the variance components σ_p^2, σ_s^2, and σ^2?

- How should you estimate the standard error of the estimated overall mean, $\hat{\mu}$?

- How should you "estimate"—or, putting it more correctly—*predict random model effects* p_i, or $s(p)_{ij}$ if these are needed?

Mixed model methods primarily use three approaches for variance component estimation: (1) procedures based on expected mean squares from the analysis of variance (ANOVA); (2) maximum likelihood (ML); and (3) residual maximum likelihood (REML), also known as restricted maximum likelihood. Of these, ML is usually discouraged, because the variance component estimates are biased downward, and hence so are the standard errors computed from them (Stroup, 2013, Chapter 4). This results in excessively narrow confidence intervals whose coverage rates are below the nominal $1 - \alpha$ level, and upwardly biased test statistics whose Type I error rates tend to be well above the nominal α level. The REML procedure is the most versatile, but there are situations for which ANOVA procedures are preferable. PROC MIXED and GLIMMIX in SAS use the REML approach by default for normally distributed data. PROC MIXED also provides optional use of ANOVA and other methods when needed. Chapter 2 presents examples in which you would want to use ANOVA rather than REML estimation.

The estimate of the overall mean in the random effects model for packages, samples, and counts is

$$\hat{\mu} = \bar{y}_{\cdots} = \sum y_{ijk} \big/ IJK$$

where I denotes the number of packages (20), J is the number of samples per package (3), and K is the number of counts per sample (2). Substituting the model equations yields

$$\sum \left(\mu + p_i + s(p)_{ij} + e_{ijk} \right) \big/ IJK$$

and taking the variance yields the following:

$$\text{Var}[\hat{\mu}] = \text{Var}\left[\sum \left(p_i + s(p)_{ij} + e_{ijk} \right) \right] \big/ (IJK)^2 = \left(JK\sigma_p^2 + K\sigma_s^2 + \sigma^2 \right) \big/ IJK$$

If you write out the ANOVA table for this model, you can show that you can estimate $\text{Var}[\hat{\mu}]$ by $MS(\text{package})/(IJK)$. Using this, you can compute the standard error of $\hat{\mu}$ by the following:

$$\sqrt{MS(\text{package})/(IJK)}$$

Hence, the confidence interval for μ becomes the following, where $1 - \alpha$ is the confidence level and

$$t_{\alpha/2, df(\text{package})}$$

is the two-sided critical value from the t distribution and $df(\text{package})$ are the degrees of freedom associated with the package source of variation in the ANOVA table.

$$\bar{y}_{\cdots} \pm t_{\alpha/2, df(\text{package})} \sqrt{MS(\text{package})/(IJK)}$$

The critical value can be computed using TINV(1 − (alpha/2),dendf,0) in SAS.

If you regard package effects as fixed, you would estimate its effect as $\hat{p}_i = \bar{y}_{i\cdots} - \bar{y}_{\cdots}$. However, because the package effects are random variables, the *best linear unbiased predictor* (BLUP) is more efficient:

$$E\left[p_i \mid y \right] = E\left[p_i \right] + \text{Cov}\left[p_i, \bar{y}_{i\cdots} \right] \left(\text{Var}\left[\bar{y}_{i\cdots} \right] \right)^{-1} \left(\bar{y}_{i\cdots} - \bar{y}_{\cdots} \right)$$

This leads to the BLUP:

$$\hat{p}_i = \left(\frac{\sigma_p^2}{\left(JK\sigma_p^2 + K\sigma_s^2 + \sigma^2 \right) / JK} \right) \left(\bar{y}_{i\cdots} - \bar{y}_{\cdots} \right)$$

When estimates of the variance components are used, the above is not a true BLUP, but an estimated BLUP, often called an *EBLUP*. Best linear unbiased predictors are used extensively in mixed models and are discussed in detail in Chapter 9.

1.6.2 Multi-location Example

The second example appeared in Output 3.7 of *SAS System for Linear Models, Fourth Edition* (Littell et al. 2002). The example is a designed experiment with three treatments observed at each of eight locations. At the various locations, each treatment is assigned to between three and 12 randomized complete blocks. A possible linear statistical model is as follows, where L_i is the ith location effect, $b(L)_{ij}$ is the ij^{th} block within location effect, is the kth treatment effect, and is the ik^{th} location by treatment interaction effect:

$$y_{ijk} = \mu + L_i + b(L)_{ij} + \tau_k + (\tau L)_{ik} + e_{ijk}$$

The modeling issues are as follows:

- Should location be a random or fixed effect?

- Depending on issue 1, the *F*-test for treatment depends on MS(error) if location effects are fixed or MS(location × treatment) if location effects are random.

- Also depending on issue 1, the standard error of treatment means and differences are affected.

The primary issue is one of *inference space*—that is, the population to which the inference applies. If location effects are fixed, then inference applies *only to those locations* actually involved in the study. If location effects are random, then inference applies to the *population represented by the observed locations*. Another way to look at this is to consider issues 2 and 3. The expected mean square for error is σ^2, whereas the expected mean square for location × treatment is $\sigma^2 + k\sigma_{TL}^2$, where σ_{TL}^2 is the variance of the location × treatment effects and k is a constant determined by a somewhat complicated function of the number of blocks at each location. The variance of a treatment mean is σ^2 / (number of observations per treatment) if location effects are fixed, but it is $[\sigma^2 + K(\sigma_{TL}^2 + \sigma_L^2)]$ / (obs/trt) if location effects are random. The inference space question, then, depends on what sources you believe contribute to uncertainty. If you believe all uncertainty comes from variation among blocks and experimental units within locations, you believe locations are fixed. If, on the other hand, you believe that variation among locations contributes additional uncertainty, then you believe locations are random. Issues of this sort first appear in Chapter 2, and reappear in various forms throughout the rest of the book.

1.6.3 Repeated Measures and Split-Plot Experiments

Because repeated measures and split-plot experiments share some characteristics or structures, they have some modeling issues in common. Suppose that three drug treatments are randomly assigned to subjects, to the ith treatment. Each subject is observed at 1, 2, ..., 7, and 8 hours post-treatment. A possible model for this study is as follows, where α represents treatment effects, τ represents time (or hour) effects, and $s(\alpha)$ represent the random subject within treatment effects:

$$y_{ijk} = \mu + \alpha_i + s(\alpha)_{ij} + \tau_k + (\alpha\tau)_{ik} + e_{ijk}$$

The main modeling issues here are as follows:

- The experimental unit for the treatment effect (subject) and for time and time × treatment effects (subject × time) are different sizes, and hence these effects require different error terms for statistical inference. *This is a feature common to split-plot and repeated measures experiments.*

- The errors, e_{ijk}, are correlated within each subject. How best to model correlation and estimate the relevant variance and covariance parameters? This is usually a question specific to repeated measures experiments.

- How are the degrees of freedom for confidence intervals and hypothesis tests affected?

- How are standard errors affected when estimated variance and covariance components are used?

Chapter 8 discusses the various forms of split-plot experiments and appropriate analysis. You can conduct the analysis using either PROC GLIMMIX or PROC MIXED. When both PROC GLIMMIX and PROC MIXED can be used, examples in this edition use PROC GLIMMIX because of its greater versatility.

Repeated measures with normally distributed data use strategies similar to split-plots for comparing means. Chapter 8 builds on Chapter 5 by adding material specific to repeated measures data. Chapter 8 discusses procedures for identifying and estimating appropriate covariance matrices. Degree of freedom issues are first discussed in Chapter 2 and appear throughout the book. Repeated measures, and correlated error models in general, present special problems to obtain unbiased standard errors and test statistics. These issues are discussed in detail in Chapter 8. Spatial models are also correlated error models and require similar procedures.

1.6.4 Fixed Treatment, Random Block, Non-normal (Binomial) Data Example

The fourth example is a clinical trial with two treatments conducted at eight locations. At each location, subjects are assigned at random to the two treatments; n_{ij} subjects are assigned to treatment i at location j. Subjects are observed to have either favorable or unfavorable reactions to the treatments. For the ij^{th} treatment-location combination, y_{ij} subjects have favorable reactions, or, in other words, $p_{ij} = y_{ij}/n_{ij}$ is the proportion of favorable reactions to treatment i at location j.

This study raises the following modeling issues:

- Clinic effects may be random or fixed, raising inference space questions similar to those just discussed.

- The response variable has a binomial, not normal, distribution.

- Because of issue 2, the response may not be linear in the parameters, and the errors may not be additive, casting doubt on the appropriateness of a linear statistical model.

Also as a consequence of issue 2, variance is a function of the mean, and is therefore not homogeneous by treatment. In addition, "residual" in the traditional linear statistical model has no meaning. How one characterizes variability at the unit of observation level must be rethought.

A possible model for this study is a generalized linear mixed model. Denote the probability of favorable reaction to treatment i at location j by π_{ij}. The generalized linear model is as follows:

$$\log\left(\frac{\pi_{ij}}{1-\pi_{ij}}\right) = \eta + \tau_i + c_j + ct_{ij}$$

Or alternatively it is as follows, where c_i are random clinic effects, τ_j are fixed treatment effects, and ct_{ij} are random clinic $\times$ treatment interaction effects:

$$\pi_{ij} = \frac{e^{\eta+\tau_i+c_j+ct_{ij}}}{1+e^{\eta+\tau_i+c_j+ct_{ij}}} = \frac{1}{1+e^{-\left(\eta+\tau_i+c_j+ct_{ij}\right)}}$$

Generalized linear mixed models are discussed in Chapters 11 through 13.

1.6.5 Repeated Measures with Non-normal (Count) Data

The fifth example appears in Output 10.39 of *SAS System for Linear Models, Fourth Edition* (Littell et al. 2002). Two treatments are assigned at random to subjects. Each subject is then observed at four times. In addition, there is a baseline measurement and the subject's age. At each time of measurement, the number of epileptic seizures is counted. The modeling issues here are as follows:

- Counts are not normally distributed.

- Repeated measures raise correlated observation issues similar to those discussed previously, but with additional complications. Specifically, because "residual" has no meaning for distributions appropriate for count data, you cannot use the residual covariance structure, as you would with normally distributed data, to account for correlated repeated measurements. You must use an alternative approach.

The model involves both factor effects (treatments) and covariates (regression) in the same model, essentially, called *analysis of covariance*.

Chapter 7 introduces analysis of covariance in mixed models. Count data in conjunction with repeated measures is an important topic in generalized linear mixed models, and is discussed in Chapter 13.

1.6.6 Repeated Measures and Split Plots with Nonlinear Effects

The final example involves five treatments observed in a randomized block experiment with 4 blocks. Each experimental unit is observed at several times over the growing season and percent emergence is recorded. Figure 1.1 shows a plot of the percent emergence by treatment over the growing season. Like the example in section 1.6.3, this is a repeated measures experiment, but the structure and model equation are similar to split-plot experiments, so similar principles apply to mixed model analysis of these data.

Figure 1.1: Treatment Means of Sawfly Data over Time

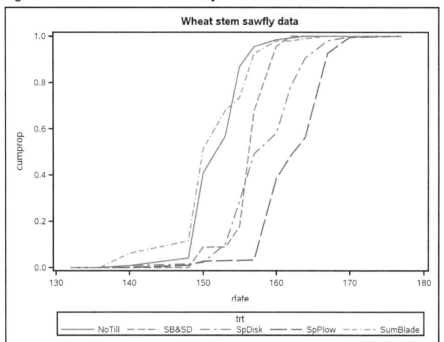

The modeling issues are as follows:

- The "usual" mixed model and repeated measures issues discussed in previous examples; plus
- The obvious nonlinear function required to describe percent emergence as a function of date.

A possible model for this experiment is as follows, where μ_{ij} is the ij^{th} treatment × date mean, w_{ik} is the random whole-plot error effect, and e_{ijk} are the repeated measures errors, possibly correlated:

$$y_{ijk} = \mu_{ij} + w_{ik} + e_{ijk}$$

The Gompertz model described earlier is a suitable candidate to model μ_{ij} as a function of date j for treatment i. The model described here is an example of a nonlinear mixed model.

Alternatively, you could model the response by using a generalized linear mixed model, assuming that

$$y_{ijk} \mid w_{ijk} \sim \text{Beta}(\mu_{ij}, \phi)$$

and

$$w_{ik} \sim N(0, \sigma_w^2)$$

and

$$\eta_{ijk} = \log(\mu_{ij}/(1-\mu_{ij})) = \eta + \tau_i + \delta_j + \tau\delta_{ij}$$

where ϕ denotes the Beta scale parameter, τ denotes treatment effects and δ denotes date effects. The advantage of this model is that beta distribution is well-suited to continuous proportion data. The disadvantage is that accounting for repeated measures correlation with generalized linear mixed models with a Beta distribution is difficult given the current state of the art.

1.7 A Typology for Mixed Models

From the examples in the previous section, you can see that contemporary mixed models cover a very wide range of possibilities. In fact, models that many tend to think of as distinct are, in reality, variations on a unified theme. Indeed, the model that only a generation ago was universally referred to as the "general linear model"—fixed effects only, normal and independent errors, homogeneous variance—is now understood to be one of the more restrictive special cases among commonly used statistical models. This section provides a framework to view the unifying themes, as well as the distinctive features, of the various modeling options under the general heading of "mixed models" that can be implemented with procedures in SAS.

As seen in the previous example, the two main features of a statistical model are (1) a *characterization of the mean*, or expected value of the observations, as a function of model parameters and constants that describe the study design, and (2) a *characterization of the probability distribution* of the observations. The simplest example is a one-factor means model where the expected value of the observations on treatment i is μ_i and the distribution is $N(\mu_i, \sigma^2)$, which leads to the linear statistical model $y_{ij} = \mu_i + e_{ij}$. The fifth example of Section 1.5 provides a more complex example: the mean model is as follows:

$$\pi_{ij} = \frac{1}{1 + e^{-(\eta + \tau_i + c_j + c\tau_{ij})}}$$

and the distribution has two parts—that of the random effects c_j and $(c\tau)_{ij}$, and that of the observations given the random effects, essentially $y_j \mid c_j, (c\tau)_{ij} \sim \text{Binomial}(n_{ij}, \pi_{ij})$. But each model follows from the same general framework.

Appendix A provides a more detailed presentation of mixed model theory. In what follows we present an admittedly simplistic overview that uses matrix notation, which is developed more fully at appropriate points throughout the book and in the appendix.

Models have two sets of random variables whose distributions we need to characterize: $\mathbf{Y}$, the vector of observations, and $\mathbf{u}$, the vector of random model effects. The models considered in this book assume that the random effects in the model follow a normal distribution, so that in general we assume $\mathbf{u} \sim \text{MVN}(\mathbf{0}, \mathbf{G})$—that is, $\mathbf{u}$ has a multivariate normal distribution with mean zero variance-covariance matrix $\mathbf{G}$. In a simple variance components model, such as the randomized block model given in Section 1.3, $\mathbf{G} = \sigma_b^2 \mathbf{I}$.

By "mean" of the observations we can refer to one of two concepts: either the *unconditional mean*, $E[\mathbf{Y}]$ or the *conditional mean* of the observations given the random model effects, $E[\mathbf{Y}|\mathbf{u}]$. In a fixed effects model, the distinction does not matter, but for mixed models it clearly does. Mixed models are mathematical descriptions of the *conditional mean* in terms of fixed effect parameters, random model effects, and various constants that describe the study design. The general notation is as follows:

- $\boldsymbol{\beta}$ is the vector of fixed effect parameters.
- $\mathbf{X}$ is the matrix of constants that describe the structure of the study with respect to the fixed effects. This includes the treatment design, regression explanatory or predictor variables, and the like.
- $\mathbf{Z}$ is the matrix of constants that describe the study's structure with regard to random effects. This includes the blocking design, explanatory variables in random coefficient designs (see Chapter 10), etc.

The mixed model introduced in Section 1.4, where observations are normally distributed, models the conditional mean as $E[\mathbf{Y}|\mathbf{u}] = \mathbf{X}\boldsymbol{\beta} + \mathbf{Z}\mathbf{u}$, and assumes that the conditional distribution of the observations given the random effects is $\mathbf{Y}|\mathbf{u} \sim \text{MVN}(\mathbf{X}\boldsymbol{\beta} + \mathbf{Z}\mathbf{u}, \mathbf{R})$, where $\mathbf{R}$ is the variance-covariance matrix of the errors. In simple linear models where errors are independent with homogeneous variances, $\mathbf{R} = \sigma^2 \mathbf{I}$. However, in heterogeneous error models (presented in Chapter 9) and correlated error models such as repeated measures or spatial models, the structure of $\mathbf{R}$ becomes very important. PROC GLIMMIX and PROC MIXED enable you to specify the structures of the $\mathbf{G}$ and $\mathbf{R}$ matrices.

The class of *generalized linear mixed models* (GLMM) has a linear model embedded within a nonlinear function—that is, $g(E[\mathbf{Y}|\mathbf{u}])$ is modeled by $\mathbf{X}\boldsymbol{\beta} + \mathbf{Z}\mathbf{u}$. The GLMM assumes normally distributed random model effects, but not necessarily normally distributed observations. For the general class accommodated by the GLMM variance of $\mathbf{Y}|\mathbf{u}$ may be characterized by a function of the mean, a scale parameter, or both. The generic expression for the variance is

$$\text{Var}\left(\mathbf{Y} \mid \mathbf{u}\right) = \mathbf{V}_\mu^{1/2} \mathbf{A} \mathbf{V}_\mu^{1/2}$$

where $\mathbf{V}_\mu = \mathrm{diag}[v(\mu)]$, $v(\mu)$ is the variance function, and $\mathbf{A}$ denotes the scale matrix. For example, for the Poisson distribution, denoting the mean as $E(\mathbf{Y}\mid\mathbf{u}) = \lambda$, the variance function is $v(\lambda_i) = \lambda_i$ and the scale matrix is $\mathbf{A} = \mathbf{I}$. Hence $\mathrm{Var}(\mathbf{Y}\mid\mathbf{u}) = \mathrm{diag}(\lambda_i)$. For the normal distribution, the scale matrix is $\mathbf{A}=\mathbf{R}$ and, because the variance does not depend on the mean, $\mathbf{V}_\mu = \mathbf{I}$. Hence $\mathrm{Var}(\mathbf{Y}\mid\mathbf{u}) = \mathbf{R}$. In certain GLMMs for repeated measures and spatially correlated data, $\mathbf{A}$ takes the form of a *working correlation* matrix. This is one, but not the only, GLMM approach for the analysis of such data.

In the most general mixed model included in SAS, the *nonlinear mixed model* (NLMM), the conditional mean is modeled as a function of $\mathbf{X}$, $\mathbf{Z}$, $\boldsymbol{\beta}$, and $\mathbf{u}$ with no restrictions; in essence, $h(\mathbf{X},\boldsymbol{\beta},\mathbf{Z},\mathbf{u})$ models E[Y|u]. Each successive model is more restrictive. In NLMMs and GLMMs, the observations are not necessarily assumed to be normally distributed. The GLMM assumes a linear predictor, although it may be embedded in a nonlinear function of the mean—in essence, $h(\mathbf{X},\boldsymbol{\beta},\mathbf{Z},\mathbf{u}) = h(\mathbf{X}\boldsymbol{\beta} + \mathbf{Z}\mathbf{u})$. The *linear mixed model* (LMM) does assume normally distributed observations and models the conditional mean directly—that is, you assume E[Y|u] = $\mathbf{X}\boldsymbol{\beta}$ + $\mathbf{Z}\mathbf{u}$. Each mixed model has a fixed effects model analog, which means that there are no random model effects and hence $\mathbf{Z}$ and $\mathbf{u}$ no longer appear in the model, and the model now applies to E[Y]. The term "mixed model" is often associated with the LMM—it is the "standard" mixed model that is implemented in PROC MIXED. However, the LMM is a special case of a GLMM. The next section presents a flowchart to associate the various models with appropriate SAS software.

This text focuses on mixed models with linear predictors, specifically LMMs and GLMMs. Table 1.3 shows the various models and their features in terms of the model equation used for the conditional mean and the assumed distribution of the observations. Although nonlinear models are not covered in this text, they are included in Table 1.3 for completeness in describing types of mixed models and their fixed-effect-only analogs.

Table 1.3. Summary of Models, Characteristics, and Related Book Chapters

Type of Model	Model of Mean	Distribution	Chapter
GLMM	$h(\mathbf{X}\boldsymbol{\beta} + \mathbf{Z}\mathbf{u})$	Y|u general, u normal	11–14
LMM*	$\mathbf{X}\boldsymbol{\beta} + \mathbf{Z}\mathbf{u}$	Y|u, u normal	2–10, 15
GLM	$h(\mathbf{X}\boldsymbol{\beta})$	Y general	11 and 12
LM*	$\mathbf{X}\boldsymbol{\beta}$	Y normal	2–4
NLMM	$h(\mathbf{X},\boldsymbol{\beta},\mathbf{Z},\mathbf{u})$	Y|u general, u normal	NA
NLM	$h(\mathbf{X},\boldsymbol{\beta})$	Y general	NA

Note: Models with linear predictor $\mathbf{X}\boldsymbol{\beta}$ and a nontrivial covariance structure that requires a RANDOM or REPEATED statement are considered mixed models.

1.8 Flowcharts to Select SAS Software to Run Various Mixed Models

SAS offers several procedures (PROCs) designed to implement the various mixed models introduced in the previous sections. PROC GLIMMIX is the flagship of the linear model procedures. It is capable of implementing a comprehensive array of GLMMs, and, because all other linear models are special cases of the GLMM, PROC GLIMMIX can compute analyses for LMM, GLM, and LM. PROC MIXED, introduced in 1992, was designed to implement LMMs. It remains a well-known and oft-used procedure, and has certain LMM-specific special-purpose features not available in PROC GLIMMIX. SAS has several fixed effects model procedures: PROC GLM implements LMs, PROC NLIN implements NLMs, and PROC GENMOD implements GLMs.

There are also several procedures, e.g., PROC LOGISTIC and PROC LIFEREG, that implement special types of GLMs; PROC REG, which implements special types of LMs; and so forth. These special-purpose procedures are not discussed in this book, but they are discussed in detail in other SAS publications as noted throughout this book. Note that PROC GLM was named before generalized linear models appeared, and it was named for "general linear models"; these are now understood not to be general at all, but the most restrictive special case among the models described in Section 1.7, and are now known simply as linear models (LM).

For NLMMs, SAS offers PROC NLMIXED and the %NLINMIX macro. The %NLINMIX macro continues to have uses that are distinct and supplementary to the NLMIXED procedure.

Figures 1.2 and 1.3 provide flowcharts to help you select the appropriate model and software for your mixed model project. The basic questions that you need to ask are as follows:

- Can you assume a normal distribution for your observations? If the model contains random effects, then this question refers to the conditional distribution of the data, given the random effects.
- Can you assume that the mean or a transformation of the mean is linearly related to the model effects? Note that "linear relation" does not mean the absence of curvature. A quadratic (in X) regression model $\beta_0 + \beta_1 X + \beta_2 X^2$ is a linear model in the β's because all the terms in the model are additive. The linear component is termed the linear predictor. Generalized linear (mixed) models imply such linearity on a certain scale, i.e. the link function $g(\bullet)$. On the other hand, the Gompertz regression equation (see Sections 1.3 and 1.6) is a nonlinear equation.
- Are all effects (except errors) fixed? Or, are there random model effects?
- Can you assume that the errors are independent? Or, as in repeated measures or spatial data, are errors possibly correlated?
- A corollary to the previous question is, are the variances among the errors homogeneous? If the answer is no, then the same modeling strategies for correlated errors are also needed for heterogeneous errors.

Once you answer these questions, you can follow the flowchart to see what kind of model you have and what SAS procedure is appropriate. Then you can refer to the relevant chapter in this book for more information about the model and procedures.

Figure 1.2: Flowchart Indicating Tools in SAS/STAT for Normal Distributed Response

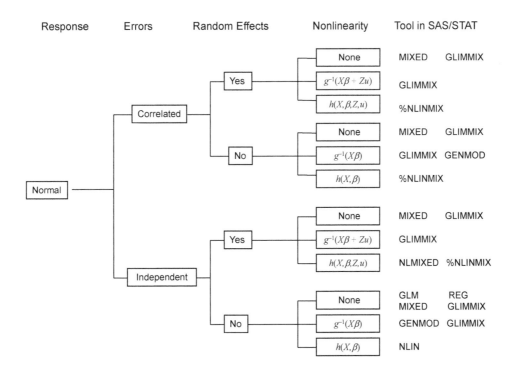

Figure 1.3: Flowchart Indicating Tools in SAS/STAT for Non-normal Distributed Response

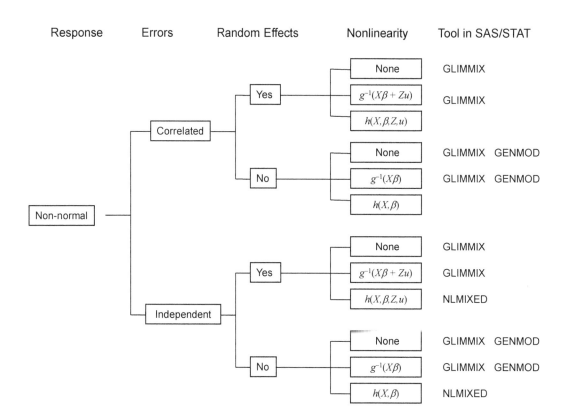

Chapter 2: Design Structure I: Single Random Effect

2.1 Introduction 19
2.2 Mixed Model for a Randomized Block Design 20
    2.2.1 Means and Variances from Randomized Block Design 21
    2.2.2 The Traditional Method: Analysis of Variance...21
    2.2.3 Expected Mean Squares 21
    2.2.4 Example: A Randomized Complete Block Design 22
2.3 The MIXED and GLIMMIX Procedures to Analyze RCBD Data 23
    2.3.1 PROC MIXED Analysis Based on Sums of Squares 23
    2.3.2 Basic PROC MIXED Analysis Based on Likelihood 26
    2.3.3 Basic PROC GLIMMIX Analysis..28
    2.3.4 Confidence Intervals for Variance Components 29
    2.3.5 Comments on Using PROC GLM for the Analysis of Mixed Models.....................................31
2.4 Unbalanced Two-Way Mixed Model: Examples with Incomplete Block Design........................32
    2.4.1 Intra-block Analysis of PBIB Data...33
    2.4.2 Combined Intra- and Inter-block PBIB Data Analysis with PROC GLIMMIX 37
2.5 Analysis with a Negative Block Variance Estimate: An Example...41
    2.5.1 Illustration of the Problem 41
    2.5.2 Use of NOBOUND to Avoid Loss of Type I Error Control..42
    2.5.3 Re-parameterization of the Model as Compound Symmetry 43
2.6 Introduction to Mixed Model Theory...44
    2.6.1 Review of Regression Model in Matrix Notation...44
    2.6.2 The RCBD Model in Matrix Notation..45
    2.6.3 Inference Basics for the Randomized Block Mixed Model 46
2.7 Summary..47

2.1 Introduction

The simplest design structures that raise mixed model issues are those with blocking. *Blocking* is a research technique used to diminish the effects of variation among experimental units. The units can be people, plants, animals, manufactured mechanical parts, or numerous other objects that are used in experimentation. *Blocks* are groups of units that are formed so that units within the blocks are as nearly homogeneous as possible. Examples of blocking criteria include batches of manufactured items, plots or benches containing plants, matched pairs of people, day on which an assay is performed, etc. In a designed experiment, the levels of the factor being investigated, called *treatments*, are *randomly assigned to units within the blocks*. However, as noted in Chapter 1, blocking can more generally be understood as a grouping method used in survey sampling (e.g. strata or clustering), observational studies (e.g. matched pairs), and the like.

An experiment conducted using blocking is called a *randomized block design*. While the methods discussed in this chapter are presented in the context of randomized block designs, you can easily adapt these methods to survey or observational study contexts. Usually, the primary objectives are to estimate and compare the means of treatments (i.e. treatments as broadly defined). In most cases, the *treatment effects* are considered *fixed* because the treatments in the study are the only ones to which inference is to be made. That is, no conclusions will be drawn about treatments that were not used in the experiment. *Block effects* are usually considered *random* because the blocks in the study constitute only a small subset of a larger set of blocks over which inferences about treatment means are to be made. In other words, the investigator wants to estimate and compare treatment means with statements of precision (confidence intervals) and levels of statistical significance (from tests of hypotheses) that are valid in reference to the entire population of blocks, not just those blocks of experimental units in the experiment. To do so requires proper specification of random effects in model equations. In turn, computations for statistical methods must properly accommodate the random effects. The model for data from a randomized block design usually contains fixed effects for treatment contributions or factors and random effects for blocking factors contributions, making it a *mixed* model.

The issue of whether blocks effects are considered fixed or random becomes especially important in blocked designs with missing data, or incomplete block designs. Analysis with random block effects enables recovery of inter-block information, and the resulting analysis is called combined inter- and intra-block analysis. For estimation and testing treatment differences, analysis with or without recovery of inter-block information is identical only in the case of a complete block design with no missing data. Otherwise, except where noted in this chapter, inter-block information adds efficiency and accuracy to the analysis.

Section 2.2 presents the randomized block model as it is usually found in basic statistical methods textbooks. The traditional analysis of variance (ANOVA) methods are given, followed by an example to illustrate the ANOVA methods. Section 2.3 illustrates mixed model analysis using the GLIMMIX and MIXED procedures to obtain the results for the example. Section 2.4 presents an analysis of data from an incomplete block design to illustrate similarities and differences between analyses with and without recovery of inter-block information with unbalanced data. Finally, Section 2.5 presents an example of an analysis with a negative block variance estimate. This presents a common dilemma for data analysts: does one allow the variance estimate to remain negative or does one set it to zero. This section presents the pros and cons of each alternative, as well as a general recommendation. Then, basic mixed model theory for the randomized block design is given in Section 2.6, including a presentation of the model in matrix notation.

2.2 Mixed Model for a Randomized Block Design

A design that groups experimental units into blocks is called a *randomized block design*. These have two forms: complete block and incomplete block. Complete block designs are generally referred to as *randomized complete block designs*, or by the acronym RCBD. In an RCBD, each treatment is applied to an experimental unit in each block. In incomplete block designs, only a subset of the treatments is assigned to experimental units in any given block. The balanced incomplete block and partially balanced incomplete block (acronym BIB and PBIB, respectively) are two common examples of this type of design. Blocked designs with missing data share modeling issues and approaches with incomplete block designs. In most—but not all—cases, each treatment is assigned to at most one experimental unit in a given block. See Section 2.4, Milliken and Johnson (2009) and Mead, et al. (2012) for complete discussions of block design strategy and structure.

Whether complete or incomplete, all randomized block designs share a common model. Assume that there are t treatments and r blocks, and that there is one observation per experimental unit. Once the treatments are selected to appear in a given block, each selected treatment is randomly assigned to one experimental unit in that block. In general, there will be N total experimental units. For complete block designs, because each of the t treatments is assigned to one experimental unit in each of the r blocks, there are $N = tr$ experimental units altogether. For incomplete block designs with the same number of experimental units in each block, there are $N = rk$ experimental units, where k denotes the number of experimental units per block.

The conventional assumptions for a randomized block model are as follows:

Letting y_{ij} denote the response from the experimental unit that received treatment i in block j, the equation for the model is as follows:

$$y_{ij} = \mu + \tau_i + b_j + e_{ij} \tag{2.1}$$

where the terms are defined as follows:

- $i = 1, 2, \dots, t$
- $j = 1, 2, \dots, r$
- μ and τ_i are fixed parameters such that the mean for the ith treatment is $\mu_i = \mu + \tau_i$
- b_j is the random effect associated with the jth block
- e_{ij} is the random error associated with the experimental unit in block j that received treatment i

Assumptions for random effects are as follows:

Block effects are distributed *normally and independently* with mean 0 and variance σ_b^2; that is, the b_j ($j = 1,2,\dots,r$) are distributed *iid* $N(0,\sigma_b^2)$.

Errors e_{ij} are distributed *normally and independently* with mean 0 and variance σ^2; that is, the e_{ij} ($i = 1,2,\dots,t; j = 1,2,\dots,r$) are distributed *iid* $N(0,\sigma^2)$. The e_{ij} are also distributed independently of the b_j.

2.2.1 Means and Variances from Randomized Block Design

The usual objectives of a randomized block design are to estimate and compare treatment means using statistical inference. Mathematical expressions are needed for the variances of means and differences between means in order to construct confidence intervals and conduct tests of hypotheses. The following results apply to complete block designs. Once these results are in place, you can adapt them for incomplete blocks, as shown below.

For the RCBD, it follows from Equation 2.1 that a treatment mean, such as $\bar{y}_{1.}$, can be written as follows:

$$\bar{y}_{1.} = \mu_1 + \bar{b}. + \bar{e}_{1.}$$

Likewise, the difference between two means, such as $\bar{y}_{1.} - \bar{y}_{2.}$, can be written as follows:

$$\bar{y}_{1.} - \bar{y}_{2.} = \mu_1 - \mu_2 + \bar{e}_{1.} - \bar{e}_{2.}$$

From these expressions, the variances of $\bar{y}_{1.}$ and $\bar{y}_{1.} - \bar{y}_{2.}$ are

$$\text{Var}\left[\bar{y}_{1.}\right] = \left(\sigma^2 + \sigma_b^2\right)/r$$

and

$$\text{Var}\left[\bar{y}_{1.} - \bar{y}_{2.}\right] = 2\sigma^2/r$$

Notice that the variance of a treatment mean $\text{Var}\left[\bar{y}_{1.}\right]$ contains the block variance component σ_b^2, but the variance of the difference between two means $\text{Var}\left[\bar{y}_{1.} - \bar{y}_{2.}\right]$ does *not* involve σ_b^2. This is the manifestation of the RCBD controlling block variation; the variances of differences between treatments are estimated free of block variation.

2.2.2 The Traditional Method: Analysis of Variance

Almost all statistical methods textbooks present analysis of variance (ANOVA) as a key component in analysis of data from a randomized block design. We assume that readers are familiar with fundamental concepts for analysis of variance, such as degrees of freedom, sums of squares (SS), mean squares (MS), and expected mean squares (E[MS]). Readers needing more information about analysis of variance may consult Littell, Stroup, and Freund (2002) or Milliken and Johnson (2009). Table 2.1 shows a standard ANOVA table for the RCBD, containing sources of variation, degrees of freedom, mean squares, and expected mean squares.

Table 2.1: ANOVA for Randomized Complete Blocks Design

Source of Variation	df	MS	E[MS]
Blocks	r − 1	MS(Blk)	$\sigma^2 + t\sigma_b^2$
Treatments	t − 1	MS(Trt)	$\sigma^2 + r\phi^2$
Error	(r − 1)(t − 1)	MS(Error)	σ^2

2.2.3 Expected Mean Squares

As the term implies, *expected mean squares* are the expectations of means squares. They are the quantities estimated by mean squares in an analysis of variance. The expected mean squares can be used to motivate test statistics, and to provide a way to estimate the variance components. For test statistics, the basic idea is to examine the expected mean square for a factor and see how it differs under null and alternative hypotheses. For example, the expected mean square for treatments, E[MS(Trt)] = $\sigma^2 + r\phi^2$, can be used to determine how to set up a test statistic for treatment differences. The null hypothesis is H$_0$: $\mu_1 = \mu_2 = \ldots = \mu_t$. The expression ϕ^2 in E[MS(Trt)] is

$$\phi^2 = (t-1)^{-1} \sum_{i=1}^{t} (\mu_i - \bar{\mu}.)^2$$

where $\bar{\mu}.$ is the mean of the μ_i. Thus, $\phi^2 = 0$ is equivalent to $\mu_1 = \mu_2 = \ldots = \mu_t$. So, if the null hypothesis is true, MS(Trt) simply estimates σ^2. On the other hand, if H$_0$: $\mu_1 = \mu_2 = \ldots = \mu_t$. is false, then E[MS(Trt)] estimates a quantity larger than σ^2. Now, MS(Error) estimates σ^2 regardless of whether H$_0$ is true or false. Therefore, MS(Trt) and MS(Error) tend to be approximately equal if H_0 is true, and MS(Trt) tends to be larger than MS(Error) if H_0: $\mu_1 = \mu_2 = \ldots = \mu_t$ is false. So a comparison of MS(Trt) with MS(Error) is an indicator of whether H_0: $\mu_1 = \mu_2 = \ldots = \mu_t$ is true or false. In this way the expected mean squares show that a valid test statistic is the ratio $F = $ MS(Trt)/MS(Error).

Expected mean squares can also be used to estimate variance components, variances of treatment means, and variances of differences between treatment means. Equating the observed mean squares to the expected mean squares provides the following system of equations:

$$MS(Blk) = \hat{\sigma}^2 + t\hat{\sigma}_b^2$$

$$MS(Error) = \hat{\sigma}^2$$

The solution for the variance components is

$$\hat{\sigma}^2 = MS(Error)$$

and

$$\hat{\sigma}_b^2 = \frac{1}{t}\left[MS(Blk) - MS(Error)\right]$$

These are called *analysis of variance* estimates of the variance components. Using these estimates of the variance components, it follows that estimates of $\text{Var}\left[\bar{y}_{1\cdot}\right]$ and $\text{Var}\left[\bar{y}_{1\cdot} - \bar{y}_{2\cdot}\right]$ are

$$\hat{\text{Var}}\left[\bar{y}_{1\cdot}\right] = \left(\hat{\sigma}^2 + \hat{\sigma}_b^2\right)/r$$

$$= \frac{1}{rt}MS(Blk) + \frac{t-1}{rt}MS(Error)$$

and

$$\hat{\text{Var}}\left[\bar{y}_{1\cdot} - \bar{y}_{2\cdot}\right] = \frac{2}{r}MS(Error)$$

The expression for

$$\text{Var}\left[\bar{y}_{1\cdot}\right]$$

illustrates a common misconception that the estimate of the variance of a treatment mean from a randomized block design is simply MS(Error)/r. This misconception prevails in some textbooks and results in incorrect calculation of standard errors by some computer software packages, as well as incorrect reporting in refereed journal articles

2.2.4 Example: A Randomized Complete Block Design

An example from Mendenhall, Wackerly, and Scheaffer (1996, p. 601) is used to illustrate analysis of data from a randomized block design.

Data for this example are presented as Data Set "Bond". There are seven blocks and three treatments. Each block is an ingot of a composition material. The treatments are metals (nickel, iron, or copper). Pieces of material from the same ingot are bonded using one of the metals as a bonding agent. The response is the amount of pressure required to break a bond of two pieces of material that used one of the metals as the bonding agent. Table 2.2 contains the analysis of variance table for the BOND data where the ingots form the blocks.

Table 2.2: ANOVA Table for BOND Data

Source of Variation	df	SS	MS	F	p-value
Ingots	6	268.29	44.72	4.31	0.0151
Metal	2	131.90	65.95	6.36	0.0131
Error	12	124.46	10.37		

The ANOVA table and the metal means provide the essential computations for statistical inference about the population means.

The ANOVA $F = 6.36$ for metal provides a statistic to test the null hypothesis H_0: $\mu_c = \mu_i = \mu_n$. The significance probability for the F test is $p = 0.0131$, indicating strong evidence that the metal means are different. Estimates of the variance components are $\hat{\sigma}^2 = 10.37$ and $\hat{\sigma}_b^2 = (44.72 - 10.37)/3 = 11.45$. Thus, an estimate of the variance of a metal mean is $(\hat{\sigma}^2 + \hat{\sigma}_b^2)/7 = 3.11$, and the estimated standard error is $\sqrt{3.11} = 1.77$. An estimate of the variance of a difference between two metal means is $2\hat{\sigma}^2/7 = 2 \times 10.37/7 = 2.96$, and the standard error is $\sqrt{2.96} = 1.72$.

2.3 The MIXED and GLIMMIX Procedures to Analyze RCBD Data

PROC GLIMMIX and PROC MIXED are procedures with several capabilities for different methods of analyzing mixed models. PROC MIXED can be used for linear mixed models (LMMs), i.e., when you can assume that the response variable has a Gaussian distribution. PROC MIXED enables you to estimate the variance components using sums of squares and expected mean squares, as described in the previous section or by using likelihood methods. PROC GLIMMIX can be used for LMMs and generalized linear mixed models (GLMMs; i.e., for both Gaussian and non-Gaussian response variables). PROC GLIMMIX uses only likelihood-based methods.

For the randomized block examples presented in this chapter, and for more complex LMM applications presented in Chapters 5 through 10, analyses obtained using PROC MIXED or PROC GLIMMIX are essentially identical. For certain advanced LMMs, not presented in this volume, PROC MIXED offers specialized capabilities that are not available in PROC GLIMMIX. On the other hand, for GLMMs with non-Gaussian data, discussed in Chapters 11 through 13, and for inference on variance components, presented in Chapter 6, PROC GLIMMIX provides capabilities that are not available in PROC MIXED. For this reason, in this section, analyses of an RCBD are shown using both procedures, but all subsequent examples in this volume use PROC GLIMMIX.

In both PROC MIXED and PROC GLIMMIX, many of the estimation and inferential methods are implemented on the basis of the likelihood function and associated principles and theory (see Appendix A, "Linear Mixed Model Theory," for details). Readers may be more familiar with the analysis of variance approach described in the previous section; those results are obtained and presented in Section 2.3.1. The likelihood method results are presented in Section 2.3.2. Output from both PROC MIXED and PROC GLIMMIX are presented so readers can see that the results are the same, but the presentation format is slightly different. The results of the analysis of variance and likelihood methods are compared and are shown to duplicate many of the results of the previous section.

There are extensive post-processing options for mean comparison estimation, testing, and plotting available with both procedures. Presentation of these options, focusing on the more extensive options available with PROC GLIMMIX, are deferred to Chapter 3.

2.3.1 PROC MIXED Analysis Based on Sums of Squares

This section contains the code to provide the analysis of the RCBD with PROC MIXED using the sums of squares approach as described in Section 2.2.4. The METHOD=TYPE3 option is used to request that Type 3 sums of squares be computed along with their expected mean squares. Those mean squares and expected mean squares are used to provide estimates of the variance components and estimates of the standard errors associated with the means and comparisons of the means.

Program

Program 2.1 shows the basic PROC MIXED statements for the RCBD data analysis.

Program 2.1

```
proc mixed data=bond cl method=type3;
   class ingot metal;
   model pres = metal;
   random ingot;
   lsmeans metal;
run;
```

The PROC MIXED statement calls the procedure. The METHOD=TYPE3 option requests that the Type 3 sums of squares method be used in estimating the variance components. You can request Type 1, 2, or 3 sums of squares. See

Milliken and Johnson (2009) or Littell and Stroup (2002) for additional detail. The CLASS statement specifies that INGOT and METAL are classification variables, not continuous variables.

The MODEL statement is an equation whose left-hand side contains the name of the response variable to be analyzed, in this case PRES. The right-hand side of the MODEL statement contains a list of the fixed effect variables, in this case the variable METAL. In terms of the statistical model, this specifies the τ_i parameters. (The intercept parameter μ is implicitly contained in all models unless otherwise declared by using the NOINT option.)

The RANDOM statement contains a list of the random effects, in this case the blocking factor INGOT, and represents the b_j terms in the statistical model.

The MODEL and RANDOM statements are the core essential statements for many mixed model applications, and the terms in the MODEL statement do not appear in the RANDOM statement, and vice versa.

Results

Results from the MODEL and RANDOM statements about the methods used appear in Output 2.1.

Output 2.1: Results of RCBD Data Analysis from PROC MIXED Using Type 3 Sums of Squares

Model Information	
Data Set	WORK.BOND
Dependent Variable	pres
Covariance Structure	Variance Components
Estimation Method	Type 3
Residual Variance Method	Factor
Fixed Effects SE Method	Model-Based
Degrees of Freedom Method	Containment

Class Level Information		
Class	Levels	Values
ingot	7	1 2 3 4 5 6 7
metal	3	c i n

Dimensions	
Covariance Parameters	2
Columns in X	4
Columns in Z	7
Subjects	1
Max Obs per Subject	21

Number of Observations	
Number of Observations Read	21
Number of Observations Used	21
Number of Observations Not Used	0

Interpretation

The "Model Information" table contains the model specifications for the data set being used, the response variable, the methods used to estimate the variance components, the approximate degrees of freedom, and the standard errors for the fixed effects.

The "Class Level Information" table lists the levels for each of the variables declared in the class statement. You should be sure that these levels are specified consistently with how the study was conducted.

The "Dimensions" table shows how many columns are in the fixed effects matrix ($\mathbf{X}$) and in the random effects matrix ($\mathbf{Z}$) parts of the model, where the linear predictor is $\mathbf{X\beta} + \mathbf{Zu}$ (see Section 1.7). For this study there are three levels of the treatment factor (metal) plus an intercept, which accounts for four columns in the $\mathbf{X}$ matrix. There are seven ingots (blocks), thus there are seven columns in the $\mathbf{Z}$ matrix. The inclusion of the RANDOM statement means that there is one variance component for the ingot effects, plus the residual variance, providing two parameters in the covariance structure of the model. There is no SUBJECT= option used in this RANDOM statement, so PROC MIXED assumes that all observations are from the same subject, a quantity that can be ignored here.

The "Number of Observations" table indicates how many observations are in the data set and how many of those observations had valid data values for all variables used in the analysis. The difference between the number in the data set and the number used is the number of observations not used in the analysis. The information in these dimension specifications must match the information that is expected from the design being analyzed. Checking these values can help determine if there are data errors that need to be addressed, because they can cause the analysis to fail.

Results

Statistical results from the MODEL and RANDOM statements appear in Output 2.2.

Output 2.2: Results of the RCBD Data Analysis from PROC MIXED Using Type 3 Sums of Squares to Estimate the Variance Components

Type 3 Analysis of Variance

Source	DF	Sum of Squares	Mean Square	Expected Mean Square	Error Term	Error DF	F Value	Pr > F
metal	2	131.900952	65.950476	Var(Residual) + Q(metal)	MS(Residual)	12	6.36	0.0131
ingot	6	268.289524	44.714921	Var(Residual) + 3 Var(ingot)	MS(Residual)	12	4.31	0.0151
Residual	12	124.459048	10.371587	Var(Residual)	.	.	.	.

Covariance Parameter Estimates

Cov Parm	Estimate	Standard Error	Z Value	Pr Z	Alpha	Lower	Upper
ingot	11.4478	8.7204	1.31	0.1893	0.05	-5.6438	28.5394
Residual	10.3716	4.2342	2.45	0.0072	0.05	5.3332	28.2618

Type 3 Tests of Fixed Effects

Effect	Num DF	Den DF	F Value	Pr > F
metal	2	12	6.36	0.0131

Interpretation

The "Type 3 Analysis of Variance" table is the usual analysis of variance table with degrees of freedom, sums of squares, mean squares, expected mean squares, error terms for effects other than the residual, *F* tests, and significance levels for these tests. The terms Var(Residual) and Var(ingot) denote the variance components σ^2 and σ_b^2, respectively. See the discussion of the "Tests of Fixed Effects" table for more detail.

The "Covariance Parameter Estimates" table gives estimates of the variance component parameters obtained by solving the set of equations from equating the observed mean squares to the expected mean squares. The estimate of σ_b^2, the block variance component, is 11.4478 (labeled "ingot"), and the estimate of σ^2, the error variance component, is 10.3716 (labeled "Residual"). The confidence intervals for the variance components are Wald confidence intervals.

The "Tests of Fixed Effects" table is like an abbreviated ANOVA table, showing a line of computations for each term in the MODEL statement. In this example, only METAL is included in the MODEL statement. The *F* statistic is used to test the null hypothesis H_0: $\mu_c = \mu_i = \mu_n$ vs. H_a (not H_0). With 2 numerator and 12 denominator degrees of freedom, the *F* value of 6.36 is significant at the 5% level (*p*-value is 0.0131). If the true METAL means are equal, then an *F*-value as large as 6.36 would occur less than 131 times in 10,000 by chance. This is the same *F* test that was obtained from the analysis of variance.

In summary, these basic PROC MIXED computations are based on sums of squares and provide the same statistical computations obtained from analysis of variance methods for a balanced data set.

2.3.2 Basic PROC MIXED Analysis Based on Likelihood

Both PROC MIXED and PROC GLIMMIX, by default, provide maximum likelihood estimates (acronym MLE) of model effects, and REML estimates of variance components. REML stands for *REsidual (or REstricted) Maximum Likelihood* (Patterson and Thompson 1971). A fundamental strength of likelihood-based methodology is its adaptability. For randomized block models, analysis of variance and likelihood-based methods produce identical results, but analysis of variance methods cannot be applied to most cases that are even slightly more complex than the randomized block, whereas likelihood-based methods can be applied to arbitrarily complex models.

When comprehensive mixed model software first became widely available—in the early 1990s—some questioned the use of REML as the default variance estimation method. Specifically, why not maximum likelihood (ML) estimates of the variance? While not shown here, you can obtain ML variance estimates by using METHOD=ML in PROC MIXED or METHOD=MSPL in PROC GLIMMIX. The resulting variance estimates will be less that the corresponding REML estimates, and the resulting confidence intervals will be narrower and test statistics will be greater. This reflects the well-known fact that ML estimates of variance components are biased downward. For example, in the one-sample case, when $y_1, y_2, ..., y_n$ is a random sample from $N(\mu, \sigma^2)$, the ML estimate of the variance is as follows:

$$\sum_i (y_i - \bar{y})^2 \Big/ n$$

whereas the sample variance—which is the simplest REML variance estimate—is as follows:

$$\sum_i (y_i - \bar{y})^2 \Big/ (n-1)$$

We know that the latter is unbiased and universally regarded as the preferred variance estimate. One can easily show that the use of ML variance estimates results in upwardly biased type I error rates (rejection rates as high as 25% for a nominal $\alpha = 0.05$), and inadequate confidence interval coverage.

Program

Program 2.2 uses the default REML method for estimating the variance components. One could exclude METHOD=REML in the PROC MIXED statement, and achieve the same results. The assumptions of normality of the various terms in the model Equation 2.1 are required in order to construct the appropriate likelihood function that is maximized. The code to provide the likelihood-based analysis is identical to that of the sums of squares method, except for the method specification.

Program 2.2

```
proc mixed data=bond method=reml;
   class ingot metal;
   model pres=metal;
   random ingot;
run;
```

The PROC MIXED statement invokes the procedure for the default method of estimation, REML. The CLASS, MODEL, and RANDOM statements are identical to those in Section 2.3.1.

Results

The results of Program 2.2 appear in Output 2.3.

Output 2.3: Results of RCBD Data Analysis from PROC MIXED METHOD=REML

Model Information	
Data Set	WORK.BOND
Dependent Variable	pres
Covariance Structure	Variance Components
Estimation Method	REML
Residual Variance Method	Profile
Fixed Effects SE Method	Model-Based
Degrees of Freedom Method	Containment

Class Level Information		
Class	Levels	Values
ingot	7	1 2 3 4 5 6 7
metal	3	c i n

Dimensions	
Covariance Parameters	2
Columns in X	4
Columns in Z	7
Subjects	1
Max Obs per Subject	21

Number of Observations	
Number of Observations Read	21
Number of Observations Used	21
Number of Observations Not Used	0

Iteration History			
Iteration	Evaluations	-2 Res Log Like	Criterion
0	1	112.40987952	
1	1	107.79020201	0.00000000

Convergence criteria met.

Covariance Parameter Estimates	
Cov Parm	Estimate
ingot	11.4478
Residual	10.3716

Type 3 Tests of Fixed Effects				
Effect	Num DF	Den DF	F Value	Pr > F
metal	2	12	6.36	0.0131

Differences between results in Output 2.3 and Output 2.2 include the following:

- The "Model Information" table shows that REML is the specified method of estimating the variance components.

- The "Iteration History" table shows the sequence of evaluations to obtain (restricted) maximum likelihood estimates of the variance components. This portion of the output is not critical to most applications, such as the present RCBD analysis.

- The "Covariance Parameter Estimates" table gives estimates of the variance component parameters. The REML estimate of σ_b^2, the block variance component, is 11.4478 (labeled "ingot"), and the estimate of σ^2, the error variance component, is 10.3716 (labeled "Residual"). For this example of a balanced data set, these variance component estimates are identical to the estimates obtained from the analysis of variance method.

Notice that the essential output you would report; that is, the variance component estimates and the test statistics for the null hypothesis of no treatment effect—in essence, the F value, 6.36, and p-value, 0.0131—are identical to the results using analysis of variance.

In summary, the default PROC MIXED computations are based on likelihood principles, but many of the results are the same as those obtained from analysis of variance methods for the RCBD.

2.3.3 Basic PROC GLIMMIX Analysis

You can use PROC GLIMMIX to compute the same analysis as PROC MIXED METHOD=REML. Because PROC GLIMMIX is the most general of the SAS mixed model procedures, most examples from this point forward use PROC GLIMMIX. The RCBD data set is shown using both procedures to enable you to see the similarities, as well as some minor differences in the format of the results.

Program

Program 2.3 shows the PROC GLIMMIX program corresponding to PROC MIXED Program 2.2 in Section 2.3.2.

Program 2.3

```
proc glimmix data=bond method=rspl;
   class ingot metal;
   model pres=metal;
   random ingot;
run;
```

The only difference is that RSPL replaces REML in the METHOD option. RSPL (Residual Subject-specific Pseudo Likelihood) is a generalized form of the REML algorithm that can be used for generalized linear mixed models (GLMMs), essentially mixed models with non-Gaussian response variable. The more general algorithm is required to enable PROC GLIMMIX to accommodate non-Gaussian data. Chapters 11, 12 and 13 cover GLMMs. Details of the RSPL algorithm are given in Appendix B. The distinction between RSPL and REML is only relevant in those chapters. With Gaussian response variables—in essence, when the data are assumed to have a normal distribution—the RSPL algorithm reduces to REML. For Gaussian data, RSPL and REML are one and the same.

Results

Output 2.4 shows selected results.

Output 2.4: Results of RCBD Data Analysis from PROC GLIMMIX

Model Information	
Data Set	WORK.BOND
Response Variable	pres
Response Distribution	Gaussian
Link Function	Identity
Variance Function	Default
Variance Matrix	Not blocked
Estimation Technique	Restricted Maximum Likelihood
Degrees of Freedom Method	Containment

Covariance Parameter Estimates		
Cov Parm	Estimate	Standard Error
ingot	11.4478	8.7204
Residual	10.3716	4.2342

Type III Tests of Fixed Effects				
Effect	Num DF	Den DF	F Value	Pr > F
metal	2	12	6.36	0.0131

Default output from PROC GLIMMIX is similar to default REML output from PROC MIXED. They differ in that the PROC GLIMMIX table of "Covariance Parameter Estimates," includes a column for the standard error whereas PROC MIXED does not. For small data sets, the standard error of the variance component estimate is not too useful, because it is based on too few degrees of freedom. Confidence intervals for variance components based on a Satterthwaite approximation or the profile likelihood are useful when Wald type confidence intervals are not. Satterthwaite and profile likelihood confidence intervals are discussed in the next section.

2.3.4 Confidence Intervals for Variance Components

Confidence intervals can be used when it is of interest to access the uncertainty about the variance components in the model. A $(1 - \alpha) \times 100\%$ confidence interval about σ^2 can be constructed by using the chi-square distribution, as

$$\frac{(b-1)(t-1)\hat{\sigma}^2}{\chi^2_{(1-\alpha/2),(b-1)(t-1)}} \leq \sigma^2 \leq \frac{(b-1)(t-1)\hat{\sigma}^2}{\chi^2_{(\alpha/2),(b-1)(t-1)}}$$

where

$$\chi^2_{(1-\alpha/2),(b-1)(t-1)}$$

and

$$\chi^2_{\alpha/2,(b-1)(t-1)}$$

are the lower and upper $\alpha / 2$ percentage points of a central chi-square distribution with $(b - 1) \times (t - 1)$ degrees of freedom, respectively. When the estimate of σ_b^2 is positive, an approximate $(1 - \alpha) \times 100\%$ confidence interval about σ_b^2 can be constructed using a Satterthwaite (1946) approximation. The estimate of σ_b^2 is a linear combination of mean squares, which in general can be expressed as

$$\hat{\sigma}_b^2 = \sum_{i=1}^{s} q_i MS_i$$

where the ith mean square is based on f_i degrees of freedom and q_i is the constant by which the ith mean square is multiplied to obtain $\hat{\sigma}_b^2$. The approximate number of Satterthwaite degrees of freedom associated with $\hat{\sigma}_b^2$ is as follows:

$$v = \frac{\left(\hat{\sigma}_b^2\right)^2}{\sum_{i=1}^{s}\left[\left(q_i MS_i\right)^2\right]/f_i}$$

For the randomized complete block, the expression is the following:

$$\hat{\sigma}_b^2 = \frac{1}{t}\left(MS(Blk) - MS(Error)\right)$$

The approximate number of degrees of freedom is as follows:

$$v = \frac{\left(\hat{\sigma}_b^2\right)^2}{\dfrac{\left(t^{-1}MS(Blk)\right)^2}{b-1} + \dfrac{\left(t^{-1}MS(Error)\right)^2}{(b-1)(t-1)}}$$

A $(1 - \alpha) \times 100\%$ confidence interval about σ_b^2 can be constructed using the chi-square distribution, as the following, where $\chi^2_{(1-\alpha/2),v}$ and $\chi^2_{\alpha/2,v}$ are the lower and upper $\alpha/2$ percentage points with v degrees of freedom, respectively:

$$\frac{v\hat{\sigma}_b^2}{\chi^2_{(1-\alpha/2),v}} \leq \sigma_b^2 \leq \frac{v\hat{\sigma}_b^2}{\chi^2_{\alpha/2,v}}$$

Program to Obtain Satterthwaite Approximation Confidence Intervals

You can use either PROC GLIMMIX or PROC MIXED to obtain Satterthwaite approximation confidence intervals about σ_b^2 and σ^2. With PROC MIXED, use the COVTEST and CL options in the PROC statement. With PROC GLIMMIX, use the COVTEST *statement* with the CL option. Program 2.4 shows the PROC GLIMMIX statements.

Program 2.4

```
proc glimmix data=bond;
   class ingot metal;
   model pres=metal;
   random ingot;
   covtest / cl;
run;
```

Results

The results of computing the estimate of the variance components and using the Satterthwaite approximation to construct the confidence interval about σ_b^2 are given in Output 2.5.

Output 2.5: Wald Confidence Intervals for Block and Residual Variance from the PROC GLIMMIX COVTEST CL Option

Covariance Parameter Estimates				
Cov Parm	Estimate	Standard Error	Wald 95% Confidence Bounds	
ingot	11.4478	8.7204	3.8811	121.55
Residual	10.3716	4.2342	5.3332	28.2618

The 95% confidence interval for the block (INGOT) variance is (3.88, 121.55) and for the residual variance is (5.33, 28.26). The confidence intervals denoted as Wald confidence intervals are in fact Satterthwaite approximate confidence intervals. The Satterthwaite degrees of freedom are computed as $df = 2 * Z^2$, where $Z =$ Estimate/(Standard Error). The confidence interval is as follows:

$$\frac{df * \text{Estimate}}{\chi^2_{1-\alpha/2,df}} \leq \sigma^2 \leq \frac{df * \text{Estimate}}{\chi^2_{\alpha/2,df}}$$

For the Ingot variance component, terms are as follows:

- $Z = 11.4478 / 8.7204 = 1.313$

- $df = 2*(1.313^2) = 3.45$

- $\chi^2_{0.025,3.45} = 0.3246$

- $\chi^2_{0.975,3.45} = 10.17$

The 95% confidence for the Ingot variance is as follows:

$$\frac{3.45*11.4478}{10.17} \leq \sigma^2_{\text{Ingot}} \leq \frac{3.45*11.4478}{0.3246}$$

or

$$3.881 \leq \sigma^2_{\text{Ingot}} \leq 121.55$$

which is the same as shown in Output 2.5.

For all but very large data sets, the Satterthwaite confidence bounds are more accurate than Wald confidence bounds and therefore recommended. You can obtain Satterthwaite bounds using either PROC GLIMMIX or PROC MIXED. An alternative procedure, available only with PROC GLIMMIX, uses the likelihood ratio. Let σ denote the vector of covariance parameters, and $\log L(\hat{\sigma})$ denote the restricted log likelihood given the REML estimates of the parameters of σ. For the ingot example,

$$\sigma' = \begin{bmatrix} \sigma_b^2 & \sigma^2 \end{bmatrix}$$

Let

$$\log L\left(\hat{\boldsymbol{\sigma}} \mid \tilde{\sigma}_b^2\right)$$

denote the restricted log likelihood for a given value—not necessarily the REML or ML estimate—of the block variance, denoted $\tilde{\sigma}_b^2$ and the estimate of the other variance components, in this case σ^2, given $\tilde{\sigma}_b^2$. We know that $-2\log(\Lambda)$ where Λ denotes the likelihood ratio, can be written as follows:

$$2\left\{\log L(\hat{\boldsymbol{\sigma}}) - \log L\left(\hat{\sigma}^2 \mid \tilde{\sigma}_b^2\right)\right\}$$

And we know that it has an approximate χ^2 distribution. Just as the Satterthwaite approximation confidence interval contains all variance component values such that the test statistic, $v\hat{\sigma}_b^2 / \sigma_b^2$, is between upper and lower quantiles of the χ_v^2 distribution, you can form a 95% confidence interval for σ_b^2 from the set of all $\tilde{\sigma}_b^2$ such that the likelihood ratio test statistic,

$$2\left\{\log L(\hat{\boldsymbol{\sigma}}) - \log L\left(\hat{\sigma}^2 \mid \tilde{\sigma}_b^2\right)\right\} < \chi^2$$

You can obtain profile likelihood confidence intervals for a variance component in two ways. The *profile likelihood ratio* (PLR) re-estimates all the other covariance parameters for each new value of the parameter for which the confidence interval is being determined. The *empirical likelihood ratio* (ELR) uses the REML estimate of σ^2 to calculate the likelihood ratio for all values of σ_b^2 being evaluated. The latter is computationally simpler and is adequate for blocked designs. You can obtain empirical profile likelihood confidence intervals using the following modification to the COVTEST statement.

```
covtest / cl(type=elr);
```

Output 2.6 shows the result.

Output 2.6: Estimated Profile Likelihood Confidence Intervals for Block and Residual Variance

			Estimated Likelihood 95% Confidence Bounds			
		Standard	Lower		Upper	
Cov Parm	Estimate	Error	Bound	Pr > Chisq	Bound	Pr > Chisq
ingot	11.4478	8.7204	2.2907	0.0500	56.4772	0.0500
Residual	10.3716	4.2342	5.1386	0.0500	25.2825	0.0500

Covariance Parameter Estimates

Notice that the confidence bounds are noticeably more precise, especially for the block variance.

2.3.5 Comments on Using PROC GLM for the Analysis of Mixed Models

Prior to the advent of mixed model methods—PROC MIXED was introduced in the early 1990s—PROC GLM was the principal SAS procedure for analyzing mixed models, even though the basic computations of PROC GLM are for fixed effects models. Statistical methods textbooks continued to present the analysis of blocked designs using PROC GLM well into the 2000s. For the *complete* block designs with *no missing data,* the GLM procedure produces results similar to the PROC MIXED analysis of variance output shown in Section 2.3.1. However, this is not true for *incomplete* blocks designs or *any* blocked designs (complete or incomplete) with missing data. PROC GLM was not designed to solve mixed model estimating equations or to compute mixed model inferential statistics. Specifically, the RANDOM statement in PROC GLM does not modify estimation or inference as do RANDOM statements in PROC GLIMMIX and PROC MIXED. The RANDOM statement in PROC GLM merely assigns sums of squares to be used to construct F values and standard errors. The sums of squares, however, are computed as if all effects are fixed.

As a result, you *cannot* use PROC GLM to implement *any* of the mixed models analyses shown subsequently in this book. In many cases, PROC GLM *does* implement an analysis that would have been considered state of the art in the 1970s. However, these analyses are known to be less accurate than the corresponding mixed model analyses. In many cases, the standard errors and test statistics obtained by PROC GLM do not correctly account for random effects. PROC GLM is an excellent tool when used for what it was intended (fixed-effects-only models), but we *emphatically discourage* its use for all applications beyond the RCBD, beginning with incomplete block designs or RCBDs with missing data. Refer to Littell, Stroup, and Freund (2002) for more detailed PROC GLM coverage.

2.4 Unbalanced Two-Way Mixed Model: Examples with Incomplete Block Design

In some applications of blocking there are not enough experimental units in each block to accommodate all treatments. *Incomplete block designs* are designs in which only a subset of the treatments is applied in each block. The treatments that go into each block should be selected in order to provide the most information relative to the objectives of the experiment.

Three types of incomplete block designs are *balanced* incomplete block designs (BIBD), *partially balanced* incomplete block design (PBIBD), and *unbalanced* incomplete block design. The word "balanced" has a specific meaning for incomplete block designs. In design theory, the meaning of "balanced" for BIB and PBIB designs results in all treatment mean estimates having the same variances (and hence the same standard error). Also, the variances of estimated treatment mean differences are the same for all pairs of treatments with BIBDs and for sets of treatments with PBIBDs. As you may suspect, it is not possible to construct BIB or PBIB designs for all possible numbers of treatments and blocks. Discovery of numbers of blocks and treatments for which BIBDs and PBIBDs can be constructed was once an active area of statistical research. With the advent of fast computers and good statistical software, the existence of BIBDs and PBIBDs for given numbers of blocks and treatments has become a less important problem. For example, you can use PROC OPTEX or the optimal design software in JMP to construct approximately balanced incomplete block designs. These designs are commonly used in many fields of research. Mead et al. (2011) have an excellent discussion of this issue.

This section presents the two most commonly used analyses for incomplete block designs. In one, called *intra-block* analysis, block effects are assumed to be fixed. In the pre-mixed-model era of statistical software, intra-block analysis was the only available method. In the other method, called *combined inter- and intra-block* analysis, block effects are assumed to be random. In most cases, using information provided by the block variance, called *recovery of inter-block information*, improves the accuracy and precision of the resulting analysis. However, the intra-block analysis is useful for introducing the distinction between Least Squares treatment means, also called *adjusted means*, and unadjusted arithmetic means, and the associated distinction between Type I tests of hypotheses and Type III tests.

You can use PROC GLM, PROC GLIMMIX or PROC MIXED to implement intra-block (fixed block effect) analysis. To do combined inter- and intra-block (random block effect) analysis, you must use either PROC GLIMMIX or PROC MIXED. PROC GLM was not designed to perform the required computations for recovery of inter-block information.

For consistency, both types of analyses are demonstrated using PROC GLIMMIX. Data from a PBIBD is used to illustrate the similarities and differences between intra-block and combined inter- and intra-block analyses. Note that the intra-block analysis shown in Section 2.5.1 is identical to the analysis that you would get if you use PROC GLM or PROC MIXED (assuming block effects fixed). The combined inter- and intra-block analysis in Section 2.5.2 is identical to the results using PROC MIXED (assuming random block effects). Finally, although the example is a PBIBD, data analysis methods in this section apply to incomplete block designs in general.

As noted above, models for an incomplete block design are the same as for an RCBD. That is, the model equation is

$$y_{ij} = \mu + \tau_i + b_j + e_{ij}$$

where $\mu_i = \mu + \tau_i$ denotes the treatment mean, b_j denotes the block effects b_j and the residual, or experimental error effects e_{ij} are assumed *iid* $N(0, \sigma^2)$. An analysis of variance table for an incomplete block design is shown in Table 2.3.

Table 2.3: Type III Analysis of Variance Table for Incomplete Blocks Design

Source of Variation	*df*	*F*
Blocks (adjusted for treatments)	r – 1	
Treatments (adjusted for blocks)	t – 1	MS(Trts adj.) / MS(Residual)
Residual	N – r – t + 1	

In the table, *r* is the number of blocks, *t* is the number of treatments, and *N* is the total number of observations. Notice that the treatments source of variation is adjusted for blocks (Littell and Stroup 2002). The treatments cannot be compared simply on the basis of the usual sum of squared differences between treatment means, because this would contain effects of blocks as well as treatment differences. Instead, a sum of squared differences must be computed between treatment means that have been adjusted to remove the block effects. The difference between the adjusted and unadjusted analyses is illustrated in Section 2.4.1.

Most statistics textbooks that cover BIBD and PBIBD present intra-block analyses. A few also present combined intra- and inter-block analysis. In older textbooks, combined inter- and intra-block analysis appears needlessly daunting. This is especially true of textbooks written before mixed model software was available, i.e., before PROC MIXED was introduced in the early 1990s, and it was not recognized that recovery of inter-block information is simply random block effect mixed model analysis. Textbooks that do cover both types of analysis are all over the map regarding advice about when to use which method of analysis. In Section 2.4.3, we address this question.

2.4.1 Intra-block Analysis of PBIB Data

Data Set PBIB contains data from Cochran and Cox (1957, p. 456). The design is a PBIBD with fifteen blocks, fifteen treatments, and four treatments per block. Data are pounds of seed cotton per plot. The *block size* is the number of treatments per block. This PBIBD has a block size of four. Each treatment appears in four blocks. Some pairs of treatments appear together within a block (e.g., treatments 1 and 2), and other treatments do not appear together in the same blocks (e.g., treatments 1 and 6).

The data appear in multivariate form; that is, with one data line per block, and the four treatment identifiers and responses given as separate variables. To arrange the data in the univariate form in which each observation has a single data line, as required for SAS mixed model procedures, use the following DATA step:

```
data pbib;
  input blk @@;
    do eu=1 to 4;
      input treat y @@;
      output;
    end;
datalines;
```

Program for Intra-block Analysis

An intra-block analysis of the PBIBD data is obtained from Program 2.5.

Program 2.5

```
proc glimmix data=pbib;
  class treat blk;
  model y=treat blk;
  lsmeans treat;
run;
```

Results

Selected results from this PROC GLIMMIX run appear in Output 2.7.

Output 2.7: Incomplete Block Design: PROC GLIMMIX Output for Intra-block Analysis

Fit Statistics	
-2 Res Log Likelihood	46.33
AIC (smaller is better)	106.33
AICC (smaller is better)	1966.33
BIC (smaller is better)	149.35
CAIC (smaller is better)	179.35
HQIC (smaller is better)	120.36
Pearson Chi-Square	2.67
Pearson Chi-Square / DF	0.09

<table>
<tr><th colspan="5">Type III Tests of Fixed Effects</th></tr>
<tr><th>Effect</th><th>Num DF</th><th>Den DF</th><th>F Value</th><th>Pr > F</th></tr>
<tr><td>treat</td><td>14</td><td>31</td><td>1.23</td><td>0.3012</td></tr>
<tr><td>blk</td><td>14</td><td>31</td><td>2.76</td><td>0.0090</td></tr>
</table>

<table>
<tr><th colspan="6">treat Least Squares Means</th></tr>
<tr><th>treat</th><th>Estimate</th><th>Standard Error</th><th>DF</th><th>t Value</th><th>Pr > |t|</th></tr>
<tr><td>1</td><td>2.8456</td><td>0.1634</td><td>31</td><td>17.41</td><td><.0001</td></tr>
<tr><td>2</td><td>2.4128</td><td>0.1634</td><td>31</td><td>14.76</td><td><.0001</td></tr>
<tr><td>3</td><td>2.4517</td><td>0.1634</td><td>31</td><td>15.00</td><td><.0001</td></tr>
<tr><td>4</td><td>2.6833</td><td>0.1634</td><td>31</td><td>16.42</td><td><.0001</td></tr>
<tr><td>5</td><td>2.8067</td><td>0.1634</td><td>31</td><td>17.17</td><td><.0001</td></tr>
<tr><td>6</td><td>2.9039</td><td>0.1634</td><td>31</td><td>17.77</td><td><.0001</td></tr>
<tr><td>7</td><td>2.7711</td><td>0.1634</td><td>31</td><td>16.96</td><td><.0001</td></tr>
<tr><td>8</td><td>2.8100</td><td>0.1634</td><td>31</td><td>17.19</td><td><.0001</td></tr>
<tr><td>9</td><td>2.9333</td><td>0.1634</td><td>31</td><td>17.95</td><td><.0001</td></tr>
<tr><td>10</td><td>2.5150</td><td>0.1634</td><td>31</td><td>15.39</td><td><.0001</td></tr>
<tr><td>11</td><td>2.8539</td><td>0.1634</td><td>31</td><td>17.46</td><td><.0001</td></tr>
<tr><td>12</td><td>3.0128</td><td>0.1634</td><td>31</td><td>18.44</td><td><.0001</td></tr>
<tr><td>13</td><td>2.6683</td><td>0.1634</td><td>31</td><td>16.33</td><td><.0001</td></tr>
<tr><td>14</td><td>2.5333</td><td>0.1634</td><td>31</td><td>15.50</td><td><.0001</td></tr>
<tr><td>15</td><td>2.8483</td><td>0.1634</td><td>31</td><td>17.43</td><td><.0001</td></tr>
</table>

Interpretation

As with the Fit Statistics output for the RCBD, only the last two lines are relevant to interpreting these results. The Pearson Chi-Square is equivalent to the residual sum of squares in an ANOVA table, and hence the Pearson Chi-square/DF gives the MS(residual) and is thus the estimated residual variance, $\hat{\sigma}^2 = 8.62$. The F value for differences between (adjusted) treatment differences is given in the Type III Tests of Fixed Effects: $F = 1.23$ and its associated p-value is 0.3012.

The least-squares means, obtained from the LSMEANS statement, are usually called adjusted means in standard textbooks. In complete block designs, the LSMEANS and the usual arithmetic means that you would calculate by hand are the same. This is not true for incomplete blocks designs, or for complete block designs with missing data. Both are examples of "unbalanced" designs in the standard design sense as defined above. Data for a given treatment in a block design with unbalance come from only a subset of the blocks. Each treatment is observed on a potentially unique subset of blocks. For example, in the PBIB example treatment 1 is observed in blocks 1, 2, 3 and 6, whereas treatment 2 is observed in blocks 3, 4, 9, and 12. If you compared unadjusted sample means of these two treatments, they would be confounded with blocks. In other words, if the sample means differ, you could not say whether it was a treatment 1 versus 2 difference, or a blocks 1, 2 and 6 versus blocks 4, 9, and 12 difference. A least squares mean adjusts for the fact that each treatment is observed on a different subset of blocks by taking the estimates of the intercept, treatment effect, and the average of all block effects. In other words, it is an estimate of what the treatment mean would have been if it had been observed in all blocks. For the PBIB, the LSMEAN for the ith treatment is defined as the estimate of $\mu + \tau_i + (1/15)\sum_j b_j$.

Program to Compare Unadjusted and Adjusted Sample Means

Program 2.6 enables you to see the difference between unadjusted sample means and adjusted, or least squares, means and the inference associated with them.

Program 2.6

```
proc glimmix data=pbib;
  class treat blk;
  model y=treat blk/htype=1,3;
```

```
   lsmeans treat / e;
   lsmeans treat / bylevel e;
run;
```

The first LSMEANS statement causes PROC GLIMMIX to compute adjusted means. The E option enables you to see which linear combination of model parameters is being used to calculate these means. The BYLEVEL option in the second LSMEANS statement causes PROC GLIMMIX to compute unadjusted sample means, and the associated E option enables you to see how these means are calculated. The HTYPE=1,3 statement obtains TYPE I and TYPE III tests of treatment effects. If you put TREAT first in the MODEL statement, the Type I tests for treatment are not adjusted for blocks, whereas the TYPE III tests are.

Results

Selected results appear in Output 2.8.

Output 2.8: Adjusted versus Unadjusted Means with Intra-block Analysis

	Type I Tests of Fixed Effects			
Effect	Num DF	Den DF	F Value	Pr > F
treat	14	31	2.48	0.0172
blk	14	31	2.76	0.0090

	Type III Tests of Fixed Effects			
Effect	Num DF	Den DF	F Value	Pr > F
treat	14	31	1.23	0.3012
blk	14	31	2.76	0.0090

Obs	Effect	treat	adj_mean	adj_stderr	unadj_mean	unadj_stderr
1	treat	1	2.84556	0.16343	2.775	0.14676
2	treat	2	2.41278	0.16343	2.400	0.14676
3	treat	3	2.45167	0.16343	2.450	0.14676
4	treat	4	2.68333	0.16343	2.950	0.14676
5	treat	5	2.80667	0.16343	2.800	0.14676
6	treat	6	2.90389	0.16343	2.925	0.14676
7	treat	7	2.77111	0.16343	2.825	0.14676
8	treat	8	2.81000	0.16343	2.725	0.14676
9	treat	9	2.93333	0.16343	2.825	0.14676
10	treat	10	2.51500	0.16343	2.450	0.14676
11	treat	11	2.85389	0.16343	2.975	0.14676
12	treat	12	3.01278	0.16343	3.125	0.14676
13	treat	13	2.66833	0.16343	2.525	0.14676
14	treat	14	2.53333	0.16343	2.425	0.14676
15	treat	15	2.84833	0.16343	2.875	0.14676

Obs	Effect	treat	blk	adj_coef4	adj_coef5	unadj_coef4	unadj_coef5
1	Intercept	_	_	1.00000	1.00000	1.00	1.00
2	treat	1	_	0.00000	0.00000	0.00	0.00
3	treat	2	_	0.00000	0.00000	0.00	0.00
4	treat	3	_	0.00000	0.00000	0.00	0.00
5	treat	4	_	1.00000	0.00000	1.00	0.00
6	treat	5	_	0.00000	1.00000	0.00	1.00

Obs	Effect	treat	blk	adj_coef4	adj_coef5	unadj_coef4	unadj_coef5
7	treat	6	_	0.00000	0.00000	0.00	0.00
8	treat	7	_	0.00000	0.00000	0.00	0.00
9	treat	8	_	0.00000	0.00000	0.00	0.00
10	treat	9	_	0.00000	0.00000	0.00	0.00
11	treat	10	_	0.00000	0.00000	0.00	0.00
12	treat	11	_	0.00000	0.00000	0.00	0.00
13	treat	12	_	0.00000	0.00000	0.00	0.00
14	treat	13	_	0.00000	0.00000	0.00	0.00
15	treat	14	_	0.00000	0.00000	0.00	0.00
16	treat	15	_	0.00000	0.00000	0.00	0.00
17	blk	_	1	0.06667	0.06667	0.00	0.00
18	blk	_	2	0.06667	0.06667	0.00	0.25
19	blk	_	3	0.06667	0.06667	0.00	0.00
20	blk	_	4	0.06667	0.06667	0.00	0.00
21	blk	_	5	0.06667	0.06667	0.25	0.00
22	blk	_	6	0.06667	0.06667	0.25	0.00
23	blk	_	7	0.06667	0.06667	0.00	0.00
24	blk	_	8	0.06667	0.06667	0.00	0.25
25	blk	_	9	0.06667	0.06667	0.25	0.25
26	blk	_	10	0.06667	0.06667	0.00	0.00
27	blk	_	11	0.06667	0.06667	0.00	0.00
28	blk	_	12	0.06667	0.06667	0.00	0.00
29	blk	_	13	0.06667	0.06667	0.00	0.25
30	blk	_	14	0.06667	0.06667	0.00	0.00
31	blk	_	15	0.06667	0.06667	0.25	0.00

The first two tables show the unadjusted (Type I) and adjusted (Type III) test of overall treatment effect. Notice that the p-values are noticeably different. Based on the adjusted test, with $p = 0.3012$, you would conclude that the treatment effect is not statistically significant; based on the Type I $p = 0.0172$, you find a statistically significant difference among the treatments. However, a careful examination of the next two tables reveals that the Type I test is confounded with block effects.

The third table shows the adjusted and unadjusted means and their respective standard errors. Notice that these means are not the same. In particular, consider treatments 4 and 5. The unadjusted means are 2.95 and 2.80, respectively, whereas the adjusted means are 2.68 and 2.81, respectively. With the unadjusted analysis, you would conclude that there is a treatment effect and that the mean of treatment 4 is greater than the mean of treatment 5. With the adjusted means, you would conclude that the mean of treatment 5 is greater, but there is insufficient evidence to conclude that a treatment effect exists. The fourth table clarifies the problem with the unadjusted means. This table shows the results of the E option for both sets of means; in the interest of space, only the coefficients of treatments 4 and 5 are given. In the usual PROC GLIMMIX output, these variables are named ROW4 and ROW5—here they are re-named ADJ_COEF4, UNADJ_COEF4, etc. The values in each column give the coefficients of the model effects used to compute the respective mean. For example, the adjusted mean for treatment 4 is computed as follows:

$$\mu + \tau_4 + 0.06667\left(\sum_{j=1}^{15} b_j\right)$$

The unadjusted mean is computed as $\mu + \tau_4 + 0.25(b_5 + b_6 + b_9 + b_{16})$. These tell you what each mean estimates. You can see that if you take the difference between the adjusted means, you estimate $\tau_4 - \tau_5$, whereas if you take the difference between the unadjusted means you estimate $\tau_4 - \tau_5 + 0.25(b_5 + b_6 + b_{15} - b_2 - b_8 - b_{13})$. With the latter, you have no way of knowing if treatments 4 and 5 are different, or if blocks 5, 6, and 15 differ from blocks 2, 8, and 13. This is why you use treatments results adjusted for blocks—in essence, Type III tests of fixed effects for treatment and default LSMEANS—and not Type I tests or hand-calculated sample means.

The means and their standard errors in intra-block analysis stem from the ordinary least squares (OLS) estimation. Thus, they do not take into account the fact that blocks are random. The adjustment of treatment means to remove block effects is a computation that treats blocks simply as another fixed effect. The intra-block analysis does not use all available information about the treatment effects, and thus it is suboptimal compared to the combined intra- and inter-block estimators provided by PROC GLIMMIX and PROC MIXED.

2.4.2 Combined Intra- and Inter-block PBIB Data Analysis with PROC GLIMMIX

When blocks are really treated as random, the result is the combined intra- and inter-block analysis. You can obtain this analysis with either the GLIMMIX or MIXED procedure.

Program

The PROC GLIMMIX statements are given in Program 2.7.

Program 2.7

```
proc glimmix data=pbib;
   class blk treat;
   model response=treat;
   random blk;
   lsmeans treat/diff;
run;
```

The primary difference between these statements and those for intra-block analysis is that BLK appears in the RANDOM statement instead of the MODEL statement. You could add the HTYPE=1,3 option to the MODEL statement, and a second LSMEANS statement using the BYLEVEL option, as shown in the previous section. You will find that the Type I and III tests, and the default and BYLEVEL means are identical with block effects assumed to be random. This is because with random block effects, the estimable function to LSMEANS is $\mu + \tau_i$ and does not require coefficients for the b_j terms. The resulting LSMEANS are adjusted, but the adjustment occurs differently than it does in intra-block analysis. This is explained in more detail below. The DIFF option causes all possible pairwise differences— there are $(15 \times 14)/2 = 105$ of them—to be computed. These are computed in this section to illustrate the role of the standard error of the difference in defining what "partially balanced" means in a PBIBD. Other mean comparison options are presented in detail in Chapter 3.

Results

Selected PROC GLIMMIX results appear in Output 2.9 for the combined intra- and inter-block analysis.

Output 2.9: Incomplete Block Design: PROC GLIMMIX Analysis

Covariance Parameter Estimates		
Cov Parm	Estimate	Standard Error
blk	0.04652	0.02795
Residual	0.08556	0.02158

Type III Tests of Fixed Effects				
Effect	Num DF	Den DF	F Value	Pr > F
treat	14	31	1.53	0.1576

treat Least Squares Means					
treat	Estimate	Standard Error	DF	t Value	Pr > |t|
1	2.8175	0.1664	31	16.93	<.0001
2	2.4053	0.1664	31	14.45	<.0001
3	2.4549	0.1664	31	14.75	<.0001
4	2.7838	0.1664	31	16.73	<.0001
5	2.8049	0.1664	31	16.86	<.0001

treat Least Squares Means					
treat	Estimate	Standard Error	DF	t Value	Pr > |t|
6	2.9107	0.1664	31	17.49	<.0001
7	2.7890	0.1664	31	16.76	<.0001
8	2.7816	0.1664	31	16.72	<.0001
9	2.8913	0.1664	31	17.37	<.0001
10	2.4911	0.1664	31	14.97	<.0001
11	2.8987	0.1664	31	17.42	<.0001
12	3.0528	0.1664	31	18.34	<.0001
13	2.6178	0.1664	31	15.73	<.0001
14	2.4913	0.1664	31	14.97	<.0001
15	2.8592	0.1664	31	17.18	<.0001

Interpretation

Information about the effect of blocks moves from the test of fixed effects output to the Covariance Parameter Estimates. The estimated block variance is $\sigma_b^2 = 0.04562$. The REML estimate of the residual variance component is 0.08556, compared to 0.086154 from the intra-block analysis (Output 2.9). Although PROC GLIMMIX output gives standard errors of variance component estimates, these are asymptotic standard errors.

The F statistic in the "Type 3 Tests of Fixed Effects" table is 1.53 with a p-value of 0.1576. Compare this to the results from the intra-block analysis (Output 2.8, $F = 1.23$, $p = 0.3012$). This smaller p-value in the mixed model analysis is the result of increased power associated with the combined intra- and inter-block estimates of the treatment effects.

The Least Squares Mean estimates of the treatment means are similar, but not identical, to the adjusted means in the intra-block analysis in Section 2.4.1. For example, the estimate of the treatment 1 mean is 2.817, compared with the intra-block estimate of 2.846. The latter is an ordinary least squares (OLS) estimate, whereas the former is a mixed model estimate, equivalent to (estimated) generalized least squares (GLS). Theoretically, the GLS estimate is superior, because it accounts for BLK being random and computes the estimate of the best linear unbiased estimate (EBLUE) accordingly, substituting estimates of the variance components for block and residual. Likewise, the standard errors in the combined inter- and intra-block analysis are different from those in Section 2.4.1. The standard error of the OLS estimate is 0.163 whereas the GLS estimate is 0.166. The former is not a valid estimate of the true standard error, for the same reason that the fixed-block-effect analysis did not compute a valid standard error estimate for a treatment mean for the RCBD data in Section 2.2.1: the random effects of blocks were ignored.

Program

In the combined inter- and intra-block PROC GLIMMIX run (Program 2.7), the differences of the least-squares means were saved to a data set with the ODS OUTPUT statement. We now want to carry out additional processing on these differences. Program 2.8 shows how. First, a data set (PAIRS) is created that contains the pairs of observations that occur together in a block in this partially balanced incomplete block design.

Program 2.8

```
data pairs;
   set pbib_mv;
   array tx{4} trt1-trt4;
   array yy{4} y1-y4;
   do i=1 to 3; do j=(i+1) to 4;
      treat  = min(tx{i},tx{j});
      _treat = max(tx{i},tx{j});
      output;
   end; end;
   keep blk treat _treat;
run;
proc sort data=pairs nodupkey; by treat _treat; run;
proc print data=pairs(obs=23); run;
```

The PAIRS data set is created from the original data in multivariate format. The variables TREAT and _TREAT are set up to match the variables by the same name in the DIFMIX data set that was created in the PROC GLIMMIX call.

Results

Output 2.10 shows the first 23 observations of the PAIRS data set. These observations correspond to the pairings of treatments within a block that involve the first two treatments.

Output 2.10: Pairs within a Block Involving Treatments 1 and 2

Obs	blk	treat	_treat
1	3	1	2
2	6	1	3
3	6	1	4
4	2	1	5
5	2	1	7
6	2	1	8
7	1	1	9
8	3	1	10
9	6	1	12
10	1	1	13
11	3	1	14
12	1	1	15
13	4	2	3
14	9	2	4
15	9	2	5
16	12	2	6
17	12	2	8
18	12	2	9
19	3	2	10
20	4	2	11
21	9	2	13
22	3	2	14
23	4	2	15

Interpretation

Treatment 1 occurs with all other treatments somewhere in a block, except for treatments 6 and 11. Similarly, treatment 2 appears with all but treatments 7 and 12. Pairs of treatments that never appear in the same block are called "disconnected pairs."

Next, the output data set of treatment mean differences was sorted by StdErr. This reveals that there are two values of standard errors. Output 2.11 shows all pairs with the greater standard error value. Output 2.12 shows a subset of the standard errors of differences with the lower standard error, specifically differences between treatment 1 or 2 and all other treatments for which the standard error is at the lower level.

Output 2.11: Least-Squares Means Differences for Disconnected Pairs

treat	_treat	Estimate	StdErr	Probt
1	6	-0.09317	0.2272	0.6846
1	11	-0.08118	0.2272	0.7233
2	7	-0.3837	0.2272	0.1013
2	12	-0.6475	0.2272	0.0077
3	8	-0.3267	0.2272	0.1605
3	13	-0.1628	0.2272	0.4789
4	9	-0.1075	0.2272	0.6395
4	14	0.2925	0.2272	0.2075
5	10	0.3138	0.2272	0.1771

treat	_treat	Estimate	StdErr	Probt
5	15	-0.05434	0.2272	0.8126
6	11	0.01199	0.2272	0.9582
7	12	-0.2638	0.2272	0.2544
8	13	0.1638	0.2272	0.4762
9	14	0.4000	0.2272	0.0882
10	15	-0.3682	0.2272	0.1153

Output 2.12: Least-Squares Means Differences for Connected Pairs Involving Treatments 1 and 2

treat	_treat	Estimate	StdErr	Probt
1	2	0.4122	0.2221	0.0729
1	3	0.3626	0.2221	0.1126
1	4	0.03369	0.2221	0.8804
1	5	0.01262	0.2221	0.9550
1	7	0.02854	0.2221	0.8986
1	8	0.03592	0.2221	0.8726
1	9	-0.07379	0.2221	0.7419
1	10	0.3265	0.2221	0.1516
1	12	-0.2353	0.2221	0.2975
1	13	0.1998	0.2221	0.3753
1	14	0.3262	0.2221	0.1519
1	15	-0.04171	0.2221	0.8522
2	3	-0.04963	0.2221	0.8246
2	4	-0.3785	0.2221	0.0983
2	5	-0.3996	0.2221	0.0817
2	6	-0.5054	0.2221	0.0299
2	8	-0.3763	0.2221	0.1002
2	9	-0.4860	0.2221	0.0363
2	10	-0.08575	0.2221	0.7020
2	11	-0.4934	0.2221	0.0337
2	13	-0.2125	0.2221	0.3461
2	14	-0.08600	0.2221	0.7012
2	15	-0.4539	0.2221	0.0495

In Output 2.11, all of the standard errors of differences between disconnected pairs are 0.2272, whereas in Output 2.12, all standard errors for differences between connected pairs are 0.2221. Although only the results for the connected pairs of treatments 1 and 2 are shown in Output 2.12, similar results are obtained for the other treatments. These standard errors differ because the treatment pairs in Output 2.11 were observed together in the same block a different number of times—in this case zero—than the pairs in Output 2.12. This is a defining characteristic of a PBIBD—there are exactly two levels of standard error of the difference. In a BIBD, there is only one level—if there is more than one level, the design is not a BIBD. The more times that treatment pairs appear together in the same block in a given design, the lower the standard error will be. Although in this example the difference is small, it is an important difference, because it reflects the decreased precision that is the result of disconnected treatment pairs. Contrasts involving treatments that do not appear in the same block are not estimated with the same precision as contrasts involving treatments that do appear in the same block. Chapter 4 covers procedures that include these principles in the design of experiments.

As noted above, textbooks that do include sections on combined inter- and intra-block analysis, i.e., assuming random block effects, often include cautionary warnings about using this analysis. Textbooks vary in the nature and extent of these warnings. Some appear to dismiss mixed model analysis altogether, while some warn against mixed model analysis when the number of blocks is "small." The definition of "small" varies. Stroup (2015) reported a simulation study on the behavior of mixed model analysis of incomplete block designs. In most cases, even when the assumptions of the randomized block mixed model are violated (including cases where the block effect distribution is bimodal or beta with most of the probability density at zero or one, the performance of the combined inter- and intra-block analysis was still equal to or superior to intra-block analysis, even with incomplete block designs with 4 blocks. The only case for which any caution seems valid is if the number of blocks is small (≤ 6) *and* the block variance is small relative to the residual variance ($\sigma_b^2/\sigma^2 < 0.5$). Otherwise, the warnings appear to be more of a holdover from an era before PROC MIXED appeared when recovery of inter-block information was difficult, and research comparing intra-block analysis to random block effect analysis focused more on "is it worth the trouble?" rather than "because it is easy with mixed-model software, is there any harm in using it?" Taking the latter perspective—the more relevant perspective given easy access to mixed model software—our answer is as follows: with the one exception noted above, no, there is no harm: you are never worse off, and you are usually better off, if you use the mixed model, random block effect approach.

2.5 Analysis with a Negative Block Variance Estimate: An Example

This section focuses on cases when the default algorithms in PROC GLIMMIX and PROC MIXED set the block variance estimate to zero. This is accompanied by a warning in the SAS LOG, "Estimated G matrix is not positive definite." Users ask if this is a problem and the answer is, "Yes, it is." This section covers an example, discusses why this occurs, why it is a problem, and what to do about it.

2.5.1 Illustration of the Problem

With this example we demonstrate a case in which the estimate of the block variance has been set to zero.

Program

The data set titled "RCBD with Negative Variance Estimate" contains data analyzed using the statements in Program 2.9.

Program 2.9

```
proc glimmix data=zero_v_ex;
 class blk trt;
 model y=trt;
 random blk;
run;
```

Results

This produces the result shown in Output 2.13.

Output 2.13: Variance Components Estimates Illustrating Set-to-Zero Default

Covariance Parameter Estimates		
Cov Parm	Estimate	Standard Error
block	0	.
Residual	8.4792	2.4477

Notice that the block variance estimate has been set to zero. Rerunning the analysis using PROC MIXED with option METHOD=TYPE3 produces an insight into why this happens.

Output 2.14: ANOVA Table Generating Negative Block Variance Estimate

Type 3 Analysis of Variance								
Source	DF	Sum of Squares	Mean Square	Expected Mean Square	Error Term	Error DF	F Value	Pr > F
trt	5	59.184969	11.836994	Var(Residual) + Q(trt)	MS(Residual)	20	1.18	0.3542
block	4	2.663237	0.665809	Var(Residual) + 6 Var(block)	MS(Residual)	20	0.07	0.9913
Residual	20	200.838496	10.041925	Var(Residual)	.	.	.	.

The MS(blk) is less than MS(residual). Recalling the ANOVA estimate of the block variance from Section 2.3.1, you can see that this results in a negative estimate. Because variance cannot be negative, the traditional approach is to set the variance estimate to zero, the lowest number within the block variance's parameter space.

Unfortunately, while setting the estimate to zero solves the problem of trying to explain how a variance can be negative (it can't), doing so has undesirable consequences. Specifically, for tests of hypotheses about treatment effects, it raises the Type I error rate relative to the nominal α-level, and it reduces the accuracy of confidence interval coverage. Using a simulation study, Littell and Stroup (2003) document the consequences of the set-to-zero default.

The reason these problems occur can be seen from the discrepancy between the residual variance estimate in the default output and the MS(residual). We know that the MS(residual) is an unbiased estimate of the residual variance. When the set-to-zero default is invoked, MS(blk) is pooled with MS(residual), as are the degrees of freedom for block and residual. The result is a downward bias in the residual variance estimate and an upward bias in the t and F statistics used to test hypotheses. The default F statistic for TRT is 1.40 versus 1.18 using the ANOVA MS(residual).

There are two ways to avoid this problem without abandoning the benefits of mixed model analysis. These are discussed in the next two sections.

First, some comments about negative variance estimates that have more to do with design than with analysis. A zero estimate may suggest a number of things. It may indicate that variation associated with the criterion used to block is relatively small compared to background noise. If so, the likelihood of data producing a MS(blk) less than MS(residual) is rather high. In such cases, the options given in the next two sections are strongly recommended. On the other hand, a zero variance estimate may suggest a flawed design. Often it means that blocking was not done in a manner consistent with the blocking criterion. See the discussion in Chapter 4 on effective versus ineffective blocking strategies. If flawed blocking is the case, all bets are off. Before proceeding, you should always do a retrospective and be willing to ask hard questions about how the design was implemented and how the data were collected.

To conclude, one common practice that we strongly discourage is pooling block and error sources of variation. This is equivalent to the set-to-zero approach, and, as noted above, is a recipe for inflated Type I error rates and poor confidence interval coverage. If the design used blocking, the data analyst must respect the design.

2.5.2 Use of NOBOUND to Avoid Loss of Type I Error Control

In this approach, you override the set-to-zero default using the option NOBOUND in the PROC statement. You can use NOBOUND in either PROC GLIMMIX or PROC MIXED.

Program

The PROC GLIMMIX statements are shown in Program 2.10.

Program 2.10

```
proc glimmix data=zero_v_ex nobound;
 class block trt;
 model y=trt;
 random block;
run;
```

Results

Output 2.15: Variance Estimates Obtained Using the PROC GLIMMIX NOBOUND Option

Covariance Parameter Estimates		
Cov Parm	Estimate	Standard Error
block	-1.5627	0.5350
Residual	10.0419	3.1755

Notice that the variance estimate for BLK corresponds to $(1/t)\left[\mathrm{MS}(blk)-\mathrm{MS}(residual)\right]=(1/6)\left[0.66-10.04\right]$ from the ANOVA table above. The residual variance estimate is now equal to the MS(*residual*). NOBOUND results in the following F statistic for treatment:

Type III Tests of Fixed Effects				
Effect	Num DF	Den DF	F Value	Pr > F
trt	5	20	1.18	0.3542

As with the variance estimates, this result agrees with the ANOVA table. The main problem with the NOBOUND option is that it makes interpreting the block variance awkward.

2.5.3 Re-parameterization of the Model as Compound Symmetry

As an alternative to NOBOUND, you can re-parameterize the randomized block model as follows to avoid the need to report a negative variance. The re-parameterized model is called a *compound symmetry* model, which is an important tool for mixed model analysis.

Re-write the model from Equation 2.1 as $y_{ij} = \mu + \tau_i + w_{ij}$, instead of $y_{ij} = \mu + \tau_i + b_j + e_{ij}$. That is, let $w_{ij} = b_j + e_{ij}$. You can easily show that $\mathrm{Var}(w_{ij}) = \sigma_b^2 + \sigma^2$ and $\mathrm{Cov}(w_{ij}, w_{i'j}) = \sigma_b^2$. It follows that the correlation between any two observations on different treatments in the same block is $\rho = \sigma_b^2 / (\sigma_b^2 + \sigma^2)$. This is called the *intra-class correlation*. The model equation $y_{ij} = \mu + \tau_i + w_{ij}$, with $\mathrm{Cov}(w_{ij}, w_{i'j})$ redefined as the intra-class covariance and denoted σ_w, is the simplest version of the compound symmetry covariance model. If $\sigma_w \geq 0$, the compound symmetry and randomized block model, with b_j defined as a random effect, are equivalent. However, unlike σ_b^2 in the randomized block model, σ_w, being a covariance, is not required to be nonnegative. The compound symmetry model enables you to interpret an apparently negative variance as a covariance. In fact, in many experiments, there are competition effects among experimental units within blocks, making negative covariance an unsurprising result.

Program

You can implement the compound symmetry model for randomized block designs using Program 2.11.

Program 2.11

```
proc glimmix;
 class blk trt;
 model y=trt;
 random trt / subject=blk type=cs residual;
run;
```

Read the RANDOM statement beginning with SUBJECT=BLK. This signifies that the residuals are assumed to be correlated within each block. TYPE=CS signifies that the correlation structure is compound symmetry. RANDOM TRT does *not* mean that TRT effects are random—it merely signifies that TRT identifies each observation within a block, and that the number of treatment levels determines the dimension of the covariance structure within each subject level, i.e., block in this case. The word RESIDUAL signifies that this covariance is part of the residual variance structure, not a random model effect. An equivalent way to write the RANDOM statement is as follows:

```
 random _residual_ / subject=blk type=cs;
```

The equivalent PROC MIXED statements are:

```
proc mixed;
 class blk trt;
 model y=trt;
 repeated / subject=blk type=cs;
run;
```

Results

The results from PROC GLIMMIX appear in Output 2.15.

Output 2.16: Compound Symmetry Covariance Estimates Obtained Using PROC GLIMMIX

Covariance Parameter Estimates			
Cov Parm	Subject	Estimate	Standard Error
CS	block	-1.5627	0.5350
Residual		10.0419	3.1755

Type III Tests of Fixed Effects				
Effect	Num DF	Den DF	F Value	Pr > F
trt	5	20	1.18	0.3542

Notice that the variance estimates are identical to those obtained using the NOBOUND option, as is the test statistic for TRT. The only difference is that the block variance has been relabeled as the CS covariance associated with block.

The compound symmetry model is the simplest form of a *marginal* model. Mixed models in which all sources of variation over and above residual appear as random effects in the linear predictor are called *conditional* mixed models. The name "conditional" is somewhat misleading: the best way to understand the distinction is that conditional mixed models enable you to compute predictions (called "Best Linear Unbiased Predictors") from linear combinations of fixed and random effects, whereas marginal models have only fixed effects in the linear predictor and account for all random variation through the residual covariance structure.

Note that the above comments are primarily applicable in cases involving designed experiments or observational studies with a clearly defined design structure (e.g. matched-pairs). In such cases, it is important to respect the design in the sense that sources of variation that are part of the design structure must be accounted for by the model in some form. On the other hand, in observational studies in which a term is included in the model because it is *suspected* to be a source of variation, but not *known* to be a source of variation, dropping the effect if it produces a set-to-zero variance estimate is preferable to the NOBOUND or compound symmetry approach.

2.6 Introduction to Mixed Model Theory

The randomized complete block design presents one of the simplest applications of mixed models. It has one fixed effect (treatments) and one random effect (blocks). In this section, we use the RCBD to introduce essential theory that underlies the mixed model. Refer to Appendix A, "Linear Mixed Model Theory," for the general setting and for additional details.

2.6.1 Review of Regression Model in Matrix Notation

The standard equation for the linear regression model is as follows:

$$y = \beta_0 + \beta_1 x_1 + \ldots + \beta_k x_k + e$$

In an application there would be *n* observed values of *y* and corresponding values of the predictor variables $x_1, \ldots, x_k$. Often the values of *y* are considered to be independent realizations with equal variance. These can be represented in matrix notation as

$$\mathbf{Y} = \mathbf{X}\boldsymbol{\beta} + \mathbf{e} \tag{2.2}$$

where the terms are defined as follows:

- **Y** is the *n* vector of observations.
- **X** is an $n \times (k + 1)$ matrix comprising a column of 1s and columns of observed values of $x_1, \ldots, x_k$.
- $\boldsymbol{\beta} = \begin{bmatrix} \beta_0 & \beta_1 & \beta_2 & \ldots & \beta_k \end{bmatrix}'$ is the *n* vector of regression coefficients.
- **e** is a vector of realizations of the errors *e*.

At this point we assume only that the error vector **e** has mean **0** and covariance matrix $\sigma^2\mathbf{I}$, denoted as $\mathbf{e} \sim (\mathbf{0}, \sigma^2\mathbf{I})$. This covariance matrix reflects the assumption of uncorrelated errors. In linear mixed models, we add the assumptions that the errors are normally distributed, denoted as $\mathbf{e} \sim N(\mathbf{0}, \sigma^2\mathbf{I})$. Note that when the normality assumption is added, lack of correlation among the errors is tantamount to independence of the errors. Refer to the expression $\mathbf{Y} = \mathbf{X}\boldsymbol{\beta} + \mathbf{e}$ as the *model equation* form of the fixed effects linear model.

Alternatively, you can rewrite Equation 2.2 as follows:

$$\mathbf{Y} \sim N\left(\mathbf{X}\boldsymbol{\beta}, \sigma^2\mathbf{I}\right). \tag{2.3}$$

Refer to this as the *probability distribution* form of the fixed effects linear model. There are two advantages to the probability distribution form. First, Equation 2.3 makes it clear that $\mathbf{X}\boldsymbol{\beta}$ models $E(\mathbf{Y})$. Second, the probability distribution form can be generalized to describe linear models for non-Gaussian data, whereas the model equation form cannot. The model equation form is useful for theoretical development of the mixed model with Gaussian (normally distributed) data, so we will continue to use it when appropriate in this book. However, it general, Equation 2.3 is the preferred form.

2.6.2 The RCBD Model in Matrix Notation

The RCBD model in Equation 2.1 can be written in matrix notation. In explicit detail, the model equation is as follows:

$$
\begin{bmatrix} y_{11} \\ \cdot \\ \cdot \\ \cdot \\ y_{t1} \\ \cdot \\ \cdot \\ y_{1r} \\ \cdot \\ \cdot \\ \cdot \\ y_{tr} \end{bmatrix} = \begin{bmatrix} 1\,1\,\ldots\,0 \\ \cdot\,\cdot\,\cdot\,\cdot \\ \cdot\,\cdot\,\cdot\,\cdot \\ \cdot\,\cdot\,\cdot\,\cdot \\ 1\,0\quad 1 \\ \cdot\,\cdot\,\cdot \\ \cdot\,\cdot\,\cdot \\ 1\,1\,\ldots\,0 \\ \cdot\,\cdot\,\cdot\,\cdot \\ \cdot\,\cdot\,\cdot\,\cdot \\ \cdot\,\cdot\,\cdot\,\cdot \\ 1\,0\quad 1 \end{bmatrix} \begin{bmatrix} \mu \\ \tau_1 \\ \cdot \\ \cdot \\ \cdot \\ \tau_t \end{bmatrix} + \begin{bmatrix} 1\,.\,\ldots\,0 \\ \cdot\,\cdot\quad\cdot \\ \cdot\quad\cdot \\ 1\,.\,\ldots\,0 \\ \cdot\,\cdot \\ \cdot\quad\cdot \\ 0\,\ldots\,1 \\ \cdot\,\cdot \\ \cdot\quad\cdot \\ 0\,\ldots\,1 \end{bmatrix} \begin{bmatrix} b_1 \\ \cdot \\ \cdot \\ b_r \end{bmatrix} + \begin{bmatrix} e_{11} \\ \cdot \\ \cdot \\ \cdot \\ e_{t1} \\ \cdot \\ \cdot \\ e_{1r} \\ \cdot \\ \cdot \\ \cdot \\ e_{tr} \end{bmatrix}
$$

The terms are defined as in Equation 2.1. In more compact matrix notation the equation is as follows:

$$\mathbf{Y} = \mathbf{X}\boldsymbol{\beta} + \mathbf{Z}\mathbf{u} + \mathbf{e} \tag{2.4}$$

The definitions are as follows:

- **Y** is the vector of observations
- **X** is the treatment design matrix
- **β** is the vector of treatment fixed effect parameters
- **Z** is the block design matrix
- **u** is the vector of random block effects
- **e** is the vector of residuals

The model Equation 2.4 states that the vector **Y** of observations can be expressed as a sum of fixed treatment effects **Xβ**, random block effects **Zu**, and random experimental errors **e**. The **Xβ** portion is defined by the MODEL statement, and the **Zu** portion is defined by the RANDOM statement. It is not necessary in this example to define the residuals **e**.

For the RCBD model in matrix notation, the random vector **u** has a multivariate normal distribution with mean vector **0** and covariance matrix $\sigma_b^2 \mathbf{I}_t$, $\mathbf{u} \sim \mathrm{N}(\mathbf{0}, \sigma_b^2 \mathbf{I}_t)$, and the random vector **e** is distributed $\mathrm{N}(\mathbf{0}, \sigma^2 \mathbf{I}_{tr})$.

As with the fixed effects linear model, you can express Equation 2.4 in probability distribution form as

$$\mathbf{Y} \mid \mathbf{u} \sim \mathrm{N}\big(\mathbf{X}\boldsymbol{\beta} + \mathbf{Z}\mathbf{u}, \mathbf{R}\big); \ \mathbf{u} \sim \mathrm{N}\big(\mathbf{0}, \mathbf{G}\big) \tag{2.5}$$

For the randomized block design as presented in this chapter, $\mathbf{R} = \sigma^2 \mathbf{I}$, and $\mathbf{G} = \sigma_b^2 \mathbf{I}_t$. As with Equation 2.3, Equation 2.5 can be adapted for mixed models with non-Gaussian data. Notice that with a mixed model, the distribution of the observation vector, **Y**, as conditional on the random model effects, and the mixed model linear predictor is used to estimate the conditional expectation, $\mathrm{E}\big(\mathbf{Y} \mid \mathbf{u}\big)$.

You can also write the marginal distribution of **Y** in model form as follows:

$$\mathbf{Y} \sim \mathrm{N}\big(\mathbf{X}\boldsymbol{\beta}, \mathbf{V}\big)$$

where $\mathbf{V} = \mathbf{ZGZ'} + \mathbf{R}$. The specific form of $\mathbf{V}$ for the randomized block design is

$$
\mathbf{V} = \begin{bmatrix} \sigma_b^2 \mathbf{J}_t & \mathbf{0}_{t\times t} & \cdots & \mathbf{0}_{t\times t} \\ \mathbf{0}_{t\times t} & \sigma_b^2 \mathbf{J}_t & \cdots & \mathbf{0}_{t\times t} \\ \mathbf{0}_{t\times t} & \mathbf{0}_{t\times t} & \ddots & \vdots \\ \mathbf{0}_{t\times t} & \mathbf{0}_{t\times t} & \cdots & \sigma_b^2 \mathbf{J}_t \end{bmatrix} + \sigma^2 \mathbf{I}_{tr}
$$

$$
= \begin{bmatrix} \sigma_b^2 \mathbf{J}_t + \sigma^2 \mathbf{I}_t & \mathbf{0}_{t\times t} & \cdots & \mathbf{0}_{t\times t} \\ \mathbf{0}_{t\times t} & \sigma_b^2 \mathbf{J}_t + \sigma^2 \mathbf{I}_t & \cdots & \mathbf{0}_{t\times t} \\ \mathbf{0}_{t\times t} & \mathbf{0}_{t\times t} & \ddots & \vdots \\ \mathbf{0}_{t\times t} & \mathbf{0}_{t\times t} & \cdots & \sigma_b^2 \mathbf{J}_t + \sigma^2 \mathbf{I}_t \end{bmatrix}
$$

where $\sigma_b^2 \mathbf{J}_t + \sigma^2 \mathbf{I}_t$ is the covariance matrix of the observations in a particular block, $\mathbf{0}_{t\times t}$ is a $t \times t$ matrix of zeros, and $\mathbf{J}_t$ is a $t \times t$ matrix of ones.

Alternatively, you can redefine σ_b^2 as the compound symmetry covariance, denoted as σ_{cs} or you can denote $\mathrm{Var}\left(y_{ij}\right) = \sigma_y^2$, define the intra-class correlation as $\rho = \sigma_{cs}/\sigma_y^2$ and write $\mathrm{Var}(\mathbf{Y})$ as the compound symmetry covariance matrix:

$$
\mathbf{V} = \sigma_y^2 \begin{bmatrix} \rho \mathbf{J}_t + (1-\rho)\mathbf{I}_t & \mathbf{0}_{t\times t} & \cdots & \mathbf{0}_{t\times t} \\ \mathbf{0}_{t\times t} & \rho \mathbf{J}_t + (1-\rho)\mathbf{I}_t & \cdots & \mathbf{0}_{t\times t} \\ \mathbf{0}_{t\times t} & \mathbf{0}_{t\times t} & \cdots & \cdots \\ \mathbf{0}_{t\times t} & \mathbf{0}_{t\times t} & \cdots & \rho \mathbf{J}_t + (1-\rho)\mathbf{I}_t \end{bmatrix}
$$

Note that in theory, $\sigma_b^2 = \sigma_{cs}$, $\sigma_y^2 = \sigma_b^2 + \sigma^2$ and $\rho = \sigma_b^2/(\sigma_b^2 + \sigma^2)$. You see the main advantage of the compound symmetry form in Section 2.5: it provides a useful way to deal with the problem of negative block variance estimates.

2.6.3 Inference Basics for the Randomized Block Mixed Model

If you want to estimate and perform inference on the fixed effects only—the treatment effects—you can use the fact that the estimate of $\boldsymbol{\beta}$ from the mixed model equations is equivalent to the solution from the generalized least squares (GLS) estimating equation $\mathbf{V}^{-1}\mathbf{X}\boldsymbol{\beta} = \mathbf{X}\mathbf{V}^{-1}\mathbf{y}$. The matrix $\mathbf{X}$ is not of full column rank and so $\mathbf{X'V}^{-1}\mathbf{X}$ is singular. You must use a generalized inverse to obtain a GLS solution of the fixed effect parameter vector $\boldsymbol{\beta}$. But the treatment means, differences between treatment means, and contrasts are estimable. Thus, no matter what generalized inverse is used, there will be a vector $\mathbf{K}$ for which $\mathbf{K'\beta}$ is equal to the mean, difference or contrast of interest. For example, choosing $\mathbf{K'} = [1,1,0,...,0]$ gives $\mathbf{K'\beta} = \mu + \tau_1 = \mu_1$. Then the general theory gives

$$
\mathrm{Var}\left[\mathbf{K}'\hat{\boldsymbol{\beta}}\right] = \left(\sigma_b^2 + \sigma^2\right)/r
$$

where $\hat{\boldsymbol{\beta}}$ is the generalized least-squares estimate. Likewise, $\mathbf{K'} = [0,1,-1,0...,0]$ gives $\mathbf{K'\beta} = \mu_1 - \mu_2$, and $\mathrm{Var}[\mathbf{K}'\hat{\boldsymbol{\beta}}] = 2\sigma^2/r$. These are the expressions presented in Section 2.2.1.

In the case of a relatively simple, balanced design such as an RCBD, the variance expressions can be derived directly from the model. This was the approach in Section 2.2.1. But more complicated, unbalanced situations require you to use the general theoretical result, $\mathrm{Var}[\mathbf{K}'\hat{\boldsymbol{\beta}}] = \mathbf{K}'\left(\mathbf{X'V}^{-1}\mathbf{X}\right)^{-}\mathbf{K}$. Given that the variance components are generally unknown and must be estimated, in practice you use the estimated variance, denoted as $\mathbf{K}'\left(\mathbf{X'\hat{V}}^{-1}\mathbf{X}\right)^{-}\mathbf{K}$, for the following inferential statistics.

If $\mathbf{k}$ is a vector (e.g. for estimating a treatment difference or a contrast), then you can use a t statistic,

$$
t = \mathbf{k}'\hat{\boldsymbol{\beta}}\Big/\sqrt{\mathbf{k}'\left(\mathbf{X'\hat{V}}^{-1}\mathbf{X}\right)^{-}\mathbf{k}}
$$

Also, if $\mathbf{k}$ is a vector, you can obtain a confidence interval for $\mathbf{K'\beta}$ with $\mathbf{k}'\hat{\boldsymbol{\beta}} \pm t_{v,\alpha/2}\sqrt{\mathbf{k}'\left(\mathbf{X\hat{V}}^{-1}\mathbf{X}\right)^{-}\mathbf{k}}$, where v denotes the degrees of freedom that are associated with the estimate of $\mathbf{k}'\left(\mathbf{X\hat{V}}^{-1}\mathbf{X}\right)^{-}\mathbf{k}$.

If **K** is a matrix, which it is for testing any hypothesis with more than 1 numerator degree of freedom, square the t ratio to get the estimated Wald statistic, $\left(\mathbf{K}'\tilde{\boldsymbol{\beta}}\right)\left[\mathbf{K}'\left(\mathbf{X}'\hat{\mathbf{V}}^{-1}\mathbf{X}\right)^{-}\mathbf{K}\right]^{-1}\mathbf{K}'\hat{\boldsymbol{\beta}}$. For complete block designs, when $\mathbf{K}'\boldsymbol{\beta}$ defines treatment difference or differences, the estimated Wald statistic reduces to $\left(\mathbf{K}'\hat{\boldsymbol{\beta}}\right)\left[\mathbf{K}'\left(\mathbf{X}'\mathbf{X}\right)^{-}\mathbf{K}\right]^{-1}\mathbf{K}'\hat{\boldsymbol{\beta}}\big/\hat{\sigma}^2$, which is equal to $SS(\mathbf{K}'\boldsymbol{\beta})/MSE$. Dividing by $\text{rank}(\mathbf{K})$ gives you $MS(\mathbf{K}'\boldsymbol{\beta})/MSE$, an F statistic.

These are the general theoretical results in the RCBD setting. They are provided to assist readers with a matrix and mathematical statistics background to better understand the methodology used in this chapter.

2.7 Summary

Chapter 2 begins with an example of a randomized block design with fixed treatments and random blocks. The importance of accounting for random effects in such a basic situation, to correctly compute the variance of a treatment mean, is demonstrated. The use of PROC GLIMMIX and PROC MIXED is introduced with explanations of how to set up the MODEL and RANDOM statements. Then, PROC GLM is briefly discussed, with emphasis on the fact that GLM is intended for fixed effect only models. We emphasize the basic applications that are handled appropriately by PROC MIXED and PROC GLIMMIX but not by PROC GLM. Then, an incomplete block design is used in Section 2.4 to illustrate some of the issues associated with unbalanced mixed model data. These include recovery of inter-block information, the difference between intra-block (fixed block) and combined inter-/intra-block (random block) analysis, and the difference between the arithmetic, or sample, mean and the least squares mean. The issue of negative "estimates" of variance components, why they matter and what to do about them, is discussed in Section 2.5. The chapter concludes with a section intended for readers with a matrix and mathematical statistics background, introducing mixed model theory relevant to estimation and inference for blocked designs.

Chapter 3: Mean Comparisons for Fixed Effects

3.1 Introduction 49
3.2 Comparison of Two Treatments 50
    3.2.1 Example Using PROC TTEST...50
    3.2.2 Analysis Using PROC GLIMMIX 51
3.3 Comparison of Several Means: Analysis of Variance 52
    3.3.1 Relationship between LSMEANS and Fixed Effects Solution....................................52
    3.3.2 Standard Errors for Mean Comparisons...54
    3.3.3 Multiple Comparisons and Planned Comparisons 57
3.4 Comparison of Quantitative Factors: Polynomial Regression..58
    3.4.1 Analysis of a Regression Experiment 58
    3.4.2 Type I versus Type III Sums of Squares...61
    3.4.3 Direct Fit of Polynomial...62
    3.4.4 Orthogonal Polynomial Contrasts 65
3.5 Mean Comparisons in Factorial Designs...67
    3.5.1 Factorial: The Basics..67
    3.5.2 A More Complex Two-Way Factorial Experiment..72
    3.5.3 Multiple Comparisons for a Factorial Experiment 74
    3.5.4 Multiple Comparisons of METHOD Means by VARIETY Using SLICE and SLICEDIFF 74
    3.5.5 Planned Comparisons in a Two-Way Factorial Experiment: CONTRAST, ESTIMATE, and LSMESTIMATE...77
    3.5.6 Simple Effect Comparisons—Using LSMESTIMATE 78
    3.5.7 Simple Effect Comparisons—Using Model Parameters: How ESTIMATE and LSMESTIMATE Differ 79
    3.5.8 Simultaneous Contrasts in Two-Way Classifications...81
    3.5.9 Comparison of Levels of One Factor within Subgroups of Levels of Another Factor......82
    3.5.10 Quantitative by Qualitative Factorial: An Example..84
    3.5.11 Example: Factorial with Two Continuous Factors 92
3.6 Summary..99

3.1 Introduction

In Chapter 1 the difference between the experiment design (blocking, experimental units, etc.) and treatment design (the factors and levels applied to the experimental units) were introduced. Chapter 2 focused primarily upon obtaining estimates of variance components, estimates of fixed effects, and overall tests of model effects for simple blocked experiment designs. However, in most cases, the overall F tests for fixed model effects represent a starting point, not a final product. Typically, you not only want to know whether there is an overall treatment difference. If there are more than two treatments, you want to know which treatments are different. How big are the treatment differences? Are they large enough to matter? Which treatment is "better"?

This chapter extends the examples from Chapter 2 to demonstrate various mean comparison procedures. This chapter also covers and builds upon some fundamental inferential concepts of linear models, which have a very rich history in statistical practice and were a core motivation for the formation of SAS Institute and PROC GLM in the 1970s. For additional discussion with lots of great examples, refer to Littell et al. (2002) and Milliken and Johnson volumes 1–3 (2009, 1989, and 2001). We focus here on core methods and examples that form the basis for treatment comparisons in a modern mixed model framework. While some of the treatment designs may be analyzed using design-specific procedures when the experiment design is a completely randomized design, we focus on using mixed model procedures (PROC GLIMMIX, in particular) even with the simple examples as it is necessary when factorial treatment designs are combined with complex experiment designs. We begin with a simple comparison of two treatments in Section 3.2. Section 3.3 presents approaches for comparing more than two treatments. Section 3.4 illustrates methods appropriate for treatment designs whose factor levels are quantitative. Sections 3.5 introduces methods for factorial treatment structures and complex quantitative by qualitative factorial designs. The examples in this chapter demonstrate the use of the LSMEANS, ESTIMATE, CONTRAST and LSMESTIMATE statements and their options to address the various goals of comparative experiments.

3.2 Comparison of Two Treatments

One of the most basic analyses is a comparison of two treatments. This typically occurs in one of two forms: independent samples (i.e. a completely randomized design with two treatments) and paired samples. A randomized block experiment with two treatments is an example of paired samples. Paired sampling gives rise to the simplest mixed model intended for comparing treatments. It is vitally important to recognize the difference between paired or blocked and independent samples, because a failure to accommodate pairing can dramatically influence conclusions about your treatments. The following example uses variation of the paired sample experiment: before- and after-treatment responses on the same experimental unit.

A combination stimulant-relaxant drug is administered to 15 animals whose pulse rates are measured before (PRE) and after (POST) administration of the drug. The purpose of the experiment is to determine whether there is a change in the pulse rate as a result of the drug. The data are in the PULSE data set in the sample library. The simplest method of analyzing a paired sample experiment is a *t* test. However, the paired comparison *t* test can be viewed as a special case of mixed model methodology. For completeness, and to establish the connection to mixed models, analyses of this example using PROC TTEST and PROC GLIMMIX are presented.

3.2.1 Example Using PROC TTEST

The appropriate *t* statistic is $t = \bar{d}/s_{\bar{d}}$, where

$$\bar{d} = \sum_i d_i / n_i$$

with d_i being the difference between the PRE and POST measurement for the ith animal, and

$$s_d = \sqrt{\sum_i (d_i - \bar{d})/(n-1)}$$

The *t* test is one of the most popular of all statistics and can be computed using PROC TTEST, one of the very first statistical procedures in all of SAS. The TTEST procedure computes two-sample *t* tests for the paired case and independent case.

Program

For the paired test, use Program 3.1.

Program 3.1

```
proc ttest;
   paired pre*post;
run;
```

The statement PAIRED PRE*POST causes the test to be computed for the paired difference PRE-POST.

Results

The results appear in Output 3.1.

Output 3.1 Paired-Difference Analysis Using PROC TTEST with the PAIRED Option

The TTEST Procedure
Difference: pre − post

N	Mean	Std Dev	Std Err	Minimum	Maximum
15	1.4667	2.3258	0.6005	-2.0000	7.0000

Mean	95% CL Mean		Std Dev	95% CL Std Dev	
1.4667	0.1787	2.7547	2.3258	1.7028	3.6681

DF	t Value	Pr > |t|
14	2.44	0.0285

Interpretation

The estimated mean difference of PRE-POST, 1.4667, appears in the column labeled MEAN. The lower and upper 95% confidence limits about the mean appear in the column labeled 95% CL Mean. This mean difference has a *t* value of 2.44 with *p* = 0.0285 indicating a statistically significant change in mean pulse rate. Since the mean is positive, the drug evidently decreases pulse rate.

3.2.2 Analysis Using PROC GLIMMIX

The data in the PULSE data set were entered with one line per animal. To analyze these data as a randomized block design using PROC GLIMMIX, the data must be stacked with separate data lines for the PRE and POST responses. Doing so also requires creating a variable to identify the observation's "treatment," that is, PRE or POST. You can obtain the stacked data using the following DATA step.

```
data pulsestack; set pulse;
   y=pre; trt="pre "; output;
   y=post; trt="post"; output;
run;
```

Now each experimental unit has two observations, one for each of the PRE and POST "treatment" levels. ANIMAL is the block in this setup.

Program

Using the stacked data, Program 3.2 shows the PROC GLIMMIX statements to analyze the experiment as a randomized block design.

Program 3.2

```
proc glimmix data=pulsestack;
   class trt animal;
   model y = trt;
   random animal;
   lsmeans trt/diff;
run;
```

Results

Output 3.2 shows the results of this analysis.

Output 3.2 Paired-Difference Analysis Using PROC GLIMMIX with random blocks

Covariance Parameter Estimates		
Cov Parm	Estimate	Standard Error
animal	4.9333	2.4301
Residual	2.7048	1.0223

Type III Tests of Fixed Effects

Effect	Num DF	Den DF	F Value	Pr > F
trt	1	14	5.96	0.0285

trt Least Squares Means

trt	Estimate	Standard Error	DF	t Value	Pr > |t|
post	62.2667	0.7136	14	87.26	<.0001
pre	63.7333	0.7136	14	89.31	<.0001

Differences of trt Least Squares Means

trt	_trt	Estimate	Standard Error	DF	t Value	Pr > |t|
post	pre	-1.4667	0.6005	14	-2.44	0.0285

Interpretation

The Covariance Parameter Estimates table shows the estimated variance between the experimental units (EUs), 4.9333, which is nearly twice the residual or within experimental unit variance, 2.7048. The intra-class correlation is 4.933/(4.933 + 2.705) = 0.65, signifying a strong correlation between measurements on the same EU. The Type III Tests of Fixed Effects has the F test for the difference between treatments. Here, the F value, 5.96, is the square of the t value obtained in the t test (Output 3.1), 2.44, and has the same p-value, 0.0285, indicating a significant effect of the drug on the animal's pulse rate. The LSMEANS statement requests the estimates of the treatment means and their difference be provided. Because the SAS procedures process names in alpha-numeric order (as default, but can be changed by using the ORDER=data option), the difference is POST-PRE and therefore is estimated as −1.4667, the opposite sign as from PROC TTEST.

In the next section, we extend the analysis from two treatments to more than two, as most experiments include multiple treatments for efficiency.

3.3 Comparison of Several Means: Analysis of Variance

In Chapter 2, Section 2.3, we began with an example of analysis of variance using the BOND data. Three different metals were used to bond two pieces of an ingot together. The amount of pressure required to break the bond was measured as the response. The seven ingots serve as complete blocks, so there are seven observations for each metal. The initial analysis results in a p-value for the Type III Tests of Fixed Effects of .0131indicating there is a significant difference in the amount of pressure required to break the bond between the three metals. Although this tells us that there is evidence that at least one treatment mean is different, it does not say which mean is different, nor does it tell us how different. For this, we need mean comparison procedures, which in mixed models are implemented using functions of the model parameters called *least squares means*, defined below in Section 3.3.1. When comparing more than two treatment levels, a natural starting point is to consider all pairwise comparisons.

3.3.1 Relationship between LSMEANS and Fixed Effects Solution

You can obtain treatment means from the LSMEANS statement. Linear combinations of means can be estimated and compared in a variety of ways, including the DIFF and SLICE options and the LSMESTIMATE, ESTIMATE, and CONTRAST statements. These statements all compute linear combinations of estimates of parameters defined in the MODEL statement with coefficients in the order of the terms in the solution.

The statement

```
model pres=metal;
```

specifies that the expected value of y_{ij} in equation (2.1) for a given metal can be represented as follows:

$$E[y_{ij}] = \mu + \tau_i = \mu_i$$

The *least squares means* are model-based estimates of these means. In other words, they are calculated from estimates of the model fixed effect parameters in the expressions: lsmean for metal $i = \hat{\mu} + \hat{\tau}_i$. The general interpretation of least squares means are as estimates of the treatment effects under a balanced design. The following program provides a simple example.

Program

Program 3.3 shows the PROC GLIMMIX statements to obtain treatment mean estimates (LSMEANS), treatment mean differences (DIFF option), confidence limits for both (CL option), ESTIMATE of the least squares mean of the nickel treatment ($\hat{\mu} + \hat{\tau}_3$), and ESTIMATE and CONTRAST for the difference between the copper and iron means ($\hat{\tau}_1 - \hat{\tau}_2$). Note that all SAS linear model procedures read levels of CLASS variables in alphabetical order (see the output in the "Results" below). Hence, τ_1 denotes the effect of the first treatment in alphabetical order (copper), τ_2 denotes the effect of the second treatment (iron) and τ_3 denotes the effect of the third (nickel). Note the correspondence of 1, −1 and 0 after METAL in the ESTIMATE and CONTRAST statements. These specify the coefficients for the respective τ_i in each statement. INTERCEPT 1 means μ is included in the terms to be estimated; absence of INTERCEPT means μ is not included. The SOLUTION option in the MODEL statement (you can abbreviate it as S) presents estimates of the fixed effect parameters.

Program 3.3

```
proc glimmix data=bond plots=(meanplot diffplot);
   class ingot metal;
   model pres = metal / solution;
   random ingot;
   lsmeans metal / diff cl;
   estimate 'nickel mean' intercept 1 metal 0   0 1;
   estimate 'copper vs iron'            metal 1 -1 0;
   contrast 'copper vs iron'            metal 1 -1 0;
run;
```

Results

Results from the SOLUTION option and the LSMEANS statement appear in Output 3.3. The ESTIMATE and CONTRAST statements appear in Output 3.4. The plots generated are in Figures 3.1 and 3.2, displayed in the next section.

Output 3.3: Results from the SOLUTION Option and LSMEANS Statements

			Solutions for Fixed Effects			
Effect	metal	Estimate	Standard Error	DF	t Value	Pr > |t|
Intercept		71.1000	1.7655	6	40.27	<.0001
metal	c	-0.9143	1.7214	12	-0.53	0.6050
metal	i	4.8000	1.7214	12	2.79	0.0164
metal	n	0	.	.	.	.

		metal Least Squares Means							
metal	Estimate	Standard Error	DF	t Value	Pr > |t|	Alpha	Lower	Upper
c	70.1857	1.7655	12	39.75	<.0001	0.05	66.3390	74.0324
i	75.9000	1.7655	12	42.99	<.0001	0.05	72.0533	79.7467
n	71.1000	1.7655	12	40.27	<.0001	0.05	67.2533	74.9467

			Differences of metal Least Squares Means						
metal	_metal	Estimate	Standard Error	DF	t Value	Pr > |t|	Alpha	Lower	Upper
c	i	-5.7143	1.7214	12	-3.32	0.0061	0.05	-9.4650	-1.9636
c	n	-0.9143	1.7214	12	-0.53	0.6050	0.05	-4.6650	2.8364
i	n	4.8000	1.7214	12	2.79	0.0164	0.05	1.0493	8.5507

Interpretation

The "Solution for Fixed Effects" table contains estimates of the fixed effects parameters. Because the **X** matrix is not of full rank, a consequence of having a classification variable in the MODEL statement and of including an intercept column in **X**, the estimates labeled "Intercept," "Metal c," "Metal i," and "Metal n" are not unbiased estimates of μ, τ_1, τ_2, and τ_3. The problem of a singular **X** matrix is solved by setting to zero the fixed effects solution corresponding to the last column of the classification effect METAL in the MODEL statement. The last level in this example "n" is the reference level. The other solutions are unbiased estimates of deviations from the reference level. The row labeled "Intercept" estimates $\mu + \tau_3$, the row labeled "Metal c" estimates $\tau_1 - \tau_3$, the row labeled "Metal i" estimates $\tau_2 - \tau_3$, and the row labeled "Metal n" estimates $\tau_3 - \tau_3 = 0$, yielding the following:

$$\hat{\mu} + \hat{\tau}_3 = 71.100$$
$$\hat{\tau}_1 - \hat{\tau}_3 = -0.9143$$
$$\hat{\tau}_2 - \hat{\tau}_3 = 4.800$$

Because there is no unique way of resolving the singularity in **X**, there is no unique way of deriving solutions. For example, changing the names of the metals in such a way that their order changes affects the choice of the reference level. However, certain linear combinations of the estimates are unique. These linear combinations correspond to *estimable functions* (See Littell, Stroup, and Freund, 2002 and Milliken and Johnson, 2009). Least squares means are such estimable functions of the fixed effects parameters.

The "Least Squares Means" table provides the model-based estimates of the least squares means. Since, for example, $\mu_1 = \mu + \tau_1 = \mu + \tau_3 + (\tau_1 - \tau_3)$, the least squares means in this example can be related easily to the estimates displayed in the "Solution for Fixed Effects" table.

$$\hat{\mu}_1 = \hat{\mu} + \hat{\tau}_1 = \hat{\mu} + \hat{\tau}_3 + (\hat{\tau}_1 - \hat{\tau}_3) = 71.1 + (-0.9142) = 70.1857$$
$$\hat{\mu}_2 = \hat{\mu} + \hat{\tau}_2 = \hat{\mu} + \hat{\tau}_3 + (\hat{\tau}_2 - \hat{\tau}_3) = 71.1 + (4.8) = 75.9$$
$$\hat{\mu}_3 = \hat{\mu} + \hat{\tau}_3 = \hat{\mu} + \hat{\tau}_3 + (\hat{\tau}_3 - \hat{\tau}_3) = 71.1 + (0.0) = 71.1$$

Because this design is balanced, the least squares means are simply the arithmetic averages of the data values from each of the treatments. This will generally not be the case for unbalanced designs.

> **Note:** Many textbooks refer to μ as the "overall mean." This is true only if we make assumptions about the model effects, in this case τ_i, that are unnecessary, and not used by any SAS linear model procedures (see Appendix A for details). It is correct to call μ the intercept, but in general it is *not correct* to call it the overall mean. Look at the "Solutions for Fixed Effects" table in Output 3.3 above: You can clearly see why this is so.

3.3.2 Standard Errors for Mean Comparisons

Along with the least squares mean and mean difference estimates, the PROC GLIMMIX listing includes the standard errors. These arise as follows. First obtain the theoretical variance of the estimator. By definition, the standard error is the square root of the estimated variance of the estimator.

Variance of a least square mean: For a paired sample with no missing data, the least square mean for treatment i is equal to the sample mean, i.e.

$$\hat{\mu} + \hat{\tau}_i = (1/b)\sum_j y_{ij}$$

You can express this in model terms as $(1/b)\sum_j (\mu + \tau_i + b_j + e_{ij})$ The variance is thus

$$\mathrm{Var}\left((1/b)\sum_j (\mu + \tau_i + b_j + e_{ij})\right) = (1/b)^2 \left(\sum_j \mathrm{Var}(\mu + \tau_i + b_j + e_{ij})\right)$$
$$= (1/b)^2 \left(b\,\mathrm{Var}(b_j) + b\,\mathrm{Var}(e_{ij})\right)$$
$$= \left(\sigma_b^2 + \sigma^2\right)/b$$

where b is the number of pairs, or blocks – in this case, $b = 7$. Thus, the estimated standard error of a least squares mean in this example is

$$\sqrt{\left(\hat{\sigma}^2 + \hat{\sigma}_b^2\right)/7} = 1.7655$$

A similar derivation gives the standard error of the difference. Begin with the difference between the two-treatment means, express the difference in terms of the model, and compute the variance:

$$(1/b)\sum_j y_{1j} - (1/b)\sum_j y_{2j} = (1/b)\sum_j \left[\left(\mu + \tau_1 + b_j + e_{1j}\right) - \left(\mu + \tau_2 + b_j + e_{2j}\right)\right]$$

$$= (1/b)\sum_j \left(\tau_1 - \tau_2 + e_{1j} - e_{2j}\right)$$

Computing the variance gives $(1/b)^2 \sum_j \text{Var}(e_{1j} - e_{2j}) = 2\sigma^2/b$.

Thus, the estimated standard error of a difference is $\sqrt{2\hat{\sigma}^2 / 7} = 1.7214$.

> **Important Note**: In this example, (and all blocked designs) the standard error of the mean depends on the block and the residual variances, whereas the standard error of the difference depends only on the residual variance. Many scientific journals make the mistake of providing only the standard error of the mean. However, the most important inference in a comparative experiment concerns treatment mean *differences*; the standard error of the estimated *difference* should be regarded as an *essential* piece of information in such publications. Except for a completely random design, you cannot determine the standard error of a difference if all you are given is the standard error of the mean.

The "Differences of Least Squares Means" table in Output 3.3 shows all possible pairwise comparisons among the three treatments. The interpretation of the results is that each row is a comparison of the mean in the column with heading metal minus the mean in the column with heading _metal. The estimated standard errors of the differences are all equal as the design is a randomized complete block with no missing data.

T values are computed to test that the differences between the respective means are zero. The results provide evidence that the means of both copper and nickel are different from iron but the copper and nickel means are not different from each other.

You can use the ESTIMATE statement for linear combinations of model effects. For illustration, consider estimating the linear combination equal to the nickel mean, μ_n. First, express the nickel mean as the estimable function $\mu_3 = \mu + \tau_3$. More explicitly, $\mu_3 = 1 \times \mu + 0 \times \tau_1 + 0 \times \tau_2 + 1 \times \tau_3$. These coefficients are used to construct the ESTIMATE statement:

```
estimate 'nickel mean' intercept 1 metal 0  0 1;
```

Similarly, the difference between the means for copper and iron is $\mu_1 - \mu_2 = \tau_1 - \tau_2$. The ESTIMATE and CONTRAST statements for this comparison are as follows:

```
estimate 'copper vs iron'        metal 1 -1 0;
contrast 'copper vs iron'        metal 1 -1 0;
```

Output 3.4 displays the results of these estimate and contrast statements.

Output 3.4: Inference about Linear Combinations of Means

		Estimates			
Label	Estimate	Standard Error	DF	t Value	Pr > |t|
nickel mean	71.1000	1.7655	12	40.27	<.0001
copper vs iron	-5.7143	1.7214	12	-3.32	0.0061

Contrasts				
Label	Num DF	Den DF	F Value	Pr > F
copper vs iron	1	12	11.02	0.0061

The "Estimates" table collects the results of the ESTIMATE statements. The nickel mean and the differences between the copper and iron means are the same as those obtained from the LSMEANS statement with the DIFF option in Output 3.4. Notice that the estimate of the nickel mean, 71.1, is equal to the solution for the Intercept in the solution table. This is due to the set to zero constraint. Therefore, the Intercept solution is *not* equal to the overall mean.

The "Contrasts" table collects the results of CONTRAST statements. The contrast of 'copper vs iron' tests the null hypothesis $H_0: \mu_1 - \mu_2 = 0$. It is associated with an F statistic of 11.02. This equals the square of the t value from the corresponding ESTIMATE statement (-3.32^2).

The ESTIMATE and CONTRAST statements are used to estimate and test hypotheses about linear combinations of terms in the mixed model, including random effects. The ESTIMATE statements in the GLIMMIX procedure allow multiple-row estimates and can adjust the corresponding t tests for multiplicity. The CONTRAST statement can consist of several linear combinations where the resulting F statistic provides a simultaneous test of the hypotheses that the set of linear combinations of the parameters are equal to zero.

The LSMEANS statement produces estimates and tests of treatment means and mean differences. The DIFF option, as the name implies, obtains mean differences. The PLOT options provide different ways of visualizing treatment means and differences. MEANPLOT shows the treatment means (Figure 3.1); the CL option places 95% confidence limits above and below each mean estimate. The DIFFPLOT (Figure 3.2) shows 95% confidence limits for all pairwise differences and plots them so that statistically significant and non-significant differences can readily be seen (once you get some practice looking at the plot!).

Important Note: Notice that the overlapping 95% confidence bars for the treatment means in Figure 3.1 must *not* be interpreted as the corresponding means are not significantly different. For example, the confidence bars for the copper and iron means overlap, but the *p*-value for the copper versus iron treatment mean difference is 0.0061. For an appropriate display of differences, see Figure 3.2.

Figure 3.1: Plot of the Least Squared Means

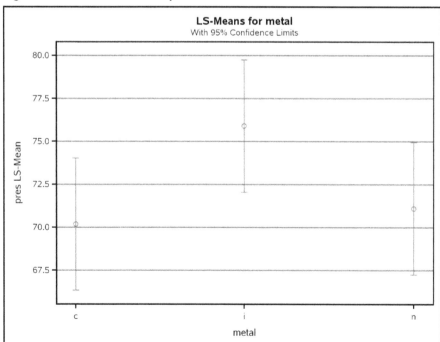

Figure 3.2: Plot of the Differences of the Least Squares Means

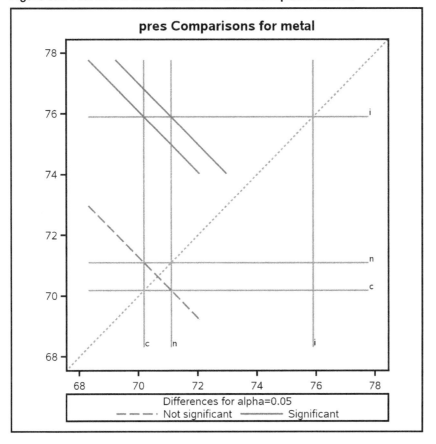

In the plot in Figure 3.2, the group means themselves are represented by both horizontal and vertical lines, labeled appropriately. The differences between means are represented by where the horizontal and vertical lines representing different means cross. The trick to this plot is that the (invisible) axis for these differences is at a 45° angle counter-clockwise from the main Y axis. Confidence intervals for the differences are shown against this alternate axis, as is the reference line for difference = 0. Thus, a difference is insignificant when the confidence interval for a difference crosses this difference = 0 line.

In this section, we have presented estimation of treatment differences and inferential statistics available with SAS mixed model procedures that control for *comparisonwise* error rate, that is, *p*-values apply to each test without regard to other tests also being made. Typically, these are used when a Type I error is not a paramount concern or avoidance of Type II error is an even bigger concern. For designs with three or more treatments, *experimentwise* error rate, that is, the probability of making at least one Type I error, is often the overriding concern. In statistical practice, the topic dealing with error control when testing more than two treatments is called *multiplicity*. The next section introduces the basic issues and tools available. Subsequent sections use examples that illustrate the major treatment designs and provide more detail for those designs.

3.3.3 Multiple Comparisons and Planned Comparisons

The *F* test for a factor in an analysis of variance tests the null hypothesis that all the factor means are equal. However, the conclusion of such a test is seldom a satisfactory end to the analysis. You usually want to know more about the differences among the means (for example, which means are different from which other means or if any groups of means have common values).

Multiple comparisons of the means are commonly used to answer these questions. There are numerous methods for making multiple comparisons, many of which are available in PROC GLIMMIX. In this chapter, only a few of the methods are illustrated.

One method of multiple comparisons is to conduct *t* tests between all possible pairs of means; this is known as the least significant difference (LSD) test. Refer to Steel and Torrie (1980) for examples.

The LSD test applies the α-level applies to each comparison, referred to as the *comparisonwise error rate*. However, if you have *t* treatments, there are $(t(t-1))/2$ possible comparisons, and in many cases it is more appropriate to be concerned with the probability of at least one Type I error. This is called the *experimentwise error rate*. If you have *c* comparisons, the experimentwise error rate is $\geq 1 - (1-\alpha)^c$, with strict equality only if all comparisons are independent – which they cannot be in an LSD test. In statistics, this is called the *multiplicity* problem.

A traditional method of dealing with multiplicity in multiple comparisons is Duncan's multiple-range test. With this test, the means are first ranked from largest to smallest. Then the equality of two means is tested by referring the difference to tabled critical points, the values of which depend on the range between the ranks of the two means tested. The larger the range of the ranks, the larger the tabled critical point (Duncan 1955).

The LSD method and, to a lesser extent, Duncan's method are frequently criticized for failing to control the Type I error rate, specifically the experimentwise error rate. In other words, the overall probability of falsely declaring some pair of means different, when in fact they are equal, is substantially larger than the stated α-level. In fact, many journals explicitly discourage the use of Duncan's multiple ranges test. PROC GLIMMIX provides several multiplicity options with varying levels of experimentwise error control. In addition to the LSD, i.e., no multiplicity adjustment, PROC GLIMMIX has options that enable the use of methods proposed by Bonferroni, Nelson, Scheffe, Sidak, and Tukey. Duncan's adjustment, specifically intended for comparisons between a control and other treatments, in also available. In addition to table-based adjustments, you can also use the SIMULATE option to obtain simulation-based inference to adjust for multiplicity.

You can request the various multiple comparison tests with the ADJUST option in the LSMEANS, ESTIMATE, and LSMESTIMATE statements in the GLIMMIX procedure.

Multiple comparison procedures, as described in the previous paragraphs, are useful when there are no pre-identified comparisons of special interest. However, in many situations there are specific comparisons known to be of particular interest. These are called preplanned comparisons because you can decide to make these comparisons prior to collecting data. Specific preplanned comparisons can be tested using the CONTRAST, ESTIMATE, LSMESTIMATE, or LSMEANS statements in PROC GLIMMIX, as discussed in Section 3.5.5, "Planned Comparisons in a Two-Way Factorial Experiment," later in this chapter. In addition, ESTIMATE, LSMESTIMATE, or LSMEANS statements enable you to estimate the size of the difference and, if desired, compute a confidence interval, as well as merely test whether the difference is zero.

3.4 Comparison of Quantitative Factors: Polynomial Regression

In many research areas, the explanatory factor is not a group of categories but rather chosen amounts of a particular treatment. These could be amounts of fertilizer or water applied to plants, or in industrial settings the temperature or pressure under which components are made. When the levels of the factor are quantitative, researchers are often interested in describing the change in the response over the change in the explanatory factor. Therefore, we want to create a regression model that adequately describes the data. One such method is to use polynomial regression. Often times the relationship between the response variable and the independent variables is a known function, which may be a nonlinear model instead of a linear model. Some such models are logistic functions that are used in the case of dose-response experiments and others follow a nonlinear function, that is, a function that cannot be expressed as a linear combination of its unknown parameters. Such cases are typically not suitable for polynomial regression unless the nonlinear curve can be adequately approximated by a low-degree polynomial. More straightforward is a direct nonlinear regression, which we do not cover here.

3.4.1 Analysis of a Regression Experiment

In many studies, the treatment design consists of quantitative levels, or amounts. Cooking time, drug dosage, irrigation volume, and storage temperature are all examples. Regression is a useful mean comparison tool in conjunction with mixed models. Polynomial regression is especially useful with linear mixed models. The following example illustrates the essential ideas.

In this example, a horticulturist is interested in the effect of added nitrogen to the final dry weight of a particular house plant. The greenhouse has six benches with room for six plants each. To account for a known gradient within the greenhouse resulting from the angle of the sun and the circulation fans, the researcher blocks by bench. The added nitrogen ranges from 0 to 200 mg/kg soil in 40 mg increments. The goal of the study is to estimate a regression equation to predict plant weight for a given amount of nitrogen applied.

In polynomial regression the number of levels of the factor determines the maximum degree polynomial we can fit. If there are T levels, you can fit a polynomial of order $T - 1$. However, it is common practice to include additional levels beyond the minimum needed to fit the polynomial that we believe will be sufficient. This enables us to test "lack of fit," that is, to confirm that the polynomial that we have chosen is adequate to describe the data (or tell us that our initial belief was incorrect). For example, Figure 3.3 shows a plot of means of the 5 levels of a quantitative treatment factor. If only the two extreme low and high levels, $X = 1$ and $X = 5$ were included in the study, it would only be possible to estimate a straight line. The curvilinear nature of the regression model would be missed. If the mid-level $X = 3$ was also observed, it would be possible to diagnose the lack of fit from linear, or you could fit a quadratic regression. However, with only three levels, you would not be able to see that the actual relationship between treatment level and response.

Figure 3.3: Possible Regression Estimates as a Function of Treatment Design

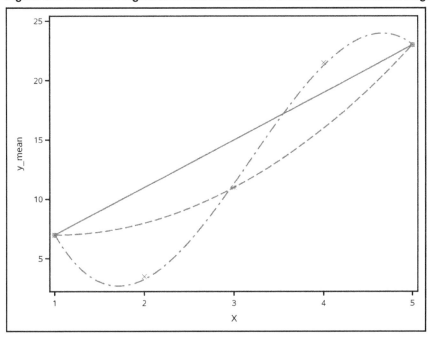

The point is that, given the number of levels of the regression factor, there is a polynomial degree that can be fit, and also one that can be "confirmed" by testing some hypotheses. Table 3.1 shows what is possible for given treatment designs.

Table 3.1: Degree Polynomial Possible

Number of levels	Fit degree	Maximum Confirm degree
2	Linear	
3	Quadratic	Linear
4	Cubic	Quadratic
5	Quartic	Cubic
6	Quintic	Quartic

This experiment has 6 levels of nitrogen (0, 40, 80, 120, 160, and 200), so we could fit a fifth-degree polynomial, though we can only confirm a fourth-degree polynomial. To develop some intuition as to which degree might best fit, we can begin the analysis by treating nitrogen as a classification variable as in ANOVA and obtain the LS Means plot.

Program

Use Program 3.4 to create a mean plot and overall effect test.

Program 3.4

```
proc glimmix data=plants;
   class bench n;
   model plant_wt=n;
   random intercept / subject=bench;
   lsmeans n / plot=meanplot(join);
run;
```

The join option causes the means to be connected, enabling you to visualize the possible polynomial fit.

Results

The mean plot is shown in Figure 3.4, and the overall test of nitrogen effect is shown in Output 3.5.

Output 3.5: Variance Estimates and Overall Test of Nitrogen Effect for Plant Weight Data

Covariance Parameter Estimates			
Cov Parm	Subject	Estimate	Standard Error
Intercept	bench	1.3723	1.1312
Residual		2.4419	0.6907

Type III Tests of Fixed Effects				
Effect	Num DF	Den DF	F Value	Pr > F
N	5	25	15.01	<.0001

The table of covariance parameter estimates in Output 3.5 gives the variance among benches $(\hat{\sigma}^2_{bench} = 1.37)$ and the variance among experimental units within benches $(\hat{\sigma}^2_{residual} = 2.44)$. Interpret the bench variance as a measure of the variability attributable to the greenhouse bench gradient. Note that for small experiments the "standard error" is a misleading statistic. That is, the standard errors of a variance estimate is useful only when you have thousands of observations. If you want to test the bench variance, use the COVTEST statement to obtain a likelihood ratio test, as shown in Chapter 6.

The *F* value for overall test of no nitrogen (N) effect is 15.01 with *p*-value < 0.0001. Figure 3.4 enables you to visualize the nitrogen effect.

Figure 3.4: Least Squares Mean Plot for Nitrogen Experiment

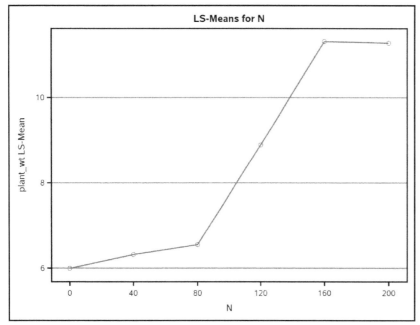

In this case we see an S-curve, common in dose-response experiments. In polynomial regression, this suggests a cubic function. Although a nonlinear regression is an alternative, we will continue with the polynomial for illustrative purposes. We have three methods that we can use to choose an adequate model to fit the data: (1) directly fitting the maximum polynomial using the Type I hypotheses, (2) creating a lack-of-fit variable and fitting the degree polynomial we believe is sufficient with the lack-of-fit testing sufficiency, and (3) using orthogonal polynomial contrasts. Notice in the ensuing examples that the model must account for all five degrees of freedom associated with nitrogen. We do this to ensure that all tests use the bench and residual variance estimates as shown in Output 3.5, that is, the appropriate variance estimates associated with the experiment design of this study.

Before we use one of the three methods to fit the regression, it is instructive to fit the model using the PROC GLIMMIX defaults. Instead of making nitrogen a classification variable as in ANOVA, we omit it from the class statement and include all of the polynomial terms in the model statement. With six levels we could fit up to a fifth degree polynomial, so we will need all five terms in the initial model statement.

Program

The full polynomial fit is implemented in the model statement in Program 3.5.

Program 3.5

```
proc glimmix data=plants;
   class bench;
   model plant_wt = n n*n n*n*n n*n*n*n n*n*n*n*n;
   random intercept / subject=bench;
run;
```

Results

Results are in Output 3.6.

Output 3.6: Selected Output from Direct Fit

Type III Tests of Fixed Effects				
Effect	Num DF	Den DF	F Value	Pr > F
N	1	26	0.30	0.5860
N*N	1	26	0.30	0.5862
N*N*N	1	26	0.29	0.5947
N*N*N*N	1	26	0.21	0.6503
N*N*N*N*N	1	26	0.13	0.7173

What is striking about the Type III Tests of Fixed Effects table is that none of our five terms are statistically significant at any reasonable level, despite the highly significant overall N effect (Output 3.5), and the plot showing an obvious visual effect of nitrogen. This obvious discrepancy results from the nature of the Type III Tests themselves. The Type III tests test the hypothesis that we can informally but instructively state as, "Do you need this variable in the model given the variation of the other variables is already removed?" Here this means we can drop any one of the terms in the polynomial and the others will pick up the slack in the fit. One reasonable next step would be to sequentially drop the highest order terms in the model until a parsimonious fit is found. Useful in this regard are Type I Sums of Squares, and the next section discusses the difference between Type I and Type III Sums of Squares.

3.4.2 Type I versus Type III Sums of Squares

Before illustrating the recommended approach to direct regression, we first digress into the different hypothesis testing options that are available within the GLIMMIX procedure. By default, PROC GLIMMIX (and PROC MIXED) use Type III Tests of Fixed Effects. The reason for this default is illustrated in Chapter 2, Section 2.4.1. However, Type III tests are not the only type of test available. In fact, there are three types of tests, Type I, Type II and Type III, available in SAS mixed model procedures. The section focuses on Type I and Type III. It is important to understand the difference, and how it affects inference and interpretation of the analysis.

Type III sums of squares are one type of *partial* sums of squares. Type III sums of squares measure the effect of a factor after accounting for the effects of all other terms in the model. For example, if we have two factors, The Type III Sums of squares for A and B are as follows:

- SS(A | B), read as "sum of squares for A after accounting for B"
- SS(B | A)

In other words, a Type III test of A tests the effect of A after accounting for the effect of B, even if A appears first in the MODEL statement. Because each test is dependent on all of the other terms in the model, the order in which we specify the terms in the model statement does not matter. As we saw in Section 2.4.1, with blocked designs the Type III tests enable you to test treatment effect adjusted for the impact of missing data or an incomplete block structure. However, in the case of regression, if you let A correspond to the linear effect and B to the quadratic, then the Type III test of linear is actually a result of SS(linear | quadratic), i.e. testing linear after fitting quadratic may not be useful.

Type I tests, on the other hand, are based on *sequential* sums of squares. That is, each test is the effect of that factor after accounting for the prior effects specified in the model. If we specify our model as

```
model y = a b;
```

then the Type I sums of squares are as follows:

- SS(A) for factor A;
- SS(B|A) for factor B.

However, if we specify the model as

```
model y = b a;
```

then the type I sums of squares are as follows:

- SS(B) for factor B;
- SS(A|B) for factor A;

The order of the effects in the model affects the results of the tests from the Type I sums of squares. In Section 2.4.1 we saw that if you fit

```
model y = trt block / htype=1;
```

you get a test of the unadjusted means, i.e. tests that are confounded with the structure of missing data. In general, when testing CLASS effects, this is an inappropriate test. However, with regression, if you fit

```
model y = n n*n / htype=1;
```

the tests correspond to the following:

- SS(N)
- SS(N*N | N)

i.e. linear regression over and above a simple intercept model, followed by quadratic over and above linear. In other words, it answers the question: Is there a linear effect in addition to not accounting for N at all, and is there a quadratic effect in addition to the linear effect? The Type I sums of squares clearly provides the answer.

Which tests are used depends upon the goal of the analysis. In most cases when we are dealing with class variables, the Type III sums of squares are preferred because they account for the design structure and possible effects of missing data. Type III tests are also handy for large designs, as they immediately provide indication of the contribution of each effect beyond the others. However, for standard polynomial regression, where order is obvious – i.e. linear first, then quadratic, etc. – the sequential Type I tests make sense. For general regression, where the standard polynomial approach is not adequate and order is not obvious, both Type 1 and Type 3 tests can be useful.

3.4.3 Direct Fit of Polynomial

The direct fit method utilizes the Type I sequential sums of squares tests to determine the degree which best fits the data.

Program

Writing out all of the terms as we did in Section 3.4.1 can be tedious. Instead, you can use a shortcut using the vertical bar symbol, | as shown in the MODEL statement of the PROC GLIMMIX statements in Program 3.6.

Program 3.6

```
proc glimmix data=plants;
   class bench;
   model plant_wt = n|n|n|n|n / htype=1;
   random intercept / subject=bench;
run;
```

The HTYPE=1 option gives you Type I tests, overriding the TYPE III test default. The vertical bar notation generates a linear predictor identical to the MODEL statement with N, N*N, etc. explicitly written as in Section 3.4.1. Specifying the MODEL statement either way will produce identical results. We will make use of this shortcut symbol frequently when analyzing factorial designs.

Results

Selected results of this program appear in Output 3.7.

Output 3.7: Selected Output from Direct Fit Using htype=1

Covariance Parameter Estimates			
Cov Parm	Subject	Estimate	Standard Error
Intercept	bench	1.3723	1.1312
Residual		2.4419	0.6907

Type I Tests of Fixed Effects				
Effect	Num DF	Den DF	F Value	Pr > F
N	1	26	67.14	<.0001
N*N	1	26	1.42	0.2442
N*N*N	1	26	4.38	0.0462
N*N*N*N	1	26	1.97	0.1718
N*N*N*N*N	1	26	0.13	0.7173

Interpretation

The covariance parameter estimates table in Output 3.7 shows the same estimates that we obtained from the default fit. The hypothesis type for the fixed effects does not affect the fit of the model itself.

Because the Type I tests of fixed effects are sequential tests, we begin at the bottom of the table to determine whether that degree term is significant in the model. We eliminate higher-order terms until we reach one that is significant. At that point we stop and retain that term and all lower-order terms in the model (whether the lower-order terms are significant or not). In this case we find that neither the fifth nor fourth degree terms add significantly to the model after the lower-order terms are included (p-values .7173 and .1718 respectively). The cubic term is significant at the $\alpha = 0.05$ level. This is consistent with our inspection of the mean plot that a third-degree polynomial describes the nitrogen effect for these data.

Knowing the cubic polynomial is the best solution, we refit the data using only those terms and request the solution. We can use the solution formula to predict plant weights for nitrogen levels not observed but within the range of the experiment.

Program

Program 3.7 obtains the solution.

Program 3.7

```
proc glimmix data=plants;
   class bench;
   model plant_wt = n|n|n / htype=1 solution;
   random intercept / subject=bench;
run;
```

Output 3.8: Solution Output from Fitting the Cubic Polynomial

Covariance Parameter Estimates			
Cov Parm	Subject	Estimate	Standard Error
Intercept	bench	1.3707	1.1308
Residual		2.4517	0.6673

Solutions for Fixed Effects					
Effect	Estimate	Standard Error	DF	t Value	Pr > |t|
Intercept	6.1791	0.7879	5	7.84	0.0005
N	-0.04113	0.03042	27	-1.35	0.1875
N*N	0.000855	0.000378	27	2.26	0.0319
N*N*N	-2.59E-6	1.241E-6	27	-2.09	0.0463

Interpretation

Notice that the variance component estimates change somewhat from those obtained from the full model. This is because the higher order polynomial terms that were in the model have now been pooled with the random effects. In the "Solutions for Fixed Effects" table, our primary interest is in the regression coefficient ESTIMATES and their standard error. Hypotheses about them have already been tested and are the motivation for fitting this reduced model. Therefore, the test statistics and associated *p*-values in this table are of little interest. Our final prediction formula is

$$\overline{\text{Plant Weight}} = 6.1791 - 0.04133n + 0.000855n^2 - 0.00000259n^3$$

where n is the amount of nitrogen in mg/kg soil.

With levels 0 through 200, the resulting regression coefficients are quite small. You might consider rescaling the N levels, e.g. dividing them by 10 and fitting the model with N=0, 4, 8, 16 and 20. The resulting regression equation would then be $6.1791 - 0.4133x + 0.08554x^2 - 0.00259x^3$, where $x = n/10$.

Direct Fit of Polynomial with Lack of Fit

With only six levels to our explanatory factor, nitrogen, it is not difficult to write the model to directly fit the full polynomial. However, it is often useful to include only the polynomial terms believed to explain the treatment effect and pool the remaining higher order terms into a single term, used to test lack of fit of the proposed polynomial model; hence, the term is called *lack of fit* in regression theory. For example, in the plant weight example, we believe a cubic regression will be adequate, so the *lack of fit* term pools the quartic and quintic effects.

In the plants data set, we currently only have the regression variable, *n*, for the level of nitrogen. In order the compute a lack of fit term, we create a new variable – call it *cn* (for the *class* version) – in the following DATA step.

```
data plants;
   set plants;
   cn = n;
run;
```

Now with these two versions of the nitrogen variable, we can directly test our third-order polynomial for lack of fit. We again make use of the Type I hypothesis tests being sequential tests, so that including the classification variable at the end of the model becomes a test of the remaining degrees of freedom for nitrogen after fitting the cubic polynomial.

Program

Program 3.8 shows the needed GLIMMIX statements.

Program 3.8

```
proc glimmix data=plants;
   class bench cn;
   model plant_wt = n|n|n cn / htype=1;
   random intercept / subject=bench;
run;
```

The variable n defines the regression (in this case $n|n|n$ specifies cubic regression) and must not be defined as a class variable. On the other hand, the cn variable does appear in the class statement. Including cn in the model statement after $n|n|n$ in conjunction with the HTYPE=1 option causes cn to act as a lack of fit term.

Results

Output 3.9 shows the results.

Output 3.9: Fixed Effect Tests Using a Lack of Fit variable.

	Type I Tests of Fixed Effects			
Effect	Num DF	Den DF	F Value	Pr > F
N	1	25	67.14	<.0001
N*N	1	25	1.42	0.2446
N*N*N	1	25	4.38	0.0466
cn	2	25	1.05	0.3635

Interpretation

Our interest is in whether the lack of fit test enables us to conclude that the cubic polynomial is sufficient to describe the effect of nitrogen on plant weight. We see that the test for cn, the lack of fit, is a two degree of freedom test because it combines the remaining two degrees of freedom for nitrogen after we have fit the cubic polynomial. This is the combined test for the fourth and fifth order terms that we included directly in the previous section. Here we have that there is no significant lack of fit, p-value 0.363. We can conclude that the cubic polynomial provides an adequate fit for these data. We would then continue as in the previous section.

3.4.4 Orthogonal Polynomial Contrasts

Using a direct fitting method as presented in the previous sections exploits the capabilities of contemporary linear model software. An alternative, developed in the pre-computer era, uses orthogonal polynomial contrasts—contrasts specifically defined for regression analysis—to partition the treatment sums of squares.

Orthogonal polynomial contrasts are contrasts defined to correspond to each order polynomial regression. In the plant weight example, this means five contrasts, one to test linear effect, one for quadratic, one for cubic, etc. By definition, coefficients in contrast statements must sum to zero. To make a set of contrasts *orthogonal*, the sum of the multiplied coefficients of any two contrasts in the set must sum to zero.

To illustrate, suppose we have a treatment design with three quantitative levels. Therefore, we have two degrees of freedom and can write two contrasts—one to test the linear trend and one the quadratic—alternatively interpreted as lack of fit from linear regression. Bearing in mind that the null hypothesis for a contrast is no effect, we determine coefficients for a linear combination of means that demonstrate no linear effect of the factor. $-1\mu_1 + 0\mu_2 + 1\mu_3$ is a possible combination. The coefficients are along a straight line on a y-axis (where the means are ordered along an x-axis). A linear slope equal to zero is equivalent to $\mu_1 = \mu_3$, whereas $\mu_1 \neq \mu_3$ indicates a straight line with a nonzero slope, i.e. a linear effect.

For the quadratic effect test, we can picture our same axes with a quadratic curve instead of a straight line. Because contrast coefficients must sum to 0, either $1\mu_1 - 2\mu_2 + 1\mu_3$ or inversely, $-1\mu_1 + 2\mu_2 - 1\mu_3$ would work for the test of a quadratic effect (and there are others). That is, departure from linear is equivalent to $\mu_2 \neq (\mu_1 + \mu_3)/2$. We can also see that either of these contrasts is orthogonal to the linear contrast, i.e. $(-1)*1 + 0*(-2) + 1*1 = 0$ and $(-1)*(-1) + 0*2 + 1*(-1) = 0$.

Tables of orthogonal polynomial contrast coefficients for varying numbers of levels of the regression factor are available in textbooks and online. These tables presume equally spaced levels. If your chosen levels are not equally spaced, you can obtain the coefficients using the ORPOL function in PROC IML. This procedure is explained in *SAS for Linear Models, 4th Edition* in Chapter 7. Chapter 5, section 5.7 of this book also shows an example that uses orthogonal polynomials for logarithmically rather than equal spaced levels.

In the plant weight example, there are six, equally spaced levels of nitrogen, meaning we can construct five mutually orthogonal contrasts to fully test the model. To implement contrasts in SAS linear mixed model software, use the basic form of the CONTRAST statement:

```
CONTRAST 'label' effect-name effect-coefficients;
```

Contrasts use the least squares means, so nitrogen must be treated as a class variable in this program. Program 3.9 shows PROC GLIMMIX statements to implement regression analysis using orthogonal polynomial contrasts.

Program 3.9

```
proc glimmix data=plants;
   class bench n;
   model plant_wt = n;
   random intercept / subject=bench;
   contrast 'Linear' n -5 -3 -1 1 3 5;
   contrast 'Quadratic' n 5 -1 -4 -4 -1 5;
   contrast 'Cubic' n -5 7 4 -4 -7 5;
   contrast 'Lack of fit' n 1 -3 2 2 -3 1,
                           n -1 5 -10 10 -5 1;
run;
```

The program includes separate CONTRAST statements to test linear, quadratic and cubic effects. Instead of separate quartic and quintic statements, this program shows how to combine quartic and quintic contrasts into a single two-degree-of-freedom test labeled "lack of fit." Output 3.10 shows the results.

Output 3.10: Results of Orthogonal Polynomial Contrasts

Covariance Parameter Estimates			
Cov Parm	Subject	Estimate	Standard Error
Intercept	bench	1.3723	1.1312
Residual		2.4419	0.6907

Type III Tests of Fixed Effects				
Effect	Num DF	Den DF	F Value	Pr > F
N	5	25	15.01	<.0001

Contrasts				
Label	Num DF	Den DF	F Value	Pr > F
Linear	1	25	67.14	<.0001
Quadratic	1	25	1.42	0.2446
Cubic	1	25	4.38	0.0466
Lack of fit	2	25	1.05	0.3635

The covariance parameter estimates and Type III test of overall N effect are identical to those in Output 3.5, as one would expect given that the CLASS and MODEL statements are the same. The contrasts results break the N effect into its regression components. Notice that the F and p-values for linear, quadratic, cubic and lack of fit are identical to those in Output 3.9, as is their interpretation.

It is possible to use the estimates from the contrasts to obtain the coefficients for the polynomial regression line (see Snedecor & Cochran and Steel & Torrie). However, in most cases, it is easier to get the estimated regression equation using the direct method.

3.5 Mean Comparisons in Factorial Designs

Two basic aspects of the design of experiments are treatment structure and error control. Choosing between randomization schemes, such as completely randomized, randomized blocks, and so on, is part of error control. This aspect is sometimes called the *experiment design*. On the other hand, the structure of the treatments consisting of the factor(s) and factor levels that are to be observed is called the *treatment design*. The *factorial* treatment design is one of the most important and widely used treatment structures. The factorial treatment design can be used with any randomization scheme, or experiment design. This section introduces the analysis of variance and mean comparison procedures used with factorial experiments.

A factorial treatment design consists of two or more treatment factors. The generic notation for factorial experiments is as follows. Factors are denoted by capital letters, beginning with A. A two-factor factorial has factors A and B. The third factor of a three-factor factorial is called factor C. Levels of each factor are denoted by lowercase letters. Factor A has a levels, factor B has b levels, and so forth. The number of levels are used to describe the design. A two-factor factorial is called an "$a \times b$ factorial treatment design." Note that all factors have at least two levels. If all factors have the same number of levels, the design is referred to as a "l^M factorial," where l denotes the number of levels per factor and M denotes the number of factors. A two-factor experiment with $a = b = 2$ is called a "2^2 factorial treatment design."

A complete factorial experiment consists of all possible combinations of levels of each factor. Levels can refer to numeric quantities of variables, such as pounds of fertilizer or temperature in degrees, as well as qualitative categories, such as names of plant varieties or drug types. An example of a factorial experiment is a study using nitrogen, phosphorus and potassium, each at three levels. Following the naming convention described above, such an experiment is called a 3^3 factorial, and has $3^3 = 27$ treatment combinations.

Factorial experiments can be used to investigate several types of treatment effects. These are as follows:

- *simple effects* (i.e. difference in mean response of levels of one factor holding the other factor or factors constant at a given level)

- *interactions* (i.e. difference in simple effects of one factor that result from changing levels of another factor; that is, do the simple effects remain constant—*no interaction*—or do they change, meaning *interaction*?)

- *main effects* (i.e. differences in mean response to levels of one factor averaged over all the levels of the other factor)

The simplest factorial treatment design is the 2×2 or 2^2 factorial. It is a good place to start to establish the essentials of understanding and working with factorial experiments.

3.5.1 Factorial: The Basics

The basics for factorial experiments include the following:

- formal notation for the factorial treatment mean

- formal definitions of simple effects, interaction and main effects in terms of the treatment means

- formal definition of the statistical model for the factorial treatment design

- introduction to contrasts that are specifically useful for factorial experiments and their connection with terms of the model

- SAS commands that are specific to factorial structure

Refer to the mean for a factorial experiment as the $A \times B$ mean or, more precisely, the $A_i \times B_j$ mean, where $i = 1, 2$ references the levels of factor A and $j = 1, 2$ references the levels for factor B. For modeling and effect definition purposes, denote the $A_i \times B_j$ mean as μ_{ij}.

Simple effects

The simple effect of A holding B constant at level B_1 is defined as $\mu_{11} - \mu_{21}$, the difference between the means of the two levels of A. The symbolic language $A \mid B_1$, read "the simple effect of A given B$_1$" is often used. Similarly, $A \mid B_2$, "simple effect of A given B$_2$," often shortened to "A given B$_2$" is defined as $\mu_{12} - \mu_{22}$; $B \mid A_1$, "B given A$_1$" is defined as $\mu_{11} - \mu_{12}$; and, "B given A$_2$" is defined as $\mu_{21} - \mu_{22}$.

Interaction

Interaction occurs when the simple effect given one level of the other factor differs from the simple effect given the other level of the other factor. That is, interaction occurs if $A \mid B_1 \neq A \mid B_2$ or, equivalently, $B \mid A_1 \neq B \mid A_2$. The measure of interaction is thus formally defined by the difference between simple effects, for example, the difference $A \mid B_1 - A \mid B_2 = \mu_{11} - \mu_{21} - (\mu_{12} - \mu_{22})$, or, alternatively, $B \mid A_1 - B \mid A_2 = \mu_{11} - \mu_{12} - (\mu_{21} - \mu_{22})$. Both expressions can be rewritten $\mu_{11} - \mu_{12} - \mu_{21} + \mu_{22}$. *Interaction* exists when simple effects are not equal; that is, when $\mu_{11} - \mu_{12} - \mu_{21} + \mu_{22} \neq 0$. Simple effects equal, that is $\mu_{11} - \mu_{12} - \mu_{21} + \mu_{22} = 0$, defines the condition of *no interaction*.

Notice that $\mu_{11} - \mu_{12} - \mu_{21} + \mu_{22}$ is a contrast. It is the simplest form of an *interaction contrast*, an important tool for the analysis of factorial experiments. We will use interaction contrasts in subsequent examples.

The interaction plot is an essential visual aid for identifying and interpreting interaction. The following three plots are representative of typical relationships among A × B means. Another interpretation of a basic two-way interaction is as a difference of the differences, or the difference of the simple effects. When the second-order difference is zero, it indicates that the first-order differences remain constant across the levels of the two factors.

Figure 3.5: Mean Plot Indicating no Interaction

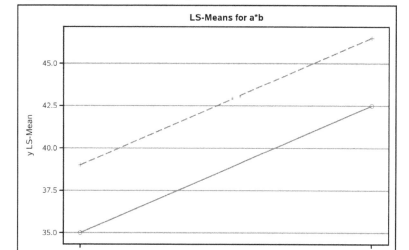

Figure 3.6: Mean Plot Indicating Interaction

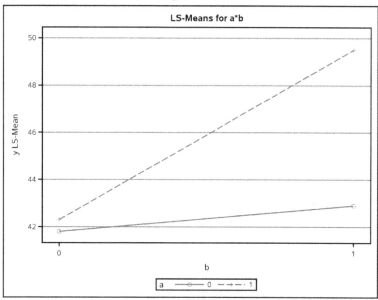

Note: $A \mid B_0 \approx 0$ and $A \mid B_1 \gg 0$.

Figure 3.7: Mean Plot Indicating Interaction

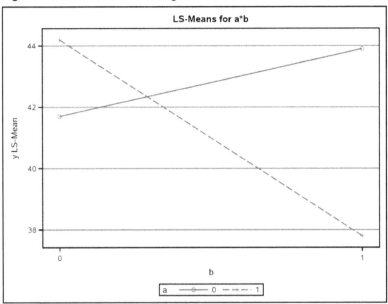

Note: $A \mid B_0 < 0$ and $A \mid B_1 > 0$.

Main effects

Main effects means, also called marginal means, are means for a given level of one factor averaged over the levels of the other factor. For example, the main effect mean for A_1 is

$$\bar{\mu}_{1.} = (1/b)\sum_{j=1}^{b}\mu_{1j}$$

where b denotes the number of levels of factor B. For a 2×2 factorial, $b = 2$, so the main effect means reduces to

$$\bar{\mu}_{1.} = (1/2)\sum_{j=1}^{2}\mu_{1j}$$

The *dot-notation* is standard short-hand for summing over all levels of the subscript replaced by a dot ($\cdot$). $\mu_{j.}$ means sum over all j, that is all levels of factor B; $\mu_{.j}$ means sum over all i, that is all levels of factor A. $\mu_{..}$ denotes the grand total, summing over everything. *Dot-notation with a bar*, $\bar{\mu}_{i.}$ means divide the total by the number of levels of j, that is the number of levels of factor B, to obtain the mean.

You can visualize the main effect means using the interaction plot. For example, plot the main effect means for A_0 and A_1 on Figure 3.5 to provide Figure 3.8: A_0 main effect mean.

Figure 3.8: Plot in Figure 3.5 with Main Effect Means Added

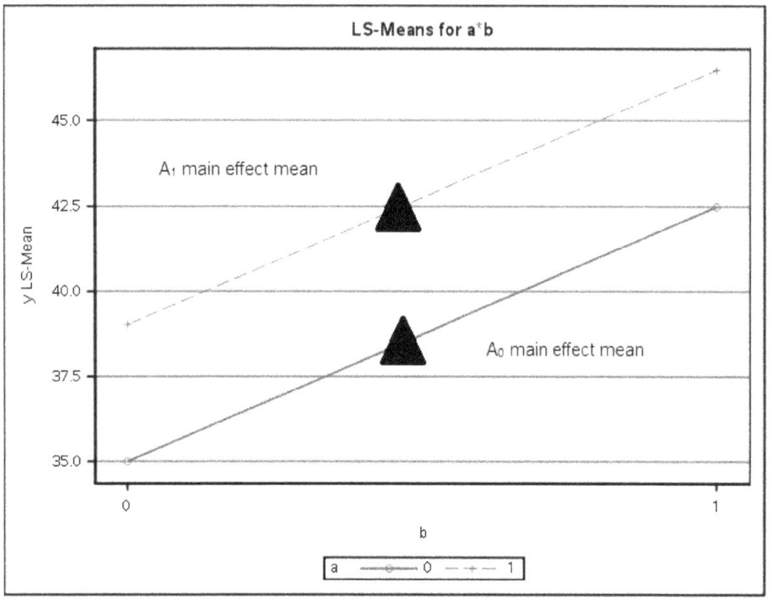

A *main effect* is defined as the difference between main effect means for a given factor. For a 2×2 factorial, the main effect of A is $\overline{\mu}_{1.} - \overline{\mu}_{2.}$, and the main effect of B is $\overline{\mu}_{.1} - \overline{\mu}_{.2}$.

Notice that main effects convey useful information about a given factor's effect *only* if the interaction is negligible. In the example plots above, the main effects are meaningful in Figure 3.5 but not in Figures 3.6 and 3.7. Reporting main effects in the presence of a non-negligible interaction is at best misleading and should not be attempted. For this reason, always start the analysis of a factorial by assessing the interaction. If the interaction is negligible, proceed to the main effects. If the interaction is not negligible, focus on simple effects *only*. Interpreting main effects in the presence of a non-negligible interaction is typically inappropriate.

Main effects, like interaction, define a contrast over the A × B treatment means. You can visualize this with Table 3.2.

Table 3.2: Contrast over the A × B Treatment Means

Factor A Levels	1		2	
Factor B Levels	1	2	1	2
A main effect	1	−1	−1	−1
B main effect	1	−1	−1	−1
A × B Interaction	1	−1	−1	1

The coefficients for the three contrasts appear in the unshaded part of the table. Notice two things:

- The contrasts are mutually orthogonal and form a complete set: therefore, they partition the three treatment degrees of freedom into three single-degree-of-freedom components.

- The interaction contrast consists of the cross-products of the coefficients of the main effects contrasts. When there are multiple main effect degrees of freedom, you can use this result to form interaction contrasts from all possible cross-products of main-effect contrasts defined on A and B.

Model for the Factorial Treatment Design

The above contrasts are important for the construction of the model for factorial experiments. For a completely randomized experiment design, the model can be expressed in one of two ways.

Cell means model is as follows:

$$y_{ijk} = \mu_{ij} + e_{ijk}$$

where y_{ijk} denotes the observation on the kth experimental unit assigned to treatment $A_i \times B_j$, and $e_{ijk} \sim \text{NI}(0, \sigma^2)$. Equivalently, you can give this model in probability distribution form as $y_{ijk} \sim \text{N}(\mu_{ij}, \sigma^2)$.

Effects model is as follows:

$$y_{ijk} = \mu + \alpha_i + \beta_j + \alpha\beta_{ij} + e_{ijk}$$

where μ denotes the intercept, α_i denotes the main effect of A, β_j denotes the main effect of B, and $\alpha\beta_{ij}$ denotes the A $\times$ B interaction.

In PROC GLIMMIX, you specify each model as follows. Both use the following:

```
proc glimmix;
   class a b;
```

The MODEL for the cell means model is

```
   model y = a*b/noint;
```

The NOINT option suppresses the intercept and A * B specifies that the only fixed effect in the model is the $A_i \times B_j$ effect. If you do not include the NOINT option, PROC GLIMMIX fits the model $y_{ijk} = \mu + \alpha\beta_{ij} + e_{ijk}$.

The MODEL for the effect means model is the following:

```
   model y = a b a*b;
```

The terms A and B specify the main effects α_i and β_j, respectively, and A * B specifies the interaction effect $\alpha\beta_{ij}$. Alternatively, you can use the following syntax:

```
   model y = a|b;
```

The vertical bar (|) tells PROC GLIMMIX to obtain all main effects and all possible products of the effects listed.

The following statements are useful for factorial experiments.

Create an interaction plot.

```
   lsmeans a*b/plots=meanplot(sliceby=a join cl);
```

The option PLOTS=MEANPLOT produces a plot of the $A \times B$ means. SLICEBY=A places the levels of B on the X-axis. JOIN connects the means for each level of A. SLICEBY=B places the levels of A on the X-axis; JOIN would then connect the B means. The SLICEBY option is essential for an interaction plot. The JOIN command is optional – connecting the means often helps you visualize important features of the treatment factor effects, especially (but not exclusively) the $A \times B$ interaction. CL provides error bars defined in terms of a 95% confidence interval on the estimated means. There is an ALPHA option, not shown here, that enables you to change the confidence level of the interval.

Obtain main effect means and differences.

```
   lsmeans a b / diff;
```

The preceding LSMEANS statement provides main effect means and their estimated differences. As mentioned above, you generally want to use this statement only if the $A \times B$ interaction is negligible, i.e. non-significant or too small to be considered scientifically important. Otherwise, use the following statement for simple effects

```
   lsmeans a*b/diff slice=(a b) slicediff=(a b);
```

The preceding LSMEANS statement provides A $\times$ B means. DIFF calls for all possible pairwise differences. SLICE computes an *F* test for the hypothesis that all B means are equal one level of A at a time (SLICE=A) or all A means are equal one level of B at a time (SLICE=B). SLICEDIFF computes all possible pairwise simple effects, either among pairs of B one level of A at a time or vice versa. You can define SLICE and SLICEDIFF on A only, B only or both (the latter is shown above).

The other PROC GLIMMIX statement useful for factorial experiments is the LSMESTIMATE statement. LSMESTIMATE has relatively little value for 2 × 2 factorials but comes into its own when you have more levels or more factors.

Examples of PROC GLIMMIX for 2 × 2 factorials with illustrations of each of these statements are given in the SAS data sets intro1, intro2, and intro3, which were used to create Figures 3.5, 3.6, and 3.7. The use and interpretation are straightforward when you have only two levels per factor. The statements become a bit more involved when you have more than two levels. The next section illustrates their use. The next example also introduces the LSMESTIMATE statement in section 3.5.6.

3.5.2 A More Complex Two-Way Factorial Experiment

Now consider a factorial with more than two levels per factor. The primary complication results from the fact that all interactions, main effects and simple effects have multiple degrees of freedom. This means that the overall tests defined by the usual effects model—A × B interaction, A and B main effects—yield inherently vague information. To work with these designs, you often must break the interaction into meaningful one-degree-of-freedom components, use these to determine non-negligible aspects of the interaction, and proceed as appropriate—i.e. with main effects or simple effects depending on the interaction results. Again, these effects should be broken into single degree-of-freedom terms that are informative and interpretable with respect to the study's objectives.

As an example, suppose three seed growth-promoting methods (METHOD) are applied to seed from each of five varieties (VARIETY) of turf grass. Six pots are planted with seed from each METHOD×VARIETY combination. The resulting 90 pots are randomly placed in a uniform growth chamber, and the dry matter yields (YIELD) are measured after clipping at the end of four weeks. Because the concern in this experiment is specifically about these five varieties and three growth methods, VARIETY and METHOD are regarded as fixed effects. A complete description of the experiment, e.g. for a scientific article, includes the treatment design, a 3 × 5 factorial, and the randomization scheme, a completely randomized design.

Data are recorded in a SAS data set called GRASSES. For convenience, the six replicate measurements are recorded in multivariate form, i.e. as Y1-Y6 in the same data line. However, SAS mixed model software requires that data be in univariate form, that is each replicate observation on YIELD must appear in a separate line. Therefore, the data set GRASSES must be rearranged to permit analysis. This data manipulation would not be necessary if the values of YIELD had originally been recorded using one data line per replication.

Program

Use Program 3.10 to convert the data from multivariate to univariate form.

Program 3.10

```
data factorial;
   set grasses;
   drop y1-y6;
   yield=y1; output;
   yield=y2; output;
   yield=y3; output;
   yield=y4; output;
   yield=y5; output;
   yield=y6; output;
run;
```

This DATA step creates a new data set, named FACTORIAL, containing the rearranged data.

It is often helpful to begin the analysis with a visual inspection of the interaction plot. This is particularly true of complex factorial experiments. You can use the PLOT option in PROC GLIMMIX to construct the interaction plot. Use the following statements:

```
proc glimmix data=factorial;
   class method variety;
   model yield = method|variety;
   lsmeans method*variety / plots=meanplot(sliceby=method join);
run;
```

The LSMEANS statement instructs SAS to compute the means and standard errors of the means of each METHOD×VARIETY combination. The MEANPLOT option creates an interaction plot of the LS means. SLICEBY=METHOD and JOIN work together to connect the VARIETY means for each METHOD enabling you to visualize METHOD and VARIETY effects.

Results

This plot appears in Figure 3.9.

Figure 3.9: Plot of Cell Means for Factorial Experiment

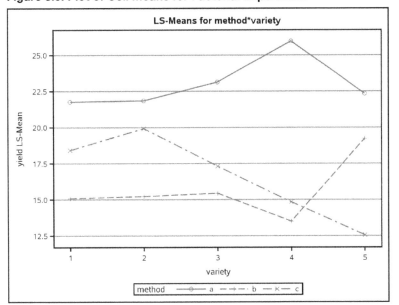

You could alternatively slice by VARIETY and draw a complementary interaction plot joining variety means with lines to show their profiles over methods. Which one you draw (or both) is a matter of personal preference and how you like to think about the interactions.

The interaction plot suggests that the differences between METHOD means depend on which VARIETY is used. This should be formally tested, however, since the graph only shows treatment means without their underlying variation.

Program

Run Program 3.11 to compute the analysis.

Program 3.11

```
proc glimmix data=factorial;
   class method variety;
   model yield=method variety method*variety;
run;
```

Both treatment factors, METHOD and VARIETY are classification variables and thus appear in the CLASS statement. The MODEL statement specifies that the analysis of YIELD is to contain sources of variation METHOD, VARIETY, and METHOD*VARIETY.

Results

Output 3.11 shows the results.

Output 3.11: Analysis of Variance for Factorial Experiment

	Type III Tests of Fixed Effects			
Effect	Num DF	Den DF	F Value	Pr > F
method	2	75	24.25	<.0001
variety	4	75	0.14	0.9648
method*variety	8	75	2.38	0.0241

Interpretation

Note that the METHOD*VARIETY effect is significant at the $p = .0241$ level, confirming the apparent interaction observed by visual inspection in Figure 3.9. Notice, however, that this test does not give any further information about the interaction. In fact, closer inspection of Figure 3.9 suggests that the interaction has many facets. For example, limiting attention to varieties 1 and 2 only, there is little visual evidence of interaction. On the other hand, limiting attention to varieties 3, 4 and 5, there is strong visual evidence of interaction, and the nature of the interaction is quite different for varieties 3 and 4 than it is for varieties 4 and 5. The next sections show how to isolate these aspects of the interaction and their associated simple effects.

3.5.3 Multiple Comparisons for a Factorial Experiment

As a general rule, if the interaction is *negligible*, you can perform multiple comparisons on the *main effect means* using the LSMEANS statement. In this case, you would use the following statement:

```
lsmeans method variety;
```

along with options shown earlier in this chapter for one-way treatment designs. On the other hand, if the interaction is not negligible, as is the case in this example, you must focus on breaking the interaction into its component parts, and then on associated simple effects that follow from the interaction components. The following sections show examples of what one might do. These examples are not intended to be exhaustive, but are intended to illustrate how to use the CONTRAST, ESTIMATE, LSMEANS, and LSMESTIMATE statements to obtain various inferential statistics likely to be of interest when analyzing a factorial experiment.

Before proceeding, two comments about *what not to do*. These are practices that either have been common in the past when statistical software was less sophisticated, or result from inadequate understanding of appropriate statistical practice for factorial treatment designs.

First comment: In the past, it was common practice to rerun the analysis with a BY statement, resulting in one analysis of variance table per level of the BY variable. However, this is very inefficient, because the error *df* for each analysis can be quite small. In essence, you are throwing out most of the data for each analysis. For example, if you do a separate analysis BY VARIETY you get ANOVAs with 2 *df* for METHOD and 10 *df* for error. This seriously reduces the power of the resulting tests. Options in PROC GLIMMIX specifically for simple effect analysis enable you to avoid this problem. The BY-group approach also directly estimates distinct residual variance components for each level of VARIETY. Such heterogeneous variances may be warranted for some data sets, and it turns out that you can also accommodate this kind of model in a single analysis on all of the data, which is the recommended approach. See later chapters on how to set up and run such heterogeneous variance models—they effectively weight observations according to the inverse of their estimated variance. In general, use BY groups only when you are sure data from distinct BY groups are independent, or when you have a very large number of groups, for example, in a genomics experiment.

Second comment: The LSMEANS statement has several options for multiple comparison tests. LSMEANS computes both main effect means and factorial treatment combination means such as METHOD*VARIETY. It will also compute multiple comparison tests for these means but with the following caveat. Multiple comparisons for testing all possible pairwise differences among treatment combination means in a factorial experiment are generally considered to be inappropriate. Several authors have written articles critical of the frequent misuse of such procedures. See, for example, Chew (1976) and Little (1978). The main point of these objections is that with factorial treatment designs, the main focus should be on interactions first, then simple effects or main effects (but not both) depending on whether the interaction is negligible or not. Multiple comparisons, when applied indiscriminately to all possible differences, tend to obscure essential information contained in the data, and make interpretation needlessly complicated and confusing. Instead, you should proceed using one of more of the following approaches.

3.5.4 Multiple Comparisons of METHOD Means by VARIETY Using SLICE and SLICEDIFF

One approach to breaking a non-negligible interaction into its component parts involves testing and estimating simple effects. The PROC GLIMMIX LSMEANS statement has two options for doing this. SLICE enables you to test overall simple effects of one factor at a specific level of the other factor. SLICEDIFF enables you to estimate pairwise simple effect differences. In this section, we illustrate each in turn. First, the SLICE option.

Suppose you want to test the overall simple effects of METHOD for each variety, i.e. test $H_0 : \mu_{Aj} = \mu_{Bj} = \mu_{Cj}$ for each variety $j = 1, 2, 3, 4, 5$. Do this with the SLICE option by including the following statement after the MODEL in the PROC GLIMMIX program given above:

```
lsmeans method*variety/slice=variety;
```

The SLICE statements produce *F* tests for simple effects. For example, SLICE=VARIETY causes a separate *F* statistic to be computed for the METHOD effect at each VARIETY. Note that you can have multiple slices in the LSMEANS statement. For example, you could use either of the following statements if you wanted to test the overall simple effect of VARIETY for each METHOD as well as the overall effect of METHOD for each VARIETY:

```
lsmeans method*variety/slice=variety slice=method;
lsmeans method*variety/slice=(variety method);
```

Results

Only the results for SLICE=VARIETY are shown here. They appear in Output 3.12.

Output 3.12: SLICE Option to Test Simple Effect of METHOD at Each VARIETY

	Tests of Effect Slices for method*variety Sliced By variety			
variety	Num DF	Den DF	F Value	Pr > F
1	2	75	3.41	0.0383
2	2	75	3.53	0.0341
3	2	75	4.90	0.0100
4	2	75	14.31	<.0001
5	2	75	7.63	0.0010

Interpretation

You can see that the magnitudes of the METHOD effects vary among the VARIETIES. You can also see that there is a statistically significant METHOD effect for every VARIETY. Unfortunately, the SLICE option does not reveal any further detail about the simple effects. To do this, additional mean comparisons are required.

Program

To do this, you use the SLICEDIFF option as shown with Program 3.12.

Program 3.12

```
proc glimmix data=factorial;
   class variety method;
   model yield = method|variety;
   lsmeans method*variety/slice=variety slicediff=variety cl adjust=tukey;
run;
```

The SLICEDIFF option provides all possible pairwise differences between levels of one factor—in this case METHOD—for each level of the factor named in the SLICEDIFF= option. Notice that you can include SLICE and SLICEDIFF options in the same statement. However, you can run SLICEDIFF without SLICE and vice versa. The CL option causes PROC GLIMMIX to compute 95% confidence limits for each simple effect difference. You can use multiplicity adjustments if desired. There are three METHODs and hence three possible pairwise differences among method means. Therefore, there are three simple pairwise simple effects for METHOD for each VARIETY. If you use a multiplicity adjustment, SLICEDIFF applies it on a per VARIETY basis. That is, the adjustment is for the three comparisons within each VARIETY, not for the 15 comparisons total for all varieties. Output 3.13 shows the SLICEDIFF output.

Results

For space reasons, the results are broken into Output 3.13 with no multiplicity adjustment and Output 3.14 with the TUKEY adjustment.

Output 3.13: Confidence Limits for Simple Effect Differences between METHOD by VARIETY Unadjusted

Simple Effect Comparisons of method*variety Least Squares Means By variety										
Simple Effect Level	method	_method	Estimate	Standard Error	DF	t Value	Pr > |t|	Alpha	Lower	Upper
variety 1	a	b	6.6833	2.5593	75	2.61	0.0109	0.05	1.5849	11.7817
variety 1	a	c	3.3500	2.5593	75	1.31	0.1945	0.05	-1.7484	8.4484
variety 1	b	c	-3.3333	2.5593	75	-1.30	0.1968	0.05	-8.4317	1.7651

Simple Effect Comparisons of method*variety Least Squares Means By variety										
Simple Effect Level	method	_method	Estimate	Standard Error	DF	t Value	Pr > |t|	Alpha	Lower	Upper
variety 2	a	b	6.6167	2.5593	75	2.59	0.0117	0.05	1.5183	11.7151
variety 2	a	c	1.9333	2.5593	75	0.76	0.4524	0.05	-3.1651	7.0317
variety 2	b	c	-4.6833	2.5593	75	-1.83	0.0712	0.05	-9.7817	0.4151
variety 3	a	b	7.6833	2.5593	75	3.00	0.0036	0.05	2.5849	12.7817
variety 3	a	c	5.8167	2.5593	75	2.27	0.0259	0.05	0.7183	10.9151
variety 3	b	c	-1.8667	2.5593	75	-0.73	0.4681	0.05	-6.9651	3.2317
variety 4	a	b	12.4667	2.5593	75	4.87	<.0001	0.05	7.3683	17.5651
variety 4	a	c	11.1333	2.5593	75	4.35	<.0001	0.05	6.0349	16.2317
variety 4	b	c	-1.3333	2.5593	75	-0.52	0.6039	0.05	-6.4317	3.7651
variety 5	a	b	3.1167	2.5593	75	1.22	0.2271	0.05	-1.9817	8.2151
variety 5	a	c	9.7833	2.5593	75	3.82	0.0003	0.05	4.6849	14.8817
variety 5	b	c	6.6667	2.5593	75	2.60	0.0111	0.05	1.5683	11.7651

Output 3.14: Confidence Limits for Simple Effect Differences between METHOD by VARIETY Adjusted

Simple Effect Comparisons of method*variety Least Squares Means By variety Adjustment for Multiple Comparisons: Tukey											
Simple Effect Level	method	_method	Estimate	Standard Error	DF	t Value	Pr > |t|	Adj P	Alpha	Adj Lower	Adj Upper
variety 1	a	b	6.6833	2.5593	75	2.61	0.0109	0.0290	0.05	0.5637	12.8029
variety 1	a	c	3.3500	2.5593	75	1.31	0.1945	0.3947	0.05	-2.7696	9.4696
variety 1	b	c	-3.3333	2.5593	75	-1.30	0.1968	0.3983	0.05	-9.4529	2.7863
variety 2	a	b	6.6167	2.5593	75	2.59	0.0117	0.0310	0.05	0.4971	12.7363
variety 2	a	c	1.9333	2.5593	75	0.76	0.4524	0.7313	0.05	-4.1863	8.0529
variety 2	b	c	-4.6833	2.5593	75	-1.83	0.0712	0.1669	0.05	-10.803	1.4363
variety 3	a	b	7.6833	2.5593	75	3.00	0.0036	0.0101	0.05	1.5637	13.8029
variety 3	a	c	5.8167	2.5593	75	2.27	0.0259	0.0659	0.05	-0.3029	11.9363
variety 3	b	c	-1.8667	2.5593	75	-0.73	0.4681	0.7469	0.05	-7.9863	4.2529
variety 4	a	b	12.4667	2.5593	75	4.87	<.0001	<.0001	0.05	6.3471	18.5863
variety 4	a	c	11.1333	2.5593	75	4.35	<.0001	0.0001	0.05	5.0137	17.2529
variety 4	b	c	-1.3333	2.5593	75	-0.52	0.6039	0.8614	0.05	-7.4529	4.7863
variety 5	a	b	3.1167	2.5593	75	1.22	0.2271	0.4465	0.05	-3.0029	9.2363
variety 5	a	c	9.7833	2.5593	75	3.82	0.0003	0.0008	0.05	3.6637	15.9029
variety 5	b	c	6.6667	2.5593	75	2.60	0.0111	0.0295	0.05	0.5471	12.7863

Interpretation

Outputs 3.13 and 3.14 give the estimated differences between the treatment combinations (Estimate), the standard error of the difference, and the DF, t statistic, and p-value for the comparison. By definition, the latter are the test statistics for the LSD mean comparison test. The Adj P gives the Tukey adjusted p-value for the comparison. Output 3.13 and 3.14 also include the lower and upper limits of the confidence interval, both the standard CI and a Tukey adjusted interval. Add the statement

```
ods output slices=s slicediffs=sd;
```

to create output SAS data sets of these tables. These tables can be helpful for sorting results or creating custom plots.

3.5.5 Planned Comparisons in a Two-Way Factorial Experiment: CONTRAST, ESTIMATE, and LSMESTIMATE

You can use the CONTRAST and ESTIMATE statements to make planned comparisons among means in a two-way classification just like you did in the one-way classification. In addition, you can use LSMESTIMATE statements, introduced in this sub-section. The LSMESTIMATE statement is similar to the ESTIMATE statement, but is often easier to work with when you have factorial treatment structure.

In the previous section, METHODs were compared separately for each VARIETY using a multiple comparison procedure. The comparisons were made separately for each variety because of the significant METHOD*VARIETY interaction. Using a multiple comparison procedure implicitly means no knowledge of the METHODs was assumed that might suggest specific comparisons among the METHOD means. Now suppose that you know something about the METHODs that suggests a specific comparison. For example, assume that METHOD A is a new technique, and METHODs B and C are industry standard techniques, assumed to be similar. You might want to compare a mean for METHOD A with the average of means for METHODs B and C, referred to here as A vs B, C. In general terms, assume you want to estimate the difference

$$\mu_A - \frac{1}{2}\left(\mu_B + \mu_C\right)$$

There are several ways to make this comparison:

- Compare A with B, C separately for each VARIETY (simple effect).
- Compare A with B, C averaged across all VARIETY levels (main effect).
- Compare A with B, C averaged across subsets of VARIETY (see text below).

Which comparison is appropriate depends on how the comparison interacts with VARIETY and whether the B and C means are sufficiently similar to justify comparing their average to the mean of A. The first comparison (simple effect) would be appropriate if the comparisons were very different from one VARIETY to the next. The second comparison (main effect) would be appropriate only if the comparison did not interact with VARIETY, that is, if the comparison had essentially the same value (aside from random noise) for all the varieties. The third comparison would be appropriate if there were subsets of varieties such that the comparison did not interact with VARIETY within the subsets.

The following sections illustrate how to use CONTRAST, ESTIMATE, and LSMESTIMATE statements to decide which of the above comparisons is appropriate and then make the comparison. For estimating comparisons, examples will initially focus on LSMESTIMATE because, as mentioned above, it is generally easier to use with factorial experiments. In subsequent sections, equivalent implementation using ESTIMATE statements will be shown. ESTIMATE and LSMESTIMATE statements differ in that ESTIMATE statements are defined in terms of the effects model whereas LSMESTIMATE statements are defined in terms of treatment LSMEANS. The ESTIMATE statement is more flexible, and is required for certain specialized applications, but the LSMESTIMATE statement is easier to use for the applications discussed here.

Writing CONTRAST and ESTIMATE statements can be tricky, especially in multiway classifications. You must use the relationship between the means and model parameters to construct CONTRAST and ESTIMATE statements. Following is a three-step process that always works:

1. Write the linear combination that you want to test or estimate in terms of means.
2. Convert means into model parameters: $\mu_{ij} = \mu + \tau_i + \nu_j + \tau\nu_{ij}$.
3. Gather like terms.

For example, suppose you want to compare A versus B and C for variety 1.

1. The comparison in terms of treatment means is $\mu_{A1} - \left(1/2\right)\left(\mu_{B1} + \mu_{C1}\right)$

2. Convert to model parameters:

$$\mu + \tau_A + \nu_1 + \tau\nu_{A1} - \left(1/2\right)\left[\left(\mu + \tau_B + \nu_1 + \tau\nu_{B1}\right) + \left(\mu + \tau_C + \nu_1 + \tau\nu_{C1}\right)\right]$$

3. Gather like terms:

$$\tau_A + \tau\nu_{A1} - \left(1/2\right)\left[\left(\tau_B + \tau\nu_{B1}\right) + \left(\tau_C + \tau\nu_{C1}\right)\right] = \tau_A - \left(1/2\right)\left(\tau_B + \tau_C\right) + \tau\nu_{A1} - \left(1/2\right)\left(\tau\nu_{B1} + \tau\nu_{C1}\right)$$

The resulting expression has the coefficients for model parameters that you can directly insert into a CONTRAST or ESTIMATE statement.

3.5.6 Simple Effect Comparisons—Using LSMESTIMATE

To set up a comparison of the first type (a comparison of A versus B, C in VARIETY 1) use the basic relationship between means. This is a simple effect comparison because you are comparing METHOD means within a particular VARIETY. Use an LSMESTIMATE statement to estimate A versus B, C in VARIETY 1 (B, C in Variety 1 means the mean of B and C in variety 1).

Writing the linear comparison in terms of cell means gives $\mu_{A1} - 0.5(\mu_{B1} + \mu_{C1})$. Before you proceed with the LSMESTIMATE statement, check the order of the LS means from the previous SAS output. The ordering of the METHOD*VARIETY coefficients is determined by the CLASS statement. In this CLASS statement, METHOD comes before VARIETY. For this reason, VARIETY levels change within METHOD levels. This can be seen in the LSMeans table in Output 3.15.

Output 3.15: LSMeans Table Showing VARIETY Changing Within METHOD

method*variety Least Squares Means						
method	variety	Estimate	Standard Error	DF	t Value	Pr > |t|
a	1	21.7667	1.8097	75	12.03	<.0001
a	2	21.8500	1.8097	75	12.07	<.0001
a	3	23.1333	1.8097	75	12.78	<.0001
a	4	25.9667	1.8097	75	14.35	<.0001
a	5	22.3333	1.8097	75	12.34	<.0001
b	1	15.0833	1.8097	75	8.33	<.0001
b	2	15.2333	1.8097	75	8.42	<.0001
b	3	15.4500	1.8097	75	8.54	<.0001
b	4	13.5000	1.8097	75	7.46	<.0001
b	5	19.2167	1.8097	75	10.62	<.0001
c	1	18.4167	1.8097	75	10.18	<.0001
c	2	19.9167	1.8097	75	11.01	<.0001
c	3	17.3167	1.8097	75	9.57	<.0001
c	4	14.8333	1.8097	75	8.20	<.0001
c	5	12.5500	1.8097	75	6.93	<.0001

Program

Now you have the information that you need to set up the LSMESTIMATE statement to go with the PROC GLIMMIX model. The required statements are

```
proc glimmix;
   class method variety;
   model yield = method variety method*variety;
   lsmestimate method*variety 'A vs B,C in V1'
      1 0 0 0 0 -.5 0 0 0 0 -.5 0 0 0 0;
```

Equivalently, you can write the LSMESTIMATE statement as

```
   lsmestimate method*variety 'A vs B,C in V1'
      2 0 0 0 0 -1 0 0 0 0 -1 0 0 0 0 / divisor=2;
```

Rather than examine output for the single LSMESTIMATE statement, make the comparison for all five varieties. You would probably want to estimate the comparison A vs B, C separately for each VARIETY if the comparison interacts with VARIETY, that is, if the value of the comparison differs from one VARIETY to the next. The next section shows how to formally test which VARIETY levels interact with the A vs B, C comparison.

As an exercise, see whether you can go through the process to get the coefficients for estimates of A versus B, C in each of VARIETY 2, 3, and 4. The A versus B, C comparison for VARIETY 5 is not shown here because there is a statistically significant difference between the B and C means given VARIETY 5 (see Output 3.13). Recall that comparing the A mean with the average of B and C only makes sense if there is no evidence that the B and C means are different.

Program 3.13 is the complete PROC GLIMMIX step with the correct LSMESTIMATE statements for A versus B, C with the four varieties for which this comparison is legitimate:

Program 3.13

```
proc glimmix;
   class method variety;
   model yield = method variety method*variety;
   lsmestimate method*variety
      'A vs B,C | V1' 2 0 0 0 0 -1 0 0 0 0 -1 0 0 0 0,
      'A vs B,C | V2' 0 2 0 0 0 0 -1 0 0 0 0 -1 0 0 0,
      'A vs B,C | V3' 0 0 2 0 0 0 0 -1 0 0 0 0 -1 0 0,
      'A vs B,C | V4' 0 0 0 2 0 0 0 0 -1 0 0 0 0 -1 0 /
      divisor=2;
run;
```

Results

The results appear in Output 3.16.

Output 3.16: Estimates of Method Differences by Variety

Effect	Label	Estimate	Standard Error	DF	t Value	Pr > |t|
		Least Squares Means Estimates				
method*variety	A vs B,C | V1	5.0167	2.2164	75	2.26	0.0265
method*variety	A vs B,C | V2	4.2750	2.2164	75	1.93	0.0575
method*variety	A vs B,C | V3	6.7500	2.2164	75	3.05	0.0032
method*variety	A vs B,C | V4	11.8000	2.2164	75	5.32	<.0001

Interpretation

Notice that the estimates differ among VARIETY levels, possibly an indication of interaction between the comparison A versus B, C and VARIETY. This is no surprise, because there was interaction between METHOD and VARIETY in the analysis of variance table (Output 3.11) in Section 3.5.2, "A More Complex Two-Way Factorial Experiment," earlier in this chapter. However, it is possible that VARIETY could interact with METHOD in general, but not interact with the comparison A versus B, C. In section 3.5.8 "Simultaneous Contrasts in Two-Way Classification," you will see how to use CONTRAST statements to test for the statistical significance of the interaction between the comparison A vs B, C and VARIETYs.

3.5.7 Simple Effect Comparisons—Using Model Parameters: How ESTIMATE and LSMESTIMATE Differ

The comparison of A with B, C in VARIETY 1 shown in the previous section uses the basic relationship between means and model parameters: $\mu_{A1} - 0.5(\mu_{B1} + \mu_{C1})$. The LSMESTIMATE statement uses the coefficients of these A × B cell means directly, because LSMESTIMATE is an *estimate* statement defined in terms of *least squares means* (LSM). The ESTIMATE statement, on the other hand, is defined in terms of the effects of the factorial statistical model, $\mu + \alpha_i + \beta_j + \alpha\beta_{ij}$. You can convert the LSMESTIMATE statement to an ESTIMATE statement as follows:

1. State the A versus B, C comparison in terms of the cell means model:
    $$\mu_{A1} - 0.5(\mu_{B1} + \mu_{C1})$$

2. Restate Step 1 in terms of the effect model parameters:
    $$\mu + \tau_A + \nu_1 + \tau\nu_{A1} - 0.5\left[\left(\mu + \tau_B + \nu_1 + \tau\nu_{B1}\right) + \left(\mu + \tau_C + \nu_1 + \tau\nu_{C1}\right)\right]$$

3. Gathering like terms gives the following:

$$\tau_A + \tau\nu_{A1} - (1/2)\big[(\tau_B + \tau\nu_{B1}) + (\tau_C + \tau\nu_{C1})\big] = \tau_A - (1/2)(\tau_B + \tau_C) + \tau\nu_{A1} - (1/2)(\tau\nu_{B1} + \tau\nu_{C1})$$

Now you have the information that you need to set up the ESTIMATE statement to go with the PROC GLIMMIX model. The required statements are as follows:

```
proc glimmix;
   class method variety;
   model yield = method variety method*variety;
   estimate 'A vs B,C in V1' method 2 -1 -1
      method*variety 2 0 0 0 0 -1 0 0 0 0 -1 0 0 0 0 /
      divisor=2;
run;
```

Notice the following:

- The μ and υ parameters disappeared from the expression, so you don't need INTERCEPT or VARIETY terms in the ESTIMATE statement. Leaving them out is equivalent to setting their coefficients equal to 0.

- The ordering of the METHOD*VARIETY coefficients is determined by the CLASS statement. In this CLASS statement, METHOD comes before VARIETY. For this reason, VARIETY levels change within METHOD levels.

- Unlike the LSMESTIMATE statement, you must include the coefficients for METHOD in the ESTIMATE statement. If you leave them out, the SAS log will print an error message that the ESTIMATE is non-estimable and the SAS listing for this ESTIMATE will be blank (try it to see what it looks like).

If you only wanted a *test* of the hypothesis $H_0 : \mu_{A1} - 0.5(\mu_{B1} - \mu_{C1}) = 0$ and do not want the estimate or standard error, you could replace the ESTIMATE statement with a CONTRAST statement containing the same coefficients:

```
contrast 'A vs B,C in V1' method 1 -.5 -.5
   method*variety 1 0 0 0 0 -.5 0 0 0 0 -.5 0 0 0 0;
```

Rather than examine output for the single ESTIMATE statement, you make the comparison for all varieties for which the A versus B, C comparison is appropriate. Guidelines for doing this are identical to those presented earlier in Section 3.5.6.

Program

As an exercise, see whether you can go through the three-step process to get the coefficients for estimates of A vs B, C in each of VARIETY 2, 3, and 4. Here is a complete PROC GLIMMIX step with the correct ESTIMATE statements for A vs B, C given VARIETY levels 1 through 4. Notice that these comparisons can be listed in a single ESTIMATE statement. You could also add and ADJUST= option to control multiplicity since you are evaluating more than one comparison.

Program 3.14

```
proc glimmix;
   class method variety;
   model yield = method|variety;
   estimate
      'A vs B,C in V1' method 2 -1 -1
         method*variety 2 0 0 0 0 -1 0 0 0 0 -1 0 0 0 0,
      'A vs B,C in V2' method 2 -1 -1
         method*variety 0 2 0 0 0 0 -1 0 0 0 0 -1 0 0 0,
      'A vs B,C in V3' method 2 -1 -1
         method*variety 0 0 2 0 0 0 0 -1 0 0 0 0 -1 0 0,
      'A vs B,C in V4' method 2 -1 -1
         method*variety 0 0 0 2 0 0 0 0 -1 0 0 0 0 -1 0 /
         divisor=2;
run;
```

Results

The results appear in Output 3.17.

Output 3.17: Estimate of Method Differences by Variety

	Estimates				
Label	Estimate	Standard Error	DF	t Value	Pr > |t|
A vs B,C in V1	5.0167	2.2164	75	2.26	0.0265
A vs B,C in V2	4.2750	2.2164	75	1.93	0.0575
A vs B,C in V3	6.7500	2.2164	75	3.05	0.0032
A vs B,C in V4	11.8000	2.2164	75	5.32	<.0001

Notice that these estimates are identical to those computed by the LSMESTIMATE statement.

3.5.8 Simultaneous Contrasts in Two-Way Classifications

This section illustrates setting up simultaneous contrasts in a two-way classification by constructing a test for significance of interaction between the comparison A versus B, C and VARIETY. The hypothesis of no interaction between A versus B, C and VARIETY is

$$H_0 : \left[\mu_{A1} - 0.5 \left(\mu_{B1} + \mu_{C1} \right) \right] = \ldots = \left[\mu_{A5} - 0.5 \left(\mu_{B5} + \mu_{C5} \right) \right]$$.

This hypothesis is actually a set of four equations, which can be written in different but equivalent ways. One way to express the equality of all the comparisons is to specify that each is equal to the last. This gives the hypothesis (H_0) in the following equations:

$$\left[\mu_{A1} - 0.5 \left(\mu_{B1} + \mu_{C1} \right) \right] = \left[\mu_{A5} - 0.5 \left(\mu_{B5} + \mu_{C5} \right) \right]$$

$$\left[\mu_{A2} - 0.5 \left(\mu_{B2} + \mu_{C2} \right) \right] = \left[\mu_{A5} - 0.5 \left(\mu_{B5} + \mu_{C5} \right) \right]$$

$$\left[\mu_{A3} - 0.5 \left(\mu_{B3} + \mu_{C3} \right) \right] = \left[\mu_{A5} - 0.5 \left(\mu_{B5} + \mu_{C5} \right) \right]$$

$$\left[\mu_{A4} - 0.5 \left(\mu_{B4} + \mu_{C4} \right) \right] = \left[\mu_{A5} - 0.5 \left(\mu_{B5} + \mu_{C5} \right) \right]$$

Going through the three-step process for each of these equations results in the following CONTRAST statement:

```
contrast 'A vs BC & Varieties'
   method*variety 1 0 0 0 -1 -.5 0 0 0 .5 -.5 0 0 0 .5,
   method*variety 0 1 0 0 -1 0 -.5 0 0 .5 0 -.5 0 0 .5,
   method*variety 0 0 1 0 -1 0 0 -.5 0 .5 0 0 -.5 0 .5,
   method*variety 0 0 0 1 -1 0 0 0 -.5 .5 0 0 0 -.5 .5;
```

As mentioned in Section 3.3.3 "Preplanned Comparison for One-Way Classification," concerning the CONTRAST statement for simultaneous comparisons in the one-way classification, there are several ways to specify a set of four equations that would be equivalent to the null hypothesis that the comparison A vs B, C is the same in all five VARIETYs. No matter how you set up the four equations, a CONTRAST statement derived from those equations will produce the results in Output 3.18.

Output 3.18: Test for A versus BC * Varieties Interaction

	Contrasts			
Label	Num DF	Den DF	F Value	Pr > F
A vs BC & Varieties	4	75	1.76	0.1450

The *F* tests for the A vs B, C * Varieties interaction in Output 3.18 is significant at the α=0.145 level. In many hypothesis testing situations, you might not consider this significant. However, like the overall METHOD*VARIETY test shown in Output 3.11, is a multiple-degree of freedom test. The overall F test had 8 numerator *df* and the test in Output 3.18 has 4 numerator *df*. This means that the F test shown in Output 3.18 is vulnerable to the same problem as the overall F test as there may be certain varieties for which A vs B, C comparison differs in a scientifically important way from the A vs B, C difference in other varieties. Because the 4 *df* for the A vs B,C*Varieties contrast is an average of four 1 *df* contrasts, if the A vs B, C interaction is concentrated in a one of single degree of freedom tests, the other 3 tests may mask it.

For this reason the test in Output 3.18 must be regarded as a preliminary test in the model-building phase. The decision should be based on a rather liberal cutoff level of significance, such as .2 or .25. You want to relax the Type I error rate in order to decrease the Type II error rate. It might be a serious mistake to declare that there is no interaction when in fact there is interaction (Type II error); you would then report main effects when you should report simple effects. The estimated main effect might not be a good representation of any of the simple effects. It is usually a less serious mistake to declare there is interaction when in fact there is not (a Type I error) and you would then report simple effects when you should report main effects. In this event, you still have unbiased estimates of simple effects, but you lose precision.

The next section illustrates partitioning the 4 *df* term above into single *df* contrasts. This will either confirm that there is no A versus B, C × VARIETY interaction or identify the specific component(s) for which an interaction does exist. Such trade-offs between Type I and Type II errors are ubiquitous throughout statistical modeling and should be kept closely in mind and related directly to the problem at hand when setting thresholds.

3.5.9 Comparison of Levels of One Factor within Subgroups of Levels of Another Factor

There are sometimes good reasons to report simple effects averaged across subgroups of levels of another factor (or factors). This is especially desirable when there are a large number of levels of the second factor. For example, if there were twenty varieties in the example instead of five, it would be tedious to report a separate comparison of methods for each of the twenty varieties, assuming it was even feasible to do so. You might want to consider trying to find subgroups of varieties such that the method comparison does not interact with the varieties within subgroups. It would be legitimate to report the method comparison averaged across the varieties within the subgroups. You should search for the subgroups with caution, however. Identification of potential subgroups should be on the basis of some prior knowledge of the varieties, such as subgroups that have some property in common.

In this example, you have already seen that for VARIETY 5 you cannot legitimately report a mean difference between METHOD A and the average of VARIETY B and C because given VARIETY 5, the B and C means differ significantly. Comparing the average of B and C to another mean makes no sense. However, this is not true for VARIETY 1 through 4. You can legitimately compare the mean of A with the average of B and C individually for each VARIETY except 5. Might there be opportunities to combine these means even further?

Suppose that VARIETY 1 and VARIETY 2 have similar genetic background, and that VARIETY 3 and VARIETY 4 have similar genetic background (but different than varieties 1 and 2). This presents a natural basis for forming subgroups. You might want to group VARIETY 1 and VARIETY 2 together and report a single result for the comparison A versus B, C averaged across these two varieties, and do the same thing for VARIETY 3 and VARIETY 4. The validity of these groupings, however, is contingent upon there being no interaction between the comparison A versus B, C and VARIETY within the groups. You could proceed using the following strategy

1. Test the interaction between A versus B,C by VARIETY within the variety 1 and 2 subgroup, and within the variety 3 and 4 subgroup.
2. If both tests in step 1 suggest negligible interaction, average over the two varieties in each group and test the interaction between A versus B,C by VARIETY across subgroups, i.e. A versus B,C × VARIETY 1&2 versus 3&4.
3. If both interactions in step 1 are negligible, you can estimate the simple effects of A versus B,C averaged over varieties 1 and 2 and, separately, over varieties 3 and 4.
4. If the interaction tested in step 2 is also negligible, you can estimate the simple effect of A versus B,C averaged over all four varieties, i.e. variety 1 through 4.

The formal hypotheses and associated contrast statements for step 1 are described here. The null hypothesis of no interaction between the comparison A vs B, C and VARIETY 1 and VARIETY 2 is

$$H_0 : \left[\mu_{A1} - 0.5\left(\mu_{B1} + \mu_{C1}\right)\right] = \left[\mu_{A2} - 0.5\left(\mu_{B2} + \mu_{C2}\right)\right]$$

It follows that the CONTRAST statement to test this hypothesis is as follows:

```
contrast 'A vs B,C*V1,V2'
    method*variety 1 -1 0 0 0 -.5 .5 0 0 0 -.5 .5 0 0 0;
```

Equivalently, it can be expressed as follows:

```
contrast 'A vs B,C*V1,V2'
   method*variety 2 -2 0 0 0 -1 1 0 0 0 -1 1 0 0 0;
```

Likewise, the null hypothesis of no interaction between A versus B, C and VARIETY 3 and VARIETY 4 is
$H_0 : \left[\mu_{A3} - 0.5\left(\mu_{B3} + \mu_{C3}\right)\right] = \left[\mu_{A4} - 0.5\left(\mu_{B4} + \mu_{C4}\right)\right]$ and the associated CONTRAST statement is

```
contrast 'A vs B,C*V3,V4'
   method*variety 0 0 2 -2 0 0 0 -1 1 0 0 0 -1 1 0;
```

For step 2, the formal statement of the null hypothesis and associated contrast statements are as follows:

$$H_0 : \left\{\left[\mu_{A1} - 0.5\left(\mu_{B1} + \mu_{C1}\right)\right] + \left[\mu_{A2} - 0.5\left(\mu_{B2} + \mu_{C2}\right)\right]\right\} - \left\{\left[\mu_{A3} - 0.5\left(\mu_{B3} + \mu_{C3}\right)\right] + \left[\mu_{A4} - 0.5\left(\mu_{B4} + \mu_{C4}\right)\right]\right\} = 0$$

Collecting terms yields the CONTRAST statement:

```
contrast 'A vs B,C*V1,V2 vs V3,V4'
   method*variety 2 2 -2 -2 0 -1 -1 1 1 0 -1 -1 1 1 0;
```

Results of these CONTRAST statements appear in Output 3.19.

Output 3.19: Interaction between A vs B, C and VARIETY Subsets

	Contrasts			
Label	Num DF	Den DF	F Value	Pr > F
A vs B,C*V1,V2	1	75	0.06	0.8136
A vs B,C*V3,V4	1	75	2.60	0.1114
A vs B,C*V1,V2 vs V3,V4	1	75	4.36	0.0401

This is almost a complete partition of the 4 *df* A vs B,C*VARIETY test from Section 3.5.8 (Output 3.18). These three contrasts are mutually orthogonal. The remaining degree of freedom would come from an A versus B, C*V1,2,3,4 versus V5 contrast. You would not include V5 since the B and C means are significantly different for V5 and not significantly different for V1, V2, V3, and V4.

You can see that the *F* test for the interaction between A versus B, C and VARIETY 1 and VARIETY 2 has a p-value of only 0.8136, which is non-significant. Assume that this interaction is negligible, and average the comparison across VARIETY 1 and VARIETY 2. On the other hand, the F test for interaction between A vs B, C and VARIETY 3 and VARIETY 4 has a *p*-value of 0.1114, which is a more ambiguous result. Certainly, there is no rigorous evidence of interaction. However, statisticians tend to be more cautious about whether to require separate estimates of A vs B, C in each of VARIETY 3 and VARIETY 4 or to combine them. Some statisticians say "pool unless the 1 *df* interaction test has p < 0.05"; others say "don't combine unless p > 0.20". Assume, for the sake of demonstration, that you do combine the A versus B, C comparison over VARIETYS 1 and 2 and another over VARIETY 3 and 4. Clearly, you cannot combine over all four varieties because the A versus B, C * V1, 2 versus V3, 4 contrast has a p-value of 0.0401. This comparison is clearly significant, meaning the A versus B, C comparison differs for the two genetic groups, VARIETY 1, 2 and VARIETY 3, 4.

To combine over the two varieties in each group, you want an estimate of

$$0.5\{[\mu_{A1} - 0.5(\mu_{B1} + \mu_{C1})] + [\mu_{A2} - 0.5(\mu_{B2} + \mu_{C2})]\}$$

for A versus B, C given V1, V2 and

$$0.5\{[\mu_{A3} - 0.5(\mu_{B3} + \mu_{C3})] + [\mu_{A4} - 0.5(\mu_{B4} + \mu_{C4})]\}$$

for A versus B, C given V3, V4. These yield the following LSMESTIMATE statement:

```
proc glimmix data=factorial;
   class method variety;
   model yield = method|variety;
```

```
lsmestimate method*variety
   'a vs b,c | v1,V2' 2 2 0 0 0 -1 -1 0 0 0 -1 -1 0 0 0,
   'a vs b,c | v3,V4' 0 0 2 2 0 0 0 -1 -1 0 0 0 -1 -1 0 /
   divisor=4,4;
run;
```

Output 3.20 shows the results.

Output 3.20: Estimate of the A vs B, C Averaged over VARIETY 1 and VARIETY 2 and over VARIETY 3 and VARIETY 4

		Least Squares Means Estimates				
Effect	Label	Estimate	Standard Error	DF	t Value	Pr > |t|
method*variety	a vs b,c | v1,2	4.6458	1.5673	75	2.96	0.0041
method*variety	a vs b,c | v3,4	9.2750	1.5673	75	5.92	<.0001
method*variety	(a vs b,c | v1,2) vs (a vs b,c | v 3,4)	-4.6292	2.2164	75	-2.09	0.0401

For clarity, you could add the A and averaged B, C means for the two groups using the following LSMESTIMATE statement:

```
lsmestimate method*variety;
   'a | v1,V2'   1 1 0 0 0 0 0 0 0 0 0 0 0 0 0 0,
   'b,c | v1,V2' 0 0 0 0 0 1 1 0 0 0 1 1 0 0 0,
   'a | v3,V4'   0 0 1 1 0 0 0 0 0 0 0 0 0 0 0 0,
   'b,c | v3,V4' 0 0 0 0 0 0 0 1 1 0 0 0 1 1 0 /
   divisor=2,4,2,4;
```

Output 3.21 shows the results.

Output 3.21: Mean of A Minus the Mean of B, C Means for Combined VARIETY Groups

		Least Squares Means Estimates				
Effect	Label	Estimate	Standard Error	DF	t Value	Pr > |t|
method*variety	a | v1,2	21.8083	1.2797	75	17.04	<.0001
method*variety	b,c | v1,2	17.1625	0.9049	75	18.97	<.0001
method*variety	a | v3,4	24.5500	1.2797	75	19.18	<.0001
method*variety	b,c | v3,4	15.2750	0.9049	75	16.88	<.0001

The estimate 4.64 in the first line of Output 3.20 is the average of the two estimates 5.02 for VARIETY 1 and 4.27 for VARIETY 2 in Output 3.17. The advantage of averaging is the smaller standard error of 1.57 for the combined estimate compared with 2.21 (see Output 3.17) for the individual estimates.

3.5.10 Quantitative by Qualitative Factorial: An Example

In the previous sections, we investigated a two-way classification design. As with a single factor design, factorial experiments are not limited to qualitative factors. In this section, we will look at the analysis of a design with one qualitative factor and one quantitative factor. In the following section, we investigate treatment design with two quantitative factors, also known as a response surface design.

This example uses data from a study with a randomized complete block experiment design and eight treatments comprising a 2 × 4 factorial treatment design. The identities of treatment factors and response variable are blinded, so they will be discussed in generic terms. Factor A is qualitative, e.g. two types of management methods. Factor B is quantitative, e.g. amounts of an additive, with levels equally spaced and amounts multiples of 0, 1, 2 and 3. The response variable is denoted Y.

The generic model for these data is

$$y_{ijk} = \mu + \alpha_i + \beta_j + \alpha\beta_{ij} + r_k + e_{ijk}$$

where terms are defined as follows:

- α_i denotes the main effect of factor A.

- β_j denotes the main effect of factor B.

- $\alpha\beta_{ij}$ denotes the A×B interaction effect.

- r_k denotes the block effect, assumed i.i.d. $N(0,\sigma_r^2)$.

- e_{ijk} denotes the residual effect, assumed i.i.d. $N(0,\sigma_e^2)$.

A typical starting place for the analysis of a qualitative × quantitative experiment is to fit the classification model as described above, using in to create an interaction plot as well as do a preliminary assessment of model effects.

Program

Use Program 3.15 to implement this step.

Program 3.15

```
proc glimmix data= qual_by_quant;
   class a b block;
   model y = a|b;
   random block;
   lsmeans a*b / plot=meanplot(sliceby=a join);
run;
```

Results

Output 3.22 shows the results.

Output 3.22: Preliminary Analysis of Qualitative × Quantitative Data

Covariance Parameter Estimates			
Cov Parm	Subject	Estimate	Standard Error
Intercept	block	0	.
Residual		10.9161	2.7290

Type III Tests of Fixed Effects				
Effect	Num DF	Den DF	F Value	Pr > F
A	1	32	7.95	0.0082
B	3	32	1.44	0.2482
A*B	3	32	1.47	0.2413

Figure 3.10: A × B Interaction Plot

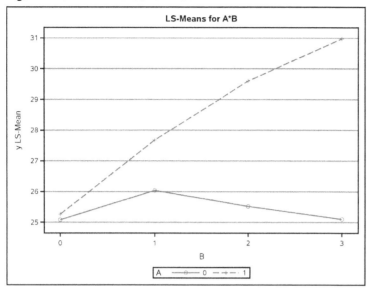

Interpretation

The first thing to notice is the "Covariance Parameter Estimates" table: the block variance estimate has been set to zero. This occurs because the solution to the REML estimating equations for the block variance is negative. As noted in Section 2.5, we must override the "set-to-zero" default using either the NOBOUND option or the compound symmetry (CS) reparameterization of the variance structure. Failing to do so risks inflating type I error rate. Use Program 3.16 to implement the NOBOUND option. This will affect the table of "Type III Tests of Fixed Effects" but it will not change the interaction plot, shown above.

You can see by inspection of the interaction plot in Figure 3.10 that there is visual evidence of a linear increase in mean response with increasing levels of factor B applied in conjunction with level 1 of factor A, whereas the effect of B in conjunction with level 0 of factor A appears to be negligible.

Program

Program 3.16 implements the NOBOUND option to override the "set-to-zero" default.

Program 3.16

```
proc glimmix data = qual_by_quant nobound;
   class a b block;
   model y = a|b;
   random block;
   lsmeans a*b / plot=meanplot(sliceby=a join);
run;
```

Results

Output 3.23 shows the covariance parameter estimates and model effect tests as amended by NOBOUND.

Output 3.23: NOBOUND-corrected Variance Estimates and Model Effect Tests for Qualitative × Quantitative Data

Covariance Parameter Estimates			
Cov Parm	Subject	Estimate	Standard Error
Intercept	block	-1.2340	0.4531
Residual		12.1502	3.2473

Type III Tests of Fixed Effects

Effect	Num DF	Den DF	F Value	Pr > F
A	1	28	7.14	0.0124
B	3	28	1.30	0.2948
A*B	3	28	1.32	0.2875

Interpretation

Using NOBOUND overrides the set-to-zero default, resulting in a more accurate estimate of residual variance (12.15 versus 10.92 without NOBOUND) and tests with better type I error control. In this data set, the results are not appreciably affected (with or without NOBOUND, the main effect of A is statistically significant and the B and A × B effects are not significant), but they could have been, as illustrated by the change in p-value for the main effect of A ($p = 0.008$ without NOBOUND, $p = 0.012$ with NOBOUND).

The striking result of the Type III tests is what is not significant. Despite visual evidence of an interaction – strong linear effect of B in conjunction with A level 1, negligible B effect with A level 0 – the overall test of the A × B effect has p-value > 0.287 – not even close to statistical significance. The apparent disconnect between visual evidence and formal statistics is an artifact of the numerator degrees of freedom of the F value for A × B: multiple numerator degree of freedom tests are notoriously underpowered, and must be partitioned into single degree of freedom components.

There are two methods for partitioning the A × B effect when B is a quantitative factor. You can either use orthogonal polynomial contrasts, or re-express the model using direct regression. Note that these are extensions of the options for single factor regression shown in Section 3.4. We begin with orthogonal polynomials.

Partition of A × B Effect Using Orthogonal Polynomials

Given that there are four levels of factor B, you can partition the B effect into linear, quadratic and cubic components. Use the partition of the B effect to obtain the needed A × B contrasts. Table 3.3 shows the strategy.

Table 3.3: Construction of Orthogonal Polynomial Interaction Contrasts by Treatment Combinations

	0				1			
	0	**1**	**2**	**3**	**0**	**1**	**2**	**3**
A				−1				1
B linear	−3	−1	1	3	−3	−1	1	3
B quadratic	−1	1	1	−1	−1	1	1	−1
B cubic	−1	3	−3	1	−1	3	−3	1
A × B linear	3	1	−1	−3	−3	−1	1	3
A × B quad	1	−1	−1	1	−1	1	1	−1
A × B cubic	1	−3	3	−1	−1	3	−3	1

First, construct main effect contrasts for A and B. Factor A only has two levels, so the only possible contrast is A level 0 versus level 1, i.e. coefficients -1 and 1. The orthogonal polynomial contrasts for factor B are linear {-3,-1,1,3}, quadratic {-1,1,1,-1} and cubic {-1,3,-3,1}. Construct the interaction contrasts by taking cross-products of the A and each B contrast. For example, for A × B linear, multiply the A level 0 coefficient (-1) by each B linear coefficient, then multiply the A level 1 coefficient by each B linear coefficient.

Program

Use Program 3.17 to implement the partition.

Program 3.17

```
proc glimmix data = qual_by_quant nobound;
   class a b block;
   model y = a|b / ddfm=kr2;
   random intercept / subject=block;
   contrast 'a' a 1 -1;
   contrast 'B linear' b -3 -1 1 3;
   contrast 'B quadratic' b -1 1 1 -1;
```

```
   contrast 'B cubic' b 1 -3 3 -1;
   contrast 'A x B linear' a*b 3 1 -1 -3 -3 -1 1 3;
   contrast 'A x B quadratic' a*b 1 -1 -1 1 1 -1 1 1 -1;
   contrast 'A x B cubic' a*b -1 3 -3 1 1 -3 3 -1;
run;
```

Results

Output 3.24 shows the results.

Output 3.24: Partition of Model Effects Using Orthogonal Polynomial Contrasts

	Contrasts			
Label	Num DF	Den DF	F Value	Pr > F
a	1	28	7.14	0.0124
B linear	1	28	3.57	0.0693
B quadratic	1	28	0.30	0.5874
B cubic	1	28	0.02	0.8770
A x B linear	1	28	3.93	0.0574
A x B quadratic	1	28	0.01	0.9391
A x B cubic	1	28	0.03	0.8707

Interpretation

The A × B linear contrast shows a marginally significant interaction with the linear term, $p = 0.0574$. Therefore, we would conclude that the effect of A is contingent on what level of B is used, and the linear effect of B is different depending on which level of factor A is used.

Looking at the A × B quadratic and A × B cubic results, you can also see why the overall A × B effect was non-significant. Assuming no missing data, the A × B effect is an average of the three orthogonal contrast effects, that is $(3.93 + 0.01 + 0.03)/3 = 1.32$, the *F*-value for the overall A×B effect.

Partition of the A × B Effect Using Direct Regression

Instead of partitioning the standard factorial effects using contrasts, you can rewrite the model in polynomial regression form. The model is as follows:

$$y_{ijk} = \mu + \alpha_i + \left(\beta_1 + \delta_{1i}\right)B_j + \left(\beta_2 + \delta_{2i}\right)B_j^2 + \left(\beta_3 + \delta_{3i}\right)B_j^3 + r_k + e_{ijk}$$

where terms are as follows:

- μ, α_i, r_k and e_{ijk} are defined as before.

- β_1, β_2 and β_3 are linear, quadratic and cubic regression coefficients, respectively.

- δ_{1i}, δ_{2i} and δ_{3i} are treatment effects on the linear, quadratic and cubic regression coefficients, respectively—that is, they are A × B linear, A × B quadratic and A × B cubic interaction terms.

- B_j is the jth level of factor B—note that B_j is a direct variable: If the levels of factor B are 0, 1, 2 and 3, then $B_1 = 0$, $B_2 = 1$, and so on.

Program

Use Program 3.18 to implement this model.

Program 3.18

```
proc glimmix data= qual_by_quant nobound;
   class a block;
   model y = a|b|b|b / htype=1,3 ddfm=kr2;
   random block;
run;
```

The right-hand terms in the MODEL statement

```
a|b|b|b
```

are SAS shorthand for the following;

```
a b a*b b*b a*b*b b*b*b a*b*b*b
```

The term `a` here fits the α_i effects; `b`, `b*b` and `b*b*b` fit the regression main effects β_1, β_2 and β_3, and `a*b`, `a*b*b` and `a*b*b*b` fit the interaction effects δ_{1i}, δ_{2i} and δ_{3i}.

Results

Results appear in Output 3.25.

Output 3.25: Variance Estimates and Type I and III Tests of Regression Model Effects

Covariance Parameter Estimates		
Cov Parm	Estimate	Standard Error
block	-1.2340	0.4531
Residual	12.1502	3.2473

Type I Tests of Fixed Effects				
Effect	Num DF	Den DF	F Value	Pr > F
A	1	28	7.14	0.0124
B	1	28	3.57	0.0693
B*A	1	28	3.93	0.0574
B*B	1	28	0.30	0.5874
B*B*A	1	28	0.01	0.9391
B*B*B	1	28	0.02	0.8770
B*B*B*A	1	28	0.03	0.8707

Type III Tests of Fixed Effects				
Effect	Num DF	Den DF	F Value	Pr > F
A	1	28	0.01	0.9355
B	1	28	0.33	0.5683
B*A	1	28	0.00	0.9598
B*B	1	28	0.06	0.8156
B*B*A	1	28	0.03	0.8632
B*B*B	1	28	0.02	0.8770
B*B*B*A	1	28	0.03	0.8707

Interpretation

The "Covariance Parameter Estimates" are identical to those computed using the factorial effects model. The "Type I Tests of Fixed Effects" results are identical to the contrast results from the factorial effects model. As we saw in the single-factor regression model in Section 3.4, the Type III test results are not useful in the context of these data.

Lack of Fit Analysis of Qualitative by Quantitative Factorial

Outputs 3.24 and 3.25 show the analysis of these data using models that account for all seven available treatment degrees of freedom—one for A, three for the main effects of B, and three for the A × B interaction. Suppose, however, that in planning the study there is good reason to believe that the effect of factor B will be linear; the four levels of factor B are observed to allow a lack-of-fit test in case the research planners are wrong about the anticipated B effect. You can extend the lack-of-fit method shown in Section 3.4.3 for use with factorial experiments.

Program

Program 3.19 fits the linear terms from the regression model but replaces the quadratic and cubic terms with a catch-all lack-of-fit term, denoted $\alpha\beta_{ij}$ in the resulting model:

$$y_{ijk} = \mu + \alpha_i + \left(\beta_1 + \delta_{1i}\right)B_j + \alpha\beta_{ij} + r_k + e_{ijk}$$

Program 3.19

```
proc glimmix data= qual_by_quant nobound;
   class a cb block;
   model y=a|b cb*a / htype=1 ddfm=kr2;
   random block;
run;
```

The term

```
cb*a
```

in the MODEL statement corresponds to the lack-of-fit effect $\alpha\beta_{ij}$. You must create the CB variable by using the program statement

```
cb=b;
```

in the DATA step.

Results

Output 3.26 shows the results.

Output 3.26: Results of Lack of Fit Analysis

Covariance Parameter Estimates		
Cov Parm	Estimate	Standard Error
block	-1.2340	0.4531
Residual	12.1502	3.2473

Type I Tests of Fixed Effects				
Effect	Num DF	Den DF	F Value	Pr > F
A	1	28	7.14	0.0124
B	1	28	3.57	0.0693
B*A	1	28	3.93	0.0574
A*CB	4	28	0.09	0.9849

Interpretation

The "Covariance Parameter Estimates" and the Type I tests of A main effect, B linear main effect, and A × B linear interaction effect are identical to those in Outputs 3.24 and 3.25. The F value for the lack-of-fit term, A*CB, is 0.09. Although it is a four-degree-of-freedom effect, the largest possible F value for any single degree of freedom component of the lack-of-fit term is $4 \times 0.09 = 0.36$. Therefore, you can conclude that the linear regression, with different slopes for each level of A, is sufficient to account for the treatment effects in these data. The next step is to estimate the coefficients of the regression equation for each level of A.

Model for Fitting Separate Regression Equations for Each Level of Factor A

The reduced model to predict Y, with linear B terms only, is

$$E\left[y_{ijk}\right] = \mu + \alpha_i + \left(\beta_1 + \delta_{1i}\right)B_j$$

The disadvantage of this model is that it is not full rank, and working with the resulting solution can be inconvenient. A more useful, full rank form of the model, is

$$E\left[y_{ijk}\right] = \beta_{0i} + \beta_{1i}B_j$$

where β_{0i} denotes the intercept for the level of factor A, and β_{1i} denotes the slope for the level of factor A. The advantage of the full rank model is that the resulting parameters estimates have a clear interpretation.

Program

Use Program 3.20 to fit the full rank model.

Program 3.20

```
proc glimmix data = qual_by_quant nobound;
   class a block;
   model y=a a*b / noint ddfm=kr2 solution;
   random block;
run;
```

Results

The solution for this model appears in Output 3.27.

Output 3.27: Solution to the Qualitative by Quantitative Factorial

Covariance Parameter Estimates		
Cov Parm	Estimate	Standard Error
block	-1.0612	0.3921
Residual	10.7675	2.6919

Solutions for Fixed Effects						
Effect	A	Estimate	Standard Error	DF	t Value	Pr > |t|
A	0	25.5040	1.1381	32	22.41	<.0001
A	1	25.5180	1.1381	32	22.42	<.0001
B*A	0	-0.04600	0.6563	32	-0.07	0.9446
B*A	1	1.9080	0.6563	32	2.91	0.0066

Interpretation

The block and residual variance estimates are different (-1.06 and 10.77 versus -1.23 and 12.15 for block and residual, reduced and full model, respectively) because the quadratic and cubic terms have been pooled with block and residual variability. The implicit assumption is that by dropping them from the model, they are now understood to be noise rather than signal. The regression equation estimates are as follows:

- for level 0 of A: $25.504 - 0.046 \times B$
- for level 1 of A: $25.518 + 1.908 \times B$

One criticism of this model is that the slope coefficient for level 0 of A is not significantly different from zero (the *p*-value for it is >0.94); there is no evidence that B, in conjunction with level 0 of factor A, affects response. A more parsimonious, but adequate and arguably more accurate model, is the following:

$$E\left[y_{ijk}\right] = \begin{cases} \beta_{00} & \text{if A=0} \\ \beta_{01} + \beta_{11}B_j & \text{if A=1} \end{cases}$$

Program

Use the DATA step and subsequent PROC GLIMMIX statements in Program 3.21 to fit this model.

Program 3.21

```
data reg;
   set qual_by_quant;
   xb = (a=1)*b;
run;

proc glimmix data=reg nobound;
   class a block;
   model y=a a*xb / noint solution;
   random block;
run;
```

The indicator function multiplied by B in the line

```
   xb = (a=1)*b;
```

creates a regression variable for B that only has value for level 1 of factor A. Thus, a linear regression over B is only fit for level 1 of A.

Results

Output 3.28 shows the results.

Output 3.28: Parameter Estimates for Parsimonious Linear Regression Model

Covariance Parameter Estimates		
Cov Parm	Estimate	Standard Error
block	-1.0206	0.3792
Residual	10.4429	2.5709

Solutions for Fixed Effects						
Effect	A	Estimate	Standard Error	DF	t Value	Pr > |t|
A	0	25.4350	0.5639	33	45.10	<.0001
A	1	25.5180	1.1216	33	22.75	<.0001
xb*A	0	0	.	.	.	.
xb*A	1	1.9080	0.6463	33	2.95	0.0058

Interpretation

The regression equations are now as follows:

- for level 0 of A: 25.435
- for level 1 of A: 25.518 + 1.908 × B

Notice that for level 1 of A the regression equation is unchanged, but for level 0, the slope is dropped. The expected response for level 0 of A is 25.435 regardless of what level of B is applied.

3.5.11 Example: Factorial with Two Continuous Factors

Factorial experiments in which all treatment factors are quantitative are also called *response surface* experiments. Although SAS has procedures specifically intended for response surface analysis, notably PROC RSREG, they fit fixed-effect-only models. However, many response surface experiments are blocked in various ways, including incomplete block structures discussed in Chapter 2, and split-plot structures discussed in Chapter 5. In addition, response surface experiments often feature non-Gaussian data, and are most appropriately analyzed using generalized linear models or generalized linear mixed models (depending on the design structure). GLMs and GLMMs are discussed in Chapters 11, 12 and 13. The purpose of this section is to introduce PROC GLIMMIX-based methods useful for analyzing factorial experiments with all quantitative factors, also known as response surface experiments. The example presented in this section uses a fixed-effects only model in order to keep the focus on model statements and plot options. You can augment these with needed RANDOM statements and DISTRIBUTION options consistent with the experiment design and type of response variable with which you are working.

The experiment in this example is a study of how the surface finish of a metal part is affected by the feed rate of the metal through the machine and the depth of the cut. There are three feed rates (0.2, 0.25 and 0.3 in/min) and fourth depths of cut (0.15, 0.18, 0.20 and 0.25mm). Therefore, feed rate could have a linear or quadratic effect, while the depth of cut could have a linear, quadratic or cubic effect. However, in response surface analysis we typically assume that a second order polynomial will be sufficient to model the data. If it is not, then it is more likely that a nonlinear surface should be fit. To test whether the second order polynomial is sufficient, you use the same lack-of-fit test discussed in Section 3.4.

Program

Program 3.22 reads in the data and begin the analysis with a plot to visualize the surface. We include both a contour plot and a 3-dimensional plot as some readers may find one more intuitive to understand the response surface than the other.

Program 3.22

```
data finish;
    do f=.2,.25,.3;
        do d=.15,.18,.20,.25;
            do rep=1 to 3;
                input surface @;
                cf = f;
                cd = d; *class copies of f and d;
                output;
                end;
            end;
        end;
    datalines;
74 64 60 79 68 73 82 88 92 99 104 96
92 86 88 98 104 88 99 108 95 104 110 99
99 98 102 104 99 95 108 110 99 114 111 107
;
run;

proc glimmix data=finish;
    model surface=f|f|d|d|d;
    store gmxfit;
run;

proc plm restore=gmxfit;
    effectplot;
run;

proc glimmix data=finish;
    class f d;
    model surface = f*d;
    lsmeans f*d;
    ods output lsmeans=lsm;
run;

 proc template;
    define statgraph surfaceplotparm;
        begingraph;
            layout overlay3d / cube=fals rotate=20 axisopts=(griddisplay=on);
                surfaceplotparm x=f y=d z=estimate;
            endlayout;
        endgraph;
    end;
run;

ods graphics / antialiasmax=5700;
proc sgrender data=lsm template=surfaceplotparm;
run;
```

Results

Figure 3.11 shows the contour plot. Figure 3.12 shows the 3-dimensional plot.

Figure 3.11: Contour Plot of Feed Rate by Cut Depth

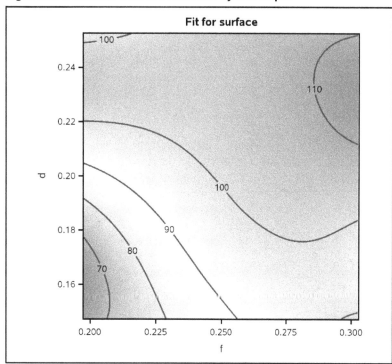

Figure 3.12: 3-D Plot of Feed Rate by Cut Depth LSMeans

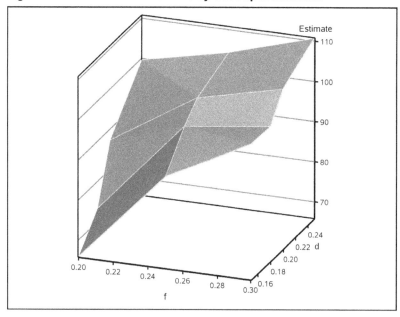

Interpretation

Both plots depict the same data, and it is a matter of preference which plot enables a better visualization. You can change the rotation of the 3-D plot using the rotate option within the layout statement of PROC TEMPLATE. It appears that as the feed rate increases, the response increases linearly or possibly quadratically. A similar response pattern can be seen across depth of cut. There also might be a linear by linear interaction due to the slight "twist" to the surface. You can verify the visual inspection with the statements in Program 3.23.

Program

You can verify the visual inspection with the statements in Program 3.23.

Program 3.23

```
proc glimmix data=finish;
   class cf cd;
   model surface=f|f|d|d@2 cf*cd / htype=1;
run;
```

Results

The output of this analysis is in Output 3.29.

Output 3.29: Analysis of Full Response Surface Model Including Lack-of-Fit

	Type I Tests of Fixed Effects			
Effect	Num DF	Den DF	F Value	Pr > F
f	1	24	103.42	<.0001
f*f	1	24	6.62	0.0167
d	1	24	71.10	<.0001
f*d	1	24	14.39	0.0009
d*d	1	24	0.63	0.4367
cf*cd	6	24	1.21	0.3349

Interpretation

As with a single quantitative factor, you begin the analysis at the bottom of the Type I Tests table to determine whether there is significant lack of fit after fitting the second-order response surface. In this case, with a p-value of .3349, you would fail to reject the null hypothesis of no lack of fit and conclude that the second-order polynomial is sufficient. Because the second-order polynomial model is sufficient, you now look for further model reduction opportunities by eliminating any other higher order non-significant terms. In this experiment, you can eliminate the d*d term as it has a p-value of .4367. All other terms remain in the model due to significant p-values. However, even if a lower order term was not significant, it is often included in the model if a higher order term including it is significant.

Program

Estimate the final fitted response surface using Program 3.24.

Program 3.24

```
proc glimmix data=finish;
   model surface = f f*f d f*d / solution;
   store gmxfit2;
run;
```

Results

The output from this model is in Output 3.30.

Output 3.30: Parameter Estimates for the Fitted Response Surface

	Parameter Estimates				
Effect	Estimate	Standard Error	DF	t Value	Pr > |t|
Intercept	-231.41	55.9055	31	-4.14	0.0002
f	1642.08	402.95	31	4.08	0.0003
f*f	-1950.00	768.74	31	-2.54	0.0164
d	776.89	154.43	31	5.03	<.0001
f*d	-2279.87	609.65	31	-3.74	0.0007
Scale	29.5481	7.5052	.	.	.

Interpretation

Using these estimates, you have the final fitted model. This model can be used to generate and plot predicted values to visualize the surface. It can also be used to identify the feed rate and cut depth that maximized (or minimizes, depending on the objective) the surface finish.

Program

You can use the statements in Program 3.25 to visualize the final fitted surface, either a contour plot or a 3-dimensional plot as best suits your visual understanding.

Program 3.25

```
proc plm restore=gmxfit2;
   effectplot;
run;

data plot_rs;
   do f=.20 to .30 by .01;
      do d=.15 to .25 by .01;
         y_hat = -231.41+1642.08*f-1950*f*f+776.89*d-2279.87*f*d;
         output;
      end;
   end;
run;

proc template;
   define statgraph surfaceplotparm;
      begingraph;
         layout overlay3d / cube=false rotate=20 axisopts=(griddisplay=on);
            surfaceplotparm x=f y=d z=y_hat;
         endlayout;
      endgraph;
   end;
run;

ods graphics / antialiasmax=5700;
proc sgrender data=plot_rs template=surfaceplotparm;
run;
```

Results

The contour plot from these statements is shown in Figure 3.13. The 3-D plot is shown in Figure 3.14.

Figure 3.13: Contour Plot of Fitted Response Surface

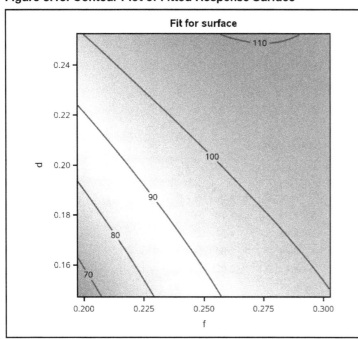

Figure 3.14: 3-Dimensional Fitted Response Surface

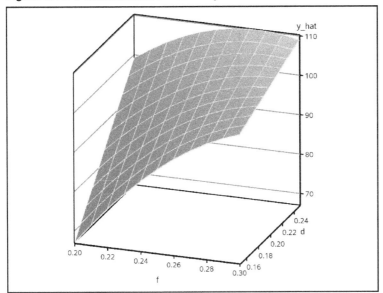

An alternative way to create the points for the plot without having to hand-code the coefficients is to append them to the original data with missing values for SURFACE. Then add the statements,

```
output out=rsp(where=(surface=.)) pred=y_hat resid=y_resid; id f d;
```

to create a SAS data set named RSP containing the response surface predictions and residuals.

An Old Fashioned but Useful Three-Dimensional Plot

For users who may find the three dimensional plot more useful in visualizing a response surface but who also may not require a publish-ready plot, the older procedure PROC G3D can provide a quick, less programming intensive look at the 3-D surface.

Program

As an alternative to the PROC TEMPLATE and PROC SGRENDER program, we present an alternate program for producing plots similar to Figure 3.12 and Figure 3.14 in Program 3.26.

Program 3.26

```
proc g3d data=lsm;
   plot f*d=estimate / rotate=30;
run;

proc g3d data=plot_rs;
   plot f*d=y_hat / rotate=30;
run;
```

Results

The plots from these statements are shown in Figure 3.15.

Figure 3.15: Three-Dimensional Response Surfaces using PROC G3D

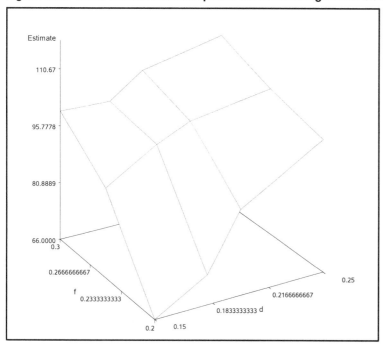

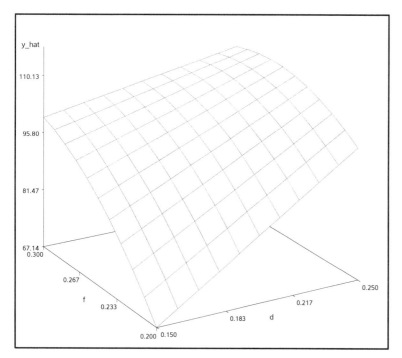

3.6 Summary

This chapter presents an extensive set of material required for *post-processing*, that is, pursuing the analysis beyond ANOVA-style tests of fixed effects. It begins with a simple two-treatment comparison, and continues with to factorial experiments with either quantitative or qualitative factors (or both).

Section 3.2 introduces the basic two-treatment comparison. This design is expanded to multiple levels in section 3.3. Section 3.4 shows post-processing methods when the factor levels are quantitative instead of qualitative. Section 3.5 presents methods for the many forms of factorial treatment structures: qualitative by qualitative, quantitative by quantitative, and quantitative by qualitative factorials of varying degrees of complexity.

Although this chapter is long, it is also introductory. Subsequent chapters expand the use of these treatment designs in conjunction with more complex experiment design structures. Specifically, Chapter 5 includes factorial treatment designs used in conjunction with multiple random effects such as split plots. Chapter 7 addresses analysis of covariance, which is conceptually similar to a qualitative by quantitative factorial.

Chapter 4: Power, Precision, and Sample Size I: Basic Concepts

4.1 Introduction **101**
4.2 Understanding Essential Background for Mixed Model Power and Precision **102**
4.3 Computing Precision and Power for CRD: An Example... **104**
    4.3.1 Creation of an Exemplary Data Set and Use of PROC GLIMMIX 104
    4.3.2 Completion of the Power Calculation... 105
4.4 Comparing Competing Designs I—CRD versus RCBD: An Example............................ **108**
    4.4.1 Revision of PROC GLIMMIX Power and Calculation Steps 108
    4.4.2 Precision of Treatment Differences with Blocking.. 108
    4.4.3 Pilot Data to Anticipate Variance Components for Precision and Power Analysis 109
    4.4.4 Precision and Power for Changing Sample Size with Blocked Design 111
4.5 Comparing Competing Designs II—Complete versus Incomplete Block Designs: An Example **112**
4.6 Using Simulation for Precision and Power... **117**
    4.6.1 Simulation to Characterize Possible Outcomes 117
    4.6.2 Simulation as an Alternative Way to Compute Precision or Power 120
    4.6.3 Simulation to Approximate Change in Variance Components 124
4.7 Summary... **129**

4.1 Introduction

Chapters 2, 3, and most of the subsequent chapters in this book focus on the analysis of data using mixed model methods. In this chapter, we turn our attention to analysis *before* data collection begins, during the planning phase of a study. Specifically, our focus in this chapter is on power, precision, sample size, and comparison of alternative designs under consideration for a prospective study.

First, a review of terminology used in this chapter.

Precision refers to the standard error, and hence the width of the confidence interval for a treatment comparison or contrast of interest. Precision analysis as discussed in this chapter refers to the expected standard error or expected confidence interval width for a proposed design. Precision analysis is especially useful when you want to compare two or more designs under consideration, because the impact of your choice of design on the expected standard error of contrasts of interest (or the expected width of their confidence intervals) gives you a highly informative way to evaluate the pros and cons of each prospective design.

The *power* of a statistical test is the probability of rejecting the null hypothesis when the alternative hypothesis is in fact true. Power equals one minus the probability of a Type II error and is also known as *sensitivity* or the *true positive rate*. For a comparative experiment, the alternative hypothesis is equivalent to the statement "a treatment difference exists." Many textbooks refer to the alternative hypothesis as the *research hypothesis*. The way hypothesis testing is most commonly done, the null and alternative hypotheses have even narrower meaning: the null says "no treatment difference exists," and the alternative says "a nonzero difference exists." Employed in this manner, power is the probability of declaring a nonzero difference to be statistically significant at a specified α-level. Note that "nonzero difference" and "scientifically relevant difference" are not equivalent. As we shall see in this chapter, being able to articulate the latter is essential for implementing power analysis. However, when you reject the null hypothesis in a conventional hypothesis test, you are merely concluding that there is evidence of a nonzero difference, not necessarily a scientifically relevant difference.

Sample size refers to the number of *legitimate* replications that are required to attain a desired level of power or precision. As we will see in this chapter, sample size is not exclusively a matter of number of observations. Design matters.

> **Important Note**: For a given sample size, different designs can have very different power and precision profiles, depending on the source, pattern, and magnitude of variance among experimental units. Mixed model-based power and precision analysis provides a powerful tool for assessing alternative designs.

The last two sentences are important, because they motivate what this chapter is and is not about. Researchers often restrict their attention to the final step of power analysis: determining the required sample size for the design that they plan to use. Typically, SAS procedures such as PROC POWER or PROC GLMPOWER are used for this step. This chapter is intentionally not about this step or these procedures. Although useful, PROC POWER and PROC GLMPOWER are limited to cases where there is a single source of variance, e.g. experimental unit variance in a completely randomized design or randomized complete block design. The POWER and GLMPOWER procedures are not designed to account for multiple random effects, recovery of inter-block information, or to assess multilevel designs. You cannot use them to compare, for example, the precision and power characteristics of a randomized block versus an incomplete block versus a split-plot design when these are three designs under consideration. Our point here is that statistical thinking about design should begin much earlier than the "compute the sample size" step. The purpose of this chapter is to present mixed model-based tools that enable you to do so. The material in this chapter is introductory. The calculations in the early sections of this chapter could be implemented with PROC POWER, but that is not the point. The point is to set the stage for examples later in this chapter, and more advanced applications in Chapter 14, that engage statistical thinking early in the planning process and that *require* mixed model-based methods.

Our focus is on *prospective* power and precision calculations, referring to the power of statistical hypothesis tests, and precision of contrast estimates for new experiments that are yet to be conducted. Such calculations can be critical in determining the size and structure of a new experimental design and in optimizing information gain from experimental units. Along with Lenth (2001) and Hoenig and Heisey (2001), we recommend against *retrospective* power calculations, in which power statistics are used to embellish analysis of a data set in hand. Conclusions from such calculations are misleading, and in fact, the power estimates themselves are generally just a function of the corresponding *p*-values. However, power calculations on current data sets can be useful from a pilot study perspective, in the sense that reasonable estimates for required parameters can be obtained from existing data, providing information needed to perform an appropriate prospective power calculation.

There is well-developed literature for power, precision and sample size calculations for a variety of simple statistical models, and for general linear models in particular. Please refer to Castelloe and O'Brien (2000), Verbeke and Molenberghs (2000), Muller and Fetterman (2002), SAS Institute Inc. (2004), as well as the documentation for the POWER and GLMPOWER procedures in SAS/STAT. As noted above, the purpose of this chapter is to move beyond this literature, to enable you to use mixed model-based statistical thinking earlier in the planning process, and to enable you to plan for designs whose complexity exceeds the capabilities of procedures such as PROC POWER and PROC GLMPOWER.

4.2 Understanding Essential Background for Mixed Model Power and Precision

Power and precision calculations for mixed models are more involved because of their more complex covariance structure (Helms 1992; Stroup 2002; Tempelman 2006; Rosa, Steibel, and Tempelman 2006; Stroup 2013), but you can implement them with either PROC GLIMMIX or PROC MIXED using theory and methodology basics, given as follows:

- The treatment effect(s) or contrast(s), defined as a linear combination $\mathbf{K}'\boldsymbol{\beta}$.
- The design matrix, $\mathbf{X}$. The number of rows corresponds to the sample size and the columns of $\mathbf{X}$ are determined by the design—usually the treatment design in particular.
- The variance-covariance matrix, $\mathbf{V}$. This matrix specifies the sources of random variation and their magnitude. In a mixed model, $\mathbf{V} = \mathbf{ZGZ}' + \mathbf{R}$. $\mathbf{G}$ gives the covariance of the random model effects, which typically correspond to the elements of the experiment design. The columns of $\mathbf{Z}$ specify the sample size and structure of the random model effects. $\mathbf{R}$ gives the variance among the experimental units, and specifies the correlation, if any, among experimental units or subsets of experimental units.

The primary result from linear mixed model theory that enables power and precision analysis is that the estimate of an estimable function, denoted $\mathbf{k}'\hat{\boldsymbol{\beta}}$, is distributed approximately $N(\mathbf{k}'\boldsymbol{\beta}, \mathbf{k}'[\mathbf{X}'\mathbf{V}^{-1}\mathbf{X}]^{-}\mathbf{k})$. From this we have the following:

- for a single degree-of-freedom contrast, defined by $\mathbf{k}'\boldsymbol{\beta}$, where $\mathbf{k}$ is a vector, the standard error of the contrast estimate is $SE(\mathbf{k}'\hat{\boldsymbol{\beta}}) = \sqrt{\mathbf{k}'(\mathbf{X}'\mathbf{V}^{-1}\mathbf{X})^{-}\mathbf{k}}$.
- a confidence interval for $\mathbf{k}'\boldsymbol{\beta}$ is thus $\mathbf{k}'\hat{\boldsymbol{\beta}} \pm t_{(\alpha,\nu)}\sqrt{\mathbf{k}'(\mathbf{X}'\mathbf{V}^{-1}\mathbf{X})^{-}\mathbf{k}}$, where t is the value from the t distribution for the $(1-\alpha)100\%$ level of confidence and ν degrees of freedom associated with the estimate of the standard error.
- for matrix $\mathbf{K}$ the test statistic for $H_0 : \mathbf{K}'\boldsymbol{\beta} = 0$ is $F = (\mathbf{K}'\hat{\boldsymbol{\beta}})'[\mathbf{K}'(\mathbf{X}'\mathbf{V}^{-1}\mathbf{X})\mathbf{K}]^{-}(\mathbf{K}'\hat{\boldsymbol{\beta}})/\text{rank}(\mathbf{K})$.

The *F* statistic, referred to in mixed model theory as the *approximate F*, has an approximate non-central *F* distribution,

$$F_{(\text{rank}(\mathbf{K}),\nu,(\mathbf{K}'\boldsymbol{\beta})'[\mathbf{K}'(\mathbf{X}'\mathbf{V}^{-1}\mathbf{X})]^{-}(\mathbf{K}'\boldsymbol{\beta}))}$$

The numerator degrees of freedom equal the rank of **K**. The denominator degrees of freedom, ν, follow from the design and sample size. The term $(\mathbf{K}'\boldsymbol{\beta})'[\mathbf{K}'(\mathbf{X}'\mathbf{V}^{-1}\mathbf{X})]^{-}(\mathbf{K}'\boldsymbol{\beta})$, often denoted φ, is the non-centrality parameter.

The design determines the **X** matrix and the structure of **V**. These, along with the anticipated values for the variance and covariance components, are required for precision analysis. Using these values, you can compute the anticipated standard error and confidence interval width of treatment differences or contrasts of potential interest.

For power analysis, in addition to the information needed for precision analysis, you also need to specify the scientifically relevant value(s) of each treatment effect of interest. For example, if you want to compare two treatment means, specifying the minimum difference that would be considered important translates to a value of the treatment effect $\mathbf{k}'\boldsymbol{\beta}$, which in this case equals $\tau_1 - \tau_2$. This enables you to calculate the noncentrality parameter for the approximate *F* statistic, and to determine what proportion of the resulting noncentral *F* distribution lies to the right of the critical value for a test at a specified α-level. Figure 4.1 illustrates the essential conceptual basis of power analysis.

Figure 4.1: Noncentral *F* for Various Noncentrality Parameters

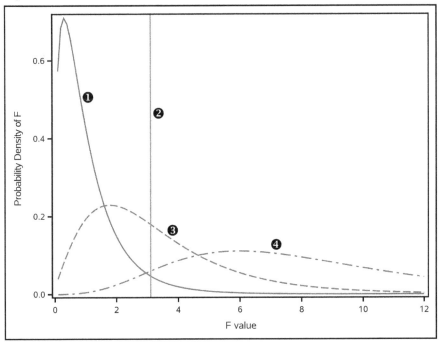

❶ Central *F*

❷ Critical value

❸ Noncentral *F*, $\varphi > 0$

❹ Noncentral *F*, $\varphi \gg 0$

Under the null hypothesis, H_0, the treatment effect $\mathbf{K}'\boldsymbol{\beta} = \mathbf{0}$. Hence, the noncentrality parameter is 0, and the *F* statistic has an approximate central *F* distribution. The *critical value* is the value of the central *F* such that the area under the curve to the right is α, the probability of a type I error, i.e. probability of rejecting H_0 when H_0 is true. The critical value is depicted by the vertical line. When the treatment effect is nonzero, the noncentrality parameter is greater than zero, shifting the distribution of the *F* statistic to the right. The greater the noncentrality parameter (i.e. the greater the treatment effect size) the more the distribution shifts to the right. Noting that you reject H_0 if the *F* statistic is greater than the critical value, the area under the curve to the right of the critical value gives the probability of rejecting H_0 when H_0 is false. That is, the area to the right of the critical value for noncentral *F* is the *power* for the corresponding treatment effect size.

You can compute precision and power analyses for mixed models using PROC GLIMMIX or PROC MIXED in the following steps:

1. Create a data set identical to the one that you will eventually use to analyze the data when it is collected, except that instead of actual data—which you do not yet have—use anticipated expected values for each treatment or treatment combination. Following O'Brien, we refer to this as the *exemplary data set*. The means that you use in the exemplary data set are not intrinsically important, but it is important that *differences* between means of treatments that you intend to compare reflect the differences that you consider to be scientifically relevant.

2. Compute the anticipated standard errors and test statistics using PROC GLIMMIX or PROC MIXED. In this step, you must provide variance and covariance values for the random model and residual effects.

3. For *precision analysis*, the standard errors from the PROC GLIMMIX or PROC MIXED step provide the needed information.

4. For *power analysis*, use the *F* value from the PROC GLIMMIX or PROC MIXED step. You can see from the definitions of the approximate *F* statistic and the noncentrality parameter given above, that multiplying the PROC GLIMMIX or PROC MIXED *F* value by the corresponding numerator degrees of freedom gives you the noncentrality parameter for the treatment differences given in the exemplary data set. You then use SAS probability functions to compute power.

In the following section, three examples of precision and power analysis are presented. Section 4.3 shows the basic procedure setting up the exemplary data set, implementing the PROC GLIMMIX step, and using the probability functions. Section 4.4 shows how to extend this procedure to compare competing designs, whose structure requires the use of mixed model analysis. Section 4.5 shows a more complex example that requires comparison of complete and incomplete block designs, and the use of recovery of inter-block information in design planning. Finally, Section 4.6 introduces the use of simulation as an additional tool to planning studies that will require mixed model analysis.

4.3 Computing Precision and Power for CRD: An Example

The example in the section introduces the essential steps that are required to implement precision and power analyses.

Suppose that a researcher wants to compare three treatments using a completely randomized design with 4 experimental units per treatment. One of treatments (referred to below as treatment C) is a reference treatment. From past experience, the mean response of treatment C is known to be approximately 50, with a variance among experimental units of $\sigma^2 = 25$. The other two treatments (referred to below as treatments A and B) have the potential to increase mean response by as much as 10. In addition, the research team agrees that the minimum increase in mean response of any practical importance is 5. To begin planning an experiment to evaluate treatments A and B relative to the control, the researchers follow the steps outlined in Section 4.2 to assess the anticipated precision and power of their proposed experiment.

4.3.1 Creation of an Exemplary Data Set and Use of PROC GLIMMIX

The programs in this section demonstrate the first two steps in the precision analysis implementation.

Programs

The first step is to create the exemplary data set as shown in Program 4.1.

Program 4.1

```
data crd;
 n=4;
 input trt$ mu;
 do eu=1 to n;
  output;
 end;
datalines;
a 60
b 55
c 50
;
```

The variable MU sets the means. For treatment C, set MU equal to 50 to reflect the researchers' knowledge. Set MU equal to 55 for either treatment A or B, and 60 for the other treatment. This enables you to assess a difference of 5—the minimum difference of practical interest—and 10, the maximum potential difference considered plausible. The DO loop creates replications determined by N. As we will see, you can change N if 4 experimental units turn out to be too few— or more than is needed—and explore the consequences of increasing or decreasing replication.

The next step is the PROC GLIMMIX—or PROC MIXED—step, shown in Program 4.2.

Program 4.2

```
proc glimmix data=crd;
   class trt;
   model mu=trt;
   parms (25)/hold=1;
   lsmeans trt / diff cl;
   contrast '5 unit diff'  trt 0 1 -1;
   contrast '10 unit diff' trt 1 0 -1;
   ods output tests3=F_overall contrasts=F_contrast;
run;
```

The CLASS and MODEL statements give the standard specification of the model for a completely randomized design. The PARMS statement specifies the experimental unit variance. The option HOLD deactivates the PROC GLIMMIX variance estimation algorithm. Instead, PROC GLIMMIX uses $\sigma^2 = 25$ for all standard error and test statistic computations. The LSMEANS DIFF and CL options enable you to obtain the anticipated standard error and confidence interval width for each pairwise treatment comparison. The CONTRAST statements enable you to obtain F values for mean differences of 5 and 10 units. The ODS OUTPUT statement creates new data sets for the overall treatment F and the F values for each contrast. These are used in the next step to determine the power of each of these tests.

Results

Output 4.1 shows the listing for the DIFFS option in the LSMEANS statement in the PROC GLIMMIX step. This is the precision analysis for this proposed study design.

Output 4.1: Precision Analysis for Three-Treatment Completely Randomized Design

			Differences of trt Least Squares Means						
trt	_trt	Estimate	Standard Error	DF	t Value	Pr > |t|	Alpha	Lower	Upper
a	b	5.0000	3.5355	9	1.41	0.1909	0.05	-2.9979	12.9979
a	c	10.0000	3.5355	9	2.83	0.0198	0.05	2.0021	17.9979
b	c	5.0000	3.5355	9	1.41	0.1909	0.05	-2.9979	12.9979

The items of interest are the STANDARD ERROR and the LOWER and UPPER confidence bounds. The standard error, 3.54, is the anticipated standard error of an estimated treatment mean difference if this study uses 4 experimental units per treatment and the error variance is $\sigma^2 = 25$. The expected width of a confidence interval for a treatment mean difference would be 16 units, e.g. $12.9979 - (-2.9979) = 15.9958 \approx 16$. You can use this information to decide whether 4 replications per treatment will provide adequate precision given the objectives of the study.

4.3.2 Completion of the Power Calculation

Once the precision analysis is complete, you can use the results to compute power, which is the fourth step in the precision and power analysis implementation.

Program

The program to compute power uses the output data sets, F_overall and F_contrast, from Program 4.2. The required SAS statements are in Program 4.3:

Program 4.3

```
data power_calc;
 set F_overall F_contrast;
 alpha=0.05;
 nc_parameter=numdf*Fvalue;
```

```
 F_critical=Quantile('F',1-alpha,numdf,dendf,0);
 Power=1-cdf('F',F_critical,numdf,dendf,nc_parameter);
run;
proc print data=power_calc;
run;
```

The data set POWER_CALC augments the data sets created from the PROC GLIMMIX TYPE III TESTS OF FIXED EFFECTS and CONTRAST listing. Specifically, multiply the FVALUE by the numerator degrees of freedom (NUMDF) to obtain the noncentrality parameter for the treatment differences specified in the exemplary DATA step. The QUANTILE function gives the value from the F distribution such that the probability of F is less than the probability given in the statement. Thus, 1-ALPHA, with ALPHA=0.05 means that the area below is 0.95 and the area above is 0.05. Using the numerator and denominator degrees of freedom from the respective F values and setting the noncentrality parameter to zero, QUANTILE gives the critical value for each F test from the ODS OUTPUT. The CDF function gives the area of the F distribution less than the first argument in the statement. Using F_CRITICAL and the NC_PARAMETER assuming the nonzero treatment differences given in the exemplary data set, PROBF gives the probability of failing to reject the hypothesis of equal treatment means. In other words, PROBF is the probability of a Type II error and 1-PROBF is the power of the test.

Results

Output 4.2 shows the PROC PRINT of the POWER_CALC data set.

Output 4.2: Power Analysis Results for Proposed Completely Randomized Design.

Obs	Effect	NumDF	DenDF	FValue	ProbF	Label	alpha	nc_parameter	F_critical
1	trt	2	9	4.00	0.0572		0.05	8	4.25649
2		1	9	2.00	0.1909	5 unit diff	0.05	2	5.11736
3		1	9	8.00	0.0198	10 unit diff	0.05	8	5.11736

Obs	F_crit_old	Power_old	Power
1	4.25649	0.55963	0.55963
2	5.11736	0.24453	0.24453
3	5.11736	0.71191	0.71191

The items of interest are the POWER calculations in the extreme right-hand column. The variable EFFECT identifies the test from the TYPE III TESTS OF FIXED EFFECTS, in this case, the overall test of equal TRT means. In most cases, this is of little interest compared to power for specific contrasts. It is shown here merely for completeness. The variable LABEL identifies specific CONTRASTS defined in the PROC GLIMMIX step. Here, you can see that with 4 replications and error variance $\sigma^2 = 25$, the power of declaring a 10-unit treatment mean difference statistically significant at the $\alpha = .05$ level is 0.71, and declaring a 5-unit difference significant is just over 0.24.

You can use the information from the power analysis in two ways. Either consider it evidence that the experiment as planned is inadequate, or as fair warning if the researcher decides to go ahead and use this study design with only 4 replications. The chance of rejecting the overall test of equal treatment means is just slightly greater that the chance of getting heads in a coin flip. The odds are against detecting a 5-unit difference if such a difference truly exists. On the other hand, if the researcher decides not to go ahead with only 4 replications, you can go back to the exemplary data set, and explore the precision and power consequences of increasing replication. You can do this by changing N in the exemplary data set, and re-running the data, PROC GLIMMIX, and power steps.

You can generate data sets for several values of "n" and then use the BY statement to evaluate power for each "n". Program 4.4 shows how.

Program

Results are shown in Output 4.3.

Program 4.4

```
data crd1;
  input trt$ mu;
 do n=4,5,6,7,15,16,17,18; **generates data for each n;
 do eu=1 to n;
  output;
 end;
```

```
 end;
datalines;
a 60
b 55
c 50
;
run;
proc sort data=crd1;
   by n; **sort data set by n;
run;
proc glimmix data=crd1 noprofile;
   by n; **evaluate for each n;
   class trt ;
   model mu=trt;
   parms (25)/hold=1,2;
   lsmeans trt / diff cl;
   contrast '5 unit diff'  trt 1 -1 0;
   contrast '10 unit diff' trt 1 0 -1;
   ods output contrasts=F_contrast;
run;
data power2;  ** compute power for each sample size;
 set F_contrast;
 alpha=0.05;
 nc_parameter=numdf*Fvalue;
 F_critical=Finv(1-alpha,numdf,dendf,0);
 Power=1-probF(F_critical,numdf,dendf,nc_parameter);
proc sort data=power2; by label;
run;
proc print data=power2; by label;
run;
```

The program generates the data set for several sample sizes per treatment using a DO loop. The data set is sorted by the sample size and then analyzed by each sample size. The results of the CONTRAST statements are stored in the data set "F_contrasts."

Results

The power for each sample size is computed and printed, which appear in Output 4.3 (only selected results for relevant sample sizes are presented).

Output 4.3: Power Computations for Selected Sample sizes for a 10-unit Difference and a 5-unit Difference for CRD

Label=10 unit diff

n	NumDF	DenDF	FValue	ProbF	alpha	nc_parameter	F_critical	Power
4	1	9	8.00	0.0198	0.05	8	5.11736	0.71191
5	1	12	10.00	0.0082	0.05	10	4.74723	**0.82679**
6	1	15	12.00	0.0035	0.05	12	4.54308	0.89889

Label=5 unit diff

n	NumDF	DenDF	FValue	ProbF	alpha	nc_parameter	F_critical	Power
16	1	45	8.00	0.0070	0.05	8.0	4.05661	0.79035
17	1	48	8.50	0.0054	0.05	8.5	4.04265	**0.81507**
18	1	51	9.00	0.0042	0.05	9.0	4.03039	0.83722

A common benchmark for adequate power is 0.8. From Output 4.3, the required replication for power = 0.8 is N = 5 for a 10-unit difference, and N = 17 for a 5-unit difference.

4.4 Comparing Competing Designs I—CRD versus RCBD: An Example

Section 4.3 concluded by increasing replication to increase power. A more efficient way to increase power, when it is possible, is to decrease the variance among experimental units. A common design strategy uses blocking—grouping experimental units into homogeneous subsets so that as much variation as possible occurs between subsets, and as little as possible occurs among experimental units within subsets.

4.4.1 Revision of PROC GLIMMIX Power and Calculation Steps

You can modify the exemplary data set and subsequent PROC GLIMMIX and power calculation steps to include block effects and the impact of blocking on experimental error variance. For this example, let σ^2_{CRD} denote the anticipated experimental error variance if the study uses a completely randomized design, and let σ^2_{RCB} denote the anticipated variance if the study uses a randomized complete block design. Let's first consider what would happen if blocking does not affect experimental unit variance.

The exemplary data and PROC GLIMMIX steps are given by SAS statements in Program 4.5.

Program 4.5

```
data rcb;
 n=4;
 input trt$ mu;
 do blk=1 to n;
  output;
 end;
datalines;
a 60
b 55
c 50
;
run;
proc glimmix data=rcb noprofile;
   class trt blk;
   model mu= trt blk;
   parms (25)/hold=1;
   lsmeans trt / diff cl;
   contrast '5 unit diff'  trt 1 -1 0;
   contrast '10 unit diff' trt 1 0 -1;
   ods output tests3=F_overall contrasts=F_contrast;
   ods html select diffs;
run;
```

The variable N now specifies the number of blocks. The TRT names and values of MU remain the same, because the same treatments will be used in the study being planned, and the same treatment mean differences are of interest. The MODEL statement now includes BLK in order to make the analysis consistent with the randomized complete block design. While this program treats block effects as fixed, you could move BLK to a RANDOM statement and treat them as random effects. As we saw in Chapter 2, for a *complete* block design, interval estimates and test statistics for treatment differences are identical for fixed and random block analysis, so you will get the same precision and power results either way. The above program eliminates the need to specify the block variance.

4.4.2 Precision of Treatment Differences with Blocking

Output 4.4 shows the precision analysis results from Program 4.5. You can compare these to precision analysis results without blocking, shown in Output 4.1, to assess the impact of blocking.

Output 4.4: Differences of Least Squares Means for RCB design

			Differences of trt Least Squares Means						
trt	_trt	Estimate	Standard Error	DF	t Value	Pr > |t|	Alpha	Lower	Upper
a	b	5.0000	3.5355	6	1.41	0.2070	0.05	-3.6511	13.6511
a	c	10.0000	3.5355	6	2.83	0.0300	0.05	1.3489	18.6511
b	c	5.0000	3.5355	6	1.41	0.2070	0.05	-3.6511	13.6511

The standard error of a treatment difference is 3.54, the same as it was with the completely randomized design with 4 experimental units per treatment. However, the anticipated width of confidence intervals for estimated treatment mean differences are now $13.65 - (-3.65) = 17.3$ units wide, compared with 16 units wide with the CRD. The confidence interval is wider with the RCB because 3 degrees of freedom are used to estimate block effects, leaving only 6 degrees of freedom for experimental error, whereas 9 degrees of freedom are available for experimental error with the CRD. Unless blocking reduces the experimental unit variance enough to offset the loss of degrees of freedom, it is counterproductive.

4.4.3 Pilot Data to Anticipate Variance Components for Precision and Power Analysis

Knowledge of the impact of blocking on experimental error variance can come for any of several sources. These include information available from published literature, from in-house data on previous similar studies, institutional memory, informed educated guesses, or pilot studies specifically intended for estimation of block and error variance for a study in the planning stage. Suppose that data from such a pilot study are available. The pilot study contains data from 20 blocks with 3 experimental units each. The blocks are similar to those being considered for use in the actual study comparing the three treatments. The data are given in data set, "Pilot Study to Estimate Error Variance for CRD vs RCBD."

Programs

Program 4.6 enables estimation of the variance components if you account for blocking. Program 4.7 enables estimates of the residual variance if you do not account for block. This enables researchers to decide whether blocking will reduce experimental error enough to offset the loss of error degrees of freedom.

Program 4.6

```
proc glimmix data=pilot_rcbd;
   class block;
   model y=/solution;
   random intercept / subject=block;
   covtest / cl(type=elr alpha=0.5);
run;
```

Program 4.7

```
proc glimmix data=pilot_rcbd;
   class eu block;
   model y=/solution;
   random intercept / subject=eu*block residual;
   covtest / cl(type=elr alpha=0.5);
run;
```

The first set of statements obtains estimates of σ_b^2 and σ_{RCB}^2. There are no treatments in the pilot data set, so the model is $y_{ij} = \mu + b_j + e_{ij}$ where $b_j \sim NI(0, \sigma_b^2)$ and $e_{ij} \sim NI(0, \sigma_{RCB}^2)$. For the second set of statements, the model is $y_{ij} = \mu + e_{ij}$ where $e_{ij} \sim NI(0, \sigma_{CRD}^2)$, i.e. the model, without treatments, for a completely randomized design. The RANDOM statement in the second set of statements specifies variance at the experimental unit level, i.e., σ_{CRD}^2. The COVTEST statements in each set of statements enable PROC GLIMMIX to compute profile likelihood confidence bounds for each variance component. The option ALPHA=0.5 specifies a 50% confidence bound, so that the lower and upper bounds approximate the lower and upper quartile, respectively. These are useful, because the point estimate of the variance from a given pilot study might be lower than the actual population variance; using it might yield a falsely optimistic assessment of required sample size. The upper confidence bound for the experimental error variance gives a more conservative precision and power analysis. However, confidence intervals for variance estimates have notoriously long right tails; using the upper bound of a 95% confidence interval is likely to yield a falsely pessimistic assessment of required sample size. The upper quartile provides a useful compromise.

Results

Output 4.5 shows the result from Program 4.6. Output 4.6 shows the results from Program 4.7.

Output 4.5: Estimates and 50% Confidence Bounds for Variance Components for RCB

				Estimated Likelihood 50% Confidence Bounds			
Covariance Parameter Estimates							
				Lower		Upper	
Cov Parm	Subject	Estimate	Standard Error	Bound	Pr > Chisq	Bound	Pr > Chisq
Intercept	block	9.4492	4.8427	6.6871	0.5000	13.1495	0.5000

Covariance Parameter Estimates							
				Estimated Likelihood 50% Confidence Bounds			
				Lower		Upper	
Cov Parm	Subject	Estimate	Standard Error	Bound	Pr > Chisq	Bound	Pr > Chisq
Residual		15.1900	3.3966	13.1581	0.5000	17.6437	0.5000

Output 4.6: Estimate and 50% Confidence Bounds for Variance Components with CRD

Covariance Parameter Estimates						
			Estimated Likelihood 50% Confidence Bounds			
			Lower		Upper	
Cov Parm	Estimate	Standard Error	Bound	Pr > Chisq	Bound	Pr > Chisq
Residual (VC)	24.3189	4.4775	21.5333	0.5000	27.6067	0.5000

Without blocking, the estimated experimental error variance is $\hat{\sigma}^2_{CRD} = 24.3$, very close to the value of 25 used in the precision and power analyses above. With blocks, the experimental error estimate is $\hat{\sigma}^2_{RCB} = 15.2$, or, if you use the more conservative upper quartile, 17.6. Use this value to assess the anticipated precision and power of a randomized block design.

Program

The revised PROC GLIMMIX step is given in Program 4.8

Program 4.8

```
proc glimmix data=rcb noprofile;
   class trt blk;
   model mu=trt;
   random blk;
   parms (0)(17.6)/hold=1,2;
   lsmeans trt / diff cl;
   contrast '5 unit diff'  trt 1 -1 0;
   contrast '10 unit diff' trt 1 0 -1;
   ods output tests3=F_overall contrasts=F_contrast;
run;
```

Results

The resulting precision analysis appears in Output 4.7.

Output 4.7: Differences of Least Squares Means for the RCB design

Differences of Least Squares Means										
Effect	trt	_trt	Estimate	Standard Error	DF	t Value	Pr > |t|	Alpha	Lower	Upper
trt	a	b	5.0000	2.9665	6	1.69	0.1429	0.05	-2.2587	12.2587
trt	a	c	10.0000	2.9665	6	3.37	0.0150	0.05	2.7413	17.2587
trt	b	c	5.0000	2.9665	6	1.69	0.1429	0.05	-2.2587	12.2587

With the impact of blocking taken into account, the anticipated standard error of a treatment mean is 2.97—versus 3.54 without blocking—and the expected width of a confidence interval for treatment mean difference is $12.26 - (-2.26) = 14.52$, compared with 16 without blocking. Completing the assessment, implement the power analysis using the same statements shown earlier in Program 4.3. Output 4.8 shows the listing.

Output 4.8: Power Computations for RCB Design

Label	NumDF	DenDF	FValue	ProbF	alpha	nc_parameter	F_critical	Power
5 unit diff	1	6	2.84	0.1429	0.05	2.8409	5.98738	0.29569
10 unit diff	1	6	11.36	0.0150	0.05	11.3636	5.98738	0.80093

As with precision, blocking has increased power. With 4 experimental units per treatment, for a 10-unit difference, power is just over 0.80 for a test at $\alpha = 0.05$, compared with an anticipated power of 0.71 without blocking.

4.4.4 Precision and Power for Changing Sample Size with Blocked Design

Program 4.9 provides the data set generation for selected numbers of blocks, the analyses, and the power computation for the two contrasts of interest. This analysis step uses PROC MIXED. You could use PROC GLMMIX and obtain identical results, at least in theory. However, occasionally, for certain values of N in the DO N=3,4,... loop, PROC GLIMMIX will give a warning that the PARMS values are "not feasible." This is an artifact of the PROC GLIMMIX algorithm. When you are working with Gaussian data, the best way around it is to use PROC MIXED instead. This issue is revisited in Chapter 14 for planning studies with non-Gaussian data.

Program 4.9

```
data rcb;
input trt$ mu;
 do n=3,4,5,6,7,8,9,10,11,12,13,14,15,16,17;  **generate different numbers of blocks;
  do blk=1 to n;
   output;
  end;
 end;
datalines;
a 60
b 55
c 50
;
run;
proc sort data=rcb; by n;**sort data by sample size or number of blocks;
run;
proc mixed data=rcb noprofile;
   by n; **analyze the data for each number of blocks;
   class trt blk;
   model mu= trt;
   random blk;
   parms (0) (17.6)/hold=1,2;
   lsmeans trt / diff cl;
   contrast '5 unit diff'  trt 1 -1 0;
   contrast '10 unit diff' trt 1 0 -1;
   ods output tests3=F_overall contrasts=F_contrast;
run;
data power3;**compute power for the contrasts from each number of blocks;
 set  F_contrast;
 alpha=0.05;
 nc_parameter=numdf*Fvalue;
 F_critical=Finv(1-alpha,numdf,dendf,0);
 Power=1-probF(F_critical,numdf,dendf,nc_parameter);
run;
proc sort data=power3; by label;
run;
proc print data=power3 noobs;by label;
run;
```

Output 4.9 gives selected results.

Output 4.9: Power Computations for Selected Sample Sizes for a 10-unit Difference and a 5-unit Difference for RCB

Label=10 unit diff

n	NumDF	DenDF	FValue	ProbF	alpha	nc_parameter	F_critical	Power
3	1	4	8.52	0.0433	0.05	8.5227	7.70865	0.59708
4	1	6	11.36	0.0150	0.05	11.3636	5.98738	**0.80093**
5	1	8	14.20	0.0055	0.05	14.2045	5.31766	0.90824

Label=5 unit diff

n	NumDF	DenDF	FValue	ProbF	alpha	nc_parameter	F_critical	Power
11	1	20	7.81	0.0112	0.05	7.8125	4.35124	0.75769
12	1	22	8.52	0.0079	0.05	8.5227	4.30095	**0.79672**
13	1	24	9.23	0.0057	0.05	9.2330	4.25968	0.83023

This provides a meaningful way of characterizing relative efficiency of competing designs by comparing the results for Output 4.3 and Output 4.9. Five replications per treatment are required for power ≥ 0.80 without blocking versus 4 replications with blocking and for a 5-unit difference, 12 experimental units per treatment are required with blocking, versus 17 without blocking. Notice that this form of characterization provides more tangible meaning than classical measures of efficiency, such as those based on mean square error. Using blocking obviously provides the most efficient design, 12 observations for the RCB versus 17 observations for the CRD to have 80% power for the 5-unit difference.

4.5 Comparing Competing Designs II—Complete versus Incomplete Block Designs: An Example

The power analyses for CRD and complete block designs in Sections 4.3 and 4.4 could have been done with conventional power and sample size software, such as PROC POWER or PROC GLMPOWER, because power in those examples depended only on treatment mean difference, number of replications, and a *single* variance. Mixed model precision and power analysis comes into its own when the standard errors and test statistics for the designs in question depend on two or more variance or covariance components. This includes designs that allow for recovery of inter-block information—e.g. the incomplete block designs covered in Chapter 2—designs with more than one experimental error variance, such as multilevel designs covered in Chapter 5, and designs with correlated errors, such as repeated measures and longitudinal designs covered in Chapter 8. For these designs, standard power and sample size software cannot be used; mixed model-based methods are *required* for accurate precision and power analysis. In this section, we introduce the approach using an incomplete block design.

Suppose that you want to design a study to compare 7 treatments, and you have 28 experimental units arranged in a grid with 7 rows and 4 columns. You want to choose the most efficient way to set up the experiment. Your options are as follows:

- Block by column and use a complete block design

- Block by row and use an incomplete block design

- Use row as a blocking criterion, but create complete blocks, e.g using all the experimental units from row 1 and the units from columns 1 through 3 in row 2 to form block 1, the units in column 4 of row 2, all the units in row 3, and the column 1 and 2 units in row 4 to form block 2, etc. Figure 4.2 shows the resulting design structure. The rows appear vertically and the columns horizontally in order to save space.

Figure 4.2: Complete Block Design Structure

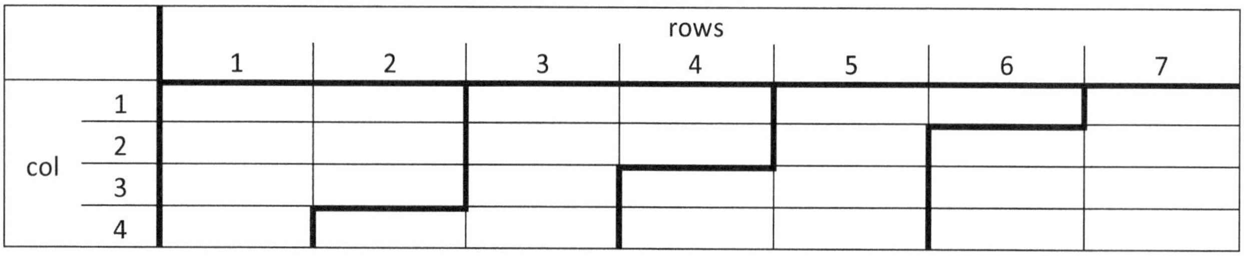

As in the CRD versus RCB comparison in Section 4.4, you can make your decision by comparing the precision of the three competing designs. Once you select the most efficient design. You can also do a power analysis to see whether 28 experimental units provide acceptable ability to detect differences considered relevant.

In order to calculate precision for these designs, you need to know how each blocking scheme affects the variance among blocks and among experimental units within blocks. Suppose you have historical data or data from a pilot study from which to estimate these variance components. The data are given in data set, "Pilot Study to Assess the Impact of Blocking on Block and Residual Variance."

Program

Use the statements in Program 4.10 to obtain the needed estimates.

Program 4.10

```
/* determine magnitude of row and column effect */
proc glimmix data=grid;
   class row col;
   model y=row col;
run;
/* obtain block and residual variance if you block on row */
proc glimmix data=grid;
   class row col;
   model y=/solution;
   random row;
   covtest / cl(type=elr alpha=0.5);
run;
/* obtain block and residual variance if you block on column */
proc glimmix data=grid;
   class row col;
   model y=;
   random col;
   covtest / cl(type=elr alpha=0.5);
run;
/* obtain block and residual variance if you construct complete blocks from parts of
multiple rows */
proc glimmix data=grid;
   class complete_block;
   model y=/solution;
   random complete_block;
   covtest / cl(type=elr alpha=0.5);
run;
/* obtain residual variance if you do not block at all */
proc glimmix data=grid;
   class row col;
   model y=;
   random intercept / subject=row*col residual;
   covtest / cl(type=elr alpha=0.5);
run;
```

The first PROC GLIMMIX program obtains an F test for ROW and COL to determine their relative effect size. The next three PROC GLIMMIX runs are essentially identical to the programs used for the pilot study in Section 4.3. The programs obtain estimates and 50% confidence bounds for the block and residual variance if you block by row, column, and the complete block composed of part of multiple rows, respectively, as described previously. The final PROC GLIMMIX run obtains an estimate and 50% confidence bounds for the residual variance if the design uses no blocking on any criterion.

Results

Output 4.10 shows the listing for the ROW and COL F test. Output 4.11 shows the variance component estimates for the three blocking schemes. Output 4.12 shows the variance estimate for an unblocked design.

Output 4.10: Tests of Row and Column Effects

	Type III Tests of Fixed Effects			
Effect	Num DF	Den DF	F Value	Pr > F
row	6	18	2.06	0.1102
col	3	18	0.70	0.5625

When evaluating the strength of a potential blocking effect, the primary consideration is the magnitude of the F value, not the p-value. If the F value is noticeably greater than one—admittedly a somewhat ambiguous judgment call—the effect is a potentially important blocking criterion. If the F value is less than one, the effect is most likely not a good candidate as a blocking criterion. You can see that blocking by ROW might be warranted, but blocking by COL is not. Output 4.11, 4.12, and 4.13 give variance component estimates and their associated confidence intervals under the three blocking schemes given earlier.

Output 4.11: Variance Component Estimates using ROW as Blocking Criterion

Covariance Parameter Estimates						
			Estimated Likelihood 50% Confidence Bounds			
			Lower		Upper	
Cov Parm	Estimate	Standard Error	Bound	Pr > Chisq	Bound	Pr > Chisq
row	1.3711	1.5262	0.5855	0.5000	2.6960	0.5000
Residual	4.7767	1.4741	3.9258	0.5000	5.8814	0.5000

Output 4.12: Variance Component Estimates using COL as Blocking Criterion

Covariance Parameter Estimates						
			Estimated Likelihood 50% Confidence Bounds			
			Lower		Upper	
Cov Parm	Estimate	Standard Error	Bound	Pr > Chisq	Bound	Pr > Chisq
col	0	.	0	1.0000	0.3063	0.5000
Residual	5.9954	1.6318	5.0172	0.5000	7.2453	0.5000

Output 4.13: Variance Component Estimates Using Complete Blocks Composed from Parts of Multiple Rows

Covariance Parameter Estimates						
			Estimated Likelihood 50% Confidence Bounds			
			Lower		Upper	
Cov Parm	Estimate	Standard Error	Bound	Pr > Chisq	Bound	Pr > Chisq
complete_block	0.1940	0.8740	0	0.7909	1.0518	0.5000
Residual	5.8445	1.6872	4.8728	0.5000	7.0874	0.5000

You can see that blocking by ROW—i.e. using 7 blocks of size 4 with block defined by ROW—minimizes the residual variance and maximizes the block variance. This is consistent with the strategy of blocking as a design tool, i.e. maximize within block homogeneity. Blocking by COL would enable the use of a complete block design, but because variation is among rows, not columns, blocking by COL results in heterogeneous experimental units within blocks and hence maximizes residual variance. Notice that attempting to form complete blocks using ROW as the apparent blocking criterion is ineffective—the blocks are scarcely less heterogeneous and residual variance is only slightly lower than blocking by COL. This is important, as many researchers form complete blocks in exactly this way, thinking that they are blocking on the appropriate criterion, but in fact disregarding the natural block size. Output 4.14 shows variance estimates from the pilot data if you simply do not block at all.

Output 4.14: Estimate of Residual Variance When Natural Block Size is Disregarded

Covariance Parameter Estimates						
			Estimated Likelihood 50% Confidence Bounds			
			Lower		Upper	
Cov Parm	Estimate	Standard Error	Bound	Pr > Chisq	Bound	Pr > Chisq
Residual (VC)	5.9954	1.6318	5.0172	0.5000	7.2453	0.5000

From Output 4.12 you can see that inept blocking is no better than not blocking at all. The residual variance with no blocking is identical to the residual variance if you block by COL. This means that a completely randomized design would provide better precision than an RCBD blocked by column, and might compete favorably with an RCBD whose blocks are constructed from multiple rows. The precision analysis shown below will provide definitive information as to how these designs compare.

Program

Once you have the variance estimates, you can implement the precision analysis. Use the following statements in Program 4.11 to obtain the precision analysis for the RCBD alternative. Use the variance estimates from the multiple-row blocking scheme. Notice that in these examples we use the upper 50% confidence bounds, not the estimates. This is a conservative choice, given that the estimates come from a small pilot study, and variance estimates from small samples are notoriously prone to uncertainty.

Program 4.11

```
data rcb;
 input blk @@;
   do eu=1 to 7;
     input trt$ @@;
     mu=12;
     output;
   end;
datalines;
 1  1 2 3 4 5 6 7
 2  1 2 3 4 5 6 7
 3  1 2 3 4 5 6 7
 4  1 2 3 4 5 6 7
;
/* Intra-block analysis */
proc glimmix data=rcb;
   class blk trt;
   model mu=trt blk;
   parms (7.09)/hold=1;
   lsmeans trt / diff cl;
run;
/* Recovery of inter-block information */
/* Combined inter-/intra-block analysis */
proc glimmix data=rcb;
   class blk trt;
   model mu=trt;
   random blk;
   parms (1.05)(7.09)/hold=1,2;
   lsmeans trt / diff cl;
run;
```

Results

Two PROC GLIMMIX runs are shown, one for intra-block (fixed block effect) analysis, one with recovery of inter-block (random block effect) analysis. Both yield identical standard errors of treatment mean differences, as expected with complete block designs. Output 4.15 and 4.16 shows the DIFF listing for the treatment 1 versus 2 comparison for intra-block and combined inter-/intra-block analysis, respectively.

Output 4.15: Precision Analysis: Treatment 1 versus 2, Using Intra-block Analysis

			Differences of trt Least Squares Means						
trt	_trt	Estimate	Standard Error	DF	t Value	Pr > |t|	Alpha	Lower	Upper
1	2	0	1.8828	18	0.00	1.0000	0.05	-3.9557	3.9557

Output 4.16: Precision Analysis: Treatment 1 versus 2, Using Recovery of Inter-block Information and Combined Inter-/Intra-block Analysis

			Differences of trt Least Squares Means						
trt	_trt	Estimate	Standard Error	DF	t Value	Pr > |t|	Alpha	Lower	Upper
1	2	-487E-18	1.8828	18	-0.00	1.0000	0.05	-3.9557	3.9557

If you use the complete block design, the anticipated standard error of a treatment mean difference is 1.88 with a 95% confidence interval width of 7.92.

Program

The alternative to the RCBD is a balanced incomplete block (BIB) design, blocking on ROW and strictly respecting the natural block size, i.e. the number of experimental units per row in the pilot study. Program 4.12 implements the precision analysis for the BIB.

Program 4.12

```
data bib;
 input blk @@;
   do eu=1 to 4;
     input trt$ @@;
```

```
    mu=12;
    output;
  end;
datalines;
 1  1 2 3 4
 2  1 2 5 6
 3  1 3 5 7
 4  1 4 6 7
 5  2 3 6 7
 6  2 4 5 7
 7  3 4 5 6
;
/* Inter-block analysis */
proc glimmix data=bib;
   class blk trt;
   model mu=trt blk;
   parms (5.88)/hold=1;
   lsmeans trt / diff cl;
run;
/* Combined Inter-/Intra-block analysis */
proc glimmix data=bib;
   class blk trt;
   model mu=trt;
   random blk;
   parms (2.7)(5.88)/hold=1,2;
   lsmeans trt / diff cl;
run;
```

Results

The results for the treatment 1 versus 2 difference appear in Outputs 4.17 and 4.18.

Output 4.17: Precision Analysis, Treatment 1 versus 2, Intra-block Analysis

			Differences of trt Least Squares Means						
trt	_trt	Estimate	Standard Error	DF	t Value	Pr > |t|	Alpha	Lower	Upper
1	2	0	1.8330	15	0.00	1.0000	0.05	-3.9070	3.9070

Output 4.18: Precision Analysis, Treatment 1 versus 2, Combined Inter-/Intra-block Analysis

			Differences of trt Least Squares Means						
trt	_trt	Estimate	Standard Error	DF	t Value	Pr > |t|	Alpha	Lower	Upper
1	2	-556E-17	1.7885	15	-0.00	1.0000	0.05	-3.8122	3.8122

Notice that with incomplete block designs, the standard errors are not the same: recovery of inter-block information increases precision. The discrepancy increases as the block variance decreases. If you use the estimate of the block variance from the pilot data instead of the upper 50% confidence bound, the standard error of a difference is 1.75. Using the more conservative upper 50% bound, the anticipated standard error is 1.79 and the expected width of a 95% confidence interval for treatment mean difference is 7.62. This compared with 7.92 for the RCBD. This means that the BIB would be expected to provide more precise estimates of treatment differences than the RCBD. Thus, the BIB is the design of choice in this example.

While not shown here, you could add expected treatment differences to the BIB exemplary data set and augment the remaining program to obtain power for contrasts of interest. The additional program statements are identical to those shown in Sections 4.3 and 4.4.

Important Note: Many design of experiments textbooks give "efficiency factors" for BIB vs. complete block designs using the same number of total observations. These "efficiency factors" are computed using an intra-block model, and assuming that residual variance is unaffected by block size. They are misleading because they ignore precision gains from recovery of inter-block information that occur for incomplete, but not for complete block designs. Moreover, it is almost never true that residual variance is unaffected by block size. It is generally easier to assure within-block homogeneity for blocks with fewer experimental units. Aside from failing to correctly identify the experimental unit, the most common abuse of design principles committed by researchers in the experimental sciences is disregarding realistic natural block size and attempting to force too many treatments into complete blocks. Using mixed model methods, as shown in this example, provides a more accurate and realistic way to compare incomplete and complete block designs than so-called "efficiency factors."

4.6 Using Simulation for Precision and Power

You can use simulation to augment the precision and power analyses covered in the previous sections of this chapter. In this section, we describe the following three uses of simulation:

1. To get an idea of what data will look like, and the range of possibilities, if you implement a given design under consideration.
2. To provide an alternative to the exemplary data/PROC GLIMMIX methods shown in previous sections for computing precision and power. Doing so also enables you to assess the accuracy of the precision and power calculations obtained using the exemplary data/PROC GLIMMIX methods.
3. To approximate the change in block and residual variance resulting from changing block size—e.g. using complete blocks when the natural block size suggests using an incomplete block design instead.

4.6.1 Simulation to Characterize Possible Outcomes

Simulation studies enable us to explore the likely behavior of statistical procedures. There was a time when writing and implementing a simulation study was a daunting task. This is no longer true, especially in the case of the design and analysis alternative discussed in this chapter. Using the DATA step and the ODS OUTPUT capability of either PROC GLIMMIX or PROC MIXED, you can easily simulate data from completely randomized or blocked designs, and explore either the average behavior of test statistics and treatment effect estimates, or specific results for several representative data sets that could arise under the mean, variance and sample size assumptions being used to plan a given study.

The methods shown in this section are useful when planning an experiment, and for statistical methods classes when introducing issues in design and analysis of research studies. Three examples are shown: a completely randomized design, a complete block design, and an incomplete block design. Each example is based on the scenario for the corresponding design used in previous sections.

The first example is a completely randomized design with three treatments and four replications per treatment. Following the assumptions given in Section 4.3, assume that the residual variance is $\sigma^2 = 25$, the mean of the reference treatment is 50, and the other two treatments have a 5 and 10 unit mean difference, respectively.

Programs

Use the DATA step in Program 4.13 to create the simulated data.

Program 4.13

```
data sim_crd;
 seed=92010015;
 residual_variance=25;
 mu_1=50;  mu_2=55; mu_3=60;
 N_replications=4;
 N_simulated_experiments=10; /* vary this number as required for a given purpose */
 /* begin creating simulated data */
 do expt=1 to N_simulated_experiments;
  do trt=1 to 3;
   mu_i=(trt=1)*mu_1+(trt=2)*mu_2+(trt=3)*mu_3;
    do exp_unit=1 to N_replications;
     e_ij=sqrt(residual_variance)*rannor(seed);
     y=mu_i+e_ij;
     output;
  end;
  end;
 end;
proc print data=sim_crd;
 where expt<3;
run;
```

Disclaimer: There are undoubtedly more elegant ways to write the above program. This is the author's "good enough for what it's for" program (to quote one of his father's favorite expressions). One advantage of this possibly less-than-elegant program is that it has proven to be student-friendly when used in design of experiments and introductory linear model courses.

The SEED is optional. Setting SEED equal to a specific number enables you to re-create the same simulated data each time to run the program. It is a good idea to run the simulation multiple times with different SEED values. Simulation results vary, at least somewhat; varying the SEED gives you a measure of variation among simulations and improves your understanding of the behaviors of the statistics of interest. The variable N_SIMULATED_EXPERIMENTS controls how many simulated experiments the DATA step creates. If you plan a detailed look at the listing for all experiments that you simulate, keep this number small, e.g. 10 as shown above. If you plan to assess average behavior, or the sampling distribution of a test statistic or estimate, you should use a much larger number: 1000 simulated experiments will usually give you an accurate idea of the sampling behavior of most statistics of interest for the designs discussed in this chapter.

For the completely randomized design, assuming an equal number of replications per treatment, you include three nested DO loops, one to create different experiments, one to treatments, and one for experimental units. The RANNOR function creates a random deviate from the standard normal—i.e. $N(0,1)$—distribution. Multiplying it by the square root of the residual variance gives you $e_{ij} \sim N(0,\sigma^2)$ for each observation. The observations simply implement the model equation, $y_{ij} = \mu + e_{ij}$. The OUTPUT statement adds each new observation to the data set. If you leave it out, the DATA step will replace each previously created observation with each newly created one, leaving you with only one observation—the 4th experimental unit, 3rd treatment, last experiment in the DO loop. Including the OUTPUT statement overrides this replacement, so your data set contains every observation created.

Once the data are created, you can either obtain the entire PROC GLIMMIX or PROC MIXED listing, or specific items of interest, for each simulated experiment. Program 4.14 gives an example of the required statements.

Program 4.14

```
/* if you just want to examine the results of several representative data sets */
proc glimmix data=sim_crd;
   by expt;
   class trt;
   model y=trt;
   lsmeans trt / diff cl;
   estimate '5 unit diff'  trt 1 -1 0,
            '10 unit diff' trt 1 0 -1 / cl;
run;
```

The key statement is BY EXPT: This causes the procedure to be executed separately for each simulated experiment. The program statements are otherwise typical statements that you would use when analyzing a completely randomized design.

If you want to characterize the behavior, e.g. the rejection rate for various hypothesis tests, the average estimate and standard error, or the confidence interval coverage for treatment comparisons of interest, you can use or adapt the following statements (Program 4.15):

Program 4.15

```
/* if you want to compute rejection rate, average treatment mean diff, etc. */
ods results off;
ods html exclude all;
proc glimmix data=sim_crd;
   by expt;
   class trt;
   model y=trt;
   lsmeans trt / diff cl;
   estimate '5 unit diff'  trt -1 1 0,
            '10 unit diff' trt -1 0 1 / cl;
   ods output tests3=F_trt estimates=trt_diff;
run;
data F_trt;
 set F_trt;
```

```
 reject=(ProbF<0.05);
run;
data trt_diff;
 set trt_diff;
 if label='5 unit diff' then do;
  cover=(Lower<5<Upper);
  reject_T=(ProbT<0.05);
  reject_CI=1-(Lower<0<Upper);
 end;
 else if label='10 unit diff' then do;
  cover=(Lower<10<Upper);
  reject_T=(ProbT<0.05);
  reject_CI=1-(Lower<0<Upper);
 end;
run;
proc sort data=trt_diff;
   by label;
run;
ods results on;
ods html select all;
proc means data=F_trt;
   var reject;
run;
proc means data=trt_diff;
   by label;
   var estimate stderr reject_T reject_CI cover;
run;
```

The key statement within PROC GLIMMIX is the ODS OUTPUT statement. This causes PROC GLIMMIX to create data sets for each item of interest. See SAS documentation under PROC GLIMMIX/DETAILS for a list of the items available for output and the names that must be used. TESTS3 creates a data set, in this case named F_TRT, that contains all the information from the TYPE III TESTS OF FIXED EFFECTS listing. TESTS3 is the ODS keyword that you must use; the data set name is your option. ESTIMATES creates a data set, in this case named TRT_DIFF, containing the content of the ESTIMATE listing. Subsequent statements define items of interest, e.g. REJECT, an indicator variable with a value of 1 if the null hypothesis was rejected, 0 otherwise, and COVER, also an indicator variable equal to 1 if the 95% confidence limits include the true treatment mean difference and 0 otherwise. The ODS RESULTS OFF and ODS HTML EXCLUDE ALL statements prevent SAS from creating a PROC GLIMMIX listing for each experiment. Without this command, you will have a listing thousands of pages long, and eventually you will exceed your computer's capacity. The ODS RESULTS ON and ODS HTML SELECT ALL turn listing back on, enabling you to obtain the results of interest from the MEANS procedure, in this case to document rejection rate and confidence interval coverage.

Results

The listings for these MEANS procedures appear in Output 4.19 and Output 4.20.

Output 4.19: Mean of REJECT Indicator Variable for Type III Test of Fixed Effects *F* value for TRT. Mean = Proportion of Null Hypotheses Rejected

	Analysis Variable :reject			
N	Mean	Std Dev	Minimum	Maximum
1000	0.5860000	0.4927949	0	1.0000000

Output 4.20: Estimates, Rejection Rates, and Confident Interval Coverage for Treatment Difference Contrasts Defined in the ESTIMATE Statement

Label=10 unit diff

Variable	Label	N	Mean	Std Dev	Minimum	Maximum
Estimate		1000	9.9651217	3.6371156	-0.5988963	21.3183425
StdErr	Standard Error	1000	3.3991076	0.7783231	1.2541856	6.8071260
reject_T		1000	0.7140000	0.4521155	0	1.0000000
reject_CI		1000	0.7140000	0.4521155	0	1.0000000
cover		1000	0.9530000	0.2117447	0	1.0000000

Label=5 unit diff

Variable	Label	N	Mean	Std Dev	Minimum	Maximum
Estimate		1000	4.8128746	3.6574217	-5.4520391	15.7012789
StdErr	Standard Error	1000	3.3991076	0.7783231	1.2541856	6.8071260
reject_T		1000	0.2210000	0.4151281	0	1.0000000
reject_CI		1000	0.2210000	0.4151281	0	1.0000000
cover		1000	0.9320000	0.2518719	0	1.0000000

Output 4.19, under the column MEAN, gives the proportion of null hypotheses rejected for the test for overall equality of treatment means. Output 4.20 gives average treatment mean difference estimates of 9.97 and 4.81, respectively—consistent with the true difference of 10 and 5. Confidence interval coverage is 95.3% and 93.2%, respectively, within the $\pm2\%$ margin of error one would expect for a simulation with 1000 experiments. Finally, the rejection rates when the true differences are 10 and 5 units, respectively, are 71.4% and 22.1%. Notice that the proportion of rejections for the overall treatment effect, 10-unit and 5-unit differences: 0.586, 0.714, and 0.221, are consistent with the power: 0.560, 0.712, and 0.245, that we obtained in Output 4.2.

4.6.2 Simulation as an Alternative Way to Compute Precision or Power

Sections 4.3 through 4.5 focused on using the exemplary data set, PROC GLIMMIX or PROC MIXED, and SAS probability functions, notably FINV and PROBF, to calculate precision and power for given treatment means, variance components, design structure, and sample size. An alternative way to obtain these calculations is via simulation. In addition, simulation can provide a more detailed insight into how the estimation and testing procedures can be expected to behave when using the design and sample size that you are evaluating. Simulation can also provide confirmation of the precision and power calculations obtained from the exemplary data set, the PROC GLIMMIX/PROC MIXED method.

The CRD example in Section 4.6.1 shows how to use simulation to do a comprehensive precision and power analysis for a proposed study using a completely randomized design. Simulating a blocked design requires additional steps to account for block variance and, if necessary, accommodate incomplete blocks.

Programs

Program 4.16 creates simulated data for blocked designs, complete and incomplete. The program creates data for the 7 block, 7 treatment, 4 experimental units per block BIB design discussed in Section 4.5. The design that you enter after the DATALINES statement and specific information about the number of EU per block, as well as treatment mean and variance component information, would need to be changed to fit the design that you are evaluating, but the structure of the program can be adapted to any blocked design. As with the program in Section 4.6.1, the "good enough for what it's for" disclaimer applies.

You could obtain a more detailed characterization of the sampling distribution of test statistics and estimators by using PROC UNIVARIATE. In the interest of space, the program and results are not shown here, but this would enable you to obtain quantiles of the sampling distribution, plot a histogram, or the like.

Program 4.16

```
data exp_dsgn;
seed=88501953;
blk_var=2.7;** block variance;
unit_var=5.88;** Experimental unit variance;
mu=12;
do expt=1 to 1000; ** generate 1000 data sets;
 do blk=1 to 7;
  blk_effect=sqrt(blk_var)*rannor(seed);
  do eu=1 to 4;
   e_ij=sqrt(unit_var)*rannor(seed);
   output;
  end;
 end;
end;
proc sort data=exp_dsgn;
   by expt blk eu;
run;
data trt_dsgn;
/* trt effects */
 tau_1=0;
```

```
    tau_2=1;
    tau_3=2;
    tau_4=3;
    tau_5=4;
    tau_6=5;
    tau_7=6;
input @@ blk;
 do eu=1 to 4;
  input trt @@;
     trt_effect=(trt=1)*tau_1+(trt=2)*tau_2+(trt=3)*tau_3
             +(trt=4)*tau_4+(trt=5)*tau_5+(trt=6)*tau_6+(trt=7)*tau_7;
   do expt=1 to 1000;
    output;
   end;
 end;
datalines;
 1  1 2 3 4
 2  1 2 5 6
 3  1 3 5 7
 4  1 4 6 7
 5  2 3 6 7
 6  2 4 5 7
 7  3 4 5 6
;
run;
proc sort data=trt_dsgn;
   by expt blk eu;
run;
data BIB;
 merge exp_dsgn trt_dsgn;
 by expt blk eu;
 y=mu+trt_effect+blk_effect+e_ij;
run;
proc print data=BIB;
   where expt<3;
run;
```

This program creates a data set with the block structure for each simulated experiment. This data set, called EXP_DSGN, re-creates the data prior to the assignment and application of treatments. The data vary as a result of variation among blocks, generated as $N(0, \sigma_b^2)$ random deviates, i.e. BLK_EFFECT = SQRT(BLK_VAR)*RANNOR(SEED), and variation among experimental units, generated as $N(0, \sigma^2)$ random deviates, where UNIT_VAR specifies the residual variance σ^2. The second data set, called TRT_DSGN, add the treatment effects, called TAU_1 through TAU_7. The second data set specifies which treatments are assigned to which blocks. Notice that you do not have to randomize the order of treatments, as you would when setting up the actual experiment. The creation of random deviates in the first data set mimics the randomization that would occur in a real experiment. Once the two data sets have been created, sort each one of them by experiment, block and experimental units, i.e. PROC SORT; BY EXPT BLK EU, merge the two data sets, and create each observation according to the model equation for a blocked design, i.e. MU+TRT_EFFECT+BLK_EFFECT+E_IJ.

Once you have created the simulated data, you can run a PROC GLIMMIX or a PROC MIXED analysis of the data, use ODS OUTPUT, and use PROC MEANS—or PROC UNIVARIATE or any other descriptive statistic procedure needed to characterize the behavior of statistics of interest. The following statements give an example. This simulation focuses on computing the average rejection rate for the overall test of no treatment effect and the contrasts for 1-unit, 2-unit, and so forth, through 6-unit treatment mean differences, and so on computing the average estimate and standard error of these treatment differences.

Program 4.17

```
ods results off;
ods html exclude all;
proc glimmix data=BIB;
   by expt; *where expt=2;
   class blk trt;
   model Y=trt;
   random intercept / subject=blk;
   lsmeans trt / diff=control('1') cl;
   contrast '1 unit diff' trt 1 -1 0 0 0 0 0;
   contrast '2 unit diff' trt 1 0 -1 0 0 0 0;
```

```
   contrast '3 unit diff' trt 1 0 0 -1 0 0 0;
   contrast '4 unit diff' trt 1 0 0 0 -1 0 0;
   contrast '5 unit diff' trt 1 0 0 0 0 -1 0;
   contrast '6 unit diff' trt 1 0 0 0 0 0 -1;
   ods output tests3=F_trt contrasts=pairwise diffs=Trt_diff;
run;
data rejection_rate;
 set F_trt pairwise;
 reject05=(probF<0.05);
run;
ods results on;
ods html select all;
proc sort data=trt_diff;
   by trt _trt;
run;
proc sort data=rejection_rate;
   by label;
run;
proc means data=trt_diff;
   by trt _trt;
   var estimate stderr;
run;
proc means data=rejection_rate;
   by label;
   var reject05;
run;
```

Results

The results appear in Output 4.21 and 4.22.

Output 4.21: Observed Rejection Rate for Selected Tests

Label=' '⇒ Overall Test of Equal Treatment Means

	Analysis Variable : reject05			
N	Mean	Std Dev	Minimum	Maximum
1000	0.7650000	0.4242110	0	1.0000000

Label=1 unit diff

	Analysis Variable : reject05			
N	Mean	Std Dev	Minimum	Maximum
1000	0.0940000	0.2919747	0	1.0000000

Label=2 unit diff

	Analysis Variable : reject05			
N	Mean	Std Dev	Minimum	Maximum
1000	0.1950000	0.3963990	0	1.0000000

Label=3 unit diff

	Analysis Variable : reject05			
N	Mean	Std Dev	Minimum	Maximum
1000	0.3640000	0.4813894	0	1.0000000

Label=4 unit diff

		Analysis Variable : reject05		
N	**Mean**	**Std Dev**	**Minimum**	**Maximum**
1000	0.5510000	0.4976411	0	1.0000000

Label=5 unit diff

		Analysis Variable : reject05		
N	**Mean**	**Std Dev**	**Minimum**	**Maximum**
1000	0.7540000	0.4308940	0	1.0000000

Label=6 unit diff

		Analysis Variable : reject05		
N	**Mean**	**Std Dev**	**Minimum**	**Maximum**
1000	0.8610000	0.3461196	0	1.0000000

You can check these results with the results you obtain if you add the treatment effects used in this simulation to the BIB example in Section 4.5. You will find that the results here are consistent with the results that you obtain with the exemplary data set plus the PROC GLIMMIX/PROC MIXED procedure.

Output 4.22: Average Estimates and Standard Errors of Treatment Means Differences

trt=2 _trt=1

Variable	Label	N	Mean	Std Dev	Minimum	Maximum
Estimate		1000	0.9046596	1.8642594	-4.4025452	6.3999524
StdErr	Standard Error	1000	1.7265354	0.2957015	0.9680036	2.8016779

trt=3 _trt=1

Variable	Label	N	Mean	Std Dev	Minimum	Maximum
Estimate		1000	1.9407380	1.8603733	-4.3597574	7.1136335
StdErr	Standard Error	1000	1.7265354	0.2957015	0.9680036	2.8016779

trt=4 _trt=1

Variable	Label	N	Mean	Std Dev	Minimum	Maximum
Estimate		1000	2.9449857	1.8076807	-2.6505719	9.3368041
StdErr	Standard Error	1000	1.7265354	0.2957015	0.9680036	2.8016779

trt=5 _trt=1

Variable	Label	N	Mean	Std Dev	Minimum	Maximum
Estimate		1000	3.9216508	1.7582896	-1.2064780	8.8651199
StdErr	Standard Error	1000	1.7265354	0.2957015	0.9680036	2.8016779

trt=6 _trt=1

Variable	Label	N	Mean	Std Dev	Minimum	Maximum
Estimate		1000	4.9127670	1.8096358	-0.8039750	10.6026114
StdErr	Standard Error	1000	1.7265354	0.2957015	0.9680036	2.8016779

trt=7 _trt=1

Variable	Label	N	Mean	Std Dev	Minimum	Maximum
Estimate		1000	5.9874874	1.8536605	0.2147694	11.4154881
StdErr	Standard Error	1000	1.7265354	0.2957015	0.9680036	2.8016779

The treatment means were structured so that the true difference between treatment 1 and treatment $i > 1$ is $i - 1$ units. For example, the difference between treatment 5 and treatment 1 is 4 units. The mean estimates are consistent with the true difference used to simulate the data. The standard error is, by definition, an estimate of the standard deviation of the sampling distribution, so the mean standard error and the standard deviation of the estimate should be close. In general, the mean standard error underestimates the standard deviation. This is a manifestation of the Kenward-Roger issue that was introduced in Chapter 2 and will be discussed in more detail in Chapters 5 and 8. Notice that the precision analysis for this design from Section 4.5 gave 1.79 as the anticipated standard error of a difference. The observed mean standard error of 1.73 in this simulation is lower, but nonetheless consistent with the anticipated value. If you re-run the simulation using the Kenward-Roger adjustment—MODEL option DDFM=KR2—the observed, bias-corrected mean standard error is 1.77.

4.6.3 Simulation to Approximate Change in Variance Components

In Section 4.5 we were able to obtain block and residual variance estimates assuming either the incomplete or complete blocking scheme, because we had pilot data from which to compute these estimates. What do you do if you do not have pilot data to work with? In this section, we present a simulation method that allows realistic comparison of competing designs via precision analysis if there are no dependable variance estimates.

As in Section 4.5 and 4.6.2, consider the 7-treatment experiment to be conducted on a 7×4 grid of experimental units. Your task is to decide whether to use a complete block design with 4 blocks or a balanced incomplete block with 7 blocks of size 4. Start by setting the value of the residual variance to be used in the PARMS statement to one. This does not mean that you assume $\sigma^2 = 1$. It means that you can interpret the standard errors that are calculated using the DIFF option to mean that the anticipated actual standard error of a difference is the STDERR value calculated for DIFF in the PROC GLIMMIX step, multiplied by the true (but as yet unknown) standard deviation σ.

Now we know that changing block size changes the residual variance, so if $\sigma^2 = 1$ when block size is 4, i.e. for the incomplete block design, it will not be one for blocks of size 7, i.e. for the complete block design. What it will be depends on the block variance with block size is 4. Stroup (2013) shows an analytical way to compute an exact block and residual variance for complete blocks given the block and residual variance for incomplete blocks. However, the method is difficult to implement, especially for users without extensive linear model background. However, you can use simulation to obtain accurate approximations. The following simulation program enables you to do so.

Program

To use the program, you need to specify the block variance assuming the smaller block size—actually the block variance relative to the residual variance because you will use $\sigma^2 = 1$ as a benchmark. When in doubt, a reasonable value to use is $\sigma_b^2 = 0.5$, meaning that the variance among blocks is half the variance among experimental units within blocks. This number is based on the authors' experience with blocked designs. In addition to the block and residual variance under the smaller block size, you also need to identify each experimental unit when you simulate the data and specify which block it will be in if you use the smaller block size and which block it will be in if you use larger, complete, blocks.

Program 4.18

```
/* create data */
/* step one - block and e.u. variation */
/*   assuming natural block size       */
data natural_variation;
seed=51722205;
b_var=0.5;
u_var=1;
mu=12;
N_Natural_blocks=7;
natural_block_size=4;
do expt=1 to 1000;
 do natural_blk=1 to N_natural_blocks;
  blk_effect=sqrt(b_var)*rannor(seed);
   do eu=1 to Natural_Block_Size;
```

```
    e_ij=sqrt(u_var)*rannor(seed);
    y=mu+blk_effect+e_ij;
    output;
   end;
  end;
 end;
run;
proc sort data=natural_variation;
   by expt natural_blk eu;
run;
/* step 2 - match e.u. to block they will be in    */
/*  under incomplete and complete block design     */
/* also give trt under complete block             */
/* so variance estimation can account for trt d.f. */
data create_rcb;
 input natural_blk eu complete_blk trt$;
 do expt=1 to 1000;
  output;
 end;
datalines;
1 1 1 a
1 2 1 b
1 3 1 c
1 4 1 d
2 1 1 e
2 2 1 f
2 3 1 g
2 4 2 a
3 1 2 b
3 2 2 c
3 3 2 d
3 4 2 e
4 1 2 f
4 2 2 g
4 3 3 a
4 4 3 b
5 1 3 c
5 2 3 d
5 3 3 e
5 4 3 f
6 1 3 g
6 2 4 a
6 3 4 b
6 4 4 c
7 1 4 d
7 2 4 e
7 3 4 f
7 4 3 g
;
run;
proc sort data=create_rcb;
   by expt natural_blk eu;
run;
/* merge data sets */
data combined;
 merge natural_variation create_rcb;
 by expt natural_blk eu;
run;
proc print;
   where expt<3;
run;
/* optional run */
/* use natural_block model to confirm     */
/*  block and residual variance estimates */
/*  equal "true" variance components      */
ods results off;
ods html exclude all;
proc glimmix data=combined;
   by expt;
   class natural_blk;
   model y= ;
```

```
    random intercept / subject=natural_blk;
    ods output covparms=nb_var_est;
run;
proc sort data=nb_var_est;
    by covparm;
run;
ods results on;
ods html select all;
proc means data=nb_var_est;
    by covparm;
    var estimate;
run;
/* determine block and residual variance */
/*    for complete block design          */
ods results off;
ods html exclude all;
proc glimmix data=combined;
    by expt;
    class complete_blk trt;
    model y=trt ;
    random intercept / subject=complete_blk;
    ods output covparms=cb_var_est;
run;
proc sort data=cb_var_est;
    by covparm;
run;
ods results on;
ods html select all;
proc means data=cb_var_est;
    by covparm;
    var estimate;
run;
```

Step 1 of the program is essentially identical to the EXP_DSGN step of the simulation program in Section 4.6.2. Step 2 replaces the TRT_DSGN DATA step with a one line per experimental unit specification of the assignment of treatments to experimental units. The column labeled NATURAL_BLK divides the experimental units into 7 blocks of size 4; the column labeled COMPLETE_BLK divided the experimental units into 4 blocks of size 7. The data sets from Steps 1 and 2 are then merged. The program contains an optional run to obtain average block and residual variance estimates using NATURAL_BLK as a blocking criterion. You can run this as a check to make sure things have been set up properly. The average block and residual variance should be close to 0.5 and 1.0, respectively. The second run is the operative run. It uses COMPLETE_BLK as the blocking criterion and includes TRT in the model to ensure that the variance estimates account for TRT degrees of freedom.

Results

Outputs 4.23 and 4.24 show the results.

Output 4.23: Average Block and Residual Variance Estimates, 7 Blocks, Block Size 4

Parameter=Intercept

	Analysis Variable : Estimate			
N	Mean	Std Dev	Minimum	Maximum
1000	0.4917714	0.4105091	0	2.3644106

Parameter=Residual

	Analysis Variable : Estimate			
N	Mean	Std Dev	Minimum	Maximum
1000	1.0049800	0.3065639	0.2667954	2.3622585

The parameter "intercept" refers to the block variance. Over the 1000 simulated experiments, the average variance estimates are $\hat{\sigma}_b^2 = 0.49$ and $\hat{\sigma}^2 = 1.00$, both extremely close to the true values of 0.5 and 1.0, as they should be for the natural block size.

Output 4.24: Average Block and Residual Variance Estimates, 4 Blocks, Block Size 7

Parameter=Intercept

	Analysis Variable : Estimate			
N	Mean	Std Dev	Minimum	Maximum
1000	0.1978456	0.2710337	0	2.2608500

Parameter=Residual

	Analysis Variable : Estimate			
N	Mean	Std Dev	Minimum	Maximum
1000	1.3117886	0.4578276	0.2215238	3.3200209

As expected, increasing block size decreases within block homogeneity and blurs the distinction among blocks, lowering the block variance and increasing residual variance. The average estimates are $\hat{\sigma}_b^2 = 0.20$ and $\hat{\sigma}^2 = 1.31$. These are the numbers that you would use to compute the standard error of a treatment mean difference for a precision analysis.

Program

If this is the information that you had for a precision analysis, the statements for the BIB and RCB would be written as shown in Program 4.19.

Program 4.19

```
data bib;
 input blk @@;
  do eu=1 to 4;
   input trt$ @@;
   mu=12;
   output;
  end;
datalines;
 1  1 2 3 4
 2  1 2 5 6
 3  1 3 5 7
 4  1 4 6 7
 5  2 3 6 7
 6  2 4 5 7
 7  3 4 5 6
;
run;
proc glimmix data=bib;
   class blk trt;
   model mu=trt;
   random blk;
   parms (0.5)(1)/hold=1,2;
   lsmeans trt / diff cl;
run;
data rcb;
 input blk @@;
  do eu=1 to 7;
   input trt$ @@;
   mu=12;
   output;
  end;
datalines;
 1  1 2 3 4 5 6 7
 2  1 2 3 4 5 6 7
 3  1 2 3 4 5 6 7
 4  1 2 3 4 5 6 7
;
run;
proc glimmix data=rcb;
   class blk trt;
   model mu=trt;
   random blk;
```

```
   parms (0.2)(1.3)/hold=1,2;
   lsmeans trt / diff cl;
run;
```

Results

The results for these two precision analyses appear in Output 4.25 and Output 4.26.

Output 4.25: Precision Analysis, Trt 1 vs. Trt 2 Mean Difference, BIB Design

			Differences of trt Least Squares Means						
trt	_trt	Estimate	Standard Error	DF	t Value	Pr > |t|	Alpha	Lower	Upper
1	2	1.35E-15	0.7385	15	0.00	1.0000	0.05	-1.5742	1.5742

Output 4.26: Precision Analysis: Treatment 1 versus Treatment 1 Mean Difference, RCB Design

			Differences of trt Least Squares Means						
trt	_trt	Estimate	Standard Error	DF	t Value	Pr > |t|	Alpha	Lower	Upper
1	2	1.48E-15	0.8062	18	0.00	1.0000	0.05	-1.6938	1.6938

The relative standard errors of a difference are 0.74 for the BIB versus 0.81 for the RCB, or more technically correct, 0.74σ versus 0.81σ where σ is the residual standard deviation given the natural block size. Clearly, the BIB would be the preferred design.

This underlines the fallacy of the classical "efficiency factor" referred to at the end of Section 4.5.

Program

You can calculate the "efficiency factor" of the BIB with 7 blocks and block size 4 versus the RCB with 4 complete blocks of size 7 with the following PROC GLIMMIX statements. Note that they each use the same exemplary data as the runs that produce Output 4.19.

Program 4.20

```
proc glimmix data=bib;
   class blk trt;
   model mu=trt blk;
   parms (1)/hold=1;
   lsmeans trt / diff cl;
   ods html select diffs;
run;

proc glimmix data=rcb;
   class blk trt;
   model mu=trt blk;
   parms (1)/hold=1;
   lsmeans trt / diff cl;
   ods html select diffs;
run;
```

Results

The results appear in Outputs 4.27 and 4.28.

Output 4.27: Intra-block Precision Results for BIB used to Calculate Efficiency Factor

			Differences of trt Least Squares Means						
trt	_trt	Estimate	Standard Error	DF	t Value	Pr > |t|	Alpha	Lower	Upper
1	2	0	0.7559	15	0.00	1.0000	0.05	-1.6112	1.6112

Output 4.28: Intra-block Precision Results for RCB Assuming Residual Variance Unchanged by Changing Block Size; Used to Calculate Efficiency Factor

			Differences of trt Least Squares Means						
trt	_trt	Estimate	Standard Error	DF	t Value	Pr > |t|	Alpha	Lower	Upper
1	2	0	0.7071	18	0.00	1.0000	0.05	-1.4856	1.4856

Assuming that residual variance is unchanged by changing blocks size—which the simulation shows is clearly not true—then the standard error for a treatment mean difference would be 0.71 for the complete block design and 0.76 for the BIB. The classical "efficiency factor" would be the ratio of these standard errors, $0.7559 / 0.7071 = 1.069$. This would be interpreted to mean that the BIB is 6.9% less efficient than the RCB. This is only true if you do not use recovery of inter-block information when you analyze data from the BIB, and if the residual variance remains the same regardless of block size. Both are summarily untrue. Using appropriate information, the relevant efficiency measure is $0.74 / 0.81 = 0.914$. In other words, appropriately assessed, the efficiency *gain* if you use the BIB is 8.6% relative to the RCB.

Note that an appropriate precision analysis to compare these designs is possible only if mixed model-based methods are used. Conventional power and sample size techniques require that you base comparisons between competing designs on the assumptions underlying the classical efficiency factor. If you use techniques that do not account for mixed model issues, chances are you will make the wrong decision.

4.7 Summary

This chapter covers the basics of mixed model methods and supporting theory to compute the precision and power in the planning stages of designing a research study. Examples focused on designs with a one source of experimental unit error, specifically on completely randomized designs and randomized block designs. Section 4.3 introduced the mixed model extension of the linear model exemplary data methods introduced by Littell and O'Brien in the 1970s. Sections 4.4 and 4.5 introduced the use of mixed model methods to compare different designs under consideration. Section 4.6 gave a brief overview of simulation-based methods for mixed model precision and power analysis.

The primary take-home message of this chapter is that while much of the "power and sample size" literature focuses on sample size determination once the design has been selected, statistical thinking involved in planning a study should begin earlier. Precision analysis enables you to compare different designs. This is important because precision and power can be greatly affected not merely by sample size, but by how a given sample size is deployed. The real value of this chapter lies in its introduction of mixed model-based methods to implement precision comparisons that are essential to planning. Sample size determination is a final step in planning. Failure to give adequate attention to the earlier steps means getting the wrong answer in the final step.

While many of the power calculations shown in this chapter can be done with procedures such as PROC POWER or PROC GLMPOWER, presenting these procedures is not the point of this chapter. The real value of mixed model-based methods lies in comparing designs in situations where there are more design options that one should consider. These are presented in Chapter 14.

Chapter 5: Design Structure II: Models with Multiple Random Effects

5.1 Introduction	**131**
5.2 Treatment and Experiment Structure and Associated Models	**132**
5.2.1 Essential Terminology: Components of Treatment and Design Structure	132
5.2.2 Possible Design Structures for 2 × 2 Factorial Treatment Design	132
5.2.3 A Final Note on the Design Structures	143
5.2.4 Determination of the Appropriate Mixed Model for a Given Layout	143
5.3 Inference with Factorial Treatment Designs with Various Mixed Models	**146**
5.3.1 Standard Errors	146
5.3.2 Variance of Treatment Mean and Difference Estimates	147
5.3.3 Completing the Standard Error: Variance Component Estimates and Degrees of Freedom	149
5.4 A Split-Plot Semiconductor Experiment: An Example	**150**
5.4.1 Tests of Interest in the Semiconductor Experiment	151
5.4.2 Matrix Generalization of Mixed Model *F* Tests	152
5.4.3 PROC GLIMMIX Analysis of Semiconductor Data	154
5.5 A Brief Comment about PROC GLM	**161**
5.6 Type × Dose Response: An Example	**162**
5.6.1 PROC GLIMMIX Analysis of DOSE and TYPE Effects	162
5.6.2 A Closer Look at the Interaction Plot	164
5.6.3 Regression Analysis over DOSE by TYPE	165
5.7 Variance Component Estimates Equal to Zero: An Example	**171**
5.7.1 Default Analysis Using PROC GLIMMIX	172
5.7.2 One Recommended Alternative: Override Set-to-Zero Default Using NOBOUND or METHOD=TYPE3	173
5.7.3 Conceptual Alternative: Negative Variance or Correlation?	174
5.8 A Note on PROC GLM Compared to PROC GLIMMIX and PROC MIXED: Incomplete Blocks, Missing Data, and Spurious Non-Estimability	**177**
5.9 Summary	**179**

5.1 Introduction

Researchers often conduct studies that call for models with two or more random model effects. These can be grouped into two broad categories: study designs with two or more blocking criteria but only one size experimental unit and study designs with more than one size experimental unit. Row and column designs such as Latin squares are the most common examples of the former. Split-plot experiments, also called hierarchical or multilevel designs, are common examples of the latter. Designs with two or more blocking criteria but only one size experimental unit may involve one-way or multiway treatment designs. Designs with more than one size experimental unit almost always involve some form of factorial or multifactor nested design. Many textbooks that cover design of experiments distinguish between the treatment structure, or *treatment design*, and the manner in which treatment combinations are assigned to experimental units. Federer (1955) refers to the latter as the *experiment design*; Milliken and Johnson (2009) refer to it as *design structure*. This chapter focuses on models for studies with multifactor treatment designs and more than one size experimental unit.

The factorial design is a fundamental construct used to illustrate the essential principles that are covered in this chapter. The factorial design is a type of treatment design and is not, by itself, completely descriptive, because it may be used in conjunction with several possible experiment designs. These include completely randomized and randomized blocks designs, described in Chapter 2, but also row-and-column, split-plot, strip-plot, nested, clustered, and other designs that give rise to two or more random model effects. Because these designs give rise to multiple random model effects, mixed models and mixed model methods are essential to their proper analysis. Repeated measures and longitudinal data are closely related to split-plot structures but involve the additional complication of serially correlated errors. Repeated measures analysis is discussed separately in Chapter 8.

As an aside, but one that is unfortunately still necessary, in the pre-mixed model computer era, split-plot analysis used fixed effects linear model software such as PROC GLM. While these procedures are adequate, if somewhat awkward, for testing overall sources of variation, they are not designed to provide appropriate standard errors for many of the treatment differences that are of interest in factorial experiments. Specifically, if scientifically important interactions exist among treatment factors, methods based on fixed effects linear models *cannot* correctly compute standard errors for simple effects of interest and *will* compute *incorrect* results. Unfortunately, many design of experiments and data analysis textbooks, even now, persist in presenting split-plot methods using these antiquated approaches. To repeat, PROC GLM was not designed to correctly compute a complete and appropriate analysis of a split-plot experiment. In fact, PROC MIXED was developed in response to a regional project undertaken to address PROC GLM's shortcomings with regard to multilevel and longitudinal data. Within SAS, use PROC GLIMMIX or PROC MIXED for split-plot experiments. This chapter shows how.

5.2 Treatment and Experiment Structure and Associated Models

Although factorial experiments are often viewed as a specific type of design, in reality they can be set up and conducted in a wide variety of ways. In this section the word factorial refers specifically to the 2×2 cross-classified treatment structure. Do not confuse it with the names used for the various experiment designs—that is, ways in which treatment combinations are assigned to experimental units, described below.

This section shows seven different ways to conduct a 2×2 factorial treatment design, each leading to a different model and analysis. The 2×2 is the simplest factorial treatment structure, and even the seven layouts shown here are not an exhaustive list of possible experiment designs! The purpose of this section is to show you how to visualize the layout (Section 5.2.1) and how to associate it with an appropriate mixed model (Section 5.2.2). The approach shown here generalizes to arbitrarily complex factorial experiments. Once you master the strategy, you can adapt it to your own data. The key concept is that different factors or factorial combinations are applied to different experimental units: identify the experimental units, and the model follows.

5.2.1 Essential Terminology: Components of Treatment and Design Structure

Suppose that you want to investigate two treatment factors, generically referred to as factor A and factor B, or A and B, respectively, each with two levels, denoted A_1 and A_2 for factor A and B_1 and B_2 for factor B. Factor A could be two types of drug, two varieties of a crop, two materials in a manufacturing process, or two different teaching methods. Factor B could be two different levels—e.g., each drug applied at a low dose (B_1) or high dose (B_2)—or it could be a distinct factor. In a factorial experiment, the treatments are cross-classified: all possible combinations of factor levels may be observed. Here, there are four treatments: A_1 applied in combination (or crossed) with B_1 (referred to as $A_1 \times B_1$, and abbreviated as AB_{11} later in this chapter); A_1 crossed with B_2 (denoted $A_1 \times B_2$, abbreviated as AB_{12}); A_2 crossed with B_1 (denoted $A_2 \times B_1$, abbreviated as AB_{21}); and A_2 crossed with B_2 (denoted $A_2 \times B_2$, abbreviated as AB_{22}). Note that factor levels are never applied alone—treatments always consist of a level of one factor in combination with a level of the other factor.

The four treatments can be observed in a variety of ways. First, each treatment must be assigned to an *experimental unit*. An experimental unit is defined as the smallest entity to which a treatment is independently applied. The word *independent* is important. For example, if you want to compare two teaching methods, you could design the experiment by assigning method A_1 to one teacher to use in her class with *n* students, and method A_2 to another teacher to use in his class. In this case, the *class* is the experimental unit. Although there are individual students in each class, once the class is assigned to a given treatment, all students in the class are assigned as well. The assignment of individual students is not independent. On the other hand, you could design the experiment by assigning individual students within a class to different teaching methods (assuming it is logistically possible to do so). For example, some students within the class could be assigned to data analysis using a calculator, whereas others could be assigned to data analysis using a computer. Then students would be the experimental units and the class would be a *blocking factor*. These two approaches imply different models and require different analyses. It is important to be very clear about how a study is conducted in order to use the right model and do the right analysis.

In the 2×2 factorial, you can conduct the experiment in a variety of ways. The next section describes seven common designs associated with a 2×2 factorial, and the associated thought process that leads to an appropriate model.

5.2.2 Possible Design Structures for 2 × 2 Factorial Treatment Design

In order to visualize the treatment combinations, levels of factor A are distinguished by shading (level A_1 not shaded, level A_2 shaded in gray) and levels of factor B are distinguished by hashing (level B_1 clear, level B_2 hashed). Figure 5.1 shows how the four resulting treatment combinations appear in subsequent illustrations.

Figure 5.1: Visualization of Treatment Codes in 2 × 2 Factorial Experiment

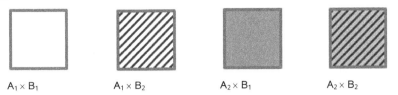

For each design structure, suppose that we have 16 experimental units, allowing us to assign four units per treatment. In other words, each treatment combination is replicated four times, although each design allocates replications in a different way. Because each design structure is different, each requires a different model for data analysis. By keeping track of the process by which treatment combinations are randomly assigned, and the resulting sources of variation implicit in each design structure, we can construct models appropriate for each structure. We begin with the simplest structure, the completely randomized design, hereafter referred to by the acronym CRD.

Completely Randomized Design (CRD)

With the CRD, each of the four A × B treatment combinations is assigned at random to four units. Figure 5.2.A shows a visualization of the 16 experimental units prior to treatment assignment, and Figure 5.2.B shows a possible random assignment of treatment combinations.

Figure 5.2: Completely Randomized Design

A

B

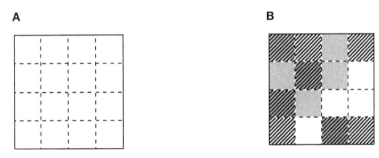

Experiment Design Skeleton ANOVA	
Source	*df*
Units	15
Total	**15**

Skelton ANOVA after Assigning Treatments	
Source	*df*
Treatments (A × B combinations)	3
Units | A, B	15 − 3 = 12
Total	**15**

Note: (A) Experiment Design Layout before Applying Treatments. (B) Final Layout after assigning Treatment Combinations.

Prior to treatment, there are 16 total experimental units and hence 15 degrees of freedom total. The treatment design has four treatment levels and hence three degrees of freedom. Typically, one would partition the degrees of freedom into A and B main effects and the A×B interaction. Other partitions are possible, and are discussed in the examples later in this chapter. You can summarize the sources of variation as shown in the tables in Figure 5.2.

There are 15 total degrees of freedom, of which three account for treatment effects. This leaves 12 degrees of freedom for "units | A, B" which you read as "unit after accounting for treatment." In standard textbooks, this source of variation is often written as "error" or "residual." We write it as "units | A, B" because, as we shall see in Chapters 11 through 13, doing so enables us to extend mixed models to data that do not follow a normal distribution. In the CRD, observations are taken on the units. Assuming normality, we can characterize the distribution of the observations as $y_{ijk} \sim N(\mu_{ij}, \sigma^2)$ where y_{ijk} denotes the observation on the kth unit $(k = 1, 2, 3, 4)$ assigned to treatment combination $A_i \times B_j$. This gives you the basis for writing an appropriate model. In Section 5.2.3 we show how to translate the assumed distribution into a statistical model and from there into PROC GLIMMIX or PROC MIXED statements.

Randomized Complete Block

Here we assume that there is a criterion that justifies dividing the 16 units into four blocks, each with four units. Treatment combinations are randomly assigned to units within each block so that each treatment combination appears exactly once in each block. Figure 5.3.A shows a visualization of the units prior to treatment assignment. Figure 5.3.B shows a possible assignment of treatments. Notice that the difference between the CRD and the RCB is that the assignment of treatments to units in the CRD is unrestricted as long as four units are assigned to each treatment combination, whereas assignment of treatments in the RCB is restricted so that each treatment appears once in each block.

Figure 5.3: Randomized Complete Block Design

A

Block 1			
Block 2			
Block 3			
Block 4			

B

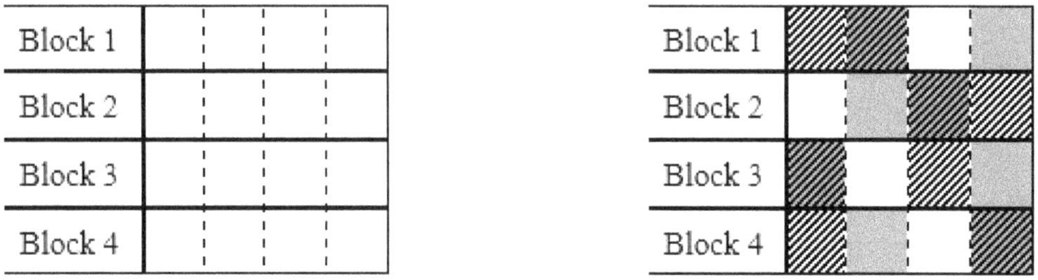

Experiment Design Skeleton ANOVA

Source	df
Block	3
Units(block)	12
Total	**15**

Skeleton ANOVA after Assigning Treatments

Source	df
Block	3
Treatment (A × B combinations)	3
Units(block)	A, B	12 − 3 = 9
Total	**15**

Note: (A) Experiment Design Layout before Applying Treatments. (B) Final Layout after assigning Treatment Combinations.

Prior to treatment, there are 15 total degrees of freedom, three of which account for blocks. The remaining 12 *df* account for units within blocks. After treatment assignment, three degrees of freedom accounts for treatments, leaving nine degrees of freedom for units. The tables in Figure 5.3 show the sources of variation and their associated degrees of freedom.

Read the source "units(block)|A, B" as "unit within block after accounting for treatment." As with the "unit" line in the CRD (Figure 5.2), for Gaussian (normally distributed) data you could write "error" or "residual" but "units(block)|A, B" allows extension to models with non-Gaussian data. Assuming normality, the distribution of observations can be written $y_{ijk} \mid r_k \sim N(\mu_{ijk}, \sigma^2)$ where r_k denotes the effect of the kth block. As discussed in Chapter 2, we typically assume $r_k \sim NI(0, \sigma_r^2)$ where "~NI" is read "normally and independently distributed," and $\mu_{ijk} = \mu_{ij} + r_k$. As with the CRD, μ_{ij} denotes the mean of treatment combination $A_i \times B_j$.

Row and Column Designs (Latin Square)

Row and column designs are used when there are two blocking criteria. Figure 5.4.A shows a visualization of the experimental units with row and column sources of variation prior to treatment assignment. The Latin square requires assignment of treatments such that each treatment combination appears once in each row and once in each column. Figure 5.4.B shows a possible assignment of treatments.

Figure 5.4: Latin Square Design

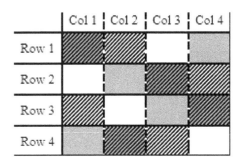

A

	Col 1	Col 2	Col 3	Col 4
Row 1				
Row 2				
Row 3				
Row 4				

Experiment Design Skeleton ANOVA

Source	df
Column	3
Row	3
Column × row = unit	9
Total	**15**

Skelton ANOVA after Assigning Treatments

Source	df
Column	3
Row	3
Treatment: A × B	3
Row × Column	A, B	9 – 3 = 6
Total	**15**

Note: (A) Experiment Design Layout before Applying Treatments. (B) Final Layout after assigning Treatment Combinations.

Read "(row × column)|A, B" as "row by column after accounting for treatment." Note that row × column combinations are the experimental units in the Latin square design. There are 15 total degrees of freedom, of which three account for rows and three for columns. Hence, prior to treatment assignment, there are $15 - 3 - 3 = 9$ degrees of freedom for experimental units. Three of these must account for treatments, leaving six degrees of freedom once treatments are assigned. The distribution of the observations, assuming normality, can be written as $y_{ijkl} \mid r_k, c_l \sim N(\mu_{ijkl}, \sigma^2)$ where r_k and c_l denote row and column effects. The mean conditional on row and column effects, μ_{ijkl} can be written $\mu_{ij} + r_k + c_l$ where, as with the CRD and RCBD, μ_{ij} denotes the treatment combination mean.

Split-Plot, Variation 1—Whole-Plot as CRD

The CRD, RCBD, and Latin square all have a single size experimental unit. Design structures in the split-plot family are different. Designs of this type, also called hierarchical or multilevel design, have two or more sizes of experimental units resulting from two or more distinct randomization steps. One of the most common reasons for difficulty fitting a mixed model is a disconnect between the design structure and the model that one is attempting to fit. Such disconnects are much more common with multilevel designs. It is important to work step by step through a process of translating the design structure to a plausible model. Skipping steps is a major cause of trouble. For this reason, in this section we break down the process step by step.

The split-plot design with the whole-plot as a CRD is the simplest multilevel design. If you follow the process shown here and for the next two variations on the split-plot, you should be able to adapt these steps to translate design structures of arbitrary complexity into plausible models.

Figure 5.5.A shows the design structure prior to any treatment assignment for the CRD split-plot design.

Figure 5.5: Split-Plot Variation 1– Whole Plot as CRD

A

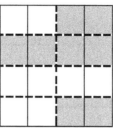

B

Experiment Design Skeleton ANOVA

Source	df
Whole-plot units	7
Split-plot units(WP)	8
Total	**15**

Skeleton ANOVA after Assigning Levels of A

Source	df
A	1
WP(A)	7 – 1 = 6
Split-plot units(WP)	8
Total	**15**

C

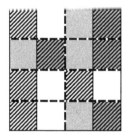

Skeleton ANOVA after Assigning Levels of B

Source	df
A	1
WP(A)	7 – 1 = 6
B(A)	2
SP(WP)	A, B	8 – 2 = 6
Total	**15**

Note: (A) Experiment Design Layout before Applying Treatments. (B) Randomization Step 1: Apply Levels of A to Whole Plots. (C) Randomization Step 2: Apply Levels of B to Split Plots.

The dashed lines demark larger experimental units, called *whole-plot experimental units*. Within each whole-plot unit are two smaller units, called *split-plot experimental units*. As an example, the whole-plot unit may be areas of a field to which irrigation is applied and the split-plots may be sections within an irrigation area where different varieties can be planted. As another example, the whole-plots may be schools, which either participate in a professional development program or serve as untreated controls, and the split-plots may be classrooms, which may receive different types of instructional curricula. The pre-treatment sources of variation can be described as follows.

There are 16 total units, hence 15 total degrees of freedom. There are eight whole-plot units, hence 7 whole-plot degrees of freedom. There are two split-plot units per whole-plot unit, hence one split-plot degree of freedom per whole plot. Because there are eight whole plots and one split-plot degree of freedom per whole plot, there are thus eight split-plot degrees of freedom altogether.

Figure 5.5.B shows the first randomization step, in which levels of factor A are applied to whole-plot units. Because there is no restriction on randomization aside from requiring that four whole plots receive A1 and four whole plots receive A2, the whole plot design is a CRD.

The shaded areas show where level A_2 is assigned. The updated table of sources of variation is now read as "WP(A)" and "whole-plot unit after accounting for factor A." Notice that factor A has two levels and hence one degree of freedom, leaving six whole plot degrees of freedom after accounting for factor A. Also notice the placement of the line for the A source of variation. Because levels of A are randomly assigned to whole plots, the whole plot is the experimental unit with respect to factor A, and the source of variation A is placed immediately above WP(A).

Figure 5.5.C shows the second randomization step: levels of B are assigned so that each level of B appears in exactly one split plot per whole plot.

The hashed plots show where level B_2 has been assigned. The table with figure 5.5.C gives the updated and final table of sources of variation.

Read "SP(WP)|A,B" as "split plot within whole plot after accounting for A and B." You can simply refer to this line as "split plot." This is the unit on which observations are taken. Write their distribution as $y_{ijk} \mid w_{ik} \sim N(\mu_{ijk}, \sigma^2)$ where w_{ik} denotes the effect of the ik^{th} whole plot, that is, the effect of the kth whole plot unit assigned to the ith level of A. Typically, we assume $w_{ik} \sim NI(0, \sigma_w^2)$. Also, $\mu_{ijk} = \mu_j + w_{ik}$. If the distributions look superficially like the distributions for the RCBD, it is because the split-plot with whole plot conducted as a CRD is actually a special case of an incomplete block design. See Milliken and Johnson (2009) for a more detailed explanation and Chapter 14 for an application of the split-plot/incomplete block relationship in the planning of experiments using mixed model methods.

Split-Plot Variation 2—Whole Plot Conducted as RCBD

This design is similar to Split Plot Variation 1, except that the whole plot experimental units are grouped into blocks according to some criterion. For example, in the irrigation and plant variety example, blocks are fields that are divided in half, with one level of irrigation applied to one half of the field and the other level of irrigation to the other half. Thus, field is the block, half-field is the whole plot, and the split plot is the same as described above. Figures 5.6.A, 5.6.B and 5.6.C show the pre-treatment, factor A randomization step, and final randomization step for this design.

Here the thick horizontal lines show the divisions between blocks and the dashed vertical lines show division between whole plots within each block.

Figure 5.6: Split-Plot Variation 2—Whole-Plot as RCBD

A

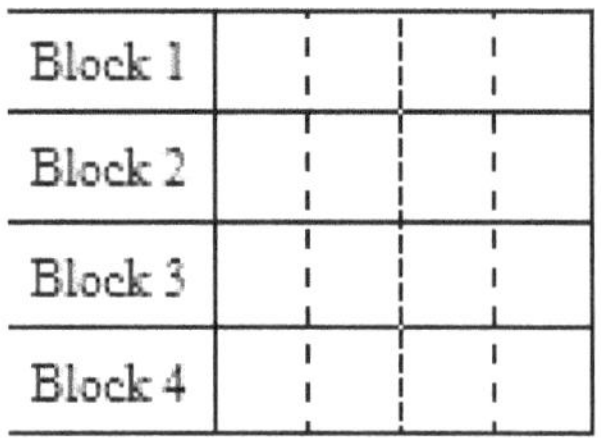

Block 1		:		:	
Block 2		:		:	
Block 3		:		:	
Block 4		:		:	

Experiment Design Skeleton ANOVA

Source	df
Block	3
Whole-plot(block)	4
Split-plot(WP)	8
Total	**15**

B

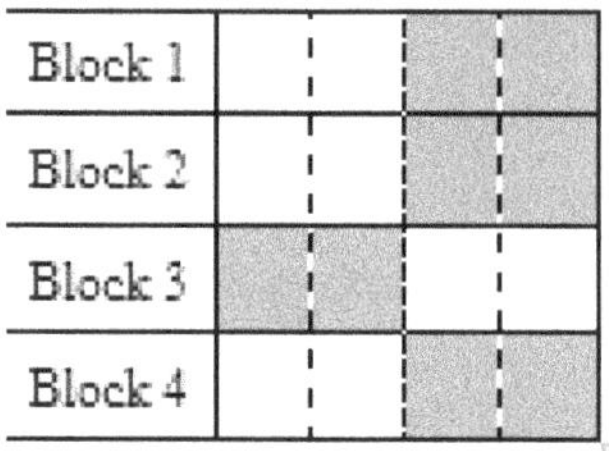

Block 1		:		:	
Block 2		:		:	
Block 3		:		:	
Block 4		:		:	

Skeleton ANOVA after Assigning Factor A

Source	df
Block	3
A	1
WP(blk) | A ➔ block × A	4 − 1 = 3
SP(WP)	8
Total	**15**

C

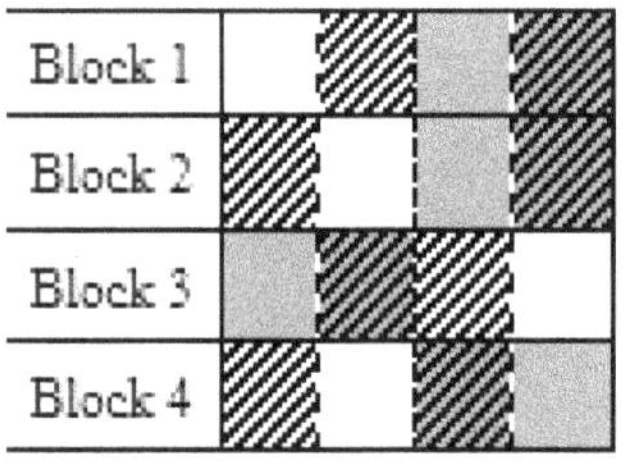

Block 1		:		:	
Block 2		:		:	
Block 3		:		:	
Block 4		:		:	

Skeleton ANOVA after Assigning Factor B

Source	df
Block	3
A	1
WP(blk) | A ➔ block × A	4 − 1 = 3
B(A)	2
SP(WP) | A, B	8 − 2 = 6
Total	**15**

Note: (A) Experiment Design Layout before Applying Treatments. (B) Layout after Randomization Step 1: Assigning Levels of A. (C) Final Layout after Randomization Step 2: Assign Levels of B.

The shaded areas show the whole plots to which A_2 has been assigned.

The hashed plots show the split plot units to which B_2 has been assigned. Table 5.1 shows the sources of variation for this design.

Table 5.1: Sources of Variation for Split-Plot with Whole Plot as RCBD

Before		After	
Source	*df*	**Source**	*df*
Block	3	Block	3
		A	1
WP(blk)	4	Block × A	4 – 1 = 3
		B	1
		A × B	1
SP(WP)	8	SP(WP) | A,B	8 – 1 – 1 = 6
Total	**15**	**Total**	**15**

Here it is helpful to see the sources of variation before and after treatments were assigned. The first two columns follow from Figure 5.6.A. The only sources of variation are block, whole plot, and split plot. There are four blocks, hence three degrees of freedom for block, two whole plots and hence one degree of freedom per block (hence four degrees of freedom for whole plot within block) and two split plot units per whole plot, as before. Levels of A are applied to the whole plot units, hence the position of A in the list of sources of variation and the fact that Factor A's one degree of freedom is removed from the whole plot source of variation. Also note that once the levels of factor A have been assigned, whole plots are uniquely identified by their block and level of A. For this reason, the whole plot effect appears in the "After" source of variation list as "Block × A." This is important, because it tells you how you will need to identify the whole plot effect in your PROC GLIMMIX or PROC MIXED statements.

You can write the distribution of the observations as $y_{ijk} \mid r_k, w_{ik} \sim N(\mu_{ijk}, \sigma^2)$ where r_k and w_{ik} denote block and whole plot effects as before. and $\mu_{ijk} = \mu_{ij} + r_k + w_{ik}$. You may find it helpful to denote the whole plot effect as ra_{ik} rather than w_{ik} to make it clear that you must reference the whole plot effect as "Block × A" in your SAS statements.

Strip-Split-Plot

This design differs from the split-plot in that there are three sizes of experimental unit, one for levels of factor A, one for levels of factor B, and one for A × B combinations. The latter results from the random assignment of levels of A and B, not from a distinct randomization. Figure 5.7.A shows the layout prior to any assignment of treatment levels.

Figure 5.7: Strip-Plot Design

A

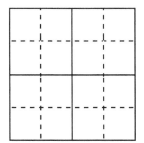

Experiment Design Skeleton ANOVA

Source	df
Blk	3
Row(blk)	4
Col(blk)	4
Row × col(blk)	4

B

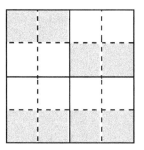

Skeleton ANOVA Adding A Effect

Source	df
Blk	3
A	1
~~Row(blk)~~ ➔ blk × A	4 – 1 = 3
Col(blk)	4
Row × col(blk)	4

C

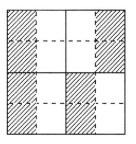

Skeleton ANOVA Adding B Effect

Source	df
Blk	3
A	1
~~Row(blk)~~ ➔ blk × A	4 – 1 = 3
B	1
~~Col(blk)~~ ➔ blk × B	4 – 1 = 3
Row × col(blk)	4

D

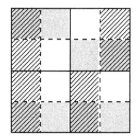

Full (Combined) Skeleton ANOVA

Source	df
Blk	3
A	1
~~Row(blk)~~ ➔ blk × A	4 – 1 = 3
B	1
~~Col(blk)~~ ➔ blk × B	4 – 1 = 3
A × B	1
Row × col(blk) ➔ blk × A × B	4 – 1 = 3

Notes: (A) Experiment Design Layout before Applying Treatments. (B) Randomization Step 1–Levels of A Assigned to "Row" experimental unit within each block. (C) Randomization Step 2 – Levels of B Assigned to "Col" experimental unit within each block. (D) Final Layout – Experiment + Treatment Design.

The experimental units are blocked into four sets of four units each. Each block of four units forms a 2 × 2 grid. It is helpful to think of each block as having rows and columns. As an example, each block could be a field, with irrigation levels applied along the rows and fertilizer levels applied along the columns. List the pre-treatment sources of variation as follows.

There are two rows and two columns per block, hence one degree of freedom for row, column and row × column within each block. There are four blocks, hence the degrees of freedom that you see in the list. Notice that row × col(blk) defines the individual units, depicted visually as the 16 individual cells in Figure 5.7.A. If observations are taken on these units, as they would be in this example, you can refer to row × col(blk) as the unit of observation.

Figure 5.7.B shows the first randomization step. Levels of A are randomly assigned to rows within each block. The shaded rows receive level A2.

Augment the list of sources of variation as follows. Place the A effect immediately above row(blk) because row(blk) is the experimental unit with respect to A. Also, once the levels of A are assigned, if you know the block and the level of A, you know the row within block; blk × A uniquely identifies row(blk). This is important because you must use blk × A in your PROC GLIMMIX or PROC MIXED statements to identity this source of variation.

Figure 5.7.C shows the next randomization step, the assignment of levels of B to columns within each block. The hashed columns receive level B2.

Augment the original sources of variation list as follows. As with the A effect, place B immediately above col(blk) to signify that col(blk) is the experimental unit with respect to B. Also, as you did with A, you now refer to col(blk) by its unique identifiers, that is, by blk × B.

You can now combine the results of the two randomization steps to form the complete design, shown in Figure 5.7.D.

Table 5.2 shows the fully augmented list of sources of variation. As with Table 5.1, you may find it helpful to see the *before* and *after* lists side by side.

Table 5.2: Sources of Variation for a 2 × 2 Factorial Experiment Conducted as a Strip-Split-Plot

Before		After	
Source	*df*	**Source**	*df*
Block	3	Block	3
		A	1
Row(blk)	4	blk × A	4 − 1 = 3
		B	1
Col(blk)	4	blk × B	4 − 1 = 3
Row × Col(blk)	4	Row × Col(blk) | A, B[a]	4 − 1 = 3
Total	**15**	**Total**	**15**

[a] Also known as *unit of observation*.

As with previous examples, if observations are assumed to follow a Gaussian distribution, the last source of variation is often referred to as "error" or "residual" or, in the context of the strip-split-plot, "error C" or "error 3." The nomenclature used in Table 5.2 is more conducive to constructing mixed models for non-Gaussian data. See Chapter 13 for examples of multilevel experiments with non-Gaussian data.

For the sources of variation, you can write the distributions that are the basis for mixed models used to analyze data from this design structure. Assuming normality, write the distribution of the observations conditional on block and experimental unit effects as $y_{ijk} \mid r_k, ra_{ik}, rb_{jk} \sim N(\mu_{ijk}, \sigma^2)$ where r_k, ra_{ik} and rb_{jk} denote block, blk × A and blk × B effects, respectively. They are assumed to be mutually independent. Each is assumed to be normally and independently distributed with mean zero and variance σ_r^2, σ_{ra}^2 and σ_{rb}^2, respectively. Following Table 5.2, partition μ_{ijk} as $\mu_{ij} + r_k + ra_{ik} + rb_{jk}$.

Split-Plot with Whole Plot Conducted as a Replicated 2 × 2 Latin Square

Figure 5.8.A shows the pre-treatment layout of design structure in which row and column gradients at the whole plot level necessitate organizing the whole plots as Latin squares.

Figure 5.8: Split-Plot Variation 3—Whole-Plot Blocked on Row and Column

A

	Col 1	Col 2	Col 3	Col 4	
Row 1					Row 3
Row 2					Row 4

Experiment Design Skeleton ANOVA

Source	df
Square	1
Row(square)	2
Column(square)	2
Row × col(square)	2
Split-plot(row × col)	8
Total	**15**

B

	Col 1	Col 2	Col 3	Col 4	
Row 1					Row 3
Row 2					Row 4

Skeleton ANOVA after Assigning Factor A

Source	df
Square	1
Row(square)	2
Column(square)	2
A	1
Row × col(square) | A	2 − 1 = 1
Split-plot(row × col)	8
Total	**15**

C

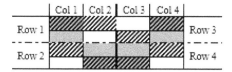

Skeleton ANOVA after Assigning Factor B

Source	df
Square	1
Row(square)	2
Column(square)	2
A	1
Row × column(square) | A	2 − 1 = 1
B(A)	2
Split-plot(Row × column) | A, B	8 − 2 = 6
Total	**15**

The solid vertical line in the middle divides the design into two parts, each consisting of two rows and two columns, separated by dashed lines. Within each row × column combination there are two sub-units. The row × column combinations are the whole plot experimental units and the sub-units are the split-plot experimental units.

Figure 5.8.B shows the first randomization step, the assignment of levels of A to whole plots.

Figure 5.8.C shows the result of the second randomization step, assigning levels of B to sub-units within each whole plot.

Table 5.3 shows the resulting sources of variation, before and after treatment assignment.

Table 5.3. Sources of Variation for Split-Plot with Whole Plot Conducted as a Latin Square

Before		After	
Source	*df*	**Source**	*df*
Row	2	Row	2
Column	2	Column	2
		A	1
Row × Column	4	Row × Column × A	4 − 1 = 3
		A	1
		A × B	1
Sub-unit(row × column)	8	Sub-unit(row × column)|A, B	8 − 1 − 1 = 6
Total	**15**	**Total**	**15**

Technically, row and column uniquely identify whole plot experimental units. We add A, and we write the whole-plot effect as "Row × Column × A" because when you write PROC GLIMMIX or PROC MIXED statements, including A will cause the PROC GLIMMIX or PROC MIXED default degree of freedom algorithm to use the correct degrees of freedom for statistics involving A effects.

From Table 5.3 you can write the distribution of the observations, conditional on row, column and whole-plot effects, as $y_{ijkl} \mid r_k, c_l, rca_{ikl} \sim N(\mu_{ijkl}, \sigma^2)$ and partition μ_{ijkl} as $\mu_{ij} + r_k + c_l + rca_{ikl}$.

5.2.3 A Final Note on the Design Structures

You can see that there are many ways to construct designs, even for relatively simple treatment structures. Why the variety? To oversimplify, the design structure must serve two goals: first, it must account for sources of variation that could otherwise be confounded with treatment effects; second, subject to the requirements of the first goal, it must keep the design as simple as possible. Split-plot structures are often used to meet these goals.

Why conduct split-plot experiments? Broadly speaking, there are three reasons:

- Out of necessity when a factor, or factorial combination, must be applied to relatively large experimental units, whereas other factors are more appropriately applied to subunits.

- For convenience: it is often simply easier to apply different factors to different sized units.

- To increase the precision of the estimated effect of the factor applied to the subunits. In general, doing so also increases the precision of the estimated interaction between the two factors relative to designs with a single size experimental unit, but decreases the precision on the other factor.

There are many other variations in addition to the design structures shown in this section. However, these seven design structures serve to show the variety of experiment designs that can be used even with a simple treatment design, and the impact that they have on constructing an appropriate mixed model for data analysis.

5.2.4 Determination of the Appropriate Mixed Model for a Given Layout

Once you have a picture of the way in which observations were obtained, as illustrated by the layouts in Figures 5.2 through 5.8, you can determine the mixed model needed to describe the sources of variation. The following strategy works if you can assume that the data can be modeled using a normal (Gaussian) distribution. Chapters 11 through 13 present adaptations of these methods for mixed models for non-Gaussian data from designs similar to those discussed in this chapter.

Assuming normality, you can use the following generic structure to write the model:

Observation = Treatment design components + Experiment design components

The treatment design components describe the sources of variation that are associated with the treatment factors. The experiment design components describe additional sources of variation introduced by the way experimental units are assigned to treatments plus random variation. In the 2×2 factorial, all seven designs share the same generic model,

$$y_{ijk} = \mu_{ij} + e_{ijk}$$

where y_{ijk} denotes the observation on the kth experimental unit assigned to the ij^{th} $A_i \times B_j$ treatment combination, μ_{ij} denotes the mean of the ij^{th} treatment combination, and e_{ijk} denotes all other variability on the observation. Notice that this is, in essence, a conversion of the distributions given in Section 5.2.2 from the probability distribution form of the model to the model equation form. In other words, for the CRD. writing $y_{ijk} \sim N(\mu_{ij}, \sigma^2)$ is equivalent to writing $y_{ijk} = \mu_{ij} + e_{ijk}$ where $e_{ijk} \sim N(0, \sigma^2)$. As the design structures shown in Section 5.2.2 increase in complexity, from a mixed model perspective, μ_{ij} remains unchanged but e_{ijk} acquires additional terms and increasing complexity.

The treatment mean is typically decomposed into main effects and interaction terms—in essence, $\mu_{ij} = \mu + \alpha_i + \beta_j + \alpha\beta_{ij}$, where μ is the overall mean or intercept, α_i and β_j are the main effects of A and B, respectively, and $\alpha\beta_{ij}$ is the A × B interaction term. Alternatively, you could decompose μ_{ij} as $\mu + \alpha_i + \beta(\alpha)_{ij}$ where $\beta(\alpha)_{ij}$ denotes the simple effect of factor B given the ith level of factor A. Main, simple, and interaction effects were introduced in Chapter 3. Section 5.3 provides additional detail in the context of the designs presented in this chapter.

The e_{ijk} term is written to match the layout or design of the study, specifically the size and assignment of experimental units. For the seven designs shown in Figure 5.1, consider Table 5.4.

Table 5.4: Model–Design Association, by Figure Number

	5.2	5.3	5.4	5.5	5.6	5.7	5.8
Effect	CRD	RCB	LS	Split-plot CR	Split-plot RCB	Strip-split-plot	Split-plot LS
Block?	No	Yes	Row Col	No	Yes	Yes	Row Col
A	eu(A*B)	blk*A*B	row*col	eu(A)	blk*A	blk*A	row*col
B	eu(A*B)	blk*A*B	row*col	B*eu(A)	blk*A*B	blk*B	row*col*B
A*B	eu(A*B)	blk*A*B	row*col	B*eu(A)	blk*A*B	blk*A*B	row*col*B

Table 5.4 gives two types of information essential to associating a model with a design: (1) are there any blocking factors (if so, what?), and (2) what is the experimental unit with respect to each of the treatment main effects and interactions? For the CRD, there is no blocking, and the experimental unit (denoted *eu* in column 5.2) is assigned to A × B combinations and hence is shared by all treatment factors.

Thus, the experiment design component, e_{ijk}, is simply an experimental error and the model can be written as follows:

$$y_{ijk} = \mu_{ij} + e_{ijk} = \mu + \alpha_i + \beta_j + \alpha\beta_{ij} + e_{ijk}$$

where e_{ijk} is typically assumed *iid* N(0, σ^2). This is the classic two-way ANOVA model.

For the RCB, there is blocking and there is only one size of experimental unit assigned to A × B treatment combinations. This experimental unit corresponds to a block × A × B combination as depicted in Figure 5.3. Hence, the experiment design component is decomposed as $E_{ijk} = r_k + e_{ijk}$, where r_k denotes the kth block effect and e_{ijk} denotes experimental error. The model is thus

$$y_{ijk} = \mu_{ij} + r_k + e_{ijk} = \mu + \alpha_i + \beta_j + \alpha\beta_{ij} + r_k + e_{ijk}$$

where the e_{ijk} are typically assumed *iid* N(0, σ^2) and the r_k are typically assumed random but may be assumed fixed depending on the circumstances. The Latin square design (Figure 5.4.C) is similar, except that separate row and column terms replace the single block term in the model.

For the split-unit designs (Figures 5.5 through 5.8), there are different-size experimental units with respect to the various treatment effects. For the CRD split-plot design (Figure 5.5), *eu(A)* denotes the whole-plot experimental unit. There must be a column in the data set (called *eu* in Table 5.4) to identify these units and you must include this variable name in the CLASS statement. Note also that main effects and their interactions may have different-sized experimental units. The extreme case is the strip-split-plot design (Figure 5.7), for which levels of A are applied to units defined by block × A combinations, levels of B are assigned to units defined by block × B, and thus A × B combinations are effectively assigned to units defined by block × A × B. The e_{ijk} term for each design reflects the information in Table 5.4.

For the design in Figure 5.5, there is no blocking, but levels of A are assigned to larger units (defined by "e.u." within A), and levels of B (and hence A × B combinations) are assigned to smaller units defined by the intersection of B and "e.u." within A. Thus, $E_{ijk} = w_{ik} + e_{ijk}$, where w_{ik} denotes random variation among "e.u." within A units (whole-plot units) and e_{ijk} denotes random variation among split-plot experimental units. The model for the design in Figure 5.6 is similar, except that the whole plot is arranged in randomized blocks, so you add a block effect, r_k, just as you did in going from the CRD to the RCB. In the split plot you must also modify the whole-plot error term accordingly (i.e., change *eu(A)* to *block*A*).

For the strip-split-plot, shown in Figure 5.7, each factor has a different-size experimental unit. Thus, $E_{ijk} = r_k + w_{ik} + v_{jk} + e_{ijk}$, to reflect block effect and random variation among block × A, block × B, and block × A × B units, respectively. The full model is thus

$$y_{ijk} = \mu + \alpha_i + w_{ik} + \beta_j + v_{jk} + \alpha\beta_{ij} + r_k + e_{ijk}$$

The final model, shown in Figure 5.8, is a split-plot design with the whole plots arranged as Latin squares. Thus, the model requires row and column blocking effects and the experimental units with respect to levels of A, row × column combinations, and with respect to B (and hence A × B), intersections of B with row × column combinations. Thus, E_{ijk} can be written as $r_k + c_l + w_{ikl} + e_{ijkl}$, where r_k and c_l denote row and column effects, respectively. Note the additional subscript, *l*, to denote column position. The final model is thus

$$y_{ijkl} = \mu + r_k + c_l + \alpha_i + w_{ikl} + \beta_j + \alpha\beta_{ij} + e_{ijkl}$$

> **Important Note**: Beginning users often add inappropriate random effects to models such as those shown in this example. *Only random effects that correspond to actual physical units in the design should appear in the model.* For example, in the split-plot design with whole-plot blocking (Figure 5.6), a block × A term (w_{ij}) appears in the model because it reflects the units assigned to levels of A. On the other hand, there is no block × B term because it is not an experimental unit with respect to any treatment factor or effect. Note the difference between this model and the split-block model, where block × B does appear in the model because it is the experimental unit for levels of B. *It is essential to maintain the relationship between the design and the way in which the* experiment design (E_{ijk}) component *is written in order for the model to be appropriate.*

This section has focused on a particular set of layouts for the 2 × 2 factorial. The main lesson, however, is that you can apply the methods of this section to any, arbitrarily complex factorial study. The basic steps are as follows:

1. Visualize the layout, as shown by example in Figures 5.2 through 5.8.
2. List the blocking criteria, if any.
3. List the treatment factor and all possible interactions.
4. Identify the experimental unit with respect to each treatment main effect and interaction.
5. Determine the fixed effects component of the model from step 3, and from step 2 for those blocking criteria that imply fixed effects.
6. Determine the random effects component of the model from step 4 (and from step 2 for random blocks). In general, there will be one random effect per experimental unit size.
7. If there are sampling units within the smallest experimental unit (e.g., if class is the experimental unit but measurements are taken on individual students within the class), then residual error corresponds to sampling unit error. Otherwise, residual error corresponds to the smallest experimental unit error and is not mentioned explicitly in the RANDOM statement.

Table 5.5 shows the CLASS, MODEL, and RANDOM statements to be used with PROC MIXED for each of the seven layouts described in Figures 5.2 through 5.8. Note that all the blocking criteria appear in the RANDOM statements. This follows the convention discussed in Chapter 2: in most cases, blocks are more naturally viewed as random effects. Note, however, that this is not a one-size-fits-all rule. There are cases in which the blocking criteria may be more appropriately regarded as fixed. Also, as discussed in Chapter 2, in the case of balanced experiments—i.e., complete block designs with no missing data—you get identical inference for treatment effects (any test, estimate, or contrast defined on A or B) regardless of whether blocks are defined as fixed or random. This is NOT the case with incomplete blocks, as in the example discussed in Section 5.7. In such cases, defining blocks as random enables you to recover intra-block information. Provided that the blocks satisfy assumptions discussed in Chapter 2, recovery of intra-block information yields more efficient inference on treatment effects.

Table 5.5: CLASS, MODEL, and RANDOM Statements for Each Design Shown in Figures 5.2 through 5.8

Design	SAS PROC MIXED—CLASS, MODEL, and RANDOM Statements
CRD (Figure 5.2)	`class a b;` `model y = a b a*b;`

RCB (Figure 5.3)	`class block a b;`
	`model y = a b a*b;`
	`random block;`

Latin square (Figure 5.4)	`class row col a b;`
	`model y = a b a*b;`
	`random row col;`

Split-plot CR (Figure 5.5)	`class eu a b;`
	`model y = a b a*b;`
	`random eu(a);`

Split-plot RCB (Figure 5.6)	`class block a b;`
	`model y = a b a*b;`
	`random block block*a;`

Split block (Figure 5.7)	`class block a b;`
	`model y = a b a*b;`
	`random block block*a block*b;`

Split-plot LS (Figure 5.8)	`class row col a b;`
	`model y = a b a*b;`
	`random row col row*col*a;`

5.3 Inference with Factorial Treatment Designs with Various Mixed Models

The basic elements of inference for factorial treatment designs – main effects, simple effects, and interaction – were introduced in Chapter 3. Their terms were defined both in terms of μ_{ij}, the treatment combination mean, and $\mu + \alpha_i + \beta_j + \alpha\beta_{ij}$, the effects model. In addition, syntax was presented for estimating these effects using the ESTIMATE, LSMEANS, and LSMESTIMATE statements. This section covers two aspects of inference not covered in Chapter 3: the impact of experiment design on standard errors – and hence test statistics – and denominator degrees of freedom.

5.3.1 Standard Errors

As shown in Section 5.2, the fixed effect component of the model, which describes the treatments, in either its mean form or effects form, is the same for all factorial treatment structures. However, the random effect component of the model depends on the layout of the design and the underlying variability among the various experimental units. This, in turn, affects standard errors of estimates of various effects. You use the standard errors of simple and main effects, interactions and contrasts, to construct their confidence intervals and test statistics. This section shows how standard errors are derived from the experiment design and the assumed sources of variation.

You can apply the methods shown in this section to any mixed model that follows from layouts such as those shown in Figures 5.2 through 5.8. The specific results vary depending on the random effects implied by the layout. Space does not permit showing the results for all possible layouts. This section focuses on the split plot with randomized block whole plot shown in Figure 5.6. It is the simplest layout with the full array of issues that arise in mixed model analysis. While the results shown in this section specifically apply to the model that follows from Figure 5.6, the methods shown here can be adapted to any layout.

As shown in Section 5.2, you can write a mixed model for Figure 5.6 in two forms:

The mean model is as follows:

$$y_{ijk} = \mu_{ij} + r_k + w_{ik} + e_{ijk}$$

The effects model is as follows:

$$y_{ijk} = \mu + \alpha_i + \beta_j + \alpha\beta_{ij} + r_k + w_{ik} + e_{ijk}$$

The effects model may be reordered as $y_{ijk} = \mu + r_k + \alpha_i + w_{ik} + \beta_j + \alpha\beta_{ij} + e_{ijk}$—that is, listing the "whole-plot" elements first, then the split-plot elements. In this section, assume that the block effects, r_k, the whole-plot error effects, w_{ik}, and the split-plot error effects, e_{ijk}, are all random effects, with the following assumptions:

- All random effects, r_k, w_{ik}, and e_{ijk} are mutually independent.
- The block effects are assumed *iid* $N(0, \sigma_R^2)$.
- The whole-plot error effects are assumed *iid* $N(0, \sigma_W^2)$.
- The split-plot error effects are assumed *iid* $N(0, \sigma^2)$.

Under these assumptions, the standard errors of the estimates of the various terms of interest can be obtained. Recall that the *standard error* is the *estimate* of the square root of the variance of the estimate of the term of interest. Hence, there are four steps in determining the standard error:

- Write the estimate of the term of interest (simple or main effect, interaction or contrast).
- Derive the variance of the estimate from step 1. This will be a function of the variances of the random model effects (σ_R^2, σ_W^2, and σ^2 in this example), called the variance components.
- Determine the estimates of the variance components σ_R^2, σ_W^2, and σ^2.
- Substitute the estimated variance components into the expression in step 2 and take the square root.

Note that the last step treats the estimated variance components as if they were known. It does not account for uncertainty associated with variance estimation. As a result, standard errors produced this way tend to be too small. Later in this chapter, and in Chapter 8, we discuss adjustments to the standard errors, e.g. an adjustment due to Kenward and Roger (1997, 2009), and the associated degrees of freedom used to construct confidence intervals and test statistics.

Nonetheless, these four steps are useful guides to see how the experiment design affects inferential statistics. First, consider steps 1 and 2.

5.3.2 Variance of Treatment Mean and Difference Estimates

For treatment combination means, μ_{ij}, the best estimate is the following:

$$\hat{\mu}_{ij} = (1/r)\sum_k y_{ijk} = \bar{y}_{ij}$$

In model terms, the variance of the estimate is as follows:

$$\begin{aligned}
\text{Var}[\bar{y}_{ij}] &= \text{Var}\left[\left(\tfrac{1}{r}\right)\sum_k \mu_{ij} + r_k + w_{ik} + e_{ijk}\right] \\
&= \left(\tfrac{1}{r}\right)^2 \sum_k \text{Var}[r_k + w_{ik} + e_{ijk}] \\
&= \left(\tfrac{1}{r}\right)^2 \sum_k [\sigma_R^2 + \sigma_W^2 + \sigma^2] = \frac{\sigma_R^2 + \sigma_W^2 + \sigma^2}{r}
\end{aligned}$$

Similar derivations yield

$$\text{Var}\left[\bar{y}_{i..}\right] = \frac{b\left(\sigma_R^2 + \sigma_W^2\right) + \sigma^2}{br}$$

for the estimated marginal mean of A_i;

$$\text{Var}\left[\bar{y}_{.j.}\right] = \frac{b\sigma_R^2 + \sigma_W^2 + \sigma^2}{br}$$

for the estimated marginal mean of B_j.

For the main effect of A, e.g., $\bar{\mu}_{1.} - \bar{\mu}_{2.}$, the variance of the estimate is as follows:

$$\text{Var}\left[\bar{y}_{1..} - \bar{y}_{2..}\right] = \text{Var}\left[\frac{1}{br}\sum_{j,k}\left(y_{1jk} - y_{2jk}\right)\right]$$

$$= \left(\frac{1}{br}\right)^2 \text{Var}\left[\sum_{j,k}\left(\mu_{1j} + r_k + w_{1k} + e_{1jk}\right) - \left(\mu_{2j} + r_k + w_{2k} + e_{2jk}\right)\right]$$

$$= \left(\frac{1}{br}\right)^2 \text{Var}\left[\sum_{j,k}\left(\mu_{1j} - \mu_{2j} + w_{1k} - w_{2k} + e_{1jk} - e_{2jk}\right)\right]$$

$$= \left(\frac{1}{br}\right)^2 \text{Var}\left[b\sum_{k}\left(w_{1k} - w_{2k}\right) + \sum_{j,k}\left(e_{ijk} - e_{2ijk}\right)\right]$$

$$= \left(\frac{1}{br}\right)^2 \left(2b^2 r\sigma_W^2 + 2br\sigma^2\right)$$

$$= \frac{2\left(b\sigma_W^2 + \sigma^2\right)}{br}$$

Similar derivation yields the variance of the main effect of B, for example, $\bar{\mu}_{.1} - \bar{\mu}_{.2}$:

$$\text{Var}\left[\bar{y}_{.1.} - \bar{y}_{.2.}\right] = \text{Var}\left[\left(\frac{1}{ar}\right)\sum_{i,k}\left(y_{i1k} - y_{i2k}\right)\right]$$

$$= \left(\frac{1}{ar}\right)^2 \text{Var}\left[\sum_{i,k}\left(\mu_{i1} + r_k + w_{ik} + e_{i1k} - \mu_{i2} - r_k - w_{ik} - e_{i2k}\right)\right]$$

$$= \left(\frac{1}{ar}\right)^2 \text{Var}\left[\sum_{i,k}\left(e_{i1k} - e_{i2k}\right)\right]$$

$$= \frac{2\sigma^2}{ar}$$

Note that the whole-plot variance, σ_W^2, appears in the main effect of A but not in the main effect of B. This is because you estimate A differences across whole plots, whereas you estimate B differences within whole plots, so the whole-plot variation is not part of the estimate.

Similar derivations yield the variances of simple effect estimators. For the simple effect of A given B, e.g., $\mu_{11} - \mu_{21}$, the variance of the estimator is the following:

$$
\begin{aligned}
\mathrm{Var}\left[\bar{y}_{11\cdot} - \bar{y}_{21\cdot}\right] &= \mathrm{Var}\left[\left(\frac{1}{r}\right)\sum_k\left(y_{11k} - y_{21k}\right)\right] \\
&= \left(\frac{1}{r}\right)^2 \mathrm{Var}\left[\sum_k\left(\mu_{11} + r_k + w_{1k} + e_{11k} - \mu_{21} - r_k - w_{2k} - e_{21k}\right)\right] \\
&= \left(\frac{1}{r}\right)^2 \mathrm{Var}\left[\sum_k\left(w_{1k} - w_{2k}\right) + \sum_k\left(e_{11k} - e_{21k}\right)\right] \\
&= \frac{2\left(\sigma_W^2 + \sigma^2\right)}{r}
\end{aligned}
$$

On the other hand, the simple effect of B given A, e.g., $\mu_{11} - \mu_{12}$, yields a different variance of the estimate:

$$
\begin{aligned}
\mathrm{Var}\left[\bar{y}_{11\cdot} - \bar{y}_{12\cdot}\right] &= \mathrm{Var}\left[\left(\frac{1}{r}\right)\sum_k\left(y_{11k} - y_{12k}\right)\right] \\
&= \left(\frac{1}{r}\right)^2 \mathrm{Var}\left[\sum_k\left(\mu_{11} + r_k + w_{1k} + e_{11k} - \mu_{12} - r_k - w_{1k} - e_{12k}\right)\right] \\
&= \left(\frac{1}{r}\right)^2 \mathrm{Var}\left[\sum_k\left(e_{11k} - e_{12k}\right)\right] \\
&= \frac{2\sigma^2}{r}
\end{aligned}
$$

Simple effects of A given B must be estimated from differences between observations in different whole plots, whereas B given A effects can be estimated from differences between observations that are entirely within the same whole plot.

5.3.3 Completing the Standard Error: Variance Component Estimates and Degrees of Freedom

From the variance of the treatment mean, difference, or contrast, you can do steps 3 and 4 described above—that is, obtain the standard error by substituting the estimates of the variance components into the variance and taking the square root. Applying these results enables *inference* in the form of either *confidence interval estimation* or *hypothesis testing*.

For *confidence intervals*, the general formula for linear combinations of the treatment combination means is *estimate* ± t_v × *standard error(estimate)*.

For *hypothesis testing*, the general approach for linear combinations of treatment means is via the following ratio:

$$
\frac{\text{estimate}}{\text{std error(estimate)}}
$$

These ratios form *t* statistics with ν degrees of freedom. Alternatively, you can square these ratios to form the *F* statistic with 1 degree of freedom in the numerator and ν denominator degrees of freedom. In both PROC GLIMMIX and PROC MIXED, the ESTIMATE statement computes the *t* statistic as well as the standard error; the CONTRAST statement computes only the *F* statistic. You can also use the CONTRAST statement to compute the general form of the *F* statistic with *k* numerator degrees of freedom. In the 2 × 2 factorial considered in this section, such hypotheses do not typically arise. However, Section 5.4 presents an example with more than two levels of a factor. The *F* statistic with *k* numerator and ν denominator degrees of freedom will be discussed in greater detail.

To obtain confidence intervals or test hypotheses, you need estimates of the components of variance. The default method for both PROC GLIMMIX and PROC MIXED is *restricted maximum likelihood* (also called *residual maximum likelihood,* hereafter referred to by its commonly used acronym, *REML*), described in Appendix A. PROC MIXED also has an option that enables you to compute estimates based on the *analysis of variance* (ANOVA). For the purpose of this discussion, ANOVA-based estimates are easier to describe in terms of their impact on standard errors and degrees of freedom. For designs described in this chapter that are *balanced* (equal number of observations per A × B × block combination), REML and ANOVA variance component estimates are identical.

For the example design based on the layout in Figure 5.5, the analysis of variance is shown in Table 5.6.

Table 5.6 Analysis of Variance for Layout in Figure 5.5

Source of Variation	df	Expected Mean Square
BLOCK	3	
A	1	$\sigma^2 + 2\sigma_W^2 + \phi_A$
BLOCK × A (whole-plot error)	3	$\sigma^2 + 2\sigma_W^2$
B	1	$\sigma^2 + \phi_B$
A × B	1	$\sigma^2 + \phi_{A*B}$
Split-plot error	6	σ^2

In Table 5.6, the ϕ are quadratic expressions for the fixed effects and have no bearing on variance component estimation. Littell et al. (2002) discuss them in detail. Also, in this discussion, the expected mean square for BLOCK is not shown, as the variance for BLOCK does not play a role in estimates or tests of treatment differences. The whole-plot and split-plot error variance components can be estimated as follows:

$$\hat{\sigma}^2 = \text{MS(Split-Plot Error), or MS(SPE) for convenience}$$

$$\hat{\sigma}_W^2 = 1/2\left(\text{MS(BLOCK} \times \text{A)} - \text{MS(SPE)}\right)$$

For a whole-plot main effect mean, $\bar{\mu}_{i\bullet}$, the variance is $(1/8)[2\sigma_W^2 + \sigma^2]$, which is estimated as $(1/8)\,\text{MS[BLOCK} \times \text{A]}$. Thus, the degrees of freedom for a confidence interval correspond to the degrees of freedom for BLOCK × A, $v = 3$.

For a split-plot main effect difference, $\mu_{\bullet 1} - \mu_{\bullet 2}$, the variance is $(1/4)\sigma^2$, which is estimated by $(1/4)\text{MS(SPE)}$. Thus, the degrees of freedom for the confidence interval correspond to the degrees of freedom for split-plot error, $v = 6$.

As a final example, consider the simple effect difference $\mu_{11} - \mu_{21}$, whose variance is $1/2[\sigma_W^2 + \sigma^2]$. The linear combination $\sigma_W^2 + \sigma^2$ cannot be estimated by a single mean square. Instead, it is estimated by the following:

$$\hat{\sigma}_W^2 + \hat{\sigma}^2 = \text{MS(SPE)} + \frac{1}{2}\left(\text{MS(BLOCK} \times \text{A)} - \text{MS(SPE)}\right)$$

$$= \frac{1}{2}\text{MS(SPE)} + \frac{1}{2}\text{MS(BLOCK} \times \text{A)}$$

The degrees of freedom can be approximated using Satterthwaite's formula. Let $\text{MS} = a_1\text{MS}_1 + \ldots + a_k\text{MS}_k$. The approximate degrees of freedom for MS are as follows:

$$v \cong \frac{(MS)^2}{\dfrac{(a_1 MS_1)^2}{df_1} + \cdots + \dfrac{(a_k MS_k)^2}{df_k}}$$

Thus, the approximate degrees of freedom for the simple effect of A for a given B are the following:

$$v \cong \frac{\left(\frac{1}{2}\text{MS(SPE)} + \frac{1}{2}\text{MS(BLOCK} \times \text{A)}\right)^2}{\dfrac{\left(\frac{1}{2}\text{MS(SPE)}\right)^2}{6} + \dfrac{\left(\frac{1}{2}\text{MS(BLOCK} \times \text{A)}\right)^2}{3}}$$

5.4 A Split-Plot Semiconductor Experiment: An Example

This example, which appeared in Littell et al. (1991, 1996, and 2002), is an experiment conducted in a semiconductor plant to study the effect of several modes of a process condition (ET) on resistance in computer chips. Twelve silicon wafers (WAFER) were drawn from a lot, and three wafers were randomly assigned to four modes of ET. Resistance in the chips was measured on chips at four different positions (POS) on each wafer after processing. The measurement was recorded as the variable RESISTANCE. The data are given as "Semiconductor Split-Plot Experiment."

The semiconductor experiment consists of two factors, ET and POS. The experimental unit with respect to ET is the wafer. The experimental unit with respect to POS is the individual chip, a subdivision of the wafer. Thus, the wafer is the whole-plot unit, and the chip is the split-plot unit.

The layout of this experiment is similar to that of Figure 5.5, the only difference being the number of levels per factor. Thus, following the table in Figure 5.5.C, a model for this experiment is

$$y_{ijk} = \mu + \alpha_i + w_{ik} + \beta_j + \alpha\beta_{ij} + e_{ijk}$$

where the following definitions apply:

- $\mu_{ij} = \mu + \alpha_i + \beta_j + \alpha\beta_{ij}$ is the mean of the ij^{th} ET × POS combination, and α_i, β_j, and $\alpha\beta_{ij}$ are the ET, POS, and ET × POS effects, respectively.

- w_{ik} is the whole-plot error effect, assumed *iid* $N(0, \sigma_W^2)$.

- e_{ijk} is the split-plot error effect, assumed *iid* $N(0, \sigma^2)$.

- w_{ik} and e_{ijk} are assumed to be independent of one another.

Littell et al. (1991) mention that correlation among the chips may actually depend on their proximity on the wafer, thus violating the assumption of independence among split-plot errors. If so, the data may be analyzed by revising the model to assume spatially dependent correlated errors. This is discussed in Chapter 8, "Analysis of Repeated Measures Data."

5.4.1 Tests of Interest in the Semiconductor Experiment

Several hypotheses are potentially of interest in this experiment. These include the following:

- No ET × POS interaction: H_0: $\mu_{ij} = \mu_{ij'}$ for all i, given $j \neq j'$; i.e., all $\alpha\beta_{ij} = 0$.

- All ET main effect means equal: H_0: $\mu_{1.} = \mu_{2.} = ... = \mu_{4.}$.

- All POS main effect means equal: H_0: $\mu_{.1} = \mu_{.2} = ... = \mu_{.4}$.

- Simple effect comparisons among specific ET levels for a given POS, e.g., H_0: $\mu_{11} - \mu_{21} = 0$.

- Simple effect comparisons among specific positions for a given ET level, e.g., H_0: $\mu_{11} - \mu_{12} = 0$.

- Contrasts, e.g., average of ET1 and ET2 versus average of ET3 and ET4 given POS2, H_0: $\frac{1}{2} (\mu_{12} + \mu_{22}) - \frac{1}{2} (\mu_{32} + \mu_{42}) = 0$.

The first three hypotheses are tested using F ratios from the analysis of variance, shown in Table 5.7.

Table 5.7: Analysis of Variance for Semiconductor Example

Source of Variation	*df*	Expected Mean Square
ET	3	$\sigma^2 + 4\sigma_W^2 + \phi_{ET}$
WAFER(ET) (whole-plot error)	8	$\sigma^2 + 4\sigma_W^2$
POS	3	$\sigma^2 + \phi_{POS}$
ET × POS	9	$\sigma^2 + \phi_{ET*POS}$
Split-plot error (SPE)	24	σ^2

The variance components can be estimated as the following:

$$\hat{\sigma}^2 = MS(SPE)$$

$$\hat{\sigma}_W^2 = 1/4 \left(MS[WAFER(ET)] - MS(SPE) \right)$$

From the ANOVA table for the semiconductor experiment, the required test statistics are as follows:

MS(ET) / MS[WAFER(ET)]	for the ET main effect
MS(POS) / MS(SPE)	for the POS main effect
MS(ET × POS) / MS(SPE)	for the ET × POS interaction

The remaining hypotheses are all single-degree-of-freedom contrasts. They can be tested using the methods shown in Section 5.3. The same degree-of-freedom issues discussed in Section 5.3.3 arise here. For example, the main effect comparison of ET1 versus ET2 can be tested using the following ratio:

$$t = \frac{\hat{\mu}_{1.} - \hat{\mu}_{2.}}{\sqrt{\frac{1}{12}\left(\hat{\sigma}^2 + 4\hat{\sigma}_w^2\right)}} = \frac{\hat{\mu}_{1.} - \hat{\mu}_{2.}}{\sqrt{\frac{1}{12}\text{MS}[\text{WAFER(ET)}]}}$$

Thus, the degrees of freedom for the t test correspond to the degrees of freedom for WAFER(ET), $\nu = 8$.

In many cases, the denominator term of the t statistic is a linear combination of mean squares. If so, the degrees of freedom for the t test must be approximated, e.g., using Satterthwaite's method. For example, the t-ratio for the test of ET1 and ET2 versus ET3 and ET4 in POS2 is as follows:

$$t = \frac{\hat{\mu}_{12} + \hat{\mu}_{22} - \hat{\mu}_{32} - \hat{\mu}_{42}}{\sqrt{\frac{4}{3}\left(\hat{\sigma}^2 + \hat{\sigma}_w^2\right)}}$$

The denominator $\hat{\sigma}^2 + \hat{\sigma}_w^2$ is estimated by MS(SPE) + (1/4){MS[WAFER(ET)] − MS(SPE)} = (1/4)MS[WAFER(ET)] + (3/4)MS(SPE). The Satterthwaite approximation yields

$$\nu \cong \frac{\left(\frac{3}{4}\text{MS}(\text{SPE}) + \frac{1}{4}\text{MS}[\text{WAFER(ET)}]\right)^2}{\dfrac{\left(\frac{3}{4}\text{MS}(\text{SPE})\right)^2}{24} + \dfrac{\left(\frac{1}{4}\text{MS}[\text{WAFER(ET)}]\right)^2}{8}}$$

Alternatively, the single-degree-of-freedom hypotheses can be tested by using F-ratios of the following form:

$$F = t^2 = \frac{\text{estimate}^2}{\text{std err}^2} = \frac{\text{MS}(\text{contrast})}{\text{MS}(\text{relevant error})}$$

Here, MS(relevant error) is the appropriate mean square or linear combination of mean squares. Thus, the F-ratio for the main effect of ET1 versus ET2 is as follows:

$$F = \frac{\text{MS}(\text{ET1 versus ET2})}{\text{MS}(\text{WAFER(ET)})}$$

The numerator has one degree of freedom and the denominator has $\nu = 8$, corresponding to the degrees of freedom for WAFER(ET). For the test of ET1 and ET2 versus ET3 and ET4 in POS2, the F-ratio is the following:

$$F = \frac{\text{MS}(\text{ET1, ET2 versus ET3, ET4 given POS2})}{\frac{1}{4}\text{MS}[\text{WAFER(ET)}] + \frac{3}{4}\text{MS}(\text{SPE})}$$

There is one degree of freedom for the numerator. The denominator degrees of freedom are determined from the Satterthwaite approximation for the linear combination of MS[WAFER(ET)] and MS(SPE).

5.4.2 Matrix Generalization of Mixed Model *F* Tests

All of the preceding F-ratios, for the overall main effects, interactions, and single-degree-of- freedom tests, are special cases of a general result for mixed models. In general, you can test hypotheses with one or more degrees of freedom by defining a **K** matrix consisting of any number of *independent* **k** vectors.

Common examples of multiple-degree-of-freedom hypotheses are overall main effect or interaction terms in the analysis of variance. For example, consider the main effect of ET.

The overall hypothesis of no ET main effect is H_0: $\mu_{1.} = \mu_{2.} = \mu_{3.} = \mu_{4.}$. This can be expressed in terms of a **K** matrix several ways. Because there are 4 levels of ET, there are 3 degrees of freedom for the ET main effect. Therefore, **K** consists of 3 independent **k** vectors, one per degree of freedom. *Any set of 3 comparisons such that H_0 is true* can be used to form **K**. For example,

$$\mathbf{K}' = \frac{1}{4}\begin{bmatrix} 1 & 1 & 1 & 1 & -1 & -1 & -1 & -1 & 0 & 0 & 0 & 0 & 0 & 0 & 0 & 0 \\ 1 & 1 & 1 & 1 & 0 & 0 & 0 & 0 & -1 & -1 & -1 & -1 & 0 & 0 & 0 & 0 \\ 1 & 1 & 1 & 1 & 0 & 0 & 0 & 0 & 0 & 0 & 0 & 0 & -1 & -1 & -1 & -1 \end{bmatrix}$$

This defines the comparisons $\mu_{1.} = \mu_{2.}$, $\mu_{1.} = \mu_{3.}$, and $\mu_{1.} = \mu_{4.}$. If all three equalities hold, then $\mu_{1.} = \mu_{2.} = \mu_{3.} = \mu_{4.}$, i.e., H_0 is true. On the other hand, see the following:

$$\mathbf{K}' = \begin{bmatrix} 1 & 1 & 1 & 1 & -1 & -1 & -1 & -1 & 0 & 0 & 0 & 0 & 0 & 0 & 0 & 0 \\ 1 & 1 & 1 & 1 & 1 & 1 & 1 & 1 & -2 & -2 & -2 & 0 & 0 & 0 & 0 & 0 \\ 1 & 1 & 1 & 1 & 1 & 1 & 1 & 1 & 1 & 1 & 1 & -3 & -3 & -3 & -3 & -3 \end{bmatrix}$$

This defines the comparisons:

$$\mu_{1.} = \mu_{2.}$$

$$1/2\left(\mu_{1.} + \mu_{2.}\right) = \mu_{3.}$$

$$1/3\left(\mu_{1.} + \mu_{2.} + \mu_{3.}\right) = \mu_{4.}$$

If these three equalities hold, they *also* guarantee that H_0: $\mu_{1.} = \mu_{2.} = \mu_{3.} = \mu_{4.}$ is true. For the main effect of ET, **K** can be composed of any three comparisons that imply $\mu_{1.} = \mu_{2.} = \mu_{3.} = \mu_{4.}$. For any **K** so constructed, the resulting *F* statistic, discussed below, will be the same.

For any linear combination **K'μ** (or estimable linear combination of the fixed effects μ, α, β, and αβ),

$$\left(\mathbf{K}'\hat{\boldsymbol{\mu}}\right)'\left[\mathbf{K}'\left(\mathbf{X}'\mathbf{V}^{-1}\mathbf{X}\right)^{-1}\mathbf{K}\right]^{-1}\left(\mathbf{K}'\hat{\boldsymbol{\mu}}\right)/\text{rank}\left(\mathbf{K}\right)$$

has an approximate chi-square distribution with rank(**K**) degrees of freedom *when V is known*. When **V** is unknown and the components of **V** are estimated (by far the more common case),

$$\left(\mathbf{K}'\hat{\boldsymbol{\mu}}\right)'\left[\mathbf{K}'\left(\mathbf{X}'\hat{\mathbf{V}}^{-1}\mathbf{X}\right)^{-1}\mathbf{K}\right]^{-1}\left(\mathbf{K}'\hat{\boldsymbol{\mu}}\right)/\text{rank}\left(\mathbf{K}\right)$$

has an approximate *F* distribution, whose numerator degrees of freedom are rank(**K**) and whose denominator degrees of freedom correspond to the degrees of freedom required to estimate **K'[X'V⁻¹X]⁻¹K**. For balanced split-plot experiments, **K'[X'V⁻¹X]⁻¹K** is estimated from either a single mean square or a linear combination of mean squares from the analysis of variance.

For example, for the main effect comparison of ET1 versus ET2,

$$\mathbf{K}' = \frac{1}{4}\begin{bmatrix} 1 & 1 & 1 & 1 & -1 & -1 & -1 & -1 & 0 & 0 & 0 & 0 & 0 & 0 & 0 & 0 \end{bmatrix}$$

$$\mathbf{K}'\left(\mathbf{X}'\hat{\mathbf{V}}^{-1}\mathbf{X}\right)^{-1}\mathbf{K} \propto \text{MS}[\text{WAFER(ET)}]$$

For the comparison of ET1 and ET2 versus ET3 and ET4 in POS2,

$$\mathbf{K}' = \frac{1}{2}\begin{bmatrix} 0 & 0 & 0 & 0 & 1 & 1 & -1 & -1 & 0 & 0 & 0 & 0 & 0 & 0 & 0 & 0 \end{bmatrix}$$

$$\mathbf{K}'\left(\mathbf{X}'\hat{\mathbf{V}}^{-1}\mathbf{X}\right)^{-1}\mathbf{K} \propto \frac{1}{4}\mathrm{MS}[\mathrm{WAFER(ET)}] + \frac{3}{4}\mathrm{MS(SPE)}$$

The *F*-ratio for other main effects and interactions, e.g., POS and ET × POS, can be constructed from appropriately defined **K** using the same logic as for ET. The numerator degrees of freedom for the resulting *F* test is the rank of **K**. The denominator degrees of freedom is determined by the ANOVA mean square implied by $\mathbf{K}'[\mathbf{X}'\mathbf{V}^{-1}\mathbf{X}]^{-1}\mathbf{K}$. The general form of the Satterthwaite approximation, from Giesbrecht and Burns (1985), is

$$\nu = \frac{2\mathrm{E}\left[\mathbf{K}'\left(\mathbf{X}'\mathbf{V}^{-1}\mathbf{X}\right)^{-}\mathbf{K}\right]^2}{\mathrm{Var}\left[\mathbf{K}'\left(\mathbf{X}'\mathbf{V}^{-1}\mathbf{X}\right)^{-}\mathbf{K}\right]}$$

Appendix A contains additional details; evaluation of the denominator requires further approximation beyond the scope of this discussion. Table 5.8 shows degree of freedom results for the semiconductor example.

Table 5.8: Degrees of Freedom for Semiconductor Example

Effect Tested	Numerator *df* (Rank)	Denominator *df* $\mathbf{K}'[\mathbf{X}'\mathbf{V}^{-1}\mathbf{X}]^{-1}\mathbf{K}$ depends on
ET	3	MS[WAFER(ET)]
POS	3	MS(SPE)
ET × POS	9	MS(SPE)

5.4.3 PROC GLIMMIX Analysis of Semiconductor Data

This section shows you how to use PROC GLIMMIX to compute the analysis of the semiconductor experiment. Three basic procedures are covered:

- Fitting the basic model
- Estimating the treatment means and differences
- Testing the hypotheses relevant to these data

Subsequent sections present examples with additional contrast and mean comparison options relevant to those applications, but not to the semiconductor data.

Program

Following Table 5.5 and noting that the layout for the semiconductor experiment is a split-plot structure with whole plots conducted in a completely randomized design (Figure 5.5), you can fit the model for these data with the PROC GLIMMIX statements in Program 5.1.

Program 5.1

```
proc glimmix data=ex_5_4;
   class et wafer position;
   model resistance=et position et*position;
   random et / subject=wafer;
run;
```

The RANDOM statement shown above is equivalent to the more obvious form, RANDOM WAFER(ET), but the form shown above is more computationally efficient.

Results

Output 5.1 shows the results.

Output 5.1: Basic PROC GLIMMIX Model Fitting Output for Semiconductor Data

Covariance Parameter Estimates			
Cov Parm	Subject	Estimate	Standard Error
et	wafer	0.1058	0.06727
Residual		0.1111	0.03209

Type III Tests of Fixed Effects				
Effect	Num DF	Den DF	F Value	Pr > F
et	3	8	1.94	0.2015
position	3	24	3.39	0.0345
et*position	9	24	0.81	0.6125

Interpretation

The main items of information are as follows:

- The estimates of σ^2 and σ_w^2, displayed in the "Covariance Parameter Estimates" table as "Residual" and "et (subject=wafer)" respectively. The default variance component estimation procedure used by PROC GLIMMIX is the REML algorithm. For balanced experiments, REML estimates are identical to the estimates obtained from the expected mean squares discussed in Section 5.3.1, provided all estimates are positive.

- The F tests for the ET and POS main effects and the ET×POS interaction, given under "Tests of Fixed Effects." The F statistics, numerator, and denominator degrees of freedom, and p-values (column "Pr > F") are identical to those that you would obtain from computing the analysis of variance (compare to Output 5.2).

Program

You can compute the analysis of variance using PROC MIXED by using the METHOD=TYPE3 option. Modify Program 5.1 as shown below in Program 5.2.

Program 5.2

```
proc mixed data=ex_5_4 method=type3;
   class et wafer position;
   model resistance=et position et*position;
   random wafer(et);
run;
```

Notice that METHOD=TYPE3 cannot be used with a RANDOM statement that has a SUBJECT= option. This produces Output 5.2.

Output 5.2: Analysis of Variance Using PROC MIXED for Semiconductor Data

Type 3 Analysis of Variance								
Source	DF	Sum of Squares	Mean Square	Expected Mean Square	Error Term	Error DF	F Value	Pr > F
et	3	3.112158	1.037386	Var(Residual) + 4 Var(wafer(et)) + Q(et,et*position)	MS(wafer(et))	8	1.94	0.2015
position	3	1.128892	0.376297	Var(Residual) + Q(position,et*position)	MS(Residual)	24	3.39	0.0345
et*position	9	0.809475	0.089942	Var(Residual) + Q(et*position)	MS(Residual)	24	0.81	0.6125
wafer(et)	8	4.274483	0.534310	Var(Residual) + 4 Var(wafer(et))	MS(Residual)	24	4.81	0.0013
Residual	24	2.667583	0.111149	Var(Residual)	.	.	.	.

In addition to the F values for the tests of ET and POSITION main effects and ET × POSITION interaction, the output also includes the sum of squares and mean squares, the expected mean squares (as previously described in Table 5.7), and the error terms for each test, as described in Table 5.8. This output also gives you an F statistic for the test of H_0: σ_w^2

= 0 (F = 5.81 for the wafer(et) effect with p-value of 0.0013). Usually in a split-plot experiment you assume that σ_w^2 is nonzero by the nature of the design, and this test is therefore of no interest. However, it is a valid test in case you do want to test σ_w^2.

Visualization of Treatment Means

As introduced in Chapter 3, you can use the PLOT=MEANPLOT option to obtain an interaction plot, enabling you to visualize the ET and POSITION effects on RESISTANCE. Add the following statement to the PROC GLIMMIX Program 5.1 shown above.

```
lsmeans et*position / plot=meanplot(sliceby=position join);
```

Figure 5.9 shows the resulting interaction plot.

Figure 5.9: Interaction Plot for Semiconductor Split Plot Data

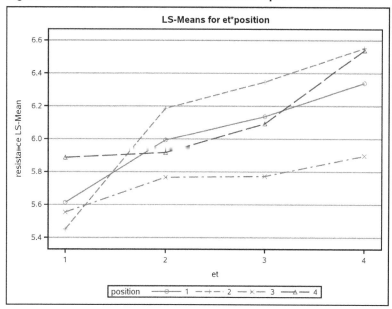

Interpretation

You can see visual evidence of a possible ET × POSITION interaction involving ET 1 and 2 only. That is, the increase in resistance between ET 1 and 2 at POSITION 2 appears to be much greater than at the other positions, especially POSITION 4. On the other hand, differences in ET 2, 3, and 4 means appear to be similar for all positions, with the possible exception of the ET 3 versus ET 4 difference at POSITION 4. These suggest specific contrasts one could use to decompose the overall test of interaction, shown above in Output 5.1. Depending on the results of the tests of interaction contrasts, one can then decide what main effects or simple effects it makes sense to test or estimate, following the strategy given in Chapter 3, Section 3.5.

Formal Decomposition of the ET × POSITION Interaction

The overall test of ET*POSITION gave an F value of 0.81 and p > 0.60. This would appear to suggest that the interaction is negligible. However, the overall test has 9 numerator degrees of freedom. It is possible that there may be single-degree of freedom aspects of the interaction that are not negligible. The interaction plot in Figure 5.9 contains hints that this might be the case. You can test this formally be decomposing the ET × POSITION interaction effect into components of potential interest. Given the visualization as discussed above, a possible decomposition is as follows:

- Is there an ET*POSITION interaction involving ET 1 and 2 and POSITION 2 and 4? Formally, test $H_0 : \mu_{12} - \mu_{22} = \mu_{14} - \mu_{24}$ or equivalently $H_0 : \alpha\beta_{12} - \alpha\beta_{22} - \alpha\beta_{14} + \alpha\beta_{24} = 0$.

- Is the interaction involving ET 1 and 2 and POSITION 1 and 3 negligible, as it appears to be? Formally, test $H_0 : \mu_{11} - \mu_{21} - \mu_{13} + \mu_{23} = 0$.

- Assuming the ET 1 versus 2 × POSITION 1 versus 3 interaction is negligible, is there an interaction involving ET 1 and 2 and POSITION 4 versus the average of positions 1 and 3? Formally, test
  $H_0 : (1/2)\left[\mu_{11} + \mu_{13} - (\mu_{21} + \mu_{23})\right] - (\mu_{14} - \mu_{24}) = 0$, or equivalently, $H_0 : \mu_{11} - \mu_{21} + \mu_{13} - \mu_{23} - 2\mu_{14} + 2\mu_{24} = 0$.

- Is the interaction involving ET 3 and 4 and POSITIONs 1, 2, and 3 negligible?

- Is there an interaction involving ET 3 and 4 and POSITION 4 versus the average of positions 1, 2, and 3?

- Is the difference between ET 2 and 3 consistent for all positions?

Program

This suggested decomposition defines the following contrast statements. Adding them to the PROC GLIMMIX statements shown earlier produces Program 5.3.

Program 5.3

```
proc glimmix data=ex_5_4;
   class et wafer position;
   model resistance=et position et*position;
   random et / subject=wafer;
contrast 'et1 v 2 x position 1 v 3'
   et*position 1 0 -1 0  -1 0 1 0  0 0 0 0  0 0 0 0;
contrast 'et1 v 2 x pos 1&3 v 4'
   et*position 1 0 1 -2  -1 0 -1 2  0 0 0 0  0 0 0 0;
contrast 'et1 v 2 x pos 2 v 4'
   et*position 0 1 0 -1  0 -1 0 1  0 0 0 0  0 0 0 0;
contrast 'et3 v 4 x pos 1v2v3'
   et*position 0 0 0 0  0 0 0 0  1 -1 0 0  -1 1 0 0,
   et*position 0 0 0 0  0 0 0 0  1 0 -1 0  -1 0 1 0;
contrast 'et3 v 4 x pos 4 v oth'
   et*position 0 0 0 0  0 0 0 0  1 1 1 -3  -1 -1 -1 3;
contrast 'et2 v 3 x all pos'
   et*position 0 0 0 0 1 -1 0 0  -1 1 0 0  0 0 0 0,
   et*position 0 0 0 0 1 0 -1 0  -1 0 1 0  0 0 0 0,
   et*position 0 0 0 0 1 0 0 -1  -1 0 0 1  0 0 0 0;
run;
```

Results

The results appear in Output 5.3.

Output 5.3: Contrasts to Decompose ET*POSITION Interaction

	Contrasts			
Label	Num DF	Den DF	F Value	Pr > F
et1 v 2 x position 1 v 3	1	24	0.19	0.6689
et1 v 2 x pos 1&3 v 4	1	24	0.64	0.4316
et1 v 2 x pos 2 v 4	1	24	3.37	0.0788
et3 v 4 x pos 1v2v3	2	24	0.03	0.9704
et3 v 4 x pos 4 v oth	1	24	0.73	0.4008
et2 v 3 x pos	3	24	0.08	0.9693

Interpretation

As expected, the contrasts for the suspected negligible interaction components, ET1 V 2 X POSITION 1 V 3, ET3 V 4 X POS 1V2V3, and ET2 V 3 X ALL POS all produce *F* values less than 1. Two of the visually suspicious components, ET1 V 2 X POS 1&3 V 4 and ET3 V 4 X POS 4 V OTH also show no evidence of statistical significance. Only the most obvious component visually, ET1 V 2 X POS 2 V 4, has a *p* value <0.10. Subject matter experts would need to help decide if that is noise (test enough hypotheses and you will eventually get a Type I error) or whether it is a genuinely consequential effect.

We will proceed with this example on the assumption that the one marginally significant interaction component is merely noise, hence interaction is negligible and it is appropriate to proceed with inference on main effects.

What this example illustrates, however, is that when you have many numerator degrees of freedom for interaction, the overall interaction test can easily mislead you. It is easy for a single degree of freedom interaction component to be averaged out by several negligible interaction components. It is important to inspect the interaction plot—looking at the data is an essential part of data analysis—and decompose the interaction effect into parts that have potential importance.

Inference on Main Effect Means

To obtain the marginal means $\mu_{i.}$ and $\mu_{.j}$, use the LSMEANS statement

```
lsmeans et position;
```

Place this line after the RANDOM statement in Program 5.3. This gives you the results shown in Output 5.4.

Output 5.4: Semiconductor Data Least Squares Means Using PROC GLIMMIX Default

				et Least Squares Means				
et	Estimate	Standard Error	DF	t Value	Pr > |t|	Alpha	Lower	Upper
1	5.6258	0.2110	8	26.66	<.0001	0.05	5.1392	6.1124
2	5.9658	0.2110	8	28.27	<.0001	0.05	5.4792	6.4524
3	6.0875	0.2110	8	28.85	<.0001	0.05	5.6009	6.5741
4	6.3325	0.2110	8	30.01	<.0001	0.05	5.8459	6.8191

				position Least Squares Means				
position	Estimate	Standard Error	DF	t Value	Pr > |t|	Alpha	Lower	Upper
1	6.0208	0.1345	24	44.78	<.0001	0.05	5.7433	6.2983
2	6.1342	0.1345	24	45.62	<.0001	0.05	5.8567	6.4117
3	5.7475	0.1345	24	42.75	<.0001	0.05	5.4700	6.0250
4	6.1092	0.1345	24	45.44	<.0001	0.05	5.8317	6.3867

The standard errors are obtained from the method presented in Section 5.4.1. For example, for the main effect mean of ET1, $\mu_{1.}$, the standard error is

$$\sqrt{\tfrac{1}{12}\left(\hat{\sigma}^2 + 4\hat{\sigma}_w^2\right)}$$

Using the variance component estimates given in Output 5.1, the standard error for $\mu_{1.}$ is

$$\sqrt{\tfrac{1}{12}[0.1111 + 4 \times 0.1058]} = 0.2110$$

The *t* ratios and their probabilities are obtained by the ratio of the estimate to the standard error, as given in Section 5.4.1. For example, the *t* ratio to test H_0: $\mu_{1.} = 0$ is

$$t = \frac{\overline{y}_{1..}}{\text{std err}(y_{1..})} = \frac{5.6258}{0.2110} = 26.66$$

Degrees of Freedom

PROC GLIMMIX and PROC MIXED have several options for denominator degrees of freedom. The default algorithm is described immediately below. With multilevel designs, you will often want to override the default. One especially useful option is the Satterthwaite procedure, described below, immediately after the description of the default degrees of freedom.

Default Degrees of Freedom

PROC GLIMMIX and PROC MIXED use containment as the default method for determining denominator degrees of freedom. For the *t* values for all least squares means, the containment method identifies the degrees of freedom for the random effect containing the effect of interest. If no random model effect contains the LSMEAN effect, then the residual degrees of freedom are used. Here, ET is contained within MS[WAFER(ET)], and therefore the degrees of freedom equal 8. POS is not contained in any random effect, so it has default denominator degrees of freedom of 24.

Override of the Default

Depending on the form of the standard error, the default may or may not be correct. For example, the standard error for the estimated ET mean is a function of the WAFER(ET) expected mean square *only*, so the default degrees of freedom are correct. However, from Section 5.4.1, the standard errors of the estimated POS mean involves a linear combination of the WAFER(ET) and residual expected mean squares.

For example, the variance of an estimated POS mean is $(1/12)(\sigma^2 + \sigma_W^2)$. The estimate of $\sigma^2 + \sigma_W^2$ is $(3/4)\text{MS[SPE]} + (1/4)\text{MS[WAFER(ET)]}$. Using Satterthwaite's procedure, the approximate degrees of freedom are as follows:

$$v = \frac{\left(\frac{3}{4}\text{MS(SPE)} + \frac{1}{4}\text{MS[WAFER(ET)]}\right)^2}{\dfrac{\left(\frac{3}{4}\text{MS(SPE)}\right)^2}{24} + \dfrac{\left(\frac{1}{4}\text{MS[WAFER(ET)]}\right)^2}{8}}$$

MS[WAFER(ET)] can be obtained from its expected mean square formula $\sigma^2 + 4\sigma_W^2$. Thus,

$$\text{MS[WAFER(ET)]} = 0.1111 + 4(0.1058) = 0.5343$$

Also, MS(SPE) = $\hat{\sigma}^2 = 0.1111$. The approximate degrees of freedom are expressed like so:

$$v = \frac{[(\frac{3}{4})0.1111 + (\frac{1}{4})0.5343]^2}{\dfrac{[(\frac{3}{4})(0.1111)]^2}{24} + \dfrac{[(\frac{1}{4})(0.5343)]^2}{8}} = 18.7$$

To get the correct degrees of freedom, you must override the default. PROC GLIMMIX and PROC MIXED provide several ways to override the default and obtain the correct degrees of freedom. By far the most straightforward way is the use of the DDFM option in the MODEL statement. For example, the MODEL statement

```
model y=resistance=et position et*position/ddfm=satterth;
```

causes the Satterthwaite approximation to be computed for every statistic throughout the procedure for which it is appropriate. In more advanced applications, the DDFM=KR2 option invokes an adjustment to standard errors and test statistics and the degree of freedom approximation due to Kenward and Roger (1997, 2009). In a balanced split plot such as this example, the DDFM=KR2 and DDFM=SATTERTH options yield identical results. However, with split plots that are unbalanced or have missing data and, more importantly, with repeated measures and spatial data, there are important differences and the DDFM=KR2 option is recommended. The DDFM=KR2 option is introduced in Section 5.7.2. However, Chapter 8 gives the most detailed presentation of the Kenward-Roger adjustment and its impact on data analysis.

Alternatively, you can directly specify denominator degrees of freedom. For example, you can use the statement

```
lsmeans position / df=18.7;
```

The results are given in Output 5.5.

Output 5.5: Least Squares Means for POS Using Specified Degrees of Freedom

position Least Squares Means					
position	Estimate	Standard Error	DF	t Value	Pr > |t|
1	6.0208	0.1345	18.68	44.78	<.0001
2	6.1342	0.1345	18.68	45.62	<.0001
3	5.7475	0.1345	18.68	42.75	<.0001
4	6.1092	0.1345	18.68	45.44	<.0001

Interpretation

The estimates, standard errors, and t ratios are the same as in Output 5.3, but the denominator degrees of freedom are different and p-values may be affected. In this case, the reported probabilities are the same because the t ratios are large.

Differences among Means

Given that there is a significant main effect of POSITION, differences among POSITION means may be of interest. Two approaches of potential interest are differences between pairs of main effect means and differences of interest if a given level of POSITION is a control or reference treatment.

Main Effect Means

From the ANOVA results, only the POSITION main effects are statistically significant. Therefore, the next logical step is specific comparisons among POSITION means. You can do this in two ways. The DIFF option in the LSMEANS statement performs pairwise comparisons. The CONTRAST and ESTIMATE statements enable you to test or estimate various linear combinations of treatment means. For example, you run the following SAS statements to pursue inference on the POSITION means. The ESTIMATE and CONTRAST statements shown here are illustrative only, and are not meant to be an exhaustive set of appropriate comparisons.

Program 5.4

```
proc glimmix data=ex_4_4;
   class wafer et position;
   model resistance=et|position / ddfm=satterth;
   random et / subject=wafer;
   lsmeans position / diff;
   estimate 'pos1 vs pos3'     position 1 0 -1 0;
   contrast 'pos1 vs pos3'     position 1 0 -1 0;
   estimate 'pos 3 vs others'  position 1 1 -3 1 / divisor=3;
   estimate 'pos3 v oth - wrong' position 1 1 -3 1;
   contrast 'pos 3 vs others'  position 1 1 -3 1;
run;
```

Note the DIVISOR option for the 'POS 3 VS OTHERS' estimate. If you omit it, you estimate $\mu_1 + \mu_2 + \mu_4 - 3\mu_3$, the difference between the sum of position 1, 2, and 4 and three times the mean of position 3. The correct statement, with the DIVISOR=3 option, estimates $(1/3)(\mu_1 + \mu_2 + \mu_4) - \mu_3$, the difference between the average mean of positions 1, 2, and 4 and the mean of position 3. For the CONTRAST statement, the DIVISOR option is unnecessary because the change of scale occurs in both the numerator and the denominator. Output 5.6 shows the results.

Output 5.6: Comparison of POSITION Least Squares Means Using LSMEANS (/ DIFF), ESTIMATE, and CONTRAST Statements

		Estimates			
Label	Estimate	Standard Error	DF	t Value	Pr > |t|
pos1 vs pos3	0.2733	0.1361	24	2.01	0.0560
pos 3 vs others	0.3406	0.1111	24	3.06	0.0053
pos3 v oth - wrong	1.0217	0.3334	24	3.06	0.0053

	Contrasts			
Label	Num DF	Den DF	F Value	Pr > F
pos1 vs pos3	1	24	4.03	0.0560
pos 3 vs others	1	24	9.39	0.0053

	Differences of position Least Squares Means				
position	_position	Estimate	Standard Error	DF	t Value	Pr > |t|
1	2	-0.1133	0.1361	24	-0.83	0.4132
1	3	0.2733	0.1361	24	2.01	0.0560
1	4	-0.08833	0.1361	24	-0.65	0.5225

Differences of position Least Squares Means						
position	_position	Estimate	Standard Error	DF	t Value	Pr > |t|
2	3	0.3867	0.1361	24	2.84	0.0090
2	4	0.02500	0.1361	24	0.18	0.8558
3	4	-0.3617	0.1361	24	-2.66	0.0138

Interpretation

First, notice that the 'POS 1 vs POS 3' estimate and the difference between the position 1 and position 3 least squares means from the DIFF option produce identical results: they represent different ways of programming the same mean difference. In general, it is easier to obtain a difference between a pair of means with the DIFF option. Use the ESTIMATE statement for linear combinations, such as 'POS 3 vs OTHERS', that cannot be obtained using the DIFF option. You can see the impact of the DIVISOR statement in the two ESTIMATE statements for position 3 versus the others: with the DIVISOR option you get a sensible estimate of the mean difference; without it you get a value multiplied by the number of means in the "others" group (in this case 3), and the result makes no sense. Note, however, that the *t* statistic is unaffected: changes of scale affect the estimates but not the tests (the standard error of the estimate changes by the same factor as the estimate itself). You can also see that for testing purposes, the CONTRAST or ESTIMATE statement output can be used interchangeably for 1 degree-of-freedom comparison. The CONTRAST statement gives you an *F* statistic; the ESTIMATE statement yields a *t* statistic. The *F* is equal to t^2 and the *p*-values are identical. The main advantage of the ESTIMATE statement is that you also get the difference estimate and its standard error. This enables you to report *how different* the means are, not merely that they are, or are not, significantly different.

Definition of a Specific Treatment as a Control

You can define a specific position as the "control" treatment. This restricts the treatment differences printed to those involving the "control." You can also adjust the *p*-value, e.g., using Dunnett's test, to control the type I error. For example, suppose POSITION 3 is the control or reference treatment. You can modify the LSMEANS statement as follows to obtain Output 5.7:

```
lsmeans position/diff=control('3') adjust=dunnett;
```

The level ('3') in parentheses identifies the control level of position. Note that it must be enclosed in single quotes. Consult the *SAS/STAT User's Guide* for a complete list of ADJUST= options.

Output 5.7: Dunnett Test of Position 3 versus Other Positions in Semiconductor Data

Differences of position Least Squares Means Adjustment for Multiple Comparisons: Dunnett-Hsu							
position	_position	Estimate	Standard Error	DF	t Value	Pr > |t|	Adj P
1	3	0.2733	0.1361	24	2.01	0.0560	0.1363
2	3	0.3867	0.1361	24	2.84	0.0090	0.0240
4	3	0.3617	0.1361	24	2.66	0.0138	0.0361

The _POSITION variable is the control. The column labeled "Pr > |t|" gives the unadjusted *p*-values, e.g., for the least significant difference test. The "Adj P" column gives the Dunnett-adjusted *p*-values. In many cases, your conclusions would not be affected by the adjustment, but you can see that they could. For example, if you use a significance level of $\alpha = 0.10$, your conclusion about the difference between position 1 and position 3 would change.

5.5 A Brief Comment about PROC GLM

The first and second editions of *SAS for Mixed Models* contained a section comparing PROC GLM with PROC MIXED for analyzing experiments with split-plots features, e.g. the designs in Figures 5.5 through 5.8. This section was motivated by the fact that many readers had been trained to use PROC GLM to analyze mixed models and needed help making the transition. Given the passage of time and the fact that mixed model methods are far more mainstream than they were when previous editions of this book were released, the decision was made not to include a detailed GLM versus PROC GLIMMIX/PROC MIXED comparison in this edition.

That said, two comments are in order. First, PROC GLM remains an excellent and comprehensive procedure for working with fixed-effect-only linear models. However, users should bear in mind that PROC GLM is a fixed-effect only program, and that PROC MIXED, and subsequently PROC GLIMMIX were developed to address known inadequacies of PROC GLM. Two cases where these inadequacies are especially evident are experiments with split plot features, as discussed in this chapter, and experiments with repeated measures, covered in Chapter 8. Put simply, PROC GLM was not designed to compute appropriate standard errors, test statistics, or confidence intervals for most mean comparisons of interest with split plot designs, and either cannot do so, or can only do so with programming heroics that are unnecessary given the ease with which PROC GLIMMIX or PROC MIXED handle the same analyses.

The second comment concerns textbooks on statistical methods or the design and analysis of experiments. Many persist in presenting the analysis of split-plot and repeated measures experiments using PROC GLM. Some merely present mixed model analysis as an afterthought. We urge authors of these textbooks to modernize their approach. To repeat what we said in the first two editions of this text: *we strongly discourage the use of PROC GLM to analyze data from experiments that clearly call for mixed models to describe relevant variation and hence require mixed model methods for data analysis.* This emphatically applies to split-plot experiments.

5.6 Type × Dose Response: An Example

This example involves data from an experiment to compare the response of two plant varieties to increasing amounts of pesticide designed to protect the plants against disease. The experiment was conducted in a greenhouse. Plants were placed on five benches, which were used as blocks to account for local variation in the greenhouse. Each bench was divided into four sections where, for convenience, levels of the pesticide were applied. Each section had two plants, one of each variety. The data set "Variety-Pesticide Evaluation" contains the data for this experiment. The variable TYPE denotes the variety, S for "susceptible" (a genotype susceptible to the disease) and R for "resistant"; the variable DOSE refers to the amount of pesticide, and the variable Y is the plant response.

The design is a split plot with the whole plot conducted in randomized complete blocks, the layout shown in Figure 5.5. DOSE is the whole-plot factor and TYPE is the split-plot factor. Thus, a model for this experiment is

$$y_{ijk} = \mu_{ij} + r_k + w_{ik} + e_{ijk}$$

where terms are defined as follows:

- y_{ijk} is the observation on the ith dose, j^{th} variety, and k^{th} block.
- μ_{ij} is the ij^{th} dose × variety mean.
- r_k is the kth block effect, assumed *iid* $N(0, \sigma_R^2)$.
- w_{ik} is the ik^{th} whole-plot (block × dose) effect, assumed *iid* $N(0, \sigma_W^2)$.
- e_{ijk} is the ijk^{th} split-plot error effect, assumed *iid* $N(0, \sigma^2)$.

The example analyses that follow show several ways to model the dose × variety means, μ_{ij}. The next section starts with the conventional partition into main effects and interactions,

$$\mu_{ij} = \mu + \delta_i + \tau_j + \delta\tau_{ij}$$

where terms are defined as follows:

- δ_i is the ith DOSE main effect.
- τ_j is the jth variety (TYPE) main effect.
- $\delta\tau_{ij}$ is the ij^{th} DOSE × TYPE interaction effect.

5.6.1 PROC GLIMMIX Analysis of DOSE and TYPE Effects

The following SAS statements, consistent with Table 5.8, obtain the variance component estimates, Type III tests of fixed effects (in this case, interaction and main effects), interaction plot, and slices for overall simple effects for the variety evaluation data. Figure 5.10 and Outputs 5.8 and 5.9 show the results.

Program 5.5

```
proc glimmix data=variety_eval;
   class block type dose;
```

```
    model y = type|dose / ddfm=satterth;
    random intercept dose / subject=block;
    lsmeans type*dose / slice=(type dose) plot=meanplot(sliceby=type join);
run;
```

Figure 5.10: Interaction Plot Produced by PROC GLIMMIX MEANPLOT Option

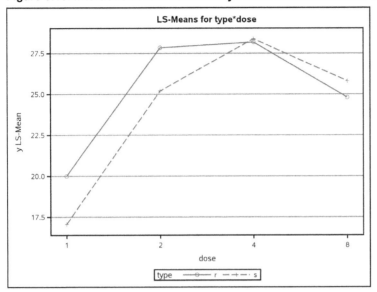

Output 5.8 Variance Estimates, Main Effect, and Interaction Tests for Variety Evaluation

Covariance Parameter Estimates			
Cov Parm	**Subject**	**Estimate**	**Standard Error**
Intercept	block	2.0735	2.7320
dose	block	4.5132	2.8291
Residual		4.3189	1.5270

Type III Tests of Fixed Effects				
Effect	**Num DF**	**Den DF**	**F Value**	**Pr > F**
type	1	16	2.78	0.1151
dose	3	12	13.63	0.0004
type*dose	3	16	2.29	0.1176

The interaction plot in Figure 5.10 suggests a quadratic response to DOSE for both TYPEs, although the resistant TYPE appears to reach maximum response at a lower DOSE than does the susceptible TYPE. Note that the PROC GLIMMIX MEANPLOT treats the levels of DOSE as CLASS effects and spaces them equally, even though in this example they are actually on a logarithmic scale. This may distort the actual response profile, a possibility that is dealt with in more detail in Section 5.6.2 below.

The "Covariance Parameter Estimates" table gives the estimates of the block, whole-plot error, and split-plot error variances components, σ_R^2, σ_W^2, and σ^2, and called "intercept, subject=block," "type, subject=block" and "residual," respectively. In this case, the variance component estimates are all positive. Section 5.7 contains a brief discussion of issues that you should consider if either the block (σ_R^2) or whole-plot error (σ_W^2) variance component estimate is zero.

The "Type 3 Tests of Fixed Effects" table gives the tests for TYPE × DOSE interactions and TYPE and DOSE main effects. As with any factorial experiment, you should consider the tests in that order: interaction first. In this case, the test for interaction has a *p*-value of 0.1176. In the next section we consider this test in more detail, because there are multiple degrees of freedom (i.e., 3 numerator *df*) associated with this test, and important interaction effects with 1 or 2 *df* may be masked. In fact, many statistical methods texts suggest treating multiple degree-of-freedom interaction tests as warranting more detailed investigation is the *p*-value is < 0.20. For the moment, assuming no interaction effect, the tests of DOSE (H$_0$: all $\delta_i = 0$ assuming no interaction) and TYPE (H$_0$: all $\tau_j = 0$ assuming no interaction) suggest that the DOSE effect is statistically significant but the TYPE effect is not.

If DOSE × TYPE effects are truly negligible, the SLICE results would not be of interest. However, for the sake of argument, and in view of the fact that the *p*-value for the overall test of interaction is <0.20, Output 5.9 shows the SLICE results.

Output 5.9 Test of SLICEs for Variety Evaluation Data

			Tests of Effect Slices for type*dose Sliced By type	
type	Num DF	Den DF	F Value	Pr > F
r	3	19.49	8.12	0.0010
s	3	19.49	13.58	<.0001

			Tests of Effect Slices for type*dose Sliced By dose	
dose	Num DF	Den DF	F Value	Pr > F
1	1	16	5.00	0.0399
2	1	16	4.03	0.0618
4	1	16	0.02	0.8810
8	1	16	0.58	0.4578

Note that the test of DOSE simple effects for given variety TYPE occurs across whole-plot experimental units and thus involves both whole-plot and split-plot error. Hence, the denominator degrees of freedom (19.5) reflect the use of Satterthwaite's approximation. For the TYPE simple effects for given DOSE levels, you can see that there appear to be large differences among varieties at low DOSE levels (i.e., low levels of pesticide protection from disease) but no statistically significant differences at higher DOSE levels. This is exactly what one would expect when comparing a resistant variety to a susceptible variety, and it suggests that we should investigate interaction in more detail.

5.6.2 A Closer Look at the Interaction Plot

Figure 5.10 showed the interaction plot from the PROC GLIMMIX MEANPLOT option, which space DOSE levels equally. In essence, Figure 5.10 shows a plot of response over log dose by TYPE. You can obtain an interaction plot over the actual DOSE levels by adding the SAS statements in Program 5.6 to the PROC GLIMMIX program given above.

Program 5.6

```
ods output lsmeans=typedosemeans;
run;

proc sgplot data=typedosemeans;
  Series y=estimate x=dose / group=type;
  Xaxis label="Dose";
  Yaxis   label="Dose x Type Mean";
  Keylegend / location=inside position=bottom title="Variety Type";
Run;
```

The ODS statement saves the least squares means to a new data set, in this case called TYPEDOSEMEANS. PROC SGPLOT uses these means to create Figure 5.11, which shows the interaction plots over DOSE.

Figure 5.11: Interaction Plot: Means over DOSE by TYPE

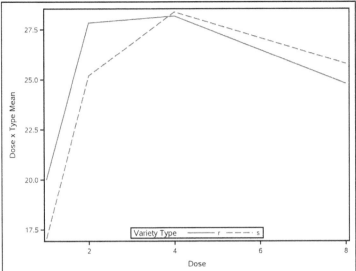

You can see from the plot that the susceptible TYPE (TYPE S) has noticeably lower mean response at low levels of DOSE. You can also see that the resistant TYPE (TYPE R) and the susceptible TYPE attain maximum response DOSE=4. The mean response of both varieties decreases somewhat when DOSE level increases from 4 to 8, but the decrease is somewhat less for the susceptible variety. This is similar to the response over LOGDOSE shown in Figure 5.10 but the logdose from MEANPLOT appears to have more of a parabolic shape than the response over DOSE, suggesting that a quadratic regression model defined on LOGDOSE might fit better. The next section pursues this idea.

5.6.3 Regression Analysis over DOSE by TYPE

The interaction plots in Figures 5.10 and 5.11 suggest that one way to characterize the variety evaluation data is to look at polynomial regression effects of dose for each type.

As discussed in Chapter 3, Section 3.5.9, you can use either a direct approach or orthogonal polynomial contrasts to fit a regression model for these data. If you do use orthogonal polynomials and fit the regression over DOSE, keep in mind that the DOSE levels are not equally spaced and the coefficients used need to reflect this. For example, you can use the ORPOL function in PROC IML to obtain the correct coefficients. For additional background refer to Littell et al. (2002, Ch. 7).

Suffice it to say that direct regression is easier and is the method that we recommend. However, for completeness, and because orthogonal polynomials are occasionally useful, this method is shown below.

Program

Use the following SAS statements in Program 5.7 to compute the PROC GLIMMIX regression analysis with orthogonal polynomial contrasts:

Program 5.7

```
proc glimmix data=variety_eval;
   class block type dose;
   model y = dose|type / ddfm=satterth;
   random intercept dose / subject=block;
   contrast 'dose linear'   dose -11 -7   1 17;
   contrast 'dose quad'     dose  20 -4 -29 13;
   contrast 'dose cubic'    dose  -8 14  -7  1;
   contrast 'type x linear' dose*type -11 -7   1 17  11   7  -1 -17;
   contrast 'type x quad'   dose*type  20 -4 -29 13 -20   4  29 -13;
   contrast 'type x cubic'  dose*type  -8 14  -7  1   8 -14   7  -1;
run;
```

The CONTRAST statements enable you to test polynomial regression, specifically the linear, quadratic, and cubic main effects and their interaction with TYPE. The coefficients reflect the geometric spacing of the dose levels 1, 2, 4, and 8. You can obtain these coefficients using the ORPOL function in PROC IML.

Results

Output 5.10 shows the results.

Output 5.10: Orthogonal Polynomial Results for DOSE Effect in Variety Evaluation Data

	Contrasts			
Label	Num DF	Den DF	F Value	Pr > F
dose linear	1	12	7.74	0.0166
dose quad	1	12	27.01	0.0002
dose cubic	1	12	6.14	0.0291
type x linear	1	16	5.82	0.0282
type x quad	1	16	0.68	0.4205
type x cubic	1	16	0.36	0.5582

Interpretation

The TYPE × LINEAR contrast indicates that the linear component of the regression over dose levels differs between the resistant and susceptible variety type. This is consistent with the plot over DOSE in Figure 5.11 showing a greater increase over dose level for the susceptible TYPE. There is no evidence that the quadratic or cubic components differ by TYPE, but there is strong evidence ($p = 0.0291$) that a quadratic regression would not fit that data and that a cubic (or possibly something else—with only 1 *df* beyond quadratic you cannot be sure) is required.

Program

Alternatively, you could fit $Log_2(DOSE)$, converting the dose levels to equally spaced levels 0, 1, 2, and 3. To do this, substitute the following CONTRAST statements, using Program 5.8

Program 5.8

```
proc glimmix data=variety_eval;
  class block type logdose;
  model y = logdose|type / ddfm=satterth;
  random intercept logdose / subject=block;
  contrast 'logdose linear' logdose -3 -1  1 3;
  contrast 'logdose quad'   logdose  1 -1 -1 1;
  contrast 'logdose cubic'  logdose -1  3 -3 1;
  contrast 'type x linear'  logdose*type -3 -1  1 3   3  1 -1 -3;
  contrast 'type x quad'    logdose*type  1 -1 -1 1  -1  1  1 -1;
  contrast 'type x cubic'   logdose*type -1 3 -3 1   1 -3  3 -1;
run;
```

These coefficients are the standard orthogonal polynomial coefficients (given in most statistical methods textbooks) for four levels.

Results

The results appear in Output 5.11.

Output 5.11: Orthogonal Polynomial Results for Log-Dose in Variety Evaluation Data

	Contrasts			
Label	Num DF	Den DF	F Value	Pr > F
logdose linear	1	12	18.25	0.0011
logdose quad	1	12	22.54	0.0005
logdose cubic	1	12	0.08	0.7780
type x linear	1	16	6.22	0.0240
type x quad	1	16	0.04	0.8515
type x cubic	1	16	0.61	0.4472

The results are similar except that there is now no evidence of lack of fit for a quadratic regression over Log(Dose) levels. The *p*-value for the "logdose cubic" term, which tests lack of fit from quadratic, is 0.7780.

Program

The next logical step would be to explore the shape of the regression equations over Log DOSE for each type. You can do this with the PROC GLIMMIX statements in Program 5.9.

Program 5.9

```
proc glimmix data=variety_eval;
   class block type logdose ;
   model y = type logdose(type) / ddfm=satterth;
   random intercept logdose / subject=block;
   contrast 'linear LogD | type R' logdose (type) -3 -1  1 3 0;
   contrast 'quad LogD   | type R' logdose (type)  1 -1 -1 1 0;
   contrast 'cubic LogD  | type R' logdose (type) -1  3 -3 1 0;
   contrast 'linear LogD | type S' logdose (type) 0 0 0 0 -3 -1  1 3;
   contrast 'quad LogD   | type S' logdose (type) 0 0 0 0  1 -1 -1 1;
   contrast 'cubic LogD  | type S' logdose (type) 0 0 0 0 -1  3 -3 1;
run;
```

This model exploits the fact that μ_{ij} can equivalently be partitioned as $\mu + \delta_i + \tau_j + \delta\tau_{ij}$ or $\mu + \tau_j + \delta(\tau)_{ij}$. Note that there is no need for the DOSE main effect to appear in the MODEL statement in order for BLOCK × DOSE, the term that identifies whole-plot error, to remain in the RANDOM statement—specified by RANDOM ... DOSE / SUBJECT=BLOCK. The CONTRAST statements are simply the linear, quadratic, and cubic orthogonal polynomial contrasts for each level of TYPE, one at a time, with the coefficients for the other type set to zero.

Results

The results appear in Output 5.12.

Output 5.12: Order of Polynomial Regression Fit by TYPE

	Contrasts			
Label	Num DF	Den DF	F Value	Pr > F
linear LogD | type R	1	19.49	6.15	0.0224
quad LogD | type R	1	19.49	17.82	0.0004
cubic LogD | type R	1	19.49	0.40	0.5322
linear LogD | type S	1	19.49	24.47	<.0001
quad LogD | type S	1	19.49	16.26	0.0007
cubic LogD | type S	1	19.49	0.02	0.8943

You can see from this output that a quadratic regression over log(DOSE) for both cultivar types is appropriate. Both "quad LogD" contrasts (given type R or S) are statistically significant ($p = 0.0004$ and 0.0007, respectively, for type R and S), and both the "cubic LogD" contrasts are nonsignificant ($p = 0.5322$ for type S, $p = 0.8943$ for type R).

Direct Regression Model and Program to Estimate It

Output 5.12 suggests that μ_{ij} can be modeled in yet a third way:

$$\mu_{ij} = \mu + \tau_j + (\beta_L + \Delta_{Li})[\log_2(\text{dose})] + (\beta_Q + \Delta_{Qi})[\log_2(\text{dose})]^2$$

where terms are defined as follows:

- β_L is the linear slope coefficient for the regression over $\text{Log}_2(\text{DOSE})$.
- Δ_{Li} is the change in slope for the ith type.
- β_Q is the quadratic coefficient for the regression over $\text{Log}_2(\text{DOSE})$.
- Δ_{Qi} is the change in quadratic coefficient for the ith type.

Program

You can estimate this model with the SAS statements in Program 5.10.

Program 5.10

```
proc glimmix data=variety_eval;
   class block type dose;
   model y=type|logdose|logdose / ddfm=satterth solution htype=1;
   random intercept dose / subject=block;
run;
```

You have to create the variable LOGDOSE=LOG2(DOSE) in the DATA step. You include DOSE in the CLASS statement in order to define whole plot error in the RANDOM statement. However, you treat LOGDOSE as a regression variable, so it is not included in the CLASS statement. The vertical bars in the effects specification of the MODEL statement cause PROC GLIMMIX to compute all possible interactions of the variables in the list. It is equivalent to the statement

```
model y = type logdose type*logdose logdose*logdose
          type*logdose*logdose;
```

In the MODEL statement, TYPE corresponds to δ_i, LOGDOSE to β_L, TYPE*LOGDOSE to Δ_{Li}, LOGDOSE*LOGDOSE to β_Q, and TYPE*LOGDOSE*LOGDOSE to Δ_{Qi}. The SOLUTION option requests a listing of the fixed effects estimates. The HTYPE=1 option causes the hypotheses to be tested sequentially. You want to do this because the default TYPE 3 tests adjust effects mentioned first in the model (e.g., linear effects) by terms mentioned later in the model (e.g., quadratic effects). In fitting polynomial regression models, you want tests that enter the model terms sequentially, starting with the lowest order polynomial, and hence you must override the default to obtain the needed hypothesis tests. Finally, the SAS statements contain an alternative model (commented out). This model includes the cubic effects. You can run this model as an alternative to the orthogonal polynomials for testing "type*linear," 'type*quad," and "type*cubic" shown above. Using the HTYPE=1 option, the results are equivalent.

Results

Output 5.13 shows the results.

Output 5.13: Regression of LOGDOSE on Y by TYPE Using Direct Regression

Solutions for Fixed Effects						
Effect	type	Estimate	Standard Error	DF	t Value	Pr > |t|
Intercept		17.0200	1.4204	19.62	11.98	<.0001
type	r	3.1690	1.2662	17	2.50	0.0228
type	s	0	.	.	.	.
logdose		10.9800	2.0181	21.45	5.44	<.0001
logdose*type	r	-1.0910	2.0334	17	-0.54	0.5985
logdose*type	s	0	.	.	.	.
logdose*logdose		-2.6800	0.6447	21.45	-4.16	0.0004
logdose*logdose*type	r	-0.1250	0.6495	17	-0.19	0.8497
logdose*logdose*type	s	0	.	.	.	.

Type I Tests of Fixed Effects				
Effect	Num DF	Den DF	F Value	Pr > F
type	1	17	2.84	0.1101
logdose	1	13	19.63	0.0007
logdose*type	1	17	6.37	0.0219
logdose*logdose	1	13	24.25	0.0003
logdose*logdose*type	1	17	0.04	0.8497

Interpretation

The "Type 1 Test of Fixed Effects" gives tests for the various model effects. The row labeled "logdose*logdose*type" tests H₀: $\Delta_{Qi} = 0$ for all levels of i. Similarly, the row labeled "logdose*logdose" tests H₀: $\beta_Q = 0$, "logdose*type" tests H₀: $\Delta_{Li} = 0$ for all i, and "logdose" tests H₀: $\beta_L = 0$. These tests suggest that while two types have different linear slopes (i.e., the Δ_{Li} terms are nonzero), they share a common quadratic LOGDOSE effect (that is, the model term $\beta_Q + \Delta_{Qi}$ can be reduced to β_Q only).

In principle, the "Solutions for Fixed Effects" table enables you to estimate the regression equation over LOGDOSE for each TYPE, although there is a much easier way to obtain the estimated coefficients of the regression equation, shown below.

If you do use the SOLUTION from Output 5.13, you must use the following steps. For example, the intercept for TYPE R is obtained by adding the estimate in the "Intercept" row (which corresponds to μ in the model) and the estimate of "type r" (which corresponds to δ_R in the model equation). The intercept for the TYPE R regression equation is thus $17.020 + 3.169 = 20.189$. Similarly, the slope for TYPE R is $\hat{\beta}_L + \hat{\Delta}_{LR}$, the sum of the "logdose" and "logdose*type R" estimates, $10.98 - 1.091 = 9.889$, and the quadratic coefficient is $\hat{\beta}_Q + \hat{\Delta}_{QR}$, the sum of the "logdose*logdose" and "logdose*logdose*type R" estimates, $-2.86 - 0.125 = -2.805$. That is, for TYPE R, the regression equation is

$$\hat{\mu}_{Rj} = 20.189 + 9.889 \times \log_2(dose_j) - 2.805 \times \left[\log_2(dose_j)\right]^2$$

Estimate Statements to Add to Program 5.10

You can add the following ESTIMATE statements to the direct regression PROC GLIMMIX program to obtain the regression parameters:

```
estimate 'B_0    for type R' intercept 1 type 1 0;
estimate 'B_Lin  for type R' logdose 1 logdose*type 1 0;
estimate 'B_quad for type R' logdose*logdose 1
                             logdose*logdose*type 1 0;
estimate 'B_0    for type S' intercept 1 type 0 1;
estimate 'B_Lin  for type S' logdose 1 logdose*type 0 1;
estimate 'B_quad for type S' logdose*logdose 1
                             logdose*logdose*type 0 1;
```

Results

Output 5.14 shows the results.

Output 5.14: Estimates of Regression Model by TYPE

Label	Estimate	Standard Error	DF	t Value	Pr > |t|
B_0 for type R	20.1890	1.4204	19.62	14.21	<.0001
B_Lin for type R	9.8890	2.0181	21.45	4.90	<.0001
B_quad for type R	-2.8050	0.6447	21.45	-4.35	0.0003
B_0 for type S	17.0200	1.4204	19.62	11.98	<.0001
B_Lin for type S	10.9800	2.0181	21.45	5.44	<.0001
B_quad for type S	-2.6800	0.6447	21.45	-4.16	0.0004

A Better Way to Estimate the Regression Equation

An alternative, and easier to understand, regression model is

$$\mu_{ij} = \beta_{0i} + \beta_{Li}\left[\log_2(dose)\right] + \beta_{Qi}\left[\log_2(dose)\right]^2$$

where terms are defined as follows:

- $\beta_{0i} = \mu + \delta_i$ is the intercept for the ith type.

- $\beta_{Li} = \beta_L + \Delta_{Li}$ is the slope for the ith type.

- $\beta_{Qi} = \beta_Q + \Delta_{Qi}$ is the quadratic regression parameter for the ith type.

Program

You can estimate this model by using PROC GLIMMIX as follows in Program 5.11.

Program 5.11

```
proc glimmix data=variety_eval;
   class block type dose;
   model y = type logdose(type) logdose*logdose(type) / noint ddfm=satterth solution;
   random intercept dose / subject=block;
   contrast 'equal quad by type?' logdose*logdose(type) 1 -1;
run;
```

In the MODEL statement, the effect LOGDOSE(TYPE) creates a linear regression parameter for each TYPE. Similarly, LOGDOSE*LOGDOSE(TYPE) creates a quadratic parameter for each TYPE. The NOINT option suppresses the SAS default of inserting μ in the model automatically. With the NOINT option, TYPE produces the parameter β_{0i} rather than the default $\mu + \delta_i$. This makes the SOLUTION output easier to read directly to get the regression equation. The CONTRAST statement is equivalent to LOGDOSE*LOGDOSE*TYPE in the previous SAS program: it tests H_0: $\beta_{QR} = \beta_{QS}$, which is equivalent to testing H_0: $\Delta_{Qi} = 0$ in the previous model. That is, if H_0 is true, then both β_{QR} and β_{QS} can be set equal to β_Q, i.e., $\Delta_{Qi} = 0$.

Results

Output 5.15 shows the results.

Output 5.15: Direct Regression by TYPE Using Nested Model

Solutions for Fixed Effects						
Effect	type	Estimate	Standard Error	DF	t Value	Pr > |t|
type	r	20.1890	1.4204	19.62	14.21	<.0001
type	s	17.0200	1.4204	19.62	11.98	<.0001
logdose(type)	r	9.8890	2.0181	21.45	4.90	<.0001
logdose(type)	s	10.9800	2.0181	21.45	5.44	<.0001
logdos*logdose(type)	r	-2.8050	0.6447	21.45	-4.35	0.0003
logdos*logdose(type)	s	-2.6800	0.6447	21.45	-4.16	0.0004

Contrasts				
Label	Num DF	Den DF	F Value	Pr > F
equal quad by type?	1	17	0.04	0.8497

Interpretation

You can see that the regression estimates and their standard errors are identical to those obtained in the previous PROC GLIMMIX program. The advantage of this approach is that you do not have to write ESTIMATE statements to make the SOLUTION output directly usable. You can also use the t values to test the null hypotheses about each regression parameter. For example, the LD_SQ(TYPE) t values test H_0: $\beta_{Qi} = 0$ for each TYPE. These are equivalent to the orthogonal polynomial contrasts shown in the nested model previously, except that this approach is much easier. You do not need to look up the contrast coefficients, or compute them for unequally spaced DOSE levels, or enter the several CONTRAST statements required. Also note that the F value for 'equal quad by type?' contrast is the same as the test for "logdose*logdose*type" in the previous direct regression program (Output 5.13). Thus, the nested program shown here is the most versatile for most analyses once you decide to model a quantitative factor such as DOSE by polynomial regression.

Extensions

The direct regression methods shown here are closely related to the *analysis of covariance*, which is considered in greater detail in Chapter 7. In many applications with quantitative factors, *nonlinear regression* models are more appropriate, provide a better fit, or provide more interpretable parameter estimates than polynomial regression.

The Final Fit

Returning to the variety evaluation data, because the analysis indicated that the quadratic regression coefficients could be considered equal, a parsimonious model would be

$$\mu_{ij} = \beta_{0i} + \beta_{Li}\left[\log_2\left(\text{dose}\right)\right] + \beta_Q\left[\log_2\left(\text{dose}\right)\right]^2$$

That is, you could use the same quadratic parameter, β_Q, for both types but retain separate intercepts, β_{0i}, and linear parameters, β_{Li}.

Program

Use the Program 5.12 to estimate the final model.

Program 5.12

```
proc glimmix data=variety_eval;
   class block type dose;
   model y=type logdose(type) logdose*logdose / noint ddfm=satterth solution;
   random intercept dose / subject=block;
run;
```

Results

The results are shown in Output 5.16.

Output 5.16 Final Regression Model Parameter Estimates for Variety Evaluation Data

		Solutions for Fixed Effects				
Effect	type	Estimate	Standard Error	DF	t Value	Pr > |t|
type	r	20.2515	1.3770	17.77	14.71	<.0001
type	s	16.9575	1.3770	17.77	12.31	<.0001
logdose(type)	r	9.7015	1.7660	13.69	5.49	<.0001
logdose(type)	s	11.1675	1.7660	13.69	6.32	<.0001
logdose*logdose		-2.7425	0.5569	13	-4.92	0.0003

For example, from the output, the regression model for TYPE R is

$$\hat{\mu}_{Rj} = 20.2515 + 9.7015 \times \log_2\left(\text{dose}_j\right) - 2.7425\left[\log_2\left(\text{dose}_j\right)\right]^2$$

5.7 Variance Component Estimates Equal to Zero: An Example

The semiconductor and variety evaluation data both had whole-plot error variance estimates greater than zero. As shown with the semiconductor data, when the variance estimates are all positive, mixed model inference on data with split plot features is identical to standard analysis of variance methods. However, when one or more of the variance component estimates is negative, then there are issues in mixed model inference that require extra care. This happens, for example, when the whole plot error mean square is less than the split plot error mean square. This example illustrates the main issues.

The example is a trial involving laboratory mice. There are four different housing conditions (denoted CONDITION 1, 2, 3, and 4) and three feeding regimes (denoted DIET: "restricted," "normal," and "supplement") under investigation. Two conditions can be handled in a single CAGE unit. Within each condition at each cage unit, mice can be separated into three diet groups. Thus, CAGE is a blocking factor, CONDITION is the whole plot treatment factor, CAGE × CONDITION combinations are the whole plot experimental units, and DIET is the split plot factor. The layout is similar to that of Figure 5.6, except that the whole plots form an incomplete block design rather than a randomized complete block design. The data are given in data set, "Mouse Condition-Diet Experiment."

Following Table 5.1, a model for these data is

$$y_{ijk} = \mu_{ij} + c_k + w_{ik} + e_{ijk}$$

where terms are defined as follows:

- μ_{ij} is the mean response for CONDITION i and DIET j.
- c_k is the effect of the kth cage unit, assumed *iid* $N(0, \sigma_C^2)$.
- w_{ik} is the effect of the ik^{th} whole plot e.u. (cage × condition) assumed *iid* $N(0, \sigma_W^2)$.
- e_{ijk} is the effect of the ijk^{th} split plot e.u. effect, assumed *iid* $N(0, \sigma^2)$.

5.7.1 Default Analysis Using PROC GLIMMIX

Following the model and the approach used in the previous examples in this chapter, you obtain the basic analysis of these data using the following SAS statements in Program 5.13.

Program 5.13

```
proc glimmix data=mice;
   class cage condition diet;
   model gain = condition|diet / ddfm=sattorth;
   random intercept condition / subject=cage;
run;
```

Output 5.17 shows the results.

Output 5.17 Standard PROC GLIMMIX Analysis of Mouse Data

Covariance Parameter Estimates			
Cov Parm	Subject	Estimate	Standard Error
Intercept	cage	3.0376	5.0791
condition	cage	0	.
Residual		27.8429	8.7672

Type III Tests of Fixed Effects				
Effect	Num DF	Den DF	F Value	Pr > F
condition	3	23.61	2.71	0.0677
diet	2	20.17	0.93	0.4090
condition*diet	6	20.17	1.73	0.1661

First, note that the estimate for the whole plot error (CAGE*CONDITION) variance component is 0. In the listing, just above the table of "Fit Statistics," you see the message:

```
Estimated G matrix is not positive definite.
```

If you use PROC MIXED, by default you will get a similar note, but it will appear in the SASLOG. With PROC MIXED, this note is followed by some additional commentary regarding the degrees of freedom. The degrees-of-freedom comment refers to the denominator degrees of freedom in the "Type 3 Tests of Fixed Effects" output.

Output 5.18 shows the analysis of variance of these data, which you can obtain using PROC MIXED with its METHOD=TYPE3 option. Using analysis of variance, there are 3 degrees of freedom for the whole plot error, instead of 23.6 shown in Output 5.17, and the ANOVA degrees of freedom for the split plot error is 16, not 20.2 as shown above. Also, the *F* value for the CONDITION main effect is 2.71 using the standard mixed model approach used by PROC GLIMMIX, whereas the analysis of variance *F*, the ratio of MS(CONDITION) to MS(CAGE*CONDITION), is 3.95.

You can drop the DDFM=SATTERTH option in PROC GLIMMIX to make the degrees of freedom agree with the analysis of variance—and, more importantly, with the structure of the design—but the *F* value is still 2.71. Obviously, there is a discrepancy between the standard mixed model results and the analysis of variance. What is going on? Which should you use?

Output 5.18: Analysis of Variance for Mouse Data—PROC MIXED

				Type 3 Analysis of Variance	
Source	DF	Sum of Squares	Mean Square	Expected Mean Square	Error Term
condition	3	171.666667	57.222222	Var(Residual) + 3 Var(cage*condition) + Q(condition,condition*diet)	MS(cage*condition)
diet	2	52.055556	26.027778	Var(Residual) + Q(diet,condition*diet)	MS(Residual)
condition*diet	6	288.388889	48.064815	Var(Residual) + Q(condition*diet)	MS(Residual)
cage	5	198.277778	39.655556	Var(Residual) + 3 Var(cage*condition) + 4.8 Var(cage)	MS(cage*condition)
cage*condition	3	43.500000	14.500000	Var(Residual) + 3 Var(cage*condition)	MS(Residual)
Residual	16	504.888889	31.555556	Var(Residual)	.

	Type 3 Analysis of Variance		
Source	Error DF	F Value	Pr > F
condition	3	3.95	0.1446
diet	16	0.82	0.4561
condition*diet	16	1.52	0.2333
cage	3	2.73	0.2185
cage*condition	16	0.46	0.7144
Residual	.	.	.

The primary issue with the default PROC GLIMMIX and PROC MIXED analysis concerns the REML estimation procedure for variance components. By definition, a variance component cannot be negative, so when the REML computing algorithm obtains a negative solution, the variance component estimate is set to 0. In theory, this could happen to either the CAGE variance, σ_C^2, or the whole plot error (CAGE*CONDITION) variance, σ_W^2. Setting either estimate to zero has a ripple effect on all subsequent analysis.

5.7.2 One Recommended Alternative: Override Set-to-Zero Default Using NOBOUND or METHOD=TYPE3

Stroup and Littell (2002) discussed the impact of negative variance component estimates on tests of fixed effects in mixed model analysis. They considered the impact of a negative solution for the block variance and for the whole plot error variance. For the former, it is easy to show by simulation that if the block variance (in this case CAGE) is set to zero, the whole plot error variance tends to be underestimated, which in turn means that the whole plot main effect (CONDITION) *F* value is overestimated. This results in an inflated Type I error rate. On the other hand, what you see for the mouse data in this example is the impact of a negative whole plot (CAGE*CONDITION) error variance estimate. If the whole plot error variance is set to zero, the whole plot main effect *F* statistic is in essence based on MS(split plot). This results in an underestimate of the *F* statistic. At the same time, the split plot and whole plot error degrees of freedom are pooled, with some additional problems with the Satterthwaite procedure, which assumes positive variance component estimates. The net result is a tendency for the Type II error rate to be inflated, although this depends on the extent to which whole plot denominator degrees of freedom are affected.

On the other hand, if you do *not* set the negative variance component estimate to zero, but allow it to remain negative, you get better control over Type I error and, for cases of negative whole plot error variance estimates, greater power. Therefore, this is the recommended procedure. You can override the set-to-zero default in one of two ways. With both PROC GLIMMIX and PROC MIXED, you can either use the NOBOUND option in the PROC statement, i.e.,

```
proc glimmix nobound;
```

Alternatively, with PROC MIXED you can use the METHOD=TYPE3 option, as shown above.. The NOBOUND option removes the lower bound of 0 from the variance components. The METHOD=TYPE3 causes PROC MIXED to estimate variance components based on the expected mean squares instead of computing REML solutions. For unbalanced data, such as incomplete block designs, the results are not equal, but they are usually close unless the data are severely unbalanced. Output 5.19 shows the results for NOBOUND and METHOD=TYPE3.

Output 5.19: NOBOUND and METHOD=TYPE3 Results Overriding Set-to-Zero Default

NOBOUND

Covariance Parameter Estimates

Cov Parm	Subject	Estimate	Standard Error
Intercept	cage	5.0288	4.7149
condition	cage	-6.2404	4.8693
Residual		31.5557	11.1566

Type III Tests of Fixed Effects

Effect	Num DF	Den DF	F Value	Pr > F
condition	3	4.718	4.31	0.0798
diet	2	16	0.82	0.4561
condition*diet	6	16	1.52	0.2333

Method=Type3

Covariance Parameter Estimates

Cov Parm	Estimate
cage	5.2407
cage*condition	-5.6852
Residual	31.5556

Type 3 Tests of Fixed Effects

Effect	Num DF	Den DF	F Value	Pr > F
condition	3	3.73	3.70	0.1271
diet	2	15.9	0.82	0.4562
condition*diet	6	15.9	1.52	0.2336

These results differ slightly. The CAGE variance estimates are 5.0292 for NOBOUND versus 5.2407 for TYPE3. The F values for CONDITION are 4.31 and 3.70, respectively. Neither is exactly equal to the analysis of variance ($F = 3.95$), but they are close. From simulation studies, there is no evidence suggesting any advantage for analysis of variance, unbounded REML, or METHOD=TYPE3 estimation. Clearly, however, you want to use either NOBOUND with PROC GLIMMIX or PROC MIXED, or METHOD=TYPE3 with PROC MIXED to estimate or test simple effects, slices, and other quantities of interest.

The degrees of freedom in Output 5.19 use the DDFM=KR2 option rather than DDFM=SATTERTH. The KR2 option uses the procedure developed by Kenward and Roger (1997, 2009). Because the KR2 option was specifically intended to account for unbalanced data in conjunction with multiple random effects or any model with correlated errors (balanced or not), it is recommended for all such applications.

5.7.3 Conceptual Alternative: Negative Variance or Correlation?

Using either the NOBOUND or METHOD=TYPE3 option presents a dilemma when you report the results. By definition, a variance must be nonnegative, yet you must report a negative variance estimate in order to control type I error or preserve power. Many authors and journal editors object to such an apparent contradiction. To address these objections, a conceptual alternative, compound symmetry, introduced in Chapter 2, can help.

In the variance components model used for the mouse data in the previous sections, the ratio

$$\frac{\sigma_W^2}{\sigma_W^2 + \sigma^2}$$

is termed the *intraclass correlation*. That is, the whole plot experimental units act as blocks with respect to the split plot experimental units. Observations within the same block are correlated. The intraclass correlation is a measure of this correlation.

Because variance components must be nonnegative, variance component models implicitly assume that the intraclass correlation is nonnegative. However, there is no conceptual reason why correlation among observations within the same whole plot experimental unit *must* be nonnegative. In fact, in many practical situations, there are interference or competition effects among adjacent experimental units that manifest themselves in negative correlation. What appears as a negative variance component estimate in the analyses from the previous sections may in fact be negative interclass correlation. In such cases, you need a more realistic model.

Compound symmetry is an alternative model of intraclass correlation that allows for negative correlation. Define

$$e_{ik} = \begin{bmatrix} e_{i1k} & e_{i2k} & ... & e_{iBk} \end{bmatrix}$$

as the vector of split plot error terms for the ik^{th} whole plot experimental unit. In the compound symmetry model, Var[e_{ik}] is defined as

$$\sigma_{CS}^2 \begin{bmatrix} 1 & \rho & ... & \rho \\ \rho & 1 & ... & \rho \\ ... & ... & ... & ... \\ \rho & \rho & ... & 1 \end{bmatrix}$$

where σ_{CS}^2 is the variance of a split plot error and ρ is the correlation between any pair of split plot errors. The model used in the previous sections is a special case, with $\sigma_{CS}^2 = \sigma_W^2 + \sigma^2$ and $\rho = \sigma_W^2 / (\sigma_W^2 + \sigma^2)$. The model can be more general.

The compound symmetry model is one of several types of mixed models that allow for *correlated errors*. They are used extensively in *repeated measures* analysis, introduced in detail in Chapter 8.

Programs

You can fit the compound symmetry model using Program 5.14.

Program 5.14

```
proc glimmix data=mice;
   class cage condition diet;
   model gain=condition|diet/ddfm=kr;
   random intercept / subject=cage;
   random diet / type=cs subject=cage*condition residual;
run;
```

The RANDOM...RESIDUAL statement replaces RANDOM CAGE*CONDITION. In general, you use the RANDOM statement with the RESIDUAL option to specify correlated error structures. The TYPE=CS option specifies the covariance structure as being of the compound-symmetric type. RANDOM CONDITION / SUBJECT=CAGE is equivalent to RANDOM _RESIDUAL_ / SUBJECT=CAGE*CONDITION—both specify the unit within which observations are correlated, in this case the whole plot experimental unit.

PROC GLIMMIX has options V and VCORR that enable you to see the entire variance covariance matrix for a given CAGE. However, this matrix contains both whole plot and split plot variance. If you want to see the estimated compound symmetry, within whole plot covariance and correlation matrices only, use the following PROC MIXED statements:

Program 5.15

```
proc mixed data=mice;
   class cage condition diet;
   model gain=condition|diet/ddfm=kr;
   random intercept / subject=cage;
   repeated / type=cs subject=cage*condition r rcorr;
run;
```

The options R and RCORR request listings of the covariance and correlation matrices, respectively, within a given CAGE × CONDITION unit.

Results

Output 5.20 shows the results.

Output 5.20: Compound Symmetry Analysis of Mouse Data

	Estimated R Matrix for cage*condition 1 1		
Row	Col1	Col2	Col3
1	25.3152	-6.2417	-6.2417
2	-6.2417	25.3152	-6.2417
3	-6.2417	-6.2417	25.3152

	Estimated R Correlation Matrix for cage*condition 1 1		
Row	Col1	Col2	Col3
1	1.0000	-0.2466	-0.2466
2	-0.2466	1.0000	-0.2466
3	-0.2466	-0.2466	1.0000

Covariance Parameter Estimates		
Cov Parm	Subject	Estimate
cage		5.0293
CS	cage*condition	-6.2417
Residual		31.5569

Type 3 Tests of Fixed Effects				
Effect	Num DF	Den DF	F Value	Pr > F
condition	3	4.72	4.31	0.0798
diet	2	16	0.82	0.4561
condition*diet	6	16	1.52	0.2334

Interpretation

The "Covariance Parameter Estimates" table shows estimates identical to the NOBOUND results, apart from some relabeling and minor rounding discrepancies between computations based on the RANDOM statement and those based on the REPEATED statement. "CS" corresponds to the estimate of CAGE*CONDITION variance, $\hat{\sigma}_W^2$, in the NOBOUND output. Here, you interpret it as the covariance between pairs of split plot experimental units. The row labeled "Residual" corresponds to the estimate of the split plot error, $\hat{\sigma}^2$, in the NOBOUND output. The "Type 3 Tests of Fixed Effects" table is identical to Output 5.19. For the "Estimated R Matrix," note that the terms on the diagonal are $\hat{\sigma}_{CS}^2 = \hat{\sigma}_W^2 + \hat{\sigma}^2 = 31.5569 - 6.2417 = 25.3152$, and the off-diagonal terms correspond to $\hat{\sigma}_W^2$.

In the "Estimated R Correlation Matrix" the off-diagonal terms are estimated interclass correlations,

$$\hat{\rho} = \frac{\hat{\sigma}_W^2}{\hat{\sigma}_W^2 + \hat{\sigma}^2} = \frac{-6.2417}{25.3152} = -0.2466$$

In general, the statements

```
random whole plot error;
```

and

```
repeated / type=cs subject=whole plot error;
```

produce identical analyses, and are in fact identical models, provided the whole plot variance component estimate is positive. If the NOBOUND option is used with the RANDOM statement, these two statements will also yield identical results. The main difference is that the compound symmetry analysis obtained using the REPEATED statement lends itself to a more palatable, and often more physically accurate, interpretation.

> **Note**: The compound symmetry alternative is viable for certain mixed model structures, such as the split-plot with well-defined whole plot and split plot variance components, when either the block or whole-plot variance has a negative solution. On the other hand, if both the block and whole-plot variance estimates are negative, or for more complex designs, such as the strip split-plot design shown in Figure 5.7, the compound symmetry approach cannot be used. In such cases, you must use either the NOBOUND option or the PROC MIXED METHOD=TYPE3, and live with the awkwardness of having to report a negative variance estimate.

5.8 A Note on PROC GLM Compared to PROC GLIMMIX and PROC MIXED: Incomplete Blocks, Missing Data, and Spurious Non-Estimability

As mentioned earlier in this chapter, there are several problems with PROC GLM compared to PROC GLIMMIX and PROC MIXED as a tool for analyzing multiple-error term factorial designs. The mouse data analysis in Section 5.7 reveals another problem, specific to the fact that the mouse data are unbalanced. In this case, the incomplete-block whole plot creates the unbalance, but unbalance also occurs when experiments are set up with complete-block whole plots but then data are lost or missing for various reasons. The problem illustrated in this section is especially serious if data from entire whole plots are missing.

Section 5.7.1 showed the analysis of variance for the mouse data. If you pursue this approach, you would logically want to include inference on the various main effect or simple effect means, and perhaps other contrasts as discussed in earlier examples. You could use the following SAS statements, which are not exhaustive, but are sufficient to illustrate why you do not want to use PROC GLM to analyze this type of data.

Program 5.16

```
proc glm data=mice;
   class cage condition diet;
   model gain=condition|diet cage cage*condition;
   lsmeans condition diet condition*diet;
run;
quit;
```

Output 5.21 shows the results.

Output 5.21: PROC GLM Output of Least Squares Means for Mouse Data

condition	gain LSMEAN
1	Non-est
2	Non-est
3	Non-est
4	Non-est

diet	gain LSMEAN
normal	57.9166667
restrict	55.5000000
suppleme	58.1666667

condition	diet	gain LSMEAN
1	normal	Non-est
1	restrict	Non-est
1	suppleme	Non-est
2	normal	Non-est
2	restrict	Non-est
2	suppleme	Non-est
3	normal	Non-est
3	restrict	Non-est
3	suppleme	Non-est
4	normal	Non-est
4	restrict	Non-est
4	suppleme	Non-est

You can see that no least squares means appear for the CONDITION or CONDITION × DIET effects. Instead, all you see is "Non-est." This means that PROC GLM has declared the CONDITION and CONDITION × DIET least squares means to be *nonestimable*. However, these means *should* be estimable, so what is the problem?

Recalling from Chapter 3, least squares means are defined as linear combinations of the fixed effects. Specifically, the CONDITION main effect least-squares means are defined as

$$\mu + \alpha_i + \frac{1}{3}\sum_j \beta_j + \frac{1}{3}\sum_j \alpha\beta_{ij}$$

where α and β refer to CONDITION and DIET, respectively. The CONDITION*DIET combination means are defined as $\mu + \alpha_i + \beta_j + \alpha\beta_{ij}$. Note that these definitions do not include random effects. In order for PROC GLM, PROC GLIMMIX, and PROC MIXED to compute least squares means, they must be *estimable*, meaning that the least squares mean must correspond to a linear combination of expected values of observations in the data set. The mixed model-based least squares means for CONDITION and CONDITION × DIET correspond to μ_i and μ_{ij} respectively, so there is no problem.

On the other hand, PROC GLM is not set up to distinguish between fixed and random effects. Instead, it defines the LSMEANS for CONDITION as

$$\mu + \alpha_i + \frac{1}{3}\sum_j \beta_j + \frac{1}{3}\sum_j \alpha\beta_{ij} + \frac{1}{6}\sum_k c_k + \frac{1}{6}\sum_k w_{ik}$$

and for CONDITION × DIET as

$$\mu + \alpha_i + \beta_j + \alpha\beta_{ij} + \frac{1}{6}\sum_k c_k + \frac{1}{6}\sum_k w_{ik}$$

including *all* effects in the model statement, regardless of whether they are fixed or random. However, three of the w_{ik} (CAGE × CONDITION combinations) are not observed. Thus, PROC GLM sets up the *estimate* of the CONDITION least squares mean as

$$\hat{\mu} + \hat{\alpha}_i + \frac{1}{3}\sum_j \hat{\beta}_j + \frac{1}{3}\sum_j \widehat{\alpha\beta}_{ij} + \frac{1}{6}\sum_k \hat{c}_k + \frac{1}{3}\sum_k I_{ik}\hat{w}_{ik}$$

where I_{ik} is equal to 1 if the ik^{th} CAGE × CONDITION combination is included in the design and 0 otherwise. However, this term fails the *estimability* criterion. That is, it cannot be expressed in terms of the expected values of the observations in the data set. The CONDITION × DIET least squares mean is similarly affected by the absent CAGE × CONDITION combination. Stroup (2013) referred to this as the "spurious non-estimability" problem.

The spurious non-estimability problem with the PROC GLM approach stems from the fact that it applies the estimability criterion indiscriminately—to random as well as fixed effects. There is no way to properly specify the model and get PROC GLM to compute least squares means for any treatment effects involving the whole plot factor unless observations are present in all whole plot blocks. The only way that PROC GLM will find estimable least squares means is to drop CAGE × CONDITION from the MODEL statement—that is, drop the whole plot error term from the analysis. If you do this, you will get results from the LSMEANS statement, but they will be incorrect for two reasons. First, they will not be adjusted for the effect of incomplete blocks. Second, all standard errors and tests will be based on an "error term" that pools MS(whole plot error) with MS(split plot error), whatever such a term estimates. In other words, you cannot use PROC GLM to analyze experiments with split plot features if they include incomplete block structure or missing whole plots. This is another reason why we recommend the use of true mixed models procedures, PROC GLIMMIX or PROC MIXED, and discourage the use of PROC GLM for all experiments with split plot structure. This includes repeated measures experiments, to be discussed in Chapter 8.

5.9 Summary

This chapter presents an extensive set of material required for analyzing factorial treatment structures with mixed models, focusing on those with hierarchical structure, i.e. more than one size experimental unit and hence multiple error terms. It begins by distinguishing between treatment structure and experiment structure, defining the factorial treatment structure and emphasizing that this treatment structure can be implemented using a variety of experiment structures. These range from simple completely randomized designs to complex split plot layouts.

Next, the chapter shows how to associate the various layouts with an appropriate mixed model. It then presented the various terms of interest in factorial experiments and how their standard errors and test statistics are affected by the experiment layout and the associated mixed model.

Three examples illustrate how to use SAS to analyze factorial data with multiple error terms. The examples all have split plot structures to illustrate the full range of mixed model issues, but the model and mean comparison methods shown could be used with any factorial structure. The main requirement is to adjust the RANDOM statement so that it accurately reflects the experiment layout. The first example (Section 5.4) is a standard two-factor factorial with qualitative factors (i.e., the factor levels are categories). The second example (Section 5.6) illustrates a two-factor factorial with factors having quantitative levels. The third example (Section 5.7) shows the inference problems that result when one or more variance component estimates are negative and what to do when this happens.

Finally, this chapter includes comments on PROC GLM, a fixed-effect-only linear model procedure, and PROC GLIMMIX and PROC MIXED—both true mixed model procedures—as tools for analyzing experiments with split plot features. The discussions focus on shortcomings of PROC GLM for this type of analysis, and why a true mixed model procedure should be the tool of choice. Section 5.5 comments on the major issues. Section 5.8 illustrates the problem of spurious non-estimability that occurs with PROC GLM in unbalanced designs with multiple error terms.

Although this chapter is long, it is also merely introductory. Subsequent chapters expand on the range of analyses with factorial treatment design and layouts with split plot features. Chapter 10 includes a section on multilocation experiments, an important and often misunderstood treatment structure with treatment and location as the factors. Chapter 8 covers repeated measures experiments, where treatment and time form a factorial structure. Chapter 13 considers split plot experiments with non-normally distributed response variables.

Chapter 6: Random Effects Models

6.1 Introduction: Descriptions of Random Effects Models..**181**	
6.1.1 Influent Example 182	
6.1.2 PROC MIXED to Estimate the Variance Components..184	
6.1.3 PROC GLIMMIX to Estimate Variance Components 184	
6.1.4 The Mixed Model Equations 185	
6.1.5 Method of Moments Estimators Using PROC MIXED...186	
6.2 One-Way Random Effects Treatment Structure: Influent Example..**188**	
6.2.1 The MIXED Procedure...188	
6.2.2 The GLIMMIX Procedure..190	
6.2.3 Comparison of the Estimation Methods Available in the MIXED and GLIMMIX Procedures.......................194	
6.3 A Simple Conditional Hierarchical Linear Model: An Example **196**	
6.3.1 PROC MIXED to Analyze the Data 197	
6.3.2 PROC GLIMMIX for the Analysis and Confidence Intervals...201	
6.4 Three-Level Nested Design Structure: An Example **202**	
6.4.1 Three-Level Nested Linear Model, an Unconditional Hierarchical Nested Linear Model 202	
6.4.2 Data Analysis Using the PROC MIXED METHOD=REML to Estimate the Variance Components 203	
6.4.3 PROC MIXED METHOD=TYPE1 to Estimate the Variance Components..............................204	
6.4.4 PROC GLIMMIX to Estimate the Variance Components and Provide ELR Confidence Intervals 204	
6.4.5 Conditional Hierarchical Linear Model or Mixed Model...205	
6.4.6 The MIXED and GLIMMIX Procedures to Fit the Model to the Data 206	
6.4.7 Unequal Variance Model 208	
6.5 A Two-Way Random Effects Treatment Structure to Estimate Heritability: An Example.......**210**	
6.5.1 PROC GLIMMIX To Analyze the Data 211	
6.5.2 PROC MIXED METHOD=TYPE3 212	
6.6 Modern ANOVA with Variance Components..**214**	
6.7 Summary...**216**	

6.1 Introduction: Descriptions of Random Effects Models

Random effects models are linear models where all the factors in the models are random variables. That is, their values are assumed to arise from a probability distribution. Random effects models are used in studies and experiments where the levels of the factors have been selected at random from a population of possible levels, and where you want to obtain information about the parameters of the distribution of those levels. The main goals of the analysis of random effects models are to do the following:

- estimate the parameters of the covariance structure of the random effects model

- test hypotheses about the parameters or functions of the parameters

- construct confidence intervals about the parameters or functions of the parameters

This chapter presents methods that are available in PROC GLIMMIX and PROC MIXED for estimating parameters of random effects models. For some simple models, we also cover procedures for testing hypotheses and for constructing confidence intervals. We then extend the methods to more complex examples in the final sections of the chapter.

The random effects model where the levels of the random effects and/or the experimental units form a nested hierarchical structure is also called the unconditional hierarchical linear model, as defined by Bryk and Raudenbush (1992). Models can be constructed to describe part of the variance between the levels of a random effect either by classifying the levels of a random effect into categories or by using continuous variables in the analysis of covariance context (see Chapter 7). The categorical variables and the continuous variables (called covariates) are considered to be fixed effects. Thus, conditional hierarchical linear models are mixed models. We describe some basic conditional hierarchical linear models in this chapter while additional models are discussed in other chapters.

Pure random effects models are applied to experiments where all the factors in the treatment structure of the designed experiment or study are random effects. The factors in the design structure are always considered as random effects (see Milliken and Johnson 2009, Chapter 4, for discussions of design and treatment structures). A factor is called a random effect if the levels of that factor selected to be included in the study or experiment are randomly selected from a population of possible levels of that factor.

6.1.1 Influent Example

Suppose you are studying the source of nitrogen contamination in the Mississippi River at New Orleans. You could go out and obtain water samples from every source of influent that eventually reaches the Mississippi River. There are thousands of influents into the Mississippi river, and it would be very expensive and time-consuming to sample every one of them (also, you most likely would want to sample them over time). Another strategy would be to identify all the influents into the river (i.e., specify the population of influents) and then randomly select, say, 100 of the influents to be actually measured. In this case, we assume that the concentration of nitrogen in the water from the influents in the population forms a distribution of nitrogen levels with mean μ_N and variance σ^2_{Infl}. By randomly selecting the influents to be sampled, we use the sample mean and variance to provide estimates of the population parameters. A model to describe the observed nitrogen concentration from the ith sample is as follows:

$$y_i = \mu_N + a_i; \ i = 1, 2..., s; \ a_i \sim N(0, \sigma^2_{Infl}) \tag{6.1}$$

Equation 6.1 is that of a single sample of size s obtained from a population with parameters μ_N and σ^2_{Infl}. Alternatively, you can express Equation 6.1 in probability distribution form as follows:

$$y_i \sim N\left(\mu_N, \sigma^2_{Infl}\right)$$

This is the type of data set you may have encountered in your first course in statistical methods, but it most likely was not represented as a model. Equation 6.1 can actually be considered to be a simple mixed model, where μ_N is the fixed effects part and a_i is the random effects part of the model. μ_N denotes the intercept or overall mean of the model. The estimates of the parameters can be obtained with PROC MIXED by using Program 6.1.

Program 6.1
```
proc mixed;
   model y = / solution;
run;
```

Alternatively, you may use PROC GLIMMIX with the same MODEL statement. The MODEL statement above includes an intercept (unless you specify the NOINT option in the MODEL statement) that provides the estimate of μ_N. The estimate of σ^2_{Infl} is computed from the residuals of the model, which are the deviations of the observations from the estimate of μ_N. (Using PROC MIXED in this context is like using a sledgehammer to drive a carpet tack, but the chapter uses this example to begin the introduction to using SAS mixed model procedures for random effects models.) The normality assumption is made to provide a distributional basis for testing hypotheses and for constructing confidence intervals about the parameters of the model. The best linear unbiased estimate (BLUE) of μ_N is $\bar{y}.$, which has the following sampling distribution:

$$\bar{y}. \sim N(\mu_N, s^{-1}\sigma^2_{Infl})$$

The best quadratic unbiased estimate (BQUE) of σ^2_{Infl} is the following:

$$\hat{\sigma}^2_{Infl} = \sum_{i=1}^{s}(y_i - \bar{y}.)^2 / (s-1)$$

The sampling distribution associated with $\hat{\sigma}^2_{Infl}$ is as follows:

$$(s-1)\hat{\sigma}^2_{Infl} / \sigma^2_{Infl} \sim \chi^2_{(s-1)}$$

Tests of hypotheses and confidence intervals are computed as described in any elementary or basic text on statistics using the chi-square distribution. We include the confidence intervals for completeness. A $(1-\alpha)$ 100% confidence interval about μ_N is as follows:

$$\bar{y}. \pm (t_{a/2,(s-1)})\hat{\sigma}_{Infl} / \sqrt{s}$$

A $(1 - \alpha)$ 100% confidence interval about σ^2_{Infl} is expressed as follows:

$$\frac{(s-1)\hat{\sigma}^2_{\text{Infl}}}{\chi^2_{\alpha/2,\,(s-1)}} < \sigma^2_{\text{Infl}} < \frac{(s-1)\hat{\sigma}^2_{\text{Infl}}}{\chi^2_{1-\alpha/2,\,(s-1)}}$$

To accommodate demands of this problem better, you most likely want to obtain information from multiple sites from each selected influent. In this case, suppose that n_i sites are randomly selected from the population of possible sites within each randomly selected influent. The number of sites may vary from influent to influent, possibly depending on the size of the influent, as you may want to select the same proportion of the possible sites from each selected influent based on approximate flow volume. Let y_{ij} denote the nitrogen concentration in the water sample taken from the jth site at the ith influent. A model to describe the collection of these measurements is as follows:

$$y_{ij} = \mu_N + a_i + e_{ij};\ i = 1,2,\ldots,\ s;\ j = 1,2,\ldots,n_i \tag{6.2}$$

where terms are defined as follows:

- $a_i \sim iid\ N(0, \sigma^2_{\text{Infl}})$

- $e_{ij} \sim iid\ N(0, \sigma^2_{\text{site}})$

Equation 6.2 is the simplest type of traditional random effects model that has two variance component parameters. The variance component σ^2_{Infl} measures the influent-to-influent variability as in Equation 6.1. The variance component σ^2_{site} measures the site-to-site variability within an influent. Equation 6.2 can again be considered a mixed effects model where μ_N is the fixed effects part of the model, a_i is the random effects part of the model, and e_{ij} is the residual part of the model. Equation 6.2 is also called a two-level hierarchical linear model (Bryk and Raudenbush 1992) because the sampled sites are nested within each sampled influent. The PROC GLIMMIX statements to fit Equation 6.2 are as follows:

Program 6.2

```
proc glimmix;
   class influent;
   model y = ;
   random influent;
run;
```

Equation 6.2 is the usual one-way random-effects treatment structure model where the levels of the treatment are the randomly selected influents. If you apply classical analysis of variance to compute sums of squares and evaluate their expected means squares, you obtain the results displayed in Table 6.1.

Table 6.1: Analysis of Variance Table for a One-Way Random Effects Treatment Structure

Source	df	Sum of Squares	Expected Mean Squares
Influents	$s - 1$	$\displaystyle\sum_{i=1}^{s} n_i (\bar{y}_{i.} - \bar{y}_{..})^2$	$\sigma^2_{\text{site}} + C\sigma^2_{\text{infl}}$
Sites (Influents)	$\displaystyle\sum_{i=1}^{s}(n_i - 1) = n_. - s$	$\displaystyle\sum_{i=1}^{s}\sum_{j=1}^{n_i}(y_{ij} - \bar{y}_{i.})^2$	σ^2_{site}

The information in Table 6.1 can be obtained by using PROC MIXED to analyze the data by specifying METHOD=TYPE1 as in Program 6.3.

Program 6.3

```
proc mixed method=type1 covtest CL;
   class influent;
   model y = ;
   random influent;
   ods output covparms=cov1
run;
```

The TYPE1 analysis produces the analysis of variance table with sums of squares, degrees of freedom, mean squares, and expected mean squares. The expected mean squares are used to determine the appropriate divisor for F statistics of the effects in the analysis.

The coefficient C is computed as follows:

$$C = \frac{n. - \dfrac{\sum\limits_{i=1}^{s} n_i^2}{n.}}{s - 1}$$

(See Chapter 18 of Milliken and Johnson 2009.) Traditional method-of-moments estimators of the variance components are obtained by equating the observed mean squares to the expected mean squares replacing the variances with estimators. The method-of-moments equations are the following:

$$MSI = \frac{\sum\limits_{i=1}^{t} n_i (\bar{y}_{i.} - \bar{y}_{..})^2}{s - 1} = \hat{\sigma}^2_{\text{site}} + C\,\hat{\sigma}^2_{\text{Infl}}$$

$$MSsite(I) = \frac{\sum\limits_{i=1}^{s}\sum\limits_{j=1}^{n_i} (y_{ij} - \bar{y}_{i.})^2}{n. - s} = \hat{\sigma}^2_{\text{site}}$$

The solution to the method of moment equations is as follows:

$$\tilde{\sigma}^2_{\text{Infl}} = \frac{MSI - MSsite(I)}{C}$$

$$\tilde{\sigma}^2_{\text{site}} = MSsite(I)$$

The method of moments estimators are the following:

$$\hat{\sigma}^2_{\text{site}} = \tilde{\sigma}^2_{\text{site}}$$

$$\hat{\sigma}^2_{\text{Infl}} = \begin{cases} \tilde{\sigma}^2_{\text{Infl}} & if\ \tilde{\sigma}^2_{\text{Infl}} > 0 \\ 0 & if\ \tilde{\sigma}^2_{\text{Infl}} \le 0 \end{cases} \tag{6.3}$$

The process of solving the method-of-moments equations does not guarantee that the solution is in the assumed parameter space. That is, the solution can yield negative values for the variance components. When that occurs, the estimate is set to zero as shown in Equation 6.3.

6.1.2 PROC MIXED to Estimate the Variance Components

PROC MIXED provides six types of estimators of the variance components. Restricted maximum likelihood (REML) estimators and maximum likelihood (ML) estimators are based on the normality assumptions stated in Equation 6.2. The third procedure is MIVQUE0, which provides estimates that are a form of method of moments estimator. The other three are methods of moments estimators based on Type 1, Type 2, or Type 3 sums of squares. The estimators obtained with the REML, MIVQUE0, TYPE1, TYPE2, and TYPE3 methods are identical for balanced data sets when the solution to the method-of-moments equations is in the parameter space. All of the estimators can be different when the data are unbalanced. Method-of-moments estimators are unbiased estimators under the assumption that random effects and errors are independently distributed. The MIVQUE0 estimators are minimum variance within the class of quadratic unbiased estimators without the assumption of normality. If you assume that the random effects are normally distributed, then the REML and ML estimators contain theoretically optimal large sample properties of maximum likelihood estimators. The likelihood estimators are obtained by maximizing the likelihood (either full or residual) function over the parameter space (see Appendix A for details).

6.1.3 PROC GLIMMIX to Estimate Variance Components

For the REML and ML estimates, which are the most modern and recommended approaches, PROC MIXED and PROC GLIMMIX provide estimates of the standard errors of the estimates of the variance components computed from the inverse of the estimated information (second derivative, Hessian) matrix. A naive Wald-type z-score can be computed as the ratio of the estimate to the corresponding estimate of its standard error to test the hypothesis $H_0: \sigma^2_{Infl} = 0$ versus H_a: $\sigma^2_{Infl} > 0$. The z-score is valid only when the sampling distribution of $\hat{\sigma}^2_{Infl}$ can be approximated by a normal distribution. But this approximation is not appropriate when the number of levels of the random treatment is small, as is the case in this example, because the sampling distribution is skewed to the right. When the number of levels is large, the z-score can be used approximately and quickly to test $H_0: \sigma^2_{Infl} = 0$ versus $H_a: \sigma^2_{Infl} > 0$ (the alternative hypothesis is one-sided).

The –2 REML Log Likelihood value is obtained by evaluating the likelihood at the selected estimators. If you want to compare two models for which the random effects of one model are a subset of the random effects of the other, you can formally test whether the additional parameters are zero with a likelihood ratio test defined on the respective –2 REML Log Likelihoods of the two models. There are some technical difficulties with this approach but it can work well; refer to Appendix A for details.

PROC GLIMMIX offers several additional methods for estimating variance components as well as the fixed effects. The scenario is more complicated here because of the assumed link function. The default method is to use the *pseudo-likelihood equations*. The pseudo-likelihood equations are identical to the mixed model equations for normally distributed data (See Appendix B and Chapter 2). Estimation methods ending in "PL" are pseudo-likelihood techniques. The first letter of the METHOD= identifier determines whether estimation is based on a residual likelihood ("R") or a maximum likelihood ("M"). The second letter identifies the expansion locus for the underlying approximation. Pseudo-likelihood methods for generalized linear mixed models can be cast in terms of Taylor series expansions (linearizations) of the GLMM. The expansion locus of the expansion is either the vector of random effects solutions ("S") or the mean of the random effects ("M"). The expansions are also referred to as the "S"ubject-specific and "M"arginal expansions. Thus, the RSPL technique is based on the residual pseudo-likelihood with the random effects solution as the expansion locus. The MSPL technique is based on the maximum pseudo-likelihood with the random effects solution as the expansion locus. The RMPL technique is based on the residual pseudo-likelihood with the mean of the random effects as the expansion locus. The MMPL technique is based on the maximum pseudo-likelihood with the mean of the random effects as the expansion locus. These methods were co-invented by at least four independent groups worldwide in the early 1990s and have proven to be very successful ever since.

For models with a few random effects, the *LAPLACE method* in PROC GLIMMIX can provide even better results than the aforementioned Taylor-series methods. Laplace's method also approximates the marginal likelihood with a Taylor series, but with a more sophisticated expansion point, and optimization is performed in one step rather than sequentially computing adjusted residuals. For models that assume normally distributed observations, Laplace's method merely reproduces maximum likelihood covariance parameter estimates. The Laplace method, as well as the *QUAD method* described below, is primarily useful for GLMMs with non-normal data; it often exhibits better asymptotic behavior and less small-sample bias than pseudo-likelihood estimators (but see Chapter 11, 12, 13, and Appendix B for a more in-depth discussion of the advantages and disadvantages of the methods available in PROC GLIMMIX). The QUAD method approximates the marginal log likelihood with an adaptive Gauss-Hermite quadrature. Compared to the LAPLACE method, estimates of GLMM variance parameters have potentially better asymptotic behavior, but the models for which parameters can be estimated by quadrature are further restricted. In addition to the conditional independence assumption, it is required that models suitable for the QUAD method can be processed by subjects. This in turn requires that all RANDOM statements have SUBJECT= effects and, in the case of multiple SUBJECT= effects, that these form a containment hierarchy. In a containment hierarchy each effect is contained by another effect, and the effect contained by all is considered "the" effect for subject processing. As is the case with Laplace, for models assuming normality, QUAD gives you maximum likelihood variance component estimates. Neither Laplace nor QUAD permit R-side covariance parameters.

The Residual methods account for the fixed effects in the construction of the objective function, which reduces the bias in covariance parameter estimates. Estimation methods involving Taylor series create pseudo-data for each optimization. Those data are transformed to have zero mean in a residual method. While the covariance parameter estimates in a residual method are the maximum likelihood estimates for the transformed problem, the fixed-effects estimates are (estimated) generalized least squares estimates. In a likelihood method that is not residual based, both the covariance parameters and the fixed-effects estimates are maximum likelihood estimates where the estimates of the covariance parameters are known to have greater bias. In some problems, residual likelihood estimates of covariance parameters are unbiased. Details of the methods are in Appendix B.

6.1.4 The Mixed Model Equations

The fixed effects part of Equation 6.2 is μ_N and is estimated by solving the mixed models equations (see Appendix A). To review briefly, the linear mixed model can be expressed as

$$\mathbf{y} = \mathbf{X}\boldsymbol{\beta} + \mathbf{Z}\mathbf{u} + \mathbf{e}$$

where the terms are defined as follows:

- **Y** is the data vector
- β is the coefficient vector corresponding to the fixed effects
- **X** is the design matrix for the fixed effects
- **U** is the coefficient vector corresponding to the random effects
- **Z** is the design matrix for the random effects part of the model
- **E** is the error vector

In this chapter it is assumed that **u** and **e** are uncorrelated random variables with zero means and covariance matrices **G** and **R**, respectively. Thus, the covariance matrix of the data vector is **V** = **ZGZ'** + **R** (see Chapter 9 for more details). The solution of the mixed model equations for β and **u** is as follows:

$$\hat{\beta} = (\mathbf{X'\hat{V}^{-1}X})^{-1}\mathbf{X'\hat{V}^{-1}y}$$
$$\hat{\mathbf{u}} = \mathbf{\hat{G}Z'\hat{V}^{-1}(y - X\hat{\beta})}$$

In PROC MIXED and PROC GLIMMIX, the SOLUTION option in the MODEL statement requests a listing of $\hat{\beta}$, and the SOLUTION option in the RANDOM statement requests a listing of $\hat{\mathbf{u}}$. Estimates of estimable linear combinations of β added to linear combinations of **u** provide predicted values of predictable functions. For Equation 6.2, the matrices above are $\beta = \mu_N \mathbf{j}_n$, $\mathbf{X} = \mathbf{j}_s \otimes \mathbf{j}_{n_i}$, $\mathbf{u}' = (a_1, a_2, \cdots, a_s)$, $\mathbf{Z} = \mathbf{I}_s \otimes \mathbf{j}_{n_i}$, $\mathbf{G} = \sigma_s^2 \mathbf{I}_s$, $\mathbf{R} = \sigma_e^2 \mathbf{I}_n$ and **e** is the random error. The notation $\mathbf{A} \otimes \mathbf{B}$ denotes the *right* direct product of matrices **A** and **B**, $\mathbf{I}_t$ denotes a $t \times t$ identity matrix, and $\mathbf{j}_n$ denotes an $n \times 1$ vector of ones.

6.1.5 Method of Moments Estimators Using PROC MIXED

The solution to the method of moments equations can be obtained with PROC MIXED by specifying either Type 1, Type 2, or Type 3 as the estimation method for the variance components. Type 1 is a sequential breakdown of sums of squares and depends on the order of the effects. Types 2 and 3 are order-independent but do not provide a partitioning of total variability as does Type 1. Types 2 and 3 differ in their moment equation construction for unbalanced data. (See Milliken and Johnson (2009) for a good description of the types of sums of squares).

Program

Program 6.4 shows the use of METHOD=TYPE3.

Program 6.4

```
proc mixed method=type3 covtest cl;
   class influent;
   model y = ;
   random influent;
run;
```

Results

The Type 3 analysis provides an analysis of variance table with expected means squares and an *F* value to test the hypothesis that the influent variance is equal to 0. The results are in Output 6.1.

Output 6.1: Type 3 Sums of Squares for the Influent Data

Type 3 Analysis of Variance								
Source	DF	Sum of Squares	Mean Square	Expected Mean Square	Error Term	Error DF	F Value	Pr > F
influent	5	1925.193608	385.038722	Var(Residual) + 6.0973 Var(influent)	MS(Residual)	31	9.04	<.0001
Residual	31	1319.779365	42.573528	Var(Residual)	.	.	.	.

Covariance Parameter Estimates							
Cov Parm	Estimate	Standard Error	Z Value	Pr Z	Alpha	Lower	Upper
influent	56.1667	36.7495	1.53	0.1264	0.05	-15.8611	128.19
Residual	42.5735	10.8446	3.93	<.0001	0.05	27.3632	75.2494

Interpretation

The estimate of the residual variance component is 42.57. The confidence interval is computed using the usual chi-square interval about a variance.

A $(1 - \alpha)100\%$ confidence interval about σ^2_{site} is as follows:

$$\frac{df \times \hat{\sigma}^2_{site}}{\chi^2_{\alpha/2, df}} < \sigma^2_{site} < \frac{df \times \hat{\sigma}^2_{site}}{\chi^2_{1-\alpha/2, df}}$$

which is 27.36 to 75.25.

A Wald-type confidence interval about $\hat{\sigma}^2_{Infl}$ is $\hat{\sigma}^2_{Infl} \pm Z_{\alpha/2}$ StandardError of $\hat{\sigma}^2_{Infl}$. The interval is -15.86 to 128.19.

An approximate $(1 - \alpha)$ 100% confidence interval about $\hat{\sigma}^2_{Infl}$ using the Satterthwaite approximation as follows:

$$\frac{v\hat{\sigma}^2_{Infl}}{\chi^2_{a/2, v}} < \sigma^2_{Infl} < \frac{v\hat{\sigma}^2_{Infl}}{\chi^2_{1-a/2, v}}$$

where v are degrees of freedom determined by using the Satterthwaite approximation. In this case, the approximate degrees of freedom are calculated as follows:

$$v = \frac{(\hat{\sigma}^2_{Infl})^2}{\frac{\left[\frac{MSI}{C}\right]^2}{s-1} + \frac{\left[\frac{MSsite(I)}{C}\right]^2}{n_. - s}}$$

The Satterthwaite approximation provides an approximation to the sampling distribution of linear combinations of mean squares. In this case

$$\hat{\sigma}^2_{Infl} = MSI/C - MSsite(I)/C$$

and the approximating sampling distribution of $v\hat{\sigma}^2_{Infl} / \sigma^2_{Infl}$ is χ^2_v. As the number of influents increases, the sampling distribution of $\hat{\sigma}^2_{Infl}$ can be approximated by a normal distribution.

When the number of influents is not large, the normal approximation will not be appropriate, because it is a symmetric distribution and the estimates of variances generally have a right-skewed sampling distribution. The Satterthwaite approximations are provided by PROC MIXED and PROC GLIMMIX for the likelihood methods of estimating variance components. For this case $C = 6.0973$ with 3.9 *df*. The resulting 95% confidence interval is 20.06 to 473.55.

Another statistic to test the hypothesis H_0: $\sigma^2_{Infl} = 0$ versus H_a: $\sigma^2_{Infl} > 0$ is as follows:

$$F_c = \frac{MSI}{MSsite(I)}$$

where the decision rule is to reject H_0 if and only if the following holds:

$$F_c > F_{\alpha, (t-1), (n_.-t)}$$

The sampling distribution of F_c is exact when the random effects are independently distributed as normal random variables. This test statistic is preferred over the *z*-score when the number of degrees of freedom associated with a random effect is small or when the test is exact. For this example the value of the F test is 9.04 based on 5 and 31 degrees of freedom with significance level <0.0001. In reality, we know that σ^2_{Infl} cannot be equal to 0, but σ^2_{Infl} may be small enough compared to σ^2_{site} to be considered negligible.

6.2 One-Way Random Effects Treatment Structure: Influent Example

The data in data set "Mississippi River" are the nitrogen concentrations in parts per million from several sites at six of the randomly selected influents to the Mississippi River. In a real-life study you would want to select many more than six sites to monitor the Mississippi River, but we use only six influents for demonstration purposes. The model in Equation 6.2 is used to describe the process, and we want to estimate the mean μ_N, the variance components, σ^2_{Infl}, and σ^2_{site}, and the predicted value for each influent, $\mu_N + a_i$.

Although our main focus at this point is statistical inference, note that this model can also be used to predict new measurements. This predicted value is simply the sum of estimated fixed and random effects. This is the first example in this book of a *best linear unbiased predictor* (BLUP), covered in greater detail in Chapter 9.

6.2.1 The MIXED Procedure

PROC MIXED is used to compute the estimates of the variance components and the population mean, predicted values for each level of influent, and predicted values for the deviations of the influent effects from the population mean using all of the methods available for estimating variance components.

Program

Program 6.5 is the PROC MIXED program to provide REML estimates of the variance components.

Program 6.5

```
proc mixed data=influent covtest cl;
   class influent;
   model y = /solution;
   random influent / solution;
/*--The following Estimate statements provide predictions of the Influent means as--*/
/*--MUhat+ahat1,… ,MUhat+ahat6                                                    --*/
   estimate 'influent 1' intercept 1 | influent 1 0 0 0 0 0;
   estimate 'influent 2' intercept 1 | influent 0 1 0 0 0 0;
   estimate 'influent 3' intercept 1 | influent 0 0 1 0 0 0;
   estimate 'influent 4' intercept 1 | influent 0 0 0 1 0 0;
   estimate 'influent 5' intercept 1 | influent 0 0 0 0 1 0;
   estimate 'influent 6' intercept 1 | influent 0 0 0 0 0 1;
/*---The following estimate statements reproduce the Solution for Random Effects---*/
/*--- as ahat1,…, ahat6                                                         ---*/
   estimate 'influent 1U' | influent 1 0 0 0 0 0;
   estimate 'influent 2U' | influent 0 1 0 0 0 0;
   estimate 'influent 3U' | influent 0 0 1 0 0 0;
   estimate 'influent 4U' | influent 0 0 0 1 0 0;
   estimate 'influent 5U' | influent 0 0 0 0 1 0;
   estimate 'influent 6U' | influent 0 0 0 0 0 1;
   ods output covparms=cvps;
run;
```

Notice that the first six ESTIMATE statements include the intercept (μ_N) and an INFLUENT effect. The vertical bar (|) separates the fixed effects (to the left of the vertical bar) and random effects (to the right). The coefficient of 1 on each effect defines the requested term as $\hat{\mu}_N + \hat{a}_i$. The second six ESTIMATE statements, e.g. "INFLUENT 1U," do not include any fixed effect; they simply request $\hat{a}_i$. The "INFLUENT xU" terms reproduce the information in the "Solutions for Random Effects" table; we include them here for illustrative purposes only. The results are displayed in Output 6.2.

Results

The results from this PROC MIXED run are shown in Output 6.2 with estimates of the variance components and solutions for the fixed and random effects.

Output 6.2: REML Estimates of the Variance Components and Estimated BLUP for Each INFLUENT

Covariance Parameter Estimates							
Cov Parm	Estimate	Standard Error	Z Value	Pr > Z	Alpha	Lower	Upper
influent	63.3211	45.2315	1.40	0.0808	0.05	22.5560	539.98
Residual	42.6583	10.8571	3.93	<.0001	0.05	27.3960	75.4984

Solution for Fixed Effects					
Effect	Estimate	Standard Error	DF	t Value	Pr > |t|
Intercept	21.2231	3.4290	5	6.19	0.0016

Solution for Random Effects						
Effect	influent	Estimate	Std Err Pred	DF	t Value	Pr > |t|
influent	1	0.3093	3.8193	31	0.08	0.9360
influent	2	-6.7193	3.9170	31	-1.72	0.0963
influent	3	-3.8979	4.0805	31	-0.96	0.3468
influent	4	2.9461	3.9870	31	0.74	0.4655
influent	5	-6.0130	4.0805	31	-1.47	0.1507
influent	6	13.3748	4.0805	31	3.28	0.0026

Estimates					
Label	Estimate	Standard Error	DF	t Value	Pr > |t|
influent 1	21.5324	2.1135	5	10.19	0.0002
influent 2	14.5038	2.3769	5	6.10	0.0017
influent 3	17.3252	2.7721	5	6.25	0.0015
influent 4	24.1692	2.5518	5	9.47	0.0002
influent 5	15.2102	2.7721	5	5.49	0.0027
influent 6	34.5979	2.7721	5	12.48	<.0001
influent 1U	0.3093	3.8193	31	0.08	0.9360
influent 2U	-6.7193	3.9170	31	-1.72	0.0963
influent 3U	-3.8979	4.0805	31	-0.96	0.3468
influent 4U	2.9461	3.9870	31	0.74	0.4655
influent 5U	-6.0130	4.0805	31	-1.47	0.1507
influent 6U	13.3748	4.0805	31	3.28	0.0026

The SOLUTION option in the MODEL statement requests the estimates of the fixed effects, which in this case is just the population mean and corresponds to the INTERCEPT. The SOLUTION option in the RANDOM statement provides predicted values of the random effects with expectation zero, which are listed as a solution for the random effect. The COVTEST option provides the estimates of the standard errors of the variance components, z-scores, and associated p-values. The CL option provides 95% confidence intervals about the variance components where the level of confidence can be controlled by the option ALPHA=xx, which yields (1–xx)100% confidence intervals.

ESTIMATE statements are used to compute predictions of predictable functions. The first set of ESTIMATE statements provides predicted values for the concentrations of nitrogen levels at each influent. These predictions are the best linear unbiased predictors (BLUP) of the nitrogen level at each influent (see Chapter 9 for a detailed discussion of BLUP). The second set of ESTIMATE statements requests predictions of the deviations from the overall mean for each influent. This set of ESTIMATE statements is included to simply show that you can obtain the solutions for the random effects through ESTIMATE statements. To obtain predictions involving the random effects, the random effects coefficients are listed after the vertical bar (|) in the ESTIMATE statement.

Program

The confidence intervals provided by PROC MIXED for the Residual and Influent variance components where estimates are obtained using the methods REML and ML are Satterthwaite-based confidence intervals. To demonstrate, you can use Program 6.6 to compute the degrees of freedom and the 95% confidence limits for each estimate from the data set created by the ODS OUTPUT statement COVPARMS=COVPS.

Program 6.6

```
data cvp1; set cvps;
/*compute Satterthwaite degrees of freedom*/
df=2*(estimate/stderr)**2;
/*Chi-Square percentage points*/
y=quantile('CHISQ', .025, df);
x=quantile('CHISQ', .975, df);
/*lower limit*/
low=df*estimate/x;
/*upper limit*/
high=df*estimate/y;
run;
proc print data=cvp1;
var CovParm Estimate StdErr df Lower Upper low high;
format df 5.1 Estimate StdErr Lower Upper low high 7.2;
run;
```

Results

The estimated degrees of freedom associated with an estimate of the variance component is $df = 2*(\text{Estimate/Stderr})^2$. Then the confidence intervals are computed using the chi-square percentage points as determined by the QUANTILE function. The results are shown in Output 6.3.

Output 6.3: Comparison of the PROC MIXED Confidence Intervals with the Satterthwaite Approximation Confidence Intervals

Obs	CovParm	Estimate	StdErr	df	Lower	Upper	low	high
1	influent	63.32	45.23	3.9	22.56	539.98	22.56	539.98
2	Residual	42.66	10.86	30.9	27.40	75.50	27.40	75.50

The confidence intervals provided by PROC MIXED for the REML method are based on the Satterthwaite approximation method. The confidence limits provided by PROC MIXED are labeled as LOWER and UPPER. The recomputed confidence intervals using the associated degrees of freedom and chi-square distribution (like Section 6.1.3) are labeled as LOW and HIGH. The two sets of intervals are identical which substantiates that the confidence intervals from PROC MIXED are based on the Satterthwaite approximation.

6.2.2 The GLIMMIX Procedure

PROC GLIMMIX can be used to obtain similar results as PROC MIXED with some slight modifications to the program. Program 6.7 shows these modifications and use of the COVTEST statement to obtain a likelihood ratio statistic for σ^2_{Infl}.

Program

The PROC GLIMMIX Program 6.7 provides REML estimates of the variance components.

Program 6.7

```
proc glimmix data=influent;
   class influent;
   model y = /solution;
   random influent / solution;
/*---Estimate statement provides predictions of the influent means as   ---*/
/*---MUhat+ahat1,…, MUhat+ahat6                                          ---*/

   estimate 'influent 1' intercept 1 | influent 1 0 0 0 0 0;
   estimate 'influent 2' intercept 1 | influent 0 1 0 0 0 0;
   estimate 'influent 3' intercept 1 | influent 0 0 1 0 0 0;
   estimate 'influent 4' intercept 1 | influent 0 0 0 1 0 0;
   estimate 'influent 5' intercept 1 | influent 0 0 0 0 1 0;
   estimate 'influent 6' intercept 1 | influent 0 0 0 0 0 1;
/*---The following estimate statements reproduce the Solution for Random Effects---*/
/*--- as ahat1,…, ahat6                                                   ---*/
   estimate 'influent 1U' | influent 1 0 0 0 0 0;
   estimate 'influent 2U' | influent 0 1 0 0 0 0;
```

```
    estimate 'influent 3U' | influent 0 0 1 0 0 0;
    estimate 'influent 4U' | influent 0 0 0 1 0 0;
    estimate 'influent 5U' | influent 0 0 0 0 1 0;
    estimate 'influent 6U' | influent 0 0 0 0 0 1;
    covtest 'influent variance=0?' 0 . / cl;
run;
```

The PROC GLIMMIX MODEL, RANDOM and ESTIMATE statements are identical to those in PROC MIXED. Their output is identical as well, and not shown here. The only difference is that the COVTEST option in the PROC MIXED statement has been replaced by the COVTEST statement in PROC GLIMMIX. This statement enables you to compute a likelihood ratio test for hypotheses about covariance parameters as well as confidence intervals for covariance parameter estimates. In Equation 6.2 there are two covariance parameters, σ^2_{Infl} and σ^2_{site}. The statement COVTEST "INFLUENT VARIANCE=0?" 0 . provides a likelihood ratio statistic to test $H_0 : \sigma^2_{\text{Infl}} = 0$. The zero tells PROC GLIMMIX to test the first variance component, and the dot (.) tells PROC GLIMMIX to allow the second variance component to take on whatever value the solution to estimation procedure produces.

You could obtain the likelihood ratio statistic by using PROC MIXED with two runs, one with the RANDOM INFLUENT statement, one without. The former gives you a "−2 ResLog Likelihood" value of 252.35, the latter gives you 267.82. The difference is a χ^2 statistic with one degree of freedom (the difference between the number of covariance parameters in the full model and the number of nonzero parameters under the null hypothesis. The value is 15.47. The PROC GLIMMIX COVTEST statement gives you this test statistic and its associated *p*-value without the need for two runs. The CL option produces the same upper and lower confidence bounds as the COVTEST CL option in PROC MIXED.

Results

The results of Program 6.7 are displayed in Output 6.4.

Output 6.4: REML Estimates of the Variance Components

			Wald 95% Confidence Bounds	
Cov Parm	**Estimate**	**Standard Error**		
influent	63.3233	45.2342	22.5563	540.04
Residual	42.6581	10.8570	27.3959	75.4980

Covariance Parameter Estimates

		-2 Res Log Like			
Label	**DF**		**ChiSq**	**Pr > ChiSq**	**Note**
influent variance=0?	1	267.82	15.47	<.0001	MI

Tests of Covariance Parameters Based on the Restricted Likelihood

MI: P-value based on a mixture of chi-squares.

The "Wald" confidence bounds, which are actually Satterthwaite bounds, are, aside from a slight rounding error, the same as those that are produced by the COVTEST option in the PROC MIXED statement. The rounding error comes from the fact that PROC GLIMMIX, in order to accommodate non-normal data, uses an updated algorithm. For normally distributed data, the estimating equations are the same but the implementation differs slightly. The "Test of Covariance Parameters" table shows the likelihood ratio test for $H_0 : \sigma^2_{\text{Infl}} = 0$. The table gives the -2 Res Log Likelihood under the null hypothesis, the test statistic, and the *p*-value, in this case <0.0001.

The Wald/Satterthwaite confidence bounds represent the traditional approach, but they are not the only way to obtain confidence bounds. An alternative uses the likelihood ratio. Let $\boldsymbol{\sigma}$ denote the vector of covariance parameters, and $\log L(\hat{\boldsymbol{\sigma}})$ denote the restricted log likelihood given the REML estimates of the parameters of $\boldsymbol{\sigma}$. For the influent example,

$$\boldsymbol{\sigma}' = \begin{bmatrix} \sigma^2_{\text{Infl}} & \sigma^2_{\text{site}} \end{bmatrix}$$

Let

$$\log L\left(\hat{\boldsymbol{\sigma}} \mid \tilde{\sigma}_{\text{Infl}}^2\right)$$

denote the restricted log likelihood for a given value (not necessarily the REML or ML estimate) of the influent variance, denoted $\tilde{\sigma}_{\text{Infl}}^2$ and the estimate of the other covariance components, in this case σ_{site}^2, given $\tilde{\sigma}_{\text{Infl}}^2$.

We know that $-2\log(\Lambda)$, where Λ denotes the likelihood ratio, can be written as

$$2\left\{\log L\left(\hat{\boldsymbol{\sigma}}\right) - \log L\left(\hat{\sigma}_{\text{site}}^2 \mid \tilde{\sigma}_{\text{Infl}}^2\right)\right\}$$

and that it has an approximate χ^2 distribution. Just as a Wald/Satterthwaite confidence interval consists of all the values of the variance component such that the test statistic—for example, $v\hat{\sigma}_{\text{Infl}}^2 / \sigma_{\text{Infl}}^2$—is between upper and lower quantiles of the χ_v^2 distribution, you can form a 95% confidence interval for σ_{Infl}^2 from the set of all $\tilde{\sigma}_{\text{Infl}}^2$ such that the likelihood ratio test statistic is as follows:

$$2\left\{\log L\left(\hat{\boldsymbol{\sigma}}\right) - \log L\left(\hat{\sigma}_{\text{site}}^2 \mid \tilde{\sigma}_{\text{Infl}}^2\right)\right\} < \chi^2$$

Program

You can obtain the likelihood-based confidence intervals for covariance parameters in two ways. The profile likelihood ratio (PLR) re-estimates all the other covariance parameters for each new value of the parameter for which the confidence interval is being determined. For example, PLR re-estimates σ_{site}^2 for each new value of σ_{Infl}^2. The empirical likelihood ratio (ELR) uses the REML estimate of σ_{site}^2 to calculate the likelihood ratio for all values of σ_{Infl}^2 that are being evaluated. Use the following PROC GLIMMIX statements to obtain the profile likelihood ratio confidence intervals.

Program 6.8

```
proc glimmix data=e_6_2 noprofile;
   class influent;
   model y = /solution;
   random influent / solution;
   covtest /cl(type=plr);
run;
```

The TYPE=PLR option accompanying CL in the COVTEST statement requests the PLR confidence limits. The NOPROFILE option in the PROC statement is required if you want a confidence interval for the residual variance, in this case σ_{site}^2.

Results

Output 6.5 contains the PRL confidence intervals about the influent variance component and about the residual variance component.

Output 6.5: Variance Component Estimates with Profile Likelihood Ratio Confidence Bound—Including NOPROFILE

	Covariance Parameter Estimates						
					Profile Likelihood 95% Confidence Bounds		
				Lower		Upper	
Cov Parm	Subject	Estimate	Standard Error	Bound	Pr > Chisq	Bound	Pr > Chisq
Intercept	influent	63.3234	45.2343	16.9953	0.0500	331.08	0.0500
Residual		42.6581	10.8570	26.9167	0.0500	73.5144	0.0500

Profile likelihood ratio confidence bounds are based on the restricted likelihood

Program

If you do not include the NOPROFILE option, you obtain estimates of the ratio of each covariance parameter to the Residual variance. Program 6.9 does not include the NOPROFILE option.

Program 6.9

```
proc glimmix data=e_6_2;
   class influent;
   model y= /solution;
   random intercept/ subject=influent solution;
   covtest / cl(type=plr);
run;
```

Results

Program 6.9 does not contain the NOPROFILE option and thus in Output 6.9 there is a confidence interval about the ratio of influent variance component divided by the residual variance and, hence, there is no confidence interval about the residual variance component.

Output 6.6: Variance Component Estimates with Profile Likelihood Ratio Confidence Bound—without NOPROFILE

| | | | | | Profile Likelihood 95% Confidence Bounds | | | | |
Cov Parm	Subject	Estimate	Standard Error	Ratio Estimate	Lower Bound	Pr > Chisq	Upper Bound	Pr > Chisq	Note
Intercept	influent	63.3233	45.2342	1.4844	0.3271	0.0500	8.2714	0.0500	R
Residual		42.6581	10.8570	1.0000					

Covariance Parameter Estimates

Profile likelihood ratio confidence bounds are based on the restricted likelihood
Bounds marked 'R' in Note column are bounds for the ratio with the residual variance.

Interpretation

If you include the NOPROFILE option, you get confidence intervals for both variance components. In this case, a 95% confidence interval for the influent variance σ^2_{Infl} is $(17.0, 331.1)$ and for the residual variance, σ^2_{site} is $(26.9, 73.5)$. If you do not include the NOPROFILE option, you get a confidence bound for the ratio $\sigma^2_{\text{Infl}}/\sigma^2_{\text{site}}$ instead of confidence bounds for the influent variance, and you do not get any confidence interval for the residual variance. Notice that the PLR confidence bounds are narrower than the default Satterthwaite bounds—e.g. PLR $(17.0, 331.1)$ for the influent variance versus Satterthwaite $(22.6, 540.0)$. (See Output 6.3.) You can show by simulation that percent coverage for the PLR and Satterthwaite methods is about the same, but Satterthwaite intervals are wider than necessary (see Wicklin 2013).

Program

Profile likelihood ratio confidence limits can be computationally demanding for models with complex covariance structure, because all of the covariance parameters are re-estimated for every prospective value examined in the construction of confidence bounds for each covariance parameter. The empirical likelihood ratio approach retains most of the advantages of PLR and is much less computationally intensive. Use Program 6.10 for the ELR approach.

Program 6.10

```
proc glimmix data=e_6_2 noprofile;
   class influent;
   model y= /solution;
   random intercept/ subject=influent solution;
   covtest / cl(type=elr);
run;
```

Results

The interesting results are to compare the widths of the ELR confidence intervals to the widths of the PLR confidence intervals. The ELR confidence intervals are in Output 6.7 and the PLR confidence intervals are in Output 6.6.

Output 6.7: Confidence Intervals Using the NOPROFILE Option and ELR

| | | | | Estimated Likelihood 95% Confidence Bounds | | | |
| | | | | Lower | | Upper | |
Cov Parm	Subject	Estimate	Standard Error	Bound	Pr > Chisq	Bound	Pr > Chisq
Intercept	influent	63.3234	45.2343	17.4465	0.0500	331.05	0.0500
Residual		42.6581	10.8570	26.9251	0.0500	73.4083	0.0500

Covariance Parameter Estimates

Estimated likelihood ratio confidence bounds are based on the restricted likelihood

The ELR 95% confidence bounds are $(17.5, 331.1)$ for influent variance and $(26.9, 73.4)$ for site (residual) variance.

These are compared with $(17.0, 331.1)$ for influent and $(26.9, 73.5)$ for residual using the PLR method. The ELR confidence intervals tend to be slightly narrower. While coverage is slightly better with PLR, the difference is negligible for most models. If you are in doubt, run a simulation for the model and scenario with which you are working and decide accordingly (see Wicklin 2013).

6.2.3 Comparison of the Estimation Methods Available in the MIXED and GLIMMIX Procedures

PROC GLIMMIX has six methods and PROC MIXED has six methods for estimating the variance components. Four of the methods for PROC MIXED use types of sums of squares, which are not available with PROC GLIMMIX. All of the methods for PROC GLIMMIX are likelihood or pseudo-likelihood based. The REML and ML methods for PROC MIXED are likelihood based while the methods TYPE1, TYPE2, TYPE3 and MIVQUE0 are sums of squares based. The sums of squares methods do not depend on normality assumptions.

For comparison purposes, the variance components for the Influent data are computed by all twelve methods and the results are in Output 6.8.

Output 6.8: Estimates of the Variance Components Using Methods PROC MIXED and PROC GLIMMIX

Method	TYPE	CovParm	Estimate	StdErr	df	Lower	Upper
REML		influent	63.3211	45.2315	3.9	22.5560	539.98
REML		Residual	42.6583	10.8571	30.9	27.3960	75.4984
TYPE 1		influent	56.1667	36.7495	4.7	-15.8611	128.19
TYPE 1		Residual	42.5735	10.8446	30.8	27.3632	75.2494
TYPE 2		influent	56.1667	36.7495	4.7	-15.8611	128.19
TYPE 2		Residual	42.5735	10.8446	30.8	27.3632	75.2494
TYPE 3		influent	56.1667	36.7495	4.7	-15.8611	128.19
TYPE 3		Residual	42.5735	10.8446	30.8	27.3632	75.2494
ML		influent	51.2509	34.3498	4.5	19.1463	360.55
ML		Residual	42.6979	10.8776	30.8	27.4111	75.6157
Mivque0		influent	45.7541	28.0460	5.3	18.2275	254.60
Mivque0		Residual	51.3914	13.1418	30.6	32.9431	91.2372
RSPL	WALD	influent	63.3233	45.2342	3.9	22.5563	540.04
RSPL	ELR	influent	63.3233	45.2342	3.9	17.4465	331.05
RSPL	WALD	Residual	42.6581	10.8570	30.9	27.3959	75.4980
RSPL	ELR	Residual	42.6581	10.8570	30.9	26.9251	73.4083
MSPL	WALD	influent	51.2541	34.3534	4.5	19.1469	360.61
MSPL	ELR	influent	51.2541	34.3534	4.5	14.7931	230.65
MSPL	WALD	Residual	42.6974	10.8774	30.8	27.4108	75.6149
MSPL	ELR	Residual	42.6974	10.8774	30.8	26.9470	73.4522
RMPL	WALD	influent	63.3233	45.2342	3.9	22.5563	540.04
RMPL	ELR	influent	63.3233	45.2342	3.9	17.4465	331.05
RMPL	WALD	Residual	42.6581	10.8570	30.9	27.3959	75.4980

Method	TYPE	CovParm	Estimate	StdErr	df	Lower	Upper
RMPL	ELR	Residual	42.6581	10.8570	30.9	26.9251	73.4083
MMPL	WALD	influent	51.2541	34.3534	4.5	19.1469	360.61
MMPL	ELR	influent	51.2541	34.3534	4.5	14.7931	230.65
MMPL	WALD	Residual	42.6974	10.8774	30.8	27.4108	75.6149
MMPL	ELR	Residual	42.6974	10.8774	30.8	26.9470	73.4522
LAPLACE	WALD	influent	51.2534	34.3528	4.5	19.1467	360.60
LAPLACE	ELR	influent	51.2534	34.3528	4.5	14.7954	230.65
LAPLACE	WALD	Residual	42.6971	10.8773	30.8	27.4106	75.6143
LAPLACE	ELR	Residual	42.6971	10.8773	30.8	26.9471	73.4520
QUAD	WALD	influent	51.2534	34.3528	4.5	19.1467	360.60
QUAD	ELR	influent	51.2534	34.3528	4.5	14.7954	230.65
QUAD	WALD	Residual	42.6971	10.8773	30.8	27.4106	75.6143
QUAD	ELR	Residual	42.6971	10.8773	30.8	26.9471	73.4520

The estimates of the influent variance are around 51 for maximum likelihood methods and around 63 for the residual maximum likelihood methods. Note that for Gaussian data, the PROC GLIMMIX methods RSPL and RMPL produce identical results, as do MSPL and MMPL. Also, for Gaussian data, RSPL and RMPL solve the same estimating equations as REML in PROC MIXED. Similarly, MSPL and MMPL solve the same estimating equations as ML in PROC MIXED.

The maximum likelihood estimates are like dividing the sum of squares by n while the residual maximum likelihood methods are like dividing by $n-1$. The LAPLACE and QUAD estimates are close to the maximum likelihood estimates. In general, the residual maximum likelihood estimates of variances are larger and less biased than the maximum likelihood estimates. For most data analysis problems the residual maximum likelihood estimates are preferable to the maximum likelihood estimates. The profile likelihood methods (PLR and ELR) available in PROC GLIMMIX produce narrower intervals with no loss in coverage, thus giving you the most accurate confidence intervals based on the least biased estimating procedure.

Deciding which method to use in practice may not always be easy. We recommend trying at least a few different ones to see how they compare as above and in subsequent analyses below. For a more rigorous comparison, we recommend running a simulation study in which you use known and reasonable ground truth assumptions and then see which methods produce results best aligned with your objectives. Simulating data in SAS is straightforward; refer to Wicklin (2013) for a complete guide. You can use BY groups within PROC MIXED or PROC GLIMMIX to fit models on each simulated data set and then collect results across them.

PROC MIXED and PROC GLIMMIX can also be used to evaluate a given data set using estimates of variance components obtained from another study or a given set of hypothesized variance components. The NOPROFILE option in the PROC MIXED statement, together with the NOITER option in the PARMS statement, forces PROC MIXED to use these values without modification by iteration. Program 6.11 uses PROC GLIMMIX to fit the data with $\hat{\sigma}^2_{Infl} = 70$ and $\hat{\sigma}^2_{site} = 25$.

Program 6.11
```
proc glimmix data=e_6_2 noprofile;
   class influent;
   model y = / solution;
   random influent / solution;
   covtest/cl(type=ELR);
   parms (70) (25) / noiter;
   ods rtf select covparms solutionr;
run;
```

The ELR confidence intervals about the variance components and the solution for the random effects are given in Output 6.9.

Output 6.9: PROC MIXED Results for Analysis with Fixed Values of the Variance Components

			\multicolumn{4}{c}{Estimated Likelihood 95% Confidence Bounds}
			\multicolumn{2}{c}{Lower}	\multicolumn{2}{c}{Upper}
Cov Parm	Estimate	Standard Error	Bound	Pr > Chisq	Bound	Pr > Chisq
influent	70.0000	49.2745	20.9107	0.0500	336.49	0.0500
Residual	25.0000	4.0939	21.5569	0.0500	102.48	0.0500

Covariance Parameter Estimates

Estimated likelihood ratio confidence bounds are based on the restricted likelihood

Solutions for Fixed Effects

Effect	Estimate	Standard Error	DF	t Value	Pr > |t|
Intercept	21.2360	3.5176	5	6.04	0.0018

Solution for Random Effects

Effect	influent	Estimate	Std Err Pred	DF	t Value	Pr > |t|
influent	1	0.3074	3.7575	31	0.08	0.9353
influent	2	-7.0206	3.8210	31	-1.84	0.0758
influent	3	-4.1402	3.9301	31	-1.05	0.3003
influent	4	3.0007	3.9072	31	0.00	0.4317
influent	5	-6.3802	3.9301	31	-1.62	0.1146
influent	6	14.1531	3.9301	31	3.60	0.0011

The predicted values of the influent means are influenced by the estimates of the variance components. In addition, the estimate of μ_N is also influenced by the method used to estimate the variance components. The REML estimate of the intercept from Output 6.1 is 21.2231 with standard error of 3.4290, where as in Output 6.9 the estimate is 21.2360 with standard error of 3.5176. Using estimates of variance components from the current data set in the above fashion often enables one to fit different fixed effect parameterizations with less computer resources than when fitting the variances and fixed effects together.

6.3 A Simple Conditional Hierarchical Linear Model: An Example

One purpose of conditional hierarchical linear models is partition variability in the levels of a random treatment by using characteristics of the levels. For example, a particular characteristic may be used to classify the levels into various groups or clusters. When the levels of the random factor are classified into groups, the groups are generally considered to be levels of a fixed effect. Thus, the resulting model is a mixed model where the fixed effects parameters correspond to the means of the newly formed groups and the random effects are the levels of the random effect nested within the levels of the fixed effect. This example applies the classification technique to data set, "Mississippi River." The influents are classified according to the type of watershed above the influent as shown in Table 6.2.

Table 6.2: Influent classification

Watershed Type 1	Watershed Type 2	Watershed Type 3
No farm land	Less than 50% farm land	More than 50% farm land
Influents 3 and 5	Influents 1, 2, and 4	Influent 6

In this case, the model is used to determine how much of the variation in the influents in Section 6.2 can be attributed to the different levels of TYPE. Thus, TYPE is considered as a fixed effect and the influents nested within a TYPE are considered as random effects. Although this section considers only the REML estimates of the variance components, other estimation methods can be applied as well.

Let y_{ijk} denote the amount of nitrogen measured from the kth site at the jth influent of the ith type, and a model to describe the collection of measurements is

$$y_{ijk} = \mu_i + a_{j(i)} + e_{ijk}; \ i = 1, 2, 3; \ j = 1, ..., n_i; \ k = 1, ..., m_{ij} \tag{6.4}$$

where the terms are defined as follows:

- $a_{j(i)} \sim iid \, N(0, \sigma_a^2)$ the jth influent within the ith type
- $e_{ijk} \sim iid \, N(0, \sigma_e^2)$ the kth site within the jth influent within the ith type

Equation 6.4 has two variance component parameters to be estimated, the same as Equation 6.2. Equation 6.4 is a mixed effects model where μ_i (i = 1,2,3) is the fixed effects part of the model, $a_{j(i)}$ is the random effects part of the model, and e_{ijk} is the residual part of the model. The notation $j(i)$ denotes that the jth level of the influent is nested within the ith type. By classifying the influents according to types, the $\mu_N + a_i$ of Equation 6.2 have been expressed as $\mu_N + a_i = \mu_i + a_{j(i)}$, where μ_i denotes that the mean level of nitrogen for influents of type i and $a_{j(i)}$ denotes the effect of the jth randomly selected influent of type i. Equation 6.4 is also called a two-level conditional hierarchical linear model (Bryk and Raudenbush 1992), because the sampling points are nested within each influent and the influents are classified according to levels of the type, a fixed effect.

The $\mathbf{X\beta}$ part of the model is the set of means, μ_i, of the types. The $\mathbf{Zu}$ part of the model are the influent effects within each type, $a_{j(i)}$ and the e_{ijk} form the residual part of the model.

6.3.1 PROC MIXED to Analyze the Data

The data set contains a fixed effect called Type of Watershed. The type of watershed is denoted by TYPE in the code. The MODEL statement now contains TYPE as a fixed effect.

Program

Program 6.12 obtains REML estimates of the variance components, estimates of the fixed effects, and computes predictions of the respective influent means:

Program 6.12

```
proc mixed data=influent covtest cl;
   class type influent;
   model y=type / solution;
   random influent(type)/solution;
/*---Estimate statement provides predictions of the influent means ---*/
   estimate 'influent 1' intercept 1 type 0 1 0 | influent(type) 1 0 0 0 0 0;
   estimate 'influent 2' intercept 1 type 0 1 0 | influent(type) 0 1 0 0 0 0;
   estimate 'influent 3' intercept 1 type 1 0 0 | influent(type) 0 0 1 0 0 0;
   estimate 'influent 4' intercept 1 type 0 1 0 | influent(type) 0 0 0 1 0 0;
   estimate 'influent 5' intercept 1 type 1 0 0 | influent(type) 0 0 0 0 1 0;
   estimate 'influent 6' intercept 1 type 0 0 1 | influent(type) 0 0 0 0 0 1;
/*---The following estimate statements reproduce the Solution for Random Effects---*/
       estimate 'influent 1U' | influent(type) 1 0 0 0 0 0;
       estimate 'influent 2U' | influent(type) 0 1 0 0 0 0;
       estimate 'influent 3U' | influent(type) 0 0 1 0 0 0;
       estimate 'influent 4U' | influent(type) 0 0 0 1 0 0;
       estimate 'influent 5U' | influent(type) 0 0 0 0 1 0;
   estimate 'influent 6U' | influent(type) 0 0 0 0 0 1;
   lsmeans type / diff;
run;
```

With the addition of TYPE of INFLUENT the individual influents become nested within a type of influent. Thus, the random influent effect is specified in the RANDOM statement using SAS nesting notation, INFLUENT(TYPE).

Results

The results in Output 6.10 correspond to the random effects part of the analysis. Output 6.10 contains the REML estimates of the variance components obtained from PROC MIXED, the solution for the random effects ($a_{j(i)}$) and the predicted means for each influent.

Output 6.10: The Random Effects Part of the Model Using PROC MIXED

		Covariance Parameter Estimates					
Cov Parm	Estimate	Standard Error	Z Value	Pr > Z	Alpha	Lower	Upper
influent(type)	14.9702	17.5422	0.85	0.1967	0.05	3.5315	1947.07
Residual	42.5136	10.7842	3.94	<.0001	0.05	27.3389	75.0789

			Solution for Random Effects				
Effect	type	influent	Estimate	Std Err Pred	DF	t Value	Pr > |t|
influent(type)	1	3	0.7653	3.1932	31	0.24	0.8122
influent(type)	1	5	-0.7653	3.1932	31	-0.24	0.8122
influent(type)	2	1	1.2295	2.7593	31	0.45	0.6590
influent(type)	2	2	-4.3259	2.8007	31	-1.54	0.1326
influent(type)	2	4	3.0964	2.8314	31	1.09	0.2826
influent(type)	3	6	-805E-16	3.8691	31	-0.00	1.0000

		Estimates			
Label	Estimate	Standard Error	DF	t Value	Pr > |t|
influent 1	20.7034	4.1423	3	5.00	0.0154
influent 2	19.1727	4.1423	3	4.63	0.0190
influent 3	16.8295	4.3989	3	3.83	0.0314
influent 4	15.6122	2.2137	3	7.05	0.0059
influent 5	18.6964	4.4444	3	4.21	0.0245
influent 6	36.4000	2.9159	3	12.48	0.0011
influent 1U	0.7653	3.1932	31	0.24	0.8122
influent 2U	-0.7653	3.1932	31	-0.24	0.8122
influent 3U	1.2295	2.7593	31	0.45	0.6590
influent 4U	-4.3259	2.8007	31	-1.54	0.1326
influent 5U	3.0964	2.8314	31	1.09	0.2826
influent 6U	-805E-16	3.8691	31	-0.00	1.0000

The REML estimates of the variance components are $\hat{\sigma}^2_{\text{Infl}} = 14.970$ and $\hat{\sigma}^2_e = 42.514$. The "Solution for Random Effects" table displays the predicted values of the effect of the individual influents with mean zero. The ESTIMATE statements provide predictions of the predictable functions for the influents with means equal to the mean of the respective types. The analysis of the fixed effects part of the model using the REML estimates of the variance components are shown in Output 6.11.

Output 6.11: The Fixed Effects Part of the Model Using PROC MIXED

		Solution for Fixed Effects				
Effect	type	Estimate	Standard Error	DF	t Value	Pr > |t|
Intercept		36.4000	4.8449	3	7.51	0.0049
type	1	-20.8000	5.9337	3	-3.51	0.0393
type	2	-16.4619	5.5168	3	-2.98	0.0584
type	3	0	.	.	.	.

	Type 3 Tests of Fixed Effects			
Effect	Num DF	Den DF	F Value	Pr > F
type	2	3	6.37	0.0832

		Least Squares Means				
Effect	**type**	**Estimate**	**Standard Error**	**DF**	**t Value**	**Pr > |t|**
type	1	15.6000	3.4259	3	4.55	0.0198
type	2	19.9381	2.6386	3	7.56	0.0048
type	3	36.4000	4.8449	3	7.51	0.0049

			Differences of Least Squares Means				
Effect	**type**	**_type**	**Estimate**	**Standard Error**	**DF**	**t Value**	**Pr > |t|**
type	1	2	-4.3381	4.3242	3	-1.00	0.3897
type	1	3	-20.8000	5.9337	3	-3.51	0.0393
type	2	3	-16.4619	5.5168	3	-2.98	0.0584

The statistic to test the equal means hypothesis (Type III Tests of Fixed Effects) has a value of 6.37 with a p-value of 0.0832. The LSMEANS or adjusted means for the levels of influent type and differences between the LSMEANS are included in Output 6.11. There is some evidence that the INFLUENT TYPE 3 mean is different from both INFLUENT TYPE 1 ($p = 0.0393$) and INFLUENT TYPE 2 ($p = 0.0584$), and there is no significant difference between the means of INFLUENT TYPE 1 and INFLUEN TYPE 2 ($p = 0.3897$).

Program

The method of moments estimators of the variance components from the TYPE3 option are obtained using Program 6.13.

Program 6.13

```
proc mixed data=influent method=type3;
   class type influent;
   model y=type/solution;
   random influent(type)/solution;
   estimate 'influent 1' intercept 1 type 0 1 0 | influent(type) 1 0 0 0 0 0;
   estimate 'influent 2' intercept 1 type 0 1 0 | influent(type) 0 1 0 0 0 0;
   estimate 'influent 3' intercept 1 type 1 0 0 | influent(type) 0 0 1 0 0 0;
   estimate 'influent 4' intercept 1 type 0 1 0 | influent(type) 0 0 0 1 0 0;
   estimate 'influent 5' intercept 1 type 1 0 0 | influent(type) 0 0 0 0 1 0;
   estimate 'influent 6' intercept 1 type 0 0 1 | influent(type) 0 0 0 0 0 1;
   lsmeans type / diff;
run;
```

Results

The methods of moments analysis (method=Type3) produces the usual analysis of variance table with sources, df, sums of squares, mean squares, expected mean squares, appropriate error term for a source, the error df, the F value and the significance level of the F value. The results are in Output 6.12.

Output 6.12: PROC MIXED Results with METHOD=TYPE3

			Type 3 Analysis of Variance				
Source	**DF**	**Sum of Squares**	**Mean Square**	**Expected Mean Square**	**Error Term**	**Error DF**	**F Value**
type	2	1500.033180	750.016590	Var(Residual) + 5.4393 Var(influent(type)) + Q(type)	0.8388 MS(influent(type)) + 0.1612 MS(Residual)	3.3584	6.01
influent(type)	3	421.638817	140.546272	Var(Residual) + 6.4848 Var(influent(type))	MS(Residual)	31	3.30
Residual	31	1319.779365	42.573528	Var(Residual)	.	.	.

Type 3 Analysis of Variance	
Source	**Pr > F**
type	0.0777
influent(type)	0.0331
Residual	.

Covariance Parameter Estimates

Cov Parm	Estimate	Standard Error	Z Value	Pr Z
influent(type)	15.1079	17.7857	0.85	0.3956
Residual	42.5735	10.7994	3.94	<.0001

Solution for Fixed Effects

Effect	type	Estimate	Standard Error	DF	t Value	Pr > |t|
Intercept		36.4000	4.8603	3	7.49	0.0049
type	1	-20.8000	5.9526	3	-3.49	0.0396
type	2	-16.4618	5.5347	3	-2.97	0.0589
type	3	0	.	.	.	.

Solution for Random Effects

Effect	type	influent	Estimate	Std Err Pred	DF	t Value	Pr > |t|
influent(type)	1	3	0.7675	3.2057	31	0.24	0.8124
influent(type)	1	5	-0.7675	3.2057	31	-0.24	0.8124
influent(type)	2	1	1.2317	2.7692	31	0.44	0.6596
influent(type)	2	2	-4.3357	2.8107	31	-1.54	0.1331
influent(type)	2	4	3.1040	2.8415	31	1.09	0.2831
influent(type)	3	6	-456E-17	3.8869	31	-0.00	1.0000

Type 3 Tests of Fixed Effects

Effect	Num DF	Den DF	F Value	Pr > F
type	2	3	6.33	0.0838

Estimates

Label	Estimate	Standard Error	DF	t Value	Pr > |t|
influent 1	20.7057	4.1578	3	4.98	0.0156
influent 2	19.1707	4.1578	3	4.61	0.0192
influent 3	16.8317	4.4136	3	3.81	0.0317
influent 4	15.6025	2.2167	3	7.04	0.0059
influent 5	18.7040	4.4593	3	4.19	0.0247
influent 6	36.4000	2.9180	3	12.47	0.0011

Least Squares Means

Effect	type	Estimate	Standard Error	DF	t Value	Pr > |t|
type	1	15.6000	3.4368	3	4.54	0.0200
type	2	19.9382	2.6478	3	7.53	0.0049
type	3	36.4000	4.8603	3	7.49	0.0049

Differences of Least Squares Means

Effect	type	_type	Estimate	Standard Error	DF	t Value	Pr > |t|
type	1	2	-4.3382	4.3384	3	-1.00	0.3910
type	1	3	-20.8000	5.9526	3	-3.49	0.0396
type	2	3	-16.4618	5.5347	3	-2.97	0.0589

The main addition to the analysis is that you get an exact F test for the hypothesis $H_0: \sigma^2_{Infl} = 0$ versus $H_a: \sigma^2_{Infl} > 0$, which has an F value of 3.30 and a p-value of .0331, while the z-score test has a p-value of .1967 in Output 6.10. The sum of squares method is a better method for testing hypotheses about the variance components than the z-score method when the number of levels of the random effect is not large (simulations show a need for at least 100 levels), or when the test based on the former is exact. The predicted means for each influent are provided by the estimates part of Output 6.12.

The means of each influent type and comparisons of those means are in the least squares means and differences of least squares means parts of Output 1.2.

6.3.2 PROC GLIMMIX for the Analysis and Confidence Intervals

If you use PROC GLIMMIX, confidence intervals about the variance components can be computed using the Wald method, the Estimated Likelihood Ratio (ELR) and the Profiled Likelihood Ratio (PLR) by including COVTEST/CL, COVTEST/CL(TYPE=ELR) or COVTEST/CL(TYPE=PLR). The variance components can be computed using six computational methods, RSPL, MSPL, RMPL, MMPL, QUAD, and LAPLACE. Output 6.13 and Output 6.14 contain the confidence intervals about the influent variance component and about the residual variance component for Wald and ELR using the six estimation techniques where TYPE of influent is included as a fixed effect in the model. The PROC MIXED confidence intervals are also included using REML, TYPE 1, TYPE 2, TYPE 3, ML and MIVQUE0.

Output 6.13: Confidence Intervals about the Residual variance from PROC MIXED and PROC GLIMMIX

Method	TYPE	CovParm	Estimate	StdErr	df	Lower	Upper
REML		Residual	42.5136	10.7842	31.1	27.3389	75.0789
TYPE 1		Residual	42.5735	10.7994	31.1	27.3632	75.2494
TYPE 2		Residual	42.5735	10.7994	31.1	27.3632	75.2494
TYPE 3		Residual	42.5735	10.7994	31.1	27.3632	75.2494
ML		Residual	42.1134	10.5947	31.6	27.1692	73.9754
Mivque0		Residual	42.3824	10.7512	31.1	27.2542	74.8483
RSPL	WALD	Residual	42.5136	10.7842	31.1	27.3389	75.0788
RSPL	ELR	Residual	42.5136	10.7842	31.1	26.8876	72.8201
MSPL	WALD	Residual	42.1129	10.5946	31.6	27.1688	73.9745
MSPL	ELR	Residual	42.1129	10.5946	31.6	26.9027	70.7096
RMPL	WALD	Residual	42.5136	10.7842	31.1	27.3389	75.0788
RMPL	ELR	Residual	42.5136	10.7842	31.1	26.8876	72.8201
MMPL	WALD	Residual	42.1129	10.5946	31.6	27.1688	73.9745
MMPL	ELR	Residual	42.1129	10.5946	31.6	26.9027	70.7096
LAPLACE	WALD	Residual	42.1127	10.5945	31.6	27.1687	73.9742
LAPLACE	ELR	Residual	42.1127	10.5945	31.6	26.9029	70.7101
QUAD	WALD	Residual	42.1127	10.5945	31.6	27.1687	73.9742
QUAD	ELR	Residual	42.1127	10.5945	31.6	26.9029	70.7101

Note: There are six methods for PROC MIXED and twelve methods for PROC GLIMMIX.

For the Residual variance component, REML, RSPL, and RMPL methods have similar or the same standard errors and confidence intervals. ML, MSPL, MMPL, LAPLACE, and QUAD have similar or the same standard errors and confidence intervals. The confidence intervals from the Residual methods have shorter widths than the other methods. The Mivque0 estimate and standard error are larger than those produced by the other methods and the confidence interval is much wider. The estimates and standard errors and confidence intervals are all identical for Type 1, Type 2, and Type 3 sums of squares (because this is a balanced data set). The Wald confidence intervals are wider than the ELR confidence intervals. A limited simulation study showed that the widths of the ELR confidence intervals are shorter than the widths of the WALD confidence intervals and that they both have the same coverage. Thus, the ELR confidence intervals seem to provide better confidence intervals than the WALD confidence intervals. The estimates and the confidence intervals for the influent variance component are in Output 6.14.

Output 6.14: Confidence Intervals about the INFLUENT(TYPE) Variance from PROC MIXED and PROC GLIMMIX

Method	TYPE	CovParm	Estimate	StdErr	df	Lower	Upper
REML		influent(type)	14.9702	17.5422	1.5	3.5315	1947.07
TYPE 1		influent(type)	15.1079	17.7857	1.4	-19.7514	49.9673
TYPE 2		influent(type)	15.1079	17.7857	1.4	-19.7514	49.9673
TYPE 3		influent(type)	15.1079	17.7857	1.4	-19.7514	49.9673
ML		influent(type)	4.8235	6.6258	1.1	0.9859	3373.29
Mivque0		influent(type)	15.4420	18.3013	1.4	3.6061	2223.55
RSPL	WALD	influent(type)	14.9703	17.5423	1.5	3.5315	1947.10
RSPL	ELR	influent(type)	14.9703	17.5423	1.5	0	180.38
MSPL	WALD	influent(type)	4.8243	6.6267	1.1	0.9861	3372.29
MSPL	ELR	influent(type)	4.8243	6.6267	1.1	0	38.7571
RMPL	WALD	influent(type)	14.9703	17.5423	1.5	3.5315	1947.10
RMPL	ELR	influent(type)	14.9703	17.5423	1.5	0	180.38
MMPL	WALD	influent(type)	4.8243	6.6267	1.1	0.9861	3372.29
MMPL	ELR	influent(type)	4.8243	6.6267	1.1	0	38.7571
LAPLACE	WALD	influent(type)	4.8233	6.6255	1.1	0.9859	3373.04
LAPLACE	ELR	influent(type)	4.8233	6.6255	1.1	0	38.7563
QUAD	WALD	Influent(type)	4.8233	6.6255	1.1	0.9859	3373.04
QUAD	ELR	Influent(type)	4.8233	6.6255	1.1	0	38.7563

Note: There are six methods for PROC MIXED and twelve methods for PROC GLIMMIX.

For the influent variance component, REML, RSPL, and RMPL methods have similar or the same standard errors and confidence intervals. ML, MSPL, MMPL, LAPLACE, and QUAD have similar or the same standard errors and confidence intervals. The confidence intervals from the Residual methods have wider widths than the other methods. The Mivque0 estimate and standard error are smaller than those produced by the other methods and the confidence interval is much narrower. The Wald confidence intervals are wider than the ELR confidence intervals. The confidence intervals produce by the TYPE 1, TYPE 2 and TYPE 3 methods are computed using the WALD method of $Estimate \pm t_{\alpha/2} \times StdError$ and need to be recalculated using the chi-square distribution with $df = 2 \times [Estimate/StdError]^2$ which would prevent the negative lower limits. The influent variance components have a computed df for each and those df can be used with the chi-square distribution to provide better confidence intervals. The confidence intervals about the residual variance used the chi-square distribution for the estimates obtained using the TYPE X sums of squares methods. The widths of the ELR confidence intervals are shorter than the widths of the WALD confidence intervals. Thus, the ELR confidence intervals seem to provide better confidence intervals than the WALD confidence intervals.

6.4 Three-Level Nested Design Structure: An Example

The data in data set "Semiconductor" are from a passive data collection study in the semiconductor industry where the objective is to determine the magnitudes of assignable causes for observed variability. The measurements are thicknesses of the oxide layer on silicon wafers determined at three randomly selected sites on each wafer. The wafers stem from eight different lots (each lot consists of 25 wafers, but only 3 wafers per lot were used in the passive data collection study). The process consists of randomly selecting eight lots of 25 wafers from the population of lots of 25 wafers. Then 3 wafers are selected from each lot of 25 for use in the oxide deposition process. After the layer of oxide is deposited, the thickness of the layer is determined at three randomly selected sites on each wafer. The structure of the study involves three sizes of experimental units in the design structure with a uniform application of a single treatment in the treatment structure. The sites on a wafer, the wafer from a lot and a lot provide the three experimental units for this study.

6.4.1 Three-Level Nested Linear Model, an Unconditional Hierarchical Nested Linear Model

A model to describe the Semiconductor data is

$$y_{ijk} = \mu + a_i + w_{j(i)} + s_{k(ij)}; \ i = 1, 2, ..., 8; \ j = 1, 2, 3; \ k = 1, 2, 3 \tag{6.5}$$

where the terms are defined as follows:

- $a_i \quad \sim \text{iid } N(0, \sigma_L^2)$
- $w_{j(i)} \sim \text{iid } N(0, \sigma_w^2)$
- $s_{k(ij)} \sim \text{iid } N(0, \sigma_s^2)$

and

- a_i is the effect of the ith randomly selected lot
- $w_{j(i)}$ is the effect of the jth randomly selected wafer from the ith lot
- $s_{k(ij)}$ is the effect of the kth randomly selected site from the jth wafer of the ith lot

In the linear models literature, Equation 6.5 has been called a three-level nested linear model or an unconditional hierarchical nested linear model. The objective of the passive data collection study is to estimate the variance components, σ_L^2, σ_w^2, and σ_s^2.

6.4.2 Data Analysis Using the PROC MIXED METHOD=REML to Estimate the Variance Components

The PROC MIXED program to fit Equation 6.5 is in Program 6.14, where lot and wafer(lot) effects are specified in the RANDOM statement and site(Wafer Lot) is the residual error (which is automatically assumed and does not need to be specified).

Program 6.14

```
proc mixed data=e_6_4 Method=REML;
   class lot wafer site;
   model Thick=;
   random lot wafer(lot);
run;
```

The mean is the only fixed effect and the residual variance corresponds to the site-to-site variance. The variance components corresponding to LOT and WAFER(LOT) measure the variability in the mean thickness of the population of lots and the variation in the mean thickness of the wafers within the population of lots, respectively.

The REML estimates of the variance components are shown in Output 6.15.

Output 6.15: Results of PROC MIXED for the Three-Level Nested Random Effects Model

Covariance Parameter Estimates							
Cov Parm	Estimate	Standard Error	Z Value	Pr > Z	Alpha	Lower	Upper
lot	129.91	76.7205	1.69	0.0452	0.05	53.1116	662.49
wafer(lot)	35.8657	14.1876	2.53	0.0057	0.05	18.7634	94.0313
Residual	12.5694	2.5657	4.90	<.0001	0.05	8.7411	19.6177

The estimates of the variance components (Estimate), the estimated standard errors of the variance components (Standard Error), a Z-Value computed as the estimate divided by the standard error, the significance level associated with the Z-Value (Pr > Z) and 95% confidence intervals for each variance component computed using the Satterthwaite approximation are contained in Output 6.15. For this study, the estimate of the lot-to-lot variance of 129.9 is four times larger than the wafer-to-wafer within-a-lot variance of 35.9, which is 2.85 times larger than the site-to-site within a wafer variance of 12.6. This provides a direct breakdown of observed variability and pinpoints lot as the key driver of the variability in the study. A next step would be to evaluate the cause of the lot-to-lot variance in order to improve the consistency of the oxide layer across the population of wafers.

The confidence intervals are Satterthwaite approximation confidence intervals using the chi-square distribution and tend to have much better small-sample coverage properties than naïve Wald confidence intervals, which are symmetric and centered about the estimates of the variance component.

6.4.3 PROC MIXED METHOD=TYPE1 to Estimate the Variance Components

Method of moments estimation provides tests of hypotheses that each of the variance components (other than the Residual) is equal to zero. The following program requests moment estimators with the METHOD=TYPE1 option.

Program 6.15

```
proc mixed data=e_6_4 Method=Type1 covtest cl;
   class lot wafer site;
   model Thick=;
   random lot wafer(lot);
run;
```

The results are given in Output 6.16 with the Type 1 analysis of variance table with sources, *df*, sums of squares, mean squares, expected mean squares, respective error tern and *df*, the *F* value and the significance level of each *F* test. There is also a summary of the estimates of the variance components obtained from the set of equations of the mean squares set equal to the expected mean squares.

Output 6.16: METHOD=TYPE1 Results for the Three-Level Nested Random Effects Model

				Type 1 Analysis of Variance				
Source	DF	Sum of Squares	Mean Square	Expected Mean Square	Error Term	Error DF	F Value	Pr > F
lot	7	9025.319444	1289.331349	Var(Residual) + 3 Var(wafer(lot)) + 9 Var(lot)	MS(wafer(lot))	16	10.73	<.0001
wafer(lot)	16	1922.666667	120.166667	Var(Residual) + 3 Var(wafer(lot))	MS(Residual)	48	9.56	<.0001
Residual	48	603.333333	12.569444	Var(Residual)	.	.	.	.

	Covariance Parameter Estimates						
Cov Parm	Estimate	Standard Error	Z Value	Pr Z	Alpha	Lower	Upper
lot	129.91	76.7205	1.69	0.0904	0.05	-20.4623	280.28
wafer(lot)	35.8657	14.1876	2.53	0.0115	0.05	8.0586	63.6729
Residual	12.5694	2.5657	4.90	<.0001	0.05	8.7411	19.6177

The method of moments estimates are as follows:

$$\hat{\sigma}_s^2 = \text{MSERROR} = 12.569$$

$$\hat{\sigma}_w^2 = \frac{\text{MSWAFER(LOT)} - \text{MSERROR}}{3} = \frac{120.167 - 12.569}{3} = 35.866$$

$$\hat{\sigma}_L^2 = \frac{\text{MSLOT} - \text{MSWAFER(LOT)}}{9} = \frac{1289.331 - 120.569}{9} = 129.907$$

For the test of the hypothesis H_0: $\sigma_L^2 = 0$ versus H_a: $\sigma_L^2 > 0$, the value of the *F* statistic is 10.73 with $p < 0.0001$. For the test of the hypothesis H_0: $\sigma_w^2 = 0$ versus H_a: $\sigma_w^2 > 0$, the value of the *F* statistic is 9.56 with $p < 0.0001$. These tests indicate that the variability among lots and the variability among wafers within a lot are significantly different from zero, i.e., they are important sources of variability in the system. The confidence intervals about the lot variance and the wafer variance are computed with the Wald method which is symmetric about the estimate of the variance component.

6.4.4 PROC GLIMMIX to Estimate the Variance Components and Provide ELR Confidence Intervals

PROC GLIMMIX with the RMPL estimation method provides estimates of the variance components. The ELR confidence intervals are obtained using the COVTEST/CL(TYPE=ERL) with the following code.

Program 6.16

```
proc glimmix data=e_6_4 Method=RMPL;
   class lot wafer site;
   Model Thick=;
   random lot wafer(lot);
```

```
       covtest/cl(TYPE=WALD);
       covtest/cl(type=ELR);

run;
```

The estimates of the variance components from PROC GLIMMIX and the Wald and ELR confidence intervals are in Output 6.17.

Output 6.17: PROC GLIMMIX Results to Provide ELR Confidence Intervals

| | | | | | | Estimated Likelihood 95% Confidence Bounds | | | |
| | | | | | | Lower | | Upper | |
Cov Parm	Estimate	Standard Error	Wald 95% Confidence Bounds		Bound	Pr > Chisq	Bound	Pr > Chisq
lot	129.91	76.7205	53.1116	662.49	45.3317	0.0500	495.32	0.0500
wafer(lot)	35.8657	14.1876	18.7634	94.0313	17.3395	0.0500	83.0924	0.0500
Residual	12.5694	2.5657	8.7411	19.6177	8.6417	0.0500	19.2692	0.0500

Covariance Parameter Estimates

Estimated likelihood ratio confidence bounds are based on the restricted likelihood

The two sets of confidence intervals are in Output 6.17 where the ELR confidence intervals are narrower than the Wald confidence intervals. The Wald intervals are computed using the Satterthwaite approximate *df* and the chi-square distribution.

The PLR confidence intervals are obtained using PROC GLIMMIX with the NOPROFILE option in with Program 6.17.

Program 6.17

```
proc glimmix data=e_6_4 Method=RMPL NOPROFILE;
   class lot wafer site;
   Model Thick=;
   random lot wafer(lot);
   covtest/cl(TYPE=WALD);
   covtest/cl(type=PLR);
run;
```

The PLR and Wald (Satterthwaite approximation) confidence intervals are in Output 6.18.

Output 6.18: PROC GLIMMIX Results to Provide PLR Confidence Intervals

| | | | | | | Profile Likelihood 95% Confidence Bounds | | | |
| | | | | | | Lower | | Upper | |
Cov Parm	Estimate	Standard Error	Wald 95% Confidence Bounds		Bound	Pr > Chisq	Bound	Pr > Chisq
lot	129.91	76.7205	53.1116	662.49	44.1667	0.0500	495.37	0.0500
wafer(lot)	35.8657	14.1876	18.7634	94.0313	17.2032	0.0500	83.4811	0.0500
Residual	12.5694	2.5657	8.7411	19.6177	8.6382	0.0500	19.2960	0.0500

Covariance Parameter Estimates

Profile likelihood ratio confidence bounds are based on the restricted likelihood

The PLR confidence intervals are close to the ELR confidence intervals, but both are narrower than the Wald (Satterthwaite) confidence intervals. The ELR confidence intervals are narrower than the PLR confidence intervals.

6.4.5 Conditional Hierarchical Linear Model or Mixed Model

A next step in this analysis is to take into account information that the engineer discovered. The engineer discovered that the lots are from two different sources and decided to add SOURCE to the model. The word SOURCE in the code for model 6.6 denotes the two different sources. The company has only two sources of lots of wafers, thus the levels of source form a fixed effect. This changes the model from the unconditional hierarchical nested linear model in 6.5 to the following conditional hierarchical nested linear model:

$$y_{ijkm} = \mu_i + a_{j(i)} + w_{k(ij)} + s_{m(ijk)}; \quad i = 1,2; \; j = 1,2,3,4; \; k = 1,2,3; \; m = 1,2,3 \tag{6.6}$$

Where the terms are defined as follows:

- $a_{j(i)} \sim$ iid N$(0, \sigma_L^2)$.
- $w_{k(ij)} \sim$ iid N$(0, \sigma_w^2)$.
- $s_{m(ijk)} \sim$ iid N$(0, \sigma_s^2)$.
- μ_i is the mean of the ith source level.
- $a_{j(i)}$ is the effect of the jth randomly selected lot from source i.
- $w_{k(ij)}$ is the effect of the kth randomly selected wafer from the jth lot from source i.
- $s_{m(ijk)}$ is the effect of the mth randomly selected site from the kth wafer of the jth lot from source i.

The μ_i represent the fixed effects part of the model, the $a_{j(i)} + w_{k(ij)}$ represent the random effects part of the model, and $s_{m(ijk)}$ is the residual part of the model. Because the model involves both random and fixed factors, Equation 6.6 is a mixed model. The discussion here is to demonstrate the process of moving from the purely random effects linear model or unconditional hierarchical linear model to the mixed model or conditional hierarchical linear model.

6.4.6 The MIXED and GLIMMIX Procedures to Fit the Model to the Data

PROC MIXED and PROC GLIMMIX are used to fit Equation 6.6 to the data.

Program

The code in Program 6.18 uses PROC MIXED to fit the mixed model.

Program 6.18

```
proc mixed data=e_6_4 covtest cl;
   class source lot wafer site;
   model Thick = source / ddfm=kr2;
   random lot(source) wafer(source lot);
   lsmeans source / diff;
run;
```

The levels of the sources, SOURCE, denote the fixed effects part of the model. Hence, SOURCE is listed in the MODEL statement. The random statement now contains LOT(SOURCE) as the lots are nested within a source and contains WAFER(SOURCE LOT) to denote the wafers are from a lot within a source. The DDFM=KR2 option in the MODEL statement adjusts the degrees of freedom for the fixed effects. The COVTEST option provides Satterthwaite approximate *df* for using the chi-square distribution to construct the confidence intervals about the variance components

Results

The results of fitting the mixed model to the thickness data are shown in Output 6.19. The output includes estimates of the means of the fixed effects and comparisons of the means that are produced by the LSMEANS statement with the DIFF option.

Output 6.19: PROC MIXED Results for the Nested Random Effects Model Using Source as a Fixed Effect

Covariance Parameter Estimates							
Cov Parm	Estimate	Standard Error	Z Value	Pr > Z	Alpha	Lower	Upper
lot(source)	119.89	77.0734	1.56	0.0599	0.05	46.1707	752.40
wafer(source*lot)	35.8657	14.1876	2.53	0.0057	0.05	18.7634	94.0313
Residual	12.5694	2.5657	4.90	<.0001	0.05	8.7411	19.6177

Type 3 Tests of Fixed Effects				
Effect	Num DF	Den DF	F Value	Pr > F
source	1	6	1.53	0.2629

Least Squares Means						
Effect	source	Estimate	Standard Error	DF	t Value	Pr > |t|
source	1	1995.11	5.7716	6	345.68	<.0001
source	2	2005.19	5.7716	6	347.43	<.0001

Differences of Least Squares Means							
Effect	source	_source	Estimate	Standard Error	DF	t Value	Pr > |t|
source	1	2	-10.0833	8.1622	6	-1.24	0.2629

The estimate of the lot-to-lot variance component is 119.89, which a little smaller when the lot source is included as a fixed effect in the model (compare to 129.91 from Output 6.18). This change is because the lot-to-lot variance component now measures the variability among lots within a source, not just the variability of lots ignoring sources. Some of the variability of the lots is attributable to the levels of SOURCE and thus is reflected in the smaller estimate in Output 6.19. Because the data set is balanced, the wafer-to-wafer variance component and the site-to-site variance component are identical for both the unconditional and conditional hierarchical linear models.

Program

The GLIMMIX procedure can also be used to provide the analysis with source in the model. The Wald and ELR confidence intervals about the model's parameters are obtained with the COVTEST statements in Program 6.19.

Program 6.19

```
proc glimmix data=e_6_4;
   class source lot wafer site;
   model Thick = source / ddfm=KR2;
   random lot(source) wafer(source lot);
   covtest/cl(TYPE=WALD);
   covtest/cl(type=ELR);
   lsmeans source / diff;
run;
```

Results

The ELR confidence intervals about the variance components, Type III test of equal source means, LSMEANS and DIFFS for the fixed effect means are included in Output 6.20

Output 6.20: PROC GLIMMIX Output with ELR Confidence Intervals

Covariance Parameter Estimates								
				Estimated Likelihood 95% Confidence Bounds				
				Lower		Upper		
Cov Parm	Estimate	Standard Error	Wald 95% Confidence Bounds		Bound	Pr > Chisq	Bound	Pr > Chisq
lot(source)	119.89	77.0734	46.1707	752.40	38.0329	0.0500	522.44	0.0500
wafer(source*lot)	35.8657	14.1876	18.7634	94.0313	17.3394	0.0500	83.0994	0.0500
Residual	12.5694	2.5657	8.7411	19.6177	8.6417	0.0500	19.2692	0.0500

Estimated likelihood ratio confidence bounds are based on the restricted likelihood

Type III Tests of Fixed Effects

Effect	Num DF	Den DF	F Value	Pr > F
source	1	6	1.53	0.2629

source Least Squares Means

source	Estimate	Standard Error	DF	t Value	Pr > |t|
1	1995.11	5.7716	6	345.68	<.0001
2	2005.19	5.7716	6	347.43	<.0001

Differences of source Least Squares Means

source	_source	Estimate	Standard Error	DF	t Value	Pr > |t|
1	2	-10.0833	8.1622	6	-1.24	0.2629

The ERL confidence intervals about the variance components are much shorter than the Wald confidence intervals (using the Satterthwaite approximation). The DDFM=KR2 option was used to provide adjusted degrees of freedom for the fixed effects.

6.4.7 Unequal Variance Model

Often factors in an experiment have an effect on the variance of the responses as well as on the mean of the responses. Because there are two sources of lots of wafers, it is possible that the lot-to-lot variability is different for each source. The last phase of this analysis is to fit a model where the lot-to-lot variance components varies with the source of lots. The heterogeneous variance component model is as follows:

$$y_{ijkm} = \mu_i + a_{j(i)} + w_{k(ij)} + s_{m(ijk)}; \ i = 1,2; \ j = 1,2,3,4; \ k = 1,2,3; \ m = 1,2,3 \qquad (6.7)$$

where the terms are defined as follows:

- $a_{j(i)} \sim$ iid N(0, $\sigma_{L_i}^2$).

- $w_{k(ij)} \sim$ iid N(0, σ_w^2).

- $s_{m(ijk)} \sim$ iid N(0, σ_s^2).

Equation 6.7 has two variance components for LOTS: σ_{L1}^2 and σ_{L2}^2 are the variances of the lots within source 1 and source 2.

Program

Program 6.20 is the PROC GLIMMIX program to fit the unequal variance model by using the GROUP=SOURCE option on the first random statement.

Program 6.20

```
proc glimmix data=e_6_4 scoring=4;
   class source lot wafer site;
   model Thick = source/ ddfm=KR2;
   random intercept/subject=lot group=source;
   random intercept/subject=wafer(source lot);
   covtest/cl(type=ELR);
   lsmeans source / diff;
   covtest "Test equality of Source Variances" general 1 -1 0 0/  cl ;
   covtest "Test wafer(source lot) is equal zero" general 0 0 1 0/  cl ;
run;
```

The SCORING=4 option for the MODEL statement requests that Fisher scoring be used in association with the estimation method up to iteration number 4. When the model is complex (the unequal variances make this model a little complex), the SCORING= *number* sometimes helps with convergence. The GROUP= option in the first RANDOM statement requests that the parameters of the associated covariance structure be varied by the group effect. Here, the lot variance component is varied by levels of the SOURCE effect. This provides a different estimate of σ^2_L for each level of

SOURCE. The COVTEST general statement provides a test of the hypothesis that the linear combination of variances is equal to zero. The first line tests the equality of the two lots variances are equal and the second line tests that the wafer(source lot) variance component is equal to 0.

Results

The results are in Output 6.21 with estimates of the variance components where there is one variance for source 1 and another variance for source 2, i.e., indicating that the sources have unequal variance.

Output 6.21: PROC GLIMMIX Results for the Conditional Hierarchical Linear Model with Unequal Variances

<table>
<tr><th colspan="7">Covariance Parameter Estimates</th></tr>
<tr><th>Cov Parm</th><th>Subject</th><th>Group</th><th>Estimate</th><th>Standard Error</th><th colspan="2">Wald 95% Confidence Bounds</th></tr>
<tr><td>Intercept</td><td>lot</td><td>source 1</td><td>17.0761</td><td>25.2888</td><td>3.2591</td><td>33158</td></tr>
<tr><td>Intercept</td><td>lot</td><td>source 2</td><td>222.71</td><td>192.80</td><td>68.1544</td><td>4008.09</td></tr>
<tr><td>Intercept</td><td>wafer(source*lot)</td><td></td><td>35.8657</td><td>14.1876</td><td>18.7634</td><td>94.0313</td></tr>
<tr><td>Residual</td><td></td><td></td><td>12.5694</td><td>2.5657</td><td>8.7411</td><td>19.6177</td></tr>
</table>

<table>
<tr><th colspan="7">Covariance Parameter Estimates</th></tr>
<tr><th></th><th></th><th></th><th colspan="4">Estimated Likelihood 95% Confidence Bounds</th></tr>
<tr><th></th><th></th><th></th><th colspan="2">Lower</th><th colspan="2">Upper</th></tr>
<tr><th>Cov Parm</th><th>Subject</th><th>Group</th><th>Bound</th><th>Pr > Chisq</th><th>Bound</th><th>Pr > Chisq</th></tr>
<tr><td>Intercept</td><td>lot</td><td>source 1</td><td>0</td><td>0.2426</td><td>252.04</td><td>0.0500</td></tr>
<tr><td>Intercept</td><td>lot</td><td>source 2</td><td>53.2111</td><td>0.0500</td><td>2045.54</td><td>0.0500</td></tr>
<tr><td>Intercept</td><td>wafer(source*lot)</td><td></td><td>17.4598</td><td>0.0500</td><td>81.2460</td><td>0.0500</td></tr>
<tr><td>Residual</td><td></td><td></td><td>8.6418</td><td>0.0500</td><td>19.2683</td><td>0.0500</td></tr>
</table>

Estimated likelihood ratio confidence bounds are based on the restricted likelihood

<table>
<tr><th colspan="5">Type III Tests of Fixed Effects</th></tr>
<tr><th>Effect</th><th>Num DF</th><th>Den DF</th><th>F Value</th><th>Pr > F</th></tr>
<tr><td>source</td><td>1</td><td>3.761</td><td>1.53</td><td>0.2883</td></tr>
</table>

<table>
<tr><th colspan="6">source Least Squares Means</th></tr>
<tr><th>source</th><th>Estimate</th><th>Standard Error</th><th>DF</th><th>t Value</th><th>Pr > |t|</th></tr>
<tr><td>1</td><td>1995.11</td><td>2.7581</td><td>3</td><td>723.37</td><td><.0001</td></tr>
<tr><td>2</td><td>2005.19</td><td>7.6821</td><td>3</td><td>261.02</td><td><.0001</td></tr>
</table>

<table>
<tr><th colspan="7">Differences of source Least Squares Means</th></tr>
<tr><th>source</th><th>_source</th><th>Estimate</th><th>Standard Error</th><th>DF</th><th>t Value</th><th>Pr > |t|</th></tr>
<tr><td>1</td><td>2</td><td>-10.0833</td><td>8.1622</td><td>3.761</td><td>-1.24</td><td>0.2883</td></tr>
</table>

Tests of Covariance Parameters Based on the Restricted Likelihood					
Label	DF	-2 Res Log Like	ChiSq	Pr > ChiSq	Note
Test equality of Source Variances	1	446.48	2.71	0.0994	DF
Test wafer(source lot) is equal zero	1	481.40	37.64	<.0001	MI

DF: P-value based on a chi-square with DF degrees of freedom.
MI: P-value based on a mixture of chi-squares.

The information in Output 6.21, provides the estimates of the lot-to-lot variance components as 17.08 and 222.71 for sources 1 and 2, respectively. The standard errors of the estimates of the SOURCE means reflect the unequal variances. That is, the estimated standard errors are higher for the source with greater variance: 2.76 for source 1 and 7.68 for source 2, respectively, each based on 3 degrees of freedom. The common lot-to-lot variance component model provides the same estimated standard error for the two SOURCE means, 5.77 based on 6 degrees of freedom (See Output 6.20). (The estimated standard errors are equal for the common lot-to-lot variance model in this case because there are equal numbers of observations from each level of SOURCE.)

Next, compare the analysis in Output 6.20 to the analysis in Output 6.21 to see the effect of unequal variances on the analysis of the fixed effects in the model. The p-value for comparing the SOURCE means changes from .2629 for the equal variance model to .2883 for the unequal variance model. This change in the p-values is due to the differences in the denominator degrees of freedom.

The estimated standard error of the difference of the two SOURCE means are identical for both analyses, 8.162. But the *df* associated with the two standard errors are different. For the two unequal variances model (one for each source of lots) the pooled estimate of the variance is based on 3.761 *df*. For the equal variances model there are 6 *df* associated with the standard error with 3 *df* coming from the variability among the lots of source 1 and another 3 *df* coming from the variability among the lots of source 2. Because these two variances are assumed to be equal, the two variances are pooled together as well as the two *df*s are pooled together. The pooling of variances and *df*s do not occur for the unequal variances situation. When the variances of the two sources are not equal, the estimated standard error of the difference is computed from a linear combination of the two variances and the associated *df* are determined by the Satterthwaite approximation. This similarity of equal standard errors of the difference disappears if the numbers of observations per level of SOURCE are not equal.

The estimates of the wafer-to-wafer and site-to-site variance components are unchanged (35.87 and 12.57, respectively). The mean of the two lot-to-lot variance components is equal to the single lot-to-lot variance component for the equal variances model ((17.08 + 222.71)/2 = 119.89). This equality occurs because there are equal numbers of observations per level of SOURCE. Because the mean of the two lot-to-lot variance components is equal to the lot-to-lot variance component for the equal variances model, the estimate of the standard error of the difference between the two sources is the same for both models. The least squares means and the difference between the two means are identical for both models. A test of the hypothesis of equal variances can be obtained by comparing the difference between the −2 Res Log Likelihood values to a chi-square distribution based on 4−3 = 1 degrees of freedom, because there are four parameters in the covariance structure for the unequal variances model and there are three parameters in the covariance structure for the equal variances model. In this case, the difference is 2.7148 based on 1 degree of freedom, and the p-value is .3173 (from the chi-square table based on 1 degree of freedom). In Output 6.21 the Test of Covariance Parameters tests the hypotheses 1) the lot to lot variances are equal with significance level 0.0994 and 2) tests the hypothesis the wafer(source lot) variance component is zero with significance level <0.0001.The results of the equal lots variances test indicate that the equal lot variance assumption is reasonable even though the lot-to-lot variance for Source 1 is 17.08 and is 222.71 for Source 2 (Each variance is based on 3 *df* so such differences are not seen to be the cause to use an unequal variance model).

6.5 A Two-Way Random Effects Treatment Structure to Estimate Heritability: An Example

The data in data set "Genetics," represent yields of five wheat families grown at four randomly selected locations. The wheat families are randomly selected from a population of wheat families in a breeding program on drought tolerance. The locations are selected from locations where the drought tolerant wheat varieties can be grown commercially. At each location, the design of the experiment is a one-way treatment structure (five wheat families) in a randomized complete block design with three blocks at each location. The objective of the study is to estimate the heritability of yield, a measure of possible genetic advancement under selection (Allard 1966). Heritability is estimated by the ratio of the estimate of the genetic variance to the phenotypic variance of a family mean. A model to describe the data is as follows:

$$y_{ijk} = \mu + l_i + f_j + lf_{ij} + b_{k(i)} + e_{ijk} \tag{6.8}$$

where terms are defined as follows:

- $i = 1, 2, 3, 4 \quad j = 1, 2, 3, 4, 5 \quad k = 1, 2, 3$.

- $l_i \sim iid\, N(0, \sigma_L^2)$ the effect of location.

- $f_j \sim iid\, N(0, \sigma_F^2)$ the effect of family.

- $lf_{ij} \sim iid\, N(0, \sigma_{LF}^2)$ the effect of family by location interaction.

- $b_{k(i)} \sim iid\, N(0, \sigma_B^2)$ the effect of blocks within a location.

- $e_{ijk} \sim iid\, N(0, \sigma_e^2)$ the plot-to-plot variation within a field measured by the block by variety interaction pooled across locations.

The additive genetic variance component is σ_F^2 and the phenotypic variance of a family mean is $\sigma_{\bar{y}_{.j.}}^2 = \sigma_L^2/4 + \sigma_F^2 + \sigma_{LF}^2/4 + \sigma_B^2/12 + \sigma_e^2/12$. For this design, heritability is defined as $h^2 = \sigma_F^2 / \sigma_{\bar{y}_{.j.}}^2$.

6.5.1 PROC GLIMMIX To Analyze the Data

The PROC GLIMMIX code in Program 6.21 is used to fit Equation 6.8 to obtain REML estimates of the variance components. There are no fixed effects to be put into the model because only the mean that corresponds to the intercept in the model needs to be estimated.

Program 6.21

```
proc glimmix data=e_6_5 ASYCOV;
  class loc fam block;
  model Yield =;
  random loc fam loc*fam block(loc);
  covtest/cl (TYPE=WALD);
  covtest/cl (type=ELR);
  ods output covtest=cov covparms=cvp asycov=asycov;
run;
```

The results of PROC GLIMMIX are in Output 6.22. Because the fixed effects part of the model consists of only the intercept, the MODEL statement contains no terms (an intercept is automatically included by PROC GLIMMIX). All other terms in the model are random effects and thus occur in the RANDOM statement. The COVTEST statements are used to provide WALD and ELR confidence intervals. The ASYCOV option provides the estimated asymptotic covariance matrix of the estimates of the variance components.

Output 6.22: PROC GLIMMIX Results Providing Estimates of the Variance Components for the Genetics Example

					Covariance Parameter Estimates			
						Estimated Likelihood 95% Confidence Bounds		
						Lower		Upper
Cov Parm	Estimate	Standard Error	Wald 95% Confidence Bounds			Bound	Pr > Chisq	Bound	Pr > Chisq
loc	613.65	540.71	185.08	12013	138.41	0.0500	5724.38	0.0500
fam	188.00	149.52	61.6103	2349.79	45.3082	0.0500	1246.04	0.0500
loc*fam	74.8616	37.8647	33.9079	280.29	28.2161	0.0500	213.07	0.0500
block(loc)	89.3208	49.9124	37.9170	404.14	32.5472	0.0500	309.79	0.0500
Residual	51.8458	12.9615	33.5297	90.7052	33.0242	0.0500	87.6871	0.0500

Estimated likelihood ratio confidence bounds are based on the restricted likelihood

Asymptotic Covariance Matrix of Covariance Parameter Estimates					
Cov Parm	CovP1	CovP2	CovP3	CovP4	CovP5
loc	292365	70.7536	-286.75	-830.41	11.2000
fam	70.7536	22357	-353.77	-187E-13	-102E-14
loc*fam	-286.75	-353.77	1433.74	11.2000	-55.9998
block(loc)	-830.41	-187E-13	11.2000	2491.24	-33.5999
Residual	11.2000	-102E-14	-55.9998	-33.5999	168.00

The estimates of the variance components are as follows:

$$\hat{\sigma}_L^2 = 613.6$$
$$\hat{\sigma}_F^2 = 188.0$$
$$\hat{\sigma}_{LF}^2 = 74.9$$
$$\hat{\sigma}_B^2 = 89.3$$
$$\hat{\sigma}_e^2 = 51.8$$
$$\hat{\sigma}_{\bar{y}_{j.}}^2 = \frac{613.6}{4} + 188.0 + \frac{74.9}{4} + \frac{89.3}{12} + \frac{51.8}{12} = 371.8$$
$$\hat{h}^2 = \frac{188.0}{371.8} = 0.506$$

The estimate of the variance component for Family provides the estimate of the additive genetic variance and the variance of a family mean is $\sigma_{\bar{y}_{j.}}^2$.

The estimate of the heritability is 0.506, indicating that 50.6% of the variability in the family means is due to additive genetic variance.

6.5.2 PROC MIXED METHOD=TYPE3

The method of analysis of variance was used to analyze this type of data since it was introduced in the 1920s (Fisher, 1925). The analysis of variance table with expected mean squares shows where the sources of variance occur. PROC MIXED can produce analysis of variance tables using TYPE1, TYPE2, TYPE3 or TYPE4 sums of squares. Most often the TYPE3 sums of squares are used to provide the analysis of variance table.

Program

The usual analysis of variance table for Equation 6.8 is constructed by the PROC MIXED statements with the METHOD=TYPE3 option, as in the Program 6.22. The model has no fixed effects, but there are four random effects and the residual. (PROC GLIMMIX does not have the capability to fit models with the Types of sums of squares.)

Program 6.22

```
proc mixed data=e_3_5 method=type3;
   class loc fam block;
   model Yield=;
   random loc fam loc*fam block(loc);
   ods output covparams=cvp;
run;
```

Results

The PROC MIXED results with the analysis of variance table and summary of the estimated variance components are displayed in Output 6.23.

Output 6.23: PROC MIXED Analysis with METHOD=TYPE3 for Genetics Example

Source	DF	Sum of Squares	Mean Square	Expected Mean Square	Error Term	Error DF
loc	3	29783	9927.777778	Var(Residual) + 5 Var(block(loc)) + 3 Var(loc*fam) + 15 Var(loc)	MS(loc*fam) + MS(block(loc)) - MS(Residual)	13.938
fam	4	10130	2532.441667	Var(Residual) + 3 Var(loc*fam) + 12 Var(fam)	MS(loc*fam)	12
loc*fam	12	3317.166667	276.430556	Var(Residual) + 3 Var(loc*fam)	MS(Residual)	32
block(loc)	8	3987.600000	498.450000	Var(Residual) + 5 Var(block(loc))	MS(Residual)	32
Residual	32	1659.066667	51.845833	Var(Residual)	.	.

Type 3 Analysis of Variance

Source	F Value	Pr > F
loc	13.73	0.0002
fam	9.16	0.0012
loc*fam	5.33	<.0001
block(loc)	9.61	<.0001
Residual	.	.

Covariance Parameter Estimates

Cov Parm	Estimate	Standard Error	Z Value	Pr Z	Alpha	Lower	Upper
loc	613.65	540.71	1.13	0.2564	0.05	-446.12	1673.42
fam	188.00	149.52	1.26	0.2086	0.05	-105.06	481.06
loc*fam	74.8616	37.8647	1.98	0.0480	0.05	0.6481	149.08
block(loc)	89.3208	49.9124	1.79	0.0735	0.05	-8.5056	187.15
Residual	51.8458	12.9615	4.00	<.0001	0.05	33.5297	90.7052

Interpretation

The analysis of variance table and expected mean squares in Output 6.23 includes statistics to test the following hypotheses:

$$H_0 : \sigma_L^2 = 0 \text{ versus } H_a : \sigma_L^2 > 0$$
$$H_0 : \sigma_F^2 = 0 \text{ versus } H_a : \sigma_F^2 > 0$$
$$H_0 : \sigma_{LF}^2 = 0 \text{ versus } H_a : \sigma_{LF}^2 > 0$$

The *p*-values corresponding to the hypotheses above are .0002, .0012, and < .0001, respectively. These tests indicate that the variance components in the model are required to adequately describe the variation in the data. The only *F* statistic with an approximate denominator *df* in Output 6.23 corresponds to the random effect LOC. The approximate df occur because the denominator for LOC is a linear combination of mean squares while the other tests use a single mean square as a denominator.

There is a large discrepancy between the *p*-values from Z values and *F* values. One reason for the discrepancy is that Z tests use an asymptotic normal sampling distribution while TYPE3 sums of squares rely on the *F* distribution. In this example, there are very few levels of the random effects. Thus, the asymptotic normal distribution of the REML estimates is most likely not appropriate. Many more levels of the factor are necessary before the asymptotic distribution becomes appropriate. The confidence intervals can be recomputed using the Satterthwaite approximation.

The variance component estimates obtained here with METHOD=TYPE3 of PROC MIXED are identical to the ones using the default METHOD=REML of PROC GLIMMIX because the data are nicely balanced. However, the printed confidence intervals for all variances except Residual from the TYPE3 analysis are computed using the symmetric Wald interval of Estimate $\pm Z \times$ StdError, leaving some undesirable lower limits less than zero. The Satterthwaite-based asymmetric intervals from the METHOD=REML analysis are much better and are recommended over the z confidence intervals.

Program

The confidence intervals in Output 6.23 can be recomputed using the Satterthwaite approximation. Program 6.23 uses the estimates of the covariance parameters that was output to the data set CVP generated by Program 6.22.

Program 6.23

```
data cvp1; set cvp;
df=2*(estimate/stderr)**2;
y=quantile('CHISQ', .025, df);
x=quantile('CHISQ', .975, df);
low=df*estimate/x;
high=df*estimate/y;
run;
proc print data=cvp1;
var CovParm Estimate StdErr ZValue Lower Upper df low high;
run;
```

Results

The Satterthwaite approximation *df* are computed as

$$df = \left[\frac{\text{Estimate of Variance}}{\text{Standard Error of Variance}} \right]^2$$

The resulting confidence intervals are computed from the chi-square distribution where the lower limit is greater than zero (Output 6.24).

Output 6.24: Recomputed Confidence Intervals using Satterthwaite Approximation

Obs	CovParm	Estimate	StdErr	ZValue	Lower	Upper	df	low	high
1	loc	613.65	540.71	1.13	-446.12	1673.42	2.5760	185.081	12013.36
2	fam	188.00	149.52	1.26	-105.06	481.06	3.1619	61.610	2349.79
3	loc*fam	74.8616	37.8647	1.98	0.6481	149.08	7.8177	33.908	280.29
4	block(loc)	89.3208	49.9124	1.79	-8.5056	187.15	6.4050	37.917	404.14
5	Residual	51.8458	12.9615	4.00	33.5297	90.7052	32.0000	33.530	90.71

The information in Output 6.24 contains the estimates of the variance components and their standard errors. The variables Lower and Upper are the default Wald confidence intervals. The line *df* are from the Satterthwaite approximation. The variables Low and High are the recomputed confidence intervals using the chi-square distribution. All of the lower bounds are positive for Low, which is not the case for Lower. The confidence interval for the Residual variance is computed by means of the Satterthwaite approximation *df* with the chi-square distribution. This fact is pointed out where Lower=Low and Upper=High. The results in Output 6.22 can be obtained from PROC MIXED as well as PROC GLIMMIX but the results in Output 6.23 can be obtained only from PROC MIXED as PROC GLIMMIX does not enable one to compute TYPE= sums of squares used to obtain method of moments estimates of the variance components.

6.6 Modern ANOVA with Variance Components

For around a century now, analysis of variance (ANOVA) and its variants and extensions like the mixed model have been arguably the most important and influential methods for analyzing experimental data. One definition of "analysis" is to "break into pieces," and if we interpret ANOVA literally in this sense, we can use it to break down total variability into constituent pieces and compare their magnitudes.

Because variance is a function of squared deviations around means, the classical way of approaching this is to compute quantities like Types 1, 2, or 3 sums of squares according to various rules associated with effects in the design. When data are nicely balanced as many examples in this book, this type of breakdown is straightforward and most all of the popular methods agree to a very close approximation if not exactly. However, when a data set becomes unbalanced, due either to data missing at random or by design, classical ANOVA becomes much less straightforward. A Type 1 analysis provides a nice sequential partitioning of the sums of squares, which sums to the total, but the values of the sums of squares depend on the order of specified effects. Sums of squares from Types 2 and 3 analyses are order-independent, but they no longer provide a meaningful partitioning of total variability because each effect is adjusted for all other effects in the model and the projections are no longer orthogonal due to data imbalance.

The more modern REML and related likelihood methods provide a solution for both balanced and unbalanced data. You simply specify all known sources of variability as random effects (even effects that you might ordinarily consider fixed for inferential purposes) and estimate their corresponding variance components using REML. The resulting estimates will isolate each source of variability appropriately, and it is reasonable to compute their sum as an estimate of total variance. Note that this sum will not be equal to the simple variance of the response because of the complex nature of the related mixed model and distributional assumptions, but it is still reasonable to compute variance proportions using it.

Program

For illustration, consider the following code, which produces the graph in Figure 6.1. The data set CVP is from the ODS OUTPUT statement in Program 6.21 where there are five variance components. The following program expresses each variance component as a proportion of the total of the variances. The included graphic is a visual indication as to the relative magnitude of the respective variance components.

Program 6.24

```
data cvp;
  set cvp;
  VarProp = estimate;
  label CovParm="Variance Component"
        VarProp="Proportion of Variance";
run;

proc stdize data=cvp out=cvp method=sum;
   var VarProp;
run;

proc sgplot data=cvp;
   vbar CovParm / response=VarProp;
run;
```

Results

The results of the code in Program 6.24 produces a bar chart where the bars representing each variance component are the proportion of the total of the variance components. PROC STDIZE computes the proportion each variance component is of the total sum of variance components. PROC SGPLOT produces the bar chart of the variation portions, as displayed in Figure 6.1.

Figure 6.1: Proportion of Variance for Genetics Example

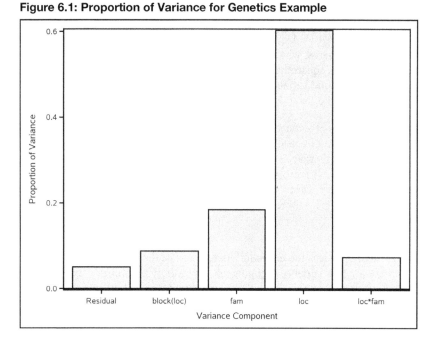

Figure 6.1 provides a simple and effective way to compare magnitudes of proportion of variance explained by each effect. The location accounts for just over 60% of the variance and family is the next highest and around three times smaller at just under 20%. The other two effects are a little larger than the residual (unexplained) variance, which is around 5%. The analysis can be continued by computing meaningful combinations and ratios of the proportions, such as various forms of genetic heritability and intra-class correlations.

This example also illustrates a case when you could intentionally specify all effects as random in order to study the proportion of variability that each component provides to the system variability You may also assign some of the effects to be fixed in mixed models designed to compare the means of the fixed effects..

6.7 Summary

Random effects arise from a probability distribution and can occur in the design structure and/or the treatment structure of an experiment. Procedures for estimating the parameters of a random effects model are demonstrated using PROC GLIMMIX and PROC MIXED. Small sample size approximations to confidence intervals using the Satterthwaite approximation are described and constructed for several examples. Unconditional and conditional hierarchical linear models are described, which are special cases of random effects and mixed linear models, respectively. Random coefficient models (Chapter 10) are a special type of mixed analysis of covariance models (see Chapter 7) and are conditional hierarchical linear models when all of the random effects are hierarchical. Variance components provide a modern way to do ANOVA, partitioning total variance into explainable pieces.

Chapter 7: Analysis of Covariance

7.1 Introduction	**217**
7.2 One-Way Fixed Effects Treatment Structure with Simple Linear Regression Models	**218**
7.2.1 Comparing the Regression Models	220
7.2.2 Summary of an Analysis of Covariance Strategy	223
7.2.3 Extensions to More Complex Regression Models	223
7.3 One-Way Treatment Structure in an RCB Design Structure—Equal Slopes Model: An Example	**223**
7.3.1 Fit the Model to Test the Slopes-Equal-to-Zero Hypothesis	224
7.3.2 Determine Whether a Common Slope Model Is Adequate to Describe the Data	226
7.3.3 Fit a Common Slope Model	227
7.3.4 Mixed Model Estimator: A Combined Estimator	232
7.4 One-Way Treatment Structure in an Incomplete Block Design Structure: An Example	**237**
7.4.1 Fit the Model to Test the Equal Slopes Hypothesis	238
7.4.2 Fit the Unequal Slopes Model	239
7.4.3 Test for Lack of Fit of the Simple Linear Regression Model	242
7.4.4 Comparing the Models at a Preselected Value of the Covariate	243
7.5 One-Way Treatment Structure in a BIB Design Structure: An Example	**246**
7.5.1 Fit the Unequal Slopes Model	246
7.5.2 Test the Equal Slopes Hypothesis	247
7.5.3 Fit Model with Unequal Slopes for Each Level of GRP	248
7.6 One-Way Treatment Structure in an Unbalanced Incomplete Block Design Structure: An Example	**254**
7.6.1 Test the Equal Slopes Hypothesis	254
7.6.2 Fit a Common Slope Model	255
7.7 Multilevel or Split-Plot Design with the Covariate Measured on the Large-Size Experimental Unit or Whole Plot: An Example	**256**
7.7.1 Fit Unequal Slopes Model and Test Slopes-Equal-to-Zero Hypothesis	257
7.7.2 Fit Factorial Effects Model for Intercepts and Slopes	258
7.7.3 Fit Model with Slopes Expressed as Main Effects of the Two Factors	259
7.7.4 Fit Model with Unequal Slopes for Each	260
7.8 Summary	**267**

7.1 Introduction

Analysis of covariance is a strategy for analyzing data from a designed experiment, sample survey, or observational study where, in addition to the response variable, one or more continuous variables are measured on each experimental unit. Ideally, the additional continuous variables, called covariates, should be determined before the treatments have been applied to the experimental units. At a minimum, the values of the covariates should not be affected by the applied treatments. The analysis of covariance is often described as a method to remove variability in the experiment by accounting for variability in the experimental units that could not be controlled by the design structure. A more global view of analysis of covariance describes it as a methodology to compare a series of regression models (Milliken and Johnson 2002). The analysis of covariance model is a model that consists of both classification, or qualitative variables and continuous, or quantitative variables. The discussion in this chapter uses treatment or treatment combination to denote the levels of the classification variables in the model and covariates to denote the continuous variables. Initial weight could be a covariate for studying weight loss drugs, which are the treatments. Covariates are primarily continuous variables, but they can be categorical or ordered categorical variables, but those topics are not discussed here.

A major objective of an analysis is to make comparisons among the levels of the treatments or treatment combinations as if the experimental units all have the same value of the covariate or covariates. This process uses regression models that describe the relationships among the response variable and the covariate (or covariates). This process is accomplished by fitting regression models to the data from each of the treatment combinations and then making comparisons among the regression lines at a common value of the covariate or set of common values of the covariates.

The basic model consists of the same functional relationship between response and the covariates with possibly different parameters for each of the treatments or treatment combinations. In essence, the basic model consists of a different regression model for each treatment or treatment combination in the treatment structure. Analysis of covariance is a strategy for making decisions about the form of the model and then comparing the model's parameters for each combination of classification variables in the treatment structure. The analysis of a one-way treatment structure in a completely randomized design structure, where the levels of the treatment are fixed effects, is used to establish the basic analysis of covariance strategy, which is the topic of Section 7.2. Most applications of analysis of covariance are to designs of experiments with fixed treatment effects and some type of blocking. A random coefficient regression model is used to describe the data when the regression models occur for each of the levels of a random effect. Random coefficient models are discussed in Chapter 10. When blocking is used in the design structure, more than one size of experimental unit is generated. Models with fixed effects and more than one size experimental unit are mixed models. Section 7.7 presents an example of the analysis of a design with more than one size of experimental unit. These examples involve blocking and demonstrate the aspects of the mixed model equations concerning the combining of information from the intra-block and inter-block analyses.

Next, the discussion expands to fixed effect treatment structure models with more complex design structures including nested and split-plot types of designs. The mixed model is very important in the analysis of complex design structures, as information about the coefficients of the covariates in the model can occur at several levels of the model. The solution of the mixed model equations combines the information from all sources into a single estimate. The following sections present models for complete block, incomplete block, and balanced incomplete block designs, as well as a multilevel or split-plot design where the covariate is measured on the large size of experimental unit.

7.2 One-Way Fixed Effects Treatment Structure with Simple Linear Regression Models

Consider a situation where data are collected from an experiment involving a one-way treatment structure in a completely randomized design, and the experimental units exhibit considerable variability that cannot be controlled by using some form of blocking. But, the researcher believes, say, from past experiences, that one or more characteristics of the experimental units can help describe some of the variability among experimental units. In this section, only one covariate is considered for the development of the strategy of analysis of covariance. Before the treatments were applied to the experimental units, the researcher measured the value of a covariate. The covariate should be considered a priori to be related to the variability observed in the experimental units. By measuring a covariate, the researcher attempts to account for variability in the experimental units that cannot conveniently be removed by blocking the experimental units into homogeneous groups. For example, in a feeding study the response to different diets may be affected by the size of the animals or the age of the animals. The animal scientist may measure the initial weight of each animal before the start of the experiment—in essence, before they are randomly assigned to the diets. The response variable can be the average daily gain of each animal computed for the amount of time that the animals are in the study. At this point the treatment structure consists of fixed effects (a set of s diets), a random sample of animals from a population of animals with initial weights denoted by x, and the response, average daily gain, denoted by Y. The average daily gain values are calculated by dividing the total amount gained during the feeding trial by the number of days the animals were on trial. A statistical model that can be used to describe the relationships among the response variable Y, the classification variable for diets, the covariate x, and the experimental units or animals is as follows:

$$y_{ij} = \alpha_i + \beta_i x_{ij} + e_{ij} \tag{7.1}$$

where the following definitions hold:

- $i = 1,2,...,s.$
- $j = 1,2,...,n.$
- $e_{ij} \sim \text{iid } N(0,\sigma_e^2).$
- α_i is the intercept of the model for treatment i.
- β_i is the slope of the model for treatment i.

Equation 7.1 represents a set of simple linear regression lines with possibly different slopes and intercepts as exhibited in Figure 7.1, where the mean of the response from the ith treatment at a given value of the covariate is expressed as $\mu(Y \mid x)_i = \alpha_i + \beta_i x$.

Figure 7.1: Three Simple Regression Lines with Unequal Slopes

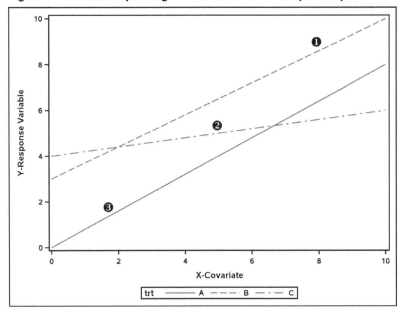

❶ $\mu(y\mid x)_B = \alpha_B + \beta_B x$

❷ $\mu(y\mid x)_C = \alpha_C + \beta_C x$

❸ $\mu(y\mid x)_A = \alpha_A + \beta_A x$

Before you use these models to describe data, you must make sure that the simple linear regression models (or the selected regression model) adequately describe the data for each treatment. This process involves identification of outliers, testing for the equality of variances, and checking the adequacy of the models for each treatment. This aspect of the analysis of covariance is often overlooked when put into the context of measuring variables to adjust for variability in the experimental units. When the analysis of covariance is cast in the context of comparing regression models, you realize that all regression diagnostics used for usual regression analysis should be used for fitting and comparing these models.

A basic philosophy is to use the simplest possible model for the covariate part of the model. That is, avoid using a more complicated model than is necessary to describe the relationship between the mean of the response variable and the covariate (Milliken and Johnson 2002). Using the simplest model prevents overfitting of the data as well as provides more degrees of freedom for estimating the error. In this light, the first hypothesis to be tested is to determine whether a model without the covariate can be used to adequately describe the data; i.e., test H_0: $\beta_1 = \beta_2 = ... = \beta_s = 0$ versus H_a: (not H_0), called the slopes-equal-to-zero hypothesis. (If you have graphed the data for each treatment, you probably already have an idea if the slopes are different from zero.) If there is evidence that the slopes are not all zero, then determine whether a model with a common slope can be used to describe the data; i.e., test H_0: $\beta_1 = \beta_2 = ... = \beta_s = \beta$ versus H_a: (not H_0), where β is unspecified. If the common slope model can be used to adequately describe the data, the process of comparing the regression models is greatly simplified. The common slope analysis of covariance model is

$$y_{ij} = \alpha_i + \beta x_{ij} + e_{ij}$$

where α_1, α_2, ..., α_s are the intercepts for treatments 1,2,...,s and β is the common slope.

As in Equation 7.1, assume $e_{ij} \sim$ iid $N(0, \sigma_e^2)$. Common slope models can be represented as shown in Figure 7.2.

Figure 7.2: Three Simple Linear Regression Models with Equal Slopes

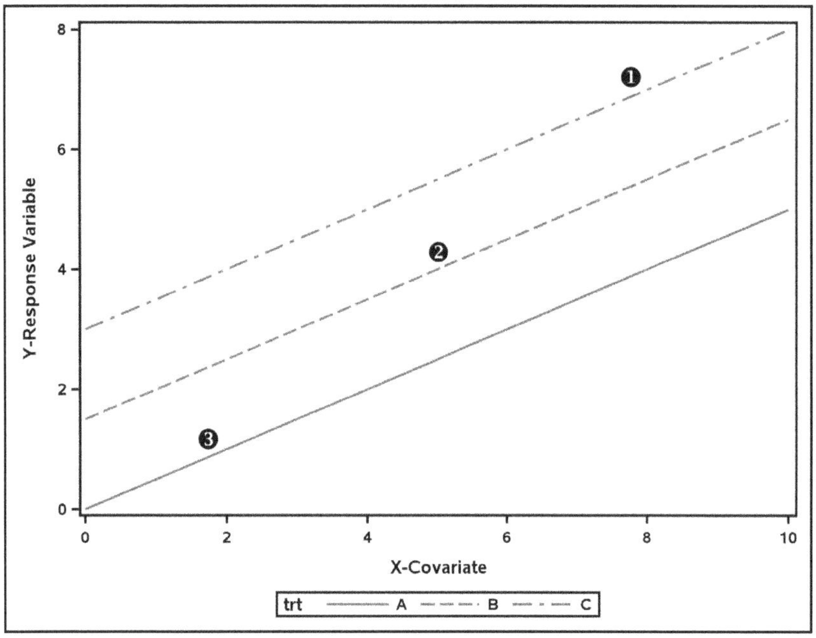

❶ $\mu\left(y\,|\,x\right)_C = \alpha_C + \beta x$

❷ $\mu\left(y\,|\,x\right)_B = \alpha_B + \beta x$

❸ $\mu\left(y\,|\,x\right)_A = \alpha_A + \beta x$

7.2.1 Comparing the Regression Models

After you decide on the form of the covariate part of the model—i.e., determine whether the covariate is useful and if so, determine the form of the slopes in the model—the next step is to make comparisons among the regression models, which may include comparisons among the intercepts, among the slopes, or among the models evaluated at specified values of the covariate. Making comparisons among the models at a specific value of the covariate, say, x_0, is equivalent to treatment comparisons as if all experimental units had a covariate value equal to x_0 (Milliken and Johnson 2002).

If the slopes are all zero, the covariate is not needed in the model, and you compare the means (intercepts for regression lines with zero slopes) using standard analysis of variance techniques (as in Chapter 3), such as testing equality of the means, investigating contrasts of the means, or carrying out multiple comparisons. If models with common slopes are adequate to describe the data, they form a series of parallel lines and can be compared by estimating the distance between the lines. The estimated regression models with common slope—i.e., the estimated means of Y for a given value of x for treatment i—are as follows:

$$\hat{\mu}(y\,|\,x)_i = \hat{\alpha}_i + \hat{\beta}x$$

$$i = 1,2, \ldots, s$$

A comparison of the regression lines for treatments one and two at $x = x^*$ is

$$\hat{\mu}(y\,|\,x^*)_1 - \hat{\mu}(y\,|\,x^*)_2 = \hat{\alpha}_1 - \hat{\alpha}_2$$

This is a comparison of the two intercepts and is independent of the value of the covariate. The quantities $\hat{\mu}(y\,|\,x^*)_i$, $i = 1,2, \ldots, s$, are predicted values obtained from the estimated regression lines evaluated at $x = x^*$, as shown in Figure 7.3. These predicted values are called *adjusted means* or *least squares means*. Also displayed in Figure 7.3 are the estimated values of the regression lines at $x = \bar{x}$. The predicted values evaluated at $x = \bar{x}$ are the usual adjusted means computed for analysis of covariance and they are designated as least squares means by SAS (LSMEANS statement). An important point is that adjusted means can be computed at values of x other than $x = \bar{x}$. Predictions from a regression model evaluated at some value $x_0 \neq \overline{x}$ can be useful. For regression models with a common slope, the differences among adjusted means involve only the intercepts. That is, they are independent of the value of the covariate (Figure 7.3).

Figure 7.3: Comparison of Equal Slopes Regression Models

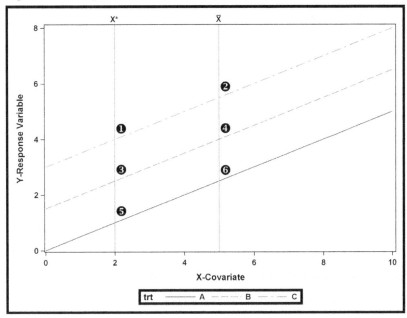

Note: $\mu(y \mid x = X^*)_k$ denotes the Mean of the kth Treatment Evaluated at x^*, and $\mu(y \mid x = \overline{X})_k$, denotes the Mean of the kth Treatment Evaluated at $\overline{X}$.

❶ $\mu\left(y \mid x = X^*\right)_C$

❷ $\mu\left(y \mid x = \overline{X}\right)_C$

❸ $\mu\left(y \mid x = X^*\right)_B$

❹ $\mu\left(y \mid x = \overline{X}\right)_B$

❺ $\mu\left(y \mid x = X^*\right)_A$

❻ $\mu\left(y \mid x = \overline{X}\right)_A$

For the unequal slopes models, the estimated mean of y for a given value of x for the ith treatment is $\hat{\mu}(y \mid x)_i = \hat{\alpha}_i + \hat{\beta}_i x$, $i = 1,2,\ldots,s$. A comparison of the regression lines for treatments one and two evaluated at $x = x^*$ is as follows:

$$\hat{\mu}(y \mid x^*)_1 - \hat{\mu}(y \mid x^*)_2 = \hat{\alpha}_1 + \hat{\beta}_1 x^* - \hat{\alpha}_2 - \hat{\beta}_2 x^* = \hat{\alpha}_1 - \hat{\alpha}_2 + \left(\hat{\beta}_1 - \hat{\beta}_2\right)x^*$$

This—unlike the common slope model—does depend on the value of the covariate. Because the comparison of treatments now depends on the value of the covariate, this model is called the unequal slopes or covariate by treatment interaction model. To provide an appropriate analysis when the slopes are unequal, the models should be compared at a minimum of three values of x, such as at a low, middle, and high value of x. Potential choices are the minimum value of x, the mean value of x, and the maximum value of x, or the lower γ percentile, the median, and the upper γ percentile of the distribution of the x values. Reasonable choices for γ are 5, 10, or 25. It is important to keep the selected values within the range of the covariate. At each of the selected values of x, contrasts of interest or multiple comparisons should be used to compare the treatments. Figure 7.4 displays three models being compared at three values of x, where the points of intersection of the models with the vertical lines are the respective adjusted treatment means. Other choices for the analysis include the following (Milliken and Johnson, 2002):

- Using a multiple comparison procedure to make pairwise comparisons between slopes in an attempt to form groups of treatments (treatments *within* a group have common slopes, and treatments *between* groups have unequal slopes).

- Constructing confidence bands about differences of models for each pair of treatments in an attempt to determine ranges of the covariate where the models are likely to have similar response levels and where the models are likely to have different response levels.

These paths of analysis are used in some of the examples that follow. But first, the discussion to this point is summarized in the next section.

Figure 7.4: Comparisons of Three Unequal Slopes Models at Three Values of X

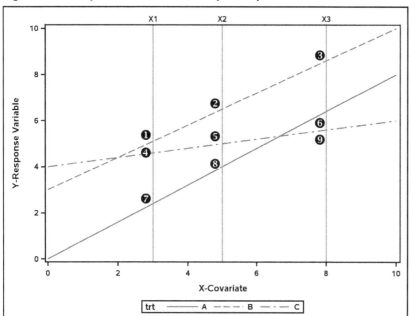

Note: $\mu(y \mid x = X^{*})_{k}$ denotes the Mean of the kth Treatment Evaluated at X^{*}.

❶ $\mu\left(y \mid x = X_{1}\right)_{B}$

❷ $\mu\left(y \mid x = X_{2}\right)_{B}$

❸ $\mu\left(y \mid x = X_{3}\right)_{B}$

❹ $\mu\left(y \mid x = X_{1}\right)_{C}$

❺ $\mu\left(y \mid x = X_{2}\right)_{C}$

❻ $\mu\left(y \mid x = X_{3}\right)_{A}$

❼ $\mu\left(y \mid x = X_{1}\right)_{A}$

❽ $\mu\left(y \mid x = X_{2}\right)_{A}$

❾ $\mu\left(y \mid x = X_{3}\right)_{C}$

7.2.2 Summary of an Analysis of Covariance Strategy

Making sure the selected functional form of the covariate part of the model does in fact describe the data is the first essential step in the analysis of covariance strategy. If the simple linear regression model is not appropriate, then a more complex model must be selected for the analysis. To this point, we have considered only the simple linear regression model as the functional form and the following discussion centers on that model. There are several ways to approach the process of determining the form of the covariate part of the model. One strategy is summarized in Table 7.1 (Milliken and Johnson, 2002). Following the steps in Table 7.1 provides a procedure to determine the form of the covariate part of the model. The resulting model can be used to compare the treatments by comparing the resulting regression models.

Table 7.1: Determining the Form of the Covariate Part of the Models for Simple Linear Regression Models

Step	Action
1	Make sure the simple linear regression model describes the data from each treatment and that regression diagnostics are used to validate the assumptions.
2	Test the hypothesis that all the slopes are equal to zero.
	(a) If fail to reject, go to step 3.
	(b) If reject, go to step 4.
3	Fit a common slope model to the data and test the hypothesis that the slope is equal to zero.
	(a) If fail to reject, compare the treatment means using analysis of variance.
	(b) If reject, use a parallel lines model and compare the treatment regression models by comparing the intercepts or adjusted means (LS-means).
4	Test the hypothesis that the slopes are equal.
	(a) If fail to reject, use a common slope model and compare the treatment regression models by comparing the intercepts or adjusted means (LS-means).
	(b) If reject, go to step 5.
5	Use the unequal slopes model.
	(a) Compare the slopes of the treatments.
	(b) Compare the models at a minimum of three values of the covariate.
	(c) Construct confidence bands about the differences of selected pairs of models.

7.2.3 Extensions to More Complex Regression Models

To this point, the discussion has focused on the simple linear regression model, but the same methodology can be extended to any regression model required to adequately describe the data. For example, a quadratic model in x may be required to describe the relationship between y and x for each treatment. You still need to select the simplest form of the covariate model by determining if the slopes are equal across treatments for x^2 as well as for x. If there are several possible covariates, then the equality of slopes must be investigated for each possible covariate. In this case, the steps in Table 7.1 must be followed for each covariate. The strategy does not involve comparing the treatments by analysis of variance unless it is decided that the slopes for all covariates across all treatments are zero. When the slopes are unequal for a covariate, the models need to be compared at a minimum of three values for that covariate. If there are k covariates with unequal slopes and the models are to be compared at combinations of three values of each covariate, then there are 3^k combinations where the models need to be compared. Thus, it is imperative that the covariate part of the model be simplified as much as possible.

7.3 One-Way Treatment Structure in an RCB Design Structure—Equal Slopes Model: An Example

The data in the data set "Average Daily Gain," are average daily gains (ADG) of steers fed for 160 days. The treatments are four diets consisting of a base ration and three levels of a feed additive added to the base ration. The objective of the experiment is to determine the optimal level of feed additive to maximize the average daily gain. The steers were housed in barns, the blocking factor, where each barn held four steers and the steers were individually fed.

The 32 steers were randomly assigned to the eight barns, and the four diets were randomly assigned to the four steers in each barn. Because the steers were of varying initial weights, the initial weights (iwt) were measured for use as a possible covariate. The model is constructed assuming that the diet effects are fixed, the barn (or block) effects are random, and the functional form of the covariate part of the model is a simple linear regression model. For step 1, a plot of the data for each diet substantiates the use of a simple linear regression model for each diet as shown in Figure 7.5, which is Step 1 of the steps in Table 7.1.

Figure 7.5: Average Daily Gain versus Initial Weight for the Steer Data

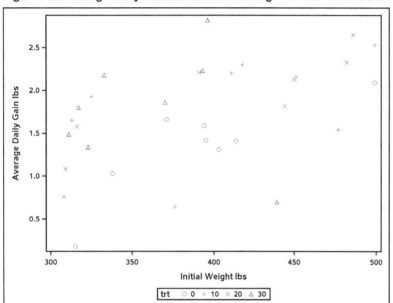

7.3.1 Fit the Model to Test the Slopes-Equal-to-Zero Hypothesis

The second step in the process for the analysis of covariance is to test the hypothesis that the slopes are all equal to zero, which in effect is asking if the covariate is linearly related to the response within any of the treatment groups. Most often a plot like Figure 7.5 will show that there is a linear relationship between the response and the covariate. The plot in Figure 7.5 shows a linear relationship, but with all of the variation within a treatment it is not obvious that the slopes are significantly different from zero. The following model is used to carry out the step 2.

A model to describe the average daily gain data as a linear function of the initial weight (x_{ij}) for each treatment is

$$y_{ij} = \alpha_i + \beta_i x_{ij} + b_j + e_{ij}$$

where the following definitions hold:

- $i = 1, 2, 3, 4$.
- $j = 1, 2,...,8$.
- α_i denotes the intercept of the ith diet model.
- β_i denotes the slope of the ith diet model.
- $b_j \sim$ iid $N(0, \sigma_b^2)$ denotes the random effect of the jth block.
- $e_{ij} \sim$ iid $N(0, \sigma_e^2)$ denotes the experimental unit error.
- b_j and e_{ij} are independent random variables.

Program

The SAS code to fit the model to test the slopes-equal-to-zero hypothesis is in Program 7.1.

Program 7.1

```
proc glimmix data=ex7_3_rcb;
   class trt blk;
   model adg=trt iwt*trt/noint solution ddfm=kr2;
   random blk;
run;
```

The NOINT option causes PROC GLIMMIX to fit a full rank model. This provides estimates of the slopes and intercepts and Type III tests that the intercepts are all equal to zero and that the slopes are all equal to zero. Selected results are presented in Output 7.1.

Results

The results are displayed in Output 7.1 with estimates of the covariance parameters, estimates of the slopes and intercepts, and Type III tests of hypotheses.

Output 7.1: Fit of the Unequal Slope Model and Test the Slopes-Equal-to-Zero Hypothesis

Covariance Parameter Estimates		
Cov Parm	Estimate	Standard Error
blk	0.2593	0.1485
Residual	0.04943	0.01703

Solutions for Fixed Effects						
Effect	trt	Estimate	Standard Error	DF	t Value	Pr > |t|
trt	0	0.4391	0.7153	19.68	0.61	0.5463
trt	10	1.4261	0.6435	20.52	2.22	0.0381
trt	20	0.4796	0.5538	21.41	0.87	0.3960
trt	30	0.2001	0.7799	19.33	0.26	0.8002
iwt*trt	0	0.002294	0.001759	17.38	1.30	0.2091
iwt*trt	10	0.001083	0.001499	17.73	0.72	0.4795
iwt*trt	20	0.003366	0.001300	17.72	2.59	0.0187
iwt*trt	30	0.004448	0.002095	17.39	2.12	0.0484

Type III Tests of Fixed Effects				
Effect	Num DF	Den DF	F Value	Pr > F
trt	4	19.08	1.30	0.3062
iwt*trt	4	17.45	3.43	0.0306

Interpretation

The "Covariance Parameter Estimates" table reports the estimates of the two variance components, one for the block-to-block variation, denoted by BLK, and one for the residual variance. The NOINT option in the MODEL statement is used so that PROC GLIMMIX fits a model with nonsingular design matrix and thus provides estimates of the intercepts and slopes, as shown in the "Solution for Fixed Effects" table. If the NOINT option is not used, the design matrix corresponding to the intercepts is singular and the estimates of the intercepts satisfy the set-to-zero restrictions (see Milliken and Johnson 2009, Chapter 6). The MODEL statement includes the IWT*TRT term in the model without the IWT term. As you will see a little later, excluding the IWT term enables the covariate part of the model to be nonsingular, thus providing estimates of the slopes. Including the IWT provides estimates of the slopes satisfying the set-to-zero restriction. The "Solution for Fixed Effects" table contains the estimates of the intercepts (Effect=TRT) and slopes (Effect=IWT*TRT) for each of the four treatments. The Type III F statistic corresponding to IWT*TRT in the "Type III Tests of Fixed Effects" table tests the hypothesis $H_0: \beta_1 = \beta_2 = \beta_3 = \beta_4 = 0$ versus H_a: (not H_0). The p-value of 0.0306 indicates that the slopes are most likely not all equal to zero. The Type III F statistic corresponding to TRT in the "Type III Tests of Fixed Effects tests" table tests the hypothesis $H_0: \alpha_1 = \alpha_2 = \alpha_3 = \alpha_4 = 0$ versus H_a: (not H_0), a comparison of the regression models at IWT=0. This does not provide meaningful comparisons, as the initial weights of the animals cannot be zero.

7.3.2 Determine Whether a Common Slope Model Is Adequate to Describe the Data

The third step is to see whether a common slope model will adequately describe the data. This is accomplished by testing the hypothesis that the slopes are all equal. The following code fits the model with the intercepts and slopes as deviations from the intercept and slope of treatment 4. In this case, the intercept of the model is α_4 and the treatment effects for the intercepts are $\alpha_i - \alpha_4$ and the same for the slopes, as defined in the following model.

$$y_{ij} = \alpha_4 + (\alpha_i - \alpha_4) + \beta_4 x_{ij} + (\beta_i - \beta_4) x_{ij} + b_j + e_{ij}$$

(7.2)

where the following definitions hold:

- $i = 1,2,3,4$.
- $j = 1,2,...,8$.
- α_i denotes the intercept of the ith diet model.
- β_i denotes the slope of the ith diet model.
- $\beta_j \sim$ iid $N(0, \sigma_b^2)$ denotes the random effect of the jth block.
- $e_{ij} \sim$ iid $N(0, \sigma_e^2)$ denotes the experimental unit error.
- b_j and e_{ij} are independent random variables.

Equation 7.2 is a reparameterization of Equation 7.1, where the slopes have been re-expressed as $\beta_i = \beta_4 + (\beta_i - \beta_4)$ In this parameterization the Type III F statistic corresponding to IWT*TRT tests the hypothesis of equal slopes, i.e., test H$_0$: $\beta_1 = \beta_2 = \beta_3 = \beta_4$ versus H$_a$: (not H$_0$).

Program

The code for fitting this reparameterized or re-expressed model is in Program7.2.

Program 7.2

The following code fits model in Equation 7.2 to the average daily gain data:

```
proc glimmix data=ex7_3_rcb;
   class trt blk;
   model adg=trt iwt iwt*trt/solution ddfm=kr2;
   random blk;
run;
```

When the MODEL statement includes the IWT term (the covariate) and the IWT*TRT term (the interaction), the model becomes singular and the set-to-zero restrictions are used to handle the singularity. The coefficient of IWT becomes the slope corresponding to the last treatment, and the coefficients of IWT*TRT become the deviations of the given treatment's slope from that of the last treatment.

Results

Selected results of fitting model 7.2 are displayed in Output 7.2 where the estimates of the fixed effects reflect the above parameterization of the model. The estimates of the covariance parameters and the Type III hypotheses of equal slopes and of equal intercepts.

Output 7.2: Fit of the Unequal Slope Model and Test the Equal Slope Hypothesis

Covariance Parameter Estimates		
Cov Parm	Estimate	Standard Error
blk	0.2593	0.1485
Residual	0.04943	0.01703

Solutions for Fixed Effects						
Effect	trt	Estimate	Standard Error	DF	t Value	Pr > |t|
Intercept		0.2001	0.7799	19.33	0.26	0.8002
trt	0	0.2390	1.0544	17.49	0.23	0.8233
trt	10	1.2260	0.9617	17.46	1.27	0.2191
trt	20	0.2795	0.9382	17.54	0.30	0.7693
trt	30	0	.	.	.	.
iwt		0.004448	0.002095	17.39	2.12	0.0484
iwt*trt	0	-0.00215	0.002808	17.49	-0.77	0.4532
iwt*trt	10	-0.00337	0.002533	17.45	-1.33	0.2011
iwt*trt	20	-0.00108	0.002508	17.53	-0.43	0.6713
iwt*trt	30	0	.	.	.	.

Type III Tests of Fixed Effects				
Effect	Num DF	Den DF	F Value	Pr > F
trt	3	17.36	0.86	0.4780
iwt	1	17.6	10.50	0.0046
iwt*trt	3	17.36	0.93	0.4485

Interpretation

The estimates of the variance components are identical to those in Output 7.1. Comparing information from the "Solution for Fixed Effects" table in Outputs 7.1 and 7.2, you see that the estimate corresponding to the IWT effect in Output 7.2 is the same as the estimate corresponding to IWT*TRT 30 in Output 7.1. The estimate corresponding to iwt*trt 0 in Output 7.2 is equal to the difference in the slopes (IWT*TRT 0) – (IWT*TRT 30) in Output 7.1. The Type III F statistic for the iwt*trt effect in the "Type III Tests of Fixed Effects" table tests the hypothesis $H_0: \beta_1 - \beta_4 = \beta_2 - \beta_4 = \beta_3 - \beta_4 = 0$ versus $H_a:$ (not H_0). This null hypothesis implies $H_0: \beta_1 = \beta_2 = \beta_3 = \beta_4 = \beta$, where β is unspecified. The p-value of 0.4485 indicates that there is insufficient evidence to conclude that the slopes are unequal. A common slope model should be adequate to describe the relationship between average daily gain and IWT across the four treatments. The Type III F statistic corresponding to the trt effect in the "Type III Tests of Fixed Effects" table tests the hypothesis $H_0: \alpha_1 - \alpha_4 = \alpha_2 - \alpha_4 = \alpha_3 - \alpha_4 = 0$ versus $H_a:$ (not H_0), which compares the regression models at IWT=0. Again, it is not meaningful to compare treatments at IWT=0 because the initial weight of the animals cannot be zero.

7.3.3 Fit a Common Slope Model

The preceding results indicate that the common slope model appears to be adequate to describe the relationship between average gain and initial weight. (Plot the residuals by treatment to verify there are no patterns.) The model with a common slope for all diets is as follows:

$$y_{ij} = \alpha_i + \beta x_{ij} + b_j + e_{ij} \tag{7.3}$$

where the following definitions hold:

- $i = 1,2,3,4$.
- $j = 1,2,...,8$.
- α_i denotes the intercept of the ith diet model.
- β denotes the common slope of the diet models.
- $\beta_j \sim$ iid $N(0, \sigma_b^2)$ denotes the random effect of the jth block.
- $e_{ij} \sim$ iid $N(0, \sigma_e^2)$ denotes the experimental unit error.
- b_j and e_{ij} are independent random variables.

Program

The SAS code to fit Equation 7.3 to the data and using the ESTIMATE and LSMEANS statements to provide the final analysis is in Program 7.3. The common slope model does not have the iwt*trt interaction term. The estimate statements provide tests for a linear trend, quadratic trend, and a cubic trend. The first LSMEANS statement provides the predicted values of the model at the average iwt. The LSMEANS statements with the AT option provides predicted values at the specified iwts.

Program 7.3

```
proc glimmix data=ex7_3_rcb;
   class trt blk;
   model adg = trt iwt/ solution ddfm=kr2;
   random blk;
   lsmeans trt / diff;
   lsmeans trt / at iwt=300;
   lsmeans trt / at iwt=500;
   ods output lsmeans=lsm;
run;
```

Results

The results of fitting Equation 7.3 to the average daily gain data are shown in Output 7.3. The estimates of the covariance parameters, the estimates of the slopes and common intercept, the Type III tests of the equality of the intercepts and the common slope equals zero, the results of the ESTIMATE statements and the results of the LSMEANS statements are shown in Output 7.3.

Output 7.3: Fit of the Equal Slope Model

Covariance Parameter Estimates		
Cov Parm	Estimate	Standard Error
blk	0.2408	0.1367
Residual	0.05008	0.01586

Solutions for Fixed Effects						
Effect	trt	Estimate	Standard Error	DF	t Value	Pr > |t|
Intercept		0.8011	0.3584	26.98	2.24	0.0339
trt	0	-0.5521	0.1149	19.99	-4.81	0.0001
trt	10	-0.06857	0.1191	20.07	-0.58	0.5713
trt	20	-0.08813	0.1164	20.02	-0.76	0.4577
trt	30	0	.	.	.	.
iwt		0.002780	0.000842	21.06	3.30	0.0034

Type III Tests of Fixed Effects				
Effect	Num DF	Den DF	F Value	Pr > F
trt	3	19.98	10.16	0.0003
iwt	1	21.06	10.89	0.0034

Estimates					
Label	Estimate	Standard Error	DF	t Value	Pr > |t|
linear	1.6367	0.3643	20	4.49	0.0002
quad	0.3954	0.1650	20.02	2.40	0.0265
cubic	0.6108	0.3538	19.94	1.73	0.0998

trt Least Squares Means					
trt	Estimate	Standard Error	DF	t Value	Pr > |t|
0	1.3320	0.1907	9.017	6.98	<.0001
10	1.8155	0.1914	9.132	9.49	<.0001
20	1.7959	0.1908	9.04	9.41	<.0001
30	1.8841	0.1923	9.289	9.80	<.0001

Differences of trt Least Squares Means						
trt	_trt	Estimate	Standard Error	DF	t Value	Pr > |t|
0	10	-0.4835	0.1129	19.95	-4.28	0.0004
0	20	-0.4639	0.1121	19.94	-4.14	0.0005
0	30	-0.5521	0.1149	19.99	-4.81	0.0001
10	20	0.01956	0.1122	19.94	0.17	0.8634
10	30	-0.06857	0.1191	20.07	-0.58	0.5713
20	30	-0.08813	0.1164	20.02	-0.76	0.4577

trt Least Squares Means						
trt	iwt	Estimate	Standard Error	DF	t Value	Pr > |t|
0	300.00	1.0829	0.2056	11.67	5.27	0.0002
10	300.00	1.5665	0.2116	12.79	7.40	<.0001
20	300.00	1.5469	0.2079	12.1	7.44	<.0001
30	300.00	1.6350	0.1973	10.17	8.29	<.0001

trt Least Squares Means						
trt	iwt	Estimate	Standard Error	DF	t Value	Pr > |t|
0	500.00	1.6389	0.2116	12.8	7.75	<.0001
10	500.00	2.1224	0.2056	11.68	10.32	<.0001
20	500.00	2.1028	0.2091	12.32	10.06	<.0001
30	500.00	2.1910	0.2241	15.15	9.78	<.0001

Interpretation

The estimates of the variance components are shown in the "Covariance Parameter Estimates" table; $\hat{\sigma}_e^2 = 0.05008$ and $\hat{\sigma}_b^2 = 0.2408$ as compared to $\hat{\sigma}_e^2 = 0.04943$ and $\hat{\sigma}_b^2 = 0.2593$ obtained from the unequal slopes models. By reducing the model to a common slope model had very little effect of the estimates of the variances. Estimates of the intercepts (using the set-to-zero solution) and of the common slope are found in the "Solution for Fixed Effects" table. The estimate of the intercept for treatment 0 is computed as $0.8011 - 0.5521 = 0.2480$. The "Type III Tests of Fixed Effects" table indicates that the common slope is significantly different from zero ($p = 0.0034$) and that the distances between the regression lines are significantly different ($p = 0.0003$). The comparisons of the intercepts (Type III test for TRT effect) are in fact comparisons of the distances between the parallel regression models, which is an interesting hypothesis.

Results

Figure 7.6 displays the four parallel regression (common slope) models, where ADG is the response variable and IWT is the regressor variable or covariate.

Figure 7.6: Estimated Regression Lines with LSMEANS and Data Points for Each Diet

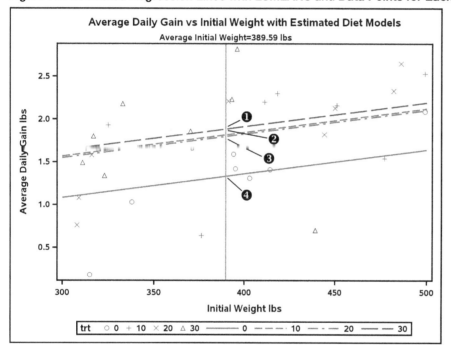

❶ LSM for 30

❷ LSM for 10

❸ LSM for 20

❹ LSM for 0

The "Least Squares Means" output provides estimates of the regression models at the average value of IWT, which in this case equals 389.59 lbs. The least squares means were also requested for values of IWT of 300 lbs and 500 lbs to provide the endpoints of the regression lines in Figure 7.6.

Because the treatment levels are quantitative—in essence, the levels of the feed additive are 0 ppm, 10 ppm, 20 ppm, and 30 ppm—the ESTIMATE statements are used to evaluate the shape of the response curve—in essence, to evaluate how the ADG means change as the amount of feed additive changes. The coefficients in the ESTIMATE statements correspond to the linear, quadratic, and cubic orthogonal polynomials for four equally spaced levels. The ESTIMATE statements were used to evaluate the curvature of the average daily gain least squares means as a function of dose or treatment. The results are shown in the "Estimates" table of Output 7.3 and indicate that there are significant linear and quadratic effects ($p = 0.002$ and $p = 0.0265$, respectively) and a marginal cubic effect ($p = 0.0998$). It is expected that the true response is of the general quadratic shape, and thus the second-degree model was used to describe the relationship among the average daily gain means and the level of dose. Program 7.4 uses the LSMEANS statement for the 4 levels of feed additive that were output in Program 7.3 as data to fit a quadratic regression model to the average daily gain values versus the levels of feed additive. The quadratic regression model is as follows:

$$\overline{ADG}_i = a + bX_i + cX_i^2 + e_i$$

where $i = 0, 10, 20, 30$.

The optimum dose is computed as follows:

$$\text{OptDose} = -\frac{b}{2c}$$

Program

The SAS code to fit the model to fit a quadratic regression model to the means, output predicted values to plot and output estimates of the parameters to provide information for the computation of the optimal dose is in Program 7.4.

Program 7.4

```
data lsm2; set lsm; if 300<iwt<400; *Select predicted means at mean iwt;
run;

***Fit Quadratic Model to the LSMEANS to estimate coefficients of a+bX+cX²;
proc glimmix data=lsm2;
model estimate=trt trt*trt/solution;
ods output ParameterEstimates=est;
output out=pred pred=p resid=r;
run;
proc print data=pred;
run;
data a; set est; if effect="Intercept"; a=estimate;
data b; set est; if effect="trt"; b=estimate;
data c; set est; if effect="trt*trt"; c=estimate;
data quad;
merge a b c;
optimum=-b/(2*c);
run;
proc print data=quad;
run;

proc sgplot data=pred;
scatter x=trt y=estimate/name="scatter";
reg x=trt y=p/degree=2 nomarkers;
refline 23.28/axis=X label="Optimum at trt=23.3";
yaxis label='Average Daily Gain lbs';
xaxis label='Dose of Treatment';
run;
```

Results

The response curve showing the relationship between the mean ADG and the levels of feed additive is displayed in Figure 7.7.

Figure 7.7: Least Squares Means as a Function of Treatment Level

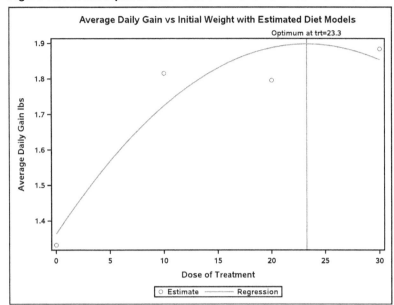

Interpretation

The pairwise comparisons results in the "Differences of Least Squares Means" table in Output 7.3 indicate that treatments 10, 20, and 30 are significantly different from the control but are not different among themselves. A quadratic function was fit to the least squares means evaluated at 389.59 lbs., and the line in Figure 7.7 is a plot of the estimated quadratic function. The maximum predicted average daily gain occurs at a dose of 23.3 ppm. The complete analysis involves using some strategy to estimate the level of feed additive that provides the optimal ADG response, a task beyond the scope of this book (for a detailed discussion of methods of estimating the optimal dose, see Remmenga et al. 1997).

7.3.4 Mixed Model Estimator: A Combined Estimator

One of the important features of the mixed models analysis is that it combines information from all parts of the model into its estimates of the fixed effects of the model. For this example, there is information about the common slope of the models from within-block comparisons as well as between-block comparisons. The mixed model estimate of the slope is constructed by combining the within-block (intra-block) information about the slope with the between-block (inter-block) information about the slope. This example provides an opportunity to demonstrate this process of information combination.

Intra-block Information and Program

The intra-block information is obtained using PROC GLIMMIX, where the following code fits the common slope model with blk included in the MODEL statement and not in a RANDOM statement. Thus, the intra-block analysis is obtained by assuming that the blocks are fixed as shown in Program 7.5.

Program 7.5

```
proc glimmix data=ex7_3_rcb;
 class blk trt;
 model adg= trt iwt blk/solution;
run;
```

Results

The results from this program 7.5 are listed in Output 7.4, which includes the estimates of the variance, common slope (bold), intercepts, and block effects and the fixed effects analysis of variance table. Because there is no RANDOM statement, the estimate of the residual variance is included in the list of parameter estimates denoted by SCALE.

Output 7.4: Fit of the Equal Slope Model to Obtain Intra-block Information about Slope

				Standard			
Effect	blk	trt	Estimate	Error	DF	t Value	Pr > |t|
Intercept			-0.1834	0.3081	20	-0.60	0.5584
trt		0	-0.5456	0.1148	20	-4.75	0.0001
trt		10	-0.05847	0.1191	20	-0.49	0.6287
trt		20	-0.08022	0.1163	20	-0.69	0.4983
trt		30	0	.	.	.	.
iwt			0.002572	0.000845	20	3.04	0.0064
blk	1		0.8697	0.1632	20	5.33	<.0001
blk	2		1.2210	0.1673	20	7.30	<.0001
blk	3		1.3292	0.1670	20	7.96	<.0001
blk	4		1.5935	0.1673	20	9.52	<.0001
blk	5		1.5182	0.1621	20	9.36	<.0001
blk	6		1.0935	0.1593	20	6.87	<.0001
blk	7		0.8508	0.1590	20	5.35	<.0001
blk	8		0	.	.	.	.
Scale			0.05000	0.01581	.	.	.

Parameter Estimates

Type III Tests of Fixed Effects

	Num	Den		
Effect	DF	DF	F Value	Pr > F
trt	3	20	10.12	0.0003
iwt	1	20	9.27	0.0064
blk	7	20	18.17	<.0001

The intra-block estimate of the common slope (row IWT in the "Solutions for Fixed Effects" table) and its associated estimated standard error based on the intra-block analysis are as follows:

$$\hat{\beta}_a = 0.002572$$

and

$$\hat{\sigma}_{\hat{\beta}_a} = 0.000845$$

Inter-block Information and Program

The inter-block model is constructed from the model of the block means $\bar{y}_{.j}$ (or totals) as

$$\bar{y}_{.j} = \bar{\alpha}. + \beta \bar{x}_{.j} + b_j + \bar{e}_{.j}$$

where the following definitions hold:

$$j = 1, 2, ..., 8$$

and

$$\text{Var}\left[\bar{y}_{.j}\right] = \text{Var}\left[b_j + \bar{e}_{.j}\right] = \sigma_b^2 + \frac{\sigma_e^2}{4} = \frac{4\sigma_b^2 + \sigma_e^2}{4}$$

The inter-block model is fit to the data using PROC GLIMMIX in Program 7.6. PROC MEANS is used to compute the block means, and the WEIGHT NADP statement scales the weighted sums of squares to make them comparable to sums of squares in Output 7.4. (Weighting by the block size is used because the variance of a block mean is a scalar multiple of the reciprocal of the block size.)

Program 7.6

```
proc sort data=ex7_3_rcb;
by blk;
run;
proc means mean n data=ex7_3_rcb;
   by blk;
   var adg iwt;
   output out=means mean = madg miwt
                    n    = nadg niwt;*Compute means for each block;
run;
proc glimmix data=means;
   model madg = miwt / solution;
   weight nadg;
run;
```

Results

The results are given in Output 7.5 where MADG and MIWT denote the block means for the ADG and IWT, respectively.

Output 7.5: Fit of the Equal Slope Model to Obtain Inter-block Information about the Slope

Model Information	
Data Set	WORK.MEANS
Response Variable	madg
Response Distribution	Gaussian
Link Function	Identity
Variance Function	Default
Weight Variable	nadg
Variance Matrix	Diagonal
Estimation Technique	Restricted Maximum Likelihood
Degrees of Freedom Method	Residual

Parameter Estimates					
Effect	Estimate	Standard Error	DF	t Value	Pr > |t|
Intercept	-2.2053	1.7570	6	-1.26	0.2561
miwt	0.01004	0.004491	6	2.24	0.0667
Scale	0.8202	0.4736	.	.	.

Interpretation

The inter-block information about the common slope is in the "Solution for Fixed Effects" portion of Output 7.5. The row corresponding to miwt (mean initial weight) yields $\hat{\beta}_r = 0.01004$ and $\hat{\sigma}_{\hat{\beta}_r} = 0.004491$.

Combined Estimate of the Common Slope and Program

The mean squared error estimate from the intra-block analysis in Output 7.4 on the scale line of the parameter estimates table is 0.05000. This is the estimate of σ_e^2. The mean squared error estimate from the inter-block analysis in Output 7.5 on the scale line of the parameter estimates table is 0.8202. This is the estimate of $\sigma_e^2 + 4\sigma_b^2$. The set of equations yielding methods of moments estimates of the variance components is as follows:

$$E[MSError(intra\text{-}block)] = \sigma_e^2$$

$$E[MSError(inter\text{-}block)] = \sigma_e^2 + 4\sigma_b^2$$

The solution to the method of moments equations for the two variance components is as follows (see Chapter 3):

$$\text{MSERROR}(intra) = 0.0500, \text{ so } \hat{\sigma}_e^2 = 0.05000$$

$$\text{MSERROR}(inter) = 0.8202$$

$$\hat{\sigma}_b^2 = \frac{\text{MSERROR}(inter) - \text{MSERROR}(intra)}{4}$$

$$= \left[\frac{0.8202 - 0.050}{4} \right]$$

$$= 0.1926$$

The combined estimate of the slope is computed as the weighted average of the intra-block estimate of the slope and the inter-block estimate of the slope where the weights are the inverses of the respective variances as follows:

$$\hat{\beta}_c = \frac{1}{\frac{1}{\hat{\sigma}_{\hat{\beta}_a}^2} + \frac{1}{\hat{\sigma}_{\hat{\beta}_r}^2}} \left[\frac{\hat{\beta}_a}{\hat{\sigma}_{\hat{\beta}_a}^2} + \frac{\hat{\beta}_r}{\hat{\sigma}_{\hat{\beta}_r}^2} \right]$$

The combined estimate of the common slope using the method of moments estimates of the variance components is $\hat{\beta}_c = 0.0028267$ and $\hat{\sigma}_{\hat{\beta}_c} = 0.00082997..$

Program 7.7 uses the preceding two estimates of the variance components (via the HOLD=1,2 option) to provide the combined estimate of the slope and its estimated standard error.

Program 7.7

```
proc glimmix data=ex7_3_rcb;
   class trt blk;
   model adg=trt iwt / solution;
   random blk;
   parms (.1926) (.0500)/ hold=1,2;
run;
```

Results

The results are in Output 7.6, where the estimate of the slope and its estimated standard error are $\hat{\beta}_c = 0.002827$ and $\hat{\sigma}_{\hat{\beta}_c} = 0.000830$, respectively (from the line IWT).

Output 7.6: Fit of the Equal Slope Model to Obtain Combined Estimate of the Slope

Covariance Parameter Estimates		
Cov Parm	Estimate	Standard Error
blk	0.1926	.
Residual	0.05000	.

Solutions for Fixed Effects						
Effect	trt	Estimate	Standard Error	DF	t Value	Pr > |t|
Intercept		0.7842	0.3460	7	2.27	0.0578
trt	0	-0.5535	0.1147	20	-4.83	0.0001
trt	10	-0.07084	0.1188	20	-0.60	0.5578
trt	20	-0.08991	0.1162	20	-0.77	0.4480
trt	30	0	.	.	.	.
iwt		0.002827	0.000830	20	3.41	0.0028

Type III Tests of Fixed Effects

Effect	Num DF	Den DF	F Value	Pr > F
trt	3	20	10.19	0.0003
iwt	1	20	11.60	0.0028

Note: The code fits the equal slope model using method of moments estimates of the Variance components (using parms (0.1926) (0.0500) / hold = 1,2;) to obtain combined intra-block–inter-block estimates of the slope and its estimated standard error.

Interpretation

The HOLD=1,2 specification in the PARMS statement forces PROC GLIMMIX to carry out the fixed effects analysis based on the specified values of the variance components. The estimate of the common slope obtained based on the method of moments estimates of the variance components from the intra- and inter-block models provides the combined estimate of the common slope described above, as shown in the IWT row of the "Solution for Fixed Effects" table. The analysis provides no standard errors for the variance components because their values have been fixed, as shown in the "Covariance Parameter Estimates" table.

Program for Combined Estimate of the Slope from REML Estimates of Covariance Parameters

Program 7.8 provides the combined estimate of the slope using the REML estimates of the covariance parameters.

Program 7.8

```
proc glimmix data=ex7_3_rcb;
   class trt blk;
   model adg=trt iwt / solution;
   random blk;
   parms (.2408) (.05008)/hold=1,2;
run;
```

Results

Output 7.7 provides the combined estimate of the slope by using the REML estimates of the variance components.

Output 7.7: Fit Equal Slope Model Using REML Estimates to Obtain Combined Estimate of the Slope

Covariance Parameter Estimates

Cov Parm	Estimate	Standard Error
blk	0.2408	.
Residual	0.05008	.

Solutions for Fixed Effects

Effect	trt	Estimate	Standard Error	DF	t Value	Pr > |t|
Intercept		0.8011	0.3557	7	2.25	0.0590
trt	0	-0.5521	0.1148	20	-4.81	0.0001
trt	10	-0.06857	0.1190	20	-0.58	0.5708
trt	20	-0.08813	0.1163	20	-0.76	0.4574
trt	30	0	.	.	.	.
iwt		0.002780	0.000833	20	3.34	0.0033

Type III Tests of Fixed Effects				
Effect	Num DF	Den DF	F Value	Pr > F
trt	3	20	10.16	0.0003
iwt	1	20	11.13	0.0033

Interpretation

The combined estimate of the common slope using the REML estimates of the variance components from PROC GLIMMIX is

$$\hat{\beta}_c = 0.002780$$

and

$$\hat{\sigma}_{\hat{\beta}_c} = 0.000833$$

which is the same as the estimate of the slope in the "Solution for Fixed Effects" table in Output 7.3.

The estimate of the standard error is a little different than in Output 7.3 where $\hat{\sigma}_{\hat{\beta}_c} = 0.000842$, due to rounding. Thus, the mixed model approach to the analysis of this model extracts more information about the common slope than a non-mixed models approach that provides only the intra-block analysis.

7.4 One-Way Treatment Structure in an Incomplete Block Design Structure: An Example

A study was conducted to determine the relationship between the amount of water put into a container and the time in seconds that it takes for the water to boil. An electric cook range was used as the heat source, where the front left-hand burner was used for each of the runs. It was also of interest to determine whether the type or shape of the container had an effect on the time to boil water, so three ceramic containers were used. The dimensions of the containers were: container A had a top diameter of 6.5 inches, was 1.25 inches deep, and had a bottom diameter of 4.75 inches; container B had a top diameter of 5.5 inches, was 1.75 inches deep, and had a bottom diameter of 4.0 inches; the corresponding dimensions for container C were 5.75, 2.25, and 3.5 inches. Four amounts of water (2 oz., 4 oz., 6 oz., and 8 oz.) were used to help establish the relationship between the amount of water and the time that it took for it to reach the boiling point. The process consisted of putting a specified amount of water into one of the containers, putting it on the range, starting the stopwatch, and stopping the watch when the water reached what was judged as complete boiling. A thermometer was not used in the boiling process. The treatment structure consisted of three types of containers and four amounts of water. The treatment combinations were randomly ordered and one replication of the twelve treatments was obtained. Then a second randomization was carried out for replication two. The two replications for two of the treatment combinations were somewhat dissimilar, so a third block was constructed involving just those two treatments. This leads to two complete blocks and one incomplete block. The listing of the data is in the data set "Cooking Times." A plot of the data is in Figure 7.8, which shows the linear relationship, Step 1.

Figure 7.8: Time to Boil Water, by Amount of Water

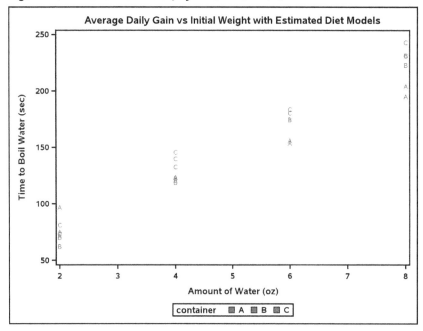

It seems reasonable that there could be a linear relationship between the amount of water put into a container and the time required for the water to reach the boiling point (this assumption will be checked later). A model used to describe a linear relationship between time and amount of water is

$$T_{ij} = \alpha_i + \beta_i W_{ij} + b_j + e_{ij}$$

where the following definitions hold:

- T_{ij} denotes the time in seconds for the water to boil.

- W_{ij} denotes the amount of water put into the container.

- $i = 1,2,3$.

- $j = 1,2,3$.

- α_i denotes the intercept of the ith container model.

- β_i denotes the slope of the ith container model.

- $b_j \sim$ iid $N(0, \sigma_b^2)$ denotes the effect of the jth block.

- $e_{ij} \sim$ iid $N(0, \sigma_e^2)$ denotes the experimental unit or run-to-run error.

- b_j and e_{ij} are independent random variables.

7.4.1 Fit the Model to Test the Equal Slopes Hypothesis

A plot of the data indicates that there is a linear relationship between the amount of water and the amount of time for the water to reach the boiling point (Figure 7.8). The second step in this analysis is to determine if the slopes are equal. Program 7.9 fits a model similar to the one for Model 7.2, including both amount and amount × container in the model.

Program 7.9

```
proc glimmix data=long;
   class container block;
   model time=container amount container*amount / solution ddfm=kr2;
   random block;
run;
```

The results for fitting the model to test for equality of slopes are in Output 7.8. Because we are interested only in the hypothesis of equal slopes, only the estimates of the variance components and the Type III tests of fixed effects are included.

Output 7.8: Fit of the Model to Test Equality of Slopes

Covariance Parameter Estimates		
Cov Parm	Estimate	Standard Error
block	94.3276	100.84
Residual	16.2661	5.4376

Type III Tests of Fixed Effects				
Effect	Num DF	Den DF	F Value	Pr > F
container	2	17.97	12.08	0.0005
amount	1	18.02	4464.10	<.0001
amount*container	2	17.95	35.09	<.0001

The p-value associated with the amount $\times$ container effect, the term testing the equal slopes hypothesis, from Output 7.8 is less than 0.0001. There is sufficient information to conclude that the slopes are not equal. The analysis continues, using the unequal slopes model.

7.4.2 Fit the Unequal Slopes Model

Once it is decided that the slopes are not equal, the next step is to compare the treatments by comparing the regression lines or characteristics of the regression lines. The strategy here is to evaluate the regression lines at several amounts of water and to perform pairwise comparisons among the predicted values.

Program

The PROC GLIMMIX code to fit the unequal slopes model is in Program 7.10.

Program 7.10

```
proc glimmix data=long;
   class container block;
   model time = container container*amount / noint solution ddfm=kr2;
   lsmeans container / at amount=2 diff;
   lsmeans container / at amount=4 diff;
   lsmeans container / at amount=6 diff;
   lsmeans container / at amount=8 diff;
   random block;
run;
```

The NOINT option in the MODEL statement prevents the inclusion of an intercept in the model, which would generate a singularity. This use of NOINT in the model yields estimates of the intercept for each container, and the solutions pertaining to the amount $\times$ container effect are estimates of the containers' slopes.

Results

The results are presented in Output 7.9, which includes estimates of the variance components, estimates of the intercepts and slopes for each model, tests of the fixed effects, least squares means at four different amounts of water, and pairwise comparisons among the container mean times within each amount of water.

Output 7.9: Fit of the Model to Test Equality of Slopes

Covariance Parameter Estimates		
Cov Parm	Estimate	Standard Error
block	94.3276	100.84
Residual	16.2661	5.4376

Solutions for Fixed Effects						
Effect	container	Estimate	Standard Error	DF	t Value	Pr > |t|
container	A	41.5075	6.3753	2.916	6.51	0.0080
container	B	17.9980	6.6975	3.487	2.69	0.0634
container	C	31.5437	6.5502	3.234	4.82	0.0143
amount*container	A	20.3037	0.6104	18.1	33.26	<.0001
amount*container	B	26.8463	0.6377	17.9	42.10	<.0001
amount*container	C	26.3032	0.6348	17.93	41.44	<.0001

Type III Tests of Fixed Effects				
Effect	Num DF	Den DF	F Value	Pr > F
container	3	6.986	15.43	0.0018
amount*container	3	17.97	1501.63	<.0001

container Least Squares Means						
container	amount	Estimate	Standard Error	DF	t Value	Pr > |t|
A	2.00	82.1149	5.9766	2.259	13.74	0.0032
B	2.00	71.6905	6.1927	2.568	11.58	0.0028
C	2.00	84.1500	6.0702	2.397	13.86	0.0024

Differences of container Least Squares Means							
container	_container	amount	Estimate	Standard Error	DF	t Value	Pr > |t|
A	B	2.00	10.4244	3.2626	18.05	3.20	0.0050
A	C	2.00	-2.0351	3.0699	17.92	-0.66	0.5158
B	C	2.00	-12.4595	3.3393	17.96	-3.73	0.0015

container Least Squares Means						
container	amount	Estimate	Standard Error	DF	t Value	Pr > |t|
A	4.00	122.72	5.8116	2.012	21.12	0.0022
B	4.00	125.38	5.9242	2.152	21.16	0.0015
C	4.00	136.76	5.8321	2.039	23.45	0.0016

Differences of container Least Squares Means							
container	_container	amount	Estimate	Standard Error	DF	t Value	Pr > |t|
A	B	4.00	-2.6607	2.1535	18.01	-1.24	0.2325
A	C	4.00	-14.0341	2.0207	17.9	-6.95	<.0001
B	C	4.00	-11.3734	2.1789	17.99	-5.22	<.0001

container Least Squares Means						
container	amount	Estimate	Standard Error	DF	t Value	Pr > |t|
A	6.00	163.33	5.9001	2.124	27.68	0.0009
B	6.00	179.08	5.9242	2.152	30.23	0.0007
C	6.00	189.36	5.8655	2.081	32.28	0.0008

Differences of container Least Squares Means							
container	_container	amount	Estimate	Standard Error	DF	t Value	Pr > |t|
A	B	6.00	-15.7458	2.2056	17.9	-7.14	<.0001
A	C	6.00	-26.0331	2.1761	17.91	-11.96	<.0001
B	C	6.00	-10.2873	2.1957	17.94	-4.69	0.0002

container Least Squares Means						
container	amount	Estimate	Standard Error	DF	t Value	Pr > |t|
A	8.00	203.94	6.2312	2.616	32.73	0.0002
B	8.00	232.77	6.1927	2.568	37.59	0.0001
C	8.00	241.97	6.1659	2.533	39.24	0.0001

Differences of container Least Squares Means							
container	_container	amount	Estimate	Standard Error	DF	t Value	Pr > |t|
A	B	8.00	-28.8309	3.3654	17.91	-8.57	<.0001
A	C	8.00	-38.0320	3.3736	17.93	-11.27	<.0001
B	C	8.00	-9.2011	3.3722	17.9	-2.73	0.0138

The variance component estimates in the "Covariance Parameter Estimates" table indicate that there was more block-to-block variation than within-block variation. The "Solution for the Fixed Effects" table provides the estimates of the slopes and intercepts. Remember that the intercepts ("container" represent predictions of the amount of time to boil the water when 0 oz. of water are used, an uninteresting prediction. The F statistics in the "Type III Tests of Fixed Effects" table test the hypotheses that all intercepts are equal to zero (container) and that all slopes are equal to zero (amount × container). Neither of these hypotheses is of interest at this point in the analysis. The "Least Squares Means" table displays predicted mean times to boiling for each of the container models at 2, 4, 6, and 8 ounces of water.

The predicted means and the data are plotted in Figure 7.9.

Figure 7.9: Data and LS-Means of Time to Boil Water as a Function of Water Amount

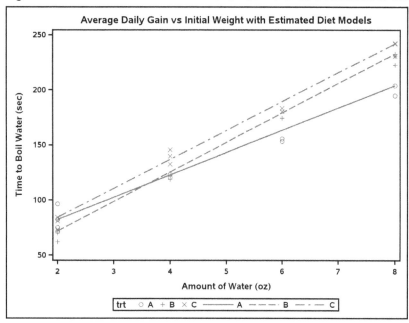

The vertical lines occur at the four levels of water. The "Differences of Least Squares Means" table shows pairwise comparisons among the container models at the four amounts of water. Without adjustment for multiplicity, there are no significant differences between A and C at 2 oz. and between A and B at 4 oz. The means for containers A, B, and C are all significantly different for amounts of 6 and 8 oz. A multiple comparison procedure, such as Tukey's method, should be used for those comparisons within a level of amount of water and possibly for making comparisons across the four levels of water.

7.4.3 Test for Lack of Fit of the Simple Linear Regression Model

The last stage in this analysis (but the first step in the process) is to carry out a test for lack of fit of the simple linear regression model to the data for each of the containers. A test for lack of fit cannot be carried out for all data sets, but when some or all of the covariates have more than one observation, a model-free estimate of the variance can be obtained and the test for lack of fit can be computed. This can be accomplished by using the amount of water as both a class and a continuous variable in the same model (Milliken and Johnson, 2002). The code to use a DATA step to generate the variable CLASS_AMT to be equal to the AMOUNT variable is in Program 7.11. The analysis in Program 7.11 fits a model with container as a class variable, amount as a continuous variable, and container*class_amt as an interaction. The Type II test for fixed effects corresponding to container*Class_amt provides the measure of the lack of fit of the unequal slopes linear regression model.

Program 7.11

```
data linear;
   set long;
   class_amt = amount;
run;
proc glmmix data=linear;
   class container class_amt block;
   model time=container amount container*amount container*class_amt / ddfm=kr2;
   random block;
run;
```

Selected results are shown in Output 7.10.

Output 7.10: Results to Test for Lack of Fit of the Simple Linear Regression Models

Class Level Information		
Class	Levels	Values
container	3	A B C
class_amt	4	2 4 6 8
block	3	1 2 3

Covariance Parameter Estimates		
Cov Parm	Estimate	Standard Error
block	85.1896	92.6933
Residual	15.5051	6.3661

Type III Tests of Fixed Effects				
Effect	Num DF	Den DF	F Value	Pr > F
container	2	11.92	13.52	0.0009
amount	0	.	.	.
amount*container	0	.	.	.
container*class_amt	6	11.92	1.18	0.3791

The "Class Level Information" table is included to show that the variable CLASS AMT has four values. The model is constructed with terms for the intercepts (CONTAINER), terms for the slopes (AMOUNT × CONTAINER), and terms for the container by amount cell means (CONTAINER × CLASS_AMT). The "Type III Tests of Fixed Effects" table provides information about the question "Given all of the other terms are in the model, do I need this term, or is there sufficient variability remaining that this term is important in the model?" The question asked by the F statistic for the CONTAINER × CLASS_AMT effect is this: given that variation about the intercepts and the variation about the slopes have been accounted for by the model, is there sufficient information for the cell means measured by the container*amt_water to still be important? The F statistic for this effect provides the lack-of-fit test for this model. The degrees of freedom for lack of fit are computed as the number of cells with data (12) minus the number of parameters in the model (3 models each with an intercept and a slope, 6), leaving 6 numerator degrees of freedom for the lack-of-fit test. The p-value for this test is 0.3791, indicating that there is insufficient information to conclude that the simple linear regression models do not fit the data for each of the treatments.

7.4.4 Comparing the Models at a Preselected Value of the Covariate

The design of the experiment used four amounts of water, and it might be of interest to construct a test of the hypothesis that the three container models are responding equally at selected values of amount of water.

Program

This can be accomplished by using CONTRAST statements, as in Program 7.12.

Program 7.12

```
proc glimmix data=linear;
   class container block;
   model time=container container*amount /ddfm=kr2 NOINT solution;
   random block;
   contrast 'Models = at 2oz'
         container 1 -1  0 container*amount 2 -2  0,
         container 1  0 -1 container*amount 2  0 -2;
run;
```

The CONTRAST statement tests the equality of container A at 2 oz. to container B at 2 oz. and the equality of container A at 2 oz. to container C at 2 oz. in a simultaneous test with two degrees of freedom.

Results

The results are in Output 7.11.

Output 7.11: Results for Comparing the Container Models at 2 oz. Amounts of Water

Covariance Parameter Estimates		
Cov Parm	Estimate	Standard Error
block	94.3276	100.84
Residual	16.2661	5.4376

Solutions for Fixed Effects						
Effect	container	Estimate	Standard Error	DF	t Value	Pr > |t|
container	A	41.5075	6.3753	2.916	6.51	0.0080
container	B	17.9980	6.6975	3.487	2.69	0.0634
container	C	31.5437	6.5502	3.234	4.82	0.0143
amount*container	A	20.3037	0.6104	18.1	33.26	<.0001
amount*container	B	26.8463	0.6377	17.9	42.10	<.0001
amount*container	C	26.3032	0.6348	17.93	41.44	<.0001

Type III Tests of Fixed Effects				
Effect	Num DF	Den DF	F Value	Pr > F
container	3	6.986	15.43	0.0018
amount*container	3	17.97	1501.63	<.0001

Contrasts				
Label	Num DF	Den DF	F Value	Pr > F
Models = at 2oz	2	17.98	7.82	0.0036

Interpretation

The "Contrasts" table in Output 7.11 provides the F value for testing the equality of the three regression models at 2 oz. of water. That is, the hypothesis H_0: $\alpha_A + 2\beta_A = \alpha_B + 2\beta_B = \alpha_C + 2\beta_C$ versus H_a: (not H_0). The p-value of 0.0036 indicates that when 2 oz. of water is used, the models are not likely to be equal.

The comparisons of the models at a specific value of the covariate can also be done by shifting the origin of the covariate to that value and then performing an analysis of covariance (Milliken and Johnson, 2002). If you want to test the equality of the regression models at $x = 6$, then compute a new variable, $x^* = x - 6$, and carry out the analysis of covariance using x^* as the covariate. The F statistic corresponding to container is a test that the container models are equal at $x = 6$.

Program

The code in Program 7.13 demonstrates this process by providing comparisons of the container models at 2, 4, 6, and 8 oz. of water.

Program 7.13

```
data test; set long;
   amt_2 = amount-2;
   amt_4 = amount-4;
   amt_6 = amount-6;
   amt_8 = amount-8;
run;
```

```
title2 "Compare the lines at 2 oz.";
proc glimmix data=test;
   class container block;
   model time=container container*amt_2 / solution ddfm=kr2;
   random block;
run;
title2 "Compare the lines at 4 oz.";
proc glimmix data=test;
   class container block;
   model time = container container*amt_4 / solution ddfm=kr2;
   random block;
run;
title2 "Compare the lines at 6 oz.";
proc glimmix data=test;
   class container block;
   model time = container container*amt_6 / solution ddfm=kr2;
   random block;
run;
title2 "Compare the lines at 8 oz.";
proc glimmix data=test;
   class container block;
   model time = container container*amt_8 / solution ddfm=kr2;
   random block;
run;
```

The DATA step computes the variables Amt_2, Amt_4, Amt_6, and Amt_8 by shifting the value of the AMOUNT variable. The DATA step is followed by four calls to PROC GLIMMIX to produce the respective comparisons. The results are shown in Output 7.12.

Results

The estimates of the variance components are identical for the 4 models. Thus, only one table with the estimates of the variance components is presented. There are four panels for comparing the container models at each of the four amounts of water.

Output 7.12: Results for Comparing the Container Models at Four Amounts of Water

Estimates of Covariance Parameters for All Comparisons

Covariance Parameter Estimates		
Cov Parm	Estimate	Standard Error
block	94.3276	100.84
Residual	16.2661	5.4376

Compare the lines at 2 oz

Type III Tests of Fixed Effects				
Effect	Num DF	Den DF	F Value	Pr > F
container	2	17.98	7.82	0.0036
amt_2*container	3	17.97	1501.63	<.0001

Compare the lines at 4 oz

Type III Tests of Fixed Effects				
Effect	Num DF	Den DF	F Value	Pr > F
container	2	17.96	26.48	<.0001
amt_4*container	3	17.97	1501.63	<.0001

Compare the lines at 6 oz

Type III Tests of Fixed Effects

Effect	Num DF	Den DF	F Value	Pr > F
container	2	17.92	72.49	<.0001
amt_6*container	3	17.97	1501.63	<.0001

Compare the lines at 8 oz

Type III Tests of Fixed Effects

Effect	Num DF	Den DF	F Value	Pr > F
container	2	17.91	69.30	<.0001
amt_8*container	3	17.97	1501.63	<.0001

Interpretation

Only one "Covariance Parameter Estimates" table is presented; the covariance parameter estimates are identical for the four models. Also, the F statistics for the equal slopes hypothesis are identical for each of the analyses. The analyses differ only in the F statistic for the test of equality of the intercepts. Using Amt_6 as the covariate, the intercept of the model has been moved to an amount of 6 oz., and thus the test of the equality of the intercepts ("container") is actually a test of the equality of the models at 6 oz. The result from the "Contrasts" table in Output 7.11 is equivalent to the results of the Container "Type III Tests of Fixed Effects" in Output 7.12 used to compare the models at 2 oz. of water.

7.5 One-Way Treatment Structure in a BIB Design Structure: An Example

The data in data set "Balanced Incomplete Block," are from four diets in a one-way treatment structure in a balanced incomplete block design structure with blocks of size three. The objectives of this example are to provide the methodology to work with the unequal slopes model and to demonstrate the use of PROC GLIMMIX with a balanced incomplete block design structure. The response variable is Y and the covariate is X.

7.5.1 Fit the Unequal Slopes Model

The unequal slopes model that describes the data is displayed in Equation 7.4:

$$y_{ij} = \alpha_i + \beta_i x_{ij} + b_j + e_{ij}, \quad (i, j) \in B \tag{7.4}$$

where the following definitions hold:

- α_i denotes the intercept of the ith diet model.

- β_i denotes the slope of the ith diet model.

- $b_j \sim$ iid $N(0, \sigma_b^2)$ denotes the effect of the jth block.

- $e_{ij} \sim$ iid $N(0, \sigma_e^2)$ denotes the experimental unit error.

- b_j and e_{ij} are independent random variables.

- B is the index set of observed diet-block combinations (i,j). That is, $B = [(1,1), (2,1), (3,1), (1,2), (2,2), (4,2), (1,3), (3,3), (4,3), (2,4), (3,4), (4,4), (1,5), (2,5), (3,5), (1,6), (2,6), (4,6), (1,7), (3,7), (4,7), (2,8), (3,8), (4,8)]$.

Program

The code in Program 7.14 translates the information from Equation 7.3 to fit the unequal slopes model to the data set.

Program 7.14

```
proc glimmix data=bib;
   class blk diet;
```

```
   model y=diet x*diet/solution ddfm=kr2;
   random blk;
run;
```

The NOINT option is *not* used in this MODEL statement. Thus, the estimates of the intercepts satisfy the set-to-zero restrictions. The DDFM=KR2 option is included to provide approximate degrees of freedom for the denominators of each test statistic and to adjust the estimated standard errors. The approximate degrees of freedom are needed because the estimates of the slopes and intercepts are combined inter- and intra-block estimates. (If the covariate X is not a term in the model, the Type III F for the $x \times$ diet effect tests the slopes-equal-to-zero hypothesis. If x is in the model along with $x \times$ diet the Type III F for the $x \times$ trt effect tests the equal slopes hypothesis.)

Results

The PROC GLIMMIX results for testing the equal slopes hypothesis are in Output 7.13.

Output 7.13: Test of the Slopes-Equal-to-Zero Hypothesis

Covariance Parameter Estimates		
Cov Parm	Estimate	Standard Error
blk	18.2499	10.0247
Residual	1.2004	0.5636

Solutions for Fixed Effects						
Effect	diet	Estimate	Standard Error	DF	t Value	Pr > |t|
Intercept		22.3678	3.1259	14.23	7.16	<.0001
diet	1	4.4295	3.4043	9.514	1.30	0.2238
diet	2	-0.4374	2.9584	9.394	-0.15	0.8856
diet	3	6.2786	3.3244	9.562	1.89	0.0896
diet	4	0	.	.	.	.
x*diet	1	0.2188	0.06451	9.475	3.39	0.0074
x*diet	2	0.4959	0.05508	9.352	9.00	<.0001
x*diet	3	0.2634	0.05767	9.509	4.57	0.0012
x*diet	4	0.4425	0.08794	9.452	5.03	0.0006

Type III Tests of Fixed Effects				
Effect	Num DF	Den DF	F Value	Pr > F
diet	3	9.323	4.43	0.0343
x*diet	4	9.375	31.75	<.0001

Interpretation

The Type III F statistic for the $x \times$ diet effect tests the hypotheses H_0: $\beta_1 = \beta_2 = \beta_3 = \beta_4 = 0$ versus H_a: (not H_0), and indicates that there is evidence to reject the null hypothesis ($p < 0.0001$). (If the covariate X is not in the model, the Type III F for the $x \times$ diet effect tests the slopes-equal-to-zero hypothesis. If x is in the model along with $x \times$ diet, the Type 3 F for the $x \times$ diet effect tests the equal slopes hypothesis.) The estimates of the intercepts use the set to zero solution and the estimates of the intercepts have no restriction, the actual slopes.

7.5.2 Test the Equal Slopes Hypothesis

The code in Program 7.15 fits the unequal slopes model to the data, but includes x as well as $x \times$ diet so that the Type III F for the $x \times$ diet effect tests $H_0 : \beta_1 = \beta_2 = \beta_3 = \beta_4 = \beta$ versus H_a : (not H_0) where β is not specified.

Program 7.15

```
proc glimmix data=bib;
   class blk diet;
   model y = diet x x*diet / solution ddfm=kr2;
   estimate 'b1-b2' x*diet 1 -1  0  0;
   estimate 'b1-b3' x*diet 1  0 -1  0;
   estimate 'b1-b4' x*diet 1  0  0 -1;
   estimate 'b2-b3' x*diet 0  1 -1  0;
   estimate 'b2-b4' x*diet 0  1  0 -1;
   estimate 'b3-b4' x*diet 0  0  1 -1;
   random blk;
run;
```

The results are in Output 7.14.

Output 7.14: Unequal Slopes Model and Test of Equal Slopes and Estimates

Covariance Parameter Estimates		
Cov Parm	Estimate	Standard Error
blk	18.2499	10.0247
Residual	1.2004	0.5636

Type III Tests of Fixed Effects				
Effect	Num DF	Den DF	F Value	Pr > F
diet	3	9.323	4.43	0.0343
x	1	9.52	97.32	<.0001
x*diet	3	9.336	5.05	0.0242

Estimates					
Label	Estimate	Standard Error	DF	t Value	Pr > |t|
b1-b2	-0.2771	0.07560	9.245	-3.67	0.0050
b1-b3	-0.04459	0.07508	9.272	-0.59	0.5668
b1-b4	-0.2238	0.1072	9.465	-2.09	0.0649
b2-b3	0.2326	0.07814	9.386	2.98	0.0149
b2-b4	0.05338	0.09787	9.352	0.55	0.5982
b3-b4	-0.1792	0.1173	9.597	-1.53	0.1589

Note: Estimate statements provide pairwise comparisons of the treatment slopes.

The Type III F statistic for the $x \times$ diet effect indicates that there is evidence to reject the equal slopes hypothesis ($p = 0.0242$). The ESTIMATE statements carry out multiple comparisons on the slopes. Based on these results (and based on the slope estimates in Output 7.13), diets 1 and 3 group together and diets 2 and 4 group together.

A new variable, GRP, is constructed to denote the two sets of diets for which the slopes are equal. The value of GRP is determined as GRP=13 for diets 1 and 3 and GRP=24 for diets 2 and 4. The slopes are different between groups and homogeneous within groups. The grouping variable enables you to take advantage of a simpler model with only two (instead of four) slopes. This leads to fewer comparisons among the diets, because you compare diets with a common slope at only one value of x whereas you compare diets with unequal slopes at a minimum of three values of x. The comparisons of the regression models with a slope for each GRP is discussed in the next section.

7.5.3 Fit Model with Unequal Slopes for Each Level of GRP

In the previous section it was decided that diets 1 and 3 had a common slope and diets 2 and 4 had a common slope. A class variable GRP is defined to have two values, "13" and "24" which is used in the model to generate the two slopes for the two groups of diets.

Program

The code in Program 7.16 fits a model with unequal slopes for the two groups. Both trt and grp are included in the CLASS statement, but only trt is used in the MODEL statement to denote the four possible intercepts and $x \times$ grp is used to denote the two different slopes.

Program 7.16

```
proc glimmix data=bib;
   class blk diet grp;
   model y = diet x*grp / solution ddfm=kr2;
   random blk;
   estimate 'diet1 at = 10.0' intercept 1 diet 1 0 0 0 x*grp 10   0;
   estimate 'diet1 at = 40.0' intercept 1 diet 1 0 0 0 x*grp 40   0;
   estimate 'diet1 at 25%= 17.0' intercept 1 diet 1 0 0 0 x*grp 17   0;
   estimate 'diet1 at 50%= 28.5' intercept 1 diet 1 0 0 0 x*grp 28.5 0;
   estimate 'diet1 at 75%= 37.0' intercept 1 diet 1 0 0 0 x*grp 37   0;
   estimate 'diet1 at mean=26.0' intercept 1 diet 1 0 0 0 x*grp 26   0;

   estimate 'diet3 at min= 10.0' intercept 1 diet 0 0 1 0 x*grp 10   0;
   estimate 'diet3 at max= 40.0' intercept 1 diet 0 0 1 0 x*grp 40   0;
   estimate 'diet3 at 25%= 17.0' intercept 1 diet 0 0 1 0 x*grp 17   0;
   estimate 'diet3 at 50%= 28.5' intercept 1 diet 0 0 1 0 x*grp 28.5 0;
   estimate 'diet3 at 75%= 37.0' intercept 1 diet 0 0 1 0 x*grp 37   0;
   estimate 'diet3 at mean=26.0' intercept 1 diet 0 0 1 0 x*grp 26   0;

   estimate 'diet2 at min= 10.0' intercept 1 diet 0 1 0 0 x*grp 0 10;
   estimate 'diet2 at max= 40.0' intercept 1 diet 0 1 0 0 x*grp 0 40;
   estimate 'diet2 at 25%= 17.0' intercept 1 diet 0 1 0 0 x*grp 0 17;
   estimate 'diet2 at 50%= 28.5' intercept 1 diet 0 1 0 0 x*grp 0 28.5;
   estimate 'diet2 at 75%= 37.0' intercept 1 diet 0 1 0 0 x*grp 0 37;
   estimate 'diet2 at mean=26.0' intercept 1 diet 0 1 0 0 x*grp 0 26;

   estimate 'diet4 at min= 10.0' intercept 1 diet 0 0 0 1 x*grp 0 10;
   estimate 'diet4 at max= 40.0' intercept 1 diet 0 0 0 1 x*grp 0 40;
   estimate 'diet4 at 25%= 17.0' intercept 1 diet 0 0 0 1 x*grp 0 17;
   estimate 'diet4 at 50%= 28.5' intercept 1 diet 0 0 0 1 x*grp 0 28.5;
   estimate 'diet4 at 75%= 37.0' intercept 1 diet 0 0 0 1 x*grp 0 37;
   estimate 'diet4 at mean=26.0' intercept 1 diet 0 0 0 1 x*grp 0 26;

   ****comparisons of means at 25%, 75%, and 50%;
   estimate 'd1-d2 75%=37'   diet 1 -1  0  0 x*grp 37   -37  ;
   estimate 'd1-d2 50%=28.5' diet 1 -1  0  0 x*grp 28.5 -28.5;
   estimate 'd1-d2 25%=17'   diet 1 -1  0  0 x*grp 17   -17  ;
   estimate 'd1-d4 75%=37'   diet 1  0  0 -1 x*grp 37   -37  ;
   estimate 'd1-d4 50%=28.5' diet 1  0  0 -1 x*grp 28.5 -28.5;
   estimate 'd1-d4 25%=17'   diet 1  0  0 -1 x*grp 17   -17  ;
   estimate 'd3-d2 75%=37'   diet 0 -1  1  0 x*grp 37   -37  ;
   estimate 'd3-d2 50%=28.5' diet 0 -1  1  0 x*grp 28.5 -28.5;
   estimate 'd3-d2 25%=17'   diet 0 -1  1  0 x*grp 17   -17  ;
   estimate 'd3-d4 75%=37'   diet 0  0  1 -1 x*grp 37   -37  ;
   estimate 'd3-d4 50%=28.5' diet 0  0  1 -1 x*grp 28.5 -28.5;
   estimate 'd3-d4 25%=17'   diet 0  0  1 -1 x*grp 17   -17  ;

   ***comparison of LSMEANS at X=26***;
   estimate 'd1-d2 at mean' diet 1 -1  0  0 x*grp 26 -26;
   estimate 'd1-d3 at mean' diet 1  0 -1  0              ;
   estimate 'd1-d4 at mean' diet 1  0  0 -1 x*grp 26 -26;
   estimate 'd2-d3 at mean' diet 0  1 -1  0 x*grp 26 -26;
   estimate 'd2-d4 at mean' diet 0  1  0 -1              ;
   estimate 'd3-d4 at mean' diet 0  0  1 -1 x*grp 26 -26;
   lsmeans diet / diff e at mean;
   lsmeans diet / diff e at x=13;
run;

data toplot; set est11;
diet=substr(label,4,1)*1;
x=substr(label,14,4)*1;
if x=40 or X=10;
```

```
proc print data=toplot; run;
proc sort data=toplot; by diet x; run; quit;

proc sgplot data=toplot;
  series x=x y=estimate/group=diet;
  refline 17/axis=X label="X=17.0";
  refline 26/axis=X label="X=26.0";
  refline 28.5/axis=X label="X=28.5";
  refline 37/axis=X label="X=37.0";
  yaxis label="Y-Response Variable";
  xaxis label="X-Covariate";
run;
```

Results

The results from the PROC GLIMMIX statements are shown in Output 7.15. The discussion refers to those sections needed for each inquiry. The results from the PROC SGPLOT statements are shown in Figure 7.10.

Output 7.15: Fit of the Model for Four Diets with Unequal Slopes for Two Groups of Diets

Class Level Information		
Class	Levels	Values
blk	8	1 2 3 4 5 6 7 8
diet	4	1 2 3 4
grp	2	13 24

Covariance Parameter Estimates		
Cov Parm	Estimate	Standard Error
blk	18.5257	10.1296
Residual	1.0378	0.4420

Solutions for Fixed Effects							
Effect	diet	grp	Estimate	Standard Error	DF	t Value	Pr > |t|
Intercept			20.9452	2.0674	15.97	10.13	<.0001
diet	1		5.3414	1.9911	11.41	2.68	0.0207
diet	2		1.1356	0.7159	11.16	1.59	0.1406
diet	3		8.1810	1.7819	11.35	4.59	0.0007
diet	4		0	.	.	.	.
x*grp		13	0.2395	0.04339	11.52	5.52	0.0002
x*grp		24	0.4892	0.04440	11.33	11.02	<.0001

Type III Tests of Fixed Effects				
Effect	Num DF	Den DF	F Value	Pr > F
diet	3	11.18	15.49	0.0003
x*grp	2	11.42	73.43	<.0001

Estimates					
Label	Estimate	Standard Error	DF	t Value	Pr > |t|
trt1 at min= 10.0	28.6818	1.7888	11.63	16.03	<.0001
trt1 at max= 40.0	35.8674	1.6507	9.08	21.73	<.0001
trt1 at 25%= 17.0	30.3584	1.6691	9.398	18.19	<.0001

Estimates					
Label	Estimate	Standard Error	DF	t Value	Pr > |t|
trt1 at 50%= 28.5	33.1129	1.5831	7.815	20.92	<.0001
trt1 at 75%= 37.0	35.1488	1.6186	8.476	21.72	<.0001
trt1 at mean=26.0	32.5141	1.5889	7.917	20.46	<.0001
trt3 at min= 10.0	31.5214	1.6911	9.816	18.64	<.0001
trt3 at max= 40.0	38.7070	1.7352	10.67	22.31	<.0001
trt3 at 25%= 17.0	33.1980	1.6099	8.3	20.62	<.0001
trt3 at 50%= 28.5	35.9525	1.5976	8.083	22.50	<.0001
trt3 at 75%= 37.0	37.9884	1.6862	9.747	22.53	<.0001
trt3 at mean=26.0	35.3537	1.5870	7.887	22.28	<.0001
trt2 at min= 10.0	26.9730	1.6779	9.614	16.08	<.0001
trt2 at max= 40.0	41.6500	1.7624	11.22	23.63	<.0001
trt2 at 25%= 17.0	30.3976	1.6018	8.164	18.98	<.0001
trt2 at 50%= 28.5	36.0238	1.6048	8.217	22.45	<.0001
trt2 at 75%= 37.0	40.1823	1.7080	10.19	23.53	<.0001
trt2 at mean=26.0	34.8007	1.5902	7.946	21.88	<.0001
trt4 at min= 10.0	25.8375	1.8151	12.21	14.24	<.0001
trt4 at max= 40.0	40.5144	1.6496	9.052	24.56	<.0001
trt4 at 25%= 17.0	29.2621	1.6862	9.775	17.35	<.0001
trt4 at 50%= 28.5	34.8882	1.5879	7.899	21.97	<.0001
trt4 at 75%= 37.0	39.0467	1.6183	8.459	24.13	<.0001
trt4 at mean=26.0	33.6652	1.5960	8.05	21.09	<.0001
t1-t2 75%=37	-5.0334	0.9404	11.21	-5.35	0.0002
t1-t2 50%=28.5	-2.9109	0.6702	11.11	-4.34	0.0011
t1-t2 25%=17	-0.03920	0.8415	11.27	-0.05	0.9637
t1-t4 75%=37	-3.8978	0.7197	11.08	-5.42	0.0002
t1-t4 50%=28.5	-1.7753	0.6456	11.15	-2.75	0.0187
t1-t4 25%=17	1.0964	1.0619	11.37	1.03	0.3233
t3-t2 75%=37	-2.1938	1.0988	11.31	-2.00	0.0705
t3-t2 50%=28.5	-0.07129	0.7364	11.19	-0.10	0.9246
t3-t2 25%=17	2.8004	0.7000	11.13	4.00	0.0020
t3-t4 75%=37	-1.0583	0.8544	11.18	-1.24	0.2409
t3-t4 50%=28.5	1.0643	0.6315	11.05	1.69	0.1199
t3-t4 25%=17	3.9360	0.8936	11.24	4.40	0.0010
t1-t2 at mean	-2.2866	0.6500	11.12	-3.52	0.0047
t1-t3 at mean	-2.8396	0.6734	11.16	-4.22	0.0014
t1-t4 at mean	-1.1510	0.6988	11.22	-1.65	0.1272
t2-t3 at mean	-13.5379	2.9888	11.36	-4.53	0.0008
t2-t4 at mean	1.1356	0.7159	11.16	1.59	0.1406
t3-t4 at mean	1.6886	0.6346	11.07	2.66	0.0221

Coefficients for diet Least Squares Means At x=26						
Effect	diet	grp	Row1	Row2	Row3	Row4
Intercept			1	1	1	1
diet	1		1			
diet	2			1		
diet	3				1	
diet	4					1

Coefficients for diet Least Squares Means At x=26

Effect	diet	grp	Row1	Row2	Row3	Row4
x*grp		13	13	13	13	13
x*grp		24	13	13	13	13

diet Least Squares Means

diet	x	Estimate	Standard Error	DF	t Value	Pr > |t|
1	26.00	35.7604	1.8226	12.29	19.62	<.0001
2	26.00	31.5545	1.7201	10.41	18.34	<.0001
3	26.00	38.6000	1.7217	10.45	22.42	<.0001
4	26.00	30.4189	1.8676	13.08	16.29	<.0001

Differences of diet Least Squares Means

diet	_diet	x	Estimate	Standard Error	DF	t Value	Pr > |t|
1	2	26.00	4.2059	1.6961	11.38	2.48	0.0299
1	3	26.00	-2.8396	0.6734	11.16	-4.22	0.0014
1	4	26.00	5.3414	1.9911	11.41	2.68	0.0207
2	3	26.00	-7.0455	1.4828	11.31	-4.75	0.0006
2	4	26.00	1.1356	0.7159	11.16	1.59	0.1406
3	4	26.00	8.1810	1.7819	11.35	4.59	0.0007

Coefficients for diet Least Squares Means At x=13

Effect	diet	grp	Row1	Row2	Row3	Row4
Intercept			1	1	1	1
diet	1		1			
diet	2			1		
diet	3				1	
diet	4					1
x*grp		13	6.5	6.5	6.5	6.5
x*grp		24	6.5	6.5	6.5	6.5

diet Least Squares Means

diet	x	Estimate	Standard Error	DF	t Value	Pr > |t|
1	13.00	31.0235	1.8833	13.29	16.47	<.0001
2	13.00	26.8176	1.7501	11	15.32	<.0001
3	13.00	33.8631	1.7588	11.11	19.25	<.0001
4	13.00	25.6820	1.9264	14.08	13.33	<.0001

Differences of diet Least Squares Means

diet	_diet	x	Estimate	Standard Error	DF	t Value	Pr > |t|
1	2	13.00	4.2059	1.6961	11.38	2.48	0.0299
1	3	13.00	-2.8396	0.6734	11.16	-4.22	0.0014
1	4	13.00	5.3414	1.9911	11.41	2.68	0.0207
2	3	13.00	-7.0455	1.4828	11.31	-4.75	0.0006
2	4	13.00	1.1356	0.7159	11.16	1.59	0.1406
3	4	13.00	8.1810	1.7819	11.35	4.59	0.0007

Figure 7.10: Four Estimated Regression Lines with Vertical Lines Drawn at Comparisons Values

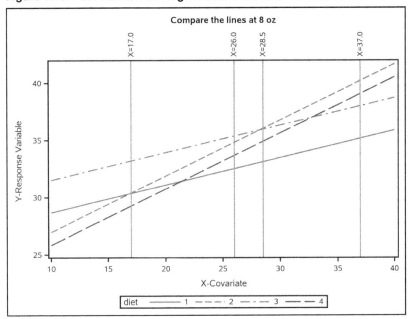

Interpretation

The "Class Level Information" table shows that the variable GRP can take on two values, 13 and 24, which indicate group membership of the diets. Simplifying the model from four slopes to two slopes did not substantially increase the estimates of the variance components, as seen from the estimates of 18.52 and 1.04 in the "Covariance Parameter Estimates" table (compare to the estimates of 18.25 and 1.20 in Output 7.14). The "Solution for Fixed Effects" table contains estimates of the slopes and intercepts. The "Type III Tests of Fixed Effects" table displays the F statistic for the test that the two slopes are equal to zero ($x \times$ grp) and the diet F statistic tests that the intercepts (models at $x = 0$) are equal (diet). Most likely these tests are not of interest. Of more interest is a comparison of the models at three or more values of x. The results in the "Estimates" table are adjusted means computed from the estimated regression models at $x = 17$ (25th percentile), $x = 26$ (the mean of the covariate values), $x = 28.5$ (the median of the covariate values), and $x = 37$ (the 75th percentile), as provided by ESTIMATE statements. The adjusted means were also computed at $x = 10$ and $x = 40$ to provide information for constructing graphs of the models; they do not correspond to any percentile of the distribution of x (estimate statements are shown, but the results are not).

The estimates labeled "$t_i–t_j$" are pairwise comparisons of the ith and j^{th} diets at the specified value of x. These comparisons are generally accomplished via the LSMEANS statement using, for example, the AT X=17.0 option. But in this case the LSMEANS statement does not provide the appropriate computations. The "Coefficients for diet Least Squares Means At x=26" table shows the correct coefficients for the intercept and the levels of diet, but it multiplies 26/2 = 13 times each slope without regard to the group to which the diet belongs. Also, the "Coefficients for diet Least Squares Means At x=13" table shows the correct coefficients for the intercept and the levels of diet, but it multiplies 13/2=6.5 times each slope without regard to the group to which the diet belongs. Thus, the LSMEANS statement is not providing the appropriate information about the regression models evaluated at the average value of X. Diets 1 and 3 and diets 2 and 4 need to be compared at only one value of X, and they are compared at $x = 26$ (mean) only. By forming groups of diets within which there are common slopes, the required number of comparisons is greatly reduced.

The graph in Figure 7.10 displays the four regression lines indicating where the models are being evaluated and compared. It verifies visually the differences between the treatments at the chosen levels of X that were computed in the estimate statements.

7.6 One-Way Treatment Structure in an Unbalanced Incomplete Block Design Structure: An Example

The data in "Unbalanced Incomplete Block" are from four treatments in a one-way treatment structure in an unbalanced incomplete block design structure with blocks of size two. This design illustrates one of the advantages of the mixed model analysis. The design is not a connected block-treatment design. But the mixed model analysis combines the intra-block and inter-block information about the fixed effects, thus extracting information about all of the treatments. The treatments can be compared using adjusted means such as those provided by the LSMEANS statement. The usual intra-block analysis, where blocks are considered as fixed effects, declares the comparisons 1 versus 3, 1 versus 4, 2 versus 3, and 2 versus 4 as non-estimable because the blocks and treatments are not connected. The response is y, and the covariate is x. A model that can be used to describe these data is as follows:

$$y_{ij} = \alpha_i + \beta_i x_{ij} + b_j + e_{ij}, \quad (i, j) \in B$$

where the following definitions hold:

- α_i denotes the intercept of the model for the ith treatment.

- β_i denotes the slope of the model for the ith treatment.

- $b_j \sim \text{iid } N(0, \sigma_b^2)$ denotes the random effect of the jth block.

- $e_{ij} \sim \text{iid } N(0, \sigma_e^2)$ denotes the experimental unit error.

- b_j and e_{ij} are independent random variables.

- B is the index set of observed treatment-block combinations as described in the example in Section 7.5.

A plot of the data, which is not included here, shows there is a linear trend between Y and X; thus, the test and results for testing the slopes equal to zero is not carried out.

7.6.1 Test the Equal Slopes Hypothesis

The model that enables one to test the equal slopes hypothesis includes x and $x*$trt as shown in Program 7.17.

Program 7.17

The following program is used to test the equal slopes hypothesis (x and $x*$trt are both in the model).

```
proc glimmix data=ex7_6_ubib;
   class blk trt;
   model y=trt x x*trt/noint solution ddfm=kr2;
   random blk;
run;
```

The results are in Output 7.16, which include the estimates of the variance components, and the Type III test of the equal slopes hypothesis.

Output 7.16: Fitting the Unequal Slopes Model and Test of the Equal Slopes Hypothesis

Covariance Parameter Estimates		
Cov Parm	Estimate	Standard Error
blk	0.02496	0.01140
Residual	0.000856	0.000489

me

Type III Tests of Fixed Effects				
Effect	Num DF	Den DF	F Value	Pr > F
trt	4	10.36	21.90	<.0001
x	1	6.959	9.50	0.0179
x*trt	3	6.481	0.61	0.6290

From the results in Output 7.16 the Type III F statistic for the $x \times$ trt effect indicate that there is no evidence to believe that the slopes are unequal ($p = 0.6290$). We conclude that a common slope model is adequate to describe the data.

7.6.2 Fit a Common Slope Model

The common slope model has x (the covariate) and not the x*trt term. The following program fits the common slope model to the data.

Program

The NOINT option in Program 7.18 is included in the MODEL statement so that the SOLUTION option provides estimates of the intercepts of the model. Without the NOINT option, the SOLUTION option provides estimates of the intercepts that satisfy the set-to-zero restrictions. The LSMEANS statement is used to compare the treatments evaluated at the mean of the x values.

Program 7.18

```
proc glimmix data=ex7_6_ubib;
   class blk trt;
   model y=trt x /noint solution ddfm=kr2;
   lsmeans trt / diff;
   random blk;
run;
```

Results

The results of fitting the common slope model to the data are given in Output 7.17, which includes the estimates of the model parameters, the least squares means, and pairwise comparisons among the means. The MODEL statement includes the NOINT option so that the solution for the fixed effects provides the estimates of the intercepts (Effect is trt). The estimate of the common slope is also included.

Output 7.17: Fitting the Common Slope Model and LSMEANS to Compare Treatments at X = 0.0449583

Covariance Parameter Estimates		
Cov Parm	Estimate	Standard Error
blk	0.02393	0.01090
Residual	0.000793	0.000373

Solutions for Fixed Effects						
Effect	trt	Estimate	Standard Error	DF	t Value	Pr > |t|
trt	1	0.5190	0.06529	10.95	7.95	<.0001
trt	2	0.6227	0.06585	11.29	9.46	<.0001
trt	3	0.3602	0.06680	11.86	5.39	0.0002
trt	4	0.4053	0.06939	13.38	5.84	<.0001
x		-2.1899	0.3970	9.472	-5.52	0.0003

Type III Tests of Fixed Effects				
Effect	Num DF	Den DF	F Value	Pr > F
trt	4	13.19	32.04	<.0001
x	1	9.472	30.42	0.0003

trt Least Squares Means					
trt	Estimate	Standard Error	DF	t Value	Pr > |t|
1	0.4206	0.06447	10.45	6.52	<.0001
2	0.5242	0.06427	10.33	8.16	<.0001
3	0.2617	0.06420	10.29	4.08	0.0021
4	0.3068	0.06475	10.62	4.74	0.0007

Differences of trt Least Squares Means						
trt	_trt	Estimate	Standard Error	DF	t Value	Pr > |t|
1	2	-0.1037	0.01649	9.023	-6.29	0.0001
1	3	0.1589	0.09102	10.39	1.75	0.1104
1	4	0.1138	0.09192	10.77	1.24	0.2421
2	3	0.2625	0.09086	10.32	2.89	0.0156
2	4	0.2174	0.09153	10.6	2.38	0.0376
3	4	-0.04510	0.01806	9.095	-2.50	0.0338

Interpretation

The LSMEANS statement provides adjusted means or estimates from the common slope regression models at $x = 0.0449583$ (the mean of the covariate). It is interesting to note that the estimated standard errors of differences between treatments 1 and 2 and treatments 3 and 4 are much smaller than the estimated standard errors of the other differences. This difference in the estimated standard errors occurs because treatments 1 and 2 occur together in six blocks and treatments 3 and 4 occur together in six blocks, but all other pairs of treatments never occur together within a block (a characteristic of an unconnected design). Thus, the within-block comparisons of treatments have estimated standard errors that do not depend on the block variance component, and the between-block comparisons of treatments have estimated standard errors that do depend on the block variance component. Because the estimate of the block variance component is approximately 30 times larger than the estimate of the experimental unit variance component, those estimated standard errors involving block effects are much larger than those not involving the block effects.

7.7 Multilevel or Split-Plot Design with the Covariate Measured on the Large-Size Experimental Unit or Whole Plot: An Example

The data in the data set "Teaching Methods I," are from a study designed to evaluate the effectiveness of three teaching methods (met). Four teachers were trained in each method. The teachers were randomly assigned to twelve classes of eight students (four females and four male students in each class). The experimental unit for the teaching method is the class of eight students. It was thought that years of experience in teaching might influence the effectiveness in delivery of the teaching method. Thus, the number of years of teaching experience for each teacher was used as a possible covariate. Part of the study was to determine whether females and males responded differently to the teaching methods. Thus, gender (gen) of the student is considered the treatment associated with experimental units at the student level.

This experiment involves two sizes of experimental units: (1) the class of eight students to which the teaching method is applied and (2) the students who differ by gender. The covariate, years of teaching experience, is measured at the class level (the teacher level, to be exact, but teachers are confounded with classes). The treatment structure is a two-way factorial arrangement with three teaching methods by two genders. The design structure consists of two sizes of experimental units. Therefore, there are two variance components in the random effects part of the model, one for the variability among students within a class by gender combination and one for the variability among classes within a teacher or method. The responses are scores on a standardized test.

7.7.1 Fit Unequal Slopes Model and Test Slopes-Equal-to-Zero Hypothesis

A plot of the data (not shown) shows that there is a possible linear relationship between the test scores and the years of experience (Step 1). The first model is to provide a test of the slopes equal to zero hypothesis.

A model involving the covariate to describe the test scores (*yijkm*) as a function of teaching method, class taught, gender of the students, and years of teaching experience is as follows:

$$y_{ijkm} = \alpha_{ik} + \beta_{ik} x_{ij} + t_{j(i)} + e_{ijkm} \tag{7.5}$$

where the following definitions hold:

- $i = 1,2,3$.
- $j = 1,2,3,4$.
- $k = 1,2$.
- $m = 1,2,3,4$.
- x_{ij} is the number of years of teaching experience (yr_ex) for the teacher teaching the jth class with the ith method.
- α_{ik} and β_{ik} are the intercept and slope associated with teaching method i and gender k.
- $t_{j(i)} \sim$ iid $N(0, \sigma_t^2)$ is the random effect of the jth class taught with the ith method.
- $e_{ijkm} \sim$ iid $N(0, \sigma_e^2)$ is the random effect associated with student m of gender k in class j taught by method i.

The *fixed effects* part of the model is $\alpha_{ik} + \beta_{ik} x_{ij}$, the *random effects* part of the model is $t_{j(i)}$, and the residual part of the model is e_{ijkm}.

Program

The code in Program 7.19 fits Equation 7.4 with separate intercepts (GEN*MET) and slopes (YR_EX*GEN*MET) for each gender–method combination.

Program 7.19

```
proc glimmix data=ex_7_7sp;
   class teacher met gen;
   model score = gen*met yr_ex*gen*met/solution noint ddfm=kr2;
   random teacher(met);
run;
```

Results

The results are listed in Output 7.18, which include the estimates of the model parameters as well as tests of the all-slopes-equal-zero hypothesis.

Output 7.18: Fit of the Unequal Slopes Model and Test Whether Slopes Are Zero

Covariance Parameter Estimates		
Cov Parm	Estimate	Standard Error
teacher(met)	1.7814	1.0748
Residual	0.6405	0.1026

Solutions for Fixed Effects

Effect	gen	met	Estimate	Standard Error	DF	t Value	Pr > |t|
met*gen	f	1	16.4231	2.3507	6.526	6.99	0.0003
met*gen	m	1	16.6538	2.3507	6.526	7.08	0.0003
met*gen	f	2	20.6993	2.0648	6.526	10.02	<.0001
met*gen	m	2	21.1351	2.0648	6.526	10.24	<.0001
met*gen	f	3	30.9821	1.8117	6.526	17.10	<.0001
met*gen	m	3	26.9345	1.8117	6.526	14.87	<.0001
y_ex*met*gen	f	1	-0.03205	0.1996	6.526	-0.16	0.8773
y_ex*met*gen	m	1	-0.03590	0.1996	6.526	-0.18	0.8627
y_ex*met*gen	f	2	0.09797	0.1620	6.526	0.60	0.5657
y_ex*met*gen	m	2	-0.09459	0.1620	6.526	-0.58	0.5788
y_ex*met*gen	f	3	-0.1518	0.1520	6.526	-1.00	0.3537
y_ex*met*gen	m	3	-0.1815	0.1520	6.526	-1.19	0.2740

Type III Tests of Fixed Effects

Effect	Num DF	Den DF	F Value	Pr > F
met*gen	6	15.55	71.52	<.0001
y_ex*met*gen	6	15.55	1.58	0.2174

Interpretation

The "Solution for Fixed Effects" table lists the estimates of the intercepts (e.g., met*gen f 1) and the slopes (e.g., yr_ex*gen*met f 1). The Type 3 *F* statistic for yr_ex*gen*met tests the slopes-equal-to-zero hypothesis and fails to provide enough evidence to conclude nonzero slopes ($p = 0.2174$). For illustration purposes, the structure of slopes is investigated to see whether by chance a simpler model involving the covariate may be appropriate.

7.7.2 Fit Factorial Effects Model for Intercepts and Slopes

The intercepts and slopes are each expressed as factorial effects in the model.

$$y_{ijkm} = (\mu + \tau_i + \gamma_k + \delta_{ik}) + (\beta + \varphi_i + \theta_k + \rho_{ik})x_{ij} + t_{j(i)} + e_{ijkm}$$
$$i = 1,2,3, \quad j = 1,2,3,4, \quad k = 1,2, \quad m = 1,2,3,4$$

(7.6)

Where the following definitions hold:

- $\alpha_{ik} = (\mu + \tau_i + \gamma_k + \delta_{ik})$.
- $\beta_{ik} = (\beta + \varphi_i + \theta_k + \rho_{ik})$.
- $t_{j(i)} \sim \text{iid } N(0, \sigma_t^2)$.
- $e_{ijkm} \sim \text{iid } N(0, \sigma_e^2)$.

The additional parameters in Equation 7.6 compared to Equation 7.5 provide factorial effect representations for the slopes and intercepts. Thus, each slope or intercept is expressed through an overall mean, an effect due to teaching method, an effect due to gender, and an effect due to the interaction between teaching method and gender. Those parameters are as follows:

- μ and β denote the overall means.
- τ_i and φ_i denote the effect of the ith teaching method (MET).
- γ_k and θ_k denote the kth gender effect (GEN).
- δ_{ik} and ρ_{ik} denote the interaction effect between the ith teaching method (MET) and the kth gender (GEN).

Program

The code in Program 7.20 fits a model with unequal slopes, expressing intercepts and slopes as factorial effects:

Program 7.20

```
proc glimmix data=ex_7_7sp;
   class teacher met gen;
   model score = met gen gen*met
                 yr_ex yr_ex*met yr_ex*gen yr_ex*gen*met/ddfm=kr2;
   random teacher(met);
run;
```

Results

The analysis of variance results of the factorial tests for the slopes and intercepts are shown in Output 7.19, which also includes the estimates of the variance components.

Output 7.19: Fit of the Unequal Slopes Model Using Factorial Effects

Covariance Parameter Estimates

Cov Parm	Estimate	Standard Error
teacher(met)	1.7814	1.0748
Residual	0.6405	0.1026

Type III Tests of Fixed Effects

Effect	Num DF	Den DF	F Value	Pr > F
met	2	6	10.09	0.0120
gen	1	78	5.30	0.0240
met*gen	2	78	10.30	0.0001
y_ex	1	6	0.46	0.5216
y_ex*met	2	6	0.33	0.7322
y_ex*gen	1	78	3.48	0.0660
y_ex*met*gen	2	78	2.24	0.1138

Interpretation

One wants to make sure that you only include covariate parts in the model that are significant so that overfitting is not a problem. The objective of the process is to use the simplest expression of the covariate part of the model as possible (Milliken and Johnson, 2002). To accomplish this, a model building process is used on the terms in the model involving the covariate or the slopes. A backward elimination process is used to simplify the covariate part of the model where the highest order interactions are considered first, which in this case is yr_ex*met*gen. The yr_ex*met*gen term has a significance level of 0.1138, indicating there is no ($p = 0.05$) evidence there is a three-way interaction.

The next step is to delete yr_ex*met*gen from the model and refit the reduced model. At this stage if the interactions yr_ex*met and yr_ex*gen have significance levels greater than 0.05, then delete the term with the largest significance level and refit the model. If the remaining two-way interaction term is still not significant, delete it and fit a common slope model and test to see whether the common slope model is significant from zero. At any step, the modeling is stopped when a covariate term is significant. The final step is to compare the treatments using the form of the slopes of the significant term.

7.7.3 Fit Model with Slopes Expressed as Main Effects of the Two Factors

The analysis in Section 7.7.3 shows that the slopes are a function of teaching and gender and not of the teaching by gender interaction.

The model with slopes as a function of the main effects (teaching and gender) only is as follows:

$$y_{ijkm} = (\mu + \tau_i + \gamma_k + \delta_{ik}) + (\beta + \varphi_i + \theta_k) \, x_{ij} + t_{j(i)} + e_{ijkm}$$

where the following definitions hold:

- $i = 1,2,3$.
- $j = 1,2,3,4$.
- $k = 1,2$.
- $m = 1,2,3,4$.
- $\alpha_{ik} = (\mu + \tau_i + \gamma_k + \delta_{ik})$.
- $\beta_{ik} = (\beta + \varphi_i + \theta_k)$ (slope as a function of teaching and gender but not their interaction).

The model is translated into code in Program 7.21 fits the model without the yr_ex*met*gen term.

Program 7.21
```
proc glimmix data=ex_7_7sp;
   class teacher met gen;
   model score = met gen gen*met yr_ex yr_ex*met yr_ex*gen/ddfm=kr2;
   random teacher(met);
run;
```

The results are listed in Output 7.20, which includes the analysis of variance tests for the remaining terms in the model.

Output 7.20: Fit of the Model with Unequal Slopes Expressed as Main Effects

Covariance Parameter Estimates		
Cov Parm	Estimate	Standard Error
teacher(met)	1.7789	1.0748
Residual	0.6602	0.1044

Type III Tests of Fixed Effects				
Effect	Num DF	Den DF	F Value	Pr > F
met	2	6	10.09	0.0120
gen	1	80	5.00	0.0281
met*gen	2	80	63.90	<.0001
y_ex	1	6	0.46	0.5216
y_ex*met	2	6	0.33	0.7322
y_ex*gen	1	80	4.20	0.0436

The Type III *F* test for the yr_ex × met effect is not significant. Thus, remove the term from the model and refit a model with unequal slopes for each gender.

7.7.4 Fit Model with Unequal Slopes for Each

The discussion in Section 7.7.3 indicates the slopes are not a function of teaching method but are possibly a function of gender. The following model expresses the slope as a function of gender.

The model with slopes as a function of the gender effects only is as follows:

$$y_{ijkm} = (\mu + \tau_i + \gamma_k + \delta_{ik}) + (\beta + \theta_k) x_{ij} + t_{j(i)} + e_{ijkm} \tag{7.7}$$

Where the following definitions hold:

- $i = 1,2,3.$
- $j = 1,2,3,4.$
- $k = 1,2.$
- $m = 1,2,3,4.$
- $\alpha_{ik} = (\mu + \tau_i + \gamma_k + \delta_{ik}).$
- $\beta_{ik} = (\beta + \theta_k)$ (slope as a function of gender only).

Program to Fit the Model

The code that fits Equation (7.7) has yr_exp and yr_exp by gender including the slopes possibly depend on gender.

Program 7.22

```
proc glimmix data=ex_7_7sp;
   class teacher met gen;
   model score = met gen gen*met yr_ex yr_ex*gen/ddfm=kr2;
   random teacher(met);
run;
```

Results

The results are in Output 7.21, which includes the analysis of variance for the remaining effects in the model.

Output 7.21: Fit of the Unequal Slopes Model for the Levels of Gender

Covariance Parameter Estimates		
Cov Parm	Estimate	Standard Error
teacher(met)	1.4665	0.7746
Residual	0.6602	0.1044

Type III Tests of Fixed Effects				
Effect	Num DF	Den DF	F Value	Pr > F
met	2	8	77.68	<.0001
gen	1	80	5.00	0.0281
met*gen	2	80	63.90	<.0001
y_ex	1	8	0.75	0.4107
y_ex*gen	1	80	4.20	0.0436

Interpretation

The Type III F statistic for the yr_ex × gen effect tests the equality of the gender slopes (one for females and one for males) and presents evidence (at the 5% significance level) that the two slopes are unequal ($p = 0.0436$). The simplified model to investigate the relationship between teaching methods and gender involving the covariate with unequal slopes for each gender and a means model for the intercepts is described by Equation 7.8.

$$y_{ijkm} = \alpha_{ik} + \beta_k x_{ij} + t_{j(i)} + e_{ijkm} \qquad (7.8)$$

where the following definitions hold:

- $i = 1,2,3.$
- $j = 1,2,3,4.$

- $k = 1, 2.$
- $m = 1, 2, 3, 4.$
- $t_{j(i)} \sim \text{iid N}\left(0, \sigma_t^2\right)$.
- $e_{ijkm} \sim \text{iid N}\left(0, \sigma_e^2\right)$.

Program to Fit the Model

Program 7.24 is used to fit Equation 7.8. The program fits the model with teaching method by gender interaction (no main effects) and years of experience by gender interaction (unequal slopes) to prove a full rank model that provides estimates of the slopes and intercepts. LSMEANS statements are used to compare the gender by teaching method means evaluated at a given number of years of teaching experience. Estimate statements are used to obtain the appropriate comparisons while LSMEANS does not provide the appropriate comparisons for all interesting comparisons.

Program 7.23

```
proc glimmix data=ex_7_7sp;
   class teacher met gen;
   model score =gen*met yr_ex*gen/noint solution ddfm=kr2;
   random teacher(met);

   lsmeans gen*met / diff at means; ;*teaching methods by gender means at average year of
teaching experience 11.4167;
   lsmeans gen*met / diff at yr_ex=5; ;*comparison of teaching method by gender means at 5
years of experience;

   lsmeans gen*met / diff at yr_ex=10; ;*comparison of teaching method by gender means at 10
years of experience;

   lsmeans gen*met / diff at yr_ex=20; ;*comparison of teaching method by gender means at 20
years of experience;

*Estimate statements to compare female and male means at teaching method 1 and specified
years of experience.
   estimate 'f-m m=1 yr_ex=5'    gen*met 1 -1 0  0 0  0 yr_ex*gen  5  -5;
   estimate 'f-m m=1 yr_ex=10'   gen*met 1 -1 0  0 0  0 yr_ex*gen 10 -10;
   estimate 'f-m m=1 yr_ex=20'   gen*met 1 -1 0  0 0  0 yr_ex*gen 20 -20;
   estimate 'f-m m=2 yr_ex=5'    gen*met 0  0 1 -1 0  0 yr_ex*gen  5  -5;
   estimate 'f-m m=2 yr_ex=10'   gen*met 0  0 1 -1 0  0 yr_ex*gen 10 -10;
   estimate 'f-m m=2 yr_ex=20'   gen*met 0  0 1 -1 0  0 yr_ex*gen 20 -20;
   estimate 'f-m m=3 yr_ex=5'    gen*met 0  0 0  0 1 -1 yr_ex*gen  5  -5;
   estimate 'f-m m=3 yr_ex=10'   gen*met 0  0 0  0 1 -1 yr_ex*gen 10 -10;
   estimate 'f-m m=3 yr_ex=20'   gen*met 0  0 0  0 1 -1 yr_ex*gen 20 -20;
*Estimate of the gender means for a specified teaching method and years of experience
   estimate 'male m=1 yr_ex=5'   gen*met 1  0 0  0 0  0 yr_ex*gen  5   0;
   estimate 'male m=1 yr_ex=10'  gen*met 1  0 0  0 0  0 yr_ex*gen 10   0;
   estimate 'male m=1 yr_ex=20'  gen*met 1  0 0  0 0  0 yr_ex*gen 20   0;
   estimate 'male m=2 yr_ex=5'   gen*met 0  0 1  0 0  0 yr_ex*gen  5   0;
   estimate 'male m=2 yr_ex=10'  gen*met 0  0 1  0 0  0 yr_ex*gen 10   0;
   estimate 'male m=2 yr_ex=20'  gen*met 0  0 1  0 0  0 yr_ex*gen 20   0;
   estimate 'male m=3 yr_ex=5'   gen*met 0  0 0  0 1  0 yr_ex*gen  5   0;
   estimate 'male m=3 yr_ex=10'  gen*met 0  0 0  0 1  0 yr_ex*gen 10   0;
   estimate 'male m=3 yr_ex=20'  gen*met 0  0 0  0 1  0 yr_ex*gen 20   0;

   estimate 'female m=1 yr_ex=5'  gen*met 0  1 0  0 0  0 yr_ex*gen  0   5;
   estimate 'female m=1 yr_ex=10' gen*met 0  1 0  0 0  0 yr_ex*gen  0  10;
   estimate 'female m=1 yr_ex=20' gen*met 0  1 0  0 0  0 yr_ex*gen  0  20;
   estimate 'female m=2 yr_ex=5'  gen*met 0  0 0  1 0  0 yr_ex*gen  0   5;
   estimate 'female m=2 yr_ex=10' gen*met 0  0 0  1 0  0 yr_ex*gen  0  10;
   estimate 'female m=2 yr_ex=20' gen*met 0  0 0  1 0  0 yr_ex*gen  0  20;
   estimate 'female m=3 yr_ex=5'  gen*met 0  0 0  0 0  1 yr_ex*gen  0   5;
   estimate 'female m=3 yr_ex=10' gen*met 0  0 0  0 0  1 yr_ex*gen  0  10;
   estimate 'female m=3 yr_ex=20' gen*met 0  0 0  0 0  1 yr_ex*gen  0  20;
run;
```

ESTIMATE statements compare genders within each teaching method at 5, 10, and 20 years of teaching experience and provide adjusted means for combinations of gender and teaching method at 5, 10, and 20 years of teaching experience. The first LSMEANS statement compares teaching methods within each gender and compares all models at the average years of teaching experience, 11.41667. The second through fourth LSMEANS statements also provide comparisons at 5, 10, and 20 years of teaching experience for comparison purposes using the AT option.

Results

The estimates of the variance components and of the fixed effects are shown in Output 7.22.

Output 7.22: Model with Intercepts for the Method-by-Gender Combinations and Two Gender Slopes

Covariance Parameter Estimates		
Cov Parm	Estimate	Standard Error
teacher(met)	1.4665	0.7746
Residual	0.6602	0.1044

Solutions for Fixed Effects							
Effect	gen	met	Estimate	Standard Error	DF	t Value	Pr > |t|
met*gen	f	1	16.4468	1.1860	8.873	13.87	<.0001
met*gen	m	1	17.5559	1.1860	8.873	14.80	<.0001
met*gen	f	2	22.2849	1.2427	8.873	17.93	<.0001
met*gen	m	2	21.3930	1.2427	8.873	17.22	<.0001
met*gen	f	3	29.6883	1.1674	8.873	25.43	<.0001
met*gen	m	3	26.2144	1.1674	8.873	22.46	<.0001
y_ex*gen	f		-0.03416	0.08883	8.873	-0.38	0.7096
y_ex*gen	m		-0.1161	0.08883	8.873	-1.31	0.2241

Type III Tests of Fixed Effects				
Effect	Num DF	Den DF	F Value	Pr > F
met*gen	6	20.96	120.44	<.0001
y_ex*gen	2	18.7	2.39	0.1187

Interpretation

The Type III F statistics in Output 7.22 test that all intercepts are equal to zero and that all slopes are equal to zero. Most likely these tests are not of much interest, but this form of the model is most convenient for constructing ESTIMATE statements because the resulting model is nonsingular and has parameters as described in the Model statement of Program 7.24. But it is very important to realize that the p-value associated with the F test for the slopes is 0.1187, and one might be tempted to exclude the covariate from the analysis. This is also true for the initial model in Output 7.18. But there is information about the slopes from the within-teacher comparisons and from the between-teacher comparisons. When within-teacher comparisons are made, the information about the covariate becomes important. The moral of the story is to always start with the full factorial representation of the slope part of the model before doing any simplification.

Results

Least squares means and pairwise comparisons of least squares means are given in Outputs 7.23, 7.24, 7.25, and 7.26, and the results of the ESTIMATE statements can be found in Output 7.27.

Output 7.23: Least Squares Means Comparing Method-by-Gender Adjusted Means at Yr_ex = 11.41667

				met*gen Least Squares Means			
gen	met	y_ex	Estimate	Standard Error	DF	t Value	Pr > |t|
f	1	11.42	16.0568	0.6388	8.873	25.13	<.0001
m	1	11.42	16.2307	0.6388	8.873	25.41	<.0001
f	2	11.42	21.8949	0.6408	8.873	34.17	<.0001
m	2	11.42	20.0677	0.6408	8.873	31.32	<.0001
f	3	11.42	29.2983	0.6397	8.873	45.80	<.0001
m	3	11.42	24.8891	0.6397	8.873	38.91	<.0001

						Differences of met*gen Least Squares Means			
gen	met	_gen	_met	y_ex	Estimate	Standard Error	DF	t Value	Pr > |t|
f	1	m	1	11.42	-0.1738	0.2874	80	-0.60	0.5469
f	1	f	2	11.42	-5.8381	0.9056	8.873	-6.45	0.0001
f	1	m	2	11.42	-4.0109	0.9056	8.869	-4.43	0.0017
f	1	f	3	11.42	-13.2415	0.9035	8.873	-14.66	<.0001
f	1	m	3	11.42	-8.8323	0.9035	8.875	-9.78	<.0001
m	1	f	2	11.42	-5.6643	0.9056	8.869	-6.25	0.0002
m	1	m	2	11.42	-3.8371	0.9056	8.873	-4.24	0.0023
m	1	f	3	11.42	-13.0676	0.9035	8.875	-14.46	<.0001
m	1	m	3	11.42	-8.6585	0.9035	8.873	-9.58	<.0001
f	2	m	2	11.42	1.8272	0.2882	80	6.34	<.0001
f	2	f	3	11.42	-7.4033	0.9076	8.873	-8.16	<.0001
f	2	m	3	11.42	-2.9942	0.9073	8.864	-3.30	0.0094
m	2	f	3	11.42	-9.2306	0.9073	8.864	-10.17	<.0001
m	2	m	3	11.42	-4.8214	0.9076	8.873	-5.31	0.0005
f	3	m	3	11.42	4.4091	0.2878	80	15.32	<.0001

Output 7.24: Least Squares Means Comparing Method-by-Gender Adjusted Means Yr_ex = 5

				met*gen Least Squares Means			
gen	met	y_ex	Estimate	Standard Error	DF	t Value	Pr > |t|
f	1	5.00	16.2760	0.8462	8.873	19.23	<.0001
m	1	5.00	16.9755	0.8462	8.873	20.06	<.0001
f	2	5.00	22.1141	0.8914	8.873	24.81	<.0001
m	2	5.00	20.8126	0.8914	8.873	23.35	<.0001
f	3	5.00	29.5175	0.8318	8.873	35.48	<.0001
m	3	5.00	25.6340	0.8318	8.873	30.82	<.0001

						Differences of met*gen Least Squares Means			
gen	met	_gen	_met	y_ex	Estimate	Standard Error	DF	t Value	Pr > |t|
f	1	m	1	5.00	-0.6995	0.3807	80	-1.84	0.0698
f	1	f	2	5.00	-5.8381	0.9056	8.873	-6.45	0.0001
f	1	m	2	5.00	-4.5366	0.9434	10.43	-4.81	0.0006
f	1	f	3	5.00	-13.2415	0.9035	8.873	-14.66	<.0001
f	1	m	3	5.00	-9.3580	0.9360	10.21	-10.00	<.0001
m	1	f	2	5.00	-5.1386	0.9434	10.43	-5.45	0.0002
m	1	m	2	5.00	-3.8371	0.9056	8.873	-4.24	0.0023

					Differences of met*gen Least Squares Means				
gen	**met**	**_gen**	**_met**	**y_ex**	**Estimate**	**Standard Error**	**DF**	**t Value**	**Pr > |t|**
m	1	f	3	5.00	-12.5419	0.9360	10.21	-13.40	<.0001
m	1	m	3	5.00	-8.6585	0.9035	8.873	-9.58	<.0001
f	2	m	2	5.00	1.3015	0.4010	80	3.25	0.0017
f	2	f	3	5.00	-7.4033	0.9076	8.873	-8.16	<.0001
f	2	m	3	5.00	-3.5199	0.9438	10.36	-3.73	0.0037
m	2	f	3	5.00	-8.7049	0.9438	10.36	-9.22	<.0001
m	2	m	3	5.00	-4.8214	0.9076	8.873	-5.31	0.0005
f	3	m	3	5.00	3.8835	0.3742	80	10.38	<.0001

Output 7.25: Least Squares Means Comparing Method-by-Gender Adjusted Means at Yr_ex = 10

				met*gen Least Squares Means			
gen	**met**	**y_ex**	**Estimate**	**Standard Error**	**DF**	**t Value**	**Pr > |t|**
f	1	10.00	16.1052	0.6482	8.873	24.84	<.0001
m	1	10.00	16.3951	0.6482	8.873	25.29	<.0001
f	2	10.00	21.9433	0.6629	8.873	33.10	<.0001
m	2	10.00	20.2322	0.6629	8.873	30.52	<.0001
f	3	10.00	29.3467	0.6448	8.873	45.51	<.0001
m	3	10.00	25.0536	0.6448	8.873	38.85	<.0001

					Differences of met*gen Least Squares Means				
gen	**met**	**_gen**	**_met**	**y_ex**	**Estimate**	**Standard Error**	**DF**	**t Value**	**Pr > |t|**
f	1	m	1	10.00	-0.2899	0.2916	80	-0.99	0.3231
f	1	f	2	10.00	-5.8381	0.9056	8.873	-6.45	0.0001
f	1	m	2	10.00	-4.1270	0.9078	8.959	-4.55	0.0014
f	1	f	3	10.00	-13.2415	0.9035	8.873	-14.66	<.0001
f	1	m	3	10.00	-8.9484	0.9046	8.916	-9.89	<.0001
m	1	f	2	10.00	-5.5482	0.9078	8.959	-6.11	0.0002
m	1	m	2	10.00	-3.8371	0.9056	8.873	-4.24	0.0023
m	1	f	3	10.00	-12.9516	0.9046	8.916	-14.32	<.0001
m	1	m	3	10.00	-8.6585	0.9035	8.873	-9.58	<.0001
f	2	m	2	10.00	1.7112	0.2982	80	5.74	<.0001
f	2	f	3	10.00	-7.4033	0.9076	8.873	-8.16	<.0001
f	2	m	3	10.00	-3.1103	0.9093	8.941	-3.42	0.0077
m	2	f	3	10.00	-9.1145	0.9093	8.941	-10.02	<.0001
m	2	m	3	10.00	-4.8214	0.9076	8.873	-5.31	0.0005
f	3	m	3	10.00	4.2931	0.2900	80	14.80	<.0001

Output 7.26: Least Squares Means Comparing Method-by-Gender Adjusted Means at Yr_ex = 20

				met*gen Least Squares Means			
gen	**met**	**y_ex**	**Estimate**	**Standard Error**	**DF**	**t Value**	**Pr > |t|**
f	1	20.00	15.7636	1.0060	8.873	15.67	<.0001
m	1	20.00	15.2343	1.0060	8.873	15.14	<.0001
f	2	20.00	21.6017	0.9555	8.873	22.61	<.0001
m	2	20.00	19.0713	0.9555	8.873	19.96	<.0001
f	3	20.00	29.0051	1.0233	8.873	28.35	<.0001
m	3	20.00	23.8928	1.0233	8.873	23.35	<.0001

					Differences of met*gen Least Squares Means				
gen	met	_gen	_met	y_ex	Estimate	Standard Error	DF	t Value	Pr > |t|
f	1	m	1	20.00	0.5293	0.4525	80	1.17	0.2456
f	1	f	2	20.00	-5.8381	0.9056	8.873	-6.45	0.0001
f	1	m	2	20.00	-3.3077	0.9654	11.41	-3.43	0.0054
f	1	f	3	20.00	-13.2415	0.9035	8.873	-14.66	<.0001
f	1	m	3	20.00	-8.1292	0.9706	11.77	-8.38	<.0001
m	1	f	2	20.00	-6.3674	0.9654	11.41	-6.60	<.0001
m	1	m	2	20.00	-3.8371	0.9056	8.873	-4.24	0.0023
m	1	f	3	20.00	-13.7708	0.9706	11.77	-14.19	<.0001
m	1	m	3	20.00	-8.6585	0.9035	8.873	-9.58	<.0001
f	2	m	2	20.00	2.5304	0.4298	80	5.89	<.0001
f	2	f	3	20.00	-7.4033	0.9076	8.873	-8.16	<.0001
f	2	m	3	20.00	-2.2910	0.9688	11.48	-2.36	0.0366
m	2	f	3	20.00	-9.9337	0.9688	11.48	-10.25	<.0001
m	2	m	3	20.00	-4.8214	0.9076	8.873	-5.31	0.0005
f	3	m	3	20.00	5.1123	0.4603	80	11.11	<.0001

Output 7.27: Compare Adjusted Gender Means at 5, 10, and 20 Years of Experience

	Estimates				
Label	Estimate	Standard Error	DF	t Value	Pr > |t|
f-m m=1 y_ex=5	-0.6995	0.3807	80	-1.84	0.0698
f-m m=1 y_ex=10	-0.2899	0.2916	80	-0.99	0.3231
f-m m=1 y_ex=20	0.5293	0.4525	80	1.17	0.2456
f-m m=2 y_ex=5	1.3015	0.4010	80	3.25	0.0017
f-m m=2 y_ex=10	1.7112	0.2982	80	5.74	<.0001
f-m m=2 y_ex=20	2.5304	0.4298	80	5.89	<.0001
f-m m=3 y_ex=5	3.8835	0.3742	80	10.38	<.0001
f-m m=3 y_ex=10	4.2931	0.2900	80	14.80	<.0001
f-m m=3 y_ex=20	5.1123	0.4603	80	11.11	<.0001
male m=1 y_ex=5	16.2760	0.8462	8.873	19.23	<.0001
male m=1 y_ex=10	16.1052	0.6482	8.873	24.84	<.0001
male m=1 y_ex=20	15.7636	1.0060	8.873	15.67	<.0001
male m=2 y_ex=5	22.1141	0.8914	8.873	24.81	<.0001
male m=2 y_ex=10	21.9433	0.6629	8.873	33.10	<.0001
male m=2 y_ex=20	21.6017	0.9555	8.873	22.61	<.0001
male m=3 y_ex=5	29.5175	0.8318	8.873	35.48	<.0001
male m=3 y_ex=10	29.3467	0.6448	8.873	45.51	<.0001
male m=3 y_ex=20	29.0051	1.0233	8.873	28.35	<.0001
female m=1 y_ex=5	16.9755	0.8462	8.873	20.06	<.0001
female m=1 y_ex=10	16.3951	0.6482	8.873	25.29	<.0001
female m=1 y_ex=20	15.2343	1.0060	8.873	15.14	<.0001
female m=2 y_ex=5	20.8126	0.8914	8.873	23.35	<.0001
female m=2 y_ex=10	20.2322	0.6629	8.873	30.52	<.0001
female m=2 y_ex=20	19.0713	0.9555	8.873	19.96	<.0001
female m=3 y_ex=5	25.6340	0.8318	8.873	30.82	<.0001
female m=3 y_ex=10	25.0536	0.6448	8.873	38.85	<.0001
female m=3 y_ex=20	23.8928	1.0233	8.873	23.35	<.0001

Interpretation

The LSMEANS results and the comparisons of the LSMEANS are in Output 7.23 through 7.26, and the results of the ESTIMATE statements are in Output 7.27. For teaching experience of 5, 10, and 20 years, only gender comparisons within a teaching method are presented. The results from the LSMEANS and ESTIMATE statements are identical, but both are presented to help understand the computation of the LSMEANS.

The importance of using the mixed models approach for this example is that the classes of eight students are blocks for gender and (like the RCB in Section 7.2) there is information about the slopes from within blocks and between blocks. The mixed model equations combine the information from the various parts of the model into combined estimators of the slopes. Using the combined estimators should generally provide estimators with smaller variances than those based on intra-block information alone.

7.8 Summary

An analysis of covariance strategy is described and demonstrated via several mixed model examples. When the model involves more than one factor in the design structure, information about the fixed effects part of the model can be extracted from several parts of the design structure. The mixed models analysis combines the information from the various parts of the design structure and about the model fixed effect parameters and provides combined estimators of the fixed effects. In particular, the estimates of the slopes corresponding to the covariates are computed from the combined information. If the design structure involves only one block—in essence, a completely randomized design structure—the usual within-block analysis extracts all of the information about the slopes from the data. When the design structure is more complex, the mixed models analysis extracts more information from the data than the usual analysis provided by an analysis where the blocks are considered as fixed effects.

A multilevel or split-plot example is presented in which the covariate was measured on the large size of experimental unit. The covariate can be measured on the large size of experimental unit, the small size of experimental unit, or on an intermediate size of experimental unit. Such examples are discussed in Milliken and Johnson (2002).

The examples in this chapter use PROC GLIMMIX for model fitting and its ESTIMATE, CONTRAST, and LSMEANS statements for post-processing. In two instances, the SLICEDIFF= option of PROC GLIMMIX is helpful to simplify and organize least squares means comparisons.

The LSMEANS statement of PROC GLIMMIX offers facilities for graphing least squares means (see Section 5.3.4) and least squares means comparisons, producing slice differences, performing analysis of means (ANOM, Ott 1967; Nelson 1982, 1991, 1993), applying enhanced multiplicity adjustments (e.g., step-down *p*-values; Westfall 1997), producing lines (lettering) output, and so on. PROC GLIMMIX makes the post-fitting analysis process easier.

A large variety of applications of analysis of covariance models including repeated measures and random coefficient models are discussed in detail in Milliken and Johnson (2002).

Chapter 8: Analysis of Repeated Measures Data

8.1 Introduction **269**
  8.1.1 Basic Concepts of Repeated Measures 269
  8.1.2 Types of Repeated Measures Analyses...270
  8.1.3 A Statistical Model for Repeated Measures...271
8.2 Mixed Model Analysis of Data from Basic Repeated Measures Design: An Example.......................... 272
  8.2.1 Historical Aside: MANOVA and the Split Plot in Time..274
  8.2.2 Repeated Measures Syntax in PROC GLIMMIX and PROC MIXED 275
  8.2.3 Comparison of Results from Two Covariance Structures 280
8.3 Covariance Structures.. 283
  8.3.1 Some Candidates 283
  8.3.2 Selection of an Appropriate Model 285
  8.3.3 Reassessment with a Means Model Accounting for Baseline Measurement...................292
8.4 PROC GLIMMIX Analysis of FEV1 Data 293
  8.4.1 FEV1 Analysis Focusing on Difference between Hour 1 and Hour 8............................297
  8.4.2 Use of Regression to Model FEV1 Change over Time...298
8.5 Unequally Spaced Repeated Measures: An Example 301
  8.5.1 Program..301
  8.5.2 Results...302
  8.5.3 Model..302
  8.5.4 Program..302
  8.5.5 Results...303
  8.5.6 Results...304
8.6 Summary... 305

8.1 Introduction

The term *repeated measures* refers to data sets with multiple measurements of a response variable on the same experimental unit. In most applications, the multiple measurements are made over a period of time. An example is growth curve data, such as monthly weight measurements of babies for the first year of their lives. Another example is drug effects data, such as measurements of pulse or respiration on patients following administration of a drug. But repeated measures can also refer to multiple measurements over space, such as thicknesses of the vertebrae of animals. In a general sense, any data that are measured repeatedly over time or space are repeated measures data. Most of this chapter uses the term in the more traditional sense, referring to sequences of measurements on experimental units in a designed experiment, sample survey, or retrospective study.

A general theme in this book is that observations from experiments tend to be correlated in some type of block-wise fashion. Random effects discussed in previous chapters are arguably the simplest form of this, in which observations that share the same level of a random effect have a common covariance, and those that have different levels are assumed independent. Repeated measures on experimental units across time and/or space opens up a large number of new ways in which observations can be correlated. We will still assume independence of observations from different experimental units, but within a unit there is an entire class of new interesting structures that we can use for effectively modeling their interrelationships. This chapter introduces these structures and unleashes some of the real inherent power and flexibility that a general mixed modeling approach can provide for analyzing experimental data.

8.1.1 Basic Concepts of Repeated Measures

A commonly occurring repeated measures study consists of a completely randomized experimental design with data collected in a sequence of equally spaced time points from each experimental unit. Much of the development of repeated measures methodology occurred in the area of human psychology. As a result, the experimental units are often called *subjects*. But "subject" could refer to an animal, a laboratory sample, or a piece of industrial equipment.

In this basic setup of a completely randomized design with repeated measures, there are two factors, *treatments* and *time*. In this sense, all repeated measures experiments are factorial experiments. Treatment is called the *between-subjects* factor because levels of treatment can change only between subjects; all measurements on the same subject represent the same treatment. Time is called a *within-subjects* factor because different measurements on the same subject are taken at different times. In repeated measures experiments, interest centers on (1) how treatment means differ, (2) how treatment means change over time, and (3) how differences between treatment means change over time. In other words, is there a *treatment main effect*, is there a *time main effect*, and is there a *treatment-by-time interaction*? These are the types of questions we may want to ask in any two-factor study. Ordinarily, the interaction would be the first question to investigate, because if it exists, then interpretation of the main effects becomes much more difficult and typically less meaningful.

There is nothing peculiar about the objectives of a repeated measures study. What makes repeated measures data analysis distinct is the *covariance structure* of the observed data. In randomized block designs, treatments are randomized to units within a block. This makes all observations within a given block equally correlated. But, in repeated measures experiments, two measurements taken at adjacent time points are typically more highly correlated than two measurements taken several time points apart. For this reason, statistical analysis usually begins with assessing the covariance structure of the data. Sections 8.2.1 and 8.2.2 are devoted to modeling the covariance structure of the example data. Appropriately modeling the covariance structure is an essential prerequisite for obtaining valid inference about treatment, time, and treatment-by-time effects.

There are similarities between repeated measures experiments and split plot experiments (see Chapter 5). You can see this by inspecting the sources of variation, shown in Table 8.1.

Table 8.1: Sources of Variation for Split Plot and Repeated Measures

Split Plot	Repeated Experiment Design	Repeated Treatment Design	Combined Repeated Measures
Factor A	—	Treatment	Treatment
Whole-plot e.u. = Block × A	Subjects	—	Between subjects = Subject(treatment)
B	—	Time	Time
A × B	—	Time × Treatment	Time × treatment
Split plot e.u.	Occasions (subject)	—	Within subjects

Note: e.u. = experimental unit.

The treatment factor (between-subjects) in a repeated measures experiment corresponds to the main-plot, a.k.a. whole-plot factor in a split plot experiment. The time factor (within-subjects) in repeated measures corresponds to the split plot factor. The experimental units to which the treatments are assigned in the repeated measures experiment are analogous to whole-plot units in the split plot experiment. The specific times experimental units that `are measured (or time intervals) correspond to split plot units. However, in a genuine split plot experiment, levels of the split plot factor are randomly assigned to split plot units within whole-plot units. Consequently, responses from different split plot units in the same whole-plot unit can be equally correlated with each other. But in repeated measures experiments, responses from occasions close in time are usually more highly correlated than responses from occasions farther apart in time. Therefore, special methods of analysis are usually needed to accommodate the correlation structure of the repeated measures.

8.1.2 Types of Repeated Measures Analyses

Three general types of statistical analyses are most commonly used for repeated measures. One method treats repeated measures data as having come from a split plot experiment. This method, variously called a *univariate analysis of variance* or a *split plot in time*, was often used before the advent of mixed model software. Another method applies *multivariate* and *univariate analysis methods* to *linear transformations* of the repeated measures. The linear transformations can be means, differences between responses at different time points, slopes of regression curves, and the like. These techniques were implemented using the REPEATED statement in PROC GLM and are illustrated in Littell, Stroup, and Freund (2002). The third method, and the focus of this chapter, applies *mixed model methods* with *special parametric structure on the covariance matrices*. This approach became computationally feasible when comprehensive mixed model software, e.g. PROC MIXED in SAS, became available. The methodology discussed in this chapter can be implemented either using PROC MIXED with the REPEATED statement or PROC GLIMMIX with the RANDOM statement in conjunction with the RESIDUAL option. As in previous chapters, most of the examples will be shown using the GLIMMIX procedure.

As noted in the introduction to this chapter, mixed model analysis involves two stages: first, fit the covariance structure; then perform inference on treatment and time effects. Littell, Pendergast, and Natarajan (2000) break these stages further into a four-step procedure for mixed model analysis:

1. Model the mean structure, usually by specification of the fixed effects.
2. Specify the covariance structure, between subjects as well as within subjects.

3. Fit the mean model accounting for the covariance structure.
4. Make statistical inference based on the results of step 3.

Other authors, such as Diggle (1988) and Wolfinger (1993a), recommend similar model-fitting and inference processes. The following sections show you how to use PROC GLIMMIX and PROC MIXED to implement these four steps.

8.1.3 A Statistical Model for Repeated Measures

Consider the experimental situation described in Section 8.1.1. Subjects are randomly assigned to a treatment factor, and measurements are made at equally spaced times on each subject. Let y_{ijk} denote the measurement at time k on the jth subject assigned to treatment i.

Following the sources of variation listed in Table 8.1, and assuming that y_{ijk} has a plausibly Gaussian distribution, a statistical model for repeated measures data is

$$y_{ijk} = \mu + \alpha_i + b_{ij} + \gamma_k + \alpha\gamma_{ik} + w_{ijk} \tag{8.1}$$

where terms are defined as follows:

- $\mu_{ik} = \mu + \alpha_i + \gamma_k + \alpha\gamma_{ik}$ is the mean for treatment i at time k, containing effects for treatment, time, and treatment × time interaction.
- b_{ij} is the *between-subjects* effect for the jth subject assigned to treatment i.
- w_{ijk} is the *within-subjects* effect for time k on the ij^{th} subject.

To see the special characteristics of the repeated measures covariance structure, it is best to start by combining the between- and within-subject effects into a single term. That is, let $e_{ijk} = b_{ij} + w_{ijk}$, where e_{ijk} can be understood as the random error associated with the measurement at time k on the jth subject that is assigned to treatment i. Hence, Equation 8.1 can be rewritten as

$$y_{ijk} = \mu_{ij} + e_{ijk} = \mu + \alpha_i + \gamma_k + \alpha\gamma_{ik} + e_{ijk} \tag{8.2}$$

Equation 8.2 is the same as the model equation for a standard factorial experiment with main effects of treatment and time, and treatment × time interaction. The distinguishing feature of a repeated measures model is the variance and covariance structure of the errors, e_{ijk}. Although treatments are randomly assigned to subjects, the levels of the repeated measures factor, in this case time, cannot be randomly assigned to units within subject. Thus, we cannot reasonably assume that the random errors e_{ijk} for the same subject are independent, so from a statistical perspective, it is typically safer to use a more general covariance structure. Instead, assume that errors for *different* subjects are independent, giving

$$\text{Cov}\left[e_{ijk}, e_{i'j'k}\right] = 0$$

if either $i \neq i'$ or $j \neq j'$.

Also, since measurements on the same subject are over a time course, they may have different variances, and correlations between pairs of measurements may depend on the length of the time interval between the measurements. Therefore, in the most general setting, we only assume

$$\text{Var}\left[e_{ijk}\right] = \sigma_k^2 \text{ and } \text{Cov}\left[e_{ijk}, e_{ijk'}\right] = \sigma_{kk'}$$

In other words, we allow the variance of e_{ijk} to depend on the measurement time k, and the covariance between the errors at two times, k and k', for the same subject, depends on the times. In the language of the GLIMMIX and MIXED procedures, this is called the *unstructured* covariance model, or TYPE=UN in SAS syntax. It is conceptually identical to the covariance structure assumed for multivariate analysis of variance (MANOVA) for repeated measures data (see next section).

At the opposite extreme is the univariate, or split plot in time approach. Return to the model given in Equation 8.1 and make the same assumptions as for a split plot experiment, that is, $b_{ij} \sim \mathrm{NI}(0,\sigma_b^2)$ and then $w_{ijk} \sim \mathrm{NI}(0,\sigma_w^2)$. Then under this model,

$$\mathrm{Var}\left[e_{ijk}\right] = \mathrm{Var}\left[b_{ij} + w_{ijk}\right] = \sigma_b^2 + \sigma_w^2 \text{ and } \mathrm{Cov}\left[e_{ijk}, e_{ijk'}\right] = \sigma_b^2 \qquad (8.3)$$

As shown in Chapters 2 and 5, this can alternatively be expressed as a *compound symmetry* model, with residual parameter $\mathrm{Var}[e_{ijk}] = \sigma_e^2$ and covariance parameter, $\mathrm{Cov}[e_{ijk}, e_{ijk'}] = \sigma_{cs}$, identified by TYPE=CS in the syntax of the GLIMMIX and MIXED procedures.

You can think of the unstructured and compound symmetry models as extremes in terms of accounting for within subject correlation. Unstructured assumes that the variance at every time and the correlation between every pair of times is unique. Compound symmetry assumes that time has no impact on either variance or within-subject correlation. In many, if not most, repeated measures experiments, correlation and—possibly—variance do depend on time, but the time dependence can be modeled more parsimoniously than UN. As you will see in the examples later in this chapter, over modeling the covariance structure (e.g. using the unstructured model when a simpler model adequately accounts for the observed covariance) reduces power and precision for fixed effects estimates and fixed effects tests, whereas under modeling (e.g. using compound symmetry when covariance is in fact time-dependent) results in underestimated standard errors and hence inflated Type I error rate and excessively narrow confidence intervals.

The example beginning in the next section illustrates how these ideas are put into practice.

8.2 Mixed Model Analysis of Data from Basic Repeated Measures Design: An Example

This repeated measures example is from Littell, Pendergast, and Natarajan (2000). It is also used in Littell, Stroup, and Freund (2002). The data appear as "Respiratory Ability." A pharmaceutical company examined effects of three drugs on respiratory ability of asthma patients. Treatments were a standard drug (A), a test drug (C), and a placebo (P). The drugs were randomly assigned to 24 patients (72 total). The assigned treatment was administered to each patient, and a standard measure of respiratory ability called FEV1 was measured hourly for 8 hours following treatment. FEV1 was also measured immediately prior to administration of the drugs. The data appear in *multivariate format*, that is, the FEV1 measurement at each hour is a distinct variable in the data set, i.e. FEV1H1 at hour 1, FEV1H2 at hour 2, etc. such that every subject has one row of data in the data set. Figure 8.1 shows profile plots for each patient.

Figure 8.1: The FEV1 Profiles by Time for Each Patient within Each Drug

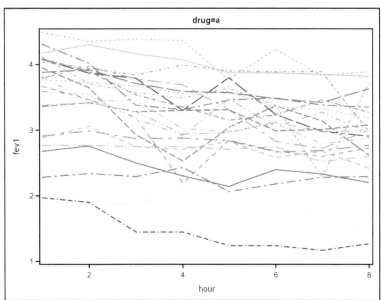

B

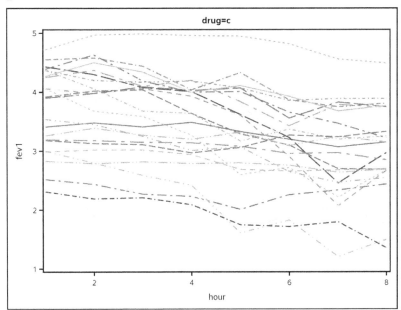

C

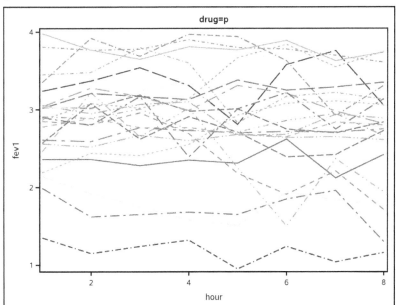

The profile plots indicate higher FEV1 values at hour 1 in the active drugs A and C than in the placebo P. Response profiles in A and C appear to decline from hour 1 to hour 8, whereas the profiles in P are basically flat, except for random disturbance. Some patients have FEV1 measures that are consistently higher or lower than those of other patients, indicating the presence of a patient random effect. This means that two measures on the same patient are correlated simply because they have the patient effect in common. Also, for a given patient, consecutive measures are possibly more highly correlated than measures that are several hours apart, although this is not readily apparent from the profile plots.

As noted above, there are often two aspects of covariance structure in the errors. First, two FEV1 measures on the same subject are likely to be more nearly the same than two measures on different subjects. Thus, measures on the same subject are usually positively correlated simply because they share common effects from that subject. This is the same phenomenon possessed by measures on the same whole-plot unit in a split plot experiment. Second, two FEV1 measures made close in time on the same subject are likely to be more highly correlated than two measures made far apart in time. This feature distinguishes repeated measures covariance structure from split plot covariance structure. In a split plot experiment, levels of the subplot factor are randomized to subplot units within whole-plot units, resulting in possible equal correlation between all pairs of measurements in or on the same whole-plot unit.

Figure 8.2: Plot of the FEV1 Means by Time for Each Drug

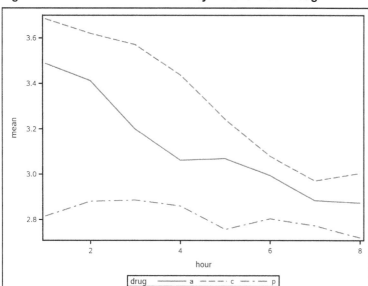

Figure 8.2 shows the FEV1 means for each drug over the eight levels of HOUR. This plot shows trends in the drug mean profiles. The means for drug P do not change much from hour 1 to hour 8. But means for drugs A and C are higher than those of drug P in the early stages and then decrease substantially. Also, the means for drug A are somewhat less that the means for drug C. The decreasing trend is more obvious in Figure 8.2 than in Figure 8.1 because of the difference in scale of the FEV1 axis.

8.2.1 Historical Aside: MANOVA and the Split Plot in Time

As mentioned earlier in this chapter, analysis of repeated measures experiments developed independently in two contexts: the MANOVA approach in human physiology, and the "split plot in time" approach in agricultural field experiments. You will see as this example is developed, the MANOVA approach and mixed model repeated measures analysis using the unstructured covariance model are conceptually similar, and the "split plot in time" approach is simply the standard mixed model analysis for a split plot experiment described in Chapter 5. In this sense, both can be viewed as special cases of the mixed model approach, but because the mixed model approach allows greater flexibility in fitting covariance structures to the data, it has replaced MANOVA and the "split plot in time" as standard practice for repeated measures. For context, it is instructive to start this example by seeing what these two approaches produce. When it was developed, the GLM procedure was designed to obtain MANOVA and "split plot in time" analyses for repeated measures.

Program

Using the multivariate format of the data, PROC GLM uses the following statements. The NOUNI option suppresses the listing of individual ANOVAs for each time, allowing only the multivariate analysis and the "split plot in time" ANOVA to be printed.

Program 8.1

```
proc glm data=fev1;
 class drug;
 model fev1h1-fev1h8=drug/nouni;
 repeated hour 8;
run;
```

Results

Output 8.1 shows the MANOVA results for the test of DRUG × HOUR (i.e. treatment × time) interaction. Output 8.2 shows the "split plot in time" results from the PROC GLM code.

Output 8.1: MANOVA Tests of Drug × Hour Interaction

MANOVA Test Criteria and F Approximations for the Hypothesis of no hour*drug Effect H = Type III SSCP Matrix for hour*drug E = Error SSCP Matrix					
S=2 M=2 N=30.5					
Statistic	Value	F Value	Num DF	Den DF	Pr > F
Wilks' Lambda	0.51191319	3.58	14	126	<.0001
Pillai's Trace	0.55490980	3.51	14	128	<.0001
Hotelling-Lawley Trace	0.82292043	3.66	14	97.495	<.0001
Roy's Greatest Root	0.60834527	5.56	7	64	<.0001
NOTE: F Statistic for Roy's Greatest Root is an upper bound.					
NOTE: F Statistic for Wilks' Lambda is exact.					

As discussed in Littell, et al. (2002), Wilk's Lambda, Pillai's Trace and the Hotelling-Lawley Trace can be used interchangeably as test statistics. For comparison with mixed models results, focus on the Hotelling-Lawley Trace, for which $F = 3.66$, and note that the denominator degrees of freedom are 97.5. You will see these numbers again when we do a mixed model analysis with the unstructured covariance model. The univariate tests provide the split plot in time analysis for hour and hour*drug interaction as shown in Output 8.2.

Output 8.2: Split Plot in Time Tests of Drug × Hour Interaction

Source	DF	Type III SS	Mean Square	F Value	Pr > F	Adj Pr > F G - G	Adj Pr > F H-F-L
hour	7	17.17039931	2.45291419	38.86	<.0001	<.0001	<.0001
hour*drug	14	6.28006632	0.44857617	7.11	<.0001	<.0001	<.0001
Error(hour)	483	30.49025937	0.06312683				

The F value for the hour * drug interaction univariate test is 7.11, whereas it was 3.66 using the MANOVA Hotelling-Lawley Trace. In this example, the *p*-values are both <0.0001, but the important thing to notice is that the F value for the split plot in time is always greater than the MANOVA F. It is not unusual to find that the split plot in time shows the treatment × time effect to be statistically significant, whereas MANOVA does not. This raises the question, "Which is most appropriate?" and the answer is, in general, neither. MANOVA tends to be too conservative for fixed effect estimates and comparisons, and the split plot in time—in essence, compound symmetry—tends to be too liberal. The following section concerns choosing an appropriate, parsimonious covariance structure for the repeated measures part of the model. We start by presenting syntax necessary to implement mixed model repeated measures analysis.

8.2.2 Repeated Measures Syntax in PROC GLIMMIX and PROC MIXED

In previous chapters, the RANDOM statement is used in PROC GLIMMIX and in PROC MIXED to model the covariance in data by specifying model random effects in the linear predictor. In most of these examples, we assume that the residuals are uncorrelated and have constant variance. By default, both PROC GLIMMIX and PROC MIXED implement this assumption. The one exception in previous chapters is the compound symmetry structure introduced in Section 2.5.3, and discussed in the context of split-plot experiments in Section 5.7.3. Compound symmetry (CS) is the simplest example of modeling covariance among residuals that share a common experimental unit; the CS model assumes equal correlation between the residuals of any two observations that share a common unit. In repeated measures, correlation between residuals of observations on the same unit typically depend on how far apart they are in time. This is called *serial correlation*. Mixed models for repeated measures extend the CS approach by providing residual covariance structures of varying complexity to account for serial correlation.

In PROC GLIMMIX, you specify residual covariance structures by adding the word RESIDUAL to the RANDOM statement. For example, in the FEV1 data the time variable is HOUR and the experimental unit on which repeated measures are taken is PATIENT(DRUG). The following statements are equivalent ways of specifying residual covariance:

```
random _residual_ / subject=patient(drug) type=cs;
random hour / subject=patient(drug) type=cs residual;
```

The SUBJECT option identifies the experimental unit on which repeated measures are taken. The TYPE option specifies the covariance structure used to model correlation between repeated measurements on that experimental unit. The second statement explicitly includes the name of the repeated measures variable, and assures that the covariance model will be computed with the data sorted by hour. The first statement is equivalent to the second, *provided that the data are sorted by HOUR before running the PROC statement.* Note that the key word RESIDUAL appears somewhere in both versions of the RANDOM statement. The example statements use TYPE=CS; examples in this chapter show different types needed to account to serial correlation in its various forms.

In PROC MIXED, the equivalent statement is as follows:

```
repeated hour / subject=patient(drug) type=cs;
```

If the data are sorted by hour, you can drop the word HOUR from this statement. Thus, REPEATED in PROC MIXED has the same meaning as RANDOM _RESIDUAL_ , as well as RANDOM with the key word RESIDUAL after the slash in PROC GLIMMIX. The change in syntax from PROC MIXED to PROC GLIMMIX represents a more modern mindset in the latter reflecting a unified view of covariance structure modeling. Historically, PROC MIXED was developed after PROC GLM, but before PROC GLIMMIX, and borrows from the former's syntax for continuity. On the other hand, unlike PROC GLM and PROC MIXED, PROC GLIMMIX is written to accommodate covariance structures for mixed models with non-Gaussian data (see Chapter 13).

For convenience, in this chapter we refer to statements that specify residual covariance structures in PROC GLIMMIX generically as "RANDOM...RESIDUAL" statements, meaning that the keyword RESIDUAL appears somewhere in the RANDOM statement. Thus, PROC GLIMMIX "RANDOM...RESIDUAL" statements are equivalent to PROC MIXED REPEATED statements.

In this section, we illustrate the basic aspects of the RANDOM...RESIDUAL and REPEATED statements. In subsequent sections of this chapter we demonstrate several types of covariance structures and how to implement them. In certain cases, it is reasonable to include both a RANDOM statement, to define random model effects, and a RANDOM...RESIDUAL or REPEATED statement to define a residual covariance structure. In other cases, use of both statements creates structures that are not mutually identifiable, and including a RANDOM statement and a RANDOM...RESIDUAL or REPEATED statement is a bad idea. Subsequent sections present examples of each case.

Turning now to the FEV1 example, we first list the sources of variance using the same framework as Table 8.1.

Table 8.2: Basic Split Plot in Time Analysis for the FEV1 Data

Source	df
Drug	2
Patient(Drug)	$3 \times (24 - 1) = 69$
Hour	7
Drug $\times$ Hour	14
Within Patients	483
Total	$(3 \times 24 \times 8) - 1 = 575$

The factors DRUG and HOUR are considered fixed effects. Therefore, these effects will appear in the MODEL statement. The factor PATIENT(DRUG) is the between-subjects random effect. It, along with within-patient variation, will be incorporated into a covariance structure associated with individual patients. The best way to describe the general form of the covariance is as follows:

$$
\mathbf{y} = \begin{bmatrix} y_{ij1} \\ y_{ij2} \\ y_{ij3} \\ y_{ij4} \\ y_{ij5} \\ y_{ij6} \\ y_{ij7} \\ y_{ij8} \end{bmatrix} \quad \mathrm{Var}\left[\mathbf{y}\right] = \begin{bmatrix} \sigma_1^2 & \sigma_{12} & \sigma_{13} & \sigma_{14} & \sigma_{15} & \sigma_{16} & \sigma_{17} & \sigma_{18} \\ & \sigma_2^2 & \sigma_{23} & \sigma_{24} & \sigma_{25} & \sigma_{26} & \sigma_{27} & \sigma_{28} \\ & & \sigma_3^2 & \sigma_{34} & \sigma_{35} & \sigma_{36} & \sigma_{37} & \sigma_{38} \\ & & & \sigma_4^2 & \sigma_{45} & \sigma_{46} & \sigma_{47} & \sigma_{48} \\ & & & & \sigma_5^2 & \sigma_{56} & \sigma_{57} & \sigma_{58} \\ & & & & & \sigma_6^2 & \sigma_{67} & \sigma_{68} \\ & & & & & & \sigma_7^2 & \sigma_{78} \\ & & & & & & & \sigma_8^2 \end{bmatrix}
$$

(8.4)

The first term, $\mathbf{y}$, denotes the vector of observations from hour 1 through hour 8 for each PATIENT. The variance of this vector, denoted $\boldsymbol{\Sigma}$, is called the covariance matrix. In its most general form, the diagonal elements give the variance of the observation at time k for the ij^{th} patient, and the off-diagonal elements in row k and column k' give the covariance between the observations at times $k \neq k'$ for the ij^{th} patient. Covariance matrices are symmetric, meaning $\sigma_{kk'}$ always equals $\sigma_{k'k}$, e.g. $\sigma_{12} = \sigma_{21}$. For this reason, to save typing, covariance matrices are almost always presented as an upper right triangle or lower left triangle, but not both. The $\boldsymbol{\Sigma}$ matrix can be simplified in various ways, to be illustrated as this example is developed.

Programs

Programs 8.2 and 8.3 show how to implement the repeated measures mixed model using the syntax introduced in Section 8.2.2. Program 8.2 uses PROC GLIMMIX. Program 8.3 uses PROC MIXED.

Recall that with PROC GLIMMIX, the RANDOM statement with the accompanying word RESIDUAL appearing in the same statement specifies the repeated measures covariance structure. The REPEATED statement in PROC MIXED serves the same function.

In this example, HOUR is the repeated measures factor. The between-subjects effect is PATIENT(DRUG). The PROC GLIMMIX statements to fit the fixed effects of DRUG, HOUR, and DRUG × HOUR interaction, with the unstructured covariance matrix $\boldsymbol{\Sigma}$ for each patient, as it appears above in Equation 8.4, are in Program 8.2.

Program 8.2

```
proc glimmix data=fev1uni;
   class drug patient hour;
   model fev1=drug hour drug*hour;
   random hour / subject=patient(drug) type=un residual v vcorr;
run;
```

The equivalent statements in PROC MIXED are in Program 8.3.

Program 8.3

```
proc mixed data=fev1uni;
   class drug patient hour;
   model fev1=drug hour drug*hour;
   repeated hour / subject=patient(drug) type=un r rcorr;
run;
```

The important elements of these statements are as follows:

1. The effect listed before the option slash (/). Here, HOUR is listed as this effect. The levels of this effect define the rows and columns of the matrix $\boldsymbol{\Sigma}$ in Equation 8.4.
2. The SUBJECT= effect defines the effect whose levels identify observations that belong to the same subject. In general, this means the between-subjects effect. In this example, all observations that share the same levels of the PATIENT(DRUG) effect represent a single subject. Observations from different subjects are uncorrelated.
3. The TYPE= option determines the covariance structure of $\boldsymbol{\Sigma}$.

Results

Output 8.3 shows the unstructured covariance parameter estimates. This listing will appear the same regardless of whether PROC GLIMMIX or PROC MIXED is used to produce it.

Output 8.3: Listing of the Unstructured Covariance Parameter Estimates

Cov Parm	Subject	Estimate	Standard Error
UN(1,1)	patient(drug)	0.4541	0.07732
UN(2,1)	patient(drug)	0.4587	0.08030
UN(2,2)	patient(drug)	0.5163	0.08790
UN(3,1)	patient(drug)	0.4441	0.07810
UN(3,2)	patient(drug)	0.4808	0.08387
UN(3,3)	patient(drug)	0.4923	0.08382
UN(4,1)	patient(drug)	0.4154	0.07584
UN(4,2)	patient(drug)	0.4688	0.08294
UN(4,3)	patient(drug)	0.4687	0.08190
UN(4,4)	patient(drug)	0.4938	0.08407
UN(5,1)	patient(drug)	0.4349	0.08090
UN(5,2)	patient(drug)	0.4943	0.08869
UN(5,3)	patient(drug)	0.4843	0.08674
UN(5,4)	patient(drug)	0.4837	0.08676
UN(5,5)	patient(drug)	0.5779	0.09839
UN(6,1)	patient(drug)	0.3934	0.07397
UN(6,2)	patient(drug)	0.4254	0.07934
UN(6,3)	patient(drug)	0.4263	0.07832
UN(6,4)	patient(drug)	0.4179	0.07773
UN(6,5)	patient(drug)	0.4945	0.08748
UN(6,6)	patient(drug)	0.4906	0.08353
UN(7,1)	patient(drug)	0.3562	0.07159
UN(7,2)	patient(drug)	0.3992	0.07776
UN(7,3)	patient(drug)	0.4021	0.07685
UN(7,4)	patient(drug)	0.4023	0.07694
UN(7,5)	patient(drug)	0.4643	0.08548
UN(7,6)	patient(drug)	0.4454	0.08016
UN(7,7)	patient(drug)	0.4994	0.08503
UN(8,1)	patient(drug)	0.3840	0.07381
UN(8,2)	patient(drug)	0.4257	0.07994
UN(8,3)	patient(drug)	0.4256	0.07884
UN(8,4)	patient(drug)	0.4251	0.07886
UN(8,5)	patient(drug)	0.4950	0.08812
UN(8,6)	patient(drug)	0.4632	0.08177
UN(8,7)	patient(drug)	0.4496	0.08106
UN(8,8)	patient(drug)	0.5031	0.08566

Output 8.3 lists the estimates of the 8 variance and $(8 \times 7)/2 = 28$ covariance parameters. UN(k,k) in the listing gives the estimate of σ_k^2. For example, the variance within the first time period is $\hat{\sigma}_1^2 = UN(1,1) = 0.4541$. UN($k,k'$) gives the estimate of the covariance $\sigma_{kk'}$. For example, $\hat{\sigma}_{12} = \hat{\sigma}_{21} = UN(2,1) = 0.4587$ is the covariance between time 1 and time 2. Notice that the listing for the unstructured covariance gives the *lower left* triangle form of the covariance matrix, not the upper right triangle given in Equation 8.4. However, because covariance matrices are symmetric, the information given in the listing is complete.

In addition to covariance estimates, there are several options available. The V option in the RANDOM.../...RESIDUAL statement requests that PROC GLIMMIX display the estimate of the Σ matrix for the first subject, and the VCORR option requests the correlation matrix, which is obtained by computing correlations from the elements of the covariance matrix. Output 8.4 shows the listing for the unstructured covariance matrix for the FEV1 data for patient 201 and drug a.

Output 8.4: FEV1 Data: Estimated Covariance Matrix—Unstructured

Row	Col1	Col2	Col3	Col4	Col5	Col6	Col7	Col8
1	0.4541	0.4587	0.4441	0.4154	0.4349	0.3934	0.3562	0.3840
2	0.4587	0.5163	0.4808	0.4688	0.4943	0.4254	0.3992	0.4257
3	0.4441	0.4808	0.4923	0.4687	0.4843	0.4263	0.4021	0.4256
4	0.4154	0.4688	0.4687	0.4938	0.4837	0.4179	0.4023	0.4251
5	0.4349	0.4943	0.4843	0.4837	0.5779	0.4945	0.4643	0.4950
6	0.3934	0.4254	0.4263	0.4179	0.4945	0.4906	0.4454	0.4632
7	0.3562	0.3992	0.4021	0.4023	0.4643	0.4454	0.4994	0.4496
8	0.3840	0.4257	0.4256	0.4251	0.4950	0.4632	0.4496	0.5031

Estimated V Matrix for patient(drug) 201 a

Interpretation

The "Estimated V Matrix for PATIENT(DRUG) 201 a" table lists the covariance matrix constructed from the covariance parameter estimates. In the unstructured case, the covariance matrix simply arranges the estimates above and below the main diagonal. In conventional matrix notation, this matrix is as follows:

$$\hat{\Sigma} = \begin{bmatrix} 0.454 & 0.458 & 0.444 & 0.415 & 0.434 & 0.393 & 0.356 & 0.384 \\ & 0.516 & 0.480 & 0.468 & 0.494 & 0.425 & 0.399 & 0.425 \\ & & 0.492 & 0.468 & 0.484 & 0.426 & 0.402 & 0.425 \\ & & & 0.493 & 0.483 & 0.417 & 0.402 & 0.425 \\ & & & & 0.577 & 0.494 & 0.464 & 0.495 \\ & & & & & 0.490 & 0.445 & 0.463 \\ & & & & & & 0.499 & 0.449 \\ & & & & & & & 0.503 \end{bmatrix}$$

Notice that there are the same elements as the UN(k,k') listing in Output 8.3. They are just presented in a different form.

This matrix reveals the essential feature of repeated measures data. The numbers on the main diagonal are the estimates of variances at hours 1 through 8, $\sigma_1^2, \ldots, \sigma_8^2$. The estimates are similar, with all values between 0.454 and 0.578. When we explore possible simplifications of the covariance structure, these values suggest that it may be reasonable to assume that the variances at different times are equal, giving $\sigma_k^2 = \sigma^2$ for all k. The numbers off the diagonal are covariance estimates between FEV1 measures at two different hours of the same subject. For example, the number 0.489 is an estimate of σ_{12}, the covariance between measures at hours 1 and 2. These covariance estimates generally decrease as the length of the time interval (called the *lag*) increases. This is consistent with the intuition that measures close in time have greater covariance (i.e. are more strongly correlated) than measures farther apart in time.

Results

The correlation matrix for the TYPE=UN covariance structure, obtained using the VCORR option, is shown in Output 8.5.

Output 8.5: Repeated Measures: Estimated Correlation Matrix—Unstructured

| | Estimated V Correlation Matrix for patient(drug) 201 a | | | | | | | |
Row	Col1	Col2	Col3	Col4	Col5	Col6	Col7	Col8
1	1.0000	0.9474	0.9393	0.8773	0.8490	0.8334	0.7479	0.8033
2	0.9474	1.0000	0.9536	0.9284	0.9050	0.8453	0.7861	0.8352
3	0.9393	0.9536	1.0000	0.9506	0.9080	0.8674	0.8109	0.8552
4	0.8773	0.9284	0.9506	1.0000	0.9055	0.8490	0.8102	0.8529
5	0.8490	0.9050	0.9080	0.9055	1.0000	0.9286	0.8642	0.9181
6	0.8334	0.8453	0.8674	0.8490	0.9286	1.0000	0.8997	0.9323
7	0.7479	0.7861	0.8109	0.8102	0.8642	0.8997	1.0000	0.8970
8	0.8033	0.8352	0.8552	0.8529	0.9181	0.9323	0.8970	1.0000

You can see the decreasing trend in correlation with increasing lag, for example, by scanning along the entries for Row 1 or Col 1.

With 8 times per subject, the unstructured covariance matrix has 36 variance and covariance parameters. On inspection of the estimated covariance and correlation matrices, we noticed that it may be reasonable to model a common variance and use a simple function to model decreasing correlation with increasing distance in time between observations. As mentioned earlier, power and precision can be increased by using a more parsimonious model, assuming that it adequately accounts for the observed variance and correlation structure of the data. We begin by comparing the unstructured results with those obtained using the compound symmetry model.

8.2.3 Comparison of Results from Two Covariance Structures

The ultimate objective of the statistical analysis is to make inference about the fixed effects of DRUG and HOUR, in the form of tests of hypotheses and confidence intervals for means and differences between means. But the inferential results about fixed effects depend on the specification of the covariance matrix of random effects. As mentioned above, an appropriately analyzed repeated measures experiment neither over- nor under-models the covariance structure. To illustrate how to do this, we begin by running the same PROC GLIMMIX program, except this time we specify *compound symmetry*. Recall that essential features of compound symmetry are: (1) equal variances at all times, $\text{Var}[y_{ijk}] = \sigma^2$ for all k, and (2) equal covariance between observations on the same subject at all pairs of times, $\text{Cov}[y_{ijk}, y_{ijk'}] = \rho\sigma^2$.

Program

The statements for specifying compound symmetric covariance structure are in Program 8.4.

Program 8.4

```
proc glimmix data=fev1uni;
   class drug patient hour;
   model fev1=drug hour drug*hour;
   random hour / sub=patient(drug) type=cs residual;
run;
```

Results

Selected results analogous to those discussed above for TYPE=UN appear in Output 8.6 through Output 8.8. In Output 8.6, there are only two parameters to be estimated for the CS structure.

Output 8.6: Covariance Parameter Estimates for Compound Symmetry

Covariance Parameter Estimates			
Cov Parm	Subject	Estimate	Standard Error
CS	patient(drug)	0.4403	0.07631
Residual		0.06313	0.004062

The structure of the estimated CS covariance matrix is shown in Output 8.7. The variances are all equal to 0.503 and the covariances are all equal to 0.440.

Output 8.7: Mixed Model Analysis of Repeated Measures: Covariance Parameter Estimates—Compound Symmetry

Estimated V Matrix for patient(drug) 201 a								
Row	Col1	Col2	Col3	Col4	Col5	Col6	Col7	Col8
1	0.5034	0.4403	0.4403	0.4403	0.4403	0.4403	0.4403	0.4403
2	0.4403	0.5034	0.4403	0.4403	0.4403	0.4403	0.4403	0.4403
3	0.4403	0.4403	0.5034	0.4403	0.4403	0.4403	0.4403	0.4403
4	0.4403	0.4403	0.4403	0.5034	0.4403	0.4403	0.4403	0.4403
5	0.4403	0.4403	0.4403	0.4403	0.5034	0.4403	0.4403	0.4403
6	0.4403	0.4403	0.4403	0.4403	0.4403	0.5034	0.4403	0.4403
7	0.4403	0.4403	0.4403	0.4403	0.4403	0.4403	0.5034	0.4403
8	0.4403	0.4403	0.4403	0.4403	0.4403	0.4403	0.4403	0.5034

The correlation matrix of the repeated measures is shown in Output 8.8. The diagonal elements are all 1.0 and the correlations (off diagonal elements) are all equal to 0.875. The correlations are computed in the usual way, as follows:

$$\hat{\rho} = \frac{\sigma_{kk'}}{\sqrt{\sigma_k^2 \sigma_{k'}^2}} = \frac{\sigma_{kk'}}{\sigma^2} = \frac{0.440}{0.503} = 0.875$$

Output 8.8: Repeated Measures: Correlations

Estimated V Correlation Matrix for patient(drug) 201 a								
Row	Col1	Col2	Col3	Col4	Col5	Col6	Col7	Col8
1	1.0000	0.8746	0.8746	0.8746	0.8746	0.8746	0.8746	0.8746
2	0.8746	1.0000	0.8746	0.8746	0.8746	0.8746	0.8746	0.8746
3	0.8746	0.8746	1.0000	0.8746	0.8746	0.8746	0.8746	0.8746
4	0.8746	0.8746	0.8746	1.0000	0.8746	0.8746	0.8746	0.8746
5	0.8746	0.8746	0.8746	0.8746	1.0000	0.8746	0.8746	0.8746
6	0.8746	0.8746	0.8746	0.8746	0.8746	1.0000	0.8746	0.8746
7	0.8746	0.8746	0.8746	0.8746	0.8746	0.8746	1.0000	0.8746
8	0.8746	0.8746	0.8746	0.8746	0.8746	0.8746	0.8746	1.0000

You see different results in the "Covariance Parameter Estimates" table when using TYPE=CS compared to TYPE=UN (compare Output 8.6 to Output 8.3). The number 0.4403, labeled "CS PATIENT(DRUG)," is the estimate of the covariance between two measures on the same patient $Cov[y_{ijk}, y_{ijk'}] = \rho\sigma^2$, where $Var[y_{ijk}] = \sigma^2$. In most cases, $\rho > 0$, and $\rho\sigma^2$ is equivalent to a between-subjects variance component σ_b^2. That is the case with this example, and we shall refer to the parameter as σ_S^2. The number .06313, labeled "Residual" in the output, is the estimate of the residual variance component. It is the variance of y_{ijk} conditional on a patient, $Var[y_{ijk}|i] = \sigma_b^2$. It follows that $\sigma^2 = \sigma_S^2 + \sigma_b^2$.

These parameters determine the covariance matrix Σ. The estimate of the matrix is as follows:

$$\hat{\Sigma} = \begin{bmatrix} 0.503 & 0.440 & 0.440 & 0.440 & 0.440 & 0.440 & 0.440 & 0.440 \\ & 0.503 & 0.440 & 0.440 & 0.440 & 0.440 & 0.440 & 0.440 \\ & & 0.503 & 0.440 & 0.440 & 0.440 & 0.440 & 0.440 \\ & & & 0.503 & 0.440 & 0.440 & 0.440 & 0.440 \\ & & & & 0.503 & 0.440 & 0.440 & 0.440 \\ & & & & & 0.503 & 0.440 & 0.440 \\ & & & & & & 0.503 & 0.440 \\ & & & & & & & 0.503 \end{bmatrix}$$

The compound symmetric covariance is highly structured with only two parameters, σ_S^2 and σ_b^2. According to this structure, the covariance between any two measures on the same subject, $\text{Cov}[y_{ijk}, y_{ijk'}]$, is equal to σ_S^2. Consequently, the correlation between any two measures on the same subject is equal to $\rho = \sigma_S^2 / (\sigma_S^2 + \sigma_b^2)$. You can see the value of this correlation, $\hat{\rho} = 0.8746$ in the off-diagonal terms in Output 8.8. Note that the compound symmetry variance estimate is approximately the average of the diagonal elements from the unstructured estimates, and similarly, the compound symmetry covariance is approximately the average of the unstructured off-diagonal elements. Both estimates are computed by REML, which also nicely handles responses missing at random. When the data are completely balanced, REML will converge in one iteration since the mixed model equations can be solved analytically.

The unstructured covariance estimates shown in Section 8.2.1 and the compound symmetry estimates shown in this section are the two extremes. We turn now to the following questions:

- What impact does the covariance structure have on inferential statistics?
- How do we decide which covariance structure better models within-subject correlation?
- Are there better, middle-ground choices that we should use instead of either unstructured or compound symmetry? If so, what are they and how do we identify them?

Output 8.9 shows the Type III Test of Fixed Effects obtained in conjunction with the unstructured and compound symmetry covariance models. Two results are shown for the unstructured covariance model, one the default *df* and the other using the DDFM=KR2 option in the MODEL statement to compute the Kenward-Roger adjustment.

Output 8.9: Type III Tests of Drug, Hour and Drug by Hour Effects under UN and CS Models

	Type III Tests of Fixed Effects			
Effect	Num DF	Den DF	F Value	Pr > F
drug	2	69	3.60	0.0327
hour	7	69	13.72	<.0001
drug*hour	14	69	4.06	<.0001

Note: Unstructured, without Kenward-Roger Adjustment

	Type III Tests of Fixed Effects			
Effect	Num DF	Den DF	F Value	Pr > F
drug	2	69	3.60	0.0327
hour	7	63	12.53	<.0001
drug*hour	14	98.06	3.66	<.0001

Note: Unstructured, with Kenward-Roger Adjustment

Type III Tests of Fixed Effects				
Effect	Num DF	Den DF	F Value	Pr > F
drug	2	69	3.60	0.0327
hour	7	483	38.86	<.0001
drug*hour	14	483	7.11	<.0001

Note: Compound Symmetry, with Kenward-Roger Adjustment

In the top panel of Output 8.9 notice that the F value for the drug×hour interaction in the default listing for UN, the unstructured covariance model, is 4.06, versus 3.66 for the Hotelling-Lawley Trace from MANOVA in Output 8.1. This is one of the problems that motivated Kenward and Roger to develop their bias correction for mixed model analysis. Except for compound symmetry with balanced designs and no missing data, use of estimated covariance parameters to compute inferential statistics results in downward biased standard errors and upward biased test statistics. Guerin and Stroup (2000) showed that the more complex the covariance structure, the more severe the bias. They also showed that the Kenward-Roger adjustment accurately addresses this bias issue. Therefore, the Kenward-Roger adjustment, implemented by the DDFM=KR2 option in PROC GLIMMIX, should be considered mandatory standard operating procedure when analyzing repeated measures data.

The middle panel of Output 8.9 shows the unstructured result with the Kenward-Roger adjustment. The F value of 3.66 is equal to the F value associated with the Hotelling-Lawley Trace. The denominator degrees of freedom are approximations: 98.06 in PROC GLIMMIX obtained using the Satterthwaite approximation discussed in Chapters 2 and 5, versus 97.5 in Output 8.1 obtained using a MANOVA-based approximation. The difference is inconsequential. The main point is the essential equivalence of MANOVA and mixed model analysis using the unstructured covariance model—*assuming you use the Kenward-Roger bias adjustment.*

The bottom panel of Output 8.9 shows the compound symmetry result, also obtained using the DDFM=KR2 option. In this case, there is no bias correction needed, but the Satterthwaite degree of freedom algorithm embedded in the KR2 option ensures that PROC GLIMMIX computes appropriate denominator degrees of freedom. Notice that this result is identical to the "split plot in time" result shown in Output 8.2.

Given that the conclusions drawn from a repeated measures analysis depend on the covariance structure you use, in the next section we address the questions "how does one decide which covariance structure to use" and "are there better, middle-ground options rather than compound symmetry or unstructured covariance."

8.3 Covariance Structures

In this section we compare several candidate covariance structures for the FEV1 data, using both graphical and information criteria to compare the covariance structures. Doing so is more or less analogous to procedures often used in selection of regression models. In the regression situation one plots the data, observes the fits of candidate models to the data, and then uses a criterion of fit to assess the various models.

8.3.1 Some Candidates

PROC GLIMMIX and PROC MIXED enable you to choose from many covariance models for Σ. The simplest model is the independent covariance model, where the within-subject error correlation is zero, and hence $\Sigma = \sigma^2 I$. In the previous sections, we considered the next simplest model, which is compound symmetry, and the most complex model, which is unstructured.

In some applications, the within-subject correlation is negligible. For example, in some agronomic and large-animal-nutrition trials, repeated measurements may occur at long enough intervals, such as monthly, where correlation is effectively zero relative to other variations. In such cases, the independence structure is acceptable. However, this should be checked before the data are analyzed assuming uncorrelated errors.

Correlation is present in most repeated measures data to some extent. When correlation is time dependent, compound symmetry (TYPE==CS in PROC GLIMMIX) does not provide an adequately covariance model. However, correlation is usually not as complex as the unstructured model (TYPE=UN in PROC GLIMMIX). We now review some of the more common alternatives to CS and UN.

Typically, correlation between observations is a function of their lag in time: adjacent observations tend to be more highly correlated than observations farther apart in time. Several models may adequately describe such correlation. Perhaps the most commonly used is the *first-order autoregressive*, or **AR(1)**, model. For the AR(1) model,

$$
\boldsymbol{\Sigma} = \sigma^2
\begin{bmatrix}
1 & \rho & \rho^2 & \cdots & \rho^{k-1} \\
  & 1 & \rho & \cdots & \rho^{k-2} \\
  &   & 1 & \cdots & \vdots \\
  &   &   & \ddots & \rho \\
  &   &   &   & 1
\end{bmatrix}
\tag{8.5}
$$

The AR(1) model assumes that $e_{ijk} = \rho e_{ij,k-1} + s_{ijk}$, where $s_{ijk} \sim iid\, N(0, \sigma_S^2)$. It follows that $\sigma^2 = \sigma_S^2 / (1 - \rho^2)$. This helps explain why independent error models tend to underestimate within-subject variance when correlation among the errors is non-negligible and depends on distance in time between observations.

Under the AR(1) model, correlation between adjacent within-subject errors is ρ, regardless of whether the pair of observations is the 1st and 2nd, 2nd and 3rd, or $(k-1)$st and kth, whereas with the unstructured model, each pair has its own correlation. The correlation is ρ^2 for any pair of errors 2 units apart, such as the 1st and 3rd. In general, errors d units apart have correlation ρ^d. Note that the AR(1) model requires estimates of just two parameters, σ^2 and ρ, whereas unstructured models require estimating $k + k(k-1)/2$ parameters.

The Toeplitz model is similar to the AR(1) model in the sense that pairs of within-subject errors separated by a common lag share the same correlation. However, errors d units apart have correlation ρ_d instead of ρ^d. Thus, for the Toeplitz model,

$$
\boldsymbol{\Sigma} = \sigma_0{}^2
\begin{bmatrix}
1 & \rho_1 & \rho_2 & \cdots & \rho_{k-1} \\
  & 1 & \rho_1 & \cdots & \rho_{k-2} \\
  &   & 1 & \cdots & \vdots \\
  &   &   & \ddots & \rho_1 \\
  &   &   &   & 1
\end{bmatrix}
=
\begin{bmatrix}
\sigma_0^2 & \sigma_{12} & \sigma_{13} & \cdots & \sigma_{1,k} \\
  & \sigma_0^2 & \sigma_{21} & \cdots & \sigma_{2,k} \\
  &   & \sigma_0^2 & \cdots & \vdots \\
  &   &   & \ddots & \sigma_{k-1,k} \\
  &   &   &   & \sigma_0^2
\end{bmatrix}
\tag{8.6}
$$

The Toeplitz covariance structure has the following elements:

$$
\sigma_{k,k+1} = \rho_1\sigma_0^2, \sigma_{k,k+2} = \rho_2\sigma_0^2, \cdots, \sigma_{k,k-1} = \rho_{k-1}\sigma_0^2
$$

The Toeplitz model is less restrictive than the AR(1) model, but it requires K parameters ($\sigma^2, \rho_1, \ldots, \rho_{k-1}$) instead of just two.

The AR(1) and Toeplitz models make sense when observations are equally spaced and the correlation structure does not change appreciably over time. A more general model that preserves the main features of these models, but allows for unequal spacing and change over time, is the first-order ante-dependence model, or ANTE(1). The model structure is the following:

$$
\boldsymbol{\Sigma} =
\begin{bmatrix}
\sigma_1^2 & \sigma_1\sigma_2\rho_1 & \sigma_1\sigma_3\rho_1\rho_2 & \cdots & \sigma_1\sigma_k\rho_1\rho_2\cdots\rho_{k-1} \\
  & \sigma_2^2 & \sigma_2\sigma_3\rho_2 & \cdots & \sigma_2\sigma_k\rho_2\rho_3\cdots\rho_{k-1} \\
  &   & \sigma_3^2 & \cdots & \vdots \\
  &   &   & \ddots & \sigma_{k-1}\sigma_k\rho_{k-1} \\
  &   &   &   & \sigma_k^2
\end{bmatrix}
$$

You can see that the ANTE(1) model assumes that the variance among observations changes over time and that correlation between pairs of observations is the product of the correlations between adjacent times between observations, so that correlation may change over time. The ANTE(1) model requires estimating $2k - 1$ parameters.

Other structures can be modified to accommodate heterogeneous variances over time, including first-order autoregressive model and Toeplitz. The modified forms of these structures are denoted ARH(1) and TOEPH, respectively, in PROC GLIMMIX and in PROC MIXED. See the SAS/STAT documentation for a complete listing of the covariance structures that are available in the GLIMMIX and MIXED procedures.

Still another covariance is derived from combining CS with AR(1). The CS component models the variation *between*-subject means using a RANDOM statement and the AR(1) component models the *within*-subject component using the RANDOM …/…RESIDUAL statement (or REPEATED statement for PROC MIXED), conditional on a particular subject. This structure is produced by Equation 8.3, which includes the random effect for subject (G side) and the AR(1) structure imposed on **R**. Thus, it can be termed AR(1)+RE. It has the following matrix form:

$$\Sigma = \sigma_b^2 \begin{bmatrix} 1 & 1 & 1 & \cdots & 1 \\ & 1 & 1 & \cdots & 1 \\ & & 1 & \cdots & 1 \\ & & & \ddots & \vdots \\ & & & & 1 \end{bmatrix} + \sigma_S^2 \begin{bmatrix} 1 & \rho & \rho^2 & \cdots & \rho^{k-1} \\ & 1 & \rho & \cdots & \rho^{k-2} \\ & & 1 & \cdots & \vdots \\ & & & \ddots & \rho \\ & & & & 1 \end{bmatrix} = \mathbf{G} + \mathbf{R}$$

(8.7)

where σ_b^2 is the between-subjects variance and σ_S^2 is the variance conditional on a subject.

Section 8.3.2 presents methods for selecting an appropriate covariance model—that is, a model that adequately accounts for within-subject correlation but does not require estimating an excessive number of covariance parameters. As with all model selection activities, evaluating covariance structure should not be a purely statistical exercise. You should first rule out covariance structures that clearly make no sense in the context of a given data set. For example, AR(1) or TOEP models are generally inappropriate if the times of observation are not equally spaced either chronologically or in terms of some meaningful criterion such as biological stage of development.

8.3.2 Selection of an Appropriate Model

You need an appropriate covariance model in order to draw accurate conclusions from repeated measures data. If you ignore important correlation by using a model that is too *simple*, you risk increasing the Type I error rate and underestimating standard errors. If the model is too *complex,* you sacrifice power and efficiency. Guerin and Stroup (2000) documented the effects of various covariance modeling decisions using PROC MIXED for repeated measures data. Their results apply equally to PROC GLIMMIX, given that both procedures use identical methodology to model Gaussian data. Their work supports the idea that repeated measures analysis is robust as long as the covariance model used is approximately correct. This is the philosophy underlying this section. Inference is severely compromised by a blatantly poor choice of the covariance model.

We illustrate two types of tools that you can use to help you select a covariance model. First are *graphical tools* to help visualize patterns of correlation between observations at different times. Second are *information criteria* that measure the relative fit of competing covariance models. As noted at the end of the last section, these methods work best when you first rule out covariance structures that are obviously inconsistent with the characteristics of the data you are analyzing.

Program

You can visualize the covariance structure by plotting the sum of squares and cross products on the same subject over lag between times of observation. Estimates of covariance among residuals are easily obtained from the following PROC MIXED statements. Notably, this is one of the few programs that can be run only with PROC MIXED, as it requires the SSCP option (which requests the sums of squares and cross products matrix), which is not available in PROC GLIMMIX.

Program 8.5

```
proc mixed data=fev1uni;
    class drug patient hour;
    model fev1 = drug|hour;
    repeated / type=un subject=patient(drug) sscp;
    ods output covparms = cov;
run;
```

Use the parameters from the sum of squares and cross products to visualize the covariance structure. The ODS statement in Program 8.5 creates a new SAS data set containing the covariances (COV). Use the following SAS statements to create a plot for visualizing a covariance model.

```
data times;
   do time1=1 to 8;
     do time2=1 to time1;
        dist=time1-time2;
        output;
     end;
   end;
run;

data covplot; merge times cov;
drop subject;
run;

proc sgplot data=covplot;
series x=dist y=estimate/group=time2 markers;
yaxis label='Covariance of Between Subj. Effects';
xaxis label='Lag' minor;
keylegend /title='From Time';
run;
```

Results

First, you create a data set (TIMES) containing the pairs of observation times and the lag between them. This data set is then merged with the covariance data set COV. A partial printout of the resulting data set COVPLOT appears in Output 8.10. The SGPLOT procedure creates a plot of the covariance between pairs of repeated measures by lag, shown in Figure 8.3.

Output 8.10: Partial Data Set Containing Lags and Estimated Covariance

time1	time2	dist	CovParm	Estimate
1	1	0	UN(1,1)	0.4541
2	1	1	UN(2,1)	0.4587
2	2	0	UN(2,2)	0.5163
3	1	2	UN(3,1)	0.4441
3	2	1	UN(3,2)	0.4808
3	3	0	UN(3,3)	0.4923
8	1	7	UN(8,1)	0.3840
8	2	6	UN(8,2)	0.4257
8	3	5	UN(8,3)	0.4256
8	4	4	UN(8,4)	0.4251
8	5	3	UN(8,5)	0.4950
8	6	2	UN(8,6)	0.4632
8	7	1	UN(8,7)	0.4496
8	8	0	UN(8,8)	0.5031

The data set COVPLOT contains the time pairs and lags and the covariance information created in the ODS step of PROC MIXED. Notice that because of the way the ODS statement constructs the data set COV, the variable Time2 is actually the observation in the pair that is taken first. In the plot shown in Figure 8.3, notice that there are seven profiles, each corresponding to the time of the first observation in the pair. Since the variable TIME2 is the first observation in the pair, this explains why you use Time2 in the SERIES statement of PROC SGPLOT.

The values plotted at lag=0 in Figure 8.3 are the variances among the observations at each of the eight times. These range from approximately 0.45 to just less than 0.60. This, and the fact that there is no trend of increasing or decreasing variance with time of observation, suggests that a covariance model with constant variance over time is probably adequate. We will more formally discuss model-fitting criteria later in this section.

Figure 8.3: Covariance as a Function of Lag in Time between Pairs of Observations

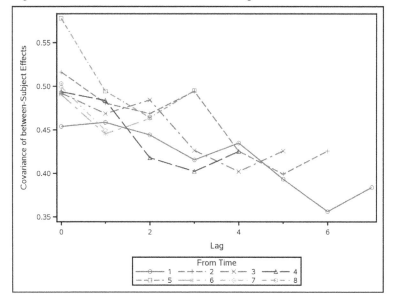

Figure 8.3 shows that for the FEV1 data, as the lag between pairs of observations increases, covariance tends to decrease. Also, the pattern of decreasing covariance with lag is approximately the same for all reference times. Start with the profile labeled "From Time 1," which gives the HOUR of the first observation of a given pair of repeated measures. The circle symbol on the plot tracks the covariance between pairs of repeated measurements whose first observation occurs at hour 1. The position of the point at lag 0 plots the sample variance of observations taken at hour 1. The plot at lag 1 gives the covariance between hours 1 and 2, lag 2 plots covariance for hours 1 and 3, and so on. Following the profile across the lags shows how the covariance decreases as lag increases for pairs of observations whose first time of observation is hour 1. There is a general pattern of decrease from approximately 0.50 at lag 1 to a little less than 0.40 at lags 4 and above. If you follow the plots labeled "From Time" 2, 3, etc., the overall pattern is similar. The covariance among adjacent observations is consistently between 0.45 and 0.50, with the HOUR of the first element of the pair making little difference. The covariance at lag 2 is a bit lower, averaging around 0.45, and does not appear to depend on the hour of the first element of the pair.

You can draw two important conclusions from Figure 8.3:

- An appropriate model must allow covariances to decrease with increasing lag, which rules out compound symmetry. Also, an equal variance assumption (across time) is reasonable. In addition, it appears that covariance is strictly a function of lag and does not depend on the time of the first observation in the pair. Therefore, unstructured, ante-dependence, or heterogeneous variance models are probably more general than necessary; there is no visual evidence of changes in variance or covariance-lag relationships over time.

- The between-subject variance component, σ_b^2, is nonzero. In fact, it is approximately between 0.35 and 0.40. Note that all of the plots of covariance decline for lags 1, 2, and 3, and then seem to flatten out. This is what should happen if the between-subjects variance component is approximately equal to the plotted covariance at the larger lags and there is AR(1) correlation among the observations within each subject. At the larger lags the AR(1) correlation, ρ^{lag}, should approach zero. The nonzero covariance plotted for larger lag results from the intra-class correlation $\rho = \sigma_b^2 / (\sigma_S^2 + \sigma_b^2)$.

Programs

You have seen results of using the UN and CS covariance structures in Sections 8.2.1 and 8.2.2. We now fit three other covariance structures to the FEV1 data: AR(1), AR(1)+RE, and TOEP. For completeness, we show SAS statements for fitting all five covariance structures. The CS structure is in Program 8.4 and the UN structure is in Program 8.5. The other three structures are implemented using Programs 8.6, 8.7, and 8.8.

Program 8.6: AR(1) Model

```
proc glimmix data=fev1uni;
   class drug patient hour;
   model fev1 = drug hour drug*hour;
   random hour / sub=patient(drug) type=ar(1) residual;
run;
```

Program 8.7: AR(1) with Additional between-Subjects [patient(drug)] effect

```
proc glimmix data=fev1uni;
   class drug patient hour;
   model fev1 = drug hour drug*hour;
   random intercept/ subject=patient(drug);
   random hour / sub=patient(drug) type=ar(1) residual;
run;
```

Program 8.8: Toeplitz Model

```
proc glimmix data=fev1uni;
   class drug patient hour;
   model fev1 = drug hour drug*hour;
   random hour / sub=patient(drug) type=toep residual;
run;
```

Results

The covariance parameter estimates for these three covariance structures are displayed in Outputs 8.11–8.13.

Output 8.11: Covariance Parameter Estimates for AR(1) Structure

Covariance Parameter Estimates			
Cov Parm	Subject	Estimate	Standard Error
AR(1)	patient(drug)	0.9219	0.01125
Residual		0.4889	0.06604

The estimates of parameters in Equation 8.5 (AR(1) structure from Output 8.11) are $\hat{\sigma}^2 = 0.4889$ and $\hat{\rho} = 0.9210$. Thus, the estimated AR(1) covariance function is $(0.4889).9219^{lag}$. The variance estimate of 0.4889 (=covariance at lag=0) seems appropriate for the plot in Figure 8.3. But for greater lags, such as lag = 7, the covariance is $(0.4889)(0.9219)^7 = 0.277$, which is too small according to the plot in Figure 8.3.

Output 8.12: Covariance Parameter Estimates for AR(1) + RE Structure

Covariance Parameter Estimates			
Cov Parm	Subject	Estimate	Standard Error
patient(drug)		0.4145	0.07551
AR(1)	patient(drug)	0.5420	0.05668
Residual		0.08337	0.01011

The estimates of parameters in Equation 8.7 (AR(1)+RE structure from Output 8.12) are $\hat{\sigma}_b^2 = 0.4145$, $\hat{\sigma}_S^2 = 0.08337$, and $\hat{\rho} = 0.542$. The estimated AR(1) covariance function is $0.4145 + (0.0833)0.542^{lag}$. Inserting lag = 0, you get a variance estimate of $0.4145 + 0.0833 = 0.4978$. Inserting higher values of the lag, you get covariance estimates that are consistent with Figure 8.3.

Output 8.13: Covariance Parameter Estimates for Toeplitz Structure

Covariance Parameter Estimates			
Cov Parm	**Subject**	**Estimate**	**Standard Error**
TOEP(2)	patient(drug)	0.4548	0.07370
TOEP(3)	patient(drug)	0.4424	0.07364
TOEP(4)	patient(drug)	0.4330	0.07359
TOEP(5)	patient(drug)	0.4167	0.07362
TOEP(6)	patient(drug)	0.4087	0.07382
TOEP(7)	patient(drug)	0.3941	0.07425
TOEP(8)	patient(drug)	0.3797	0.07577
Residual		0.4927	0.07375

In the notation of Equation 8.6, the estimates of variance and covariance parameters (Toeplitz structure from Output 8.13) are $\hat{\sigma}_0^2 = 0.4548$, $\hat{\sigma}_{1,2} = 0.4424$, $\hat{\sigma}_{1,3} = 0.4330$, ... , $\hat{\sigma}_{1,8} = 0.3797$. The correlation estimates are, for example, $\hat{\rho}_1 = 0.4548 / 0.4927 = 0.9231$. The TOEP($d + 1$) parameters estimate covariance up to lag d with the covariances set to 0 for points greater than lag d. For example, TOEP(2) estimates correlation between repeated measures $d = 1$ unit apart in time and sets the correlations to zero for repeated measures more than 1 unit apart in time.

Figure 8.4 shows covariances plotted versus lag for five models; AR(1), AR(1)+RE, CS, TOEP, and UN. Except for UN, these covariance relationships can be expressed as a function of lag, meaning that there is only one covariance value for a given lag. Points on the graphs for the functional covariance structures are joined as curves (line segments in the case of TOEP). The unconnected points represent the covariance values from the UN model.

Figure 8.4: Covariance versus Lag for Five Covariance Models

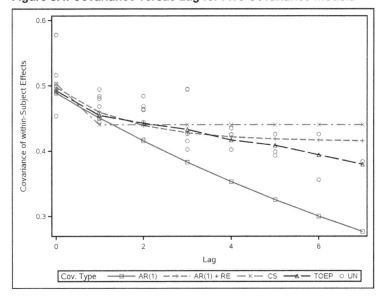

The compound symmetry covariance is represented by the point (0, 0.503) followed by the flat line across all lags with covariance 0.440. The plot with a covariance decreasing from approximately 0.50 to 0.27 as lag increases is what one would expect to see with AR(1) covariance. The plot that decreases from approximately 0.50 to 0.42 is the expected plot from the AR(1) + RE model. You can see that the plots of observed covariance functions in Figure 8.4 correspond most closely to the AR(1) + RE and TOEP models.

Information Criteria for Comparing Covariance Structures

Output from PROC GLIMMIX and PROC MIXED includes values under the heading "Fit Statistics." These include –2 times the Residual (or REML) Log Likelihood (labeled "–2 Res Log Likelihood"), and three *information criteria*. In theory, the greater the residual log likelihood, the better the fit of the model. However, somewhat analogously to R^2 in multiple regression, you can always improve the log likelihood by adding parameters to the point of absurdity.

Information criteria printed by PROC GLIMMIX attach penalties to the log likelihood for adding parameters to the model. The penalty is a function of the number of parameters. Each of the information criteria equals −2 Res Log Likelihood *plus* −2 times a function involving the number of covariance model parameters. For example, the penalty for the compound symmetry model is a function of 2, because there are two covariance parameters, σ^2 and ρ. The penalty for an unstructured model is a function of $k(k + 1)/2$ (there are k variances and $k(k − 1)/2$ covariances). Hence, the residual log likelihood for an unstructured model is *always* greater than the residual log likelihood for compound symmetry, but the penalty is always greater as well. Unless the improvement in the residual log likelihood exceeds the size of the penalty, the simpler model yields the lower information criterion and is thus the preferred covariance model.

Two commonly used information criteria are those of Akaike (1974) and Schwarz (1978). A more recent information criterion is a finite-population corrected Akaike criterion developed by Burnham and Anderson (1998). The Akaike information criterion is often referred to by the abbreviation AIC. The finite-population corrected AIC has the abbreviation AICC. Schwarz's Bayesian information criterion is usually referenced as BIC or SBC. Hence, we use BIC, in concert with PROC GLIMMIX output. Refer to SAS Help and Documentation for a complete explanation of how these terms are computed.

The basic idea for repeated measures analysis is that among the models within-subject covariance that are considered plausible in the context of a particular study (for example, biologically or physically reasonable) the model that *minimizes* AIC, AICC, or BIC is preferred. When AIC, AICC, or BIC is close, the simpler model is generally considered preferable in the interest of using a parsimonious model.

Keselman et al. (1998) compared AIC and BIC for their ability to select the "right" covariance model. Their study used SAS 6.12, which used a formula to compute BIC that was updated in SAS 8.0. Guerin and Stroup (2000) compared the information criteria, using SAS 8.0, for their ability to select the "right" model *and* for the impact of choosing "the wrong" model based on the Type I error rate.

They found that AIC tends to choose more complex models than BIC. They found that choosing a model that is too simple affects Type I error control more adversely that choosing a model that is too complex. When Type I error control is the highest priority, AIC is the model-fitting criterion of choice. However, if loss of power is relatively more serious, BIC may be preferable. AICC was not available at the time of the Guerin and Stroup study; a reasonable inference from their study is that its performance is similar to AIC, but somewhat less likely to choose a more complex model. Thus, loss of power is less than with AIC, but still greater than with BIC. Refer to Burnham and Anderson (1998) for further discussion on the distinctions between AIC and BIC. They also provide more conceptual formulations about whether to consider an infinite set of models or a finite set, somewhat analogously to the distinctions that we make in this book between fixed and random effects and narrow and broad inference spaces.

You can compare candidate covariance models by running PROC MIXED with the same fixed effects model, varying the RANDOM and REPEATED statements to obtain the AIC, AICC, and BIC for all candidate models. For the FEV1 data, the Toeplitz and AR(1)+RE models appear to warrant consideration based on the covariance plots.

Results for Fit Statistics

Fit statistics for these models are produced from Programs 8.7 and 8.8, and the results appear in Outputs 8.14 and 8.15.

Output 8.14: Fit Statistics for AR(1)+RE Model with FEV1 Data

Fit Statistics	
-2 Res Log Likelihood	296.05
AIC (smaller is better)	302.05
AICC (smaller is better)	302.09
BIC (smaller is better)	308.88
CAIC (smaller is better)	311.88
HQIC (smaller is better)	304.77
Generalized Chi-Square	46.02
Gener. Chi-Square / DF	0.08

The value of −2 Residual Log Likelihood is 296.05, and the AR(1)+RE model has three parameters, so the AIC is equal to $296 + 2(3) = 302.05$. The AICC has a small correction for estimating parameters, yielding a value of 302.09. The BIC value is 308.88, larger that AIC, but not greatly so, because of the relatively small number of parameters.

Output 8.15: Fit Statistics for Toeplitz Model with FEV1 Data

Fit Statistics	
-2 Res Log Likelihood	276.99
AIC (smaller is better)	292.99
AICC (smaller is better)	293.25
BIC (smaller is better)	311.20
CAIC (smaller is better)	319.20
HQIC (smaller is better)	300.24
Generalized Chi-Square	271.99
Gener. Chi-Square / DF	0.49

The value of -2 Res Log Likelihood for TOEP is 276.99, which is less than the value of -2 Res Log Likelihood for AR(1) + RE (296.05) because TOEP is a more general structure than AR(1)+RE. The TOEP model has eight parameters, so the AIC is equal to $276.99 + 2(8) = 292.99$. The AICC is slightly larger at 293.25. The BIC value is 311.2, which is larger than AIC, but again not greatly so because there are still only a modest number of parameters.

The AIC and AICC for the Toeplitz model are slightly better than the AIC and AICC for AR(1)+RE. But the BIC is slightly worse for TOEP than for AR(1) + RE. You could use either model, but the AR(1) + RE would generally be considered preferable because it is a simpler model.

For completeness you can also fit the compound symmetry and unstructured models.

> **Note**: Importantly, about compound symmetry, Toeplitz, and unstructured models, in the AR(1) + RE model above, you use both a RANDOM statement for the between-subjects effect, PATIENT(DRUG), and a RANDOM .../...RESIDUAL (REPEATED in PROC MIXED) statement for the AR(1) covariance among repeated measures within subjects. The AR(1) component accommodates covariance over and above that induced by between-subjects variation. These two sources of variation are distinct and clearly identifiable AR(1) models. However, this is not true for compound symmetry, Toeplitz, and unstructured covariance.

Program Statements Inappropriate for the Compound Symmetry Model

In Section 8.3.1 you saw that compound symmetry and the model with random between-subjects effect and independent errors are equivalent. Thus, the between-subjects variance component, σ_b^2, and compound symmetry covariance are not identifiable. This situation also holds, in more complex form, for Toeplitz and unstructured covariance. Therefore, you should *not* use a RANDOM statement for the effect used as SUBJECT= effect in the REPEATED statement for these covariance structures. For example, the SAS statements in Program 8.9 are inappropriate for the compound symmetry model.

Program 8.9

```
proc glimmix data=fev1uni;
   class drug hour patient;
   model fev1 = drug|hour basefev1;
   random intercept / subject=patient(drug);
   random hour / type=cs subject=patient(drug) residual;
run;
```

The two RANDOM statements are redundant. Each is a stand-alone specification of the same covariance structure. Included together in the program, they create an identifiability issue that must be resolved. If you want to specify the compound symmetry (CS) covariance structure, you must delete the RANDOM INTERCEPT / SUBJECT=PATIENT(DRUG) statement. For Program 8.9 as written, PROC GLIMMIX (or its PROC MIXED equivalent) may or may not converge. If it does converge, either the patient(drug) or the compound symmetry parameter will be set to zero.

Usually, you should attempt to use separate RANDOM and RANDOM...RESIDUAL statements (or RANDOM and REPEATED statements if you are using PROC MIXED) for structures such as AR(1), particularly when covariance-by-lag plots as in Figure 8.3 show evidence of nonzero between-subjects variation. Guerin and Stroup (2000) showed that failure to model a separate between-subjects random effect can adversely affect inference on time and treatment × time effects.

Results

The AIC, AICC, and BIC results are given in the following table. Also computed are values for the AR(1) model without the RANDOM PATIENT(DRUG) statement.

Table 8.33: Information Criteria for Different Covariance Models

Model	AIC	AICC	BIC
Compound symmetry	400.55	400.57	405.10
AR(1) with random patient(drug)	302.05	302.09	308.88
AR(1) without random patient(drug)	335.61	335.63	340.16
Toeplitz	292.99	293.25	311.20
Unstructured	269.46	274.64	351.42

You can see that the unstructured model actually has the best AIC and AICC. However, it is a distinctly poor choice according to the BIC. This illustrates the tendency of AIC, and to a lesser extent of AICC, to "choose" more complex models. In this case, given the covariance plots, choosing the unstructured model on the basis of the AIC is probably "modeling overkill," unless there is some compelling medical or biological process that supports the unstructured model. The covariance with AR(1) and no random patient(drug) is not a correct model. The covariance model with the AR(1) and the RANDOM statement has the smallest BIC and is likely an appropriate choice to represent the correlation structure in the data.

8.3.3 Reassessment with a Means Model Accounting for Baseline Measurement

In studies with repeated measures, it is common to have a pre-treatment measure, called a *baseline*. This permits the use of each subject as its "own control" to assess the effect of treatment over time. Such a measure is included in the FEV1 data set, with the variable name BASEFEV1. Baseline variables are usually used as *covariates* (Milliken and Johnson 2002). You can refit the means model to include BASEFEV1 as a covariate, output the resulting covariance and correlation matrices, and plot them using the same approach used for Figure 8.3.

Program

The revised PROC MIXED statements for the baseline covariate model are in Program 8.10.

Program 8.10

```
proc mixed data=fev1uni;
   class drug hour patient;
   model fev1 = drug|hour basefev1;
   repeated / type=un sscp subject=patient(drug) rcorr;
   ods output covparms = cov;
run;
```

Using the output data sets of the covariances (COV) with the code in Program 8.5, the plots of the covariances can be obtained as in Figure 8.5.

Figure 8.5: Covariance as a Function of Lag in Time between Pairs of Observations

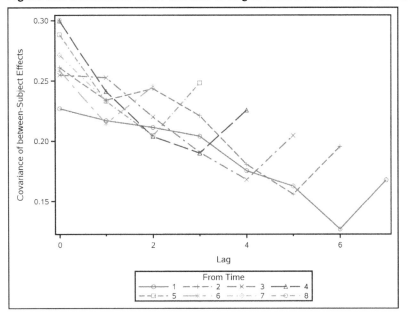

The pattern of Figure 8.5 is similar to that of Figure 8.3 except that using BASEFEV1 as a covariate substantially reduces the variance from approximately 0.50 (see Figure 8.3) to less than 0.30 as shown in Figure 8.5. With increasing lag the covariance appears to reach an asymptote between 0.15 and 0.20. Again, this suggests a between-subjects variance between 0.15 and 0.20, and an additional within-subject covariance model with covariance a decreasing function of lag but independent of time.

Note also that because the fixed effects have changed, AIC and BIC values are not directly comparable to those from previous sections because we are using REML. This also raises an important consideration, which is that changes in the mean model directly impact the covariance structure. In one sense, all effects account for variability in the responses and compete to explain it. A repeated measures covariance structure effectively models variability in the residuals of the response after subtracting out the mean model specified by the fixed effects. So it is critical to carefully consider the entire model that you have specified and make sure that it parsimoniously accounts for all known sources of variation in the experiment in a way that aligns with the experimental design and experimental unit structure.

8.4 PROC GLIMMIX Analysis of FEV1 Data

Once you have selected the covariance model, you can proceed with the analysis of baseline covariate and the treatment effects just as you would in any other analysis of variance or, in this case, analysis of covariance.

Program

Start the analysis with the following PROC GLIMMIX statements where covariance structure of the repeated measures is AR(1).

Program 8.11

```
proc glimmix data=fev1uni;
  class drug patient hour;
  model fev1=basefev1 drug|hour/ddfm=kr2;
  random intercept / subject=patient(drug);
  random hour / subject=patient(drug) type=ar(1) residual;
  lsmeans drug*hour / slice=drug slicediff=hour plot=meanplot(sliceby=drug join);
  covtest 'between subject variance = 0?' zeroG;
run;
```

Results

Note the use of the DDFM=KR2 option to obtain bias corrected inferential statistics and Satterthwaite approximate degrees of freedom. You should always use the Kenward-Roger option when analyzing repeated measures data. The

SLICE, SLICEDIFF, and MEANPLOT options enable you to characterize, at least in a preliminary way, the interaction between DRUG and HOUR. The results are discussed below.

The COVTEST statement with the ZEROG option enables you to test $H_0 : \sigma_b^2 = 0$ —in essence, that the between-subject variance is equal to zero. By default, for this particular data set, the COVTEST produces the results in Output 8.16.

Output 8.16: Difficulty with the COVTEST Statement with ZEROG Option

Tests of Covariance Parameters Based on the Restricted Likelihood					
Label	DF	-2 Res Log Like	ChiSq	Pr > ChiSq	Note
between subject variance = 0?	1	.	.	.	

Along with this listing, the following statement appears in the SASLOG:

```
WARNING: Optimization failed during setup because the function value cannot be improved.
```

For most data sets, this will not happen. If it does, try adding the following statement:

```
nloptions technique=nrridg;
```

The NLOPTIONS changes the algorithm that PROC GLIMMIX uses on default (quasi-Newton) to the Newton-Raphson with ridging the algorithm used by PROC MIXED. Most of the time, the two algorithms produce identical results, but occasionally, one works when the other does not. In this case, changing to NRRIDG gives the result in Output 8.17.

Output 8.17: Testing the Between-Subject Variance Equal to Zero with COVTEST

Tests of Covariance Parameters Based on the Restricted Likelihood					
Label	DF	-2 Res Log Like	ChiSq	Pr > ChiSq	Note
between subject variance = 0?	1	275.04	28.00	<.0001	MI

You can verify that this is the appropriate result by noting from the fit statistics in Section 8.3 that the -2 RES LOG LIKE for the model with the between-subject variance included is 247.03. Hence, aside from rounding error, the -2 log likelihood ratio χ^2 is 28.0. Reject the null hypothesis ($p < 0.0001$) and retain the between-subject effect in the model for the rest of the analysis.

Note the COVTEST result for variance components is not a classical chi-square test because the null hypothesis is on the boundary of the parameter space. PROC GLIMMIX automatically detects this situation and adjusts the p-value accordingly.

Proceeding with the analysis, Output 8.18, 8.19, and Figure 8.6 show selected results produced by the PROC GLIMMIX statements given in Program 8.11. The Type 3 tests for the fixed effects are given in Output 8.18.

Output 8.18: Type 3 Tests of Fixed Effects from Analysis of Covariance for FEV1 Data

Type III Tests of Fixed Effects				
Effect	Num DF	Den DF	F Value	Pr > F
basefev1	1	68	75.91	<.0001
drug	2	68.84	7.28	0.0014
hour	7	394.7	17.12	<.0001
drug*hour	14	424.3	3.94	<.0001

You can see that the two main results are as follows:

- There is very strong evidence of a relationship between the baseline covariate BASEFEV1 and the subsequent responses FEV1. The *p*-value is <0.0001.

- There is strong evidence of a DRUG × HOUR interaction ($p < 0.0001$). That is, changes in the response variable FEV1 over time are not the same for all DRUG treatments.

As with any factorial structure, inference on the DRUG and HOUR main effects should not proceed until the DRUG × HOUR interaction is understood. Begin by visualizing the mean responses, adjusted for the baseline effect. Figure 8.6 shows the interaction plot produced by the MEANPLOT option.

Figure 8.6: Interaction Plot of Adjusted Means for Each Drug over Hour

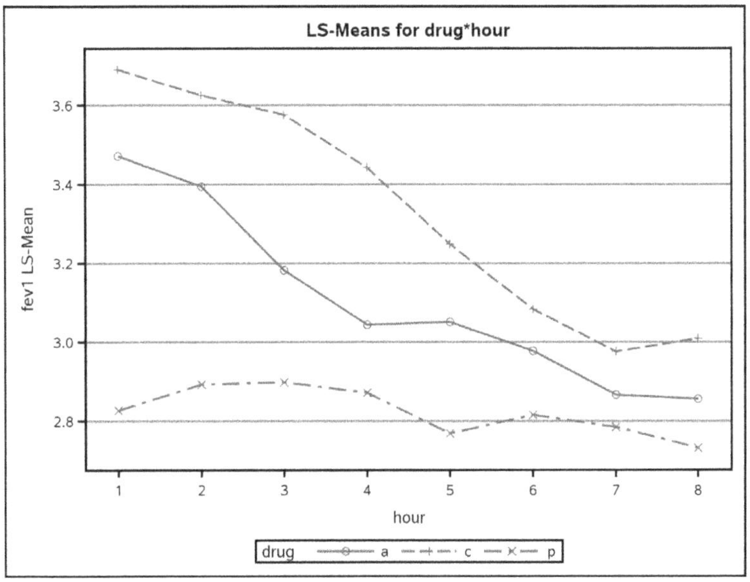

You can see that after adjustment for the baseline covariate, the mean responses for the two drugs, A and C, are much greater than those for the placebo, P, for the first hours of measurement. This suggests that the two drugs do improve respiratory performance relative to the placebo initially after the patient uses them. Also, for the two drugs the means of the responses gradually decrease over time, whereas for the placebo, P, changes little over time. The change appears to be approximately linear over time with a negative slope. This suggests fitting a linear regression over HOUR, possibly with a quadratic term to account for decreasing slope as HOUR increases, and testing its interaction with HOUR. Alternatively, depending on the objectives, you might want to test DRUG differences at specific hours during the experiment. Inference along these lines continues in the next section. First, however, Output 8.19 shows results from the SLICE and SLICEDIFF options. These provide a preliminary characterization of the DRUG and HOUR simple effect prior to doing more targeted CONTRAST or regression analysis.

Output 8.19: Simple Effect Statistics for FEV1 Repeated Measures Analysis of Covariance

	Tests of Effect Slices for drug*hour Sliced By drug			
drug	Num DF	Den DF	F Value	Pr > F
a	7	394.7	10.10	<.0001
c	7	394.7	13.79	<.0001
p	7	394.7	1.10	0.3621

Simple Effect Comparisons of drug*hour Least Squares Means By hour							
Simple Effect Level	drug	_drug	Estimate	Standard Error	DF	t Value	Pr > |t|
hour 1	a	c	-0.2182	0.1494	107.3	-1.46	0.1471
hour 1	a	p	0.6447	0.1495	107.3	4.31	<.0001
hour 1	c	p	0.8629	0.1494	107.3	5.78	<.0001
hour 2	a	c	-0.2303	0.1494	107.3	-1.54	0.1262
hour 2	a	p	0.5022	0.1495	107.3	3.36	0.0011
hour 2	c	p	0.7325	0.1494	107.3	4.90	<.0001
hour 3	a	c	-0.3941	0.1494	107.3	-2.64	0.0096
hour 3	a	p	0.2838	0.1495	107.3	1.90	0.0602
hour 3	c	p	0.6779	0.1494	107.3	4.54	<.0001
hour 4	a	c	-0.3978	0.1494	107.3	-2.66	0.0090
hour 4	a	p	0.1730	0.1495	107.3	1.16	0.2496
hour 4	c	p	0.5708	0.1494	107.3	3.82	0.0002
hour 5	a	c	-0.1966	0.1494	107.3	-1.32	0.1912
hour 5	a	p	0.2830	0.1495	107.3	1.89	0.0610
hour 5	c	p	0.4796	0.1494	107.3	3.21	0.0018
hour 6	a	c	-0.1066	0.1494	107.3	-0.71	0.4773
hour 6	a	p	0.1617	0.1495	107.3	1.08	0.2816
hour 6	c	p	0.2683	0.1494	107.3	1.80	0.0753
hour 7	a	c	-0.1091	0.1494	107.3	-0.73	0.4670
hour 7	a	p	0.08175	0.1495	107.3	0.55	0.5855
hour 7	c	p	0.1908	0.1494	107.3	1.28	0.2043
hour 8	a	c	-0.1528	0.1494	107.3	-1.02	0.3087
hour 8	a	p	0.1238	0.1495	107.3	0.83	0.4092
hour 8	c	p	0.2767	0.1494	107.3	1.85	0.0668

The SLICE table provides a test of the overall HOUR simple effect by DRUG. For drugs A and C, the p-values are <0.0001, providing formal confirmation of the decrease over hour for the two test drugs seen in the interaction plot. Drug P, on the other hand, has a p-value >0.36, which is formal confirmation of the lack of change over hours seen in the interaction plot.

The SLICEDIFF table gives you detailed information about the differences among drugs at each hour. The main results are as follows:

- The adjusted mean FEV1 for Drugs A and C differ significantly ($p \leq 0.05$) only at HOUR 3 and HOUR 4, when the respiratory performance of drug A drops more rapidly than drug C.

- Drug C shows significantly ($p < 0.001$) better respiratory performance than drug P through hour 5. At hour 6 the mean performance of drug C is still 0.27 ($\pm$ 0.15) units better than drug P, and the p-value is still marginally significant ($p = 0.075$). At hours 7 and 8 drug C fails to show evidence of better performance.

- Drug A shows significantly better mean performance ($p < 0.001$) than drug P at hours 1 and 2, and marginally better mean performance ($p < 0.07$) at hours 3 and 5. At hours 4, 6, 7 and 8, mean difference between drug A and P is less than 0.2 ($\pm$ 0.15) units with p-values > 0.2.

Outputs 8.18 and 8.19 provide preliminary statistics. Sections 8.4.1 and 8.4.2 provide more targeted analyses. These are meant to be examples, not an exhaustive review of analyses one should do, nor are they necessarily prescriptive. These examples may or may not fit your objectives or address the questions your data are intended to answer. These examples merely illustrate possible approaches and are mainly intended to illustrate the use of various post-processing options that are available with SAS mixed model software when you are analyzing repeated measures data.

8.4.1 FEV1 Analysis Focusing on Difference between Hour 1 and Hour 8

In addition to the interaction plot and the SLICE and SLICEDIFF simple effect results, you may need to do more targeted inference to address objectives of particular interest. One possibility, illustrated here, involves estimating the change from hour 1 to hour 8 for each drug, and comparing those changes. You can do this using the ESTIMATE, LSMESTIMATE, and CONTRAST statements. The purpose of this section in partly to review the inferential statistics associated with this objective, but mainly to illustrate the ESTIMATE, LSMESTIMATE, and CONTRAST statements in the repeated measures context.

For the ith drug, the difference between the FEV1 mean at hour 1 and hour 8 can be written in terms of the mean model as $\mu_{i1} - \mu_{i8}$, and in terms of the effects model as $\gamma_1 - \gamma_8 + \alpha\gamma_{i1} - \alpha\gamma_{i8}$.

These translate to the following ESTIMATE and LSMESTIMATE statements:

```
estimate 'hour 1 vs hour 8, drug P' hour 1 0 0 0 0 0 0 -1
   drug*hour 0 0 0 0 0 0 0 0  0 0 0 0 0 0 0 0  1 0 0 0 0 0 0 -1,
  'hour 1 vs hour 8, drug A' hour 1 0 0 0 0 0 0 -1
   drug*hour 1 0 0 0 0 0 0 -1  0 0 0 0 0 0 0 0  0 0 0 0 0 0 0 0,
  'hour 1 vs hour 8, drug C' hour 1 0 0 0 0 0 0 -1
   drug*hour 0 0 0 0 0 0 0 0  1 0 0 0 0 0 0 -1  0 0 0 0 0 0 0 0 / e cl;
 lsmestimate drug*hour
  'hour 1 vs hour 8, drug P' 0 0 0 0 0 0 0 0  0 0 0 0 0 0 0 0  1 0 0 0 0 0 0 -1,
  'hour 1 vs hour 8, drug A' 1 0 0 0 0 0 0 -1  0 0 0 0 0 0 0 0  0 0 0 0 0 0 0 0,
  'hour 1 vs hour 8, drug C' 0 0 0 0 0 0 0 0  1 0 0 0 0 0 0 -1  0 0 0 0 0 0 0 0 / e cl;
```

The ESTIMATE statements must be written in terms of the effects model, whereas the LSMESTIMATE statement is based on the means model. In the authors' experience, one of the most frequent problems that novice users have with the ESTIMATE statement occurs when they write the coefficients using the means model and neglect to include the coefficients for the HOUR effect. The LSMESTIMATE statement is more forgiving in this regard. Also, both the ESTIMATE and LSMESTIMATE statements enable you to define multiple comparisons in a single statement. For both statements, use the CL option to obtain confidence intervals for the estimated differences. The "e" option requests the estimable functions of the model's fixed effects parameters or of the least squares means. Output 8.20 shows the listing for these two statements.

Output 8.20: Hour 1 versus Hour 8 Difference, by Drug from ESTIMATE and LSMESTIMATE

			Estimates					
Label	Estimate	Standard Error	DF	t Value	Pr > |t|	Alpha	Lower	Upper
hour 1 vs hour 8, drug P	0.09458	0.08258	157.3	1.15	0.2538	0.05	-0.06853	0.2577
hour 1 vs hour 8, drug A	0.6154	0.08258	157.3	7.45	<.0001	0.05	0.4523	0.7785
hour 1 vs hour 8, drug C	0.6808	0.08258	157.3	8.24	<.0001	0.05	0.5177	0.8440

				Least Squares Means Estimates					
Effect	Label	Estimate	Standard Error	DF	t Value	Pr > |t|	Alpha	Lower	Upper
drug*hour	hour 1 vs hour 8, drug P	0.09458	0.08258	157.3	1.15	0.2538	0.05	-0.06853	0.2577
drug*hour	hour 1 vs hour 8, drug A	0.6154	0.08258	157.3	7.45	<.0001	0.05	0.4523	0.7785
drug*hour	hour 1 vs hour 8, drug C	0.6808	0.08258	157.3	8.24	<.0001	0.05	0.5177	0.8440

There are two important things to notice:

- The ESTIMATE and LSMESTIMATE statement results are identical.

- For drugs A and C, the beginning to end—hour 1 vs. hour 8—mean differences are 0.615 and 0.681, respectively, with 95% confidence intervals (0.45,0.78) and (0.52,0.84) respectively, whereas for drug P, the estimated change is 0.09548 with a confidence interval that includes zero.

The latter result is consistent with the interaction plot in Figure 8.6. The mean respiratory performance for drugs A and C is relatively high at hour 1 and decreases over time, whereas the respiratory performance of drug P is relatively low at hour 1 and does not change appreciably over time.

It may be of interest to compare these differences in addition to estimating them. For example, you may want to compare the beginning-to-end change for drugs A and C, and, if they are similar, compare their average to drug P's beginning-to-end change. These translate into the following contrasts:

- $\mu_{A1} - \mu_{A8} - \mu_{C1} + \mu_{C8} = \alpha\gamma_{A1} - \alpha\gamma_{A8} - \alpha\gamma_{C1} + \alpha\gamma_{C8}$.

- $\frac{1}{2}(\mu_{A1} - \mu_{A8} - \mu_{C1} + \mu_{C8}) - (\mu_{P1} - \mu_{P8}) = \frac{1}{2}(\alpha\gamma_{A1} - \alpha\gamma_{A8} - \alpha\gamma_{C1} + \alpha\gamma_{C8}) - (\alpha\gamma_{P1} - \alpha\gamma_{P8})$.

Use the following CONTRAST statements to implement these comparisons:

```
contrast 'hour 1 vs 8 x drug A vs C'
    drug*hour 1 0 0 0 0 0 0 -1  -1 0 0 0 0 0 0 1  0 0 0 0 0 0 0 0;
contrast 'hour 1 vs 8 x drug P vs A&C'
    drug*hour 1 0 0 0 0 0 0 -1  1 0 0 0 0 0 0 -1  -2 0 0 0 0 0 0 2;
```

Because contrasts depend only on the ratio of their coefficients and not on the literal values of the coefficients, you can use integer coefficients 1 and 2, rather than 0.5 and 1 in the second CONTRAST statement. Output 8.21 shows the results.

Output 8.21: CONTRAST Results to Compare Hour 1 to Hour 8 Changes

	Contrasts			
Label	Num DF	Den DF	F Value	Pr > F
hour 1 vs 8 x drug A vs C	1	159.6	0.31	0.5756
hour 1 vs 8 x drug P vs A&C	1	159.6	30.04	<.0001

Consistent with the interaction plots and the estimates in Output 8.20, the difference in beginning-to-end change between drugs A and C is negligible, whereas the difference between their average change and the hour 1 vs. hour 8 change for drug P is statistically significant ($p < 0.0001$).

8.4.2 Use of Regression to Model FEV1 Change over Time

From the plot in Figure 8.6, there appears to be a linear regression of FEV1 on HOUR with a negative slope. The slope for drug P appears to be obviously different from drugs A and C, whereas if the slopes from drugs A and C are different, the difference is subtler. The slopes appear to be less negative as HOUR increases, indicating a possible quadratic trend. You can test these impressions. One approach is to write orthogonal polynomial contrasts for linear, quadratic, etc. effects and, more importantly, their interactions with treatment contrasts of interest. You can do this far less tediously using analysis of covariance methods.

Program

Create a new data set with a new variable H where H is equal to HOUR as follows:

```
data fev1regr;
   set fev1uni;
   h=hour;
run;
```

Use the PROC GLIMMIX statements in Program 8.12 to do a preliminary assessment of the proposed model where HOUR is a class variable and H is a continuous variable

Program 8.12

```
proc glimmix data=fev1regr;
 class drug patient hour;
 model fev1=basefev1 drug|h|h drug|hour/htype=1;
 random intercept / subject=patient(drug);
 random hour / subject=patient(drug) type=ar(1) residual;
run;
```

Results

You can see that this program is similar to analysis of covariance for qualitative × quantitative factorial treatment structures presented in Chapter 3. Here, there is an additional covariate, BASEFEV1. The DRUG|H|H causes PROC

GLIMMIX to compute statistics for the main effects of DRUG, linear HOUR (H), quadratic HOUR (H*H) and interactions of linear and quadratic HOUR with DRUG. These interactions test whether the linear and quadratic aspects of the regression on HOUR are parallel among drugs. The DRUG|HOUR term in conjunction with the HTYPE=1 option computes the leftover effects of HOUR after accounting for linear and quadratic regression, and DRUG*HOUR, the interaction between the leftover HOUR and DRUG*HOUR effects. Taken together, HOUR and DRUG*HOUR can be interpreted as lack-of-fit from quadratic regression.

When you attempt to run this program, you get the following in the SAS Log:

```
WARNING: The initial estimates did not yield a valid objective function.
```

Although you can use PROC GLIMMIX and PROC MIXED interchangeably for most mixed model analysis with Gaussian data, this is one case in which PROC MIXED is preferred. If you implement the above program, substituting the following statement:

```
repeated hour / subject=patient(drug) type=ar(1);
```

for the RANDOM...RESIDUAL statement in the PROC GLIMMIX program, you get the following in the SAS Log:

```
WARNING: Stopped because of infinite likelihood.
```

Program

You can get around this problem by including NOPROFILE with the PARMS statement in the PROC MIXED statements of Program 8.13.

Program 8.13

```
proc mixed data=fev1_u noprofile;
 class drug patient hour;
 model fev1=basefev1 drug|h|h hour drug*hour/  htype=1;
 random intercept / subject=patient(drug);
 repeated hour / subject=patient(drug) type=ar(1);
 parms (0.4145)(0.08337)(0.5420)/ hold=1,2,3;
run;
```

Results

The main idea here is that when the lack of fit terms HOUR and DRUG*HOUR are used in conjunction with direct regression parameters, both PROC GLIMMIX and PROC MIXED often struggle. The fix is to use the variance components estimated from CLASS effects-only model. That is, use the statements used to produce Outputs 8.18 through 8.20, and use the NOPROFILE option in the PROC statement and the HOLD option in the PARMS statement to prevent re-estimation of the variance components. This is similar to the "trick" used to Chapter 4 to do power and precision analysis. Often, this "trick" will work with PROC GLIMMIX, but it works more reliably with PROC MIXED. Finally, notice that the NOPROFILE option reverses the order of the AR(1) variance and correlation terms, so pay attention to this when you implement similar programs.

Output 8.22 shows the results.

Output 8.22: Type I (Sequential) Tests: Preliminary Assessment of Regression on Hour

Type 1 Tests of Fixed Effects				
Effect	Num DF	Den DF	F Value	Pr > F
basefev1	1	482	36.68	<.0001
drug	2	68	3.50	0.0357
h	1	482	102.65	<.0001
h*drug	2	482	17.21	<.0001
h*h	1	482	0.43	0.5120
h*h*drug	2	482	2.19	0.1134
hour	5	482	1.26	0.2795
drug*hour	10	482	1.56	0.1149

The important elements are as follows:

- Neither DRUG × HOUR nor HOUR is significant, indicating no lack of fit from the quadratic model—in essence, no third- or higher-order regression effects.

- Neither quadratic HOUR (H*H) nor DRUG × quadratic HOUR (DRUG*H*H) is statistically significant at ($p \leq$ 0.05). The DRUG *H*H term tests the equality of quadratic regressions, if any, for the treatments. Because there is no evidence of unequal quadratic regression coefficients, the next test for an overall quadratic trend using the quadratic main effect, H*H, which is also not significant at ($p \leq 0.05$). Taken together, these terms indicate that there is no evidence of quadratic regression effects.

- DRUG × H is statistically significant at ($p \leq 0.05$),) indicating evidence of unequal linear regressions of FEV1 on HOUR for the three drug treatments.

Program

You can now fit separate regressions of FEV1 on HOUR for each drug using the statements in Program 8.14

Program 8.14

```
proc glimmix data=fev1_u;
 class drug patient hour;
 model fev1=drug basefev1 drug*h/noint solution;
 random intercept / subject=patient(drug);
 random hour / subject=patient(drug) type=ar(1) residual;

run;
```

Results

Once you remove the lack of fit terms, the problem running PROC GLIMMIX disappears. Output 8.23 shows the results.

Output 8.23: Estimates of Regression Parameters by DRUG for FEV1 Data

Solutions for Fixed Effects						
Effect	drug	Estimate	Standard Error	DF	t Value	Pr > |t|
drug	a	1.1487	0.2943	68	3.90	0.0002
drug	c	1.4407	0.2920	68	4.93	<.0001
drug	p	0.5146	0.2912	68	1.77	0.0817
basefev1		0.8947	0.1027	501	8.71	<.0001
h*drug	a	-0.08887	0.01161	501	-7.66	<.0001
h*drug	c	-0.1057	0.01161	501	-9.11	<.0001
h*drug	p	-0.01583	0.01161	501	-1.36	0.1732

The estimated slopes for drug A and C, −0.089 and −0.106 respectively, are both negative and significantly different from zero, whereas the slope for drug P, −0.016, is not significantly different from zero. These results are consistent with the interaction plot and other results just discussed.

You could add the following CONTRAST statements to Program 8.14 to see if there is evidence that regressions for drug A and C are different. You could also test the placebo versus the treated drugs.

```
contrast 'equal intercept drug A vs C' drug 1 -1 0;
contrast 'equal intercept avg drug A&C vs P' drug 1 1 -2;
contrast 'equal slope drug A vs C' drug*h 1 -1 0;
contrast 'equal slope avg drug A&C vs P' drug*h 1 1 -2;
```

The results are shown in Output 8.24.

Output 8.24: Test of Equality of Regression for Drugs

	Contrasts			
Label	Num DF	Den DF	F Value	Pr > F
equal intercept drug A vs C	1	68	3.69	0.0589
equal intercept avg drug A&C vs P	1	68	35.12	<.0001
equal slope drug A vs C	1	501	1.05	0.3063
equal slope avg drug A&C vs P	1	501	32.83	<.0001

There is some evidence that the intercepts are different ($p = 0.0589$), indicating a difference between drugs A and C immediately after the treatment is applied. There is no evidence of a difference in slopes ($p = 0.3063$) of Drugs A and C. As expected, there is strong evidence that the regression for drug P is different from the average regression of drugs A and C. Both the intercept and slope of Drug P are significantly different ($p < 0.0001$) from the average intercept and slope of Drugs A and C.

This concludes the analysis of the FEV1 data. The methods up to this point are appropriate when repeated measures are taken at equally spaced times (or distances). In the next section, we consider variations on these methods when observations are unequally spaced.

8.5 Unequally Spaced Repeated Measures: An Example

In the longitudinal data setting, in which repeated measures on subjects occur over time, it is often the case that the measurements are made on time intervals that are not equal.

8.5.1 Program

For example, consider the heart rate profiles in Figure 8.7, generated by the code in Program 8.15. (See "Heart Rates," in "Data Sets," for the complete data set.)

Program 8.15

```
data hr;
   input patient drug$ basehr hr1 hr5 hr15 hr30 hr1h;
   array hra{5}  hr1 hr5 hr15 hr30 hr1h;
   do i = 1 to 5;
      if (i = 1) then minute = 1;
      else if (i = 2) then minute = 5;
      else if (i = 3) then minute = 15;
      else if (i = 4) then minute = 30;
      else minute = 60;
      hours  = minute / 60;
      hours1 = hours;
      hr = hra{i} ;
      output;
   end;
   drop i hr1 hr5 hr15 hr30 hr1h;
   datalines;
...datalines...
run;

proc sgplot data=hr noautolegend;
series x=minute y=hr/group=patient lineattrs=(pattern=1 color=black);
refline 1 5 15 30 /axis=x;

run;
```

8.5.2 Results

The statements in Program 8.15 provide the graph in Figure 8.7 where the vertical lines show the times (minutes) when the heart rates were measured.

Figure 8.7: Unequally Spaced Repeated Heart Rate Measurements for 24 Patients

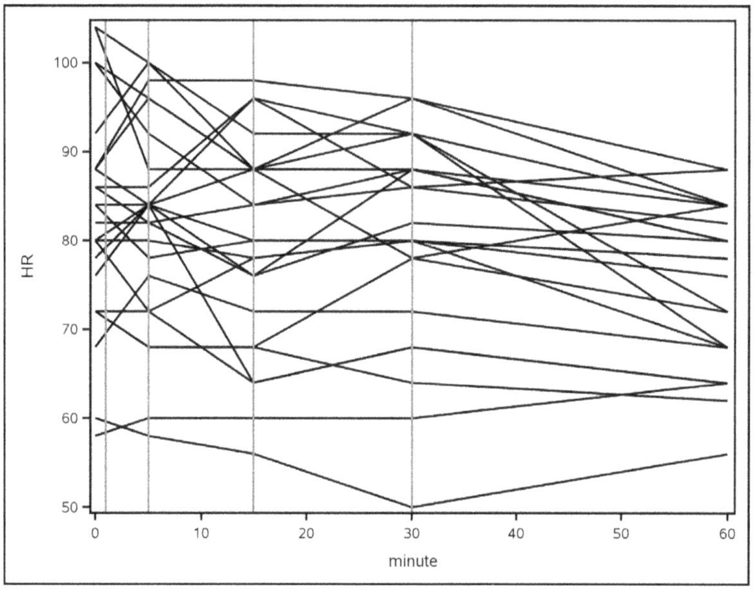

Note: Vertical Lines Drawn at Measurement Intervals.

These data, from the pharmaceutical industry, consist of repeated measurements on the heart rates of 24 patients at 5 unequally spaced time intervals: 1 minute, 5 minutes, 15 minutes, 30 minutes, and 1 hour. Each patient is subjected to one of three possible drug treatment levels: a, b, and p, the last being a placebo.

8.5.3 Model

For data of this sort, it is sensible to consider some type of time series covariance structure, where the correlations of the repeated measurements are assumed to be smaller for observations that are farther apart in time. Another option for unequally spaced repeated measures is the random coefficient model, discussed in Chapter 10.

However, many of the time series covariance structures considered in previous sections of this chapter are inappropriate because they assume equal spacing. The structures that are inappropriate include AR(1), TOEP, and ANTE(1). The CS and UN structures are still appropriate; however, CS assumes that the correlations remain constant, and UN is completely general (often overly so). However, there are covariance structures that occupy middle ground between the extremes of CS and UN that allow for unequal spacing. This section focuses on those structures.

To fit a time series type of covariance structure in which the correlations decline as a function of distance apart in time, you can use any one of the spatial structures that are available in PROC GLIMMIX and PROC MIXED. Something that all of the spatial structures have in common is that they model the within-subject covariance as a function of the distance between observations. The covariance between observations at time k and k' is k', $\sigma_{kk'} = \sigma^2 f(d)$, where. $d = |k - k'|$.

The most common of these are SP(POW) (spatial power law), for which , $f(d) = \rho^d$, SP(GAU) (Gaussian), for which, $f(d) = \exp(-d^2/\rho^2)$ and SP(SPH) (spherical), for which $f(d) = 1 - (3d/2\rho) + (d^3/2\rho^3)$ when $d < \rho$ and 0 otherwise. In general, these covariance structures are meant to be used with two-dimensional spatial data. However, they can be used for repeated measures in time. The connection is that the unequally spaced data can be viewed as a spatial process in one dimension.

Notice that the SP(POW) structure for unequally spaced data provides a direct generalization of the AR(1) structure for equally spaced data. For this reason, it is especially useful for unequally spaced repeated measures.

8.5.4 Program

The PROC GLIMMIX code in Program 8.16 is used to fit the SP(POW) covariance structure to the heart rate data.

Program 8.16

```
proc glimmix data=hr order=data;
   class drug hours patient;
   model hr = drug|hours basehr/ddfm=kr2;
   random intercept / subject=patient(drug);
   random hours / type=sp(pow)(minute)
     subject=patient(drug) residual;
   covtest 'between subject variance = 0?' zeroG;
   nloptions technique=nrridg;
run;
```

8.5.5 Results

The ORDER=DATA option is used in the PROC GLIMMIX statement to preserve the ordering of the levels of the class variable HOUR (time is coded here in hours). If you use the RANDOM...RESIDUAL statement as it is written above, the ORDER option is actually superfluous, because RANDOM HOUR orders the data correctly. However, if you use the statement RANDOM _RESIDUAL_ / SUBJECT=PATIENT(DRUG) TYPE=SP(POW)(MINUTE), then the ORDER statement becomes crucial, because the RANDOM _RESIDUAL statement will not "know" how to properly order the data in the correct time sequence.

The variable MINUTE after TYPE=SP(POW) informs the procedure what to use to determine distance between observations within each subject, in order to compute $f(d)$. Notice that MINUTE must *not* appear in the CLASS statement because it must be treated as a continuous variable.

The fixed effects model consists of different cell means for each drug-hour combination, and the baseline heart rate is included as a covariate. Finally, the NLOPTIONS statement is included as it was in the previous example to enable PROC GLIMMIX to compute the likelihood ratio test for the between-subjects variance component.

Selected results appear in Output 8.25.

Output 8.25: Fit Statistics, Covariance Estimates, Type 3 Tests, and COVTEST Results for Heart Rate Data

Fit Statistics	
-2 Res Log Likelihood	727.15
AIC (smaller is better)	733.15
AICC (smaller is better)	733.39
BIC (smaller is better)	736.69
CAIC (smaller is better)	739.69
HQIC (smaller is better)	734.09
Generalized Chi-Square	3812.21
Gener. Chi-Square / DF	36.66

Covariance Parameter Estimates			
Cov Parm	Subject	Estimate	Standard Error
Intercept	patient(drug)	38.0650	16.4077
SP(POW)	patient(drug)	0.9008	0.04315
Residual		36.6558	8.3720

Type III Tests of Fixed Effects				
Effect	Num DF	Den DF	F Value	Pr > F
drug	2	20.59	1.48	0.2505
hours	4	58.58	5.12	0.0013
drug*hours	8	64.24	1.07	0.3953
basehr	1	19.91	23.40	0.0001

Tests of Covariance Parameters Based on the Restricted Likelihood					
Label	DF	-2 Res Log Like	ChiSq	Pr > ChiSq	Note
between subject variance = 0?	1	732.22	5.07	0.0122	MI

Most results in Output 8.25 are variations on the same theme as you used to interpret the results for the FEV1 data. While not shown here, you could compute the information criteria for competing covariance structures appropriate for unequally spaced data, e.g. CS and UN. The SP(POW) spatial covariance structure was used here where the estimate of ρ is 0.90. The covariance function $f(d) = \rho^d$ where in this case d is the distance, in minutes, between a pair of observations within a given patient. The Type 3 Tests tell you that the baseline, BASEHR, has a significant linear relationship with the heart rate observations, and that there is evidence of an HOUR effect, but no statistically significant evidence of a DRUG effect on changes in heart rate over time. While not shown here, you could use MEANPLOT to construct an interaction plot to allow you to visualize the effects over HOUR.

Program

One item of possible interest that you can obtain from PROC MIXED but not from PROC GLIMMIX is the within-subjects covariance and correlation matrices. PROC GLIMMIX enables you to compute the covariance matrix for the observations, called the *V matrix*, but it involves both the within- and between-subjects variance. If you could drop the between-subjects effect from the linear predictor, then the V and R matrices would be equivalent, but the COVTEST result tells you that the between-subjects effect must remain in the linear predictor, so you cannot do this. Instead, use the PROC MIXED code in Program 8.17.

Program 8.17

```
proc mixed data=hr order=data;
   class drug hours patient;
   model hr = drug|hours basehr;
   random int / subject=patient(drug);
   repeated hours / type=sp(pow)(minute) sub=patient(drug) r rcorr;
run;
```

The R option requests the printout of the conditional (within-subjects) covariance matrix corresponding to the first level of PATIENT(DRUG), and RCORR prints this matrix in correlation form.

8.5.6 Results

Selected output from Program 8.17 is shown in Output 8.26.

Output 8.26: Covariance and Correlation Matrices for Unequally Spaced Model

Estimated R Matrix for patient(drug) 201 p					
Row	Col1	Col2	Col3	Col4	Col5
1	36.6560	21.7845	7.6673	1.6010	0.06980
2	21.7845	36.6560	12.9014	2.6939	0.1175
3	7.6673	12.9014	36.6560	7.6539	0.3337

Estimated R Matrix for patient(drug) 201 p					
Row	Col1	Col2	Col3	Col4	Col5
4	1.6010	2.6939	7.6539	36.6560	1.5982
5	0.06980	0.1175	0.3337	1.5982	36.6560

Estimated R Correlation Matrix for patient(drug) 201 p					
Row	Col1	Col2	Col3	Col4	Col5
1	1.0000	0.5943	0.2092	0.04368	0.001904
2	0.5943	1.0000	0.3520	0.07349	0.003204
3	0.2092	0.3520	1.0000	0.2088	0.009104
4	0.04368	0.07349	0.2088	1.0000	0.04360
5	0.001904	0.003204	0.009104	0.04360	1.0000

The "Estimated R Matrix for patient 201" table reveals the estimate of σ^2 to be 36.66. This is not the variance of an observation however, which is $36.66 + 38.06 = 74.72$ (see Output 8.26). σ^2 represents the variance among the repeated measures for a given patient. Note how the covariance becomes much smaller for time points that are farther apart. The correlations in the "Estimated R Correlation Matrix for patient 201" table reveal the same decline.

The estimate of ρ for this example is 0.9008 (SP(POW) in Output 8.25 in Covariance Parameter Estimates). The scale of this estimate depends on the scale selected for the MINUTE variable; however, the fixed effects estimates and their standard errors are scale invariant.

8.6 Summary

Repeated measures data need mixed models because of correlations between measurements on the same subject. Modeling the covariance structure is a preliminary step in the analysis of repeated measures data using mixed model methodology. The MIXED and GLIMMIX procedures have several covariance structures available for valid estimation of covariance in the data. An example from respiratory ability of asthma patients used the first-order autoregressive structure.

Missing data can have a devastating effect on multivariate methods of repeated measures analysis because subjects with incomplete data are discarded. Mixed model methodology using PROC GLIMMIX and PROC MIXED do not require complete data. The respiratory ability of asthma patients example data with some values randomly deleted can be used as an illustration.

Chapter 9: Best Linear Unbiased Prediction (BLUP) and Inference on Random Effects

9.1 Introduction 307
9.2 Examples Motivating BLUP.. 308
    9.2.1 Breeding Random Effects Model 308
    9.2.2 Machine-Operator Two-Way Mixed Model 308
    9.2.3 Multilocation Model with Multiple Error Terms... 309
    9.2.4 Dose-Response Random Coefficient Regression Model.. 310
9.3 Obtainment of BLUPs in the Breeding Random Effects Model.. 311
    9.3.1 Program Using the GLIMMIX Procedure 311
    9.3.2 Relationship between Sire Means and BLUPs.. 314
9.4 Machine-Operator Two-Factor Mixed Model 316
    9.4.1 Model 316
    9.4.2 Program to Obtain Estimates and Predictors 317
    9.4.3 Intermediate Inference Space BLUP.. 319
    9.4.4 Broad Inference Space BLUP 320
    9.4.5 Comparison with Operator Effects Fixed Model—Narrow Inference Space and Fixed Effects Models....... 320
9.5 A Multilocation Example... 322
    9.5.1 Modeling Issues for a Multicenter Trial 323
    9.5.2 Analysis with Fixed Center Effects.. 324
    9.5.3 Analysis with Random Center Effects 327
    9.5.4 Center-Specific Inference in Multicenter Example... 329
9.6 Matrix Notation for BLUP... 334
9.7 Summary 337

9.1 Introduction

This book focuses primarily on fixed-effects estimation and testing with mixed models in designed experiments. The primary role of random effects and covariance structure in these models is in determining appropriate standard errors of an estimated fixed effect difference or to form test statistics that exhibit nominally accurate statistical properties in a frequentist or empirical Bayes framework. In other cases, notably in Chapter 6, estimates of the variance components themselves are of intrinsic interest. This can be especially useful in a classical "analysis of variance" mindset, in which "analysis" refers to partitioning total variance into understandable pieces and statistically comparing their magnitudes. Both of these general situations are forms of statistical *inference*, in which the goal is a fundamental understanding and explanation of the phenomena under study and how they have given rise to the data at hand.

Complementary to inference is *prediction,* in which we attempt to forecast data that is currently unseen. Of course, the best way to predict something accurately is to fully understand it. While we rarely comprehend a real-life data-generating mechanism completely, we can often model it fairly well and use fitted models to generate predictions for it. Such activity is very popular now in the data mining and machine learning communities via an ever-increasing range of algorithms such as boosted trees and neural networks. In some cases, the sole purpose is to obtain good predictions and the prediction model can be a complete black box. Here we do not want to go that far, but rather focus on some ways to move from inference to prediction in the mixed model context. Refer to Schmueli (2010) for a more general and in-depth discussion and practical examples of the explain-predict dialectic. For our purposes, it turns out that, while primarily being a very effective inference engine, mixed models have a special and interesting predictive side to them as well.

One of the main features distinguishing mixed model methodology from conventional linear model methods is the ability to estimate "realized values of random variables"—that is, specific random effects or linear functions of random effects. In seminal work, Henderson (1963) developed a procedure for predicting breeding values of randomly selected sires in animal genetics experiments. To do this, he derived estimates of the random sire effects in a mixed model. He called this procedure *best linear unbiased prediction (BLUP)*. Harville (1976) shows that Henderson's method has a strong theoretical basis: it can be justified as an extension of the Gauss-Markov theorem. More recently, the use of predictors based on estimated random effects has gained widespread acceptance and has been applied to statistical problems in many disciplines. BLUPs are a form of empirical Bayes shrinkage estimators, also known as regularized estimators under a squared (L2) norm and have theoretically optimal properties under the usual mixed model assumptions.

The purpose of this chapter is to introduce the fundamental concepts of best linear unbiased prediction, hereafter referred to as BLUP, and to demonstrate their use with PROC GLIMMIX and PROC MIXED. Section 9.2 presents some introductory motivating examples. Sections 9.3 through 9.6 revisit the examples in depth and in levels of increasing complexity to show how you can use mixed model procedures for best linear unbiased prediction. If you are familiar with matrix notation, Section 9.7 presents an overview of the basic ideas and theory of BLUP in those terms.

9.2 Examples Motivating BLUP

This section presents a number of examples to illustrate the distinction between estimation—as defined in classical linear model theory—and BLUP. These are some basic cases in which the latter is warranted. McLean et al. (1991) discuss the related concept of inference spaces available in working with mixed models. Robinson (1991) and discussants provide an excellent in-depth coverage of BLUP and its connections to many branches of statistical theory.

9.2.1 Breeding Random Effects Model

The pure random effects model is discussed in Chapter 6. A common example occurs in animal breeding, in which a group of bulls are randomly selected. Each bull is mated to a number of cows, and a trait of interest (e.g., weight gain) is measured in the offspring. The model for such an experiment is as follows:

$$y_{ijk} = \mu + s_i + d(s)_{ij} + e_{ijk}$$

where terms are defined as follows:

- y_{ijk} is the measurement on the kth offspring of the jth dam (cow) mated to the ith sire (bull).
- μ is the intercept.
- s_i is the effect of the ith sire (random).
- $d(s)_{ij}$ is the effect of the jth dam mated to the ith sire (random).
- e_{ijk} is the residual.

The effects s_i, $d(s)_{ij}$, and e_{ijk} are each *iid* normal with mean 0 and variances σ_S^2, σ_D^2, and σ^2, respectively. In addition, all random effects are assumed to be independent of one another.

Typically, the initial purpose of such experiments is to estimate the variance associated with the random effects (e.g., sire and dam). In this example, for example, researchers typically want to know whether a trait can be inherited and if so, how much of the inheritance is paternal or maternal. Variance component estimates are used to estimate heritability as the proportion of variability attributable to genetic variation.

A subsequent objective of many such trials is to identify superior animals for breeding purposes. For example, if the trait of interest does turn out to be strongly inherited, say, through the sire, then the animal breeder would want to identify the best sires for future breeding. In order to do this, the sire breeding value, $\mu + s_i$, must be estimated. In our mixed model this is a linear combination of a fixed effect, μ, and a random effect, s_i. We can use generalized least squares to estimate μ and BLUP to estimate each s_i.

As an aside, the difference between fixed and random effects can be illustrated with this nested model. Suppose that each of the sires represents a particular breed—e.g., sire 1 is an Angus, sire 2 is a Hereford, etc. If there is one sire per breed, then it is reasonable to regard sire (now "breed") as a fixed effect. However, if the sires are a random sample from one or more sets of breeds, then sire would be considered a random effect for a standard analysis. The inclusion of specific breeds in the experiment is a reproducible decision, whereas the random sampling of sires from a population of bulls from the same breed is not.

9.2.2 Machine-Operator Two-Way Mixed Model

The two-way mixed model was discussed in Chapter 2. McLean et al. (1991) used the following example from a manufacturing application to illustrate inference on random effects in a two-way model. Different machines used in a production process are to be compared. Machine operators are randomly selected from a population of possible operators. Each operator runs each machine; two observations are taken for each operator-machine combination.

The resulting model is

$$y_{ijk} = \mu + \tau_i + O_j + \tau O_{ij} + e_{ijk} \tag{9.1}$$

where terms are defined as follows:

- y_{ijk} is the kth observation on the ith machine run by the jth operator.
- μ is the intercept.
- τ_i is the effect of the ith machine (fixed).
- O_j is the effect of the jth operator (random).
- τO_{ij} is the ij^{th} machine-by-operator interaction.
- e_{ijk} is random error.

The operator, machine-by-operator, and error effects are assumed *iid* normal with mean 0 and variance components σ_O^2, σ_{MO}^2, and σ^2, respectively.

The analyses discussed in Chapter 2 focus on inference about fixed effects, in this case, the machine effects. For example, you can estimate the mean performance of the ith machine as $\mu + \tau_i$, or estimate or test the difference between machines, e.g., the first and second machines, $\tau_1 - \tau_2$. These estimates and tests address the objective of assessing machine performance, say, for the purpose of choosing the best machine.

In this study, a manager may also be interested in assessing the performance of various operators under his or her supervision. The manager might want to know the performance of the jth operator averaged over all machines,

$$\mu + (1/m) \sum_i \tau_i + O_j$$

where m is the number of machines in the study. The manager might also want to assess the performance of a given operator on a specific machine, $\mu + \tau_i + O_j + \tau O_{ij}$. These objectives must be addressed by estimating the required linear combinations of fixed and random effects, i.e., the required BLUPs.

9.2.3 Multilocation Model with Multiple Error Terms

Mixed models with multiple error terms are introduced in Chapter 5. A common type of multierror model in which BLUP may be of interest occurs in a multilocation trial. Examples of multilocation trials include medical and pharmaceutical research, where similar experiments are often conducted at several clinics or hospitals, or technology-transfer research in agriculture, where similar experiments are often conducted at several farms. The purpose of such trials is to broaden the scope of inference, for example, to a wide variety of situations that might be encountered when an experimental treatment is adopted for practical use.

A typical multilocation trial is conducted as follows. Each of t treatments is replicated r times at each of s sites or locations. Ideally, the sites are a random sample from a target population. How well this ideal is met in practice can be a controversial matter; assume that sites are random for this discussion. The model implied by such a trial is

$$y_{ijk} = \mu + s_i + r(s)_{ij} + s\tau_{ik} + e_{ijk} \tag{9.2}$$

where terms are defined as follows:

- y_{ijk} is the observation on the jth replication on the kth treatment at the ith site or location.
- s_i is the site effect (random).
- $r(s)_{ij}$ is the replication within-site effect (random).
- τ_k is the treatment effect (fixed).
- $s\tau_{ik}$ is the site-by-treatment interaction (random).

The effects s_i, $r(s)_{ij}$, $s\tau_{ik}$, and e_{ijk} are each assumed *iid* normal with mean 0 and variances σ_S^2, σ_{RS}^2, σ_{RT}^2, and σ^2, respectively. The random effects are assumed independent of one another.

In conventional fixed effects analysis of multilocation trials, inference focuses on average treatment performance throughout the target population. Thus, estimates of treatment means, expressed as $\mu + \tau_k$, or differences between two treatments, $\tau_k - \tau_{k'}$, are the main objectives.

In many practical situations, you may be interested in the specific performance of treatments at a given site. For example, you may want to know the site-specific treatment mean, expressed as $\mu + s_i + \tau_k + s\tau_{ik}$, or a site-specific treatment difference, $\tau_k - \tau_{k'} + s\tau_{ik} - s\tau_{ik'}$. These estimates are of particular interest if you suspect that different treatments perform better under different environmental conditions, represented by the various locations in the trial.

Traditionally, site-specific inference has been approached first by determining if a significant site-by-treatment interaction exists and then by analyzing each site separately if the interaction is present. However, this approach limits the power and precision of inference at each site. The mixed model approach using BLUP permits site-specific inference using information from the entire trial for all sites simultaneously.

9.2.4 Dose-Response Random Coefficient Regression Model

Random coefficient regression models are discussed in detail in Chapter 10. These models lend themselves to applications for which BLUP is useful. Two examples are illustrative.

In clinical trials, a common objective is to assess the relationship between drug dosage and a physiological response. Suppose that subjects are randomly assigned to receive a given dosage of a drug. The subjects' response is then measured. A model for these data is as follows:

$$y_{ij} = \beta_0 + s_i + (\beta_1 + d_i) X_{ij} + e_{ij}$$

where terms are defined as the following:

- y_{ij} is the response of the ith subject at the jth dose level
- β_0 is the fixed intercept
- β_1 is the fixed slope
- s_i is the random deviation of the ith subject's intercept from β_0
- d_i is the random deviation of the ith subject's slope from β_1
- X_{ij} is the jth dose level assigned to subject i
- e_{ij} is random error

The random effects, s_i, d_i, and e_{ij} are assumed *iid* normal with mean 0 and variance components σ_S^2, σ_D^2, and σ^2, respectively.

In conventional regression theory, the *subject-specific* terms, s_i and d_i, do not appear in the model. Inference focuses on estimating the intercept and slope and using them to obtain predicted response to a given dose level, i.e., $\hat{\beta}_0 + \hat{\beta}_1 X_{ij}$. The estimates of intercept, slope, and predicted response are implicitly averages over the entire population of subjects.

In the mixed model that includes the random regression coefficients, s_i and d_i, the same *population-average* estimates used in conventional regression can also be obtained. However, in a clinical trial where the subjects happen to be patients under treatment for an illness, the specific response of a given patient to drug dosage may also be of interest. The attending physician, for example, may want to know how an individual patient responds to a given dose.

In the random coefficient mixed model, you assume that the population-average relationship between dose and response is given by the conventional regression equation, $\beta_0 + \beta_1 X_{ij}$, but each subject's specific response to dosage can be estimated by

$$\beta_0 + s_i + (\beta_1 + d_i) X_{ij}$$

The terminology "population average" versus "subject-specific" is due to Zeger et al. (1988). The subject-specific estimate is a form of BLUP.

Another example, presented in Section 9.6, concerns pharmaceutical shelf life. In a stability trial, a sample of batches is observed over time to monitor changes in the response variable, called the stability limiting characteristic. Typically, this characteristic gets worse over time until it reaches a point at which the product is no longer considered acceptable for use. In many stability trials, this decline is linear over time and can be modeled using linear regression. The linear predictor has the same form as the multipatient dose response clinical trial. Current practice is to use analysis of covariance models similar to those presented in Chapter 7, but a promising alternative is to use batch-specific BLUPs of the intercept and slope, written as $\beta_0 + b_{0i}$ and $\beta_1 + b_{1i}$ respectively.

9.3 Obtainment of BLUPs in the Breeding Random Effects Model

How do you compute BLUPs? It is actually quite easy in SAS. The same approach to writing ESTIMATE statements for fixed effects applies to BLUPs as well, with one additional item of syntax. This section considers a data set based on the animal breeding example introduced in Section 9.2.1. Five sires are randomly sampled from a population, and each sire is mated to two dams. Two offspring per sire-dam combination are observed, and the average daily gain (ADG) of each offspring is recorded. The data are given as "Breeding." The model for this data set is model (9.1) in Section 9.2.1.

As noted in Section 9.2.1, animal breeders are often interested in the breeding value of the ith sire, that is, the BLUP of the predictable function: $\mu + s_i$. Actually, three BLUPs for the ith sire might be defined. The first is $\mu + s_i$, the population-wide or broad inference space BLUP, which predicts the performance of the ith sire across the entire population of dams to which he might potentially be mated. The second is $\mu + s_i + (\frac{1}{2})\Sigma d(s)_{ij}$, the narrow inference space BLUP assessing the performance of the sire on those dams to which he was actually mated. The third is the conditional mean, $\mu + s_i + d(s)_{ij}$, a "dam-specific" BLUP assessing the performance of a specific sire-by-dam combination.

9.3.1 Program Using the GLIMMIX Procedure

You can obtain BLUPs and accompanying mixed model results by using PROC GLIMMIX.

Program

BLUPs are computed in three different ways in Program 9.1, using specifications in the RANDOM, OUTPUT, and ESTIMATE statements. The latter directly compute the three BLUPs defined above.

Program 9.1

```
proc glimmix data=breeding;
   class sire dam;
   model adg = / ddfm=kr2 s;
   random sire dam(sire) / s;
   estimate 'sire 1 BLUP "broad" '
            intercept 1 | sire 1 0;
   estimate 'sire 1 BLUP "narrow" '
            intercept 2 | sire 2 0
             dam(sire) 1 1 0 0  0 0  0 0  0 0 / divisor=2;
   estimate 'sire 1 BLUP with dam 1'
            intercept 1 | sire 1 0
            dam(sire) 1 0;
   ods output solutionr=sr estimates=ests;
   output out=blups_rock pred(blup noilink)=eblup;
run;
```

Some things to note about this program follow:

- This model has no fixed effects (other than an intercept, which is included by default). Therefore, the MODEL statement serves primarily to identify the dependent variable (ADG) and no independent variables appear after the "=" sign.

- The MODEL statement also includes the DDFM=KR2 option. This is important for two reasons. First, similar to discussions (e.g., of Satterthwaite's approximation) in Chapters 5 and 8, the prediction error variance of the BLUPs may involve a linear combination of variance components. The degrees of freedom used to construct interval estimates or evaluate tests should take this into account. Second, the prediction error variance computed with estimated variance components tends to be biased downward. This is similar to the underestimation of standard errors with unbalanced and repeated measures data (see Chapter 5), but the effect can be even more severe in cases like this. For BLUPs, the DDFM=KR2 option invokes a bias correction due to Prasad and Rao (1990) and Harville and Jeske (1992).

- The model effects, SIRE and DAM(SIRE), are both random and thus appear in the RANDOM statement. The S (SOLUTION) option produces a table of the "estimates" (actually "predictors") of the SIRE and DAM(SIRE) effects. These are BLUPs.

- You use the ESTIMATE statement to define predictable functions for observed SIRE and DAM combinations. All fixed effect coefficients must appear first and then all random effect coefficients. Fixed and random effect coefficients must be separated by a vertical bar (|).

- The only fixed effect is the intercept, μ. All other coefficients appear to the right of the vertical bar.

- As with ESTIMATE statements shown in previous chapters for fixed effects only, all coefficients for an effect following the last one specified are set to 0. For example, in the first ESTIMATE statement, "sire 1 BLUP broad," SIRE 1 0 causes the coefficients for the remaining sire effects (s_3, s_4, and s_5) to default to zero. DAM(SIRE) 0 sets all coefficients for dam to zero. Alternatively, you can explicitly give all the coefficients for every effect in the model for the predictable function: $\mu + s_1$. The ESTIMATE statement then appears as follows:

```
estimate 'sire 1 BLUP broad'
         intercept 1 |
         sire 1 0 0 0 0
         dam(sire) 0 0 0 0 0 0 0 0 0 0;
```

The second ESTIMATE statement gives all coefficients explicitly for the predictable function defining the narrow inference space BLUP, $\mu + s_1 + (\frac{1}{2})\Sigma d(s)_{1j}$. The third ESTIMATE statement uses defaults to define the function specific to the sire 1, dam 1 BLUP, $\mu + s_1 + d(s)_{11}$.

- The ODS statement creates new SAS data sets, SR and ESTS, containing results from the RANDOM / SOLUTION and ESTIMATE statements, respectively. You can use these data sets for subsequent analyses and graphics.

- The OUTPUT statement creates a new SAS data set, BLUPS_ROCK, with the same number of rows as the input data set, 20 in this case. The option PRED(BLUP NOILINK)=EBLUP instructs PROC GLIMMIX to create a variable in this data set named EBLUP that contains BLUPs for each row constructed in the same way as the third ESTIMATE statement. Refer to the PROC GLIMMIX documentation for details on all the options that are available in the OUTPUT statement.

- If you add extra rows to the input table with missing values for ADG, you can obtain BLUPs for unobserved combinations of SIRE and DAM corresponding to the values of these variables that you specify in the extra rows. The new BLUPs will appear in the BLUPS_ROCK data set. If any of the levels you specify for SIRE or DAM are not one of the original levels in the observed data, a BLUP value of 0 will be assigned to that level for its random effect estimate.

- This code will also work with PROC MIXED, except you need to delete the OUTPUT statement and instead add the option OUTP=EBLUP to the MODEL statement.

Results

The results are given in Output 9.1.

Output 9.1: PROC GLIMMIX Output for Breeding Random Effects Model

Covariance Parameter Estimates		
Cov Parm	Estimate	Standard Error
sire	0.05130	0.05896
dam(sire)	0.03701	0.03668
Residual	0.03870	0.01731

Solutions for Fixed Effects

Effect	Estimate	Standard Error	DF	t Value	Pr > |t|
Intercept	2.3300	0.1261	4	18.48	<.0001

Solution for Random Effects

Effect	sire	dam	Estimate	Std Err Pred	DF	t Value	Pr > |t|
sire	1		-0.1243	0.1980	4.31	-0.63	0.5620
sire	2		-0.05809	0.1980	4.31	-0.29	0.7828
sire	3		0.1759	0.1980	4.31	0.89	0.4211
sire	4		-0.2001	0.1980	4.31	-1.01	0.3655
sire	5		0.2065	0.1980	4.31	1.04	0.3518
dam(sire)	1	1	-0.1056	0.1887	4.975	-0.56	0.6002
dam(sire)	1	2	0.01593	0.1887	4.975	0.08	0.9360
dam(sire)	2	1	-0.2048	0.1887	4.975	-1.09	0.3275
dam(sire)	2	2	0.1629	0.1887	4.975	0.86	0.4276
dam(sire)	3	1	-0.00058	0.1887	4.975	-0.00	0.9976
dam(sire)	3	2	0.1275	0.1887	4.975	0.68	0.5295
dam(sire)	4	1	0.05588	0.1887	4.975	0.30	0.7791
dam(sire)	4	2	-0.2002	0.1887	4.975	-1.06	0.3375
dam(sire)	5	1	0.1270	0.1887	4.975	0.67	0.5309
dam(sire)	5	2	0.02196	0.1887	4.975	0.12	0.9119

Estimates

Label	Estimate	Standard Error	DF	t Value	Pr > |t|
sire 1 BLUP "broad"	2.2057	0.1859	8.915	11.86	<.0001
sire 1 BLUP "narrow"	2.1609	0.1003	12.12	21.55	<.0001
sire 1 BLUP with dam 1	2.1002	0.1428	16.1	14.71	<.0001

Interpretation

In Output 9.1, the REML estimates of the variance components are given under "Covariance Parameter Estimates." The estimate of the sire variance, σ_S^2, is 0.0513. The estimated dam variance, σ_D^2, is 0.0370, and the estimated residual variance is 0.0387.

The estimate of the intercept, $\hat{\mu} = 2.33$, is given in the "Solution for Fixed Effects" table. Solutions for the SIRE and DAM(SIRE) effects appear under "Solution for Random Effects." For example, the predictor for the first SIRE is $\hat{s}_i = -0.1243$ and the predictors for the dams mated to sire 1, DAM(SIRE) 1 1 and DAM(SIRE) 1 2, are

$$\widehat{d(s)}_{11} = -0.1056$$

and

$$\widehat{d(s)}_{12} = 0.01593$$

The standard errors of prediction are relatively large for this example and resulting *p*-values are not significant by common standards, and this is typical given the shrunken nature of the BLUPs and the underlying assumption that the random effects have arisen from a normal distribution with mean zero. BLUPs are often used more for ranking and selection rather than searching for classical statistical significance.

The "Estimates" output gives the three BLUPs. The column labeled "Estimate" gives the estimated BLUP. Technically, it is not an estimate, but a predictor. The "Std Error" is technically not a standard error but is the square root of the estimated prediction error variance (the prediction standard error). These are fine points of mixed model jargon. For practical purposes, estimates and predictors have similar roles in inference, as do standard errors and square root prediction error variances. Unless otherwise noted, the rest of this chapter uses *standard error* to refer to the square root prediction error variance. Note that the standard errors shown here are corrected for bias using the Prasad-Rao procedure—a consequence of the DDFM=KR2 option.

For the three predictable functions, the results are shown in Table 9.1.

Table 9.1: ESTIMATE Statement Results

Label	Predictable Function	BLUP	Std. Error
sire 1 broad	$\mu + s_1$	2.206	0.1859
sire 1 narrow	$\mu + s_1 + (\frac{1}{2})\Sigma d(s)_{1j}$	2.161	0.1003
sire 1 dam1	$\mu + s_1 + d(s)_{11}$	2.100	0.1428

The BLUPs are not the same. This is typical of changes in the inference space among BLUPs. In this case, the prediction for sire 1 for the entire population of dams is higher than for the average of the dams to which he was actually mated. This relationship is specific to these data and does not necessarily hold in general. The prediction error is largest for broad inference, smallest for narrow inference, and in between the two for dam-specific inference. This relationship *does* hold in general. In narrow inference, you have data on the specific sire-dam combinations you are predicting. In broad inference, your predictions apply to sire-dam combinations that are theoretically possible but have not been observed. Broad inference, therefore, is made with less precision than narrow inference: with broad inference there is more uncertainty and hence greater variability.

PROC GLIMMIX initially computes the standard error by substituting the REML variance component estimates into the formula for the prediction error variance assuming known variance components. These formulae are given in Appendix A. This is often called the *naive* method of estimating prediction error variance. Kackar and Harville (1984) showed that the naive estimate is biased downward. They suggested a correction for the bias. When the DDFM=KR2 option is in effect, the GLIMMIX procedure applies the Prasad-Rao-Harville-Jeske standard error adjustment. Refer to the PROC GLIMMIX documentation for additional details and references.

9.3.2 Relationship between Sire Means and BLUPs

These data illustrate the relationship between the estimate of a mean and its BLUP analog. Whereas a fixed effects mean is a simple average—reflecting the assumption that the entire population of levels has been observed in the data set—the BLUP is a regression toward the overall mean based on the variance components of the model effects. Regression toward the mean is sometimes called *shrinkage estimation*. Note that REML estimation automatically estimates the proper degree of shrinkage without the need for hand-tuning, and furthermore, this estimate is optimal in terms of mean-squared error under the standard mixed model assumptions.

Program to Visualize BLUP Shrinkage

To visualize BLUP shrinkage for this example, run Program 9.2.

Program 9.2

```
proc means data=blups_rock noprint;
   by sire;
   var adg eblup;
   output out=brm mean= / autoname;
run;

data brms;
   set brm;
   pair = _n_;
   stat = "mean";
   value = adg_mean;
   output;
   stat = "blup";
   value = eblup_mean;
   output;
run;
```

```
proc sgplot data=brms;
   series x=stat y=value / group=sire;
run;
```

Results and Interpretation

This code produces Figure 9.1. The raw means for the five sires are on the left side and connected to their corresponding BLUPs on the right side. Note how the lines pinch mildly toward the center when going from left to right, which represents a small degree of shrinkage for this example. If the variance component estimates had been smaller, then the shrinkage would be more severe. Conversely, as the variance component estimates grow larger, there is less and less shrinkage. In fact, one view of fixed effects is as "random effects with infinite variance", or a completely flat, noninformative prior in Bayesian terms.

Figure 9.1: Illustration of Shrinkage for Breeding Example

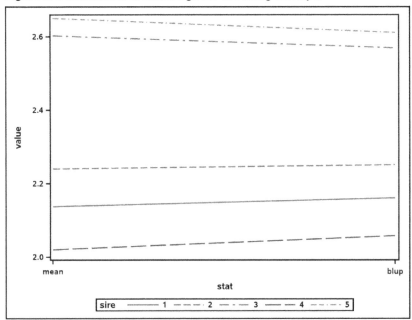

The shrinkage estimator, or BLUP, has its origins in an exercise in Mood (1950). Paraphrasing it in the context of the sire and dam example, it goes something like this. Suppose average daily gain (a.d.g.) has a Gaussian distribution $N(\mu, \sigma_S^2)$. An offspring of sire i has an average daily gain of $\bar{y}_{i\bullet}$. Suppose observed a.d.g. for a given offspring has a Gaussian distribution centered at the offspring's true a.d.g. with a variance of σ^2. What is the maximum likelihood estimate of the offspring's a.d.g.? Hint: it is *not* $\bar{y}_{i\bullet}$. The correct answer, which is the maximum of the posterior density of the offspring's a.d.g., is the best linear unbiased predictor, $\hat{\mu} + \hat{s}_i$ where $s_i \sim N(0, \sigma_S^2)$. Henderson was a student in Mood's class, and it is this exercise that played a pivotal role in his development of BLUP theory and applications.

For sire 1, the sample mean is $\bar{y}_{1\bullet\bullet} = 2.1375$. Its "broad" BLUP is $\mu + s_1$. Because μ is a fixed effect, you estimate it from the overall sample mean $\bar{y}_{\bullet\bullet\bullet} = 2.33$. The random effect, s_1, is estimated from its conditional mean, $E[s_1 \mid \{y_{ijk}\}]$, where $\{y_{ijk}\}$ denotes the set of all observations. In this case, this reduces to $\hat{s}_{1,BLUP} = E[s_1 \mid \bar{y}_{1\bullet\bullet}]$, which is equal to

$$E[s_1] + \text{Cov}[s_1, \bar{y}_{1\bullet\bullet}](Var[\bar{y}_{1\bullet\bullet}])^{-1}(\bar{y}_{1\bullet\bullet} - \bar{y}_{\bullet\bullet\bullet})$$

Since $E[s_1] = 0$, this is equal to the following:

$$0 + \sigma_S^2 \times \left[\frac{\sigma^2 + 2\sigma_D^2 + 4\sigma_S^2}{12} \right]^{-1} \times (\bar{y}_{1\bullet\bullet} - \bar{y}_{\bullet\bullet\bullet})$$

Substituting the estimates of the variance components and means yields the following:

$$\hat{s}_1 = 0.0513 \times \frac{12}{(0.0387 + 6 \times 0.03701 + 12 \times 0.0513)} \times (2.1375 - 2.33) = -0.1243$$

Thus, the estimated sire 1 BLUP is $\hat{\mu} + \hat{s}_1 = 2.33 - 0.1243 = 2.2057$, as seen in Output 9.1.

The basic idea of a shrinkage estimator is that it *moves* the sire mean toward the overall mean, avoiding potential mean squared error due to noisiness or lucky anomalies in the data. The degree of shrinkage depends on the magnitude of the variance components. A large sire variance results in very little shrinkage, whereas a smaller variance results in more shrinkage toward μ.

The advantage of the shrinkage estimate is that estimated means well above or below μ are regressed toward μ consistent with the magnitude of σ_S^2 relative to the total variance of the observations. Thus, extreme means are attenuated by knowledge of the underlying variability, and the risk of misinterpreting the data is reduced. This is a central concept of BLUP and in the related fields of empirical Bayes and Bayesian statistical theory, as well as regularization in machine learning.

As a note on terminology, strictly speaking, BLUP assumes that the variance components are known. In practice, you use estimated variance components, so the resulting predictor is not a true BLUP, but is to a good approximation. In mixed model vernacular, the predictor calculated using the estimated variance components is more properly called an empirical BLUP, or *EBLUP*. Given common usage of the acronym "BLUP", we use it loosely to refer to either form.

This section is meant to be a very basic introduction to BLUP in a breeding context, but we want to mention that it continues to be an active area of research in many advanced related areas. Refer to Vitezica et al (2013) and Azevedo et al (2015) for some modern applications in genomics.

9.4 Machine-Operator Two-Factor Mixed Model

The second example is based on the machine-operator study described in Section 9.2.2 and illustrates various BLUP concepts from Section 9.3. This example focuses on using PROC GLIMMIX to obtain the BLUPs discussed in Section 9.3 and on relationships between these BLUPs and estimable functions frequently computed using when operator effects are treated as fixed.

Two different types of machine (variable MACHINE) are compared. Three operators (variable OPERATOR) are randomly sampled from a population. Two observations are taken on each operator for each machine. The response variable (Y) is a performance criterion of interest in the study. The data are given in data set "Machine Operators."

9.4.1 Model

The mixed model for this study is model 9.1 given in Section 9.2.2.

In mixed model applications, there are three basic types of functions of the model effects of potential interest. See Section 9.7 for additional information about the underlying mixed model theory. The types of functions in the context of this example are

- *Estimable functions.* These are estimable linear combinations of fixed effects only. These correspond to broad inference for the machines in the McLean et al. (1991) terminology and population-average inference using the Zeger et al. (1988) terminology. Consider these two examples:

  - *e1* Machine 1 mean, $\mu + \tau_1$

  - *e2* Machine difference, $\tau_1 - \tau_2$

- *Narrow inference predictable functions.* These are predictable functions that limit inference to the operators actually observed. Inference is based on conditional expectations given the observed operators. This is narrow inference as described by McLean et al. (1991). Consider these two examples:

  - *e3* Machine 1 BLUP given observed operators:

$$\mu + \tau_1 + (1/3)\sum_j O_j + (1/3)\sum_j \tau O_{1j}$$

  - *e4* Machine difference BLUP given observed operators:

$$\tau_1 - \tau_2 + (1/3)\left[\sum_j \tau O_{1j} - \sum_j \tau O_{2j}\right]$$

- *Subject-specific predictable functions.* These are BLUPs that are applicable to individual operators. Consider these three examples:

  ○ *e5* Operator 1 BLUP, averaged over all machines:

  $$\mu + (1/2)\tau_1 + O_1 + (1/2)\sum_j \tau O_{i1}$$

  ○ *e6* BLUP for operator 1 using machine 1:

  $$\mu + \tau_1 + O_1 + \tau O_{11}$$

  ○ *e7* BLUP for the difference between machines specific to operator 1:

  $$\tau_1 - \tau_2 + \tau O_{11} - \tau O_{21}$$

9.4.2 Program to Obtain Estimates and Predictors

ESTIMATE statements provide you with full flexibility to compute the exact BLUPs you want. Although it can sometimes be tedious to specify numerous statements and get all their coefficients correct, over time you will develop a proficiency with them, as well as a valuable set of previous examples to use as templates.

Programs

You can obtain BLUPs for the functions from the preceding section by using the following PROC GLIMMIX statements in Program 9.3.

Program 9.3

```
proc glimmix data=machine;
   class machine operator;
   model y=machine/ddfm=kr2;
   random operator machine*operator;
   lsmeans machine;
   estimate 'BLUE - mach 1'
         intercept 1 machine 1 0;
   estimate 'BLUE - diff'
         machine 1 -1;
   estimate 'BLUP - m 1 narrow'
         intercept 3 machine 3 0 |
         operator 1 1 1 machine*operator 1 1 1 0 0 0 / divisor=3;
   estimate 'BLUP - diff narrow'
         machine 3 -3 |
         machine*operator 1 1 1 -1 -1 -1 / divisor=3;
   estimate 'BLUP - oper 1'
         intercept 2 machine 1 1  |
         operator 2 0 0 machine*operator 1 0 0 1 0 0 / divisor=2;
   estimate 'BLUP -  m 1 op 1'
         intercept 1 machine 1 0 |
            operator 1 0 0 machine*operator 1 0 0 0 0 0;
   estimate 'BLUP - diff op 1'
         machine 1 -1 | machine*operator 1 0 0 -1 0 0;
run;
```

The ESTIMATE statements labeled "BLUE" are the two broad or population-averaged estimable functions. The ESTIMATE statements labeled "BLUP...narrow" correspond to the two narrow inference space BLUPs. The final set of three ESTIMATE statements refers to the subject-specific BLUPs.

Before discussing the results, we present an alternative set of PROC GLIMMIX statements. The above statements for the BLUPs are written to follow the form of the linear predictor, $\mu + \tau_i + O_j + \tau O_{ij}$ literally. While this approach is clear and easy when you have a small number of random effects, it becomes tedious and unmanageable as the number of random effect levels increases. The following statements use the SUBJECT specification in the RANDOM statement.

Program 9.4

```
proc glimmix data=machine;
   class machine operator;
   model y=machine/ddfm=kr2;
```

```
    random intercept machine / subject=operator;
    lsmeans machine;
    estimate 'BLUE - mach 1'
            intercept 1 machine 1 0;
    estimate 'BLUE - diff'
            machine 1 -1;
    estimate 'BLUP - m 1 narrow' intercept 3 machine 3 0 |
            intercept 1 machine 1 / subject 1 1 1 divisor=3;
    estimate 'BLUP - diff narrow' machine 3 -3 | machine 1 -1 /
            subject 1 1 1 divisor=3;
    estimate 'BLUP - oper 1' intercept 2 machine 1 1 |
            intercept 2 machine 1 1 / subject 1 0 0 divisor=2;
    estimate 'BLUP - m 1 op 1' intercept 1 machine 1 0 |
            intercept 1 machine 1 0 / subject 1 0 0;
    estimate 'BLUP - diff op 1' machine 1 -1 |
            machine 1 -1 / subject 1 0 0;
run;
```

Written using the SUBJECT=OPERATOR option, PROC GLIMMIX "understands" INTERCEPT / SUBJECT=OPERATOR as the O_j effect, and MACHINE / SUBJECT=OPERATOR as the τO_{ij} effect. The SUBJECT option in the ESTIMATE statement makes the predictable function applicable to the jth operator level as specified by the coefficients following SUBJECT. For example, SUBJECT 1 0 refers to operator 1, SUBJECT 0 1 refers to operator 2, and SUBJECT 1 1 1 directs PROC GLIMMIX to sum over all three operators. Thus, the "BLUP – M 1 NARROW statement is read as follows:

$$\mu + \tau_1 + (1/3)\sum_j \left(O_j + \tau O_{1j}\right)$$

Results

The results of program 9.4 are given in Output 9.2.

Output 9.2 PROC GLIMMIX Output for Machine-Operator Two-Way Mixed Model

Covariance Parameter Estimates			
Cov Parm	Subject	Estimate	Standard Error
Intercept	operator	0.1073	0.1498
machine	operator	0.05100	0.07656
Residual		0.04853	0.02802

Solutions for Fixed Effects						
Effect	machine	Estimate	Standard Error	DF	t Value	Pr > |t|
Intercept		51.9567	0.2467	2.973	210.59	<.0001
machine	1	-1.0083	0.2240	2	-4.50	0.0460
machine	2	0	.	.	.	.

Solution for Random Effects							
Effect	machine	Subject	Estimate	Std Err Pred	DF	t Value	Pr > |t|
Intercept		operator 1	0.2295	0.2836	1.965	0.81	0.5046
machine	1	operator 1	0.1200	0.2508	1.347	0.48	0.6983
machine	2	operator 1	-0.01097	0.2508	1.347	-0.04	0.9707
Intercept		operator 2	0.08515	0.2836	1.965	0.30	0.7927
machine	1	operator 2	-0.1311	0.2508	1.347	-0.52	0.6741
machine	2	operator 2	0.1716	0.2508	1.347	0.68	0.5924
Intercept		operator 3	-0.3147	0.2836	1.965	-1.11	0.3844
machine	1	operator 3	0.01107	0.2508	1.347	0.04	0.9704
machine	2	operator 3	-0.1606	0.2508	1.347	-0.64	0.6135

Estimates					
Label	Estimate	Standard Error	DF	t Value	Pr > |t|
BLUE - mach 1	50.9483	0.2467	2.973	206.50	<.0001
BLUE - diff	-1.0083	0.2240	2	-4.50	0.0460
BLUP - m 1 narrow	50.9483	0.08993	6	566.53	<.0001
BLUP - diff narrow	-1.0083	0.1272	6	-7.93	0.0002
BLUP - oper 1	51.7366	0.1151	6.698	449.30	<.0001
BLUP - m 1 op 1	51.2979	0.1724	7.885	297.48	<.0001
BLUP - diff op 1	-0.8773	0.2567	7.976	-3.42	0.0092
BLUP - m 1 interm	50.9483	0.1584	2	321.65	<.0001
BLUP - op 1 broad	51.6820	0.2391	2.989	216.15	<.0001

machine Least Squares Means					
machine	Estimate	Standard Error	DF	t Value	Pr > |t|
1	50.9483	0.2467	2.973	206.50	<.0001
2	51.9567	0.2467	2.973	210.59	<.0001

Interpretation

Major points about the output follow:

- For the broad and narrow inference space, the estimates of the machine means are the same, 50.9483. However, the standard errors for the two inference spaces are different. The standard error for the broad space is 0.2467. For the narrow BLUP the standard error is 0.0899.

- The standard error in the broad inference space results from determining the variance of an estimated machine mean or difference, as derived in Chapters 2 and 4. The standard error for the narrow inference space is what you would get if you defined OPERATOR (and hence MACHINE × OPERATOR) as fixed, rather than random. The same result holds for the machine difference as well. The two inference spaces yield identical estimates, −1.008, but the standard errors, 0.224 for broad inference and 0.1272 for narrow inference, are different.

- Again, the broad standard error results from the same derivations of the variance of treatment differences presented in previous chapters. The narrow standard error corresponds to the standard error you would obtain if operator effects were defined as fixed.

  The subject-specific BLUPs are computed using methods discussed in Section 9.7 and Appendix A. Unlike the broad and narrow space estimates and predictors, their standard errors do not have any straightforward, easy-to-derive formula, which is why good mixed model software is essential for this important case.

9.4.3 Intermediate Inference Space BLUP

McLean et al. (1991) discussed a third inference space, which they called *intermediate* inference. For example, an alternative to the two predictable functions for the machine 1 mean presented above is

$$\mu + \tau_1 + (1/3)\sum_j O_j$$

This predictable function is conditioned on the operator main effects but not on the operator-machine interactions. For a manager assessing a machine's performance with a particular group of operators, this makes sense if operator performance averaged over machines is predictable, but specific interactions are not.

Aside from its potential application, this function has some theoretical features that help shed light on traditional ways of doing things in PROC GLM. You can compute the intermediate BLUP in PROC GLIMMIX (or PROC MIXED) using the following statement:

```
estimate 'BLUP - m 1 interm'
        intercept 3 machine 3 0 |
        intercept 1 machine 0 / subject 1 1 1 divisor=3;
```

The result is included in Output 9.2 above.

As was the case for the broad and narrow machine 1 means, the estimate is the same, 50.9483. But the standard error is different. It is 0.158—less than the broad but greater than the narrow space standard error. You can derive this standard error by defining the machine and operator main effects as fixed, but the machine-by-operator effects as random.

9.4.4 Broad Inference Space BLUP

You can also vary the inference space for subject-specific BLUPs. For example, a broad space predictable function for operator 1 averaged across machines is

$$\mu + (1/2)\tau_1 + O_1$$

This function assumes that you can estimate the machine effects and predict the operator 1 effect but that you do not want to restrict inference to the particular way in which operator 1 interacted with the machines in this study. Thus, this is broader inference than results from including the τO_{i1} effects.

You can compute the broad space BLUP for operator 1 in PROC GLIMMIX using the following statement:

```
estimate 'BLUP - op 1 broad'
        intercept 2 machine 1 1  |
        intercept 2 machine 0 / subject 1 0 0 divisor=2;
```

The results appear in the last row of the "Estimates" table in Output 9.2. The predictor is 51.682, with a standard error of 0.2391.

9.4.5 Comparison with Operator Effects Fixed Model—Narrow Inference Space and Fixed Effects Models

Although OPERATOR effects fit the definition of random effect in this example, it is instructive to see what estimates result if we treat OPERATOR effects as fixed. The estimable or predictable functions for the various inference spaces considered in the previous section provide insight into the interpretation of fixed effect inference, particularly standard errors. You can use PROC GLIMMIX or PROC MIXED to compute the fixed effects analysis, but computing it using PROC GLM is especially revealing.

Program

To compute the analysis using PROC GLM, use Program 9.5:

Program 9.5

```
proc glm data=machine;
   class machine operator;
   model y = machine|operator;
   random operator machine*operator/test;
   lsmeans machine operator machine*operator/stderr;
   lsmeans machine/stderr e=machine*operator;
   estimate 'diff' machine 1 -1/e;
run;
```

Results

The results appear in Output 9.3 and Output 9.4.

Output 9.3 PROC GLM Results for Machine-Operator Two-Way Model

Source	Type III Expected Mean Square
machine	Var(Error) + 2 Var(machine*operator) + Q(machine)
operator	Var(Error) + 2 Var(machine*operator) + 4 Var(operator)
machine*operator	Var(Error) + 2 Var(machine*operator)

machine	y LSMEAN	Standard Error	Pr > |t|
1	50.9483333	0.0899305	<.0001
2	51.9566667	0.0899305	<.0001

operator	y LSMEAN	Standard Error	Pr > |t|
1	51.7625000	0.1101420	<.0001
2	51.5675000	0.1101420	<.0001
3	51.0275000	0.1101420	<.0001

machine	operator	y LSMEAN	Standard Error	Pr > |t|
1	1	51.3550000	0.1557642	<.0001
1	2	50.8400000	0.1557642	<.0001
1	3	50.6500000	0.1557642	<.0001
2	1	52.1700000	0.1557642	<.0001
2	2	52.2950000	0.1557642	<.0001
2	3	51.4050000	0.1557642	<.0001

Interpretation

The LSMEANS for machine are computed using estimable functions with the same coefficients as the narrow space BLUP for machine

$$\mu + \tau_1 + (1/3)\sum_j O_j + (1/3)\sum_j \tau O_{1j}$$

The estimate of the LSMEANS for machine is the same (e.g., 50.9483 for machine 1) as that obtained for the broad, narrow, and intermediate estimates from Program 9.4 in PROC GLIMMIX shown in Output 9.2.

Output 9.4 PROC GLM Machine-Operator Output

Least Squares Means
Standard Errors and Probabilities Calculated Using the Type III MS for machine*operator as an Error Term

machine	y LSMEAN	Standard Error	Pr > |t|
1	50.9483333	0.1583947	<.0001
2	51.9566667	0.1583947	<.0001

Coefficients for Estimate diff		Row 1
Intercept		0
machine	1	1

Coefficients for Estimate diff		Row 1
machine	2	-1
operator	1	0
operator	2	0
operator	3	0
machine*operator 1 1		0.3333333333
machine*operator 1 2		0.3333333333
machine*operator 1 3		0.3333333333
machine*operator 2 1		-0.333333333
machine*operator 2 2		-0.333333333
machine*operator 2 3		-0.333333333

Parameter	Estimate	Standard Error	t Value	Pr > |t|
diff	-1.00833333	0.12718097	-7.93	0.0002

Interpretation

There are a few key details to highlight from this analysis:

- The default standard error for the LSMEANS for machine is the standard error for the *narrow space BLUP*—0.0899.

- Traditionally, you override the default error term using the optional error term E=MACHINE*OPERATOR to account for the fact that OPERATOR effects are random. The resulting standard error is 0.159. Using this option results in the *intermediate space BLUP* estimate and standard error.

- The ESTIMATE statement to assess the difference between machines in PROC GLM uses the same coefficients and yields the same results as the narrow space BLUP for machine difference. The ESTIMATE statement in PROC GLM has no option to override the default standard error.

- PROC GLM cannot compute the broad space estimates and standard errors for machine means and differences. They can be computed in PROC GLIMMIX or PROC MIXED. This is important because in the vast majority of practical applications, the broad inference space is of primary—if not exclusive—interest.

- The least squares means for OPERATOR and MACHINE × OPERATOR are computed by standard linear model methods for fixed effects. They do not in general yield the same results as the corresponding BLUPs computed in PROC GLIMMIX or PROC MIXED. PROC GLM cannot compute subject-specific BLUPs. For the model as defined in this example, the OPERATOR and MACHINE × OPERATOR estimates computed by PROC GLM are inappropriate.

The ANOVA table and the *F* values computed using the RANDOM statement with the TEST option in PROC GLM are correct. This is one of the few aspects of the PROC GLM analysis that are correct for this model.

9.5 A Multilocation Example

The summary section of Chapter 5 mentioned multilocation experiments as an important class of factorial experiments. The typical features of multilocation data are as follows:

- Treatments form one factor (often, the treatments themselves may have a factorial structure).

- Locations form another factor.

- Location × treatment interactions and location-specific treatment simple effects are often of interest.

- Locations are typically a sample of a larger population and hence most appropriately modeled as random effects.

- Thus, inference on location × treatment and location-specific treatment simple effects requires BLUP methodology.

This section illustrates multilocation mixed model analysis using the following example. The example is a multicenter trial to compare four treatments. Treatments are observed at each of nine centers or locations. At each center, a randomized complete block design with three blocks is used. Two natural candidates for random effects are the centers and blocks within centers. Perhaps most importantly, if treatment effects are different at different centers, then a third random effect would be represented as a treatment by center interaction.

The data appear as "Multicenter Trial."

9.5.1 Modeling Issues for a Multicenter Trial

As also described in model Equation 9.2, these data can be described by the model

$$y_{ijk} = \mu + \tau_i + c_j + \tau c_{ij} + b(c)_{jk} + e_{ijk}$$

where terms are defined as follows:

- y_{ijk} denotes the observation on the ith treatment on the kth block at the jth center.
- μ denotes the intercept.
- τ_i is the effect of the ith treatment.
- c_j is the effect of the jth center.
- τc_{ij} is the ij^{th} center × treatment interaction effect.
- $b(c)_{jk}$ is the effect of the kth block at the jth center.
- e_{ijk} is random residual associated with the ijk^{th} observation.

The block effects are random, mutually independent, and distributed $N(0, \sigma_B^2)$, and random residual effects are independent and distributed $N(0, \sigma^2)$. The remaining assumptions depend on the specifics of the study and are considered controversial by many statisticians. There are two primary issues:

- Should center effects be considered fixed or random?
- Should the center × treatment effect be included in the model?

It is not the purpose of this section to resolve this controversy. There are situations for which one model approach may clearly be appropriate and other situations for which the same model approach is clearly not appropriate. There is no "one size fits all" set of assumptions. In this section we first review the circumstances that should accompany each set of assumptions and then illustrate the analysis. Because this chapter concerns best linear unbiased prediction, most of the focus is on the random locations case, especially when location-specific treatment effects, a form of BLUP, are of interest.

First, a brief review of the circumstances that warrant the various assumptions.

Should center effects be considered fixed or random? Following the discussion in Chapters 1 and 2, the relevant question is "Do the centers observed constitute the entire population of interest, or are they a sample of a larger target population?" Is there something special about the centers included in the study, or would any set of representative centers be suitable for the study? Put another way, do center effects represent a sample that would allow variation among centers to be described plausibly by a probability distribution? If center effects do not plausibly represent a probability distribution and have been deliberately selected for specific reasons (similar to how you select treatment levels), then they should be considered fixed. Otherwise, they are random. Center effects are often considered fixed simply because otherwise there would too few denominator degrees of freedom to test treatment effects. This "reasoning by convenience" is fallacious. It is easy to show by simulation that it is an open invitation to drastically excessive Type I error rates.

Should the center × treatment effect be included in the model? The rationale for excluding center × treatment from the model follows the experimental unit criterion for identifying terms that belong in the model discussed in Chapter 5. For the multicenter trial in this example, the experimental unit is block × center × treatment. Center × treatment does not correspond to any physical unit in the design. However, if you exclude it from the model, you implicitly assume that treatment effects must be identical at all locations. In many, if not most, multicenter trials, this is a questionable leap of faith. The relevant question to ask is thus, Can center-specific differences in treatment effect be ruled out? If the answer to this question is "no" or "not sure," then center × treatment should be included in the model, at least initially.

The next two subsections present both alternatives: subsection 9.5.2 covers the location effects fixed model; 9.5.3 covers location effects random. This will allow us to compare and contrast the results and interpretation.

9.5.2 Analysis with Fixed Center Effects

You use the following PROC GLIMMIX statements in program 9.6 to implement the basic elements of the analysis, assuming that the center effects are fixed. To reiterate from the discussion above, you assume center (or location) effects are fixed if they *are* the entire population being studied or if they have been deliberately selected for specific reasons. For example, locations may represent particular soil types or climatic conditions in an agronomic trial or well-defined socioeconomic or risk groups in a clinical trial. Historically, especially in the days before PROC MIXED, this was considered the "standard" analysis.

Program 9.6

```
proc glimmix data=MultiCenter;
   class center block treatment;
   model response=center treatment center*treatment;
   random block / subject=center;
   lsmeans treatment;
   lsmeans center*treatment/slice=center;
run;
```

Output 9.5 shows relevant results from this analysis.

Output 9.5 Multicenter Data Analysis with Fixed Center Effects

Covariance Parameter Estimates			
Cov Parm	Subject	Estimate	Standard Error
block	center	0.005719	0.005085
Residual		0.03475	0.006688

Type III Tests of Fixed Effects				
Effect	Num DF	Den DF	F Value	Pr > F
center	8	18	22.80	<.0001
treatment	3	54	8.23	0.0001
center*treatment	24	54	1.45	0.1306

treatment Least Squares Means					
treatment	Estimate	Standard Error	DF	t Value	Pr > |t|
1	2.9196	0.03871	54	75.41	<.0001
2	2.7304	0.03871	54	70.53	<.0001
3	2.9200	0.03871	54	75.42	<.0001
4	2.9589	0.03871	54	76.43	<.0001

Tests of Effect Slices for center*treatment Sliced By center				
center	Num DF	Den DF	F Value	Pr > F
A	3	54	0.54	0.6544
B	3	54	2.22	0.0965
C	3	54	0.66	0.5777
D	3	54	2.89	0.0439
E	3	54	2.85	0.0456
F	3	54	2.45	0.0735
G	3	54	3.72	0.0167
H	3	54	3.49	0.0217
I	3	54	0.97	0.4120

Interpretation

From the "Type 3 Tests of Fixed Effects" table, start with the test of no center × treatment interaction. The *F* value, 1.45, and *p*-value, 0.1306, appears to indicate that there is no evidence of an interaction—that is, no evidence of center-specific treatment effects (however, more about this later). This appears to justify assessing treatment main effects. The treatment *F* value is 8.23 with $p < 0.0001$. The treatment least squares means indicate that the mean response to treatment 2 (2.73) is less than the other treatments, which range from 2.91 to 2.96. You could add a DIFF option to the first LSMEANS statement to obtain interval estimates or tests of specific pairwise differences, or you could add CONTRAST or ESTIMATE statements to address specific objectives. These are not shown here, but are similar to examples in previous chapters.

Note that as with any factorial experiment, inference is a two-step process:

1. Center × treatment interaction is evaluated first. If it is non-negligible, you focus on simple effects (for example, starting with the "Tests of Effect Slices" output).
2. Only if interaction is deemed negligible does one proceed to inference on the treatment main effects.

In this study, both treatment and center × treatment effects are tested using the residual error term. Hence, there are 54 denominator degrees of freedom for each test.

Although the test for center × treatment interaction *appears* to be non-significant, we should be cautious about proceeding to main effects for two reasons. First, many statistical methods texts—for example, Snedecor and Cochran (1989) and Milliken and Johnson (2009)—warn against concluding that the interaction is negligible when there are multiple numerator degrees of freedom for interaction and the *p*-value is <.20. Second, on the "Tests of Effect Slices" table in Output 9.5, three of the nine centers (A, C, and I) show no evidence of treatment effect. Two centers, B and F, show at best marginal evidence. Only four of the nine centers show statistically significant differences among the treatment means. Output 9.6 shows the center × treatment least squares means for these four centers (D, E, G, and H, where treatment effects are clearly significant; in the interest of space, the other centers are not shown). You can visualize these differences by adding the following option to the LSMEANS statement:

```
lsmeans center*treatment / slice=center plot=meanplot(sliceby=treatment join);
```

Figure 9.2: Interaction Plot Showing Treatment Effect by Center

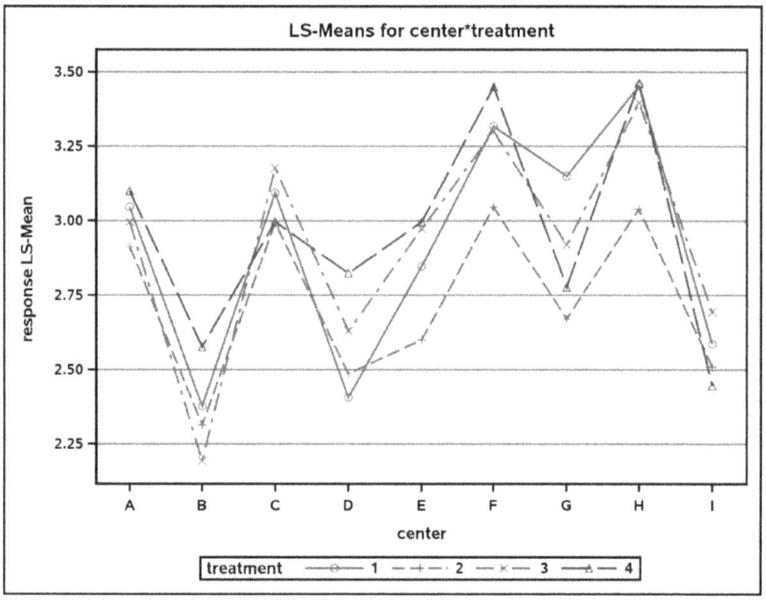

Notice that the treatment differences are visually most obvious at centers E, F, G, and H, whereas the treatment means are visually similar at centers A, C and I. Also, the degree to which the profile lines deviate from being parallel to one another is a visual indication of the strength of treatment × center interaction.

Output 9.6: Center × Treatment Least Squares Means for Centers with Significant Treatment Effects

center	treatment	Estimate	Standard Error	DF	t Value	Pr > |t|
D	1	2.4067	0.1161	54	20.72	<.0001
D	2	2.4867	0.1161	54	21.41	<.0001
D	3	2.6300	0.1161	54	22.64	<.0001
D	4	2.8233	0.1161	54	24.31	<.0001
E	1	2.8467	0.1161	54	24.51	<.0001
E	2	2.6000	0.1161	54	22.39	<.0001
E	3	2.9733	0.1161	54	25.60	<.0001
E	4	2.9967	0.1161	54	25.80	<.0001
G	1	3.1500	0.1161	54	27.12	<.0001
G	2	2.6700	0.1161	54	22.99	<.0001
G	3	2.9200	0.1161	54	25.14	<.0001
G	4	2.7767	0.1161	54	23.91	<.0001
H	1	3.4533	0.1161	54	29.73	<.0001
H	2	3.0400	0.1161	54	26.17	<.0001
H	3	3.3967	0.1161	54	29.25	<.0001
H	4	3.4633	0.1161	54	29.82	<.0001

Comments on Center × Treatment LS Means

Of the four centers that show unambiguously significant treatment effects, two of them, D and G, show a pattern of treatment differences unlike the pattern among main effect means. At center D, the mean of treatment 1 is less than the mean of treatment 2 and the mean of treatment 3, while it is noticeably greater than that of treatment 2, is substantially less than the mean of treatment 4. For center G, treatments 2 and 4 have means that are moderate, whereas treatments 1 and 3 have relatively high means.

There are two ways to look at the implications of the slices by center and center × treatment least squares means. First, one can make them the focus of the analysis. Second, one can dismiss them as relatively unimportant and proceed with inference based on treatment main effects only.

The rationale for the former approach, focusing on simple effects, is as follows. The *F* test for center × treatment effect has 24 *numerator* degrees of freedom. Many statistical methods texts warn about the lack of power of tests with many numerator degrees of freedom. Snedecor and Cochran (1989), for example, suggest that when degrees of freedom for interaction are large, the interaction should not be disregarded unless the *p*-value is much greater than α-levels one would usually use—e.g., greater than 0.20. By this argument, the center × treatment *p*-value, 0.1306, should be considered evidence of non-ignorable interaction and further inference should be on center-specific simple effects.

The rationale for the latter approach, focusing on main effects, is as follows. You could argue that the center-specific effects observed in these data are just an expression of minor localized differences in the population. By this argument, simple effect inference would be regarded as "ghost-chasing" or overinterpreting the data, and thus a distraction from the "big picture"—i.e., differences among main effect means.

The *p*-values shown here are unadjusted. For these data, if they were adjusted for multiplicity, for example, using Bonferroni's procedure, the apparent significance might disappear. However, even with such adjustments, dilemmas of the sort illustrated by these data are possible. Clearly, this is a judgment call. There are data sets where this approach can be justified. Such a judgment requires experience and knowledge of the subject matter of the study, as well as a sense of the ever-present tradeoffs between false positives and false negatives and losses associated with them. This argument could easily be rephrased, "the center-specific effects observed in these data are just an expression of localized variation in the population," which essentially defines centers as random effects.

9.5.3 Analysis with Random Center Effects

With the random (or location) effects model, the center effects, c_j, are assumed to be mutually independent and distributed N(0, σ_C^2) and the center × treatment effects, τc_{ij}, are assumed to be mutually independent and distributed N(0, σ_{TC}^2). The most common forms of inference are population-wide (broad)—that is, inference on treatment means, $\mu + \tau_i$ or location- (center-) specific. The center-specific case is equivalent to subject-specific inference discussed in previous sections of this chapter. Interest would typically focus on treatment effects at specific centers or sets of centers.

A special case of BLUP, called "narrow inference" in this discussion, produces results similar to the fixed center-effects model. In multilocation trials, you ordinarily would not be interested in narrow inference unless you consider locations fixed. However, it is of interest for the sake of comparison; this section presents an example.

Basic Analysis and Population-Averaged Inference

You can use Program 9.7 to compute the basis analysis—that is, estimates of variance components, overall tests of treatment effects, and estimates of and comparisons among treatment LS-means.

Program 9.7

```
proc glimmix data=MultiCenter;
   class center block treatment;
   model response=treatment / ddfm=KR2;
   random intercept block treatment /subject=center;
   lsmeans treatment / diff;
run;
```

Results

Output 9.7 shows relevant results.

Output 9.7 Random Center Effect Analysis of Multicenter Data: Broad Inference

Covariance Parameter Estimates		
Cov Parm	Subject	Estimate
Intercept	center	0.1034
block	center	0.005719
treatment	center	0.005170
Residual		0.03475

Type 3 Tests of Fixed Effects				
Effect	Num DF	Den DF	F Value	Pr > F
treatment	3	24	5.69	0.0043

Least Squares Means						
Effect	treatment	Estimate	Standard Error	DF	t Value	Pr > |t|
treatment	1	2.9196	0.1164	9.9	25.07	<.0001
treatment	2	2.7304	0.1164	9.9	23.45	<.0001
treatment	3	2.9200	0.1164	9.9	25.08	<.0001
treatment	4	2.9589	0.1164	9.9	25.41	<.0001

Interpretation

The block(center) and error variance component estimates are identical to those obtained with fixed center effect analysis ($\hat{\sigma}_B^2 = 0.0057$, $\hat{\sigma}^2 = 0.03475$). The center and center × treatment variance components are $\hat{\sigma}_C^2 = 0.1034$ and $\hat{\sigma}_{TC}^2 = 0.0517$, respectively. The treatment means are identical to those in the fixed center analysis, but the standard errors are not. For fixed centers, the standard error of a mean is

$$\sqrt{\frac{\hat{\sigma}^2 + \hat{\sigma}_B^2}{36}} = 0.03871$$

whereas for random centers the standard error is

$$\sqrt{\frac{\hat{\sigma}^2 + \hat{\sigma}_B^2 + 4\hat{\sigma}_{TC}^2 + 4\hat{\sigma}_C^2}{36}} = 0.1164$$

Similarly, with random center effects, the standard error of a treatment difference is

$$\sqrt{\frac{2\left(\hat{\sigma}^2 + 4\hat{\sigma}_{TC}^2\right)}{36}} = 0.061$$

whereas with the fixed center analysis the standard error would be based on $\hat{\sigma}^2$ only. The standard errors reflect differences in the sources of random variations assumed to affect treatment effects in the two models. The interval estimates that you obtain from the random center analysis are assumed to apply to the entire population of centers, of which the centers in the data set are only a sample. On the other hand, the interval estimates for treatment means obtained from fixed center analysis assume that the centers in the data set are the population. From a random center perspective, they are similar to "narrow" inference space treatment mean BLUPs.

Narrow Inference Space Treatment Means

The narrow inference space treatment mean BLUPs are defined using the same estimable function as fixed center analysis uses to compute treatment least squares means: $\mu + \tau_i + \bar{c}_. + \overline{(\tau c)}_{i.}$. In the random center effect analysis, you add ESTIMATE statements to the PROC GLIMMIX program shown in the last section to compute these BLUPs. For example, for treatment 1, consider the following ESTIMATE statements:

```
estimate 'trt 1 LS Mean'
    intercept 1 treatment 1 0 0 0;
estimate 'trt 1 BLUP "Narrow"'
    intercept 9 treatment 9 0 0 0 |
    intercept 1 treatment 1 0 0 0 /
    subject 1 1 1 1 1 1 1 1 1 divisor=9;
estimate 'trt 1 BLUP "alt"'
    intercept 9 treatment 9 | intercept 1 /
    subject 1 1 1 1 1 1 1 1 1 divisor=9;
estimate 'trt1 vs trt2'
    treatment 1 -1 0;
estimate 'trt 1 v 2 BLUP'
```

```
treatment 9 -9 0 0 | treatment 1 -1 0 0 /
subject 1 1 1 1 1 1 1 1 1 divisor=9;
```

The first statement reproduces the random center least squares means. The second statement applies the definition of the least-square mean for the fixed center analysis. Note that center and center × treatment effects appear to the right of the vertical bar (|), as they are random effects in this analysis. The third statement is a modified BLUP, similar to the "intermediate" inference space BLUP introduced in Section 9.4. The final two statements estimate the difference between treatments 1 and 2: the first between least squares means as defined in the random center model; the second between treatment 1 and 2 BLUPs, whose coefficients are identical to the difference between least squares means in the fixed center effect model. Output 9.8 shows the results.

Output 9.8: Estimates Comparing LS-Means versus BLUPs for Treatment Means

	Estimates				
Label	Estimate	Standard Error	DF	t Value	Pr > |t|
trt 1 LS Mean	2.9196	0.1164	9.898	25.07	<.0001
trt 1 BLUP "Narrow"	2.9196	0.03871	67.93	75.41	<.0001
trt 1 BLUP "alt"	2.9196	0.04553	26.52	64.12	<.0001
trt1 vs trt2	0.1893	0.06102	24	3.10	0.0049
trt 1 v 2 BLUP	0.1893	0.05073	54	3.73	0.0005

Interpretation

"Trt 1 LS Mean" and "trt 1 BLUP 'narrow'" yield estimates and standard errors identical to random center and fixed center least squares means, respectively. You can see that the estimates and standard errors are identical to the random center LS-mean and the fixed center LS-mean for treatment 1, respectively. Likewise, the "trt1 vs trt2" estimate is identical to the difference between treatment 1 and 2 LS-means for the random center output, whereas the "trt 1 v 2 BLUP" produces output identical to the fixed center estimates of treatment difference. These estimates help clarify what the random and fixed center analyses are doing. The random center effect analysis produces interval estimates based on assuming that uncertainty results from the centers being a sample of the population, whereas the fixed center analysis assumes that uncertainty results only from experimental error within centers. If centers represent a larger population, the latter interval estimate is unrealistic. The alternate "trt 1 BLUP" allows for uncertainty to result from variation in treatment effects among centers, but not from variation in the centers themselves.

9.5.4 Center-Specific Inference in Multicenter Example

Center-specific inference means that you assess center main effect BLUPs, center × treatment BLUPs, and simple effect differences between treatments at specific centers. As in previous examples, you use BLUPs rather than means because the BLUPs, unlike the means, use information about the variance among random center effects. Conventional means are not appropriate because they imply estimable functions based on both treatment and center effects; this implication is misleading, and produces inappropriate interval estimates, because center is not a fixed effect.

Obtainment of BLUPs

To illustrate, suppose you want the BLUP for treatment 1 at center A. The predictable function for this BLUP is $\mu + \tau_1 + c_A + \tau c_{1A}$. Similarly, for treatment 2, the BLUP is $\mu + \tau_2 + c_A + \tau c_{2A}$. The center-specific difference between treatment 1 and 2 is thus $\tau_1 - \tau_2 + \tau c_{1A} - \tau c_{2A}$. Similar BLUPs can be constructed for any center × treatment combination or treatment difference at any given center.

You can also compute BLUPs for centers (averaged over all treatments), or differences between centers, if these are of interest in a particular study. For example, the predictable function for the BLUP of center A is

$$\mu + \left(1/4\right)\sum_i \tau_i + c_A + \left(1/4\right)\sum_i \tau c_{iA}$$

The BLUP of the difference between two centers would be, for example,

$$c_A - c_B + \left(1/4\right)\sum_i \tau c_{iA} - \left(1/4\right)\sum_i \tau c_{iB}$$

for center A versus center B. An alternative center A BLUP would be $\mu + \frac{1}{4} \Sigma \tau_i + c_A$. This would broaden the inference space to allow variation among treatment effects at each center (the center × treatments effects) to be considered a contributor to uncertainty in this predictor. The BLUP for center difference with the equivalent inference space would be $c_A - c_B$.

You can expand the application of center-specific treatment differences to obtain the BLUP equivalent of the center × treatment SLICE in the fixed center analysis. For example, the simultaneous contrast

$$\tau_1 - \tau_2 + \tau c_{1A} - \tau c_{2A}$$
$$\tau_1 - \tau_3 + \tau c_{1A} - \tau c_{3A}$$
$$\tau_1 - \tau_4 + \tau c_{1A} - \tau c_{4A}$$

defines the BLUP equivalent for the slice among treatments for center A. This set is based on the result that the set of contrasts comparing treatment 1 to 2, 1 to 3, and 1 to 4 jointly imply that all treatment effects are equal. You could use any three independent contrasts such that if they are all zero, then the treatment effects are equal, and obtain the same result.

Implementation Using PROC GLIMMIX

You can compute these BLUPs using the following PROC GLIMMIX statements (Program 9.8):

Program 9.8

```
proc glimmix data=MultiCenter;
   class center block treatment;
   model response=treatment/ddfm=KR;
   random intercept block treatment / subject =center;
   estimate 'trt1 at center A blup'
            intercept 1 treatment 1 0 0 0 |
            intercept 1 treatment 1 0 0 0 / subject 1 0;
   estimate 'trt2 at center A blup'
            intercept 1 treatment 0 1 0 0 |
            intercept 1 treatment 0 1 0 0 / subject 1 0;
   estimate 'trt3 at center A blup'
            intercept 1 treatment 0 0 1 0 |
            intercept 1 treatment 0 0 1 0 / subject 1 0;
   estimate 'trt4 at center A blup'
            intercept 1 treatment 0 0 0 1 |
            intercept 1 treatment 0 0 0 1 / subject 1 0;
   estimate 'trt1 at center B blup'
            intercept 1 treatment 1 0 0 0 |
            intercept 1 treatment 1 0 0 0 / subject 0 1 0;
   estimate 'trt2 at center B blup'
            intercept 1 treatment 0 1 0 0 |
            intercept 1 treatment 0 1 0 0 / subject 0 1 0;
   estimate 'trt3 at center B blup'
            intercept 1 treatment 0 0 1 0 |
            intercept 1 treatment 0 0 1 0 / subject 0 1 0;
   estimate 'trt4 at center B blup'
            intercept 1 treatment 0 0 0 1 |
            intercept 1 treatment 0 0 0 1 / subject 0 1 0;
   estimate 'trt 1 v 2 at center A'
            treatment 1 -1 0 0 | treatment 1 -1 0 0 / subject 1 0;
   estimate 'trt 1 v 3 at center A'
            treatment 1 0 -1 0 | treatment 1 0 -1 0 / subject 1 0;
   estimate 'trt 1 v 4 at center A'
            treatment 1 0 0 -1 | treatment 1 0 0 -1 / subject 1 0;
   contrast 'slice at center A'
            treatment 1 -1 0 0 | treatment 1 -1 0 0,
            treatment 1 0 -1 0 | treatment 1 0 -1 0,
            treatment 1 0 0 -1 | treatment 1 0 0 -1 / subject 1 0;
   contrast 'slice at center A'
            treatment 1 -1 0 0 | treatment 1 -1 0 0,
            treatment 0 1 -1 0 | treatment 0 1 -1 0,
            treatment 0 1 0 -1 | treatment 0 1 0 -1 / subject 1 0;
   contrast 'slice at center B'
            treatment 1 -1 0 0 | treatment 1 -1 0 0,
```

```
              treatment 1 0 -1 0 | treatment 1 0 -1 0,
              treatment 1 0 0 -1 | treatment 1 0 0 -1 / subject 0 1 0;
   ods select Estimates Contrasts;
run;
```

Results and Interpretation

Note that the contrast entitled 'slice at center A' shows two different sets of independent comparisons among the treatments that both define the overall equality of treatment effects. You can see from the results shown in Output 9.9 that they produce identical results.

Output 9.9: PROC GLIMMIX Location-Specific Results for Multicenter Data

	Estimates				
Label	Estimate	Standard Error	DF	t Value	Pr > |t|
trt1 at center A blup	3.0443	0.09687	26.93	31.43	<.0001
trt2 at center A blup	2.8723	0.09687	26.93	29.65	<.0001
trt3 at center A blup	3.0291	0.09687	26.93	31.27	<.0001
trt4 at center A blup	3.0879	0.09687	26.93	31.88	<.0001
trt1 at center B blup	2.4172	0.09687	26.93	24.95	<.0001
trt2 at center B blup	2.2668	0.09687	26.93	23.40	<.0001
trt3 at center B blup	2.3608	0.09687	26.93	24.37	<.0001
trt4 at center B blup	2.5060	0.09687	26.93	25.87	<.0001
trt1 at center H blup	3.3797	0.09687	26.93	34.89	<.0001
trt2 at center H blup	3.1213	0.09687	26.93	32.22	<.0001
trt3 at loc H blup	3.3624	0.09687	26.93	34.71	<.0001
trt4 at center H blup	3.4099	0.09687	26.93	35.20	<.0001
trt 1 v 2 at center A	0.1720	0.1112	8.89	1.55	0.1566
trt 1 v 3 at center A	0.01517	0.1112	8.89	0.14	0.8945
trt 1 v 4 at center A	-0.04360	0.1112	8.89	-0.39	0.7041

	Contrasts			
Label	Num DF	Den DF	F Value	Pr > F
slice at center A	3	8.89	1.43	0.2971
slice at center A	3	8.89	1.43	0.2971
slice at center B	3	8.89	1.63	0.2510
slice at center C	3	8.89	1.19	0.3682
slice at center D	3	8.89	1.98	0.1877
slice at center E	3	8.89	2.57	0.1203
slice at center F	3	8.89	2.42	0.1339
slice at center G	3	8.89	2.30	0.1465
slice at center H	3	8.89	2.86	0.0978
slice at center I	3	8.89	1.11	0.3965

The "Estimates" table shows BLUPs for the four treatments at centers A, B, and H. The SAS code for center H was not shown in the program, but it is a straightforward adaptation of the code for centers A and B. The ESTIMATE statements can easily be adapted to the other centers as well.

The BLUPs are similar, but not equal, to the center × treatment least squares means for the fixed center analysis shown in Output 9.6. The differences are as follows:

- The BLUPs are shrinkage estimators as described in Section 9.4.3 and are regressed toward the mean.

- The standard errors reflect differences in the sources of variation considered random.

The SLICE BLUPs test the same differences, conceptually, as the fixed center slices, except these, too, are based on shrinkage estimators and on a broader inference space. Output 9.9 shows the results for all slices. In the interest of space, the SAS statements for centers C though I are omitted, but are defined similarly to those for centers A and B.

In many multilocation and multicenter trials, there are questions regarding the *stability* of treatments. In other words, do the same treatments perform well or poorly in all locations, or are there as-yet-unknown subpopulations such that some treatments perform optimally at certain types of locations whereas other treatments are better suited for other locations? By assessing the simple effects of treatments at each location using the BLUPs demonstrated in this example, the stability issue can be addressed using mixed model methods.

Note that for this example, the BLUP-based slices do not show nearly the extent of discrepancies seen in the fixed center slices. When fixed center analysis is used inappropriately for centers that are a sample of the population, the slices based in center × treatment least squares means (Output 9.5) tend to be overly sensitive to variation in treatment effects among centers. In other words, use of fixed center analysis when center effects are more appropriately regarded as random increases the Type I error rate. Using a model as much in line as possible with reality will help you make better decisions on any particular problem.

Output 9.10 shows results for BLUP-based slices defined using the same contrasts, but omitting the DDFM=KR2 option. This shows what happens when the standard errors are not corrected for bias and degrees of freedom are not approximated. You can see that the Type I error rate tends to be increased without the DDFM=KR2 correction. The DDFM=SATTERTH option corrects the degrees of freedom, but not the standard errors. The Type I error rate is lower without the DDFM option, but it is still excessive.

Output 9.10: PROC GLIMMIX Center-Specific Results for Multicenter Data, No DDFM=KR2 Option

	Contrasts			
Label	Num DF	Den DF	F Value	Pr > F
slice at center A	3	24	1.98	0.1434
slice at center A	3	24	1.98	0.1434
slice at center B	3	24	2.26	0.1077
slice at center C	3	24	1.65	0.2052
slice at center D	3	24	2.75	0.0651
slice at center E	3	24	3.55	0.0294
slice at center F	3	24	3.35	0.0357
slice at center G	3	24	3.19	0.0419
slice at center H	3	24	3.95	0.0201
slice at center I	3	24	1.53	0.2319

Finally, you can define BLUPs on subsets of centers. For example, the following statements allow you to look at the four treatment BLUPs at their corresponding slices for three subsets of the centers:

- A and C, two centers with no significant treatment effects

- B, D, and I, three centers with marginally significant or nonsignificant differences among the means and somewhat different ranks among the treatment BLUPs than at other centers

- E though H, the four centers with significant slices in the fixed center analysis

These subsets are mainly for demonstration. Obviously, you could define other subsets that would be of greater interest, depending on additional specifics about the centers or the objectives of the study. The SAS statements are as follows.

```
estimate 'trt1 @ Centers A,C'
      intercept 2 treatment 2 0 0 0 |
      intercept 1 treatment 1 0 0 0 / subject 1 0 1 0 divisor=2;
estimate 'trt2 @ Centers A,C'
      intercept 2 treatment 0 2 0 0 |
      intercept 1 treatment 0 1 0 0 / subject 1 0 1 0 divisor=2;
estimate 'trt3 @ Centers A,C'
      intercept 2 treatment 0 0 2 0 |
      intercept 1 treatment 0 0 1 0 / subject 1 0 1 0 divisor=2;
estimate 'trt4 @ Centers A,C'
      intercept 2 treatment 0 0 0 2 |
```

```
            intercept 1 treatment 0 0 0 1 / subject 1 0 1 0 divisor=2;
estimate 'trt1 @ Centers B,D,I'
            intercept 3 treatment 3 0 0 0 |
            intercept 1 treatment 1 0 0 0 / subject 0 1 0 1 0 0 0 0 1 divisor=3;
estimate 'trt2 @ Centers B,D,I'
            intercept 3 treatment 0 3 0 0 |
            intercept 1 treatment 0 1 0 0 / subject 0 1 0 1 0 0 0 0 1 divisor=3;
estimate 'trt3 @ Centers B,D,I'
            intercept 3 treatment 0 0 3 0 |
            intercept 1 treatment 0 0 1 0 / subject 0 1 0 1 0 0 0 0 1 divisor=3;
estimate 'trt4 @ Centers B,D,I'
            intercept 3 treatment 0 0 0 3 |
            intercept 1 treatment 0 0 0 1 / subject 0 1 0 1 0 0 0 0 1 divisor=3;
estimate 'trt1 @ Centers E,F,G,H'
            intercept 4 treatment 4 0 0 0 |
            intercept 1 treatment 1 0 0 0 / subject 0 0 0 0 1 1 1 1 0 divisor=4;
estimate 'trt2 @ Centers E,F,G,H'
            intercept 4 treatment 0 4 0 0 |
            intercept 1 treatment 0 1 0 0 / subject 0 0 0 0 1 1 1 1 0 divisor=4;
estimate 'trt3 @ Centers E,F,G,H'
            intercept 4 treatment 0 0 4 0 |
            intercept 1 treatment 0 0 1 0 / subject 0 0 0 0 1 1 1 1 0 divisor=4;
estimate 'trt4 @ Centers E,F,G,H'
            intercept 4 treatment 0 0 0 4 |
            intercept 1 treatment 0 0 0 1 / subject 0 0 0 0 1 1 1 1 0 divisor=4;
contrast 'slice at Centers A,C'
            treatment 2 -2 0 0 | treatment 1 -1 0 0,
            treatment 2 0 -2 0 | treatment 1 0 -1 0,
                treatment 2 0 0 -2 | treatment 1 0 0 -1 / subject 1 0 1 0;
contrast 'slice at Centers B,D,I'
            treatment 3 -3 0 0 | treatment 1 -1 0 0,
            treatment 3 0 -3 0 | treatment 1 0 -1 0,
            treatment 3 0 0 -3 | treatment 1 0 0 -1 / subject 0 1 0 1 0 0 0 0 1;
contrast 'slice at Centers E,F,G,H'
            treatment 4 -4 0 0 | treatment 1 -1 0 0,
        treatment 4 0 -4 0 | treatment 1 0 -1 0,
        treatment 4 0 0 -4 | treatment 1 0 0 -1 / subject 0 0 0 0 1 1 1 1 0;
```

Output 9.11 shows the results using the DDFM=KR2 option.

Output 9.11: PROC GLIMMIX Multicenter Results for Subsets of Centers

	Estimates				
Label	Estimate	Standard Error	DF	t Value	Pr > |t|
trt1 @ Centers A,C	3.0679	0.07035	36.84	43.61	<.0001
trt2 @ Centers A,C	2.9011	0.07035	36.84	41.24	<.0001
trt3 @ Centers A,C	3.0733	0.07035	36.84	43.69	<.0001
trt4 @ Centers A,C	3.0884	0.07035	36.84	43.90	<.0001
trt1 @ Centers B,D,I	2.5316	0.05891	48.12	42.98	<.0001
trt2 @ Centers B,D,I	2.3946	0.05891	48.12	40.65	<.0001
trt3 @ Centers B,D,I	2.5469	0.05891	48.12	43.24	<.0001
trt4 @ Centers B,D,I	2.6078	0.05891	48.12	44.27	<.0001
trt1 @ Centers E,F,G,H	3.1365	0.05226	59.24	60.02	<.0001
trt2 @ Centers E,F,G,H	2.8969	0.05226	59.24	55.43	<.0001
trt3 @ Centers E,F,G,H	3.1231	0.05226	59.24	59.76	<.0001
trt4 @ Centers E,F,G,H	3.1575	0.05226	59.24	60.42	<.0001

Contrasts				
Label	Num DF	Den DF	F Value	Pr > F
slice at Centers A,C	3	17.58	2.27	0.1162
slice at Centers B,D,I	3	32.41	3.23	0.0352
slice at Centers E,F,G,H	3	53.11	7.24	0.0004

The results in the "Estimates" table tend to suggest that, despite difference in individual centers, the patterns of differences among the means for the three subsets of centers are similar. The "Contrasts" table shows treatment effect *p*-values ranging from 0.0004 to 0.1162. These discrepancies are considerably less than among individual centers. Depending on the context and specific objectives, this output may be taken as evidence that there are differences among subpopulations represented by the three subsets or as evidence that treatment effects are similar enough among all centers to justify population-wide or broad inference on the treatment means.

9.6 Matrix Notation for BLUP

This section presents the basic concepts and terminology of best linear unbiased prediction in matrix notation. This section focuses on application and interpretation. Appendix A contains additional theoretical detail.

The basic form of a linear mixed model is

$$y_j = \sum_i \beta_i X_{ji} + \sum_k u_k Z_{jk} + e_j$$

where terms are defined as follows:

- y_j is the jth observation.
- β_i are fixed effect parameters.
- X_{ji} are constants associated with the fixed effects.
- u_k are random effects.
- Z_{jk} are constants associated with the random effects.
- e_j is the jth residual error.

Specific forms of the linear models were discussed in Section 9.2 and in the previous chapters. Alternatively, you can write the mixed model in matrix form as $\mathbf{Y} = \mathbf{X}\boldsymbol{\beta} + \mathbf{Z}\mathbf{u} + \mathbf{e}$.

The expected value of an observation is

$$E[\mathbf{Y}] = E[\mathbf{X}\boldsymbol{\beta} + \mathbf{Z}\mathbf{u} + \mathbf{e}] = \mathbf{X}\boldsymbol{\beta}$$

because the expected values of the random effect vector **u** and the error vector **e** are 0. This is called the *unconditional expectation*, or the mean of **Y** averaged over all possible **u**. The subtlety of this quantity is important: in practical terms, the observed levels of the random effects are a random sample of a larger population. The unconditional expectation is the mean of **Y** over the *entire population*.

The conditional expectation of **Y** given **u**, denoted $E[\mathbf{Y}|\mathbf{u}]$, is

$$E[\mathbf{Y}|\mathbf{u}] = \mathbf{X}\boldsymbol{\beta} + \mathbf{Z}\mathbf{u}$$

In practical terms, this is the mean of **Y** *for the specific set* of levels of the random effect *actually observed*.

The unconditional mean is thus a population-wide average, whereas the conditional mean is an average specific to an observed set of random effects. Because the set of observed levels of the random factors is not an *exact* duplicate of the entire population, the conditional and unconditional means are not equal, in general.

We complete a full linear mixed model specification by adding the following distributional assumptions, where, as usual, N refers the normal (Gaussian) probability distribution and a tilde (~) is shorthand for "is distributed as"

$$\mathbf{u} \sim \mathrm{N}(\mathbf{0}, \mathbf{G})$$

$$\mathbf{Y} \mid \mathbf{u} \sim \mathrm{N}(\mathbf{X\beta} + \mathbf{Zu}, \mathbf{R})$$

$$\mathbf{Y} \sim \mathrm{N}(\mathbf{X\beta}, \mathbf{V})$$

$$\mathbf{V} = \mathrm{Var}[\mathbf{Y}] = \mathbf{ZGZ'} + \mathbf{R}$$

Assuming initially that $\mathbf{G}$ and $\mathbf{R}$ are known, a primary goal is to estimate $\mathbf{\beta}$ and $\mathbf{u}$. Applying standard linear model theory leads to a foundational set of equations:

$$\begin{bmatrix} \mathbf{X'R^{-1}X} & \mathbf{X'R^{-1}Z} \\ \mathbf{Z'R^{-1}X} & \mathbf{Z'R^{-1}Z} + \mathbf{G^{-1}} \end{bmatrix} \begin{bmatrix} \tilde{\mathbf{\beta}} \\ \tilde{\mathbf{u}} \end{bmatrix} = \begin{bmatrix} \mathbf{X'R^{-1}y} \\ \mathbf{Z'R^{-1}y} \end{bmatrix}$$

These are known as Henderson's mixed model equations, or simply as the *mixed model equations*. Note that they are an extended version of usual linear model normal equations, and the inverse of $\mathbf{G}$ regularizes / ridges the random effects. The solutions are

$$\begin{bmatrix} \tilde{\mathbf{\beta}} \\ \tilde{\mathbf{u}} \end{bmatrix} = \begin{bmatrix} \mathbf{X'R^{-1}X} & \mathbf{X'R^{-1}Z} \\ \mathbf{Z'R^{-1}X} & \mathbf{Z'R^{-1}Z} + \mathbf{G^{-1}} \end{bmatrix}^{-} \begin{bmatrix} \mathbf{X'R^{-1}y} \\ \mathbf{Z'R^{-1}y} \end{bmatrix}$$

$$= \begin{bmatrix} \left(\mathbf{X'V^{-1}X}\right)^{-1} \mathbf{X'V^{-1}y} \\ \mathbf{GZ'V^{-1}}\left(\mathbf{y} - \mathbf{X}\left(\mathbf{X'V^{-1}X}\right)^{-1} \mathbf{X'V^{-1}y}\right) \end{bmatrix}$$

Since the right-most term in the parentheses for the random effects solution is the same as the fixed effects estimate, we can also write

$$\tilde{\mathbf{u}} = \mathbf{GZ'V^{-1}}\left(\mathbf{y} - \mathbf{X}\tilde{\mathbf{\beta}}\right)$$

When $\mathbf{G}$ and $\mathbf{R}$ (and thus also $\mathbf{V}$) are unknown, we estimate them using restricted maximum likelihood (see Appendix A) and then plug their estimates into the preceding equations to obtain estimates of $\mathbf{\beta}$ and $\mathbf{u}$ from $\mathbf{y}$.

The BLUP formula $\tilde{\mathbf{u}} = \mathbf{GZ'V^{-1}}\left(\mathbf{y} - \mathbf{X}\tilde{\mathbf{\beta}}\right)$ can be derived in several ways; see Appendix A, Robinson (1991), and Huber (2013). For some additional intuition behind how and why BLUP works, split this formula into three parts, each enclosed in brackets as follows:

$$[\mathbf{G^{1/2}}][\mathbf{G^{1/2}Z'V^{-1/2}}][\mathbf{V^{-1/2}}\left(\mathbf{y} - \mathbf{X}\tilde{\mathbf{\beta}}\right)]$$

Working from right to left, the term on the right represents the original data standardized to have mean 0 and identity covariance matrix, a set of canonical residuals. The middle term represents the correlation matrix between the data and the random effects, which rotates and projects the residuals into "BLUP space". Then finally the term on the left rescales the mapped residuals to have appropriate variance. This is an illustration of the powerful elegance of matrix algebraic representations of statistical models.

BLUPs as defined above are centered around zero, but can be shifted by combining them with fixed effect estimates. Recall that in the previous chapters, statistical inference is based on linear combinations of the fixed effects. Linear combinations of fixed effects, denoted $\Sigma_i \mathbf{K}_i \mathbf{\beta}_i$, are called *estimable functions* if they can be constructed from a linear combination of unconditional means of the observations. That is, if $\mathbf{K'\beta} = \mathbf{T'E}[\mathbf{Y}] = \mathbf{T'X\beta}$ for some $\mathbf{T}$, then it is estimable. Quantities such as regression coefficients, treatment means, treatment differences, contrasts, and simple effects in factorial experiments are all common examples of estimable functions.

Estimable functions do not depend on the random effects. The examples discussed in Section 9.2 introduced linear combinations of both the $\mathbf{\beta}_i$ and $\mathbf{u}_j$ of interest in many practical situations. A generalization of the estimable function is required for such cases. Linear combinations of the fixed and random effects, $\mathbf{K'\beta} + \mathbf{M'u}$, can be formed from linear combinations of the conditional means. Such linear combinations are called *predictable functions*. A function $\mathbf{K'\beta + M'u}$ is predictable if its $\mathbf{K'\beta}$ component is estimable.

The mixed model equations, discussed in Appendix A, provide solutions for both estimable and predictable functions. Using the mixed model equation solution for β in an estimable function results in the *best linear unbiased estimate* (BLUE) of $\mathbf{K'\beta}$. For predictable functions, the solutions for β and $\mathbf{u}$ provide the best linear unbiased *predictor* (BLUP) of $\mathbf{K'\beta + M'u}$.

To summarize, linear combinations of fixed effects only are called estimable functions. The solution of the mixed model equations results in estimates, or BLUEs, of $\mathbf{K'\beta}$. Linear combinations of fixed *and* random effects are called predictable functions. Solving the mixed model equations yields *predictors*, or BLUPs, of $\mathbf{K'\beta + M'u}$.

Estimates, or BLUEs, and predictors, or BLUPs, imply different targets of statistical inference. Various terminology has been developed to describe the differences. McLean et al. (1991) discussed the *inference space* and defined *broad* versus *narrow* inference. Zeger et al. (1988) discussed *population-wide* versus *subject-specific* inference. To oversimplify, *broad* and population-wide generally refer to inference based exclusively on fixed effects and estimable functions, whereas *narrow* and subject-specific generally refer to inference based on predictable functions.

Technically, the broad/narrow and population-wide/subject-specific terminology is not interchangeable, and the distinctions are somewhat subtler. You can better understand the distinctions with a specific example. The machine-operator example introduced in Section 9.2.2 and developed in Section 9.4 is a good place to start.

The unconditional mean of an observation is $E[y_{ijk}] = \mu + \tau_i$. If you wanted an estimate of the average performance of the ith machine over the entire population of operators—those actually observed in the study *and* those in the population but not observed—you would estimate $\mu + \tau_i$. Similarly, if you wanted to estimate the average difference between two machines over the entire population, you would estimate $\tau_i - \tau_{i'}$. Both of these terms involve only fixed effects, and thus they are *estimates*.

Alternatively, you may want to assess the performance of a machine for the specific set of operators observed. Perhaps the machine's designer wants an estimate over the entire population, but as the manager of your company, you want to know how *your* operators, as a group, are doing. If so, you want to determine the conditional mean, $\mu + \tau_i + (1/J)\Sigma O_j + (1/J)\Sigma\Sigma\tau O_{ij}$, where J is the number of operators. In terms of a difference, you want to determine $\tau_i - \tau_{i'} + (1/J)\,\Sigma\Sigma[\tau O_{ij} - \tau O_{i'j}]$. These expressions represent an example of what McLean et al. (1991) called the *narrow* inference space. They would not necessarily be called *subject-specific*, because while they narrow the inference space, they restrict attention to a group of operators, not a specific operator. Narrow inference terms are *predictors* because they involve both fixed and random effects. You can see that narrow inference terms share the same estimable functions as their broad inference analogs, but the narrow space terms have additional random effects.

Finally, suppose, as a manager, you want to use the study to evaluate an individual employee or to determine which machine is best to assign to that particular operator. In such cases, you do not want averages. You want a quantity that is specific to a given operator. To assess a given operator, averaged over all machines, you want to determine one of two possible predictable functions:

$$\mu + \left(\frac{1}{I}\right)\sum_i \tau_i + O_j + \left(\frac{1}{I}\right)\sum_i \sum_j \tau O_{ij} \tag{9.3}$$

or

$$\mu + \left(\frac{1}{I}\right)\sum_i \tau_i + O_j \tag{9.4}$$

where I is the number of machines. The narrow space BLUP is obtained from Equation 9.3, whereas Equation 9.4 yields the broad space BLUP. To assess a specific operator's performance on a given machine, you want to determine the conditional mean, $\mu + \tau_i + O_j + \tau O_{ij}$. To compare an individual operator's performance on the two machines, you want to determine $\tau_i - \tau_{i'} + \tau O_{ij} - \tau O_{i'j}$. Each of these are what Zeger et al. (1988) called *subject-specific* terms. If you drop the random effects components of each subject-specific predictable function, you have its population-wide analog.

In the end, your choice of mixed model and associated inference space will depend on the problems that you are trying to solve and associated questions that you are trying to answer.

9.7 Summary

The chapter presents an introduction to best linear unbiased prediction (BLUP) and the distinction between estimation and prediction in mixed models. Section 9.2 surveys several examples to illustrate types of studies for which estimates and predictors that are of interest in practical situations. Section 9.3 covers predictors in a strictly random effects model. Section 9.4 presents a two-way model with one effect fixed. In addition to working through the analysis, this example shows the consequence of modeling an effect as fixed with regard to the implied inference space. Section 9.5 gives a detailed illustration of approaches that you can use with multilocation studies. Section 9.6 presents an example in which you can use BLUP to address an objective that calls for estimation of a lower percentile, not a measure of central tendency. Finally, Section 9.7 presents additional detail on the theory and methodology of inference on random effects.

This chapter discusses different methods of obtaining BLUPs that are available in PROC GLIMMIX and other mixed modeling procedures. The SOLUTION option in the RANDOM statement provides direct estimates. Output data sets from the MODEL statement with appropriate options combine random effect solutions with fixed effects estimates for row-by-row predictions. Finally, ESTIMATE and CONTRAST statements enable you to create customized BLUP functions that are tailored for a particular purpose and help elucidate the inner workings of this powerful methodology.

Chapter 10: Random Coefficient Models

10.1 Introduction 339
10.2 One-Way Random Effects Treatment Structure in a Completely Randomized Design Structure: An
Example 342
    10.2.1 Model: Simple Linear Regression Model with Random Coefficients...342
    10.2.2 Program..342
    10.2.3 Results..343
    10.2.4 Program to Fit a Model 344
    10.2.5 Results..344
    10.2.6 Program to Calculate the Values of Intercepts and Slopes...346
    10.2.7 Results..346
    10.2.8 Program to Assemble and Construct Data for Regression Lines 347
    10.2.9 Results..347
10.3 Random Student Effects: An Example 348
    10.3.1 Model: Simple Linear Regression Models with Additional Fixed Effects 348
    10.3.2 Analysis with Fixed Effects and Random Coefficients...348
10.4 Repeated Measures Growth Study: An Example 353
    10.4.1 Repeated Measures Analysis 355
    10.4.2 Random Coefficient Analysis..357
    10.4.3 Test of Lack of Fit..363
10.5 Prediction of the Shelf Life of a Product 364
    10.5.1 Example: A Pharmaceutical Stability Trial—Essential Background...365
    10.5.2 Estimation Using Best Linear Unbiased Prediction...367
    10.5.3 Estimation Using Fixed Effects Analysis of Covariance...371
    10.5.4 Estimation Using the "Naive" Mixed Model Approach...375
10.6 Summary 376

10.1 Introduction

Data that have a nested or hierarchical structure are common in a wide variety of disciplines, and similar methods for analyzing such data are found in these disciplines under different guises. The analyses considered here fall under the headings of *random coefficient models* and *empirical Bayes models* in the statistics literature (Laird and Ware 1982, Strenio, Weisberg, and Bryk 1983, Rutter and Elashoff 1994, Wolfinger, 1996). Analogous terms in the educational and social science literature are *hierarchical linear models* and *multilevel linear models* (see, for example, Goldstein 1987, Bryk and Raudenbush 1992, and contributions in a special issue of the *Journal of Educational and Behavioral Statistics,* 1995). A primary objective of this chapter is to describe these models and illustrate how to fit random coefficient models using PROC GLIMMIX and PROC MIXED. Section 10.5 shows an application of a random coefficient models for the prediction of shelf life of a product.

The basic structure of random coefficient models builds on the analysis of covariance models discussed in Chapter 7. There linear regression models are used to include continuous variables (covariates) as independent variables in the model. In Chapter 7 the regression coefficients for the covariates were assumed to be fixed effects—that is, unknown fixed parameters that were estimated from the data.

In this chapter the regression coefficients for one or more covariates are assumed to be a random sample from some population of possible coefficients; hence the term *random coefficients*. Random coefficient models are sensible whenever the data arise from independent subjects or clusters and the regression model for each subject or cluster can be assumed to be a random deviation from some population of regression models.

The standard random coefficient model involves a random intercept and slope for each subject. Let y_{ij} denote the measurement of the jth observation on the ith subject, and x_{ij} is the regressor or independent variable that is measured on the jth observation of the ith subject, then the random coefficient model can be written as

$$y_{ij} = a_i + b_i x_{ij} + e_{ij}$$

$$(10.1)$$

where terms are defined as follows:

$$i = 1, 2, \ldots, t$$

$$j = 1, 2, \ldots, n_i$$

$$\begin{bmatrix} a_i \\ b_i \end{bmatrix} \sim iid \ \text{N}\left(\begin{bmatrix} \alpha \\ \beta \end{bmatrix}, \mathbf{G} \right)$$

$$\mathbf{G} = \begin{bmatrix} \sigma_a^2 & \sigma_{ab} \\ \sigma_{ab} & \sigma_b^2 \end{bmatrix}$$

and

$$e_{ij} \sim iid \ \text{N}\left(0, \sigma^2\right)$$

In Equation (10.1) it is assumed that the intercept and slope are correlated. Often, one tests this assumption, i.e. tests $\text{H}_0 : \sigma_{ab} = 0$, and if H_0 is not rejected, the analysis can proceed with a simplified

$$\mathbf{G} = \begin{bmatrix} \sigma_a^2 & 0 \\ 0 & \sigma_b^2 \end{bmatrix}$$

Equation 10.1 can be expressed as

$$y_{ij} = \alpha + a_i^* + \beta x_{ij} + b_i^* x_{ij} + e_{ij} \tag{10.2}$$

where terms are defined as follows:

$$i = 1, 2, \ldots, t$$

$$j = 1, 2, \ldots, n_i$$

$$a_i^* = a_i - \alpha$$

$$b_i^* = b_i - \beta$$

$$\begin{bmatrix} a_i^* \\ b_i^* \end{bmatrix} \sim iid \ \text{N}\left(\begin{bmatrix} 0 \\ 0 \end{bmatrix}, \mathbf{G} \right)$$

and

$$e_{ij} \sim iid \ \text{N}\left(0, \sigma^2\right)$$

Equation (10.2) can be expressed in terms of a mixed model as

$$y_{ij} = \alpha + \beta x_{ij} + a_i^* + b_i^* x_{ij} + e_{ij} \tag{10.3}$$

The terms in the model are $i = 1, 2, \ldots, t$ $j = 1, 2, \ldots, n_i$. The terms in Equation 10.3 are defined as follows:

- $\alpha + \beta x_{ij}$ is the fixed effects part of the model.
- $a_i^* + b_i^* x_{ij}$ is the random effects part of the model.
- e_{ij} is the residual part of the model.

Finally, Equation 10.3 can be expressed as follows:

$$y_{ij} = \alpha + \beta x_{ij} + e_{ij}^{*} \qquad\qquad (10.4)$$

where terms are defined as follows:

$$i = 1, 2, ..., t$$

$$j = 1, 2, ..., n_i$$

$$E\left[y_{ij}\right] = \alpha + \beta x_{ij}$$

$$e_{ij}^{*} = a_i^{*} + b_i^{*} x_{ij} + e_{ij}$$

and

$$\mathrm{Var}\left[y_{ij}\right] = \left[1, x_{ij}\right] \mathbf{G} \begin{bmatrix} 1 \\ x_{ij} \end{bmatrix} + \sigma^2$$

The equation $E[y_{ij}] = \alpha + \beta x$ is the mean of the distribution of the regression models. A graphical representation of this model is displayed in Figure 10.1. The random regression lines for each subject deviate from the overall population regression line (solid line), $\mu(y \mid x) = \alpha + \beta x$. For this graph, the covariance between intercept and slope, σ_{ab}, is small, because there is no real relationship between a subject's intercept and slope.

Figure 10.1: Several Simple Linear Regression Models from a Random Sample of Treatments with the Population Model

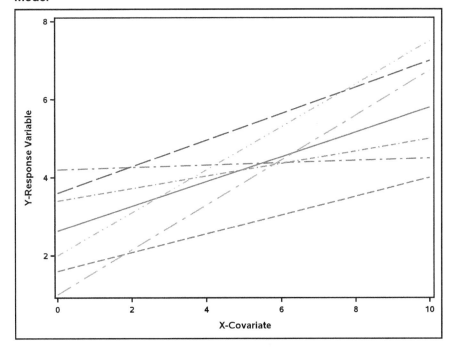

The random coefficient model is a conditional hierarchical linear model (Bryk and Raudenbush 1992) where the experimental units are nested within the randomly selected levels of the subjects. It is possible to introduce additional levels of hierarchy as well as more than two random coefficients at each level. The first two examples in the next section consider only the standard random intercept-slope model just described, and the third example consists of a quadratic random coefficient model with three random coefficients. Using the notation from the previous section, the analyses of the examples consist of estimating α, β, $\mathbf{G}$, and σ^2 and of testing hypotheses about the parameters.

10.2 One-Way Random Effects Treatment Structure in a Completely Randomized Design Structure: An Example

The data in Data Set "Winter Wheat," are from ten varieties of wheat that were randomly selected from the population of varieties of hard red winter wheat adapted to dry climate conditions. The experimental units are 1-acre plots of land in a 60-acre field. The varieties were randomly assigned to six, 1-acre plots of land in the field. It was thought that the preplanting moisture content of the plots could have an influence on the germination rate and hence on the eventual yield of the plots. Thus, the amount of preplanting moisture in the top 36 inches of the soil was determined from a soil core from the center of each plot. The response is yield in bushels per acre (YIELD), and the covariate is the measured amount of preplanting moisture (MOIST), which was measured before planting the varieties on the plots. Because the varieties were randomly selected, the resulting regression model for each variety is a random model selected from the population of variety models. The fixed effects of the model are the population intercept and slope, which are the expected values of the population of the intercepts and slopes of the varieties.

10.2.1 Model: Simple Linear Regression Model with Random Coefficients

The following model, similar to Equation 10.1, describes these data:

$$y_{ij} = a_i + b_i x_{ij} + e_{ij} \qquad (10.5)$$

where terms are defined as follows:

$$i = 1, 2, \ldots, 10$$

$$j = 1, 2, \ldots, 6$$

$$\begin{bmatrix} a_i \\ b_i \end{bmatrix} \sim iid \ \ N\left(\begin{bmatrix} \alpha \\ \beta \end{bmatrix}, \mathbf{G} \right)$$

$$\mathbf{G} = \begin{bmatrix} \sigma_a^2 & \sigma_{ab} \\ \sigma_{ab} & \sigma_b^2 \end{bmatrix}$$

and

$$e_{ij} \sim iid \ \ N\left(0, \sigma^2\right)$$

10.2.2 Program

Program 10.1 fits model 10.5 to the data where VARIETY is a class variable, MOIST (abbreviation for moisture content), and COVTEST is used to evaluate the importance of σ_{ab}.

Program 10.1

```
proc glimmix data=wheat noprofile;
   class variety;
   model yield = moist / solution;
   random int moist / type=un sub=variety solution G Gcorr;
   covtest / cl(type=elr);
   covtest "Test cov a and b = 0" general 0 1 0 0;
   ods output ParameterEstimates=fixed solutionr=random;
run;
```

The SUBJECT=VARIETY option in the RANDOM statement specifies that the intercept and slope of one variety are independently distributed from the intercepts and slopes of other varieties. The option TYPE=UN in the RANDOM statement specifies the covariance structure for a subject's random effects. TYPE=UN calls for an unstructured (2×2) covariance matrix, comprising the variance of the random intercepts (σ_a^2), the variance of the random slopes (σ_b^2), and their covariance (σ_{ab}). The effects INT and MOIST in the RANDOM statement, together with the SUBJECT=VARIETY option, instruct PROC GLIMMIX to add a random intercept and a random slope for each variety to the random effects part of the model, i.e., the RANDOM statement int most/subject=variety; models variety (the intercepts) and

Moist*Variety (the slopes). The fixed effects part specified by the MODEL statement consists of a fixed intercept (automatically included through the MODEL statement) and a fixed slope for MOIST. The COVTEST statement with the CL option requests estimated standard errors and 95% confidence intervals for the covariance parameters. The option (Type=elr) requests the confidence intervals be computed using the estimated likelihood ratio. The confidence intervals for variances are constructed using the Satterthwaite type approximation with degrees of freedom equal to $2 \times (z\text{-score})^2$. The confidence interval about the covariance is computed using the Wald interval. The ODS OUTPUT statement provides two data sets, one with the fixed effects parameter estimates and one with the predictions of the intercepts and slopes for each level or subject of the random effects. The options G, GCORR, and SOLUTION provide the estimated covariance matrix and correlation matrix for the random effects (intercepts and slopes).

10.2.3 Results

The results are given in Output 10.1, with the main emphasis placed on testing $\sigma_{ab} = 0$, as well as additional results produced by the code.

Output 10.1: Results for Covariance Parameters and Fixed Effects

Fit Statistics	
-2 Res Log Likelihood	186.15
AIC (smaller is better)	194.15
AICC (smaller is better)	194.90
BIC (smaller is better)	195.36
CAIC (smaller is better)	199.36
HQIC (smaller is better)	192.82
Generalized Chi-Square	20.42
Gener. Chi-Square / DF	0.35

Estimated G Matrix			
Effect	Row	Col1	Col2
Intercept	1	18.8948	-0.07272
moist	2	-0.07272	0.002394

Estimated G Correlation Matrix			
Effect	Row	Col1	Col2
Intercept	1	1.0000	-0.3419
moist	2	-0.3419	1.0000

Covariance Parameter Estimates							
				Estimated Likelihood 95% Confidence Bounds			
				Lower		Upper	
Cov Parm	Subject	Estimate	Standard Error	Bound	Pr > Chisq	Bound	Pr > Chisq
UN(1,1)	variety	18.8948	9.1112	9.6527	0.0500	52.0478	0.0500
UN(2,1)	variety	-0.07272	0.08242	-0.1527	0.0500	0.07258	0.0500
UN(2,2)	variety	0.002394	0.001349	0.001045	0.0500	0.007279	0.0500
Residual		0.3521	0.07902	0.2339	0.0500	0.5643	0.0500

Estimated likelihood ratio confidence bounds are based on the restricted likelihood

	Solutions for Fixed Effects				
Effect	Estimate	Standard Error	DF	t Value	Pr > |t|
Intercept	33.4339	1.3985	9	23.91	<.0001
moist	0.6617	0.01678	9	39.42	<.0001

Tests of Covariance Parameters Based on the Restricted Likelihood					
Label	DF	-2 Res Log Like	ChiSq	Pr > ChiSq	Note
Test cov a and b = 0	1	187.12	0.97	0.3242	DF

DF: p-value based on a chi-square with DF degrees of freedom.

The "Solution for the Fixed Effects" table gives $\hat{\alpha} = 33.4348$ and $\hat{\beta} = 0.6617$. Based on the RANDOM statement, REML estimates of the variance and covariance components are obtained from the "Estimated G Matrix" and "Covariance Parameters Estimates" table as the following:

$$\hat{\mathbf{G}} = \begin{bmatrix} 19.1328 & -0.07377 \\ -0.07377 & 0.002401 \end{bmatrix}$$
$$\hat{\sigma}^2 = 0.3511$$

The second covtest statement provides a test of the hypothesis that $\sigma_{ab} = 0$. The value of the test statistic is based on the restrictive likelihood approach that is demonstrated in the next section. The value of the Chi-square statistic is 0.97 and is based on 1 *df*. The associated significance level is 0.3242, indicating that there is not sufficient evidence to conclude that $\sigma_{ab} \neq 0$. The SOLUTION option in the RANDOM statement provides the EBLUPs of the variety effects for the intercepts and slopes. The "Solution for Random Effects" table in Output 10.2 contains the predicted values for the deviations of the varieties' intercepts from the population mean intercept (the first variety's intercept is labeled "Intercept variety 1" which is a prediction of a_1). The deviations of the varieties' slopes from the population mean slope (the first variety's slope is labeled "moist variety 1" which is a prediction of b_1) for each variety.

10.2.4 Program to Fit a Model

Since there is not enough evidence to conclude that $\sigma_{ab} \neq 0$, the next step in the process is to fit a model with $\sigma_{ab} = 0$. To specify $\sigma_{ab} = 0$ use TYPE=UN(1) in the RANDOM statement as shown in Program 10.2.

Program 10.2

```
proc glimmix data=wheat noprofile;
   class variety;
   model yield = moist / solution;
   random int moist / type=un(1) sub=variety solution G Gcorr;
   covtest / cl(type=elr);
   ods output ParameterEstimates=fixed solutionr=random;
run;
```

10.2.5 Results

Output 10.2 contains the fit statistics where the covariance between a and b has been set to zero and the -2 Res Log Likelihood has a value of 187.11. The value of -2 Res Log Likelihood in Output 10.1 with $\sigma_{ab} \neq 0$ has a value of 186.15. Because the two models are nested with respect to the covariance parameters, a likelihood ratio test can be carried out. The difference between the two likelihoods is $187.11 - 186.15 = 0.96$. This statistic has a Chi-square distribution based on 1 df, which is the same as the Test for Covariance Parameters Based on the Restrictive Likelihood in Output 10.1. Also, the model with $\sigma_{ab} = 0$ has smaller information criteria than the model that estimates σ_{ab} indicating the model with $\sigma_{ab} = 0$ fits the data better.

Output 10.2: Results for Random Effects

Fit Statistics	
-2 Res Log Likelihood	187.11
AIC (smaller is better)	193.11
AICC (smaller is better)	193.56
BIC (smaller is better)	194.02
CAIC (smaller is better)	197.02
HQIC (smaller is better)	192.12
Generalized Chi-Square	20.55
Gener. Chi-Square / DF	0.35

Covariance Parameter Estimates				Estimated Likelihood 95% Confidence Bounds			
				Lower		Upper	
Cov Parm	Subject	Estimate	Standard Error	Bound	Pr > Chisq	Bound	Pr > Chisq
UN(1,1)	variety	18.2825	8.7973	8.0117	0.0500	55.1524	0.0500
UN(2,1)	variety	0	.	0	1.0000	0	1.0000
UN(2,2)	variety	0.002291	0.001299	0.000790	0.0500	0.007724	0.0500
Residual		0.3543	0.07996	0.2350	0.0500	0.5689	0.0500

Estimated likelihood ratio confidence bounds are based on the restricted likelihood

Solutions for Fixed Effects					
Effect	Estimate	Standard Error	DF	t Value	Pr > |t|
Intercept	33.4108	1.3761	9	24.28	<.0001
moist	0.6619	0.01647	9	40.19	<.0001

Solution for Random Effects						
Effect	Subject	Estimate	Std Err Pred	DF	t Value	Pr > |t|
Intercept	variety 1	0.9444	1.4870	40	0.64	0.5290
moist	variety 1	-0.04866	0.02080	40	-2.34	0.0244
Intercept	variety 2	-2.2271	1.5020	40	-1.48	0.1460
moist	variety 2	-0.06849	0.02696	40	-2.54	0.0151
Intercept	variety 3	-0.3504	1.4923	40	-0.23	0.8156
moist	variety 3	0.06626	0.02195	40	3.02	0.0044
Intercept	variety 4	0.7015	1.4589	40	0.48	0.6332
moist	variety 4	-0.02294	0.02352	40	-0.97	0.3354
Intercept	variety 5	1.0728	1.6596	40	0.65	0.5217
moist	variety 5	-0.01874	0.02536	40	-0.74	0.4643
Intercept	variety 6	4.6292	1.4448	40	3.20	0.0027
moist	variety 6	0.02469	0.01958	40	1.26	0.2146
Intercept	variety 7	-10.5861	1.4329	40	-7.39	<.0001
moist	variety 7	0.05120	0.02191	40	2.34	0.0245
Intercept	variety 8	2.3977	1.4613	40	1.64	0.1087
moist	variety 8	0.02317	0.02180	40	1.06	0.2943
Intercept	variety 9	-0.1414	1.4932	40	-0.09	0.9250
moist	variety 9	0.02289	0.02191	40	1.04	0.3024

Solution for Random Effects

Effect	Subject	Estimate	Std Err Pred	DF	t Value	Pr > |t|
Intercept	variety 10	3.5594	1.7867	40	1.99	0.0532
moist	variety 10	-0.02940	0.02777	40	-1.06	0.2962

The estimates of the variance components (with $\sigma_{ab} = 0$) from the "Estimated G Matrix" and "Covariance Parameter Estimates" tables are as follows:

$$\hat{\mathbf{G}} = \begin{bmatrix} 18.2825 & 0 \\ 0 & 0.002291 \end{bmatrix}$$

$$\hat{\sigma}_e^2 = 0.3543$$

The estimates of the fixed effects intercept and slope have changed slightly compared to Output 10.1. There was little evidence in Output 10.1 that $\sigma_{ab} \neq 0$ (the 95% confidence interval about the covariance is -0.2378 to 0.09027).

These deviations of intercepts and deviations of slopes can be used with the estimates of α and β to construct a plot of the family of simple linear regression lines. The values of α and β are in the data set FIXED, and the predicted deviations for each variety's intercept and slope are in the data set RANDOM (generated with the ODS OUTPUT statement in the preceding program).

10.2.6 Program to Calculate the Values of Intercepts and Slopes

The following program can be used to calculate the values of the intercepts (a_i) and the values of the slopes (b_i) as shown in Output 10.3. The variables FINT and FSLOPE contain the fixed effect estimates of the intercept and slope, and the variables RINT and RSLOPE are the predicted deviations for the intercepts and slopes for each variety.

Program 10.3

```
data lines;
   merge random(where=(effect='Intercept') rename=(estimate=rint))
        random(where=(effect='moist'    ) rename=(estimate=rslope));
   if _n_ = 1 then merge
           fixed(where=(effect='Intercept') rename=(estimate=fint))
           fixed(where=(effect='moist'    ) rename=(estimate=fslope));
   intercept = fint   + rint;
   slope     = fslope + rslope;
   keep subject fint fslope rint rslope intercept slope;
run;
proc print data=lines;
   var subject fint rint intercept fslope rslope slope;
run;
```

10.2.7 Results

The predicted intercepts (variable INTERCEPT) and predicted slopes (variable SLOPE) for each variety were obtained by merging the solution for random effects and the parameter estimates and are displayed in Output 10.3.

Output 10.3: Predicted Slopes and Intercepts for Each Variety

Obs	Subject	fint	rint	intercept	fslope	rslope	slope
1	variety 1	33.4108	0.9444	34.3552	0.6619	-0.04866	0.61321
2	variety 2	33.4108	-2.2271	31.1837	0.6619	-0.06849	0.59338
3	variety 3	33.4108	-0.3504	33.0604	0.6619	0.06626	0.72813
4	variety 4	33.4108	0.7015	34.1123	0.6619	-0.02294	0.63893
5	variety 5	33.4108	1.0728	34.4836	0.6619	-0.01874	0.64313
6	variety 6	33.4108	4.6292	38.0400	0.6619	0.02469	0.68656
7	variety 7	33.4108	-10.5861	22.8247	0.6619	0.05120	0.71307
8	variety 8	33.4108	2.3977	35.8085	0.6619	0.02317	0.68504
9	variety 9	33.4108	-0.1414	33.2694	0.6619	0.02289	0.68476
10	variety 10	33.4108	3.5594	36.9702	0.6619	-0.02940	0.63247

The fixed effect for the slope (fslope) is added to each of the random effects slopes (rslope) to provide the slopes for each of the varieties. The fixed effect for the intercept (fint) is added to each of the random effects intercepts (rint) to get the intercept for each of the varieties.

10.2.8 Program to Assemble and Construct Data for Regression Lines

Regression lines are constructed by evaluating the model for each variety at MOIST=10 and 60 and then connecting the two points. Program 10.4 retrieves data sets from Program 10.3, puts them together, and constructs the data required for making Figure 10.2.

Program 10.4

```
data plotlines; set lines;
moist=10;
pred=intercept+moist*slope;
output;
moist=60;
pred=intercept+moist*slope;
output;
if subject="variety 1" then do;
   subject="Pop Mean";
moist=10;
pred=fint+moist*fslope;
output;
moist=60;
pred=fint+moist*fslope;
output;
end;
run;

*proc print data=plotlines;
*run;

proc sort data=plotlines; by subject;
proc sgplot data=plotlines;
   series x=moist y=pred/group=subject;
   xaxis label='Moisture Content of Plot';
   yaxis label='Predicted Yields';
run;
```

10.2.9 Results

Figure 10.2 displays the set of predicted regression lines for the ten varieties and the estimate of the population mean (solid line in center of bundle).

Figure 10.2: Predicted Simple Linear Regression Models from a Random Sample of Varieties with the Estimated Population Model

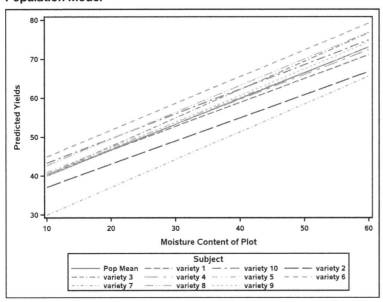

Equation 10.5 specifies a covariance between the intercepts and slopes. Sometimes a model with $\sigma_{ab} = 0$ describes the data as well as the model where the covariance is estimated as was the case for the wheat variety data. Fitting an unstructured covariance matrix can also be numerically difficult, and a model without covariances between the random effects provides less difficulty. Notice that even if all entries of the (2×2) unstructured covariance matrix are positive, the resulting covariance matrix may not be *positive definite*.

10.3 Random Student Effects: An Example

Kreft et al. (1994) analyze data from the Second International Mathematics Study (SIMS). Here 3,691 eighth-grade students are measured on mathematics achievement tests, and the hierarchical structure of the data is due to the fact that these students are grouped into 190 classes. The raw data are given in Data Set 10.3, "Mathematics Study."

10.3.1 Model: Simple Linear Regression Models with Additional Fixed Effects

A multilevel analysis of these data begins by constructing a model at the student level involving any explanatory variables measured on the students. For this example, Kreft et al. (1994) use the standard regression model:

$$\left(\text{GAIN}\right)_{ij} = \beta_{0j} + \beta_{1j} \left(\text{PRETOT}\right)_{ij} + e_{ij}$$

Here, $(\text{GAIN})_{ij}$ is the gain on the score of a particular achievement test of the ith student in the jth class and $(\text{PRETOT})_{ij}$ is the sum of some pretest score items for the same student. The residual errors e_{ij} are assumed to be independent and identically distributed Gaussian random variables with mean zero and variance σ^2.

Next, the regression coefficients β_{0j} and β_{1j} are assumed to arise from a model at the class level. Assuming initially that there are no class-level variables, the basic model to consider here is

$$\beta_{0j} = \gamma_{00} + d_{0j}$$
$$\beta_{1j} = \gamma_{10} + d_{1j}$$

where the class-level disturbance terms (d_{0j}, d_{1j}) are assumed to be independent and identically distributed bivariate Gaussian random variables with zero mean and variance-covariance matrix $\mathbf{G}$ where

$$\begin{bmatrix} d_{0j} \\ d_{1j} \end{bmatrix} \sim iid \ \text{N}\left(\mathbf{0}, \mathbf{G}\right), \text{ where } \mathbf{G} = \begin{bmatrix} \sigma_{00} & \sigma_{10} \\ \sigma_{10} & \sigma_{11} \end{bmatrix}$$

Substituting the expressions for β_{0j} and β_{1j} into the student-level model produces the following single-equation formulation:

$$\left(\text{GAIN}\right)_{ij} = \gamma_{00} + \gamma_{01} \left(\text{PRETOT}\right)_{ij} + d_{0j} + d_{1j} \left(\text{PRETOT}\right)_{ij} + e_{ij}$$

This equation reveals that the hierarchical linear model is actually the same as the random coefficient model considered in previous sections. The mean model consists of the two parameters γ_{00} and γ_{10}, and the variance model has a random intercept d_{0j}, a random slope d_{1j}, and a residual error e_{ij}. The fixed effects part of the model is $\gamma_{00} + \gamma_{10}(\text{PRETOT})_{ij}$, the random effects part of the model is $d_{0j} + d_{1j}(\text{PRETOT})_{ij}$, and the residual part of the model is e_{ij}.

10.3.2 Analysis with Fixed Effects and Random Coefficients

The single-equation formulation is probably easiest to translate into PROC MIXED code because all of the fixed effects must be placed together in the MODEL statement and all of the random effects are specified in the RANDOM statement.

Program with PROC MIXED

For this example, appropriate PROC MIXED code is shown in Program 10.5.

Program 10.5

```
proc mixed data=sims covtest cl;
   class class;
   model gain = pretot / s ddfm=kr2;
```

```
    random int pretot / subject=class type=un s;
    ods output solutionf=est solutionr=rand;
run;
```

The DATA= option in the PROC MIXED statement specifies the SAS data set to use for the analysis. The COVTEST option requests the estimated standard error and z-score, and the CL option indicates that confidence intervals about the covariance parameters are to be included.

The CLASS statement looks a bit unusual here because the variable CLASS shares the same name. The purpose of the CLASS statement is to treat the listed variables as classification rather than continuous variables. This is done for the variable CLASS, which indicates the class of a particular student.

The MODEL statement specifies the mean model effects. An intercept is included by default, corresponding to γ_{00}, and the variable PRETOT models the γ_{10} term. Because PRETOT is not in the CLASS statement, it is treated as a continuous effect with a single degree-of-freedom regression. The S (=SOLUTION) option requests that the estimates of γ_{00} and γ_{10} be printed along with their estimated standard errors and corresponding t statistics.

The RANDOM statement is the mechanism for specifying the terms involving d_{0j} and d_{1j}. The INTERCEPT effect corresponds to the d_{0j}. INTERCEPT is a keyword automatically interpreted by PROC MIXED as an effect with all 1s. PRETOT corresponds to the $d_{1j}(\text{PRETOT})_{ij}$ term in the model. The SUBJECT=CLASS option is important because it instructs PROC MIXED regarding the index j and when it changes. Observations from different classes are assumed to be independent. The TYPE=UN option sets up G as an unstructured (2×2) matrix with the three parameters σ_{00}, σ_{01}, and σ_{11}

PROC MIXED includes the homogeneous residual error e_{ij} in the model by default.

Results

The results of this analysis are shown in Output 10.4.

Output 10.4: Results of from PROC MIXED Random Student Effects Model with DDFM=KR2

		Covariance Parameter Estimates						
Cov Parm	Subject	Estimate	Standard Error	Z Value	Pr Z	Alpha	Lower	Upper
UN(1,1)	class	14.4797	2.6993	5.36	<.0001	0.05	10.3642	21.6578
UN(2,1)	class	-0.2337	0.1016	-2.30	0.0214	0.05	-0.4328	-0.03456
UN(2,2)	class	0.009192	0.004940	1.86	0.0314	0.05	0.004004	0.03847
Residual		22.2362	0.5519	40.29	<.0001	0.05	21.1930	23.3588

	Solution for Fixed Effects				
Effect	Estimate	Standard Error	DF	t Value	Pr > |t|
Intercept	7.0595	0.3665	165	19.26	<.0001
pretot	-0.1860	0.01620	126	-11.48	<.0001

Type 3 Tests of Fixed Effects				
Effect	Num DF	Den DF	F Value	Pr > F
pretot	1	126	131.86	<.0001

The "Covariance Parameter Estimates" table displays the estimates of σ_{00}, σ_{10}, and σ_{11}, and σ^2 in the Estimate column. The Standard Error column displays approximate standard errors of the estimates based on the fact that they are asymptotically normal. A corresponding z-score and p-value are also printed, testing whether the parameter is different from zero. These tests can, however, be unreliable in small samples.

The "Solution for Fixed Effects" table prints estimates of the mean model parameters γ_{00} and γ_{10}. The "Type 3 Tests of Fixed Effects" table prints an F test for testing $\gamma_{10} = 0$. This hypothesis is strongly rejected. Because this F statistic has only 1 numerator degree of freedom, it is equal to the square of the *t* statistic for PRETOT in the "Solution for Fixed Effects" table and the *p*-values are the same.

Program with PROC GLIMMIX

An interesting comparison is to compare the results when using PROC GLIMMIX with the DDFM=KR2 option to those from PROC MIXED in Output 10.4, as shown in Program 10.6.

Program 10.6

```
proc glimmix data=sims cl;
   class class;
   model gain = pretot / s ddfm=kr2;
   random int pretot / subject=class type=un s;
   covtest/cl(type=ELR);
ods output solutionf=est solutionr=rand;
run;
```

Results

The covariance parameters with ELR confidence intervals, the estimates of the fixed effects parameters, and the Type III test of the fixed effects are included in Output 10.5. The results from Output 10.5 are added to Table 10.1 under the column of GLIMMIX.

Output 10.5: PROC GLIMMIX results with DDFM=KR2 option

Covariance Parameter Estimates							
				Estimated Likelihood 95% Confidence Bounds			
				Lower		Upper	
Cov Parm	Subject	Estimate	Standard Error	Bound	Pr > Chisq	Bound	Pr > Chisq
UN(1,1)	class	14.4891	2.7013	12.4593	0.0500	17.1641	0.0500
UN(2,1)	class	-0.2340	0.1017	-0.2340	1.0000	-0.1593	0.0500
UN(2,2)	class	0.009202	0.004942	0.004976	0.0500	0.01564	0.0500
Residual		22.2358	0.5519	21.2153	0.0500	23.3222	0.0500

Estimated likelihood ratio confidence bounds are based on the restricted likelihood

Solutions for Fixed Effects					
Effect	Estimate	Standard Error	DF	t Value	Pr > |t|
Intercept	7.0596	0.3666	164.5	19.26	<.0001
pretot	-0.1860	0.01620	126.2	-11.48	<.0001

Type III Tests of Fixed Effects				
Effect	Num DF	Den DF	F Value	Pr > F
pretot	1	126.2	131.84	<.0001

For comparison, Table 10.1 reproduces a portion of Table 1 from Kreft et al. (1994) with additional results from PROC MIXED and PROC GLIMMIX. It displays REML results for the preceding model from three other software packages. They are seen to agree closely with the PROC MIXED and PROC GLIMMIX results.

Table 10.1: Comparison of PROC MIXED and PROC GLIMMIX REML Results for SIMS Data from Other Software Packages

Parameter	GENMOD	HLM	ML3	MIXED	GLIMMIX
γ_{00}	7.060	7.060	7.060	7.060	7.060
γ_{10}	-0.186	-0.186	-0.186	-0.186	-0.186
σ_{00}	14.52	14.53	14.49	14.48	14.49

Parameter	GENMOD	HLM	ML3	MIXED	GLIMMIX
σ_{10}	−0.234	−0.237	−0.234	−0.234	−0.234
σ_{11}	0.009	0.009	0.009	0.009	0.009
σ^2	22.23	22.23	22.24	22.24	22.24

The intercept and slope for each class were put together as for the previous examples, and the regression lines were evaluated at pretest total of 0 and 40. The resulting predicted regression lines for each class as well as the estimated population linear regression model are displayed in Figure 10.3, where the dashed line denotes the population model.

Program to Extract Information and Provide Predicted Values

Program 10.7 shows the code used to extract the necessary information and provide the predicted values to generate the intercepts and slopes for each class.

Program 10.7

```
data lines;
   merge rand(where=(effect='Intercept') rename=(estimate=rint))
         rand(where=(effect='pretot'   ) rename=(estimate=rslope));
   if _n_ = 1 then merge
         est(where=(effect='Intercept') rename=(estimate=fint))
         est(where=(effect='pretot'   ) rename=(estimate=fslope));
   intercept = fint   + rint;
   slope     = fslope + rslope;
   pretot=0; Gain=intercept; output;
   pretot=40; gain=intercept+40*slope;output;
   keep class fint fslope rint rslope intercept slope gain pretot;
run;
data mean; set lines; if _N_=1;
class=191;
pretot=0; gain=fint;output;
pretot=40; gain=fint+40*fslope;output;
run;
data linesnew;
merge lines mean(rename=(pretot=meanpretot gain=meangain));
run;
proc print data=linesnew;
run;

proc sort data=lines; by class pretot; run;

proc sgplot data=linesnew noautolegend;
   series x=pretot y=gain/group=class lineattrs=(color=ltgray pattern=1);
   series x=meanpretot y=meangain/lineattrs=(color=black pattern=1 thickness=3);
   xaxis label='Pre-test Total Score';
   yaxis label='Gain in Score';
run;
```

Results

The code in Program 10.7 extracts the intercepts and slopes for each of the 190 classes and gets predicted values for the pretot =0 and 40.

Figure 10.3: Predicted Simple Linear Regression Models from a Random Sample of Classes with the Estimated Population Model

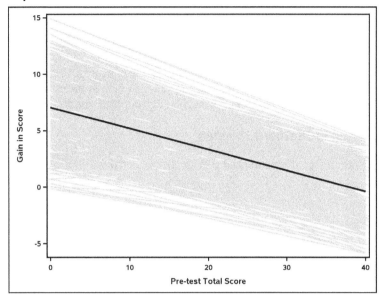

A question you might ask with 190 classes is this: "Are there sufficient observations so that one could use the Wald of Z confidence interval?" The confidence intervals were recomputed using "Estimate+1.96*Standard Error. The Wald confidence intervals for σ_{00}, σ_{10}, σ_{11}, and σ^2 are 9.19 to 19.78, −0.43 to −0.034, 0.0005 to 0.019, and 21.15 to 23.32, respectively. Even with this large of sample size, the Wald intervals, which are centered at the estimate, do not have the same characteristics as the ELR confidence intervals that are more like intervals computed from a Chi-square distribution.

Program to Fit PROC MIXED with the Satterthwaite Approximation

The final comparisons involve comparing DDFM=SATTERTH with PROC MIXED to those that use DDFM=KR2. Program 10.9 fits PROC MIXED with DDFM=SATTERTH (the Satterthwaite approximation to the degrees associated with fixed effects).

Program 10.8

```
proc mixed data=sims covtest cl;
   class class;
   model gain = pretot / s ddfm=satterth;
   random int pretot / sub=class type=un s;
run;
```

Results

The results for using DDFM=SATTERTH with PROC MIXED are shown in Output 10.6.

Output 10.6: Results of Random Student Effects Model with DDFM=SATTERTH

		Covariance Parameter Estimates						
Cov Parm	Subject	Estimate	Standard Error	Z Value	Pr Z	Alpha	Lower	Upper
UN(1,1)	class	14.4797	2.6993	5.36	<.0001	0.05	10.3642	21.6578
UN(2,1)	class	-0.2337	0.1016	-2.30	0.0214	0.05	-0.4328	-0.03456
UN(2,2)	class	0.009192	0.004940	1.86	0.0314	0.05	0.004004	0.03847
Residual		22.2362	0.5519	40.29	<.0001	0.05	21.1930	23.3588

Solution for Fixed Effects

Effect	Estimate	Standard Error	DF	t Value	Pr > |t|
Intercept	7.0595	0.3658	165	19.30	<.0001
pretot	-0.1860	0.01610	126	-11.56	<.0001

Type 3 Tests of Fixed Effects

Effect	Num DF	Den DF	F Value	Pr > F
pretot	1	126	133.57	<.0001

The main difference between the results in Outputs 10.4, 10.5, and 10.6 are in the computation of the estimated standard errors for the fixed effects. The method used to compute the estimated standard errors for the fixed effects in Output 10.6 (with DDFM=SATTERTH) is the model-based method, while the method used in Output 10.5 (with DDFM=KR2) is the Prasad-Rao-Jeske-Kackar-Harville method. The estimated standard errors in Output 10.5 are a little larger than those in Output 10.6, thus demonstrating the increasing effect of the Prasad-Rao-Jeske-Kackar-Harville method. This adjustment is also evident in the values of the F statistics, which are smaller with the Prasad-Rao-Jeske-Kackar-Harville method.

10.4 Repeated Measures Growth Study: An Example

The growth of animals is determined by measuring the same animal at several times during the growth period of concern. This process generates repeated measures data. The data for this example come from studying the growth of pigs after weaning for 30 days. The weight of each pig is measured at days 0, 6, 12, 18, 24, and 30 after weaning. Plots of the data show (Figures 10.4, 10.5, and 10.6) that the growth exhibits a quadratic response as a function of days. The objective of the experiment was to determine if any of three treatments had an effect on the growth response. The data appear as Data Set "Pig Growth." These data are in multivariate form, where repeated measurements of an animal correspond to different variables. A SAS data set in univariate form—as required by PROC MIXED and PROC GLIMMIX—is produced with Program 10.9.

Program 10.9

```
data pigs;
   set pigsx;
   array days{6} day:;
   do i=1 to 6;
      day = (i-1)*6;
      weight = days{i};
      output;
   end;
   keep trt pig weight day;
run;
```

Figures 10.4, 10.5, and 10.6 show the growth curves (connect the dots between measurements) of the 20 pigs assigned to each of the three treatments.

Figure 10.4: Weight Data for Pigs Assigned to Treatment 1

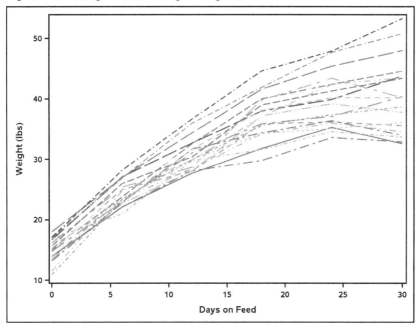

Figure 10.5: Weight Data for Pigs Assigned to Treatment 2

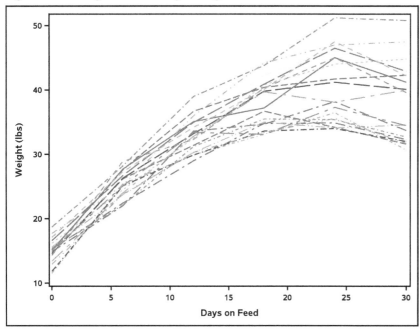

Figure 10.6: Weight Data for Pigs Assigned to Treatment 3

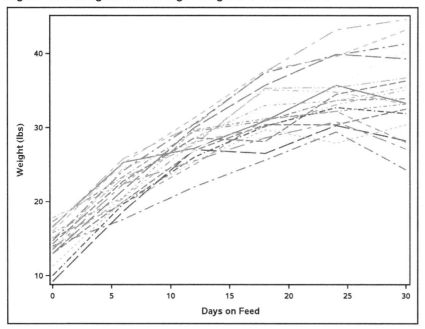

10.4.1 Repeated Measures Analysis

One approach to the analysis of this data set is to carry out a repeated measures analysis of variance where the REPEATED statement is used to model the covariance structure of the repeated measures. Since the measurements are made at equally spaced time points, an AR(1) covariance structure is a possibility. The repeated measures model is

$$wt_{ijk} = \mu + \tau_i + \delta_k + \tau\delta_{ik} + p_{ij} + e_{ijk}$$
$$i = 1, 2, 3 \quad j = 1, 2, ..., 20 \quad k = 1, 2, ..., 6$$

where $\mu + \tau_i + \delta_k + \tau\delta_{ik}$ is the fixed effects part of the model where τ_i is the treatment effect, δ_k is the day effect, $\tau\delta_{ik}$ is the treatment by day interaction effect, p_{ij} is the pig random effect, and e_{ijk} is the random effect of a measurement made on the kth day of the jth pig assigned to treatment i. It is assumed that

$$p_{ij} \sim iid \; N\left(0, \sigma_{pig}^2\right)$$

and

$$
\begin{bmatrix} e_{ij1} \\ e_{ij2} \\ e_{ij3} \\ e_{ij4} \\ e_{ij5} \\ e_{ij6} \end{bmatrix}
\sim iid \; N \left(
\begin{bmatrix} 0 \\ 0 \\ 0 \\ 0 \\ 0 \\ 0 \end{bmatrix},
\sigma_e^2
\begin{bmatrix}
1 & \rho & \rho^2 & \rho^3 & \rho^4 & \rho^5 \\
\rho & 1 & \rho & \rho^2 & \rho^3 & \rho^4 \\
\rho^2 & \rho & 1 & \rho & \rho^2 & \rho^3 \\
\rho^3 & \rho^2 & \rho & 1 & \rho & \rho^2 \\
\rho^4 & \rho^3 & \rho^2 & \rho & 1 & \rho \\
\rho^5 & \rho^4 & \rho^3 & \rho^2 & \rho & 1
\end{bmatrix}
\right)
$$

Program 10.10 fits this model.

Program 10.10

```
proc glimmix data=pigs;
   class trt day pig;
   model weight=trt day day*trt / ddfm=kr2;
   random pig / subject=trt;
   random day / subject=pig(trt) type=ar(1) residual;
   lsmeans day*trt;
run;
```

The RANDOM statement specifies $p_{ij} \sim iid$ N$(0, \sigma_{pig}^2)$ and the RANDOM DAY statement with RESIDUAL specifies that DAY is the repeated measurement, that pig(trt) is the subject effect, and that the covariance structure of the repeated measurements has the AR(1) structure.

The results of the analysis are given in Output 10.7. This analysis does not assume any functional relationship between weight and time. The treatment by day means are computed and can be compared. For example, it is probably of interest to compare the treatment means within each day of measurement.

Output 10.7 Results of Repeated Measures Analysis with TYPE=AR(1)

Covariance Parameter Estimates			
Cov Parm	Subject	Estimate	Standard Error
pig	trt	1.7575	5.8912
AR(1)	pig(trt)	0.8175	0.08380
Residual		14.5603	6.5044

Type III Tests of Fixed Effects				
Effect	Num DF	Den DF	F Value	Pr > F
trt	2	56.45	10.06	0.0002
day	5	222.2	384.13	<.0001
trt*day	10	240.8	3.93	<.0001

trt*day Least Squares Means						
trt	day	Estimate	Standard Error	DF	t Value	Pr > |t|
1	0	14.9450	0.9033	93.52	16.55	<.0001
1	6	24.3300	0.9033	93.52	26.94	<.0001
1	12	30.9000	0.9033	93.52	34.21	<.0001
1	18	36.8950	0.9033	93.52	40.85	<.0001
1	24	39.7600	0.9033	93.52	44.02	<.0001
1	30	40.4450	0.9033	93.52	44.78	<.0001
2	0	15.1250	0.9033	93.52	16.74	<.0001
2	6	25.4550	0.9033	93.52	28.18	<.0001
2	12	32.9800	0.9033	93.52	36.51	<.0001
2	18	37.9700	0.9033	93.52	42.04	<.0001
2	24	40.6850	0.9033	93.52	45.04	<.0001
2	30	38.6050	0.9033	93.52	42.74	<.0001
3	0	14.3950	0.9033	93.52	15.94	<.0001
3	6	21.9850	0.9033	93.52	24.34	<.0001
3	12	27.7050	0.9033	93.52	30.67	<.0001
3	18	31.8900	0.9033	93.52	35.31	<.0001
3	24	34.2500	0.9033	93.52	37.92	<.0001
3	30	34.4200	0.9033	93.52	38.11	<.0001

The estimate of the autoregressive correlation in the "Covariance Parameter Estimates" table is 0.8175, the estimate of the pig-to-pig variability within a treatment is 1.7574, and the estimate of the residual variance is 14.5604. From the "Type 3 Tests of Fixed Effects" table we see that there is a significant day $\times$ treatment interaction ($p < 0.0001$), so only the day by treatment means were requested. Pairwise comparisons of treatment within a day are of interest, but these are not displayed here.

10.4.2 Random Coefficient Analysis

From the graphics it looks like there is a possible quadratic relationship between weight and day of measurement. A quadratic model that can be used to describe the weight on the kth day of the jth pig from the ith treatment is the following:

$$wt_{ijk} = a_{ij}^* + b_{ij}^* day_k + c_{ij}^* day_k^2 + e_{ijk}$$

$$i = 1, 2, 3, \quad j = 1, 2, ..., 20, \quad k = 1, 2, ..., 6$$

The animals in the study represent a random sample of pigs from a population of pigs, so the quadratic model used to represent a pig's growth represents a realization from the population of quadratic models. This can be expressed through the following distributional assumptions:

$$\begin{bmatrix} a_{ij}^* \\ b_{ij}^* \\ c_{ij}^* \end{bmatrix} \sim N\left(\begin{bmatrix} \alpha_i \\ \beta_i \\ \gamma_i \end{bmatrix}, \begin{bmatrix} \sigma_a^2 & \sigma_{ab} & \sigma_{ac} \\ \sigma_{ab} & \sigma_b^2 & \sigma_{bc} \\ \sigma_{ac} & \sigma_{bc} & \sigma_c^2 \end{bmatrix} \right)$$

and

$$e_{ijk} \sim iid \ N(0, \sigma_e^2)$$

If you let $a_{ij}^* = \alpha_i + a_{ij}$, $b_{ij}^* = \beta_i + b_{ij}$, $c_{ij}^* = \gamma_i + c_{ij}$, the model can be expressed as follows:

$$wt_{ijk} = [\alpha_i + a_{ij}] + [\beta_i + b_{ij}] day_k + [\gamma_i + c_{ij}] day_k^2 + e_{ijk}$$

$$= \alpha_i + \beta_i day_k + \gamma_i day_k^2 + a_{ij} + b_{ij} day_k + c_{ij} day_k^2 + e_{ijk}$$

$$i = 1, 2, 3, \quad j = 1, 2, ..., 20, \quad k = 1, 2, ..., 6$$

and

$$\begin{bmatrix} a_{ij} \\ b_{ij} \\ c_{ij} \end{bmatrix} \sim N\left(\begin{bmatrix} 0 \\ 0 \\ 0 \end{bmatrix}, \begin{bmatrix} \sigma_a^2 & \sigma_{ab} & \sigma_{ac} \\ \sigma_{ab} & \sigma_b^2 & \sigma_{bc} \\ \sigma_{ac} & \sigma_{bc} & \sigma_c^2 \end{bmatrix} \right)$$

and

$$e_{ijk} \sim iid \ N(0, \sigma_e^2)$$

$\alpha_i + \beta_i day_k + \gamma_i day_k^2$ is the fixed effects part of the model, $a_{ij} + b_{ij} day_k + c_{ij} day_k^2$ is the random effects part of the model, and e_{ijk} is the residual part of the model. The fixed effects part of the model can be rewritten for analysis purposes as $\alpha_i + \beta_i day_k + \gamma_i day_k^2 = (\alpha_0^* + \alpha_i^*) + (\beta_0^* + \beta_i^*) day_k + (\gamma_0^* + \gamma_i^*) day_k^2$, where

$$\alpha_0^* = \alpha_3, \ \alpha_i^* = \alpha_i - \alpha_3, \ \beta_0^* = \beta_3, \ \beta_i^* = \beta_i - \beta_3, \ \gamma_0^* = \gamma_3$$

and $\gamma_i^* = \gamma_i - \gamma_3$.

Program

Use Program 10.11 to fit the model.

Program 10.11

```
proc glimmix data=pigs;
   class trt pig;
   model weight=trt day day*trt day*day day*day*trt/ddfm=kr2;
   random int day day*day / subject=pig(trt) type=un g gcorr;
   covtest / cl;
run;
```

The MODEL statement is used to specify the fixed effects part of the model,

$$(\alpha_0^* + \alpha_i^*) + (\beta_0^* + \beta_i^*)day_k + (\gamma_0^* + \gamma_i^*)day_k^2$$

where trt day day*trt day*day day*day*trt correspond to α_i^*, β_0^*, $\beta_i^* day_k$, γ_0^*, and $\gamma_i^* day_k^2$ respectively. The intercept of the model is α_0^*. This representation enables you to test the equality of the α_i, the equality of the β_i and the equality of the γ_i. The RANDOM statement is used to specify the random effects part of the model, $a_{ij} + b_{ij} day_k + c_{ij} day_k^2$ where int, day, day*day specify a_{ij}, b_{ij} and c_{ij}, respectively and TYPE=UN specifies the covariance matrix of the regression model coefficients. The GCORR option enables you to see the correlation matrix among the random coefficient regression terms.

Results

The results are shown in Output 10.8.

Output 10.8: Covariance and Correlation Estimates for Quadratic Random Coefficient Model

Estimated G Matrix				
Effect	Row	Col1	Col2	Col3
Intercept	1	1.6751	0.03796	0.003899
day	2	0.03796	0.000093	0.000366
day*day	3	0.003899	0.000366	2.748E-6

Estimated G Correlation Matrix				
Effect	Row	Col1	Col2	Col3
Intercept	1	1.0000	3.0433	1.8175
day	2	3.0433	1.0000	22.9238
day*day	3	1.8175	22.9238	1.0000

Covariance Parameter Estimates					
Cov Parm	Subject	Estimate	Standard Error	Wald 95% Confidence Bounds	
UN(1,1)	pig(trt)	1.6751	0.6719	0.8697	4.4662
UN(2,1)	pig(trt)	0.03796	0.06055	-0.08071	0.1566
UN(2,2)	pig(trt)	0.000093	0.009372	.	.
UN(3,1)	pig(trt)	0.003899	0.002163	-0.00034	0.008138
UN(3,2)	pig(trt)	0.000366	0.000269	-0.00016	0.000894
UN(3,3)	pig(trt)	2.748E-6	0.000010	2.596E-7	7.675E14
Residual		2.1563	0.2273	1.7719	2.6816

The "Estimated G Matrix" table provides the estimated variances and covariances associated with individual pig regression models within a treatment,

$$\hat{G} = \begin{bmatrix} \hat{\sigma}_a^2 & \hat{\sigma}_{ab} & \hat{\sigma}_{ac} \\ \hat{\sigma}_{ab} & \hat{\sigma}_b^2 & \hat{\sigma}_{bc} \\ \hat{\sigma}_{ac} & \hat{\sigma}_{bc} & \hat{\sigma}_c^2 \end{bmatrix} = \begin{bmatrix} un(1,1) & un(2,1) & un(3,1) \\ un(2,1) & un(2,2) & un(3,2) \\ un(3,1) & un(3,2) & un(3,3) \end{bmatrix}$$

$$= \begin{bmatrix} 1.6751 & 0.03796 & 0.0039 \\ 0.03796 & 0.000093 & 0.00037 \\ 0.0039 & 0.00037 & 2.748E-6 \end{bmatrix}$$

Notice that the estimate of the variance for the quadratic (day*day) random regression coefficient σ_c^2 is essentially zero. In addition, the "estimated G correlation matrix" shows impossible values for the correlations.

Clearly, analysis cannot continue with the model parameterization used in Program 10.11. You have three choices: 1) drop the quadratic random regression coefficient, 2) assume the random regression coefficients are uncorrelated or 3) use the model Program 10.11 is intended to fit but use a different TYPE= specification. Three possibilities are TYPE=CHOL, TYPE=FA0(3) and TYPE=UNR. All three are available in PROC GLIMMIX; FA0(3) and UNR are available with PROC MIXED. TYPE=CHOL fits a Cholesky factorization of the unstructured covariance matrix that guarantees that it will be at least non-negative definite. TYPE=FA0(3) fits a factor-analytic structure without the diagonal matrix used in the full FA(3) factor analytic structure. In principle, it is similar to the Cholesky factorization. TYPE=UNR fits the variance terms of the unstructured covariance matrix, but it fits correlations rather than covariance terms in the off-diagonal, thus ensuring that correlation estimates are within the parameter space.

With these data, TYPE=CHOL and TYPE=FA0(3) give similar estimates of the covariance parameters and correlations. TYPE=UNR gives different covariance and correlation estimates. Subsequent analysis is similar for all three TYPES.

Program

Program 10.12 shows statements using PROC GLIMMIX to fit the unstructured random coefficient model using TYPE=UNR. Also included, but commented out, is the equivalent statement for TYPE=FA0(3).

Program 10.12

```
proc glimmix data=pigs;
   class trt pig;
   model weight=trt day day*trt day*day day*day*trt/ddfm=kr2;
   random int day day*day/subject=pig(trt) type=unr g gcorr;
   *random int day day*day / subject=pig(trt) type=fa0(3) g gcorr;
   covtest 'corr=0?' diagG / cl;
   covtest 'corr=0?' . . . 0 0 0 .;
   covtest 'day*day zero' . . 0 . 0 0 .;
run;
```

The three COVTEST statements enable you to test various aspects of the covariance structure. The first two statements are equivalent ways to test H_0 : all covariance terms $(\sigma_{ab}, \sigma_{ac}, \sigma_{bc})$ equal zero. The third statement tests all of the covariance terms involving the quadratic random regression coefficient, $H_0 : \sigma_c^2 = 0, \sigma_{as} = 0, \sigma_{bc} = 0$; this test addresses the question, "should day*day be dropped from the RANDOM statement?" The positions of the zeroes in the COVTEST statements correspond to the order in which the covariance parameters appear in the "Covariance Parameter Estimates" table.

Results

Results for the covariance and correlation estimates appear in Output 10.9.

Output 10.9. Covariance, Correlation and COVTEST Results for TYPE=UNR with Quadratic Random Coefficient Model

Estimated G Matrix				
Effect	Row	Col1	Col2	Col3
Intercept	1	1.7742	0.02298	0.004359
day	2	0.02298	0.005116	0.000172
day*day	3	0.004359	0.000172	0.000011

Estimated G Correlation Matrix				
Effect	Row	Col1	Col2	Col3
Intercept	1	1.0000	0.2412	1.0000
day	2	0.2412	1.0000	0.7347
day*day	3	1.0000	0.7347	1.0000

Covariance Parameter Estimates					
Cov Parm	Subject	Estimate	Standard Error	Wald 95% Confidence Bounds	
Var(1)	pig(trt)	1.7742	0.6655	0.9548	4.3755
Var(2)	pig(trt)	0.005116	0.008905	0.000843	169.94
Var(3)	pig(trt)	0.000011	8.512E-6	3.51E-6	0.000134
Corr(2,1)	pig(trt)	0.2412	0.8225	-1.3709	1.8533
Corr(3,1)	pig(trt)	1.0000	0	.	.
Corr(3,2)	pig(trt)	0.7347	1.7723	-2.7389	4.2083
Residual		2.0434	0.1877	1.7202	2.4677

Tests of Covariance Parameters Based on the Restricted Likelihood					
Label	DF	-2 Res Log Like	ChiSq	Pr > ChiSq	Note
corr=0?	3	1574.79	23.86	<.0001	DF
corr=0?	3	1574.79	23.86	<.0001	DF
day*day zero	3	1565.51	14.58	0.0022	--

Interpretation

The values in the "Estimated G Matrix" table replace those in given above following Output 10.8. The "Estimated G Correlation Matrix" contains values that are all within the parameter space. However, one value, the correlation between random intercept and quadratic day component, is equal to one—right at the upper bound of the parameter space for correlations. For these data, if you use TYPE=FA0(3), you will also find that one of the correlation estimates is exactly equal to one. This results from the fact that the variance component estimate for the quadratic random regression term is essentially zero. The "Tests of Covariance Parameters" table shows Chi-square values of 23.86 for the test that all correlations are equal to zero, and 14.58 for the test of the quadratic (day*day) random regression coefficient. The former provides evidence that you cannot assume that correlations among the random coefficient regression effects are zero. The latter is an artifact of the near-zero quadratic random regression variance component estimate. In subsequent analyses, this term is dropped

Program

Program 10.13 gives statements to continue the analysis, focusing on tests of treatment and day effects.

Program 10.13

```
proc glimmix data=pigs;
 class trt pig;
  model weight=trt day day*trt day*day day*day*trt/ddfm=kr2;
  random int day /subject=pig(trt) type=unr g gcorr;
run;
```

Results

Results appear in Output 10.10.

Output 10.10: Type 3 Tests for TYPE=UNR without Quadratic Random Coefficient

Type III Tests of Fixed Effects				
Effect	Num DF	Den DF	F Value	Pr > F
trt	2	99.74	0.87	0.4223
day	1	227.7	2583.00	<.0001
day*trt	2	227.7	25.01	<.0001
day*day	1	237	1311.40	<.0001
day*day*trt	2	237	27.81	<.0001

The "Type 3 Tests of Fixed Effects" table indicate that you would fail to reject H_0: $\alpha_1 = \alpha_2 = \alpha_3$ versus H_a: (not H_0) ($p = 0.4223$ from trt source), reject H_0: $\beta_1 = \beta_2 = \beta_3$ versus H_a: (not H_0) ($p < 0.0001$ from the day × trt source), and reject H_0: $\gamma_1 = \gamma_2 = \gamma_3$ versus H_a: (not H_0) ($p < 0.0001$ from the day × day × trt source). Thus, the population models for the three treatments could have a common intercept, different coefficients for DAY, and different coefficients for DAY × DAY.

Program

The treatments can be compared at any value of DAY. The LSMEANS statements are used to provide estimates of the regression models at selected values of DAY (0 to 30). Use Program 10.14 to obtain the results of the LSMEANS statements.

Program 10.14

```
proc glimmix data=pigs;
   class trt pig;
   model weight=trt day day*trt day*day day*day*trt/ddfm=kr2;
   random int day /subject=pig(trt) type=unr g gcorr;
   lsmeans trt/at day=0 diff;
   lsmeans trt/at day=6 diff;
   lsmeans trt/at day=12 diff;
   lsmeans trt/at day=18 diff;
   lsmeans trt/at day=24 diff;
   lsmeans trt/at day=30 diff;
run;
```

Results

The results appear in Output 10.11.

Output 10.11: Least Squares Means and Pairwise Comparisons of Differences between the Quadratic Random Coefficient Models at each Day

trt Least Squares Means

trt	day	Estimate	Standard Error	DF	t Value	Pr > |t|
1	0.00	14.8993	0.3578	99.74	41.65	<.0001
2	0.00	14.9589	0.3578	99.74	41.81	<.0001
3	0.00	14.3536	0.3578	99.74	40.12	<.0001

Differences of trt Least Squares Means

trt	_trt	day	Estimate	Standard Error	DF	t Value	Pr > |t|
1	2	0.00	-0.05964	0.5059	99.74	-0.12	0.9064
1	3	0.00	0.5457	0.5059	99.74	1.08	0.2834
2	3	0.00	0.6054	0.5059	99.74	1.20	0.2343

trt Least Squares Means

trt	day	Estimate	Standard Error	DF	t Value	Pr > |t|
1	6.00	24.2017	0.4206	57.85	57.54	<.0001
2	6.00	25.5676	0.4206	57.85	60.78	<.0001
3	6.00	21.9951	0.4206	57.85	52.29	<.0001

Differences of trt Least Squares Means

trt	_trt	day	Estimate	Standard Error	DF	t Value	Pr > |t|
1	2	6.00	-1.3659	0.5949	57.85	-2.30	0.0253
1	3	6.00	2.2066	0.5949	57.85	3.71	0.0005
2	3	6.00	3.5725	0.5949	57.85	6.01	<.0001

trt Least Squares Means

trt	day	Estimate	Standard Error	DF	t Value	Pr > |t|
1	12.00	31.4213	0.6143	63.81	51.15	<.0001
2	12.00	33.2731	0.6143	63.81	54.17	<.0001
3	12.00	27.8317	0.6143	63.81	45.31	<.0001

Differences of trt Least Squares Means

trt	_trt	day	Estimate	Standard Error	DF	t Value	Pr > |t|
1	2	12.00	-1.8519	0.8687	63.81	-2.13	0.0369
1	3	12.00	3.5896	0.8687	63.81	4.13	0.0001
2	3	12.00	5.4414	0.8687	63.81	6.26	<.0001

trt Least Squares Means

trt	day	Estimate	Standard Error	DF	t Value	Pr > |t|
1	18.00	36.5580	0.8117	60.77	45.04	<.0001
2	18.00	38.0754	0.8117	60.77	46.91	<.0001
3	18.00	31.8633	0.8117	60.77	39.25	<.0001

Differences of trt Least Squares Means

trt	_trt	day	Estimate	Standard Error	DF	t Value	Pr > |t|
1	2	18.00	-1.5174	1.1479	60.77	-1.32	0.1912
1	3	18.00	4.6947	1.1479	60.77	4.09	0.0001
2	3	18.00	6.2121	1.1479	60.77	5.41	<.0001

trt Least Squares Means

trt	day	Estimate	Standard Error	DF	t Value	Pr > |t|
1	24.00	39.6119	1.0107	57.15	39.19	<.0001
2	24.00	39.9745	1.0107	57.15	39.55	<.0001
3	24.00	34.0899	1.0107	57.15	33.73	<.0001

Differences of trt Least Squares Means

trt	_trt	day	Estimate	Standard Error	DF	t Value	Pr > |t|
1	2	24.00	-0.3626	1.4294	57.15	-0.25	0.8006
1	3	24.00	5.5220	1.4294	57.15	3.86	0.0003
2	3	24.00	5.8846	1.4294	57.15	4.12	0.0001

trt Least Squares Means

trt	day	Estimate	Standard Error	DF	t Value	Pr > |t|
1	30.00	40.5829	1.2392	59.49	32.75	<.0001
2	30.00	38.9704	1.2392	59.49	31.45	<.0001
3	30.00	34.5114	1.2392	59.49	27.85	<.0001

Differences of trt Least Squares Means							
trt	_trt	day	Estimate	Standard Error	DF	t Value	Pr > |t|
1	2	30.00	1.6125	1.7526	59.49	0.92	0.3612
1	3	30.00	6.0714	1.7526	59.49	3.46	0.0010
2	3	30.00	4.4589	1.7526	59.49	2.54	0.0136

The least squares means are estimates of the three treatment regression models evaluated at 0, 6, 12, 18, 24, and 30 days after initiation of the treatments. Those means are graphed in Figure 10.7. One of the problems with using the quadratic model is that there is an estimated decline in weight from days 24 to 30 for treatment 2, which is probably not real. What is important is that the selected model adequately describes the data in the range of the data and the quadratic models seem to do a good job. The next section presents a test for lack of fit of the quadratic regression models. The "Differences of Least Squares Means" table provides pairwise comparisons among the three treatment models evaluated at a specific number of days. There are no significant differences among the three models at day 0 (as one would expect), all means are significantly different at day 6, the means of treatments 1 and 2 are not significantly different for days 12 to 30, but treatments 1 and 2 means are significantly different from the mean of treatment 3 for days 12 to 30. These conclusions can be visualized by the graph in Figure 10.7.

Figure 10.7: Models for the Pig Growth Data

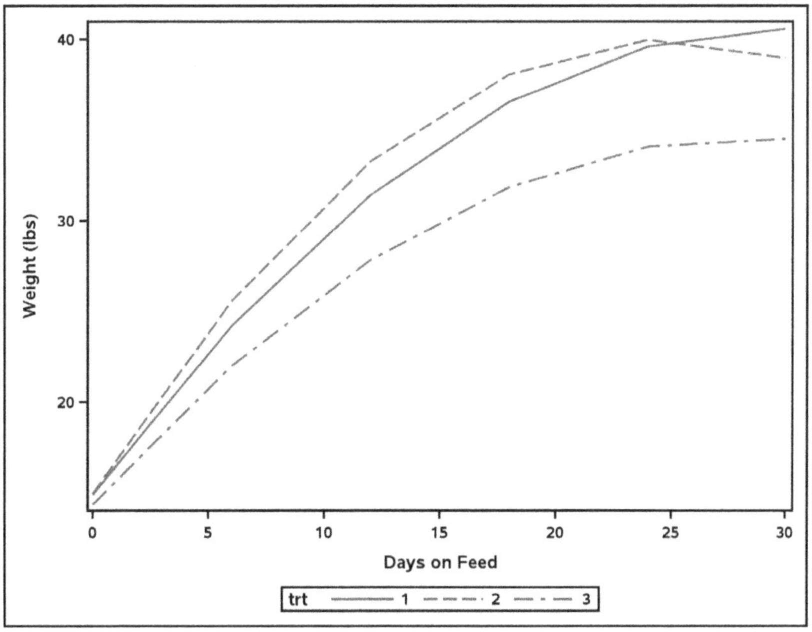

10.4.3 Test of Lack of Fit

The final step in this analysis is to evaluate whether the quadratic models adequately describe the data. The variable DAY needs to be used as a class variable and as a continuous variable in the same model specification, so the first step is to generate a new variable XDAY=DAY. Then, construct a model with the desired regression part of the model and include the term XDAY*TRT, where both XDAY and TRT are in the CLASS statement. If you request the Type 1 analysis using the option HTYPE=1, then the F statistic associated with the XDAY*TRT source provides the statistic to test the lack of fit of the regression model to describe the DAY*TRT means.

Program

The code to provide the test for lack of fit is in Program 10.15.

Program 10.15

```
data pigs; set pigs;
   xday=day;
run;
proc glimmix data=pigs;
   class trt pig xday;
   model weight=trt day day*trt day*day day*day*trt xday*trt/
```

```
                        ddfm=kr2 htype=1;
   random int day /subject=pig(trt) type=unr;
covtest / cl;
run;
```

Results

The results of the lack of fit test are given in Output 10.12.

Output 10.12: Test for Lack of Fit of Quadratic Random Coefficient Model

| | | | | Wald 95% | |
Cov Parm	Subject	Estimate	Standard Error	Confidence Bounds	
Var(1)	pig(trt)	0.7756	0.3729	0.3625	2.6673
Var(2)	pig(trt)	0.02453	0.005248	0.01679	0.03922
Corr(2,1)	pig(trt)	0.7342	0.2493	0.2456	1.2228
Residual		2.1629	0.2026	1.8149	2.6221

Covariance Parameter Estimates

Type I Tests of Fixed Effects

Effect	Num DF	Den DF	F Value	Pr > F
trt	2	57	11.56	<.0001
day	1	57	1292.47	<.0001
day*trt	2	57	6.38	0.0032
day*day	1	228	1326.74	<.0001
day*day*trt	2	228	28.14	<.0001
trt*xday	9	228	1.31	0.2336

The "Type 1 Tests of Fixed Effects" table provides sequential tests for the effects in the model. The question addressed by the source labeled "trt*xday" is: given all previously listed (=all other) terms in the model, do they describe all of the pattern in the "trt*xday" means or is a more complex model more appropriate? In this case, the p-value is 0.2336, indicating that the quadratic regression model is adequate to describe the xday × trt means. A small p-value would indicate that the model does not adequately describe the data. The analysis can also be carried out using the Type 3 Tests of Fixed Effects, but in that table the sources for all terms except trt × xday have zero degrees of freedom and zero F statistics. This occurs because the Type 3 Tests are adjusted for all other terms in the model. So, when trt × xday is in the model, all of the variation among the means is described, and there is no variability left for other terms in the model.

A nonlinear model that is monotonic over time would most likely be a better representation of the data, but that model is not considered here.

10.5 Prediction of the Shelf Life of a Product

Predicting the shelf life of a product is an excellent application of random coefficient regression models. There are several ways to design and analyze shelf life studies that depend on the type of data being collected and the expected degradation process. Informally, think of shelf life as the time a product performs acceptably. Performance is measured by response variables called stability limiting characteristics. Shelf life corresponds to the time at which the stability limiting characteristics no longer meet specified acceptance criteria; labeled shelf life (e.g. the expiration date that appears on a product's label) is in essence a prediction of how long the product can be expected to meet acceptance criteria.

This example focuses on a pharmaceutical stability trial. The data are given in Data Set "Stability Trial." Section 10.5.1 provides relevant background for three alternative analyses presented in Sections 10.5.2, 10.5.3, and 10.5.4. The analysis in Section 10.5.2 uses random coefficient regression in conjunction with best linear unbiased prediction. The analyses in Sections 10.5.3 and 10.5.4 do not, but provide instructive lessons regarding mixed model inference.

10.5.1 Example: A Pharmaceutical Stability Trial—Essential Background

The "Stability Trial" data were collected in accordance with the International Conference on Harmonization's Q1E (2003) guidelines for the conduct and analysis of such trials. The guidelines state that a minimum of three batches must be observed over time. Suggested times of observation are 0, 3, 6, 9, 12, and 18 months after manufacture. Additional observations are sometimes taken at 24 months and occasionally at 36 months. The data set has three batches and has observations through 24 months. The response variable is normalized so that 100 is the population mean stability limiting characteristic at time zero, i.e. when the product is manufactured. If the stability limiting characteristic is decreasing, as is the case in these data, 90 is typically set as the lower acceptance limit; if it is increasing, 110 is typically the upper acceptance limit.

The Q1E document uses linear regression over time to describe essential principles to be followed in shelf life estimation, specifically the following model:

$$y_{ij} = \beta_0 + \delta_{oi} + \left(\beta_1 + \delta_{1i}\right)M + e_{ij}$$

where $M = \{0,3,6,8,12,18,...\}$ denotes the number of months post-manufacture, β_0 and β_1 denote population average intercept and slope coefficients δ_{0i} and δ_{1i} denote the deviation of the ith batch intercept and slope from the population average, and e_{ij} denotes measurement error for the observation on the ith batch at the jth month. The distribution of the random variable $Y_i \mid M \sim N\left(\beta_0 + \delta_{0i} + \left(\beta_1 + \delta_{1i}\right), \sigma_Y^2\right)$ is often referred to as the *product distribution*. The analyses in subsequent sections use variations on this model.

Shelf life is determined by setting Y to 90 and solving for M once the regression coefficients are estimated. The Q1E procedure begins by testing $H_0 : \delta_{0i} = 0$ for all i, and $H_0 : \delta_{1i} = 0$ for all i. Depending on the result, shelf life is determined either using β_0 and β_1 (if you fail to reject both hypotheses), using the batch-specific intercept ($\beta_0 + \delta_{0i}$) and common slope , β_1 , or using the batch-specific slope ($\beta_1 + \delta_{1i}$) and batch-specific intercept if you reject both hypotheses. For a decreasing stability limiting characteristic, e.g. potency, the estimated shelf life is

$$SL = \left(90 - \text{intercept}\right)/\text{slope}$$

While current guidelines call for δ_{0i} and δ_{1i} to be treated as fixed effects, there is increasing realization that 1) this procedure is at odds with the stated goal (*predicting* how long future batches can be expected to meet acceptance criteria), and 2) shelf life can be determined more accurately by treating batch effects $\left(\delta_{0i}$ and $\delta_{1i}\right)$ as random and using best linear unbiased prediction. By treating δ_{0i} and δ_{1i} as fixed effects, the currently mandated procedure by definition limits the inference space to only those batches actually observed, thus precluding inference on "all future batches."

A more appropriate model is thus

$$y_{ij} = \beta_0 + b_{oi} + \left(\beta_1 + b_{1i}\right)M$$

where

$$\begin{bmatrix} b_{0i} \\ b_{1i} \end{bmatrix} \sim N\left(\begin{bmatrix} 0 \\ 0 \end{bmatrix}, \begin{bmatrix} \sigma_0^2 & \sigma_{01} \\ \sigma_{01} & \sigma_1^2 \end{bmatrix}\right)$$

(10.6)

You can simplify the model if the random intercept and slope effects, b_{0i} and b_{1i} can be assumed to be independent, in essence, if $\sigma_{01} = 0$. Modeling b_{0i} and b_{1i} as random eliminates the need to test for equal slopes and equal intercepts, as one would do in a fixed effects model. It also means that in order to ensure that "all future batches" last at least as long as the stated shelf life, it is reasonable to estimate shelf life using the best linear unbiased predictors, $\beta_0 + b_{0i}$ and $\beta_1 + b_{1i}$ of the shortest lived batch. Figures 10.8, 10.9, and 10.10 help you visualize why this is so.

Figure 10.8: Hypothetical Population of Batch Regressions and Associated Shelf Lives

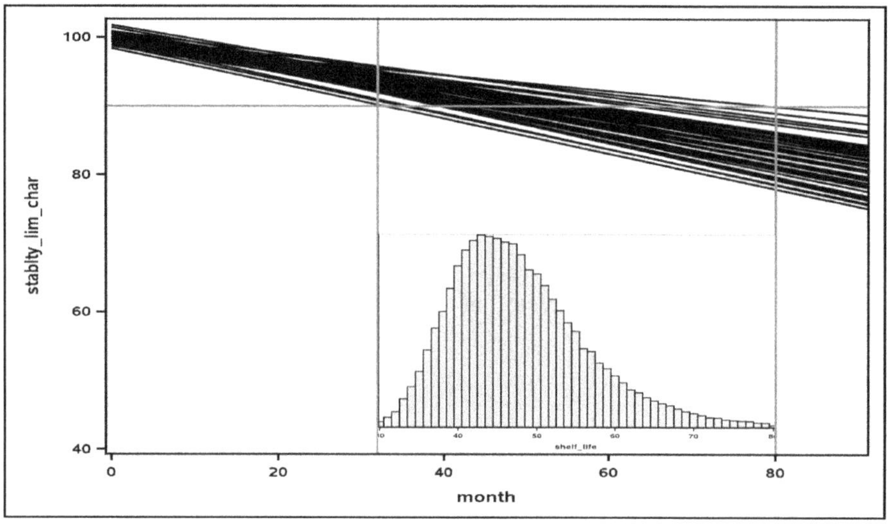

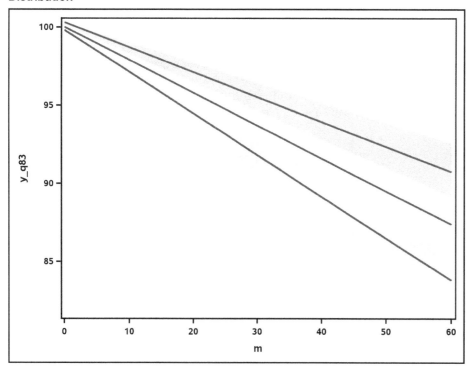

Figure 10.8 illustrates the product distribution (the bundle of regression lines) and the shelf-life distribution (the inset histogram) over time. You can see that there is variability in both intercept and slope. The point at which the regression line for the "stablty_lim_char" intersects 90 is the shelf life for that particular batch. You can see that focusing on central tendency would result in approximately 50% of future batches expected to fail to meet the acceptance criterion for the stated shelf life. On the other hand, you can use batch-specific BLUPs of the regression over months to obtain estimates that are consistent with the mandated objective of shelf-life estimation. Figures 10.9 and 10.10 illustrate.

Figure 10.9: Expected Regression over Time of 3 Batches Relative to Minimum and Maximum of Product Distribution

The three solid lines show the expected regressions of the three batches observed in the stability trial. The three shaded areas show the lower, middle and upper one-third of the distribution of the regression lines. You can see that focusing on the shortest-lived regression gets you close, but over estimates the lower limit of the distribution of batches. In fact, the lower solid line traces the 16-2/3 percentile—i.e. the median of the lower one-third of the distribution of batch regressions. This would mean that if you use the expected shelf life of the shortest-lived batch as your estimate, you expect 16-2/3% of future batches to have a shorter shelf life than your estimate. This may constitute an unacceptably high risk, especially if the consequences of a product failing to be effective for its entire stated lifetime are serious. An alternative is to use a lower confidence bound of the batch-specific regression coefficients of the shortest-lived batch.

Figure 10.10: Plot Depicting 5th Percentile of Product Distribution Relative to Expected Regression over Time of 3 Batches

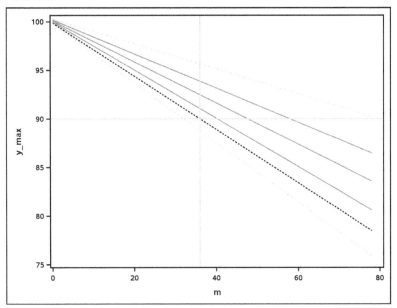

The lower confidence limit of the shortest-lived batch provides an estimate of the regression over time for a batch whose percentile is somewhere between 0 and 16-2/3. For example, if the mandate is to provide a shelf life estimate such that the probability that all future batches will last at least that long, the percentile of the lower confidence limit can be adjusted accordingly. For example, if the mandated probability level is 95%, you would want the estimate based on the lower-confidence limit to correspond to the 5th percentile of the product distribution. This translates approximately to taking the lower confidence bound of a 70% confidence interval about the batch-specific estimate of the shortest-lived batch. Why 70% confidence interval? The 15th percentile of the lower one-third of the distribution corresponds approximately to the 5th percentile of the overall population. Note that these batch-specific regression "estimates" ("predictors" to be precise) must be obtained via best linear unbiased prediction.

In fact, Stroup and Quinlan (2015) provide evidence that a lower confidence bound of the BLUP of the shortest-lived batch provides an estimate of shelf life that is accurate and addresses the "all future batches" mandate.

10.5.2 Estimation Using Best Linear Unbiased Prediction

The data given in "Stability Trial" are from three batches, each with measurements taken on drug efficacy at 0, 3, 6, 9 12, 18, and 24 months. In this section, the proposed method is illustrated by using the batch with the shortest-lived BLUP. That is, use the batch that shows the most deviation from the other batches. If the material degrades over time, then the batch that goes below the acceptance criteria determines the shelf life.

Program

Start by plotting the data, using Program 10.16.

Program 10.16

```
proc sgplot data=stability_demo;
   reg x=month y=y/group=batch;
   refline 90 ;
   xaxis label='Months of Storage';
   yaxis label='Remaining Amount' min=89;
run;
```

Results

Figure 10.11: displays the plot of each data set with the predicted regression lines.

Figure 10.11: Stability Trial Data by Batch, with Linear Regression for each Batch Superimposed

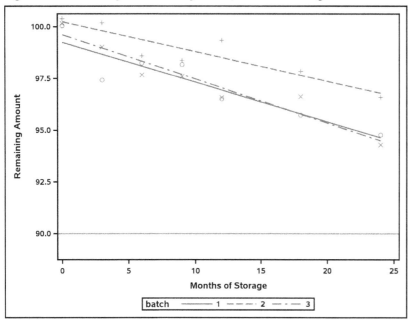

Each batch begins with Y (the stability limiting characteristic) close to 100. Each batch shows approximately linear degradation over time, with some measurement error as evidenced by deviation from the regression lines. Batch 2 appears to degrade more slowly than batches 1 and 3.

Program to Test for Noncorrelation of Intercept and Slope Coefficients

Next, test $H_0 : \sigma_{01} = 0$ to see if the random intercept and slope coefficients are uncorrelated, which is accomplished by using the SAS statements in Program 10.17.

Program 10.17

```
proc glimmix data=stability_demo;
   class batch;
   model y = month;
   random intercept month / subject=batch type=un gcorr;
   covtest 'b0 and b1 indep?' . 0 . .;
   ods html select covparms gcorr covtests;
run;
```

TYPE=UN specifies the covariance matrix of the random intercept and slope as

$$\text{Var}\begin{bmatrix} b_{0i} \\ b_{1i} \end{bmatrix} = \begin{bmatrix} \sigma_0^2 & \sigma_{01} \\ \sigma_{01} & \sigma_1^2 \end{bmatrix}$$

Use the GCORR option to see the estimate of the correlation matrix,

$$\text{Corr}\left(\begin{bmatrix} b_{0i} \\ b_{1i} \end{bmatrix}\right) = \begin{bmatrix} 1 & r_{01} \\ r_{01} & 1 \end{bmatrix}$$

The covariance parameters to be estimated are, in order, $\sigma_0^2, \sigma_{01}, \sigma_1^2$ and σ^2, labeled UN(1,1), UN(2,1), UN(2,2) and RESIDUAL in the PROC GLIMMIX listing. The sequence "dot zero dot dot" (. 0 . .) directs COVTEST to test the hypothesis that the second covariance parameter, UN(2,1) = σ_{01}, is equal to zero, while allowing the other covariance parameters to be set to their REML solutions.

Results

Output 10.13 shows selected results.

Output 10.13: Covariance, Correlation, and COVTEST Results for Stability Data

Estimated G Matrix			
Effect	Row	Col1	Col2
Intercept	1	0.08398	0.02418
month	2	0.02418	0.000279

Estimated G Correlation Matrix			
Effect	Row	Col1	Col2
Intercept	1	1.0000	4.9962
month	2	4.9962	1.0000

Covariance Parameter Estimates			
Cov Parm	Subject	Estimate	Standard Error
UN(1,1)	batch	0.08398	0.2582
UN(2,1)	batch	0.02418	0.01646
UN(2,2)	batch	0.000279	0.001328
Residual		0.4288	0.1566

Tests of Covariance Parameters Based on the Restricted Likelihood					
Label	DF	-2 Res Log Like	ChiSq	Pr > ChiSq	Note
Cov b0 and b1 = 0	1	52.5467	3.05	0.0808	DF

DF: p-value based on a chi-square with DF degrees of freedom.

In this case, the information in "Estimated G Correlation Matrix" is most important. Specifically, correlation is by definition, between -1 and 1; the off-diagonal term, 4.9962, is out of the parameter space, an impossible value. This tells you that TYPE=UN is a nonsense model for this particular data set. The COVTEST result, likelihood ratio $\chi^2 = 3.05$ tends to support this, as do the information criteria (not shown here). The AICC is 60.35 for the UN model, 60.15 for the model with σ_{01} not included.

Program to Predict the Batch-Specific BLUPs of Regression Coefficients

The model with b0 and b1 being uncorrelated can be used to predict the batch-specific BLUPs of regression coefficients, as shown in Program 10.18.

Program 10.18

```
proc glimmix data=stability_demo;
class batch;
model y=month / ddfm=kr2 s cl;
random intercept month / subject=batch type=un(1) s;
covtest / cl;
/* estimate BLUPs - a.k.a. batch-specific intercept & slope */
estimate 'b0 blup batch 1' intercept 1 | intercept 1 / subject 1 0 0 cl alpha=0.30;
estimate 'b1 blup batch 1' month 1 | month 1 / subject 1 0 0 cl alpha=0.30;
estimate 'b0 blup batch 2' intercept 1 | intercept 1 / subject 0 1 0 cl alpha=0.30;
estimate 'b1 blup batch 2' month 1 | month 1 / subject 0 1 0 cl alpha=0.30;
estimate 'b0 blup batch 3' intercept 1 | intercept 1 / subject 0 0 1 cl alpha=0.30;
estimate 'b1 blup batch 3' month 1 | month 1 / subject 0 0 1 cl alpha=0.30;
ods output estimates=ests;
run;
```

The MODEL and RANDOM statements implement the model shown in Equation 10.7. Given the GCORR and COVTEST results above, TYPE=UN is deleted from the RANDOM statement to provide the 0 correlation between b_{0i} and b_{1i}. The ESTIMATE statements compute BLUPs of the batch-specific intercept, $\hat{\beta}_0 + \hat{b}_{0i}$, and slope, $\hat{\beta}_1 + \hat{b}_{1i}$. Use ALPHA=0.30 for lower confidence bounds that approximate the lower 5th percentile of the product distribution, as illustrated in Figure 10.10.

Results

Output 10.14 shows the result with estimates of the fixed effect parameters and predictions of the random effect intercept and slope deviations for each batch.

Output 10.14; Covariance, Fixed, and Random Effects Estimates and Batch-Specific Regression Coefficient BLUPs

					Covariance Parameter Estimates

Cov Parm	Subject	Estimate	Standard Error	Wald 95% Confidence Bounds	
UN(1,1)	batch	0.2806	0.4525	0.04955	2154.64
UN(2,1)	batch	0	.	.	.
UN(2,2)	batch	0.001287	0.002303	0.000207	76.8727
Residual		0.4057	0.1421	0.2261	0.9308

Solutions for Fixed Effects

Effect	Estimate	Standard Error	DF	t Value	Pr > |t|	Alpha	Lower	Upper
Intercept	99.6981	0.3823	1.846	260.79	<.0001	0.05	97.9143	101.48
month	-0.1829	0.02728	1.846	-6.70	0.0263	0.05	-0.3102	-0.05561

Solution for Random Effects

Effect	Subject	Estimate	Std Err Pred	DF	t Value	Pr > |t|
Intercept	batch 1	-0.3484	0.5061	1.511	-0.69	0.5815
month	batch 1	-0.01212	0.03782	1.233	-0.32	0.7943
Intercept	batch 2	0.5023	0.5061	1.511	0.99	0.4530
month	batch 2	0.03274	0.03782	1.233	0.87	0.5225
Intercept	batch 3	-0.1539	0.5061	1.511	-0.30	0.7976
month	batch 3	-0.02061	0.03782	1.233	-0.55	0.6678

Estimates

Label	Estimate	Standard Error	DF	t Value	Pr > |t|	Alpha	Lower	Upper
b0 blup batch 1	99.3497	0.4639	16.85	214.15	<.0001	0.3	98.8536	99.8458
b1 blup batch 1	-0.1950	0.03628	13.15	-5.38	0.0001	0.3	-0.2341	-0.1559
b0 blup batch 2	100.20	0.4639	16.85	215.99	<.0001	0.3	99.7043	100.70
b1 blup batch 2	-0.1501	0.03628	13.15	-4.14	0.0011	0.3	-0.1893	-0.1110
b0 blup batch 3	99.5442	0.4639	16.85	214.57	<.0001	0.3	99.0481	100.04
b1 blup batch 3	-0.2035	0.03628	13.15	-5.61	<.0001	0.3	-0.2426	-0.1644

The ESTIMATE column gives the batch-specific BLUPs of the intercept (b0) and slope (b1). For example, in the "Solutions for Fixed Effects" the intercept and slope estimates are 99.70 and −0.18, respectively; the random coefficient estimates for batch 3 are -0.15 and -0.02; the resulting BLUPs, shown in the "Estimates" table, are 99.70 − 0.15 = 99.55 for the intercept and -0.18-0.02= -0.20 for the slope. The LOWER column in the "Estimates" table gives the lower bounds of these BLUPs. Use the latter if the goal is to estimate the shelf life as the time at which the 5th percentile of the product distribution intercepts the acceptance criterion (see Figure 10.10). You can hand calculate the shelf-life estimates for each batch. For example, if you use batch 3—the shortest-lived batch—then the lower confidence limits yield an estimated shelf life of $(90 - 99.0481)/{-0.2426} = 37.2905$, or 37 months.

Program for an Alternative Way to Generate Output 10.12

Alternatively, you can use Program 10.19 to generate Output 10.12.

Program 10.19

```
data b0 b1;
  set ests;
  if substr(label,1,1)="b"; batch=substr(label,15,1);
  if substr(label,2,1)="0" then do;
   intercept=lower;
   output b0; end;
  if substr(label,2,1)="1" then do slope=lower; output b1;
  end;
run;

**the following merges the information from the intercepts and slopes for each batch and
computes the shelf life;

data b0; set b0; drop slope; run;
data b1; set b1; drop intercept; run;
proc sort data=b0; by batch; run;
proc sort data=b1; by batch; run;
data life; merge b0 b1; by batch;
 shelf_life=(90-intercept)/slope;
run;
proc print data=life;
 var label batch intercept slope shelf_life;
run;
```

These statements assume that the results of the ESTIMATE statements from Program 10.16 were output into a data set called "ests". Then the intercepts and slopes are put into separate data sets with some name changes. Next, combine the slope and intercept data sets and compute the estimated shelf life.

Results

The results are shown in Output 10.15.

Output 10.15: Re-computing Shelf Life for Each Batch

Obs	Label	batch	intercept	slope	shelf_life
1	b1 blup batch 1	1	98.8536	-0.23415	37.8121
2	b1 blup batch 2	2	99.7043	-0.18929	51.2682
3	b1 blup batch 3	3	99.0481	-0.24264	37.2905

The predicted shelf lives are 37.8, 51.3 and 37.3 for batches 1, 2, and 3, respectively. Given the discussion of Figures 10.8, 10.9, and 10.10, if the mandated acceptable risk is 5%, then the 37-month value based on the lower confidence bounds is the desired estimate.

10.5.3 Estimation Using Fixed Effects Analysis of Covariance

As noted in the introduction to this section, for pharmaceutical shelf-life estimation, the current guidelines—Q1A (1992) and Q1E (1992)—mandate using a fixed effects analysis of covariance model. The protocol is as follows:

Test for "poolability." This entails one, possibly two, tests:

1. Test for equality of slopes, $H_0 : \delta_{1i} = 0$ for all *i*. If you reject, use the unequal slopes analysis of covariance model, as described in Chapter 7. If you fail to reject, go to "Poolability step 2."

2. Test for equality of intercepts, $H_0 : \delta_{0i} = 0$. If you reject, use the equal slopes analysis of covariance model. If you fail to reject, do not include any batch-specific effects in the model.

Thus, the possible models are as follows:

- Unequal slopes. Linear predictor $\beta_0 + \delta_{oi} + (\beta_1 + \delta_{1i})M$ or equivalently $\beta_{0i} + \beta_{1i}M$

- Equal slopes, unequal intercepts: $\beta_0 + \delta_{oi} + \beta_1 M$ or equivalently $\beta_{0i} + \beta_1 M$

- Common intercept and slope, $\beta_0 + \beta_1 M$

Once you select the model according to protocol, estimate shelf life. If you select either the unequal slopes or equal slopes, unequal intercept model, use the shortest-lived batch. If you use the common intercept and slope model, use the common regression. Shelf life is determined by tracking the lower confidence bound of the regression line in question if the stability limiting characteristic is decreasing, or the upper bound if the stability limiting characteristic is increasing over time. The last month for which this confidence bound remains within the acceptance region is the estimated shelf life.

Program

Use Program 10.20 to implement the poolability test.

Program 10.20

```
proc glimmix data=stability_demo;
   class batch;
   model y=batch|month/htype=1,3;
run;
```

The Type 1 and 3 Tests of MONTH*BATCH allow you to test for equal slopes. The Type 1 Test of BATCH allows you to test for equal intercepts.

Results

Output 10.16 shows the results for the "poolability" tests.

Output 10.16: Test Statistics for Equal Slopes and Equal Intercepts Tests

Type I Tests of Fixed Effects				
Effect	Num DF	Den DF	F Value	Pr > F
batch	2	15	10.97	0.0012
month	1	15	100.48	<.0001
month*batch	2	15	1.28	0.3070

Type III Tests of Fixed Effects				
Effect	Num DF	Den DF	F Value	Pr > F
batch	2	15	1.50	0.2541
month	1	15	100.48	<.0001
month*batch	2	15	1.28	0.3070

The F value for the test of equal slopes, i.e. MONTH*BATCH, is 1.28 with a p-value of 0.3070. The F value for the Type 1 Test of MONTH—the test of equal intercepts—is 10.97 with a p-value of 0.0012. Following protocol, you proceed using the equal slope, unequal intercept model.

Program

Alternatively, you could test for equal intercepts using the equal slopes analysis of covariance model. Use Program 10.21 to fit the equal slopes model.

Program 10.21

```
proc glimmix data=stability_demo;
 class batch;
 model y=batch month;
run;
```

Results

Output 10.17 shows the result.

Output 10.17: Test for Equal Intercepts Using Equal Slopes ANCOVA Model

	Type III Tests of Fixed Effects			
Effect	Num DF	Den DF	F Value	Pr > F
batch	2	17	10.62	0.0010
month	1	17	97.29	<.0001

As before, the test for BATCH is the test of equal intercepts. $F = 10.62$ and $p = 0.0010$, similar to the F and p-values from Output 10.16.

Program

Once the type of model is selected, then proceed to complete the estimation of shelf life. The model has equal slopes and unequal intercepts and is fit by the code in Program 10.22.

Program 10.22:

```
proc glimmix data=stability_demo;
   class batch;
   model y=batch month / noint s;
   lsmeans batch / at month=43 cl alpha=0.10;
   lsmeans batch / at month=44 cl alpha=0.10;
run;
```

Results

Notice that the MODEL statement defines the equal slope, unequal intercept analysis of covariance model. The LSMEANS statements give you the predicted stability limiting characteristic for MONTH specified using the AT option, using the linear predictor $\hat{y}_{iM} = \beta_{0i} + \beta_1 M$. The MODEL options NOINT and S allow you to print the estimated regression parameters. Output 10.18 shows the results.

Output 10.18: Regression Parameter Estimates and LSMEANS Results for Stability Data, Using Q1A/Q1E Mandated Protocol

			Parameter Estimates							
Effect	batch	Estimate	Standard Error	DF	t Value	Pr > |t|	Alpha	Lower	Upper
batch	1	99.1531	0.3157	17	314.12	<.0001	0.05	98.4871	99.8190
batch	2	100.64	0.3157	17	318.83	<.0001	0.05	99.9750	101.31
batch	3	99.3003	0.3157	17	314.59	<.0001	0.05	98.6344	99.9663
month		-0.1829	0.01854	17	-9.86	<.0001	0.05	-0.2220	-0.1438
Scale		0.4429	0.1519	.	.	.	.	.	.

			batch Least Squares Means						
batch	month	Estimate	Standard Error	DF	t Value	Pr > |t|	Alpha	Lower	Upper
1	43.00	91.2892	0.6566	17	139.02	<.0001	0.1	90.1469	92.4315
2	43.00	92.7770	0.6566	17	141.29	<.0001	0.1	91.6347	93.9193
3	43.00	91.4365	0.6566	17	139.25	<.0001	0.1	90.2942	92.5788

batch Least Squares Means									
batch	month	Estimate	Standard Error	DF	t Value	Pr > |t|	Alpha	Lower	Upper
1	44.00	91.1063	0.6738	17	135.21	<.0001	0.1	89.9341	92.2784
2	44.00	92.5941	0.6738	17	137.42	<.0001	0.1	91.4220	93.7663
3	44.00	91.2536	0.6738	17	135.43	<.0001	0.1	90.0814	92.4257

The estimated slope parameter, given by MONTH in the "Parameter Estimates" table is −0.1829, interpreted as a 0.1829 unit-per-month, or 2.2 unit per year, decrease. If you use the lower confidence limit, −0.222, the annual rate of decrease is $12 \times 0.222 = 2.66$ units. You can see that BATCH 1 has the lowest intercept and hence will decrease to the lower acceptance limit first. The relevant information in the LSMEANS table is the LOWER column. It gives you the lower confidence bound of $\hat{y}_{LM}$. You can see that for BATCH 1 it is 90.1 at 43 months and 89.9 at 44 months. Following the protocol, the estimated shelf life is 43 months.

Comment on the Discrepancy between Fixed Effects ANCOVA and BLUP

The estimated shelf life is 42 months, using the mandated fixed effects ANCOVA model, and 37 months using the BLUP alternative. Figure 10.12 helps visualize why there is a discrepancy.

Figure 10.12: Expected Lower Confidence Bound of Regression Estimated by Common Slopes Model, Relative to 5th Percentile of Product Distribution

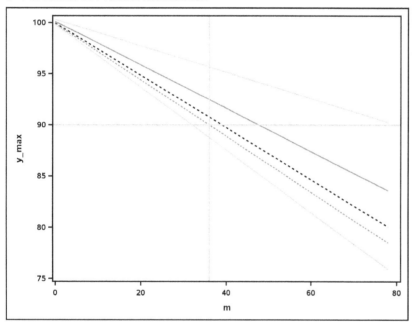

The solid black line shows the regression line from which the Q1E fixed effects ANCOVA model obtains the shelf life estimate. Although intended to be "conservative" the regression line's expected percentile value is actually the $\Phi\left(-1.65/\sqrt{3}\right) = 0.17$, i.e. the 17th percentile of the population of regression lines. On the other hand, the regression line from which the BLUP-based shelf life estimate is obtained is constructed to target the 5th percentile of the population. In other words, the risk associated with the Q1E procedure when the equal slopes model is selected is actually 0.17. Figure 10.12 illustrates that the expected value of the Q1E estimate is approximately 41 months. If the actual estimate is equal to the expected value of its sampling distribution, the best estimate of the probability that a future batch fails before the stated shelf life is 0.17. Recall that the actual Q1E estimate for the data in this example is 43 months. You can see from Figure 10.12 that the risk of product failure before 43 months is approximately 0.3.

The other issue with the Q1E procedure is the inference space. By definition, the inference space of a fixed batch model is limited to only those batches actually observed. On the other hand, the Q1E mandate clearly calls for the shelf life estimate to apply to "all future batches." Hence, there is a disconnect between the model and the stated objective. If the goal is to make a *prediction* about future batches, then using a random batch model is what best linear unbiased *predictors* are intended to do.

10.5.4 Estimation Using the "Naive" Mixed Model Approach

An obvious question suggested by the above discussion is why not use a mixed model to address the inference space issue? Specifically, use the random coefficient mixed model used in the BLUP approach shown above. Quinlan, et al. (2013) investigate this model under the assumption that the mixed model means "poolability" is a nonissue and shelf life can be determined from the lower confidence bound of the predicted value, $\hat{y}_M = \hat{\beta}_0 + \hat{\beta}_1 Month$, obtained using mixed model methodology.

You can implement this procedure by using Program 10.23.

Program 10.23

```
proc glimmix data=stability_demo;
  class batch;
  model y=month / ddfm=kr2 s cl;
  random intercept month / subject=batch;
  estimate 'yhat at 36' intercept 1 month 36/ cl alpha=0.10;
  estimate 'yhat at 37' intercept 1 month 37/ cl alpha=0.10;
run;
```

The ESTIMATE statements allow you to track the lower confidence bound of $\hat{y}_M$ as it approaches the acceptance limit. Use ALPHA=0.10 to target the lower 5th percentile.

Output 10.19 shows selected results.

Output 10.19: Selected Output from the "Naive" Mixed Model Approach

Covariance Parameter Estimates			
Cov Parm	Subject	Estimate	Standard Error
Intercept	batch	0.2806	0.4525
month	batch	0.001287	0.002303
Residual		0.4057	0.1421

Solutions for Fixed Effects								
Effect	Estimate	Standard Error	DF	t Value	Pr > |t|	Alpha	Lower	Upper
Intercept	99.6981	0.3823	1.846	260.79	<.0001	0.05	97.9143	101.48
month	-0.1829	0.02728	1.846	-6.70	0.0263	0.05	-0.3102	-0.05561

Estimates								
Label	Estimate	Standard Error	DF	t Value	Pr > |t|	Alpha	Lower	Upper
yhat at 36	93.1144	0.9366	1.763	99.42	0.0003	0.1	90.1121	96.1167
yhat at 37	92.9315	0.9618	1.746	96.62	0.0003	0.1	89.8241	96.0389

The table of "Covariance Parameter Estimates" shows the estimated estimates of the intercept variance, $\hat{\sigma}_0^2$, the slope variance, $\hat{\sigma}_1^2$, and residual (measurement error) variance, $\hat{\sigma}^2$. The "Solutions for Fixed Effects" gives the estimated regression equation, $99.7 - 0.1829 \times$ Month. The lower confidence bound at 36 months is 90.1; the lower confidence bound at 37 months is 89.8. The shelf life estimate is therefore 36 months.

We call this the "naive" mixed model approach because, done this way, the confidence interval width depends on the number of batches sampled. With 3 batches, the confidence interval is sufficiently imprecise—and hence wide—to more or less correspond to the estimates obtained using batch-specific BLUP. However, if you increase the number of batches, the confidence interval narrows: the implicit target percentile tends toward the median, and the risk of future batches failing to remain within acceptance criteria increases accordingly. In other words, the more you replicate, the greater the risk of a shelf life estimate that a high proportion of future batches will fail to meet. The BLUP approach ameliorates this undesirable tendency. This explains why we call the mixed model approach shown in this section "naive."

As with the Q1E procedure, the problem with the "naive" mixed model approach is that it focuses on *estimation* rather than on mixed model *prediction*.

10.6 Summary

Data structures appropriate for this chapter consist of repeated measurements on independent subjects. The random coefficients model for such data is effectively an analysis of covariance for each subject; however, the coefficients from these regression models are assumed to have arisen from a normal probability distribution. Three examples were used to illustrate the important features of the model: one where the subjects are treatments, another where the subjects are students and a repeated measures growth study. A fourth example provides methods to predict shelf life of a product. Only linear random coefficient models were discussed in this chapter, but nonlinear random coefficient models are quite useful, as in the growth study in Section 10.4. You can fit nonlinear random coefficient models by using PROC NLMIXED, a topic for the future and beyond the scope of this introductory book.

Chapter 11: Generalized Linear Mixed Models for Binomial Data

11.1 Introduction **377**	
11.2 Three Examples of Generalized Linear Mixed Models for Binomial Data **378**	
11.2.1 Binomial O-Ring Data..378	
11.2.2 Binomial Data in a Multicenter Clinical Trial 379	
11.2.3 Binary Data from a Dairy Cattle Breeding Trial...379	
11.3 Example 1: Binomial O-Ring Data..**380**	
11.3.1 Standard Generalized Linear Model Regression with Binomial Data 380	
11.3.2 A Generalized Linear Model Alternative: Logistic Regression..................................381	
11.4 Generalized Linear Model Background..**383**	
11.4.1 Generalized Linear Model Overview 383	
11.4.2 Probability Distributions and Log Likelihoods 384	
11.4.3 The Structure of the Generalized Linear Model 386	
11.4.4 From GLM to GLMM...387	
11.4.5 Conditional and Marginal Models 388	
11.4.6 Estimates, Standard Errors, and Confidence Intervals 391	
11.4.7 Deviance, Goodness of Fit, and Hypothesis Testing 391	
11.4.8 Estimation Methods in PROC GLIMMIX 392	
11.5 Example 2: Binomial Data in a Multicenter Clinical Trial...**394**	
11.5.1 Two Pre-GLMM Analyses: The Normal Approximation and the Angular Transformation..........................395	
11.5.2 GLMM Analysis of Binomial Using Logit (Canonical) Link Function 398	
11.5.3 Clinic-Specific Treatment Effects 406	
11.5.4 Marginal GLMM Analysis of Binomial Using Logit Link 409	
11.6 Example 3: Binary Data from a Dairy Cattle Breeding Trial **412**	
11.7 Summary...**417**	

11.1 Introduction

The linear mixed models in the previous chapters assume that the observations are normally distributed. In this chapter and in Chapters 12 and 13, we present mixed models for data that do not follow a normal distribution. We begin with a historical note and a vocabulary convention to be used in these three chapters. Johann Carl Friedrich Gauss is credited with the normal, also called the Gaussian, distribution. In this chapter, we use "Gaussian" distribution exclusively. The term "normal" implies that non-normally distributed data are in some sense "abnormal." This seems pejorative. In many disciplines, data with non-Gaussian distributions are the rule, not the exception—Gaussian data would be considered highly abnormal in these disciplines. To avoid the appearance of vocabulary favoritism, we will use "Gaussian distribution" rather than "normal distribution."

Linear mixed models (LMMs), that is, mixed models for Gaussian data differ from *generalized* linear mixed models (GLMMs) in several respects. First, you can write a Gaussian LMM either in model equation form—observation = fixed effects + random effects + residual—or in probability distribution form. On the other hand, you must write a GLMM in probability distribution form. In fact, for many distributions, "residual" has no meaning. Second, with LMMs, the linear combination of fixed and random effects directly models the mean. However, for non-Gaussian data, or for cases in which there are restrictions on the range of allowable values for predictable functions, it is usually better to use the "fixed effects + random effects" linear combination to model a function of the mean, called a *link function*. Third, the distinction between conditional and marginal models is more consequential for GLMMs. With Gaussian data, choosing between a conditional or marginal LMM affects how one models and interprets covariance structure, but does not affect estimation and inference for fixed effects. This is not the case for GLMMs. Marginal models have a different target of inference than conditional models; deciding which is appropriate is a crucial—and often misunderstood—aspect of working with non-Gaussian data.

One pre-GLMM approach to handling non-Gaussian data is to use various data transformations in conjunction with standard linear model methods. The more commonly used transformations are discussed in introductory statistical methods texts such as Steel and Torrie (1980) and Snedecor and Cochran (1989). Box and Cox (1964) discuss such transformations in considerable depth. Although the GLMM link function superficially resembles a transformation, there are important differences that will be clarified in the examples of this chapter for binomial data and Chapter 12 for count data.

Nelder and Wedderburn (1972) introduce the *generalized linear model* (GLM), a comprehensive extension of the fixed-effect-only linear model. In this class of models, the mean of the data is expressed in terms of a monotonic function of a linear model, and the parameters are estimated by maximum likelihood. Originally developed for members of the exponential family of distributions, GLMs have been extended to a much broader range of applications. For example, *quasi-likelihood* methods for independent data enable statistical estimation and inference based on only the mean and variance model of the data, without the specification of a joint distribution. Similarly, likelihood-based techniques have been developed for cases where the joint distribution of the data is unknown or difficult to determine, but a conditional distribution can be specified. This scenario is important for developments discussed below, where the distribution of the data is known conditional on random effects. Examples in this chapter and in Chapters 12 and 13 illustrate models of this type.

Between the publication of Nelder and Wedderburn's 1972 paper and the 1990s, a number of articles extended the GLM to various special-purpose mixed model applications. Breslow and Clayton (1993) presented a unifying approach tying together the underlying principles of the *generalized linear mixed model* (GLMM). Independently, Wolfinger and O'Connell (1993) developed a similar methodology for GLMMs and implemented it in the GLIMMIX macro. In 2005, the functionality of this macro was enhanced and incorporated as a SAS/STAT procedure, PROC GLIMMIX. In 2008, the GLIMMIX procedure was augmented with several options and additional statements that greatly extended its capability and versatility.

The purpose of Chapters 11 through 13 is to introduce the basic concepts of the GLMM and to show how to use PROC GLIMMIX to fit basic GLMMs. Chapter 11 focuses on binary and binomial response variables, that is, responses with two alternatives (e.g. yes/no, dead/alive, defective/not defective). Section 11.2 introduces three examples to be developed in subsequent sections. Section 11.3 presents a linear regression model as an introductory illustration of what is wrong with standard linear models for non-Gaussian data, and how GLMs address the problem. Section 11.4 gives an introduction to GLMs and GLMMs. The authors intend Section 11.4 to be a "gentle introduction," but with the understanding that the GLMM is arguably the most technically difficult topic in this book. Many readers will find Section 11.4 tough going and may want to skip ahead to the examples in Sections 11.5 and 11.6. Chapter 12 presents GLMMs for discrete counts. The examples in Chapters 11 and 12 use simple designs. Chapter 13 covers GLMMs with more complex design structure—split-plots and repeated measures.

11.2 Three Examples of Generalized Linear Mixed Models for Binomial Data

As mentioned above, many practical applications call for mixed model methods, but the data do not meet the assumptions of the standard mixed linear model. This section presents three examples in which the response variable involves two categories.

11.2.1 Binomial O-Ring Data

Following the 1986 Challenger space shuttle disaster, investigators focused on a suspected association between O-ring failure and low temperature at launch. Data documenting the presence or absence of primary O-ring thermal distress in the 23 shuttle launches preceding the Challenger mission appear in Dalal et. al (1989) and are reproduced in Agresti (1996). The data consist of the temperature at launch, in Fahrenheit degrees, the total number of shuttle launches at that temperature and the number of launches in which thermal distress occurred. Denote the total number of launches at a given temperature by n_j, where j is a subscript referencing the jth temperature. Temperatures at launch ranged from 53 to 81 degrees with a total of 16 temperature values within this range. Hence, $j = 1$ references 53 degrees, $j = 2$ references 57 degrees, and so on through 81 degrees, referenced by $j = 16$. The number of thermal distress incidents at the jth temperature is denoted by y_j. Thus, the sample proportion of launches in which thermal distress occurred is denoted by $p_j = y_j / n_j$.

Analysis of the O-ring data focuses on estimating a linear regression of temperature on proportion of launches in which thermal distress occurred. The standard linear regression model is as follows:

$$p_j = \beta_0 + \beta_1 X_j$$

where X_j denotes the actual temperature referenced by subscript j, e.g. $X_1 = 53$, ... , $X_{16} = 81$. As we will see in Section 11.3, there is an obvious problem with this approach, in that it yields predicted proportions, $\hat{p}_j$ that are not necessarily bounded by 0 and 1. Addressing the problem of obtaining predicted values that are within the allowable range of proportions provides the initial motivation for the generalized linear model (GLM). Section 11.3.2 introduces logistic regression, a GLM for linear regression with proportion data, as a preferred method of analyzing the O-ring data.

11.2.2 Binomial Data in a Multicenter Clinical Trial

Beitler and Landis (1985) discuss data from a clinical trial involving 2 drug treatments and 8 clinics. The 8 clinics represent a sample from a larger target population. At the jth clinic ($j = 1,2,...,8$), n_{i1} subjects were randomly assigned to receive treatment 1, and n_{2j} subjects were randomly assigned to treatment 2. Each subject was classified as having a "favorable" or "unfavorable" response to the treatment. The number of "favorable" responses to the ith treatment at the jth clinic is denoted y_{ij}, and the sample proportion of "favorable" responses for the ij^{th} treatment-clinic combination is denoted $p_{ij} = y_{ij}/n_{ij}$.

The objective of the trial is to determine the effect of treatment and clinic on the probability of a "favorable" response. If we take the approach used in the first ten chapters of this book, then a possible linear mixed model for this trial is:

$$p_{ij} = \mu + \tau_i + c_j + e_{ij} \tag{11.1}$$

where terms are defined as follows:

- μ denotes the intercept.

- τ_i denotes the ith treatment effect.

- c_j denotes the jth clinic effect, assumed iid $N(0, \sigma^2)$

- e_{ij} denotes the residual, assumed iid $N(0, \sigma^2)$

Because clinics were sampled from the population, the clinic effects are considered random.

There are at least three problems with applying the conventional mixed model methods to Equation 11.1. First, given that the response variable is the number of favorable outcomes out of the number of patients at each treatment × clinic combination, the presumed distribution is Binomial(n_{ij}, π_{ij}) where π_{ij} denotes the probability of a favorable response to treatment i at clinic j. Standard LMM assumptions of normality and homogeneity of variance are thus violated by definition. Second, although the probability of a favorable response clearly must be between 0 and 1, there is no guarantee that estimates of π_{ij} obtained from models that fit the linear predictor directly to p_{ij} will satisfy this restriction; predicted probabilities that are negative or greater than one are entirely possible. Finally, estimates obtained from Equation 11.1 do not, in fact, estimate the binomial probability, π_{ij}. Equation 11.1 estimates the expected value of p_{ij}, called the *marginal mean*, which is not equal to the probability π_{ij}. This is our first example of the distinction between the *conditional* and *marginal* inference target, a critically important issue in mixed models for non-Gaussian data. Section 11.4.4 formally introduces *conditional* and *marginal* models. Section 11.5.1 presents the LMM analysis of Equation 11.1 in order to help make these issues tangible.

Beitler and Landis (1985) present a procedure for analyzing these data that anticipates the generalized linear mixed model, although they do not develop their approach within the GLMM framework. Also, their model does not address the need for restrictions on predicted probabilities, nor does their approach show any awareness of the conditional/marginal model issue. Sections 11.5.2 and 11.5.4 present *conditional* and *marginal* models for the multicenter binomial data in this example and show how to use the GLIMMIX procedure for the analysis.

11.2.3 Binary Data from a Dairy Cattle Breeding Trial

In the previous example, there were n_{ij} favorable/unfavorable responses per treatment × clinic combination making it possible to calculate a sample proportion, $p_{ij} = y_{ij}/n_{ij}$. In many disciplines, only one observation per experimental unit is possible; the response variable, therefore, must be binary. Stroup (2013) presented an example provided by Bello, et al. (2006). This is a much-simplified adaptation to illustrate modeling binary data with a GLMM while avoiding any possibly distracting complications.

In this example, randomly selected males are mated to two females. Each female typically has one or two offspring. Less commonly, some females have three offspring. The response variable concerns a trait in the offspring. Define the response variable as follows:

$$y_{ijk} = \begin{cases} 0 \text{ if the trait is not present} \\ 1 \text{ if the trait is present} \end{cases}$$

A possible model is $y_{ijk} = \mu + m_i + f(m)_{ij} + o(f,m)_{ijk}$, where m_i denotes the effect of the ith male, $f(m)_{ij}$ denotes the effect of the jth female mated to the ith male, and $o(f,m)_{ijk}$ denotes the effect of the kth offspring from the ij^{th} parent pair. Because males and females represent a sample, all model effects except μ are assumed to be random.

This model has all of the problems listed for the binomial model above in Section 11.2.1. They are exacerbated by the fact that there is usually only one binary observation per offspring.

11.3 Example 1: Binomial O-Ring Data

Section 11.3.1 describes the O-ring data used to investigate the Challenger space shuttle disaster of 1986. The data are given in Challenger Thermal Distress Data. The variables are temperature in Fahrenheit degrees at launch (TEMP), total number of launches at that temperature (TOTAL), and number of launches at that temperature in which O-ring thermal distress occurred (TD). Analysis focuses on fitting a linear regression of TD on TEMP and obtaining predicted proportion of launches with thermal distress at various temperatures. Section 11.3.1 shows results using standard linear models. The problems with these results motivate the need to do something different. Section 11.3.2 introduces logistic regression, a common GLM for binomial data, and shows how it addresses the problems encountered with the standard linear model.

11.3.1 Standard Generalized Linear Model Regression with Binomial Data

The linear regression model based on linear model theory can be written as follows:

$$p_j = y_j/n_j = \beta_0 + \beta_1 X_j + e_j$$

where X_j denotes the jth temperature level—i.e. $X_1 = 53, X_2 = 57, ..., X_{16} = 81$ — p_j denotes the observed proportion of launches n which thermal distress occurred, and e_j denotes random residual. Note that the observed proportion is the ratio of thermal distress incidents at the jth temperature (y_j) relative to the number of launches (n_j).

Program

Program 11.1 implements this model.

Program 11.1

```
proc glimmix data=Challenger;
 proportion=td/total;
 model proportion=temp/solution;
 estimate 'p_hat at 50 deg' intercept 1 temp 50;
 estimate 'p_hat at 60 deg' intercept 1 temp 60;
 estimate 'p_hat at 70 deg' intercept 1 temp 70;
 estimate 'p_hat at 80 deg' intercept 1 temp 80;
run;
```

You must define the sample proportion response variable. You can do this with the program statement PROPORTION=TD/TOTAL. The MODEL statement option SOLUTION gives you the estimates of the intercept and slope, $\hat{\beta}_0$ and $\hat{\beta}_1$. The ESTIMATE statements compute the predicted proportion of thermal distress incidents for selected temperatures. The ESTIMATE statements in this example cover the range between 50 and 80 degrees. You can add other temperatures if needed.

Results

Output 11.1 shows the results.

Output 11.1: Estimated Regression Coefficients and Predicted Proportions of Thermal Distress with Standard Linear Regression Model

Parameter Estimates					
Effect	Estimate	Standard Error	DF	t Value	Pr > |t|
Intercept	3.1803	0.6417	14	4.96	0.0002
temp	-0.04152	0.009231	14	-4.50	0.0005
Scale	0.08580	0.03243	.	.	.

Estimates					
Label	Estimate	Standard Error	DF	t Value	Pr > |t|
p_hat at 50 deg	1.1041	0.1906	14	5.79	<.0001
p_hat at 60 deg	0.6888	0.1112	14	6.20	<.0001
p_hat at 70 deg	0.2736	0.07374	14	3.71	0.0023
p_hat at 80 deg	-0.1417	0.1247	14	-1.14	0.2751

Interpretation

The estimated regression parameters are intercept, $\hat{\beta}_0 = 3.18$, and slope, $\hat{\beta}_1 = -0.0415$. The estimated residual variance is $\hat{\sigma}^2 = 0.0858$. The regression coefficient estimates suggest an obvious problem with this approach: proportions are constrained to be between 0 and 1, but there is nothing to keep the predicted value $\hat{\beta}_0 + \hat{\beta}_1 X$ within these boundaries. Indeed, you can see in the "Estimates" table that the predicted proportions at 50 and 80 degrees are 1.1 and −0.14 respectively, both of which are nonsense estimates.

Less obvious, but equally important, there is a disconnect between the assumptions of the model and the presumptive distribution of y_j. It makes sense to assume $y_j \sim \text{Binomial}(n_j, \pi_j)$ where π_j denotes the probability of a thermal distress incident at the jth temperature. The assumptions underlying the standard linear model imply $E(y_j/n_j) = \beta_0 + \beta_1 X_j$ and $\text{Var}(y_j/n_j) = \sigma^2$, whereas if we assume y_j follows a binomial distribution, then $E(y_j/n_j) = \pi_j$ and $\text{Var}(y_j/n_j) = \pi_j(1-\pi_j)/n_j$. Therefore, $\hat{\beta}_0 + \hat{\beta}_1 X_j$ should equal $\hat{\pi}_j$, which, given the results in the table of "Estimates," is clearly not true. In addition, in the standard linear model, the residual variance is a distinct parameter, whereas in the binomial, the variance is a function of the mean, and the concept of "residual" has no real meaning. These reasons suggest the need for a better approach for non-Gaussian data.

11.3.2 A Generalized Linear Model Alternative: Logistic Regression

The rationale for the GLM begins with inspection of the log-likelihood function, which, for the binomial, is the natural log of the probability distribution function. Using notation from Section 11.3.1, the probability density function (PDF) of the thermal distress response variable is:

$$f(y_j) = \binom{n_j}{y_j} \pi_j^{y_j} (1 - \pi_j)^{y_j}$$

and its natural log is as follows:

$$\log[f(y_j)] = y_j \log[\pi_j/(1-\pi_j)] + n_j(1-\pi_j) + \log\left[\binom{n_j}{y_j}\right]$$

The term multiplied by the response variable, in this case the term multiplied by y_j, $\log[\pi_j/(1-\pi_j)]$ is called the *natural*, or *canonical parameter*. Nelder and Wedderburn (1972) argue that because the data are linear in the natural parameter, it makes more sense to fit a linear model to the natural parameter than it does to fit a model directly to the response variable, or, to put it more precisely, to the mean of the response variable. In other words, a regression model

$\log[\pi_j/(1-\pi_j)] = \beta_0 + \beta_1 X_j$ would be a sensible linear regression model for binomial data. The term $\log[\pi_j/(1-\pi_j)]$ is called the *logit* and hence this regression model is referred to as *logistic regression.*

Once you estimate the regression equation, you have an estimate of the logit. This is called the *model scale* estimate. Once you have the model scale estimate, you can solve for $\hat{\pi}_j$ the estimated probability of a thermal distress incident at temperature *j*, which, for the Challenger data was the main goal of the data analysis. Solving for π_j gives $\pi_j = 1/[1 + \exp\{-(\beta_0 + \beta_1 X_j)\}]$. This is called the *data scale* estimate. Notice that unlike $\beta_0 + \beta_1 X$, the data scale estimate $1/[1 + \exp\{-(\beta_0 + \beta_1 X_j)\}]$ cannot be less than 0 nor greater than 1. In addition, the logistic regression model has no residual term e_j and hence no distinct variance component. Once you have an estimate of π_j you have the estimate of the variance, $\pi_j(1-\pi_j)/n_j$ as well.

Program

You can implement the logistic regression for the Challenger data using Program 11.2.

Program 11.2

```
proc glimmix data=Challenger;
 model td/total=temp/dist=binomial link=logit solution;
 estimate 'p_hat at 50 deg' intercept 1 temp 50/ilink;
 estimate 'p_hat at 60 deg' intercept 1 temp 60/ilink;
 estimate 'p_hat at 70 deg' intercept 1 temp 70/ilink;
 estimate 'p_hat at 80 deg' intercept 1 temp 80/ilink;
run;
```

A response variable is the form of Y/N, or in this case TD/TOTAL, is automatically treated as a binomial response variable, i.e. the assumed distribution is $Y \sim \text{Binomial}(N, \pi)$. The left-hand side of the model equation is called the *link function*. By default, PROC GLIMMIX uses LOGIT as the link function for binomial response variables. The MODEL statement options DIST and LINK define the response variable distribution and the LINK function to be used for the analysis. In this example, however, DIST and LINK are unnecessary because the binomial and logit are assumed by default; they are shown here for completeness and to establish syntax that you will need in more complicated examples. The ESTIMATE statement computes estimates on the model scale—in this case estimated logits. The ILINK option causes the ESTIMATE statement to compute the model scale estimate. ILINK is short for *inverse link*, the function that converts the model scale estimate to the data scale.

Results

Output 11.2 shows selected results.

Output 11.2: Logistic Regression Coefficient Estimates and Predicted Probabilities

Parameter Estimates					
Effect	Estimate	Standard Error	DF	t Value	Pr > |t|
Intercept	15.0429	7.3786	14	2.04	0.0608
temp	-0.2322	0.1082	14	-2.14	0.0500

Estimates							
Label	Estimate	Standard Error	DF	t Value	Pr > |t|	Mean	Standard Error Mean
p_hat at 50 deg	3.4348	2.0232	14	1.70	0.1117	0.9688	0.06121
p_hat at 60 deg	1.1131	1.0259	14	1.09	0.2962	0.7527	0.1909
p_hat at 70 deg	-1.2085	0.5953	14	-2.03	0.0618	0.2300	0.1054
p_hat at 80 deg	-3.5301	1.4140	14	-2.50	0.0256	0.02847	0.03911

Interpretation

The estimated regression coefficients for intercept and slope are $\hat{\beta}_0 = 15.04$ and $\hat{\beta}_1 = -0.232$, respectively. Thus, for the jth temperature, you estimate its logit as $15.04 - 0.232 X_j$, e.g. for 50 degrees $15.04 - 0.232 \times 50 = 3.435$. In the table of

"Estimates," the estimated logits (and, in general, the model scale estimates) appear in the column labeled ESTIMATE. The data scale estimates, in this case the estimated probabilities $\hat{\pi}_j$ appear in the column labeled MEAN. For example, the estimated probability for 50 degrees is obtained by applying the inverse link to the logit, i.e. $1/[1+\exp\{-(3.435)\}] = 0.969$. Standard errors associated with the model and data scale estimates are obtained using computations described in Section 11.4.5. You can see that the estimated probabilities obtained from logistic regression are all within the parameter space and make sense. As a final note, the estimated probability of O-ring thermal distress is over 0.96 at 50 degrees. When Challenger had its fatal launch, the temperature was in the 30s.

11.4 Generalized Linear Model Background

Generalized linear models (GLMs) are extensions of fixed effects linear models to cases where data are independent and standard linear model assumptions associated with the Gaussian (a.k.a. "normal") distribution are violated. Generalized linear *mixed* models (GLMMs) extend GLMs to accommodate random model effects. This section presents a "gentle" introduction to the GLM and GLMM. A more comprehensive overview of GLMM theory and methods, and how PROC GLIMMIX implements them, appears in Appendix B. See Stroup (2013) for a comprehensive, in-depth presentation of the GLMM.

The goal of this section is to present the main ideas so that (1) the methods presented in Sections 11.5 and 11.6, and in Chapters 12 and 13, are understandable and (2) the available statements and options of the GLIMMIX procedure have an adequate context.

11.4.1 Generalized Linear Model Overview

Standard linear models are defined directly in terms of the observations. Many introductory texts introduce the generic form of the model as "observation = systematic component + random residual." For example, the linear model for a one-way analysis of variance is usually written as follows:

$$y_{ij} = \mu + \tau_i + e_{ij}$$
$$e_{ij} \sim \text{NI}\left(0, \sigma^2\right)$$

$$(11.2)$$

where ~NI means "normally and independently distributed." Another way to write this model, essential for making the transition to generalized linear models, is in terms of the distribution of the data. Equation 11.2 can be equivalently expressed as follows:

$$y_{ij} \sim \text{NI}\left(\mu + \tau_i, \sigma^2\right)$$
$$\text{E}\left(y_{ij}\right) = \mu + \tau_i$$
$$\text{Var}\left(y_{ij}\right) = \sigma^2$$

$$(11.3)$$

You can see that y_{ij} is assumed to have mean $\mu + \tau_i$ and variance σ^2, and that the "systematic component" directly models the mean. Equation 11.2 is called the *model equation form* and Equation 11.3 is called the *probability distribution form*. As we shall see, the probability distribution form lends itself naturally to extension to non-Gaussian observations, whereas the model equation form does not.

For models that are given in model equation form, the expected value of the observation is a linear combination of the model fixed effects. In regression models, these effects provide predicted values of the expected value of an observation given as X. In an analysis of variance model, the effects can be used to estimate means or compare means of various treatments, where functions of $\text{E}(y_{ij})$ represent treatment means or other estimable functions of interest.

For standard mixed models, such as those discussed up to this point in this book, we simply add random effects where appropriate, or elaborate the covariance structure, or both. For example, for a randomized block design, the model equation form is commonly written as follows:

$$y_{ij} = \mu + \tau_i + b_j + e_{ij}$$
$$b_j \sim \text{NI}\left(0, \sigma_b^2\right)$$
$$e_{ij} \sim \text{NI}\left(0, \sigma^2\right)$$

$$(11.4)$$

Equation 11.4 can be re-expressed in probability distribution form as follows:

$$
\begin{aligned}
y_{ij} \mid b_j &\sim \mathrm{NI}\!\left(\mu_{ij}, \sigma^2\right) \\
\mathrm{E}\!\left(y_{ij} \mid b_j\right) &= \mu_{ij} \\
\mu_{ij} &= \mu + \tau_i + b_j \\
\mathrm{Var}\!\left(y_{ij} \mid b_j\right) &= \sigma^2
\end{aligned}
\tag{11.5}
$$

Note that the marginal mean of the Gaussian mixed model is $\mathrm{E}(y_{ij})$, which for Equation 11.5 is $\mu + \tau_i$. The mean of the block effect is zero; therefore, b_j does not appear in the marginal mean. As before, the primary objective of the standard linear model is to estimate the expected value of the observations. In the mixed model, we either focus on the conditional mean, $\mathrm{E}(y_{ij} \mid b_j)$ or the marginal mean. The former implies BLUPs defined by predictable functions (as discussed in Chapters 9 and 10), the latter implies estimable functions defined on fixed effects only. Like the standard linear model, the Gaussian linear mixed model is defined directly in terms of the mean, the only difference being the inclusion of random model effects—or complex covariance structure (i.e. one that requires using a RANDOM or REPEATED statement)—in the mixed model.

This modeling strategy works well for Gaussian data. However, problems arise with non-Gaussian data. These include inefficient or inaccurate estimates, estimates outside the range of permissible values, misleading *p*-values in hypothesis tests, and so on. When the data are non-Gaussian and the analysis requires a mixed model, these problems are often magnified.

Instead of using a modeling strategy that depends on Gaussian assumptions, Nelder and Wedderburn used the assumed log likelihood of the observations as the basis for a more generally applicable linear model. To understand their strategy, we begin in Section 11.4.2 by contrasting the Gaussian (for continuous response variables whose distribution follows— at least approximately—a bell-shaped curve) and the Binomial (for yes/no variables). In Chapter 12, we extend the Nelder-Wedderburn strategy to the Poisson distribution (for discrete counts).

11.4.2 Probability Distributions and Log Likelihoods

The log likelihood is written as the natural log of the probability density, or probability distribution function. For a given set of observations, denoted *y* in the distributions given below, maximizing the function with respect to each parameter gives the maximum likelihood estimate. For Gaussian data, the maximum likelihood and least squares estimates happen to agree. This is not true of other distributions. Maximum likelihood is the more generalizable approach, and thus the basis for developing the GLM and GLMM. The following distributions illustrate the essential building blocks of this approach.

Gaussian

For the Gaussian distribution, the probability density function of *y* is:

$$
f(y) = \left(\frac{1}{\sqrt{2\pi\sigma^2}}\right) \exp\!\left[-\frac{(y-\mu)^2}{2\sigma^2}\right]
$$

where μ is the mean and σ^2 is the variance. The log-likelihood function is thus:

$$
l(\mu, \sigma^2; y) = -\left(\frac{1}{2}\right)\log(2\pi\sigma^2) - \frac{(y-\mu)^2}{2\sigma^2} = -\frac{1}{2}\left\{\frac{(y-\mu)^2}{\sigma^2} + \log(2\pi\sigma^2)\right\}
\tag{11.6}
$$

Binomial

For the binomial distribution with *n* trials and a success probability of π, the familiar form of the probability distribution function of *y* is

$$
f(y) = \binom{n}{y}\pi^y (1-\pi)^{n-y}
$$

and the log-likelihood function is thus:

$$l(\pi; y) = y \, \log\left(\frac{\pi}{1-\pi}\right) + n \, \log(1-\pi) + \log\binom{n}{y}$$

For modeling purposes, it is useful to re-express the binomial log likelihood in terms of the sample proportion, y/n, as follows:

$$l(\pi; y) = ny \, \log\left(\frac{\pi}{1-\pi}\right) + n \, \log(1-\pi) + \log\binom{n}{y} \tag{11.7}$$

Common Features of the Log-Likelihood

You can re-express the Gaussian and binomial log-likelihood functions, Equations 11.6 and 11.7, respectively, as follows:

$$\text{Gaussian: } l(\mu,\sigma^2; y) = -\frac{1}{2}\left\{\frac{-2y\mu + \mu^2 + y^2}{\sigma^2} + \log(2\pi\sigma^2)\right\} = \frac{y\mu - (\mu^2/2)}{\sigma^2} - \frac{1}{2}\left\{\left(\frac{y}{\sigma}\right)^2 + \log(2\pi\sigma^2)\right\}$$

$$\text{Binomial: } l(\pi; y) = \frac{y \, \log\left[\pi/(1-\pi)\right] - \log\left[1/(1-\pi)\right]}{1/n} + \log\binom{n}{y}$$

The log-likelihood functions for these distributions have a common form,

$$l(\theta,\phi; y) = \frac{y\theta - b(\theta)}{a(\phi)} + c(y,\phi) \tag{11.8}$$

where θ is termed the "natural" (or "canonical") parameter and ϕ is a scale parameter.

You can see that the mean, μ is the natural parameter for the Gaussian distribution and the logit is the natural parameter for the binomial. You can also see that the variance, σ^2 is the scale parameter for the Gaussian distribution, whereas the "scale" parameter for the binomial is $1/n$. You must estimate the scale parameter in a Gaussian distribution, whereas it is known for the binomial. The Gaussian is called a *two-parameter* distribution because it has distinct mean and scale parameters, whereas the binomial is called a *one-parameter* distribution because the mean and variance both depend on a single parameter, π.

Distributions whose log likelihood can be written in the form of Equation 11.8 are said to be members of the linear *exponential family* of distributions. The fact that y is multiplied by θ is important. This idea is introduced in Section 11.3.2 and developed in more detail in Section 11.4.3. Note that the natural parameter, θ, is always a function of the mean. It is often helpful to write the natural parameter as a function of the mean, i.e. $\theta(\mu)$. Also, the variance can be expressed as a function of the mean and $a(\phi)$. Specifically,

$$\text{Var}(Y) = v(\mu)a(\phi)$$

where $v(\mu)$ denotes the *variance function*—the function of the mean involved in Var(Y). For example, the variance function of the binomial distribution is $\pi(1-\pi)$. On the other hand, the variance function for the Gaussian distribution is $v(\mu) = 1$, because its variance does not depend on the mean. For the binomial and Gaussian distributions, the various functions can be summarized as shown in Table 11.1.

Table 11.1: Functions for Binomial and Gaussian Distributions

	Binomial/n	**Gaussian**
Mean	π	μ
$\theta(\mu)$	$\log[\pi/(1-\pi)]$	μ

	Binomial/*n*	**Gaussian**
$a(\phi)$	$1/n$	σ^2
$v(\mu)$	$\pi(1-\pi)$	1
$\text{Var}(Y)$	$\pi(1-\pi)/n$	σ^2

Notice that for the binomial distribution the mean appears in the variance function. This is commonplace in the exponential family of distributions. The independence of the mean and the variance for the Gaussian distribution is an exception. In other words, only with the Gaussian distribution can you determine the degree of variability independently from the mean. For other distributions in the exponential family, knowing the mean also determines the degree of variability, at least up to the function $a(\phi)$. This has far-reaching consequences for model formulation and estimation.

11.4.3 The Structure of the Generalized Linear Model

Inspection of the generic form of the log likelihood in Equation 11.8 reveals a central idea of the *generalized* linear model (GLM): y is multiplied by θ in the log likelihood, that is, the observations are linear in the natural parameter. This calls into question the traditional model equation form of the linear model. The model equation form of the linear model makes sense with Gaussian data because the mean is the natural parameter. However, for distributions whose natural parameter is a function of the mean, not the mean itself, and hence the observations are not linear in the mean, it makes more sense to do something different.

The "something different" is the generalized linear model. The GLM has three essential components:

- the distribution of the observations
- the linear predictor
- the link function

The distribution of the observations was discussed in Section 11.4.1. Nelder and Wedderburn (1972) initially developed the GLM for response variables whose distribution belongs to the exponential family. Following a paper by Wedderburn (1974), they extended the GLM to response variables for which you could specify a *quasi-likelihood*. Putting it as non-technically as possible, if you can specify a response variable's mean, natural parameter, variance function, and scale parameter, you can use GLM methodology.

Linear Predictor

The *linear predictor* is the linear combination of model effects that describes how the explanatory variables affect the mean. For example, in a one-way ANOVA model, the linear predictor is $\mu + \tau_i$. In a polynomial regression, the linear predictor is as follows:

$$\sum_{j=0}^{p} \beta_j X^j$$

For a randomized block design, the usual linear predictor is $\mu + \tau_i + b_j$.

The linear predictor is often introduced as "everything but the error term" in the model equation. In model equation form, the generic expression is as follows:

$$Y = \text{linear predictor} + e \tag{11.9}$$

To reiterate from the beginning of this section, Equation 11.9 is only useful for Gaussian data. The *probability distribution* form can be used for all linear models. Here, the GLM fits the linear predictor to a function of the expected value—denoted $g(\mu)$ – that has meaning in the context of the distribution of the observations. Nelder gave $g(\mu)$ its name in GLM terminology: it is called the *link function*, that is, the function that "links" the linear predictor to the mean.

Link and Inverse Link Functions

The notation for the GLM follows McCullagh and Nelder (1989), using the character η to denote the link function. For example, for a blocked design whose primary response variable is Gaussian, we could write the linear predictor as

$\eta_{ij} = \eta + \tau_i + b_j$. Notice that we replace μ by η to denote the intercept. This is to avoid the temptation to incorrectly refer to μ as the "overall mean." The *inverse link* function expresses the expected value of the observations as a function of the linear predictor. The inverse link is alternatively denoted $\mu = g^{-1}(\eta)$ or $\mu = h(\eta)$. In most models, there is a one-to-one correspondence between the link and inverse link functions. One notable exception occurs with models for categorical data when the response variable has three or more categories; these are beyond the scope of this chapter.

The log-likelihood function reveals some of the basic considerations for choosing a link function. First, the observations are linear with respect to the *natural parameter*, θ . For Gaussian data, $\theta = \mu$. Because the likelihood is linear in μ , it is reasonable to fit a model directly to μ , or equivalently to *Y*. In generalized linear model terms, the link function is equal to the mean, that is, $\eta = \mu$. This is called the *identity link*.

On the other hand, for binomial data, the observations are linear in the logit, $\eta = \log[\pi/(1-\pi)]$. Thus, as illustrated in Section 11.3.2, fitting a linear model to the logit is more reasonable than fitting a model directly to π (or *Y*). Fitting a model to $\log[\pi/(1-\pi)]$ gives rise to the *logistic model*. A regression model fit to the logit is called *logistic regression*. An ANOVA model fit to the logit is called *logistic* ANOVA. The inverse link for the logistic model is $\pi = 1/\{1 + \exp(-\eta)\}$.

In each of these examples, the natural parameter is used as the link function. A link function of this form is called the *canonical link function*. Although it is common to choose the canonical link, this is neither required nor necessarily recommended. The example in Section 11.6 shows binomial data modeled with the *probit* link; the rational for using it instead of the logit is explained in the introduction to that section.

11.4.4 From GLM to GLMM

The GLM involves fixed model effects only. However, as we have seen in previous chapters, most linear models require some mixed model aspect, either random model effect(s), a covariance structure that must be specified, or both. Development of generalized linear *mixed* models (GLMMs) began almost as soon as Nelder and Wedderburn introduced the GLM. Two publications, Zeger and Liang (1986) and Liang and Zeger (1986), introduced *generalized estimating equations* for *working covariance* models. Often called *GEE-type* models, these are special cases of generalized linear mixed models. Section 11.5.44 presents an example of this type of model for binomial data.

GEE-type models enable GLMs to be used for study designs that can be modeled by a fixed effect linear predictor and a correlated error structure, for example, repeated measures data, blocked designs, and relatively simple split-plots. Generalized estimating equations, known by their acronym GEE, are essentially GLM analogs of generalized least squares. Generalized estimating equations enable estimation and inference with these models, but do not accommodate random effects. Two subsequent publications, Breslow and Clayton (1993) and Wolfinger and O'Connell (1993), provided the basis for extending the GLM to linear predictors with random effects. Wolfinger and O'Connell's *pseudo-likelihood* (PL) is the default algorithm for estimation and inference in PROC GLIMMIX.

In essence, GLMMs are GLMs with either one or more random model effects, or a covariance structure that goes beyond the GLM's $\text{Var}(Y) = a(\phi)v(\mu)$ of a standard GLM, or both. In SAS terms, linear models can be divided into four basic categories, summarized along with their acronyms, in Table 11.2.

Table 11.2: The Four Categories of Linear Models

Distribution of Observations	Model Specification Statement	
	MODEL only	**MODEL RANDOM**
Gaussian	Linear Model (LM) (historically called "General" Linear Model)	Linear Mixed Model (LMM)
Non-Gaussian	Generalized Linear Model (GLM)	Generalized Linear Mixed Model (GLMM)

In terms of acronyms, the root acronym is LM—linear model. Add "G" for *generalized* if the data are non-Gaussian. Add "M" for *mixed* if you need to use a RANDOM statement in PROC GLIMMIX (or RANDOM or REPEATED in PROC MIXED) to fully specify the model.

The required elements to specify a GLMM are as follows:

- *The distribution of the observations.* In a mixed model, this is actually the distribution of the observations *conditional* on the random model effects. This distinction has important implications that are described in the examples that follow in this chapter and in Chapters 12 and 13.

- *The linear predictor.* If there are random model effects, include them in the linear predictor. For example, the usual linear predictor for a randomized block design is $\eta_{ij} = \eta + \tau_i + b_j$. As we have seen in previous chapters, in most cases, the block effect, b_j is assumed to be random.

- *The link function.* Some distributions have more than one option for linking the linear predictor and the mean of the observations. You should specify which link function you are using.

- *The distribution of the random effects.* If there are random model effects, you must specify their assumed distribution. In a GLMM, random model effects are typically assumed to have a Gaussian distribution with mean 0. As with other mixed models, the covariance structure can be any well-defined multivariate normal covariance.

- *The residual covariance structure.* If there is a residual covariance structure, it must be described.

Recall from Chapters 2 and 5 that mixed models whose linear predictor contains random effects are called *conditional models*. Whereas models with a fixed-effects-only linear predictor, but with a residual covariance structure that requires a RANDOM statement (or REPEATED statement in PROC MIXED), are called *marginal models*. With Gaussian data, you can construct conditional and marginal versions of mixed models that are identical with respect to fixed effect estimation and inference. Sections 2.5.3 and 5.7.3 cover examples. This is not the case for conditional and marginal models with non-Gaussian data. With GLMMs, conditional and marginal models have different targets of inference; deciding which target is appropriate is an essential part of constructing a GLMM. The next section elaborates on this important concept.

11.4.5 Conditional and Marginal Models

The GLMM has estimation and inference issues that are not present in the LM, LMM, or GLM. In the LM, GLM, and LMM, it is clear that the objective is to estimate the mean, i.e. the expected value of the observations, and to obtain confidence intervals or test hypotheses about differences or other contrasts defined in terms of the mean.

When *generalized* and *mixed* appear together, estimation and inference become more complicated. To understand why, we need to take a closer look at the way we model how the data arise. Specifically, two distributions define a mixed model. One is the distribution of the observed data given the random model effects, and the other is the distribution of the random model effects. For example, consider the distributions we would use to model the multi-clinic study introduced in Section 11.2.2 and covered in detail in Section 11.5. If we assume Gaussian data, then $y_{ij} \mid c_j \sim N(\mu + \tau_i + c_j, \sigma^2)$, the distribution of the observations given the clinics, and $c_j \sim N(0, \sigma_c^2)$, the distribution of the clinic effects. Although these are the distributions that model how the data arise, we cannot observe either distribution directly. Instead, we can only observe the data, the y_{ij} whose distribution is $y_{ij} \sim N(\mu + \tau_i, \sigma_c^2 + \sigma^2)$ with the additional fact that the covariance of two observations on different treatments in the same clinic is $Cov(y_{ij} y_{i'j}) = \sigma_c^2$. This is called the *marginal* distribution.

Notice that the fixed effect component of the distribution of $y_{ij} \mid c_j$ and the marginal distribution of y_{ij} are the same, in this case $\mu + \tau_i$. This result holds when the conditional distribution of the observations given the random effects is Gaussian, but not when the conditional distribution is non-Gaussian. This is best illustrated with an example. Figure 11.1 presents distributions that define a multi-clinic GLMM with binomial data. The two distributions that give rise to the data are the random clinic effect distribution, $c \sim N(0, \sigma_c^2)$, and the observations given the clinics, $y \mid c \sim \text{Binomial}(n, \pi)$. Figure 11.1 depicts the distributions when $\sigma_c^2 = 2$, $n = 40$ and $\pi = 0.25$, values similar to the estimated clinic variance and probability of a favorable outcome for treatment 1 in the multicenter example presented in Section 11.5.

Figure 11.1: Distributions That Define Multicenter Binomial Data

A

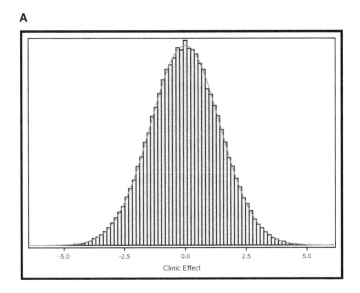

B

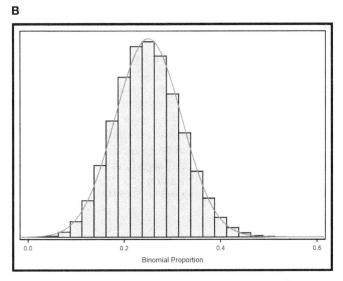

C

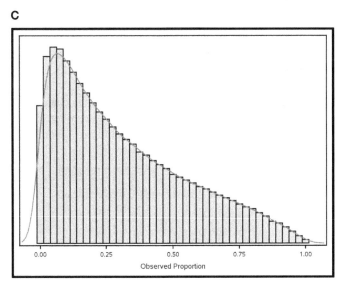

Note: (A) Distribution of clinic effects, $c \sim N(0,2)$. (B) Distribution of observations given clinics, $y \mid c \sim$ Binomial$(40, 0.25)$. (C) Distribution of observations we can see; marginal distribution of y.

The left-hand plot (A) shows the distribution of the clinic effects. The middle plot (B) shows the distribution of the observations given the clinics, plotted in terms of the sample proportion, Y/N. The vertical bars show the binomial distribution. Superimposed on panel (B) is the normal distribution with the same mean and variance as the binomial. Note that the mean is $\pi = 0.25$. With $n = 40$, the binomial is sufficiently symmetrical so that the normal approximation holds. The right-hand plot (C) shows the distribution that we actually observe—the marginal distribution of the observations. Unlike the "parent" distributions, it is right-skewed, not symmetrical. The normal approximation clearly would not be appropriate. Moreover, the mean of the marginal distribution is 0.31, not 0.25.

The mean of the distribution of the observations given the random model effects, and the mean of the marginal distribution are not the same. For modeling and inference, they have different interpretations and address different objectives. Each has a legitimate purpose, and each is inappropriate if not used for that purpose. Therefore, when you work with a GLMM, you have the additional responsibility of understanding the distinction and using a GLMM capable of addressing your intended objective. The examples in Section 11.5 and in subsequent chapters will elaborate on this crucial idea.

In GLMM language, *conditional* GLMMs target the mean of the observations given the random effects, whereas *marginal* GLMMs target the marginal mean. Conditional GLMMs have random model effects in the linear predictor (and hence one or more RANDOM statements without the word RESIDUAL) and they allow BLUPs. Marginal GLMMs do not have random model effects (and hence the RANDOM statement that must include the word RESIDUAL). Marginal GLMMs embed all random effect information in the residual covariance. In SAS jargon that has its origins in the first edition of this book (*SAS System for Mixed Models*, 1996), the covariance structure of random model effects is called "G-side" covariance and residual covariance, e.g. the covariance structure of marginal models, is called "R-side" covariance.

As a further note on language, marginal models for non-Gaussian data are sometimes referred to as "GEE-type models." The acronym *GEE* comes from *generalized estimating equations* (Liang and Zeger, 1986; Zeger and Liang, 1986), a computing algorithm developed for GLMs with a residual covariance structure. In the context of GEE, residual covariance is called the "working covariance structure." Putting it as non-technically as possible, parameters of the working covariance are not true scale, correlation, or covariance parameters; they play a similar role, but they specify a *quasi-likelihood* as defined in Section 11.4.3. In other words, conditional, G-side, GLMMs are defined by actual probability distributions, whereas marginal models for non-Gaussian data are defined by a quasi-likelihood with a working covariance structure. PROC GLIMMIX uses the pseudo-likelihood computing algorithm instead of generalized estimating equations for marginal models with non-Gaussian data, but the model definition of a "GEE-type" model and a GLMM with R-side-only covariance is identical. For this reason, in the context of marginal GLMMs, we often refer to R-side covariance as "working covariance."

Conditional and marginal GLMMs target different means. The specifics depend on the model and the distribution, but Figure 11.1 conveys the general idea. The most important question this raises is which model and associated target of inference, conditional or marginal, should you use? The answer lies in the shape of the distribution (C) in Figure 11.1, the only distribution we can observe directly. Marginal distributions associated with GLMMs tend to be highly skewed. Consequently, the mean can be a misleading measure of central tendency. In the example in Figure 11.1, the median of the distribution of the observations shown in panel (C) is 0.25, the probability of a favorable outcome in the "parent" distribution shown in panel (B), whereas the mean is 0.31. In technical terms, the former is denoted $E(y \mid c)$, the mean of the observations conditional on the random effects, and the latter is denoted $E(y)$, the marginal mean. A conditional GLMM targets $E(y \mid c)$; a marginal GLMM targets $E(y)$. Income data provide a good way to think about when each quantity would be a valid target of inference. Income data tend to be strongly right-skewed. If we want to characterize the income of a typical household in the population, we report median income. In GLMM terms, we use a conditional GLMM to estimate $E(y \mid c)$, specifically $E(y \mid c = 0)$ (because "typical clinic" implies average clinic; $c = 0$ defines average clinic). If we want to characterize how much money is in the economy, we need the marginal mean. In this case, in GLMM terms, we should use the marginal model.

Beyond this generic overview, the conditional versus marginal issue is best clarified through the examples presented later in this chapter and in Chapters 12 and 13.

11.4.6 Estimates, Standard Errors, and Confidence Intervals

You use the inverse link to obtain predicted values of μ from the estimated model effects. For example, if you fit a linear regression, the linear predictor is $\beta_0 + \beta_1 X$. Therefore,

$$\hat{\mu} = g^{-1}\left(\hat{\beta}_0 + \hat{\beta}_1 X\right)$$

For the Gaussian distribution, $\hat{\mu} = \hat{\beta}_0 + \hat{\beta}_1 X$, since $\eta = \mu$. For the binomial, $\eta = \log[\pi/(1-\pi)]$ and hence $\hat{\pi} = 1/\{1 + \exp[-(\hat{\beta}_0 + \hat{\beta}_1 X)]\}$. Estimates with the linear predictor, or linear combinations of effects in the linear predictor are called *model scale* estimates. Estimates obtained with the inverse link are called *data scale* estimates.

Because the link and inverse link are non-linear functions, they cannot necessarily be used for estimates of treatment differences. For example, with the linear predictor for a one-way treatment design, the linear predictor for a treatment mean is $\eta + \tau_i$ and the estimable function for a treatment is the difference between treatment i and treatment i' is $\tau_i - \tau_{i'}$. These are both model scale estimates. In a logistic model, $\hat{\eta} + \hat{\tau}_i$ estimates $\log[\hat{\pi}_i/(1-\hat{\pi}_i)]$, and therefore $1/\{1 + \exp[-(\hat{\eta} + \hat{\tau}_i)]\}$ estimates π_i. The data scale estimate is $\hat{\pi}_i$. However, $1/\{1 + \exp[-(\hat{\tau}_i - \hat{\tau}_{i'})]\}$ does not estimate $\tau_i - \tau_{i'}$. Instead, $\hat{\tau}_i - \hat{\tau}_{i'} = (\hat{\eta} + \hat{\tau}_i) - (\hat{\eta} + \hat{\tau}_{i'})$ estimates $\log[\hat{\pi}_i/(1-\hat{\pi}_i)] - \log[\hat{\pi}_{i'}/(1-\hat{\pi}_{i'})]$, or equivalently $\log\{[\hat{\pi}_i/(1-\hat{\pi}_i)]/[\hat{\pi}_{i'}/(1-\hat{\pi}_{i'})]\}$, the log of the odds-ratio. Therefore, $\exp(-(\hat{\tau}_i - \hat{\tau}_{i'}))$ gives you an estimate of the odds-ratio. This is as close to a data-scale estimate as you can get with a direct function of $\hat{\tau}_i - \hat{\tau}_{i'}$.

You can go through an analogous process for other link functions. These will be illustrated in the examples later in this chapter and in Chapters 12 and 13. The primary rule of thumb is that the inverse link is useful for estimates of means, but not differences. For differences, you need to determine what the model scale contrast estimates and how, or even if, it can be expressed as something meaningful on the data scale.

When you obtain estimates on the model scale, PROC GLIMMIX obtains their associated standard errors. Appendix B provides a general overview of estimation and inference for generalized linear models, including how estimates and standard errors are computed. As a general rule, estimates should be accompanied by their standard errors in any statistical report. Therefore, if you report a data scale estimate, you should also report a data scale standard error. Data scale standard errors can be obtained from model scale standard errors using the *Delta Rule* approximation. Specifically, the Delta Rule approximation is $SE[h(\hat{\eta})] = [\partial[h(\eta)]/\partial\eta] \times SE(\hat{\eta})$, where $\hat{\eta}$ denotes the model-scale estimate and $h(\hat{\eta})$ denotes the data scale estimate. For canonical link functions, the derivative can be shown to equal the variance function. For example, the Delta Rule for an estimated probability in a logistic model is $SE[\hat{\pi}] = [\hat{\pi}(1-\hat{\pi})] \times SE(\hat{\eta})$. Link functions other than canonical links require that you obtain the appropriate derivative. The PROC GLIMMIX option ILINK implements the inverse link and Delta Rule for link functions available in PROC GLIMMIX.

A final note concerning confidence intervals. Often, in addition to reporting estimates and standard errors, you want to report confidence intervals. The standard formula for confidence intervals is $\text{estimate} \pm t \times SE(\text{estimate})$. For GLMs this is valid on the model scale, but not on the data scale. In other words, $\hat{\eta} \pm t \times SE(\hat{\eta})$ yields a valid confidence interval, but $h(\hat{\eta}) \pm t \times SE[h(\hat{\eta})]$ does not. This is because, except for the Gaussian case, the inverse link is non-linear. Therefore, the resulting data scale confidence interval should be asymmetric. You can obtain a valid data scale confidence interval by applying the inverse link to the lower and upper confidence bounds of the model scale confidence interval. The correct data scale confidence interval has lower and upper confidence bounds $h[\hat{\eta} - t \times SE(\hat{\eta})]$ and $h[\hat{\eta} + t \times SE(\hat{\eta})]$, respectively.

11.4.7 Deviance, Goodness of Fit, and Hypothesis Testing

Two important test procedures with the GLM and GLMM are *goodness of fit*, and hypothesis testing of estimable functions, such as treatment differences, contrasts, regression coefficients, etc. These are described in non-technical terms in this section. See Appendix B for an in-depth description of the underlying theory and computational details.

Goodness of Fit

Goodness of fit refers to the adequacy with which a model accounts for variability in the data. With Gaussian data, model inadequacy typically occurs when important terms have been left out of the linear predictor. For example, trying to fit a linear regression to a nonlinear dose-response relationship, or omitting the whole plot error term when analyzing a split plot experiment will result in model inadequacy.

With non-Gaussian data, there are additional reasons for model inadequacy in addition to those given above for Gaussian data. The most important of these is *overdispersion*. Overdispersion occurs when the model fails to adequately account for all the sources of variability in the data. For example, GLMs that model discrete counts often use the Poisson distribution (see Chapter 12 for examples). In the Poisson distribution, the mean equals the variance. If the Poisson assumption holds, the observed variance should be approximately equal to the observed mean. In practice, this often is not what we see; instead, the observed variance greatly exceeds the mean, and the discrepancy increases as the mean increases. Overdispersion can be a serious problem. Models with overdispersion produce downward-biased standard errors, and hence inflated test statistics and excessively narrow confidence intervals. As will be clear from the examples in this chapter and in Chapters 12 and 13, the first thing that you should do when you run an analysis with a GLM or GLMM is look at *goodness-of-fit* statistics.

Goodness-of-fit statistics measure model adequacy, the degree to which a particular model accounts for the variability in the data. The two most common goodness-of-fit statistics for detecting overdispersion in the GLM and GLMM are the *deviance* and the *Pearson* χ^2. With Gaussian data, these two statistics are identical and equal to the SS(residual). With non-Gaussian data, the deviance and Pearson χ^2 statistics are not equal, but tend to be close. PROC GLIMMIX computes the Pearson χ^2, but not the deviance.

For distributions other than the Gaussian, the Pearson χ^2 estimates a scale parameter over and above the terms in the model. For example, in a GLM with a binomial response variable, consider the variance expression. Note that this is not the variance of a binomial response variable; it is called an extra-dispersion (or overdispersion) parameter. If the binomial GLM adequately fits the data, this extra-dispersion parameter should effectively disappear, i.e. equal one. In other words, for the binomial, the scale parameter is known, and you should not need to estimate an additional parameter. For GLMs, PROC GLIMMIX includes Pearson χ^2 in the Fit Statistics listing as PEARSON CHISQ/DF. For the binomial GLM, PEARSON CHISQ/DF should equal one, or at least be close. If it is substantially greater than one, this is a red flag— evidence of overdispersion, and hence evidence that the rest of the analysis cannot necessarily be trusted. Sections 12.3.2 and 13.3.2 give examples where overdispersion is present and present ways of dealing with the issue.

For GLMMs, PROC GLIMMIX includes a Generalized Chi-Square statistic by default. However, the Pearson χ^2 is the preferred statistic for diagnosing overdispersion. You can obtain the Pearson statistics by using either METHOD=LAPLACE or METHOD=QUADRATURE, discussed below in Section 11.4.8. For GLMMs, Pearson χ^2 appears in the Conditional Fit Statistics listing.

Hypothesis Testing

As with confidence interval estimation, the basic building block of hypothesis testing is the estimable function. Examples of estimable functions are treatment differences, contrasts, and predicted values in regression. The two most common approaches to hypothesis testing with linear models are *likelihood ratio tests* and *Wald statistics*. For Gaussian data the two are equivalent, and, in cases where ANOVA-style *F* statistics can be constructed, one can derive a GLMM *F* statistic from either the likelihood ratio or Wald approach. With the GLM and GLMM, likelihood ratio and Wald statistics are not the same. However, they tend to be close, and with GLMs, there is no consistent evidence that one is preferable to the other. This is also the case for GLMMs, but with GLMMs, the Wald approach is considerably more flexible and computationally viable. For this reason, PROC GLIMMIX provides Wald-based statistics for all tests of hypotheses.

The Wald statistic can be shown to have an approximate χ^2 distribution, with degrees of freedom equal to the numerator of degrees of freedom of the test you are implementing. The Wald statistic divided by the numerator degrees of freedom has an approximate *F* distribution. Appropriate use of the Wald-based test can be divided into two cases. In case 1, the scale parameter is a known constant, and does not need to be estimated. In case 2, at least one variance or covariance component must be estimated, including the scale parameter if it is unknown. In case 1, you should use the Wald statistic. In case 2, you should use the approximate *F statistic*. Both PROC GLIMMIX and PROC MIXED compute approximate *F* statistics by default. However, both have a CHISQ option, which you should use in case 1.

Details of the underlying theory and computing details are given in Appendix B.

11.4.8 Estimation Methods in PROC GLIMMIX

This section provides an overview of the estimation methods, focusing on when you would want to use each method and why. The examples in this chapter and Chapters 12 and 13 give in-context specifics illustrating the use of these options. Appendix B provides additional technical detail of the underlying theory and methodology.

The GLIMMIX procedure implements GLMs using maximum likelihood. Recall the generic form of the log likelihood for a GLM from Equation 11.8:

$$\left[y\theta - b(\theta) \right] / \phi + c(y, \phi)$$

The canonical parameter θ is a function of μ and hence a function of the parameter vector β through the inverse link function, $h(X\beta)$. Maximizing

$$\left[y\theta - b(\theta)\right]/\phi$$

with respect to β provides maximum likelihood estimates of the model effects.

For the GLMM, the log likelihood involves the distribution of the observations conditional on the random effects, $y \mid b$, and the distribution of the random effects. The log likelihood is thus the log of

$$\int f(y \mid b) f(b) db$$

This integral can be written in simplistic terms for illustrative purposes as follows:

$$\int \exp\left\{\left[\left(y\theta_{X\beta+Zb} - b(\theta)\right)/\phi\right]\right\}\left(2\pi\sigma^2\right)^{-\frac{1}{2}} \exp\left(b^2/2\sigma^2\right) db$$

where $\theta_{X\beta+Zb}$ denotes the canonical parameter to indicate that it is a function of the mixed model linear predictor.

In general, this integral is intractable; maximizing the log likelihood thus requires some form of approximation. The most common can be divided into linearization methods and integral approximation methods. Linearization methods include pseudo-likelihood (PL; Wolfinger and O'Connell,1993) and penalized quasi-likelihood (PQL) and marginal quasi-likelihood (MQL) (Breslow and Clayton,1993). Integral approximation methods include the LAPLACE approximation, and adaptive Gauss-Hermite QUADRATURE (Pinheiro and Bates, 1995). By default, PROC GLIMMIX uses a REML-like version of PL — METHOD=RSPL in PROC GLIMMIX syntax.

The six basic estimation methods for GLMMs are controlled by the METHOD= option of the PROC GLIMMIX statement. These were introduced in Chapter 6. This section expands on the Chapter 6 discussion to describe aspects unique to GLMMs. The methods are METHOD=RSPL (the default), RMPL, MSPL, MMPL, LAPLACE, and QUADRATURE. The abbreviations are deciphered as follows. LAPLACE and QUADRATURE (or METHOD=QUAD) are self-explanatory. If the last two letters are PL, then the method is one of the four variations of pseudo-likelihood.

In PL, a linearization is applied by creating a pseudo-variable, denoted here as $y*$, from the first-order Taylor series approximation of $g(y)$ evaluated at μ, where $g(\bullet)$ is the link function of the GLMM. The pseudo-variable defines a pseudo-model $y* = X\beta + Zb + e*$ that is handled computationally as if $y*$ is a Gaussian response variable in a mixed model. The first letter of the METHOD= identifier determines whether the log likelihood is formed as a *residual* (restricted) log likelihood or a *maximum* log likelihood. The second letter identifies the locus of the expansion. In a **S**ubject-specific expansion, the linearization is carried out about current estimates of fixed and random effects. This is the approach taken by Wolfinger and O'Connell (1993). In a **M**arginal expansion, the linearization is carried out about a current estimate of the fixed effects, with the expected value of the random effects set to 0. Breslow and Clayton (1993) call this the marginal quasi-likelihood (MQL) approach.

There are advantages and disadvantages to each method. In the vast majority of applications, you will want to use either the RSPL default or the LAPLACE or QUADRATURE integral approximation method. This discussion is therefore limited to these options.

The RSPL default enables you to do the following:

- use the DDFM=SATTERTH , KR, and KR2 options
- use the RESIDUAL option with the RANDOM statement, essential for analysis of marginal GLMMs, and any other application that requires a working covariance
- compute REML-like estimates of variance components, thus avoiding the downward bias known to exist with ML variance estimates

Pseudo-likelihood is less computationally demanding than integral approximation. PL has the following drawbacks:

- Because a pseudo-likelihood depends on a pseudo-model, you cannot use it to compute likelihood ratio tests. Specifically, if you want to test variance components using the COVTEST statement, or compare covariance structures using information criteria, you should use integral approximation. The COVTEST statement used in conjunction with PL will give you a pseudo-likelihood ratio statistic, but it is not clear what, if anything, this statistic means.

- PL will not give you a Pearson χ^2 statistic. If you want an overdispersion diagnostic, you must use integral approximation to compute it.

- The linearization on which PL depends assumes that $y^* \mid b$ is approximately normal. In cases where this is not true (e.g. binary data, binomial data with small N and p close to 0 or 1, highly skewed count data), linearization provides a poor approximation and hence PL results can be severely biased.

Integral approximation enables you to do the following:

- obtain the Pearson χ^2 statistic to assess overdispersion

- obtain information criteria to compare among plausible covariance models

- obtain valid likelihood ratio statistics from the PROC GLIMMIX COVTEST statement to test covariance components

On the other hand, integral approximation has the following drawbacks:

- Variance components estimates are ML. They exhibit the same downward bias described in Chapter 2, and hence are prone to producing inflated test statistics and excessively narrow confidence intervals.

- You cannot use DDFM=SATTERTH, KR, or KR2. Their unavailability can exacerbate the test statistic inflation already present because of ML variance bias.

- You cannot use integral approximation unless you have a well-defined likelihood. Specifically, this precludes using QUADRATURE or LAPLACE in conjunction with a model that has a residual covariance (RANDOM … RESIDUAL) structure, such as a GEE-type model with a working covariance. It also makes QUADRATURE and LAPLACE more vulnerable to model misspecification.

For integral approximation, LAPLACE and QUADRATURE have advantages and disadvantages. Quadrature with a single quadrature point is equivalent to the Laplace approximation. However, the number of quadrature points can be increased, allowing greater accuracy. On the other hand, QUADRATURE is more computationally demanding than LAPLACE, and the discrepancy increases as you increase the number of quadrature points. More importantly, QUADRATURE can be overwhelmed by model complexity. The QUADRATURE has a FASTQUAD option that alleviates this problem, at least to some extent. If you have more than one random effect or multiple random statements with the same subject, use the FASTQUAD option. However, with a single random effect, FASTQUAD has no effect. However, for more complex models, e.g. repeated measures models for non-Gaussian data presented in Chapter 13, you may find LAPLACE to be the only viable integral approximation method.

In short, there is no valid one-size-fits-all advice for which METHOD specification to use. Specific wisdom and experience will be shared as we present the examples in this and the next two chapters.

11.5 Example 2: Binomial Data in a Multicenter Clinical Trial

Section 11.2.2 describes an experiment involving two treatments conducted at eight randomly sampled clinics. The data, published in Beitler and Landis (1985), are given as Data Set 11.5, "Clinics." At the jth CLINIC (j=1,2,...,8), n_{ij} subjects are assigned to the ith treatment (TRT) (I =1,2). At the ij^{th} treatment-clinic combination, y_{ij} subjects respond favorably and the remaining $n_{ij} - y_{ij}$ do not. The number of patients for the ij^{th} CLINIC by TRT combinations is denoted by NIJ in the data set; the number of favorable responses y_{ij} is denoted by FAV. The response variable of interest was the proportion of favorable responses, $p_{ij} = y_{ij}/n_{ij}$, or FAV/NIJ.

Conditional on the jth clinic, the distribution of y_{ij} is Binomial(n_{ij}, π_{ij}), where π_{ij} denotes the probability of a subject assigned to TRT i at CLINIC j having a favorable response. Thus, conditional on the jth clinic, the distribution of the sample proportion is $p_{ij} \mid$ clinic effects~ Binomial(n_{ij}, π_{ij})$/n_{ij}$. Table 11.3 shows a summary of the characteristics of the conditional likelihood.

Table 11.3: Features of Conditional Likelihood

Expression	Function	Value
Conditional mean	μ_{ij}	π_{ij}
Natural parameter	$\theta(\mu_{ij})$	$\log[\pi_{ij}/(1-\pi_{ij})]$
Variance function	$v(\mu_{ij})$	$\pi_{ij}(1-\pi_{ij})$
Scale parameter	$a(\phi_{ij})$	$1/n_{ij}$

Section 11.5.1 reviews two pre-GLMM analyses still commonly used at the time this edition is written. Although neither should be used given the availability of GLMM methodology via PROC GLIMMIX, it is important for readers to understand why they should not be used. Each analysis reveals issues that underline the rationale for using GLMM analysis instead. Consider these two pre-GLMM analyses examples of what not to do.

Section 11.5.2 presents two variations on the conditional GLMM for binomial data with random effects. The first is the standard model that you would ordinarily use. The second is useful when the solution to the clinic variance is negative. The second variation also provides an insight into the distinction between a conditional and marginal model. Section 11.5.2 focuses on broad inference. That is, inference on treatment means and differences representative of the population from which the eight clinics in this study were sampled. Section 11.5.3 shows additional, clinic-specific analysis using best linear unbiased prediction.

Section 11.5.4 covers a marginal model appropriate for the clinic data. This section concludes with a summary of the differences in implementation and interpretation of the conditional and marginal models.

11.5.1 Two Pre-GLMM Analyses: The Normal Approximation and the Angular Transformation

Introductory statistical methods courses usually cover the normal approximation to the binomial. These include rules of thumb for deciding when the binomial proportion can be treated as a Gaussian random variable. For example, in some textbooks, the rule is: for proportions less than 0.5, if $N \times p \geq 5$, where N is the number of Bernoulli observations per experimental unit, one can use the normal approximation. Other textbooks give $N \times p \geq 10$.

Program

In the GLIMMIX procedure, you can use Program 11.3 to implement an analysis of the clinic data using the normal approximation.

Program 11.3

```
proc glimmix data=clinics;
 class clinic trt;
 pct=fav/Nij;
 model pct=trt;
 random intercept / subject=clinic;
 lsmeans trt / diff;
run;
```

Results

Results are given in Output 11.3.

Output 11.3: Analysis of Multi-clinic Binomial Data Using Normal Approximation

	Type III Tests of Fixed Effects			
Effect	Num DF	Den DF	F Value	Pr > F
trt	1	7	3.34	0.1105

trt Least Squares Means					
trt	Estimate	Standard Error	DF	t Value	Pr > |t|
cntl	0.2942	0.1080	7	2.72	0.0296
drug	0.4097	0.1080	7	3.79	0.0068

There are two problems with these results, one obvious, the other subtler.

The obvious problem involves the standard error. They are both 0.1080. This follows from the default assumption of homogeneity of variance. However, with binomial data, the variance is known to be proportional to $\pi(1-\pi)$. The standard errors in this listing cannot be correct.

The subtler problem concerns the estimates, 0.29 for CNTL and 0.41 for DRUG. In linear model theory, we know these are best linear unbiased estimates of the mean—or at least approximately "best" given that we use the estimated clinic variance to obtain 0.29 and 0.41. However, "unbiased estimates" of what mean? Recalling the discussion in Section 11.4.4, there are two potential targets of inference—the conditional mean and the marginal mean for each treatment. The conditional means are actual probabilities. That is, estimates of π_{CNTL} and π_{DRUG} as defined in the conditional distribution of the observations given the clinics. The marginal means are the averages of the proportions over the clinics. Conditional means characterize the probability of a favorable outcome for each treatment at a typical clinic. In most basic research, this is the appropriate target of inference. These are not what you estimate with the normal approximation. Instead, 0.29 and 0.41 are estimates of the marginal means. With multi-clinic binomial data with proportions less than 0.5, these are means of strongly right-skewed distributions.

To address these problems, most statistical methods textbooks recommend variance-stabilizing transformations based on Barlett's (1947) article. The standard variance stabilizing transformation for binomial data is the angular transformation—also known as the arc sine square root transformation,

$$\sin^{-1}\left(\sqrt{p_{ij}}\right)$$

In the pre-GLMM era, transformations were standard practice. However, generalized linear models are demonstrably more accurate than transformations, especially when the model contains random effects.

Program

Program 11.4, shows how to implement the angular transformation—with the caveat that it is mainly an illustration of what not to do, and why not to do it, compared to the binomial GLMM that follows in Section 11.5.2.

Recalling the discussion in Section 11.4.4, there are two potential targets of inference—the conditional mean and the marginal mean for each treatment. The conditional means are actual probabilities; that is, estimates of and as defined in the conditional distribution of the observations given the clinics.

Program 11.4

```
proc glimmix data=clinics;
  class clinic trt;
  arcsin_pct=arsin(sqrt(fav/Nij));
  model arcsin_pct=trt;
  random intercept / subject=clinic;
  lsmeans trt/cl;
  ods output lsmeans=lsm;
run;
```

The PROC GLIMMIX step implements the analysis using the same model as the normal approximation. The only difference is the use of the transformed response variable. When you use transformed data, the treatment means are means on the transformation scale, in this case, the arc sine square root. Any treatment mean differences or contrasts are thus computed on the angular transformation scale. To make the means understandable, data analysts often "back transform" the results. That is, the treatment mean estimators are computed using the inverse of the arc sine square root function.

Results

Selected results appear in Output 11.4.

Output 11.4: Selected Results from Analysis Using Angular Transformation

Covariance Parameter Estimates

Cov Parm	Subject	Estimate	Standard Error
Intercept	clinic	0.1094	0.06784
Residual		0.03282	0.01754

Type III Tests of Fixed Effects

Effect	Num DF	Den DF	F Value	Pr > F
trt	1	7	4.30	0.0767

trt Least Squares Means

trt	Estimate	Standard Error	DF	t Value	Pr > |t|	Alpha	Lower	Upper
cntl	0.4931	0.1333	7	3.70	0.0077	0.05	0.1777	0.8084
drug	0.6810	0.1333	7	5.11	0.0014	0.05	0.3656	0.9963

Interpretation

The only useable listing directly from PROC GLIMMIX as shown in Output 11.4 is the *F* test for treatment effect given in the Type 3 Tests of Fixed Effects table. The LSMEANS are computed on the angular transformation scale. The ESTIMATE is the mean of

$$\sin^{-1}\left(\sqrt{p_{ij}}\right)$$

for the ith treatment. The standard error and confidence bounds are also computed on that scale. Similarly, the Covariance Parameter Estimates, for CLINIC, $\hat{\sigma}_C^2 = 0.1094$, and for RESIDUAL, $\hat{\sigma}^2 = 0.03282$, are variances of the angular transformed proportions. These are neither interpretable nor useful to most users.

Program

You can implement the back-transformation using the ODS OUTPUT statement and the subsequent DATA step shown in Program 11.5.

Program 11.5

```
data back_transform;
 set lsm;
 trt_mean=(sin(estimate))**2;
 s_e_mean=2*sin(estimate)*cos(estimate)*stderr;
 LCL =(sin(lower))**2;
 UCL =(sin(upper))**2;
proc print data=back_transform;
 var trt estimate StdErr Lower Upper trt_mean s_e_mean LCL UCL;
run;
```

The ODS OUTPUT statement creates a data set with the means and their standard errors on the arc sine square root scale. Use $[\sin(\text{LSMean})]^2$ to obtain the back-transformed means. Compute the lower and upper confidence limits as $[\sin(\text{Lower})]^2$ and $[\sin(\text{Upper})]^2$, respectively, where "lower" and "upper" are the confidence limits on the angular transformation scale. Use the Delta method to obtain the back-transformed standard error, which employs a first order derivative approximation. Let ψ denote the least squares mean. The Delta method gives the approximation

$$SE\left(\text{back-transformed mean}\right) = \{\partial[\sin(\psi)]^2 / \partial\psi\} \times SE(\hat{\psi}) = 2[\sin(\hat{\psi})][\cos(\hat{\psi})] \times SE(\hat{\psi}).$$

Results

Output 11.5 shows the results for the back-transformed means.

Output 11.5: Back-transformed Mean, Standard Error, and Confidence Bounds

Obs	trt	Estimate	StdErr	Lower	Upper	trt_mean	s_e_mean	LCL	UCL
1	cntl	0.4931	0.1333	0.1777	0.8084	0.22404	0.11120	0.03126	0.52299
2	drug	0.6810	0.1333	0.3656	0.9963	0.39632	0.13045	0.12784	0.70469

The back-transformed means given in Output 11.5 provide approximations of the estimated proportion on the original data scale. The estimates, called TRT_MEAN in the table, are 0.224 and 0.396 for the CNTL and DRUG treatments, respectively. Notice that the lower and upper confidence limits, called LCL and UCL, are obtained by back-transforming the LOWER and UPPER bounds (0.178, 0.808) for CNTL and (0.366, 0.996) for DRUG. They are *not* obtained using the back-transformed standard error, called S_E_MEAN.

While the standard errors and resulting confidence intervals and test statistics from the angular transformation do reflect the relationship between the proportion and the variance known to exist with binomial data, there are still two important problems. First, it is not clear what the back-transformations actually estimate. The back-transformation simply converts the mean of the transformed proportions by applying the inverse of the transformation. The result, as shown in Stroup (2013), is neither the conditional mean (the binomial probability) nor the marginal mean. Second, with mixed models, the transformation affects the random effects as well as the response variable. Affecting the response variable is the purpose of the transformation; affecting the random effect—and the distributional assumptions associated with it—is an unintended, and undesirable, consequence. The bottom line: the use of transformations is not a viable option for mixed models and should be regarded as a strategy of last resort.

What is needed is a modeling strategy that targets the binomial probability—or to be more technically correct, the mean of the distribution of the observations conditional on the random effects—when it is the appropriate target of inference. This will be presented in the next section. In addition, we need a legitimate method of analysis, not the normal approximation shown above, when the marginal mean is the target of inference. This will be shown in Section 11.5.4.

11.5.2 GLMM Analysis of Binomial Using Logit (Canonical) Link Function

Using the canonical link, a conditional GLMM for the clinic data can be defined by the following:

$$\eta_{ij} = \log\left[\pi_{ij} / \left(1 - \pi_{ij}\right)\right] = \eta + \tau_i + c_j + \tau c_{ij} \tag{11.10}$$

where terms are defined as follows:

- η is the intercept.

- τ_i is the effect of the ith TRT.

- c_j is the effect of the jth CLINIC, assumed i.i.d. $N(0, \sigma_c^2)$.

- τc_{ij} is the ij^{th} TRT × CLINIC interaction effect, assumed i.i.d. $N(0, \sigma_{tc}^2)$.

Note that because the clinics are a random sample, the CLINIC and TRT × CLINIC effects are random. This is called the conditional model because the random clinic effects appear in the linear predictor, and the distribution of the observations is conditional on the random effects, that is,

$$y_{ij} \mid c_j, \tau c_{ij} \sim \text{Binomial}\left(n_{ij}, \pi_{ij}\right)$$

You can define an equivalent model using compound symmetry by combining c_j and τc_{ij} into a single random effect, denoted here as ct_{ij}. The resulting model follows:

$$\eta_{ij} = \log\left[\pi_{ij}/\left(1-\pi_{ij}\right)\right] = \eta + \tau_i + ct_{ij} \tag{11.11}$$

where terms are defined as follows:

- η and τ_i are defined as above

- ct_{ij} is the ij^{th} TRT $\times$ CLINIC interaction effect. Within the jth clinic, the TRT×CLINIC effects have a compound symmetry structure; that is,

$$\mathbf{c}_j = \begin{bmatrix} ct_{1j} \\ ct_{2j} \end{bmatrix} \sim N\left(\begin{bmatrix} 0 \\ 0 \end{bmatrix}, \begin{bmatrix} \sigma^2 + \sigma_{cs} & \sigma_{cs} \\ \sigma_{cs} & \sigma^2 + \sigma_{cs} \end{bmatrix}\right)$$

Equation 11.11 is similar to the equivalence of the random block and compound symmetry models introduced in Chapters 2 and 5. As is the case with the Gaussian compound symmetry models, if $\sigma_c^2 \geq 0$ then the compound symmetry covariance σ_{cs} is equivalent to the clinic effect variance σ_c^2 and the compound symmetry scale parameter σ^2 is equivalent to the TRT CLINIC variance σ_{ct}^2. However, in the compound symmetry model, σ_{cs} is not required to be nonnegative, and hence is useful in cases when you get a negative solution for the estimate of the clinic variance.

Most of this section focuses on the standard conditional model, $\eta_{ij} = \eta + \tau_i + c_j + \tau c_{ij}$, from Equation 11.10, but concludes with a brief look at the compound symmetry alternative (Equation 11.11).

Keep in mind that there are two possible targets of inference, the probability of a favorable outcome for the ith treatment, denoted π_i, or the marginal mean for the ith treatment, here denoted as μ_i. This section focuses on the former, and therefore on the conditional model as written above. Section 11.5.4 shows how to implement the analysis if the marginal mean is the target.

We recommend fitting this model in two steps. First, run PROC GLIMMIX using an integral approximation method to check for overdispersion and to test the TRT $\times$ CLINIC interaction, i.e. test $H_0 : \sigma_{tc}^2 = 0$. Once you complete the first step, and make any needed adjustments to the model, run the second step, with your analysis focused on treatment effects, estimated differences, and so on.

Program

Use the PROC GLIMMIX statements in Program 11.6 for the first step.

Program 11.6

```
proc glimmix data=clinics method=quad;
   class clinic trt;
   model fav/nij = trt;
   random intercept trt / subject=clinic;
   covtest 'interaction=0?'. 0;
run;
```

The syntax is similar to what you use to fit a mixed model with Gaussian data. The important difference in this example is the use of the *events/trials* syntax to specify the binomial proportion in the MODEL statement. The numerator variable is the number of events or "successes" (in this case, FAV), and the denominator is the total number of trials (NIJ) for a given fixed-by-random effect combination. Thus, the response variable, the sample proportion, is FAV/NIJ. The events/trials syntax is also used in PROC GENMOD and PROC LOGISTIC. If you use this syntax, PROC GLIMMIX defaults to fitting a model for binomial data and chooses the logit link as the default link.

The RANDOM statement is specified with SUBJECT=CLINIC. Although the statement above is equivalent to RANDOM CLINIC TRT*CLINIC, the quadrature option, METHOD=QUAD, requires a subject to be specified. The COVTEST statement computes a likelihood ratio test for $H_0 : \sigma_c^2 = 0$. After the title, there is a dot followed by a zero. The dot enables the clinic variance to be estimated as usual, but the zero applies to the TRT×CLINIC variance thereby obtaining the test statistic.

Results

Output 11.6 shows selected results.

Output 11.6: Binomial Example—LOGIT Link—Preliminary Analysis—Selected Output

Model Information	
Data Set	WORK.CLINICS
Response Variable (Events)	fav
Response Variable (Trials)	nij
Response Distribution	Binomial
Link Function	Logit
Variance Function	Default
Variance Matrix Blocked By	clinic
Estimation Technique	Maximum Likelihood
Likelihood Approximation	Gauss-Hermite Quadrature
Degrees of Freedom Method	Containment

Class Level Information		
Class	Levels	Values
clinic	8	1 2 3 4 5 6 7 8
trt	2	cntl drug

Dimensions	
G-side Cov. Parameters	2
Columns in X	3
Columns in Z per Subject	3
Subjects (Blocks in V)	8
Max Obs per Subject	2

Optimization Information	
Optimization Technique	Dual Quasi-Newton
Parameters in Optimization	4
Lower Boundaries	2
Upper Boundaries	0
Fixed Effects	Not Profiled
Starting From	GLM estimates
Quadrature Points	5

Fit Statistics for Conditional Distribution	
-2 log L(fav | r. effects)	48.78
Pearson Chi-Square	7.91
Pearson Chi-Square / DF	0.49

Covariance Parameter Estimates

Cov Parm	Subject	Estimate	Standard Error
Intercept	clinic	1.9601	1.1942
trt	clinic	0.01140	0.1597

Tests of Covariance Parameters Based on the Likelihood

Label	DF	-2 Log Like	ChiSq	Pr > ChiSq	Note
interaction=0?	1	74.0445	0.01	0.4704	MI

MI: p-value based on a mixture of chi-squares.

Interpretation

The "Model Information" table provides information about how the GLIMMIX procedure forms the model and about the method of estimation. In this case, the Gauss-Hermite maximum likelihood procedure was specified by METHOD=QUAD. The "Model Information" also confirms that the distribution of the observation conditional on the random effects is binomial and that the logit link is used for the model.

The "Dimensions" table gives the dimension of the parameter space. "G-side cov. parameters" confirms that there are two variance components—CLINIC and TRT * CLINIC. "Columns in X" and Columns in Z" provide information about the size of for the fixed effects, called the X matrix, and the random effects, called the Z matrix. In this case, there are three fixed effects, intercept and the two treatment effects, one for CNTL and one for DRUG. Similarly, there are three corresponding levels of the random effects per CLINIC. "Subjects" gives the number of levels of the effect named in the SUBJECT= option in the RANDOM statement, in this case 8, the number of clinics. There are two observations per clinic, one for each treatment. Each observation consists of FAV, the number of favorable responses, and NIJ, the number of patients on a given treatment at a given clinic.

The "Fit Statistics for Conditional Distribution" gives the Pearson χ^2/DF statistic used as an overdispersion diagnostic. If this statistic is substantially greater than 1, it constitutes evidence of overdispersion. The term "substantially greater" involves part art, part science. Like correlation, no exact dividing line exists between "negligible" and "substantial." In this case, the value is 0.49, less than one and hence not evidence of overdispersion.

The covariance parameters give estimates of the CLINIC and TRT × CLINIC variance. These are variance components on the logit scale. Note that the logit is the log of the odds. The CLINIC variance measures variation in the log odds among clinics, where the odds are pooled over all treatment levels. The TRT × CLINIC variance measures variation in the log odds ratio among clinics. In this case, the estimated TRT × CLINIC variance is 0.01, evidence that the log odds ratio is relatively constant from clinic to clinic. On the other hand, the CLINIC variance estimate is 1.96, suggesting that variation among clinics in the overall odds does exist.

The "Tests of Covariance" table gives the likelihood ratio χ^2 statistic for $H_0 : \sigma_{tc}^2 = 0$. The value of the test statistic is 0.01, with one degree of freedom and a *p*-value of 0.47. There is insufficient evidence to reject the null hypothesis, i.e. insufficient evidence of a nonzero variance among the log odds ratio among clinics.

Taken together, the Pearson χ^2/df overdispersion statistic and variance component test results suggest that we could continue with a reduced model, dropping the TRT × CLINIC effect as unnecessary. On the other hand, retaining the term enables you to obtain clinic-specific BLUPs, shown in Section 11.5.3. In addition, there is a case for respecting the design (and the actual restrictions on randomization that occurred) and retaining all terms that follow from the design structure, as long as doing so does no harm. For this data set, because $\hat{\sigma}_{tc}^2$ is so small, and the data set is small as well, whether you retain TRT × CLINIC or not has little impact on your conclusions about the TRT fixed effects. You can verify this by dropping TRT × CLINIC from the RANDOM statement and rerunning the analysis.

For the sake of illustration, we continue with the analysis retaining TRT × CLINIC. In addition, subsequent analysis uses the default, REML-like pseudo-likelihood procedure rather than integral approximation. This follows from the discussion of the pros and cons of pseudo-likelihood and integral approximation in Section 11.4.8. In this case, the binomial *N* (the number of subjects in the TRT × CLINIC groups) is large enough and the binomial probabilities for each treatment are far enough from 0 and 1 that the distributions of $y_{ij} \mid c_j, ct_{ij}$ are reasonably symmetric. In addition, the number of replicate clinics (8) is small enough for non-negligible downward bias to occur with maximum likelihood variance components estimates, these estimates are downward biased just as they are with Gaussian data. Claassen (2014), Stroup and Claassen (2018) and Claassen and Stroup (2018) show that under these conditions, RSPL is the method of choice.

Program

Use the PROC GLIMMIX statements in Program 11.7 to proceed with the analysis.

Program 11.7

```
proc glimmix data=clinics;
 class clinic trt;
 model fav/nij=trt;
 random intercept trt / subject=clinic;
 lsmeans trt / ilink diff oddsratio cl;
run;
```

The CLASS, MODEL, and RANDOM statements are as before. The LSMEANS statement obtains estimates of treatment means and differences on the model—in the case *logit*—scale. Specifically, the least square means are defined as $\log[\hat{\pi}_i/(1-\hat{\pi}_i)] = \hat{\eta} + \hat{\tau}_i$, where $\hat{\pi}_i$ denotes the probability of a favorable outcome given treatment *i*. The ILINK option causes data scale estimates to be computed using the inverse link, that is, $\hat{\pi}_i = 1/\{1 + \exp[-(\hat{\eta} + \hat{\tau}_i)])\}$. Usually, you will want to report the ILINK results, not the estimate of the logit. The DIFF option computes $\hat{\tau}_{CNTL} - \hat{\tau}_{DRUG}$, which estimates the log odds-ratio, $\log\{[\hat{\pi}_{CNTL}/(1-\hat{\pi}_{CNTL})]/[\hat{\pi}_{DRUG}/(1-\hat{\pi}_{DRUG})]\}$. Note that ILINK does not apply to differences, only to LSMEANS per se. Applying the inverse link function to $\log\{[\hat{\pi}_{CNTL}/(1-\hat{\pi}_{CNTL})]/[\hat{\pi}_{DRUG}/(1-\hat{\pi}_{DRUG})]\}$ results in a nonsense statistic. For binomial data, the appropriate data scale statistic for a difference is the odds-ratio. The ODDSRATIO option causes GLIMMIX to compute $\exp(\hat{\tau}_{CNTL} - \hat{\tau}_{DRUG}) = [\hat{\pi}_{CNTL}/(1-\hat{\pi}_{CNTL})]/[\hat{\pi}_{DRUG}/(1-\hat{\pi}_{DRUG})]$. The CL option obtains 95% confidence bounds for all estimates—means, differences, model, and data scale.

Results

Output 11.7 shows the results.

Output 11.7: Selected PROC GLIMMIX Listing for Binomial GLMM

Model Information	
Data Set	WORK.CLINICS
Response Variable (Events)	fav
Response Variable (Trials)	nij
Response Distribution	Binomial
Link Function	Logit
Variance Function	Default
Variance Matrix Blocked By	clinic
Estimation Technique	Residual PL
Degrees of Freedom Method	Containment

Fit Statistics	
-2 Res Log Pseudo-Likelihood	50.30
Generalized Chi-Square	13.55
Gener. Chi-Square / DF	0.97

Covariance Parameter Estimates

Cov Parm	Subject	Estimate	Standard Error
Intercept	clinic	2.0103	1.2716
trt	clinic	0.06057	0.2043

Type III Tests of Fixed Effects

Effect	Num DF	Den DF	F Value	Pr > F
trt	1	7	5.06	0.0592

trt Least Squares Means

trt	Estimate	Standard Error	DF	t Value	Pr > |t|	Alpha	Lower	Upper	Mean	Standard Error Mean	Lower Mean	Upper Mean
cntl	-1.1650	0.5657	7	-2.06	0.0784	0.05	-2.5026	0.1727	0.2378	0.1025	0.07567	0.5431
drug	-0.4164	0.5606	7	-0.74	0.4818	0.05	-1.7422	0.9093	0.3974	0.1343	0.1490	0.7128

Differences of trt Least Squares Means

trt	_trt	Estimate	Standard Error	DF	t Value	Pr > |t|	Alpha	Lower	Upper	Odds Ratio	Lower Confidence Limit for Odds Ratio	Upper Confidence Limit for Odds Ratio
cntl	drug	-0.7485	0.3326	7	-2.25	0.0592	0.05	-1.5351	0.03803	0.473	0.215	1.039

Interpretation

The "Model Information" reiterates most of what appeared in the METHOD=QUAD run above. The key difference is the "Estimation Technique." Here, the default "Residual PL," algorithm is used, that is, residual, or REML-like, pseudo-likelihood. Under "Fit Statistics," the −2 Res Log Pseudo-Likelihood is an artifact of the pseudo-variable; it has little intrinsic meaning. For the logit model, the generalized chi-square/DF is the sum of squared differences between the observed and expected pseudo-variable, weighted by the binomial variance function and divided by the residual degrees of freedom. A more general formal definition appears in Appendix B. The "Gener. Chi-square/DF" is 0.97. The generalized χ^2/df is, according to the PROC GLIMMIX documentation, "the usual residual dispersion estimate." For distributions that do not have a residual dispersion parameter—the binomial is one such distribution (the Poisson, covered in Chapter 12, is the other)—"Gener. Chi-square/DF" can be interpreted as an overdispersion parameter estimate, and hence values substantially greater than one indicate the presence of overdispersion. Here, the value of 00.97 does not appear to raise any red flags. However, the generalized χ^2 can be misleading as an indicator of model fit, and is not recommended as a model checking statistic. Use the Pearson χ^2, obtained with METHOD=QUAD or METHOD=LAPLACE, instead.

The "Covariance Parameter Estimates" table provides an estimate of the CLINIC variance, $\hat{\sigma}_C^2 = 2.01$, and the TRT × CLINIC variance, $\hat{\sigma}_{tc}^2 = 0.06$. Notice the difference between these and the estimates obtained from quadrature, 1.96 and 0.01, from Output 11.5. The discrepancy is typical of REML versus ML variance component estimates; METHOD=QUAD produces ML estimates whereas "residual PL" gives you REML-like estimates. In cases where the number of random effect subjects is small, as is the case here with 8 clinics, and most, if not all, n_{ij} are not close to 1 (all are and most are >10), ML estimates are biased downward with the same undesirable effect on type I error control and confidence interval coverage noted earlier in this book for Gaussian data.

The F value and the p-value in the "Type III Tests of Fixed Effects" are interpreted as would any other F test for overall treatment effect. The statistics on the left side of the table of treatment least squares means include the ESTIMATE, standard error, and confidence bounds (LOWER and UPPER) of each least squares mean. Note these are on the *logit* scale. The right side of the table lists the corresponding values on the original data scale—these estimates are labeled MEAN, STANDARD ERROR MEAN, LOWER MEAN, and UPPER MEAN, respectively. The estimated probabilities of a favorable response are $\hat{\pi}_{CNTL} = 0.238$ and $\hat{\pi}_{DRUG} = 0.398$, with standard errors of 0.103 and 0.134, respectively. Notice that the confidence bounds are obtained by applying the inverse link to the model-scale confidence bounds, *not* by using the data scale standard error.

Similarly, the table of treatment differences provides information about the model—or log odds-ratio—scale on the left side and the estimated odds-ratio, 0.473, and its lower and upper confidence bound on the right side.

Alternative Conditional GLMM for Clinic Data

Instead of using the standard conditional model, you could obtain an essentially equivalent analysis using the compound symmetry (CS) reparameterization given in Equation 11.11). A good time to try this is when the standard model estimates the clinic variance to be zero and your listing contains the message: "Estimated G matrix is not positive definite." As in examples where this occurred presented in Chapters 2 and 5, Type I error control and confidence interval coverage are better for the CS model than for the set-to-zero default.

In this example, the clinic variance is positive, and therefore the standard and CS models give equivalent results. From this perspective, there is no need to use the CS model instead of the standard model. Nonetheless, we present the CS model. If you do encounter a set-to-zero result, you should use the statements in Program 11.8. In addition, comparing the RANDOM statements in Program 11.8 and Program 11.11, shown in the next section for the marginal model, helps illustrate the difference between these models from a SAS programming point of view.

Program

Program 11.8 shows the PROC GLIMMIX statements to implement the CS equivalent of the standard model in Program 11.7.

Program 11.8

```
proc glimmix data=clinics;
 class clinic trt;
 model fav/nij=trt;
 random trt / subject=clinic type=cs;
 lsmeans trt / ilink diff oddsratio cl;
run;
```

These statements are identical to those in Program 11.7, except for the RANDOM statement. In the standard model, the statement RANDOM INTERCEPT TRT / SUBJECT=CLINIC specifies two random effects, CLINIC and TRT × CLINIC, both with the default TYPE=VC variance structure. Recall that TYPE=VC means that all random effects are assumed to be independent with a variance component as each random effect's only parameter. In the CS model, the RANDOM statement specifies only TRT × CLINIC effects (the ct_{ij} effects in Equation 11.11) and defines the two effects within each clinic (one for each TRT) as correlated with TYPE=CS defining the correlation structure.

Results

Results appear in Output 11.8.

Output 11.8: Selected Results from CS Parameterization of Conditional GLMM for Binomial Data

Model Information	
Data Set	WORK.CLINICS
Response Variable (Events)	fav
Response Variable (Trials)	nij
Response Distribution	Binomial
Link Function	Logit
Variance Function	Default
Variance Matrix Blocked By	clinic
Estimation Technique	Residual PL
Degrees of Freedom Method	Containment

Fit Statistics	
-2 Res Log Pseudo-Likelihood	50.30
Generalized Chi-Square	13.55
Gener. Chi-Square / DF	0.97

Covariance Parameter Estimates			
Cov Parm	Subject	Estimate	Standard Error
Variance	clinic	0.06057	0.2043
CS	clinic	2.0103	1.2716

Type III Tests of Fixed Effects				
Effect	Num DF	Den DF	F Value	Pr > F
trt	1	14	5.06	0.0410

trt Least Squares Means												
trt	Estimate	Standard Error	DF	t Value	Pr > |t|	Alpha	Lower	Upper	Mean	Standard Error Mean	Lower Mean	Upper Mean
cntl	-1.1650	0.5657	14	-2.06	0.0586	0.05	-2.3783	0.04831	0.2378	0.1025	0.08484	0.5121
drug	-0.4164	0.5606	14	-0.74	0.4699	0.05	-1.6189	0.7860	0.3974	0.1343	0.1654	0.6870

Differences of trt Least Squares Means												
trt	_trt	Estimate	Standard Error	DF	t Value	Pr > |t|	Alpha	Lower	Upper	Odds Ratio	Lower Confidence Limit for Odds Ratio	Upper Confidence Limit for Odds Ratio
cntl	drug	-0.7485	0.3326	14	-2.25	0.0410	0.05	-1.4620	-0.03510	0.473	0.232	0.966

Interpretation

The "Model Information" table provides similar information to the listing for the standard model. The "Gener. Ch-Square/DF" in the "Fit Statistics" table is 0.97, equal to the generalized χ^2/df for the standard model. The covariance parameter estimates are CS, $\hat{\sigma}_{cs} = 2.01$, equivalent to the CLINIC variance $\hat{\sigma}_c^2 = 2.01$ for the standard model, and the "variance" estimate, $\hat{\sigma}^2 = 0.06$.

The F value for TRT given in the "Type III Tests of Fixed Effects" table is 5.06. Although this is the same as the -value for the standard model, the denominator degrees of freedom are not. Output 11.7 shows 7 *DenDF* for the standard model, whereas Output 11.8 shows 14 *DenDF* for the CS model. This is because the CS model combines the standard model's c_j and τc_{ij}, each with 7 *df*, into a single term, ct_{ij}, with all 14 *df* now associated with ct_{ij}. The containment rule uses the random effect that contains TRT in both cases, but in the standard model, the TRT × CLINIC effect has 7 *df*, whereas in the CS model it has 14 *df*. You can eliminate the discrepancy by using the Satterthwaite approximate *df*, which you can obtain by using either the DDFM=SATTERTH or DDFM=KR2 option in the MODEL statement. We recommend the latter, because it also invokes the Kenward-Roger bias correction for standard errors and test statistics. Doing so in this example gives $F = 4.26$, *DenDF* = 4.61, and $p = 0.0987$.

The data scale LSMEANS, which estimates the probability of a favorable outcome at a typical clinic, is 0.238 with a standard error of 0.103 for the CNTL treatment, and 0.398 with a standard error of 0.134 for the DRUG treatment. These are the same as the estimates and standard errors in Output 11.7 for the standard model. If you use the KR2 option, both the standard and CS model give the upper and lower data scales confidence limits as (0.08, 0.54) for CNTL and (0.15, 0.71) for DRUG. If you do not use the DDFM option, the confidence limits will not agree because of the discrepancy in denominator *df* noted above. The same is true for the ODDSRATIO, 0.473 for both models. The confidence interval will agree for both models if you use DDFM, KR2 being the recommended option.

11.5.3 Clinic-Specific Treatment Effects

In addition to providing estimates and inferential statistics that focus on π_i, the probability for the ith treatment, the conditional model enables you to obtain clinic-specific BLUPs. On the model scale, using the standard Equation 11.10, these are computed as follows:

$$\hat{\eta} + \hat{\tau}_i + \hat{c}_j + \widehat{\tau c}_{ij}$$

Clinic-specific BLUPs of difference between the CNTL and DRUG treatment are thus $\hat{\tau}_1 - \hat{\tau}_2 + \widehat{\tau c}_{1j} - \widehat{\tau c}_{2j}$.

Program

Program 11.9 illustrates the statements used to obtain these BLUPs for clinics 1 and 2.

Program 11.9

```
proc glimmix data=clinics;
 class clinic trt;
 model fav/nij=trt/s;
 random intercept trt / subject=clinic s;
 estimate 'CNTL Clinic 1 BLUP' intercept 1 trt 1 0
    | intercept 1 trt 1 0 / subject 1 0 ilink cl;
 estimate 'DRUG Clinic 1 BLUP' intercept 1 trt 0 1
    | intercept 1 trt 0 1 / subject 1 0 ilink cl;
 estimate 'CNTL Clinic 2 BLUP' intercept 1 trt 1 0
    | intercept 1 trt 1 0 / subject 0 1 0 ilink cl;
 estimate 'DRUG Clinic 2 BLUP' intercept 1 trt 0 1
    | intercept 1 trt 0 1 / subject 0 1 0 ilink cl;
 estimate 'diff Clinic 1' trt 1 -1 | trt 1 -1
    / subject 1 0 exp cl;
 estimate 'diff Clinic 2' trt 1 -1 | trt 1 -1
    / subject 0 1 0 exp cl;
run;
```

The S options in the MODEL and RANDOM statements cause PROC GLIMMIX to print to solutions for the fixed and random effects. The ESTIMATE statement syntax to obtain the BLUPs was introduced in Chapter 9 and follows the same form here. The coefficients in the BLUP estimate statements to the left of the vertical bar identify the fixed effects η and τ_i. The coefficients to the right of the vertical bar identify the random effects, c_j and τc_{ij}. The coefficients following SUBJECT identify the clinic for the random effects' clinic. For example, SUBJECT 1 0 specifies clinic 1, SUBJECT 0 1 0 specifies clinic 2. Use similar syntax for the differences. You can add additional statements for the other clinics; the statements are identical except that the SUBJECT option changes. For example, SUBJECT 0 0 1 specifies clinic 3, SUBJECT 0 0 0 1 specifies clinic 4, and so on.

Results

Output 11.9 shows selected results.

Output 11.9: Clinic-Specific Estimates for Clinics 1 and 2

Solutions for Fixed Effects						
Effect	trt	Estimate	Standard Error	DF	t Value	Pr > |t|
Intercept		-0.4164	0.5606	7	-0.74	0.4818
trt	cntl	-0.7485	0.3326	7	-2.25	0.0592
trt	drug	0	.	.	.	.

Solution for Random Effects

Effect	trt	Subject	Estimate	Std Err Pred	DF	t Value	Pr > |t|
Intercept		clinic 1	-0.1234	0.5974	0	-0.21	.
trt	cntl	clinic 1	0.08734	0.2314	0	0.38	.
trt	drug	clinic 1	-0.09106	0.2312	0	-0.39	.
Intercept		clinic 2	1.7837	0.6167	0	2.89	.
trt	cntl	clinic 2	0.05064	0.2342	0	0.22	.
trt	drug	clinic 2	0.003097	0.2349	0	0.01	.
Intercept		clinic 3	0.9464	0.6207	0	1.52	.
trt	cntl	clinic 3	-0.06918	0.2345	0	-0.30	.
trt	drug	clinic 3	0.09770	0.2345	0	0.42	.
Intercept		clinic 4	-1.3151	0.7109	0	-1.85	.
trt	cntl	clinic 4	-0.01770	0.2409	0	-0.07	.
trt	drug	clinic 4	-0.02192	0.2403	0	-0.09	.
Intercept		clinic 5	-0.6180	0.6709	0	-0.92	.
trt	cntl	clinic 5	-0.09628	0.2398	0	-0.40	.
trt	drug	clinic 5	0.07766	0.2388	0	0.33	.
Intercept		clinic 6	-1.6248	0.8098	0	-2.01	.
trt	cntl	clinic 6	-0.03395	0.2433	0	-0.14	.
trt	drug	clinic 6	-0.01500	0.2425	0	-0.06	.
Intercept		clinic 7	-0.7290	0.7812	0	-0.93	.
trt	cntl	clinic 7	-0.01010	0.2422	0	-0.04	.
trt	drug	clinic 7	-0.01186	0.2423	0	-0.05	.
Intercept		clinic 8	1.6801	0.7352	0	2.29	.
trt	cntl	clinic 8	0.08924	0.2410	0	0.37	.
trt	drug	clinic 8	-0.03862	0.2415	0	-0.16	.

Estimates

Label	Estimate	Standard Error	DF	t Value	Pr > |t|	Alpha	Lower	Upper	Mean	Standard Error Mean	Lower Mean	Upper Mean
CNTL Clinic 1 BLUP	-1.2010	0.3285	7	-3.66	0.0081	0.05	-1.9777	-0.4243	0.2313	0.05840	0.1216	0.3955
DRUG Clinic 1 BLUP	-0.6309	0.3057	7	-2.06	0.0779	0.05	-1.3537	0.09201	0.3473	0.06930	0.2053	0.5230
CNTL Clinic 2 BLUP	0.6694	0.3303	7	2.03	0.0823	0.05	-0.1117	1.4505	0.6614	0.07398	0.4721	0.8101
DRUG Clinic 2 BLUP	1.3704	0.4102	7	3.34	0.0124	0.05	0.4004	2.3404	0.7974	0.06626	0.5988	0.9122
diff Clinic 1	-0.5701	0.3706	7	-1.54	0.1678	0.05	-1.4464	0.3061	Non-est	.	.	.
diff Clinic 2	-0.7010	0.4045	7	-1.73	0.1267	0.05	-1.6575	0.2556	Non-est	.	.	.

	Estimates		
Label	Exponentiated Estimate	Exponentiated Lower	Exponentiated Upper
CNTL Clinic 1 BLUP	.	.	.
DRUG Clinic 1 BLUP	.	.	.
CNTL Clinic 2 BLUP	.	.	.
DRUG Clinic 2 BLUP	.	.	.
diff Clinic 1	0.5654	0.2354	1.3581
diff Clinic 2	0.4961	0.1906	1.2912

Interpretation

The first table shows the "Solutions for Fixed Effects," that is, $\hat{\eta}$ and the $\hat{\tau}_i$.

The second table shows the "Solutions for Random Effects"—that is, the $\hat{c}_j$ and $\widehat{\tau c}_{ij}$.

The third table, the first table of "Estimates," shows the BLUP analog of the least squares means for clinics 1 and 2.

The fourth table, the second table of "Estimates," shows the treatment differences for clinics 1 and 2. For example, the solution for the fixed intercept is $\hat{\eta} = -0.4164$, the CNTL fixed effect is $\hat{\tau}_{CNTL} = -0.7485$, the effect of clinic 1 is

$$\hat{c}_1 = -0.1234$$

and the treatment × clinic effect is

$$\widehat{\tau c}_{CNTL,1} = 0.08734$$

Thus, the model-scale BLUP is $\text{logit}(\hat{\pi}_{C,1}) = -0.4164 - 0.7485 - 0.1234 + 0.08734 = -1.201$. Applying the inverse link, the clinic 1, CNTL treatment BLUP is $\hat{\pi}_{C,1} = 0.2313$. The model scale log odds ratio for clinic 1 is obtained from

$$\hat{\tau}_C - \hat{\tau}_D + \widehat{\tau c}_{C,1} - \widehat{\tau c}_{D,1} = -0.7485 - 0 + 0.08734 - (-0.09106) = -0.5701$$

Applying the EXP option yields the clinic-specific odds-ratio, 0.5654, called "Exponentiated Estimate" in the output.

You can obtain the same clinic-specific BLUPs with the CS model. The only difference is that the treatment BLUPs are computed as $\hat{\eta} + \hat{\tau}_i + \widehat{ct}_{ij}$ rather than $\hat{\eta} + \hat{\tau}_i + \hat{c}_j + \widehat{\tau c}_{ij}$.

Program

Program 11.10 shows the required statements.

Program 11.10

```
proc glimmix data=clinics;
 class clinic trt;
 model fav/nij=trt / ddfm=kr2;
 random trt / subject=clinic type=cs;
 estimate 'CNTL Clinic 1 BLUP' intercept 1 trt 1 0
    | trt 1 0 / subject 1 0 ilink cl;
 estimate 'DRUG Clinic 1 BLUP' intercept 1 trt 0 1
    | trt 0 1 / subject 1 0 ilink cl;
 estimate 'CNTL Clinic 2 BLUP' intercept 1 trt 1 0
    | trt 1 0 / subject 0 1 0 ilink cl;
 estimate 'DRUG Clinic 2 BLUP' intercept 1 trt 0 1
    | trt 0 1 / subject 0 1 0 ilink cl;
```

```
estimate 'diff Clinic 1' trt 1 -1 | trt 1 -1
    / subject 1 0 exp cl;
estimate 'diff Clinic 2' trt 1 -1 | trt 1 -1
    / subject 0 1 0 exp cl;
run;
```

Results

Output 11.10 shows the results for the ESTIMATE statements.

Output 11.10: Clinic-Specific Estimates for Clinic 1 and 2 Using Conditional CS Model

Estimates													
Label	Estimate	Standard Error	DF	t Value	Pr > |t|	Alpha	Lower	Upper	Mean	Standard Error Mean	Lower Mean	Upper Mean
CNTL Clinic 1 BLUP	-1.2010	0.4202	14	-2.86	0.0126	0.05	-2.1022	-0.2998	0.2313	0.07471	0.1089	0.4256
DRUG Clinic 1 BLUP	-0.6309	0.3727	14	-1.69	0.1126	0.05	-1.4301	0.1684	0.3473	0.08448	0.1931	0.5420
CNTL Clinic 2 BLUP	0.6694	0.3752	14	1.78	0.0961	0.05	-0.1353	1.4741	0.6614	0.08403	0.4662	0.8137
DRUG Clinic 2 BLUP	1.3704	0.5557	6.576	2.47	0.0452	0.05	0.03900	2.7018	0.7974	0.08976	0.5097	0.9371
diff Clinic 1	-0.5701	0.5981	2.543	-0.95	0.4220	0.05	-2.6824	1.5421	Non-est	.	.	.
diff Clinic 2	-0.7010	0.6763	1.351	-1.04	0.4503	0.05	-5.4621	4.0601	Non-est	.	.	.

Estimates			
Label	Exponentiated Estimate	Exponentiated Lower	Exponentiated Upper
CNTL Clinic 1 BLUP	.	.	.
DRUG Clinic 1 BLUP	.	.	.
CNTL Clinic 2 BLUP	.	.	.
DRUG Clinic 2 BLUP	.	.	.
diff Clinic 1	0.5654	0.06840	4.6746
diff Clinic 2	0.4961	0.004245	57.9822

Interpretation

The results above are identical to those obtained with standard model, shown in Output 11.9. You will notice discrepancies in the standard errors and confidence interval widths because the standard model statements in Program 11.9 did not use the DDFM=KR2 option. If you use DDFM=KR2 for both the standard model and the CS model, the standard errors and confidence intervals, as well as the BLUPs, will be identical.

11.5.4 Marginal GLMM Analysis of Binomial Using Logit Link

In the previous section, inference focused on π, interpreted as the probability of a favorable response for a typical patient at a typical clinic in the case of least squares means, and a typical patient at clinic j in the case of the clinic-specific BLUPs. Obtaining BLUPs requires using the conditional model, and inference focused on π is the appropriate target for most research. However, in some studies, the marginal mean, not the probability, is the appropriate target.

Recall the discussion in Section 11.4.4. If the objective is to estimate the prevalence of favorable (or unfavorable) responses across the entire population, focus shifts to the marginal mean. Recall that fitting a mixed model to the sample proportion, and assuming that the normal approximation holds for the sample proportion gives an unbiased estimate of the marginal mean, but the standard errors and resulting test statistics are flawed.

Targeting the marginal mean calls for a marginal GLMM, often referred to as a GEE model. Suppose, instead of fitting the conditional model to the Beitler-Landis example, as we did in Section 11.5.2, we want to fit the marginal model. We write the marginal model as follows:

- Linear Predictor: $\eta_i = \eta + \tau_i$

- Link function: logit

- Observations y_{ij} "~" quasi-Binomial with mean $n_{ij}\mu_{ij}$ and residual covariance $\mathbf{R}_W$, also called the R-side covariance or the working covariance.

- Residual covariance:

$$\mathbf{R}_W = \begin{bmatrix} \varphi + \sigma_w & \sigma_w \\ \sigma_w & \varphi + \sigma_w \end{bmatrix},$$

where φ is a working scale parameter and σ_w is a working covariance.

The linear predictor contains only fixed effects. Therefore, it is not possible to compute clinic-specific BLUPs. The mean, μ_{ij}, is the marginal proportion of favorable responses, not the probability as in the conditional model, as illustrated in Figure 11.1 (see Section 11.4.5). The R-side scale and covariance parameters are analogous to the variance and covariance parameters in the conditional compound symmetry model presented in Section 11.5.3.

Note that because you are using an R-side covariance in conjunction with non-Gaussian data, you cannot specify a distribution for the observations. You can only refer to their *quasi-likelihood*. In this case, the quasi-likelihood has a binomial structure, hence the term "quasi-Binomial" in the model specification. Quasi-likelihoods and working covariance structures are the defining characteristics of marginal GLMMs.

Program

Use Program 11.11 to implement the marginal GLMM for the Beitler-Landis data.

Program 11.11

```
proc glimmix data=clinics ic=q;
 class clinic trt;
 model fav/nij=trt;
 random trt / subject=clinic type=cs residual;
 lsmeans trt / ilink diff oddsratio cl;
covtest 'no clinic effect?' 0 .;
run;
```

The CLASS, MODEL, and LSMEANS statements are identical to those used for the conditional GLMM in the previous section. The RANDOM statement defines the residual, or R-side compound symmetry covariance, also often referred to as a working covariance. Notice that the syntax of this statement is identical to the CS conditional model, except for the addition of the word RESIDUAL. This illustrates an important difference between Gaussian and non-Gaussian mixed models.

With Gaussian data, the RANDOM statement with the word RESIDUAL defines the covariance among observations within each subject, in this case CLINIC. The compound symmetry parameter can be thought of as the CLINIC effect. Adding the word RESIDUAL does not change the estimates treatment means or differences. With non-Gaussian data, we see this equivalence in the using the CS conditional model *without* the key word RESIDUAL in the RANDOM statement. However, adding RESIDUAL changes the model from conditional to marginal, changes the covariance to a working covariance, thereby altering the interpretation of the covariance parameters, and redirects estimation from π to the marginal mean.

By default, information criteria are not computed for marginal GLMMs, because they are computed using pseudo-data. Pseudo-data are model-specific, meaning that different models computing different pseudo-data, and hence the resulting information criteria are not meaningful for comparing different models. However, you can use the option IC=Q to compute information criteria based on pseudo-data. These are shown here so that you can see what the output looks like and the accompanying warning. The COVTEST option produces a pseudo likelihood ratio test, that is, a likelihood ratio test based on the pseudo-data computed fitting the compound symmetry model. Because the pseudo-likelihoods with and without the compound symmetry parameter are computed using the same pseudo-data, the resulting statistic can be used to test $H_0 : \sigma = 0$. You can interpret this as a test of the CLINIC effect.

> **Note**: Because marginal GLMMs are by definition based on quasi-likelihoods, you cannot use the integral approximation methods LAPLACE or QUAD. Integral approximation methods require a true likelihood and therefore can only be used with conditional GLMMs.

Results

Results for the marginal GLMM appear in Output 11.11.

Output 11.11: Analysis of Multi-Clinic Binomial Data with Marginal GLMM

Fit Statistics	
-2 Res Log Pseudo-Likelihood	43.08
Pseudo-AIC	47.08
Pseudo-AICC	48.17
Pseudo-BIC	47.24
Pseudo-CAIC	49.24
Pseudo-HQIC	46.00
Generalized Chi-Square	13.07
Gener. Chi-Square / DF	0.93

Fit statistics based on pseudo-likelihoods are not useful for comparing models that differ in their pseudo-data.

Covariance Parameter Estimates			
Cov Parm	Subject	Estimate	Standard Error
CS	clinic	4.7998	2.8400
Residual		0.9336	0.5040

Type III Tests of Fixed Effects				
Effect	Num DF	Den DF	F Value	Pr > F
trt	1	7	3.85	0.0904

trt Least Squares Means												
trt	Estimate	Standard Error	DF	t Value	Pr > |t|	Alpha	Lower	Upper	Mean	Standard Error Mean	Lower Mean	Upper Mean
cntl	-0.6510	0.4142	7	-1.57	0.1600	0.05	-1.6303	0.3284	0.3428	0.09330	0.1638	0.5814
drug	-0.1775	0.4140	7	-0.43	0.6809	0.05	-1.1564	0.8013	0.4557	0.1027	0.2393	0.6903

Differences of trt Least Squares Means

trt	_trt	Estimate	Standard Error	DF	t Value	Pr > |t|	Alpha	Lower	Upper	Odds Ratio	Lower Confidence Limit for Odds Ratio	Upper Confidence Limit for Odds Ratio
cntl	drug	-0.4734	0.2411	7	-1.96	0.0904	0.05	-1.0436	0.09677	0.623	0.352	1.102

Tests of Covariance Parameters
Based on the Residual Pseudo-Likelihood

Label	DF	-2 Res Log P-Like	ChiSq	Pr > ChiSq	Note
no clinic effect?	1	51.4403	8.36	0.0038	DF

Interpretation

As with analysis of the conditional GLMM, the "Fit Statistics" table gives you the residual log pseudo-likelihood and the generalized Chi-square statistic. By default, these are the only statistics that you will see in the "Fit Statistics" table. Here, because we added the IC=Q option, we also see information criteria based on the pseudo-likelihood, along with the warning, "Fit statistics based on pseudo-likelihoods are not useful for comparing models that differ in their pseudo-data." As the warning implies, these information criteria have no practical application. Unlike the conditional GLMM, the generalized Chi-square has no goodness-of-fit interpretation. For marginal GLMMs, generalized χ^2/df estimates the working scale parameter, ϕ. The "Covariance Parameter Estimates" table provides estimates of the working covariance, $\hat{\sigma} = 4.7998$, and the working scale, $\hat{\phi} = 0.93$. The "Tests of Covariance Parameter" table gives the pseudo-likelihood χ^2 statistic, 8.36, with its associated p-value of 0.0038. Use this statistic to test $H_0 : \sigma = 0$; there is sufficient evidence to reject H_0 which, as noted earlier, you can interpret as evidence of a CLINIC effect.

The "Type III Test of Fixed Effects" provides the F statistic for the test of overall treatment effect. Notice that the F value is lower than the F value from the conditional GLMM—3.85 versus 5.98—and the corresponding p-value is higher. This is typical of marginal GLMMs with binomial data. You can see why by looking at the least square means. The estimated proportions are $\hat{\mu}_{CNTL} = 0.34$ and $\hat{\mu}_{DRUG} = 0.46$. Compared to the estimated probabilities, $\hat{\pi}_{CNTL} = 0.24$ and $\hat{\pi}_{DRUG} = 0.40$, the marginal means are closer to 0.5. This results from the fact that the marginal distribution is strongly right-skewed with the probability is less than 0.5, and therefore the mean will always be to the right of the true probability. As a result, the estimated odds-ratio for the marginal model will be closer to one than the estimate from the conditional model—in this case 0.623 versus 0.485 in the previous analysis.

To summarize, if your inference target is the probability of a favorable response for a typical member of the population, the results from the conditional model, e.g. $\hat{\pi}_{CNTL} = 0.24$ and $\hat{\pi}_{DRUG} = 0.40$, are appropriate. On the other hand, if the target is the overall proportion affected throughout the population, and the number of patients at each clinic in the data set accurately reflects the distribution of patient numbers in the population, then base inference on statistics from the marginal GLMM, e.g. $\hat{\mu}_{CNTL} = 0.34$ and $\hat{\mu}_{DRUG} = 0.46$.

11.6 Example 3: Binary Data from a Dairy Cattle Breeding Trial

Section 11.2.3 described a breeding trial in which 24 randomly selected males were each mated to 2 females. Each female had a number of offspring, typically one or two, but occasionally three. Each offspring was evaluated for the presence or absence of a particular trait of interest. The data are given in the Breeding Trial data set. The males are identified by the variable S (for "sire") and females by the letter D (for "dam"). The response variable TRAIT has a value of 0 if the trait is absent, or 1 if the trait is present. Denoting y_{ijk} as the response for the kth offspring of the jth dam ($j = 1, 2$) mated to the ith sire, ($i = 1, 2, ..., 24$), $y_{ijk} \sim \text{Binary}(p_{ij})$ where p_{ij} denotes the probability of the trait occurring in an offspring from sire i mated to dam j.

In breeding trials, researchers focus on two primary objectives: 1) estimating variance components, usually as a first step in estimating heritability; and 2) obtaining breeding values, i.e. best linear unbiased predictors of sire or dam performance used for selection.

Because the response variable is binary and sire and dam both represent samples of their respective populations, a candidate model uses the linear predictor $\eta_{ij} = \eta + s_i + d(s)_{ij}$, where s_i denotes the sire effect and is assumed to be distributed $NI(0, \sigma_S^2)$ and $d(s)_{ij}$ denotes the dam effect, assumed to be distributed $NI(0, \sigma_D^2)$. In Section 11.2.3 a term for offspring, $o(s)_{ijk}$, was also included in the model. If the data were Gaussian, $o(s)_{ijk}$ would be the residual term. However, because the data are binary, and with so few offspring per dam, there is insufficient information to estimate an offspring term. However, because it is a potential source of variation, we should pay attention to evidence of overdispersion in the analysis.

In the multi-clinic trial in Section 11.5, we used the canonical link, the logit, because researchers in clinical trials report treatment effects in terms of odds ratios. Logistic models lend themselves naturally to estimation and inference with odds and odds ratios. Geneticists, on the other hand tend to favor the *probit* link, defined as $\eta_{ij} = \Phi^{-1}(p_{ij})$, or, more informatively, in terms of the inverse link $p_{ij} = \Phi(\eta_{ij})$, where Φ denotes the Gaussian cumulative distribution function. One way to conceptualize the probit link is to imagine a process with a Gaussian distribution. The process itself is unobservable; the only thing we see is the consequence of the process, a binary response. The probit link enables geneticists to use interpretations of variance components developed in quantitative genetics using the Gaussian distribution as a framework. The assumption is that the model effects are operating on the underlying, unobservable process.

Program

Use Program 11.12 to fit this model.

Program 11.12

```
proc glimmix data=binary method=quad;
 class s d;
 model trait(event='1')= / link=probit distdist=binary solution;
 random intercept d / subject=s;
run;
```

By default, PROC GLIMMIX models on the 0 value of a binary variable. The option (EVENT='1') overrides the default, causing PROC GLIMMIX to model p_{ij} as the probability that TRAIT=1. The options LINK and DIST specify that TRAIT, given the random effects, has a binary distribution and that the probit link is to be used. By default, PROC GLIMMIX uses the link for binary and binomial data. Unless the response variable appears in Y/N form, PROC GLIMMIX defaults to the Gaussian distribution unless the DIST= option specifies the desired distribution. Notice that the MODEL statement lists no variables to the right of the equal sign. This is because the only fixed effect in this model is the intercept, which PROC GLIMMIX includes in the model by default. The statement RANDOM INTERCEPT D / SUBJECT=S is equivalent to RANDOM S D(S). However, because the quadrature option requires you to specify a SUBJECT, you must use the RANDOM statement as shown in Program 11.7. Consistent with the discussion of pros and cons of quadrature versus the default pseudo-likelihood estimation method for binary and binomial data, use quadrature. The number of binary observations per litter is small—certainly one to three is very small. In such cases, pseudo-likelihood variance estimates are known to be biased, whereas quadrature alleviates the bias issue. Recall that the opposite was true for the multi-clinic example is Section 11.5, where the number of patients per clinic is larger than the litter sizes in this example, but there are fewer clinics, and hence integral approximation methods show downward bias typical of maximum likelihood estimates, whereas the pseudo-likelihood default produces REML-like variance estimates.

Results

Selected results appear in Output 11.12.

Output 11.12: PROC GLIMMIX Listing for Analysis of Binary Breeding Trial Data

Model Information	
Data Set	WORK.BREEDING_TRIAL
Response Variable	trait
Response Distribution	Binary
Link Function	Probit
Variance Function	Default
Variance Matrix Blocked By	s

Model Information	
Estimation Technique	Maximum Likelihood
Likelihood Approximation	Gauss-Hermite Quadrature
Degrees of Freedom Method	Containment

Optimization Information	
Optimization Technique	Dual Quasi-Newton
Parameters in Optimization	3
Lower Boundaries	2
Upper Boundaries	0
Fixed Effects	Not Profiled
Starting From	GLM estimates
Quadrature Points	7

Fit Statistics for Conditional Distribution	
-2 log L(trait | r. effects)	55.13
Pearson Chi-Square	38.20
Pearson Chi-Square / DF	0.42

Covariance Parameter Estimates			
Cov Parm	Subject	Estimate	Standard Error
Intercept	s	0.5228	0.7550
d	s	1.0798	1.0397

Solutions for Fixed Effects					
Effect	Estimate	Standard Error	DF	t Value	Pr > |t|
Intercept	0.7749	0.3366	23	2.30	0.0307

Interpretation

The "Model Information" table confirms that the binary distribution, probit link, and quadrature method are being used. The "Optimization Information" table tells you that the quadrature approximation of the log likelihood uses 7 quadrature points. The Pearson Chi-Square/DF statistic of 0.42 in the "Fit Statistics for Conditional Distribution" table provides no evidence of overdispersion. The "Covariance Parameter Estimates" give sire and dam variance component estimates on the probit scale. These can be used to calculate heritability estimates, i.e. the proportion of observed variation in the trait under investigation attributable to genetic factors. For example, heritability attributable to sires using the probit model is defined as sire variance divided by sum of sire, dam and residual variance. Because the probit link implicity assumes an underlying but unobservable standard normal process, it follows that the "residual variance," while not estimated, is set to one. See Gianola (1982) and Heringstad, et al. (2003) for discussions of the rationale for doing so in the context of the probit link function. For these data, the estimated heritability attributable to sire is $0.523/(0.523 + 1.08 + 1) = 0.201$, or approximately 20%. The INTERCEPT estimate gives the estimated overall likelihood of the trait of interest on the probit scale. Note that this is a probit, not a probability. You need to use the inverse link to convert it to a probability. You can do this with an ESTIMATE statement, as shown in Program 11.13.

The objectives of this study were 1) to compute sire heritability and 2) to compute breeding values. The heritability calculation was shown above. Breeding values are best linear unbiased predictors (BLUPs). A common breeding value is for sires. In this example, it is defined as $\hat{\eta} + \hat{s}_i$ for the ith sire. From the "Solution for Fixed Effects" table, we know that

$\hat{\eta} = 0.7749$. You can use the SOLUTION option in the RANDOM statement to obtain the breeding values (BLUPSs) for all sires. For sire 1, this listing appears as follows:

				Std Err			
Effect	**d**	**Subject**	**Estimate**	**Pred**	**DF**	**t Value**	**Pr > |t|**
Intercept		s 1	0.2745	0.7096	43	0.39	0.7007
d	1	s 1	0.3513	0.9052	43	0.39	0.6998
d	2	s 1	0.2157	0.9379	43	0.23	0.8192

Solution for Random Effects

You can see that $\hat{s}_i = 0.2745$ and hence the breeding value for sire 1 is $0.7749 + 0.2745 = 1.0494$.

Program

To understand more completely how the BLUPs are computed, you can use the statements in Program 11.13 to obtain breeding values for all 24 sires. Note that these ESTIMATE statements are shown in detail for completeness. In practice, if you have a large number of sires, constructing ESTIMATE statements for every sire can be tedious, if not overwhelming. There is macro code that you can use, which is accessible via a SAS Usage Note online at http://support.sas.com/kb/37109. You can also use the RANDOM / SOLUTION option as described above or prediction options in the MODEL statement.

Program 11.13

```
proc glimmix data=breeding_trial method=quad;
class s d;
model trait(event='1') = / link=probit d=binary;
random intercept d / subject=s;
estimate 'pop avg proportion' intercept 1 /  cl ilink;
 estimate 'sire  1 breeding value' intercept 1 | intercept 1 / subject 1 cl ilink;
 estimate 'sire  2 breeding value' intercept 1 | intercept 1 / subject 0 1 cl ilink;
 estimate 'sire  3 breeding value' intercept 1 | intercept 1 / subject 0 0 1 cl ilink;
 estimate 'sire  4 breeding value' intercept 1 | intercept 1 / subject 0 0 0 1 cl ilink;
 estimate 'sire  5 breeding value' intercept 1 | intercept 1 / subject 0 0 0 0 1 cl ilink;
 estimate 'sire  6 breeding value' intercept 1 | intercept 1 / subject 0 0 0 0 0 1 cl ilink;
 estimate 'sire  7 breeding value' intercept 1 | intercept 1 / subject 0 0 0 0 0 0 1 cl
ilink;
 estimate 'sire  8 breeding value' intercept 1 | intercept 1 / subject 0 0 0 0 0 0 0 1 cl
ilink;
 estimate 'sire  9 breeding value' intercept 1 | intercept 1 / subject 0 0 0 0 0 0 0 0 1 cl
ilink;
 estimate 'sire 10 breeding value' intercept 1 | intercept 1 / subject 0 0 0 0 0 0 0 0 0 1
cl ilink;
 estimate 'sire 11 breeding value' intercept 1 | intercept 1 / subject 0 0 0 0 0 0 0 0 0 0 1
cl ilink;
 estimate 'sire 12 breeding value' intercept 1 | intercept 1 / subject 0 0 0 0 0 0 0 0 0 0 0
1 cl ilink;
 estimate 'sire 13 breeding value' intercept 1 | intercept 1 / subject 0 0 0 0 0 0 0 0 0 0 0
0 1 cl ilink;
 estimate 'sire 14 breeding value' intercept 1 | intercept 1 / subject 0 0 0 0 0 0 0 0 0 0 0
0 0 1 cl ilink;
 estimate 'sire 15 breeding value' intercept 1 | intercept 1 / subject 0 0 0 0 0 0 0 0 0 0 0
0 0 0 1 cl ilink;
 estimate 'sire 16 breeding value' intercept 1 | intercept 1 / subject 0 0 0 0 0 0 0 0 0 0 0
0 0 0 0 1 cl ilink;
 estimate 'sire 17 breeding value' intercept 1 | intercept 1 / subject 0 0 0 0 0 0 0 0 0 0 0
0 0 0 0 1 cl ilink;
 estimate 'sire 18 breeding value' intercept 1 | intercept 1 / subject 0 0 0 0 0 0 0 0 0 0 0
0 0 0 0 0 1 cl ilink;
 estimate 'sire 19 breeding value' intercept 1 | intercept 1 / subject 0 0 0 0 0 0 0 0 0 0 0
0 0 0 0 0 0 1 cl ilink;
 estimate 'sire 20 breeding value' intercept 1 | intercept 1 / subject 0 0 0 0 0 0 0 0 0 0 0
0 0 0 0 0 0 1 cl ilink;
 estimate 'sire 21 breeding value' intercept 1 | intercept 1 / subject 0 0 0 0 0 0 0 0 0 0 0
0 0 0 0 0 0 0 1 cl ilink;
 estimate 'sire 22 breeding value' intercept 1 | intercept 1 / subject 0 0 0 0 0 0 0 0 0 0
```

```
0 0 0 0 0 0 0 0 0 1 cl ilink;
 estimate 'sire 23 breeding value' intercept 1 | intercept 1 / subject 0 0 0 0 0 0 0 0 0 0
0 0 0 0 0 0 0 0 0 1 cl ilink;
 estimate 'sire 24 breeding value' intercept 1 | intercept 1 / subject 0 0 0 0 0 0 0 0 0 0
0 0 0 0 0 0 0 0 0 0 1 cl ilink;
run;
```

The INTERCEPT before and after the vertical bar (|) obtain fixed intercept (η) and random sire (s_i) estimates, respectively. The SUBJECT option specifies which sire to use.

Results

Output 11.13 shows the results.

Output 11.13: BLUPs of Sire Breeding Values

					Estimates								
Label	Estimate	Standard Error	DF	t Value	Pr > |t|	Alpha	Lower	Upper	Mean	Standard Error Mean	Lower Mean	Upper Mean
pop avg proportion	0.7749	0.3366	23	2.30	0.0307	0.05	0.07858	1.4712	0.7808	0.09946	0.5313	0.9294
sire 1 breeding value	1.0495	0.7831	23	1.34	0.1933	0.05	-0.5706	2.6695	0.8530	0.1801	0.2841	0.9962
sire 2 breeding value	1.0495	0.7831	23	1.34	0.1933	0.05	-0.5706	2.6695	0.8530	0.1801	0.2841	0.9962
sire 3 breeding value	1.0857	0.7924	23	1.37	0.1839	0.05	-0.5535	2.7248	0.8612	0.1753	0.2900	0.9968
sire 4 breeding value	0.7953	0.6511	23	1.22	0.2343	0.05	-0.5516	2.1421	0.7868	0.1893	0.2906	0.9839
sire 5 breeding value	1.1322	0.8014	23	1.41	0.1711	0.05	-0.5255	2.7900	0.8712	0.1684	0.2996	0.9974
sire 6 breeding value	0.5293	0.6851	23	0.77	0.4477	0.05	-0.8880	1.9466	0.7017	0.2376	0.1873	0.9742
sire 7 breeding value	1.0985	0.7921	23	1.39	0.1788	0.05	-0.5402	2.7371	0.8640	0.1729	0.2945	0.9969
sire 8 breeding value	0.1611	0.8530	23	0.19	0.8518	0.05	-1.6034	1.9256	0.5640	0.3359	0.05443	0.9729
sire 9 breeding value	0.3549	0.7532	23	0.47	0.6420	0.05	-1.2033	1.9130	0.6387	0.2821	0.1144	0.9721
sire 10 breeding value	0.09339	0.9574	23	0.10	0.9231	0.05	-1.8871	2.0739	0.5372	0.3803	0.02957	0.9810
sire 11 breeding value	1.0495	0.7831	23	1.34	0.1933	0.05	-0.5706	2.6695	0.8530	0.1801	0.2841	0.9962
sire 12 breeding value	0.2562	0.7998	23	0.32	0.7516	0.05	-1.3983	1.9107	0.6011	0.3088	0.08102	0.9720
sire 13 breeding value	0.6040	0.6719	23	0.90	0.3780	0.05	-0.7859	1.9939	0.7271	0.2234	0.2160	0.9769
sire 14 breeding value	0.4615	0.7113	23	0.65	0.5229	0.05	-1.0100	1.9330	0.6778	0.2551	0.1563	0.9734
sire 15 breeding value	0.8485	0.6435	23	1.32	0.2003	0.05	-0.4826	2.1797	0.8019	0.1791	0.3147	0.9854
sire 16 breeding value	0.9963	0.7748	23	1.29	0.2113	0.05	-0.6064	2.5991	0.8405	0.1882	0.2721	0.9953
sire 17 breeding value	1.0857	0.7924	23	1.37	0.1839	0.05	-0.5535	2.7248	0.8612	0.1753	0.2900	0.9968
sire 18 breeding value	0.4615	0.7113	23	0.65	0.5229	0.05	-1.0100	1.9330	0.6778	0.2551	0.1563	0.9734

							Estimates					
Label	Estimate	Standard Error	DF	t Value	Pr > |t|	Alpha	Lower	Upper	Mean	Standard Error Mean	Lower Mean	Upper Mean
sire 19 breeding value	0.6452	0.6636	23	0.97	0.3410	0.05	-0.7274	2.0179	0.7406	0.2150	0.2335	0.9782
sire 20 breeding value	1.0495	0.7831	23	1.34	0.1933	0.05	-0.5706	2.6695	0.8530	0.1801	0.2841	0.9962
sire 21 breeding value	1.0495	0.7831	23	1.34	0.1933	0.05	-0.5706	2.6695	0.8530	0.1801	0.2841	0.9962
sire 22 breeding value	0.5706	0.6340	23	0.90	0.3775	0.05	-0.7410	1.8822	0.7159	0.2149	0.2293	0.9701
sire 23 breeding value	0.6452	0.6636	23	0.97	0.3410	0.05	-0.7274	2.0179	0.7406	0.2150	0.2335	0.9782
sire 24 breeding value	0.4966	0.6675	23	0.74	0.4644	0.05	-0.8841	1.8774	0.6903	0.2354	0.1883	0.9698

Interpretation

As with any other ESTIMATE listing, the ESTIMATE, STANDARD ERROR and LOWER and UPPER confidence bounds are given on the model (in the case, probit) scale. The data scale estimates are given as MEAN, STANDARD ERROR MEAN, LOWER MEAN, and UPPER MEAN. For example, the probit of sire 1 is 1.0495, whereas the predicted probability that an offspring of sire 1 has the trait of interest is 0.853. Assuming that having the trait is a good thing, the best sire is sire 5, whose offspring have a predicted probability of 0.8712.

11.7 Summary

Chapter 11 begins with an overview of the problems presented by non-Gaussian (i.e. non-normal) response variables, the most common of which is binary or binomial. Section 11.1 presents a brief summary of the major differences between LMMs for Gaussian data and GLMMs for non-Gaussian data, as well as a history from pre-generalized linear model approaches to non-Gaussian data through the introduction of GLMMs. Section 11.2 introduces three prototypical examples of GLMMs with a binomial or binary response, and Section 11.3 covers the first of these, a basic generalized binomial regression framework. Section 11.4 provides more in-depth coverage of generalized linear model concepts and required model elements. Formal GLMM statistical theory appears in Appendix B. The remaining two examples of GLMMs with binomial data are presented Sections 11.5 and 11.6. Another common type of non-Gaussian data, discrete counts, is discussed in Chapters 12. Binomial and count data with more complex design structure are presented in Chapter 13.

Chapter 12: Generalized Linear Mixed Models for Count Data

12.1 Introduction 419
12.2 Three Examples Illustrating Generalized Linear Mixed Models with Count Data 420
    12.2.1 Completely Randomized Design with Discrete Counts 420
    12.2.2 Count Data from a Blocked Design 420
    12.2.3 Linear Regression with Discrete Counts 421
12.3 Overview of Modeling Considerations for Count Data 421
    12.3.1 Poisson Models and Their Motivation 421
    12.3.2 Overdispersion and Count Data 422
    12.3.3 Negative Binomial Models and Their Motivation 423
    12.3.4 Alternative Distributions for Count Data 423
12.4 Example 1: Completely Random Design with Count Data 424
    12.4.1 Default Test Statistics and Confidence Intervals in PROC GLIMMIX 424
    12.4.2 When to Override the PROC GLIMMIX Defaults: the CHISQ and DDFM=NONE Options ...425
    12.4.3 Alternative Analysis if Overdispersion is Considered Non-Negligible 427
12.5 Example 2: Count Data from an Incomplete Block Design..429
    12.5.1 Naive Analyses: ANOVA and GLMM with Overdispersion...429
    12.5.2 Poisson Mixed Model 432
    12.5.3 Negative Binomial GLMM 437
    12.5.4 Poisson or Negative Binomial GLMM: Model Selection...441
    12.5.5 Marginal Model for Count Data in a Blocked Design 442
    12.5.6 A Warning Regarding Blocks Effects Fixed or Random..445
12.6 Example 3: Linear Regression with a Discrete Count Dependent Variable 445
    12.6.1 Naive GLMM with Overdispersion...446
    12.6.2 Conditional GLMMs that Account for Overdispersion 448
    12.6.3 GLMM for Regression on Count Data When the Marginal Mean is the Intended Target...451
12.7 Blocked Design Revisited: What to Do When Block Variance Estimate is Negative 453
    12.7.1 Adjustment for Poisson-Normal GLMM 454
    12.7.2 Adjustment for Negative Binomial GLMM 455
12.8 Summary 456

12.1 Introduction

Generalized linear mixed models (GLMMs) for non-Gaussian response variables were introduced in Chapter 11, using examples with binary and binomial data. This chapter continues the introduction to GLMMs with examples involving count data. The term "count data" refers to response variables that can have only nonnegative integer values, that is, $y = 0,1,2$, and so on. Examples include the number of incidents of atrial fibrillation or seizure in a given period, number of plants in a plot, number of animals in a given domain, number of insurance claims, etc.

Introductory probability and mathematical statistics texts usually present the Poisson as the standard distribution for counts. That is, if Y is a discrete count random variable, then $Y \sim \text{Poisson}(\lambda)$, where λ is the mean (e.g. average number of seizures or plants or insurance claims per unit of time, space). The Poisson distribution has three characteristics that are relevant to modeling count data. First, the mean and variance are equal, that is, $E(Y) = \lambda = \text{Var}(Y)$. Second, the natural parameter is $\theta = \log(\lambda)$, the natural log of the mean parameter. Third, even with λ as low as 5 or 6, the shape of the Poisson distribution closely approximates the Gaussian distribution.

Because the Poisson is the presumptive distribution for count data and the Gaussian approximation holds even for relatively small mean counts, users in pre-GLMM days were tempted to use standard linear mixed models for count data. The problems with doing so are similar to those presented in Chapter 11 for binomial data. First, the assumption of equal variance for standard ANOVA and regression models is violated because the variance changes with the mean. Second, as we saw in Section 11.4.4, when there are random model effects, even if the random effects are distributed Gaussian, and the conditional distribution of the data given the random effects is Poisson but closely approximates the Gaussian, the actual distribution of the observed data is typically not Gaussian, but strongly right-skewed. As a result, standard Gaussian linear mixed models are poor candidates for count data. The pre-GLMM fix for both of these problems was to use a variance stabilizing transformation, the square root of Y and natural log of Y—or $Y + 1$ if there are zero counts in the data—are the most common transformations that appear in statistical methods textbooks. However, as we saw in Chapter 11, using variance stabilizing transformations with mixed models tends to be counterproductive.

In addition to the problems described in the preceding paragraph, the Poisson distribution can be a poor choice for modeling count data. In practice, observed count data often have variance considerably larger than the mean. In many cases, especially with biological count data, the negative binomial distribution provides a better fit than the Poisson distribution. For the negative binomial random variable with mean $E(Y) = \lambda$, the variance is $\text{Var}(Y) = \lambda + \phi\lambda^2$, where $\phi > 0$ is a scale parameter. There are compelling biological as well as statistical reasons why the negative binomial is often the preferred distribution for modeling count data. See Young and Young (1998) and Hilbe (2011).

In this chapter, examples of GLMMs with count data are presented. As in Chapter 11, focus is on deriving a plausible model from a study design description, interpreting diagnostics to distinguish between cases when the Poisson is the preferred distribution from cases that call for the negative binomial, implementing the selected GLMM and interpreting the results.

12.2 Three Examples Illustrating Generalized Linear Mixed Models with Count Data

This section introduces three examples in which the response variable is a discrete count. Each example is developed in detail in sections 12.4, 12.5, and 12.6, respectively.

12.2.1 Completely Randomized Design with Discrete Counts

Date set "CRD Count" contains data from a completely randomized design with two treatments and observations on six replications per treatment. The response variable is a discrete count. The example is intentionally generic—its main purpose is to illustrate when to override the approximate F and approximate t algorithms that PROC GLIMMIX uses by default for test statistics and confidence intervals, respectively. In this example, we assume that the response variable has a Poisson distribution and use the log link function with the standard linear predictor for a completely randomized design. That is, $y_{ij} \sim \text{Poisson}(\lambda_i)$ and $\log(\lambda_i) = \eta + \tau_i$ where λ_i denotes the expected count for the ith treatment, η denotes the intercept, and τ_i denotes the ith treatment effect. The key feature of this example is the absence of any random model effects or scale parameters to be estimated.

12.2.2 Count Data from a Blocked Design

Data set "BIB Count" contains data from a balanced incomplete block design with seven treatments arranged in seven blocks, each with four treatments. Figure 12.1 shows the layout.

Figure 12.1: Balanced Incomplete Block Layout for Block Design with Counts

	Block						
	1	2	3	4	5	6	7
Treatments	3	2	7	1	2	4	5
	2	6	3	7	3	7	6
	1	5	1	4	7	2	4
	4	1	5	6	6	5	3

Treatments are divided into three groups: treatments 1 and 2 form group 1; treatments 3, 4 and 5 form group 2; treatments 6 and 7 form group 3. The response variable is a discrete count.

A pre-GLMM approach would fit a model to $\log(C)$, where C denotes the observed count, or $\log(C + 1)$ if there are zero counts. A GLMM approach would use the natural parameter, $\log(\lambda)$. A linear predictor for these data is thus:

$$\eta_{ij} = \eta + \tau_i + b_j$$

where terms are defined as follows:

- η denotes the intercept.

- τ_i denotes the ith treatment effect.

- b_j denotes the jth block effect, assumed $\text{NI}\left(0, \sigma_b^2\right)$.

Section 12.5 presents three variations on the GLMM—the Poisson GLMM, negative binomial GLMM and marginal, "GEE-type," model for analyzing these data, and discusses when each model would be appropriate. Section 12.7 presents variations on these models when the block variance solution is negative and the PROC GLIMMIX default sets the estimate to zero—the GLMM version of the NOBOUND issue introduced in Chapter 2.

12.2.3 Linear Regression with Discrete Counts

Data set "Manufacturing Counts" are from a study conducted on eight lots from a manufacturing process. Samples from each lot were exposed to a finishing treatment (called X in the data set) in amounts varying in increments of 2 from 0 to 10. The response variable is the number of aberrant micro-sites in the finished product. Ideally, there should not by any aberrant micro-sites, but it is known that if there are fewer than 10, there is no discernable impact on the product's performance. Thus, the objective of data analysis is to predict the effect of finishing treatment on the number of aberrant micro-sites and to determine what level of finishing treatment is required to ensure that the expected number of aberrant micro-sites is less than 10.

Denote the response variable in this example, the number of aberrant micro-sites, by C. The standard pre-GLMM approach would be to fit a regression model to the log of C, or, more precisely, to $\log(C + 1)$ since there are zero counts in the data set. For a GLMM, $\log(\lambda)$, where λ denotes the expected count, is the natural parameter for the Poisson distribution, and is commonly used as the link function for models for Poisson and negative binomial models. A linear predictor for these data can be written as follows:

$$\eta_{ij} = B_{0i} + B_{1i} X_j \tag{12.1}$$

where terms are defined as follows:

- η_{ij} denotes $\log(C_{ij} + 1)$ and C_{ij} is the count for the ith lot, j^{th} level of X if the pre-GLMM approach is used, or η_{ij} denotes $\log(\lambda_{ij})$ for the GLMM.

- B_{0i} denotes the intercept for the ith lot.

- B_{1i} denotes the slope for the ith lot.

Alternatively, you can express Equation 12.1 as follows:

$$\eta_{ij} = \beta_0 + b_{0i} + (\beta_1 + b_{1i}) X_j \tag{12.2}$$

where terms are defined thus:

- β_0 denotes the overall intercept.

- b_{0i} denotes the effect of the ith lot on the intercept, assumed $\sim N(0, \sigma_0^2)$.

- β_1 denotes the overall slope.

- b_{1i} denotes the effect of the ith lot on the slope, assumed $\sim N(0, \sigma_1^2)$.

Note that, relating Equation 12.1 to Equation 12.2, $B_{0i} = \beta_0 + b_{0i}$ and $B_{1i} = \beta_1 + b_{1i}$. Section 12.6 presents pre-GLMM, Poisson GLMM, and negative binomial GLMM analyses for these data, all using the GLIMMIX procedure. The section concludes with a comparison of the three analyses.

12.3 Overview of Modeling Considerations for Count Data

In this section, a summary of the distributions most commonly used to model count data, their motivation and their pros and cons is presented. We focus on the Poisson and negative binomial, the two most frequently used distributions. See Appendix B for details of how these distributions fit into GLMM theory and methodology. See Stroup (2013) for a comprehensive, in-depth presentation of the GLMM.

12.3.1 Poisson Models and Their Motivation

The standard motivation for the Poisson distribution begins by supposing that you have a grid divided into N cells of equal size. An object arrives in any given cell with probability p. All arrivals are assumed to be mutually independent. Thus, the expected number of arrivals into the grid, i.e. the expected count, is $\lambda = Np$, and the probability of Y arrivals follows a binomial distribution. The Poisson arises by supposing that you divide the grid into ever smaller cells, but λ remains constant. In other words, the grid size remains constant, N goes to infinity, the cell size thus goes to zero, while $\lambda = Np$ remains constant. The limiting distribution is the Poisson. Formally, subject to the constraint that $\lambda = Np$ remains constant as $N \to \infty$,

$$\lim_{N \to \infty} \binom{N}{Y} (\lambda/N)^Y (1-\lambda/N)^{N-Y} = e^{-\lambda}\lambda^Y / Y!$$

equals the PDF of the Poisson random variable. The Poisson log-likelihood is thus

$$\log\left(e^{-\lambda}\lambda^Y / Y!\right) = Y \log(\lambda) - \lambda - \log(Y!)$$

(12.3)

Relating Equation 12.3 to the generic form of the exponential family log-likelihood

$$\frac{y\theta - b(\theta)}{a(\phi)} + c(y,\phi)$$

the natural (or canonical) parameter is $\theta = \log(\lambda)$ and the scale parameter is $\phi = 1$ (that is, $a(\phi) = \phi = 1$).

From the generalized linear modeling perspective, the important characteristics of the Poisson distribution are the expected value and variance, $E(Y) = \lambda = \text{Var}(Y)$ and the natural parameter, $\theta = \log(\lambda)$. The important assumption of the process giving rise to the Poisson is that arrivals are assumed to be mutually independent. The assumptions of independence and equality of mean and variance have important implications for modeling certain kinds of data, notably biological counts. These are discussed in Section 12.3.2.

12.3.2 Overdispersion and Count Data

Using the Poisson distribution to model count data implies that the mean and variance are equal. In practice, the observed mean and variance will be somewhat unequal because of sampling variation. However, the observed variance is often considerably greater than the mean. This is an example of *overdispersion*, introduced in the context of binomial data in Chapter 11. Whenever the observed sample variance exceeds the variance accounted for by the model being fit, overdispersion is said to exist. Overdispersion is a problem because standard errors used to construct confidence intervals are underestimated, the resulting confidence intervals are too narrow, and test statistics are inflated, increasing the likelihood of false positives when testing hypotheses.

As shown in the binomial examples in Chapter 11, the primary diagnostic for overdispersion in the GLIMMIX procedure is the Pearson χ^2/df. If you have evidence of overdispersion, you must account for it. With count data, there are two strategies for doing so: either you can modify the Poisson-based model to accurately describe the mean-variance relationship, or you can change the assumed distribution to something else. The usual "something else" is the negative binomial distribution. The remainder of this section describes strategies for retaining the Poisson distribution by accounting for overdispersion, but also describes why this can be problematic. Sections 12.3.3 and 12.3.4 give alternative distributions and their motivation.

In the early literature of generalized linear models, the standard "fix" for over dispersed count data was to multiply the variance by a scale parameter. In other words, assume a mean, or expected value, of λ and a variance of $\varphi\lambda$ where φ denotes a scale parameter. To account for overdispersion, $\varphi > 1$. This modifies the Poisson log-likelihood from Equation 12.3 to

$$\left[\left(Y\log(\lambda) - \lambda\right)/\varphi\right] - \log(Y!)$$

(12.4)

In reality, Equation 12.4 is not a true log-likelihood. It is a quasi-likelihood. A quasi-likelihood is not the log of a true probability distribution, as is a true log-likelihood, but its structure allows estimation and inference using generalized linear model theory and methodology. The scale parameter, φ, is often referred to as the *overdispersion parameter*.

With the advent of the generalized linear mixed model, use of the overdispersion parameter has fallen out of favor. To understand why, it is helpful to look at modeling in its design context. The simplest way to do this is to consider a completely randomized design, in which treatments are randomly assigned to experimental units. The thought process presented below extends to more complex designs, such as the randomized block design in Section 12.5 and the split-plot with counts presented in Chapter 13.

In the CRD, for observations on experimental units there are two potential sources of variation: variability resulting from the difference between treatment means, and variability from the uniqueness of each experimental unit. In a Gaussian linear model, the linear predictor $\eta + \tau_i$ accounts for treatment mean variation and the variance, σ^2 accounts for intrinsic variability among experimental units. In a Poisson GLM for count data, using the Gaussian linear model template, the linear predictor is $\log(\lambda_i) = \eta + \tau_i$. Hence, the Poisson GLM defines both the mean and the experimental unit variance as $\lambda_i = \exp(\eta + \tau_i)$. However, if there is additional variability over and above the treatment effect, analogous to the error or residual term in a Gaussian linear model, then variance will be underestimated because there is no provision for experimental unit uniqueness. For this reason, we often refer to $\log(\lambda_i) = \eta + \tau_i$ as the *naive GLM* for the CRD.

A design-based approach to overdispersion in a Poisson model is to add a random model effect to account for experimental unit uniqueness. That is, use the linear predictor $\log(\lambda) = \eta + \tau_i + u_{ij}$, where $u_{ij} \sim \text{NI}(0, \sigma_u^2)$. In GLM terminology, this is often called a Poisson-normal model. Note that it is a conditional GLMM. See Chapter 11 for definitions or marginal and conditional models, and an explanation of their targets of inference. With a CRD, using the quasi-likelihood scale parameter as in Equation 12.4 gives you a marginal model. The examples in Section 12.5 how overdispersion strategies extend to conditional and marginal GLMMs in the context of modeling count data with blocked designs.

12.3.3 Negative Binomial Models and Their Motivation

Section 12.3.2 concluded with the Poisson-normal model. An alternative way of looking at the design-based approach to model-building with count data yields the negative binomial distribution. Instead of assuming a Poisson(λ) distribution for the observations, assume that the observations have a distribution conditional on an experimental unit effect, that is $Y | u$ follows a Poisson(λu) distribution, where $u \sim \text{Gamma}(1/\phi, \phi)$ and ϕ is the scale parameter. The marginal distribution of Y is negative binomial with mean λ and variance $\lambda + \phi\lambda^2$. The log likelihood for the negative binomial, written in GLM-friendly form, is

$$y\log\left[\lambda\phi/(1+\lambda\phi)\right] - (1/\phi)\log(1+\lambda\phi) + \log\binom{y+(1/\phi)-1}{y}$$

(12.5)

See Hilbe (2011) for a comprehensive discussion of the negative binomial distribution in the context of modeling.

In a completely randomized design, denote the observation on the jth experimental unit for the ith treatment as y_{ij}. The conditional distribution given the ij^{th} experimental unit effect is $y_{ij} | u_{ij} \sim \text{Poisson}(\lambda_i u_{ij})$, where λ_i denotes the mean, or expected count, of the ith treatment. The natural parameter is $\log(\lambda_i u_{ij}) = \log(\lambda_i) + \log(u_{ij})$. This is equivalent to using the linear predictor $\log(\lambda_i) = \eta + \tau_i$ and assuming a negative binomial distribution for the observations. This model is similar to the Poisson-normal model in that it arises from the same design perspective, and it replaces the Gaussian experimental unit effect, $u_{ij} \sim \text{NI}(0, \sigma_u^2)$, by $\log(u_{ij})$ where u_{ij} is assumed to have a Gamma distribution. Negative binomial GLMMs are often called Poisson-Gamma GLMMs.

A less mathematical, more process-oriented motivation for the negative binomial revisits the original development of the Poisson, the grid with N cells. Instead of the cell being occupied or not, suppose each cell can, in theory, be occupied by 0, 1, 2, ... individuals. Start with two cells and two individuals. Individuals can both be in cell 1, both be in cell 2, or one each in cells 1 and 2. Assuming a binomial process, the probabilities are ¼, ¼ and ½, respectively. Alternatively, you could assume a Bose-Einstein process, in which the probabilities are 1/3 both each outcome. Then, instead of assuming that the next individual is equally likely to go the either cell, assume that the next individual is more likely to go to the cell that is already occupied. The equally likely process leads to the Poisson; the more likely to go to the occupied cell leads to the negative binomial. The latter more realistically models biological counts because living organisms tend to aggregate rather than to spread out at random. See Young and Young (1998) for a complete development of these ideas.

12.3.4 Alternative Distributions for Count Data

Although the Poisson and negative binomial are the two distributions for count data with pre-defined DISTRIBUTION options in the GLIMMIX procedure, there are other distributions one might consider. In particular, suppose that you want to see if you can justify using the Poisson rather than the negative binomial distribution. One approach would be to test the hypothesis that the negative binomial variance can be simplified from $\lambda + \phi\lambda^2$ to λ, that is, test $H_0 : \phi = 0$.

However, as you can see in Equation 12.5, the negative binomial log likelihood includes a term $1/\phi$ that you cannot evaluate at $\phi = 0$ and hence you cannot obtain a likelihood ratio statistic for this test.

The *generalized Poisson* is an alternative to the negative binomial. Although it is heavier tailed than the negative binomial, its characteristics are similar. The log likelihood is

$$y \log(\lambda\gamma) - \log(\lambda\gamma) - \gamma - \log(y!)$$

where $\gamma = \lambda + \phi y$, and ϕ is the scale parameter whose interpretation is equivalent to the negative binomial scale parameter. The expected value of the generalized Poisson is $E(Y) = \mu = \lambda/(1-\phi)$ and the variance is $\mathrm{Var}(Y) = \lambda/(1-\phi)^3 = \mu/(1-\phi)^2$. See Joe and Zhu (2005) for additional details.

Example 45.14 in the SAS Documentation for the GLIMMIX procedure shows how to implement the generalized Poisson. Doing so requires writing program statements to define the log likelihood and the variance function. You can adapt these program statements for use with the models presented in Sections 12.4 through 12.6. However, because this chapter is intended to be an introduction rather than an advanced application, these examples focus on the Poisson and negative binomial exclusively, and not the generalized Poisson.

12.4 Example 1: Completely Random Design with Count Data

Section 12.2.1 described a completely randomized design with two treatments, six replications per treatment, and a response variable that is a discrete count.

In this section, we use what we have called a "naive" generalized linear model to analyze the data. We do this with the caveat that in practice, you want to pay attention to evidence of overdispersion and account for it if present. However, in some cases, this example being one of them, overdispersion is negligible and the "naive" GLM provides a defensible analysis. In such cases, PROC GLIMMIX has default settings for test statistics and confidence intervals that should be overridden. The purpose of this section is to show how and why.

12.4.1 Default Test Statistics and Confidence Intervals in PROC GLIMMIX

As given in Section 12.2.1, the "naive" GLM for these data has the following elements:

- Distribution: $y_{ij} \sim \mathrm{Poisson}(\lambda_i)$, where y_{ij} denotes the jth observation on the ith treatment.

- Link Function: $\eta_i = \log(\lambda_i)$.

- Linear Predictor: $\eta_i = \eta + \tau_i$, where η denotes the intercept and τ_i denotes the treatment effect.

Program

Use Program 12.1 to implement this model.

Program 12.1

```
proc glimmix data=crd_counts;
 class trt;
 model y=trt / d=poisson;
 lsmeans trt / ilink cl;
run;
```

Results

Output 12.1 shows the results of interest in this example.

Output 12.1: Fit Statistics, Default Test Statistics, and Confidence Intervals for CRD Model

Fit Statistics	
-2 Log Likelihood	62.36
AIC (smaller is better)	66.36
AICC (smaller is better)	67.69

Fit Statistics	
BIC (smaller is better)	67.33
CAIC (smaller is better)	69.33
HQIC (smaller is better)	66.00
Pearson Chi-Square	11.99
Pearson Chi-Square / DF	1.20

Type III Tests of Fixed Effects				
Effect	Num DF	Den DF	F Value	Pr > F
trt	1	10	4.45	0.0612

trt Least Squares Means												
trt	Estimate	Standard Error	DF	t Value	Pr > |t|	Alpha	Lower	Upper	Mean	Standard Error Mean	Lower Mean	Upper Mean
0	2.6150	0.1104	10	23.68	<.0001	0.05	2.3689	2.8610	13.6667	1.5092	10.6857	17.4793
1	2.2513	0.1325	10	17.00	<.0001	0.05	1.9562	2.5464	9.5000	1.2583	7.0722	12.7613

Interpretation

As with the examples presented in Chapter 11, the "Pearson Chi-Square/DF" that appears in the "Fit Statistics" table is the primary overdispersion diagnostic. Here, Pearson $\chi^2/DF = 1.20$, which can be interpreted as negligible-to-marginal evidence of overdispersion. In Section 12.4.3, we present an alternative model to use if we conclude that $\chi^2/DF = 1.20$ constitutes marginal evidence and that we need to account for overdispersion. For now, to illustrate the main idea of this section, we proceed assuming that overdispersion is negligible and the "naive" GLM is adequate.

The approximate F value in the "Type III Tests of Fixed Effects" table is 4.45, with a p-value of 0.0612. Notice that the p-value is determined using an F distribution with 10 denominator degrees of freedom. For the model in this example, this is a problem. In Section 11.3.6, two cases were presented for hypothesis testing with a generalized linear model: Case 1, when there is no random model effect or scale parameter to be estimated, and Case 2, when there is a random model effect or unknown scale parameter. For Case 1, a chi-square test, not an F test, should be used. The F test is only appropriate for Case 2. In this example, we are in Case 1. The approximate F statistic given in the default PROC GLIMMIX listing is overly conservative. In the next Section we will see how to obtain the appropriate χ^2 test statistic.

The confidence intervals for the treatment model scale ESTIMATE and data scale MEAN have the same issue as the Type III test statistic. The model scale confidence interval is computed as $(\hat{\eta} + \hat{\tau}_i) \pm t_{10} \times SE(\hat{\eta} + \hat{\tau}_i)$, which would be appropriate if the standard error depended on estimates of unknown covariance components. However, it does not. Therefore, the appropriate formula to obtain the confidence interval is $(\hat{\eta} + \hat{\tau}_i) \pm z \times SE(\hat{\eta} + \hat{\tau}_i)$, where z is the value from the standard normal distribution. Note that the reasoning here is essentially the same as introductory statistics "use χ^2 and z if the variance is known, F and t if the variance is estimated."

12.4.2 When to Override the PROC GLIMMIX Defaults: the CHISQ and DDFM=NONE Options

Continuing from the previous section, because PROC GLIMMIX is a mixed model program, its default reflects the assumption that most of the time it will be used with models that require at least one covariance parameter estimate. However, when you do use PROC GLIMMIX for a fixed effect GLM, it is important to use it appropriately.

A rule is as follows: If there is no RANDOM statement *and* you are working with a distribution that does not have an unknown scale parameter (e.g. binomial or Poisson), use χ^2 and z. To do so, you must override the PROC GLIMMIX default. If there is at least one RANDOM statement *or* you are working with a distribution that does have an unknown scale parameter (e.g. negative binomial), use the default F and t.

As this example satisfies the "no RANDOM statement *and* distribution with no scale parameter" criteria, you should override the PROC GLIMMIX default and use the χ^2 form of the Wald statistic and compute confidence intervals using the standard normal, or z. There are two options to override the PROC GLIMMIX defaults: CHISQ and DDFM=NONE. The former affects the test statistics generated by the MODEL statement only, the "Type III Tests of Fixed Effects." The latter affects computations throughout the PROC GLIMMIX program, including the CONTRAST, ESTIMATE, LSMEANS, and LSMESTIMATE statements. For this reason, we recommend using DDFM=NONE. In the section, we illustrate the results obtained with each option.

Program

Program 12.2 shows a modification of Program 12.1 using the CHISQ option.

Program 12.2

```
proc glimmix data=crd_counts;
 class trt;
 model y=trt / d=poisson chisq;
 lsmeans trt / ilink cl;
run;
```

Results

Relevant results appear in Output 12.2.

Output 12.2: Test Statistics and Confidence Intervals Computed using CHISQ Option

| | Type III Tests of Fixed Effects | | | | | |
Effect	Num DF	Den DF	Chi-Square	F Value	Pr > ChiSq	Pr > F
trt	1	10	4.45	4.45	0.0350	0.0612

| | | | | trt Least Squares Means | | | | | | | | |
trt	Estimate	Standard Error	DF	t Value	Pr > |t|	Alpha	Lower	Upper	Mean	Standard Error Mean	Lower Mean	Upper Mean
0	2.6150	0.1104	10	23.68	<.0001	0.05	2.3689	2.8610	13.6667	1.5092	10.6857	17.4793
1	2.2513	0.1325	10	17.00	<.0001	0.05	1.9562	2.5464	9.5000	1.2583	7.0722	12.7613

Interpretation

The "Type III Tests of Fixed Effects" table gives two sets of test statistics, the approximate F and the χ^2. In this case, the tests statistics are equal, $F = \chi^2 = 4.45$. The "chi-square" value is the true Wald statistic. The F value is computed as Wald/(numerator df). In this case, numerator $df = 1$. The important difference is between the p-values, 0.061 versus 0.035, the latter being the appropriate value to use for this model. The difference stems from the fact that the motivation for the F distribution is to account for uncertainty associated with estimating the variance. Because there is no variance to estimate with this model, there is no need to account for such uncertainty.

On the other hand, the "trt Least Squares Means" table is identical to the default table in Output 12.1. For example, the model-scale confidence bounds for TRT 0 are 2.369 and 2.861 in both tables. These bounds are computed using $(\hat{\eta} + \hat{\tau}_i) \pm t_{10} \times SE(\hat{\eta} + \hat{\tau}_i)$, and are thus unnecessarily accounting for uncertainty in estimating a variance that in this case does not exist.

Program

To compute appropriate test statistics and confidence intervals, use the DDFM=NONE option, as shown in Program 12.3. DDFM=NONE causes PROC GLIMMIX to evaluate F and t with infinite denominator degrees of freedom, making them equivalent to χ^2 and z respectively.

Program 12.3

```
proc glimmix data=crd_counts;
 class trt;
 model y=trt / d=poisson ddfm=none;
 lsmeans trt / ilink cl;
run;
```

Results

Results appear in Output 12.3.

Output 12.3: Test Statistics and Confidence Intervals Computed Using DDFM=NONE Option

	Type III Tests of Fixed Effects			
Effect	Num DF	Den DF	F Value	Pr > F
trt	1	Infty	4.45	0.0350

									trt Least Squares Means		
trt	Estimate	Standard Error	DF	t Value	Pr > |t|	Alpha	Lower	Upper	Mean	Standard Error Mean	Lower Mean	Upper Mean
0	2.6150	0.1104	Infty	23.68	<.0001	0.05	2.3985	2.8314	13.6667	1.5092	11.0069	16.9692
1	2.2513	0.1325	Infty	17.00	<.0001	0.05	1.9917	2.5109	9.5000	1.2583	7.3279	12.3160

Interpretation

The "Type III Tests of Fixed Effects" provide the same test statistic and *p*-value as the appropriate values from the CHISQ option—4.45 and $p = 0.035$. The confidence bounds are obtained from the formula $(\hat{\eta} + \hat{\tau}_i) \pm t_\infty \times SE(\hat{\eta} + \hat{\tau}_i)$, which is equivalent to $(\hat{\eta} + \hat{\tau}_i) \pm z \times SE(\hat{\eta} + \hat{\tau}_i)$. For example, the confidence bounds for TRT 0 are 2.399 and 2.831, whereas they were 2.369 and 2.861 in the previous runs. The difference may seem small, but you can easily show via simulation that DDFM=NONE results in accurate confidence interval coverage for GLMs with no covariance or scale parameter to estimate, whereas coverage accuracy suffers under the PROC GLIMMIX default.

12.4.3 Alternative Analysis if Overdispersion is Considered Non-Negligible

In the previous sections, overdispersion was deemed to be negligible and hence using the "naive" GLM to analyze the data could be defended. In practice, it may be better to explicitly account for unit-level variation. From the discussion in Section 12.3, we know that there are a number of ways to do this. In the early days of generalized linear modeling, McCullach and Nelder (1989) suggested adding a scale parameter to the Poisson variance to adjust for overdispersion. You can do this in PROC GLIMMIX by adding a RANDOM RESIDUAL_statement. Subsequent work has cast doubt on the effectiveness of this strategy (see Stroup, 2013). Either adding a unit-level random effect to the linear predictor or changing the assumed distribution to the negative binomial have emerged as preferred strategies. All three have in common the fact that they require estimation of a scale or covariance parameter. Hence, the PROC GLIMMIX approximate *F* and *t* defaults are appropriate and should not be overridden in these cases.

Program

For example, Program 12.4 shows statements required for a Poisson model adding a unit-level effect to account for overdispersion. The required elements of this model, using the same notation as above with the "naive GLM, are as follows.

- Distribution: $y_{ij} \mid u_{ij} \sim \text{Poisson}(\lambda_{ij})$ where u_{ij} denotes the experimental unit level effect, assumed $\sim \text{NI}(0, \sigma_u^2)$.
- Link function: $\eta_{ij} = \log(\lambda_{ij})$.
- Linear Predictor: $\eta_{ij} = \eta + \tau_i + u_{ij}$.

Program 12.4

```
proc glimmix data=crd_counts method=quad;
 class trt eu;
 model y=trt / d=poisson;
```

```
lsmeans trt / ilink cl;
/*random eu(trt);*/
random intercept / subject=eu(trt);
covtest 'overdispersion?' zeroG;
run;
```

Add EU to the CLASS statement and RANDOM INTERCEPT / SUBJECT=EU(TRT) to specify the unit-level random effect. This form of the RANDOM statement is equivalent to RANDOM ET(TRT) (included but commented out). If you want to test $H_0 : \sigma_u^2 = 0$, which is in essence a test of overdispersion, add the COVTEST statement. When you include the COVTEST statement, you must also use integral approximation (either METHOD=LAPLACE or QUAD) to obtain a valid likelihood ratio test. If you use METHOD=QUAD, you must also use the form of the RANDOM statement that specifies a SUBJECT. The ZEROG option in the COVTEST statement defines a test that all elements of the G matrix— the covariance matrix of the random model effects—are equal to zero. In this case, the only element of the G matrix is σ_u^2, so ZEROG causes PROC GLIMMIX to compute the test statistic for $H_0 : \sigma_u^2 = 0$.

Notice that because you now have a RANDOM statement and hence a variance component to estimate, the PROC GLIMMIX defaults using the *F* and *t* distributions are appropriate—you do not need and should not use the CHISQ or DDFM=NONE options that appeared in Programs 12.2 and 12.3.

Results

Output 12.4 shows relevant results.

Output 12.4: Selected Results for Poisson CRD Model with Unit-Level Random Effect

Covariance Parameter Estimates			
Cov Parm	Subject	Estimate	Standard Error
Intercept	eu(trt)	0	.

Type III Tests of Fixed Effects				
Effect	Num DF	Den DF	F Value	Pr > F
trt	1	10	4.45	0.0612

trt Least Squares Means											
trt	Estimate	Standard Error	DF	t Value	Pr > |t|	Alpha	Lower	Upper	Mean	Standard Error Mean	Lower Mean	Upper Mean
0	2.6150	0.1104	10	23.68	<.0001	0.05	2.3689	2.8610	13.6667	1.5092	10.6857	17.4793
1	2.2513	0.1325	10	17.00	<.0001	0.05	1.9562	2.5464	9.5000	1.2583	7.0722	12.7613

Tests of Covariance Parameters Based on the Likelihood					
Label	DF	-2 Log Like	ChiSq	Pr > ChiSq	Note
overdispersion?	1	62.3554	0.00	1.0000	MI

Interpretation

The "Covariance Parameter Estimates" table shows the unit-level variance "Estimate," $\hat{\sigma}_u^2 = 0$. With a zero estimate of the unit-level variance, the *p*-value for the associated test of $\sigma_u^2 = 0$ is one. This appears to confirm the decision in the previous sections to use a GLM assuming negligible overdispersion. In this case, the test statistics and confidence intervals are identical to the PROC GLIMMIX default shown in Output 12.1. In general, accounting for overdispersion makes tests more conservative and confidence intervals wider. When there is evidence of overdispersion, you must account for it. However, in this example, doing so appears to be unnecessary and would needlessly sacrifice power and precision.

12.5 Example 2: Count Data from an Incomplete Block Design

Section 12.2.2 gave a description of an experiment conducted as a balanced incomplete design with seven treatments and seven blocks each with four experimental units. The response variable of primary interest is a discrete count. Researchers want to compare treatment effects on mean counts.

In the pre-GLMM era, this experiment would have been analyzed in one of two ways, either applying standard ANOVA to the count variable directly, or using a variance stabilizing transformation, such as the natural log. The justification for the former stems from the fact that, except for very small expected counts, the normal approximation to the Poisson holds. The justification for the latter stems from the fact that because the mean and variance of Poisson random variables are equal, ANOVA's equal variance assumption must be violated if there is a nonzero treatment effect—the analysis must be modified accordingly. In the GLMM era, we regard both analyses as naive. These, along with what we call the "naive Poisson GLMM" are discussed in Section 12.5.1. Variations on non-naive Poisson models are presented in Section 12.5.2. Negative binomial models are presented in Section 12.5.3.

12.5.1 Naive Analyses: ANOVA and GLMM with Overdispersion

To understand why we characterize the models in this section as "naive" we begin with a review of the sources of variation we must account for when analyzing a blocked design, and the probability processes we conceptualize as giving rise to the data. These are summarized in Table 12.1.

Table 12.1: Sources of Variation and Probability Processes in a Blocked Design

Source	Effect Type	Notation	Density Function [Presumed Distribution]
Block	random	b	$f(b)$ [Gaussian]
Treatment	fixed	τ	NA
experimental unit(block) / unit of observation	random	y^{a}	$f(y \mid b)$ [Poisson or negative binomial] [b]

Note: NA = nonapplicable.

[a] The variable y denotes the observed response variable taken of the unit of observation; strictly speaking not an "effect."

[b] Poisson GLMM may require additional random effect at experimental unit level to account for overdispersion.

Table 12.1 gives us two insights relevant to deciding how to model count data from a blocked design.

First, any model that we use must account for all sources of variation in the list under SOURCE, including variability attributable to uniqueness at the experimental unit level that is not accounted for by block and treatment effects. Any model with a one-to-one correspondence between parameters and sources of variation can be regarded as "sensible." Models that fail to account for all sources of variation can be regarded as *naive*. Models that have redundant parameters can be regarded as *nonsense* models. A model considered sensible may not necessarily be the best choice, as there may be competing sensible models. However, a naive or nonsense model is never a good choice.

The second insight from Table 12.1 concerns the distribution of the observations. Although we conceptualize the data as arising from two probability processes, characterized by $f(b)$ and $f(y \mid b)$, neither of these distributions is directly observable. We can only observe the data, and hence only directly observe the marginal distribution of the observations, $f(y)$. Even if $f(b)$ and $f(y \mid b)$ are both symmetric, $f(y)$ for count data is strongly right-skewed. The Gaussian mixed model justified by the normal approximation to the Poisson, presented in Section 12.5.1, and the marginal GLM presented in Section 12.5.5 both estimates of the mean of $f(y)$. However, we know that there are compelling arguments against using the mean as the measure of central tendency for strongly skewed distributions. The Poisson conditional GLMM presented in Section 12.5.2 and the negative binomial conditional GLMM presented in 12.5.3 represent attempts to target a more reasonable measure of central tendency. Specifically, their broad inference targets to $E(y \mid b)$ when $b = 0$, interpreted as the expected count for a typical member of the population. For the count data models discussed in this chapter and in Chapter 13, the mean of $f(y)$, or more precisely, the marginal mean, is substantially greater.

In most cases, the "expected count for a typical member of the population" is the appropriate target of inference, not the marginal mean. This explains why assuming the normal approximation to the Poisson for counts, and using standard

ANOVA, or a standard Gaussian mixed model, is inappropriate. Any analysis that assumes normality will result in unbiased estimates of the marginal mean. See Section 12.5.5 for an elaboration of this point

As a point of reference for appropriate analyses, presented in Section 12.5.2 and 12.5.3, the *F* value for the overall test of treatment effect and the estimated means from standard analysis assuming normality are shown in Output 12.5.

Program

You can obtain them using the PROC GLIMMIX statements in Program 12.5.

Program 12.5

```
proc glimmix data=bib_counts;
 class block trt;
 model count=trt;
 random intercept /subject=block;
 lsmeans trt;
run;
```

Results

Output 12.5 shows the results.

Output 12.5: Treatment LSMEANS from Standard Gaussian Mixed Model for Count Data

	Type III Tests of Fixed Effects				
Effect	Num DF	Den DF	F Value	Pr > F
trt	6	15	1.54	0.2333

	trt Least Squares Means				
trt	Estimate	Standard Error	DF	t Value	Pr > |t|
1	28.8442	8.3402	15	3.46	0.0035
2	30.1062	8.3402	15	3.61	0.0026
3	15.7676	8.3402	15	1.89	0.0782
4	13.7165	8.3402	15	1.64	0.1208
5	21.6334	8.3402	15	2.59	0.0203
6	5.7771	8.3402	15	0.69	0.4991
7	5.4050	8.3402	15	0.65	0.5267

Interpretation

As an additional point of reference, Output 12.6 shows selected results of analysis with the same Gaussian mixed model but using the log variance stabilizing transformation instead of the actual counts.

Program

You can obtain these results with Program 12.6.

Program 12.6

```
proc glimmix data=bib_counts;
 class block trt;
 log_c=log(count);
 model log_c=trt;
 random intercept / subject=block;
 lsmeans trt;
 ods output lsmeans=lsm;
run;
data back_transform;
 set lsm;
```

```
 mu=exp(estimate);
 stderr_mu=mu*stderr;
proc print data=back_transform;
 var estimate stderr mu stderr_mu;
run;
```

The program statement LOG(COUNT) creates the response variable LOG_C. There are no zero counts in the data set for this example. If there were, you should use LOG(COUNT+1). The LSMEANS statement computes treatment means of the log counts. Standard practice is to report back-transformed counts, obtained by taking EXP(ESTIMATE) where ESTIMATE is the least squares mean for a given treatment. Using the Delta Rule, the standard error of the back-transformed mean is obtained by multiplying the standard error of the least squares mean by the back-transformed mean. The LSMEANS statement in PROC GLIMMIX does not have an EXP option, but you can easily use ODS OUTPUT to create a new data set with the least squares means information and define the back transformation with program statements as shown.

Results

Results are in Output 12.6

Output 12.6: Selected Results from Gaussian Mixed Model Analysis on Log Count

	Type III Tests of Fixed Effects				
Effect	Num DF	Den DF	F Value	Pr > F
trt	6	15	1.25	0.3364

Obs	Estimate	StdErr	mu	stderr_mu
1	2.9701	0.6072	19.4933	11.8373
2	2.8647	0.6072	17.5446	10.6540
3	2.3328	0.6072	10.3065	6.2586
4	2.0691	0.6072	7.9180	4.8082
5	2.6345	0.6072	13.9360	8.4626
6	1.4938	0.6072	4.4539	2.7046
7	1.3301	0.6072	3.7813	2.2962

The analysis with the log transformation gives a *p*-value for treatment of 0.3364. Keep this value in mind for comparison with the Poisson and negative binomial based analyses in Sections 12.5.2 and 12.5.3. You can easily show via simulation that the log transformation has very poor power characteristics for testing treatment mean differences relative to Poisson and negative binomial GLMMs. The latter control Type I error, as well as the log transformation, are distinctly more powerful when treatment differences exist.

In addition to the *p*-value, notice that the back-transformed means are noticeably lower than the least squares means from the analysis assuming normality shown in Output 12.5. These estimates will be of interest as we consider GLMMs in Sections 12.5.2 and 12.5.3.

The final model we consider in this section is the "naive" Poisson GLMM. Often, data analysts new to generalized linear models will simply borrow statements from mixed model analysis and add an option in the MODEL statement that specifies the distribution and another in the LSMEANS statement to obtain data scale estimates of the treatment means. For this example, doing so gives the following PROC GLIMMIX program:

Program

Program 12.7 shows the program statements for the "naïve" Poisson GLMM.

Program 12.7

```
proc glimmix data=bib_counts method=quadrature;
class block trt;
model count=trt / d=poi;
random intercept /subject=block;
lsmeans trt / ilink;
```

The program also includes METHOD=QUADRATURE in order to obtain the Pearson χ^2/DF overdispersion diagnostic to highlight the primary weakness of this approach.

Results

Relevant results appear below in Output 12.7.

Output 12.7: Conditional Fit Statistics and *p*-value for Test of Overall Treatment Effect from "Naive" Poisson GLMM

Fit Statistics for Conditional Distribution	
-2 log L(count | r. effects)	301.68
Pearson Chi-Square	184.96
Pearson Chi-Square / DF	6.61

Type III Tests of Fixed Effects				
Effect	Num DF	Den DF	F Value	Pr > F
trt	6	15	18.34	<.0001

Interpretation

You can see that the Pearson overdispersion diagnostic is 6.61, strong evidence of overdispersion. The statistics for the test of treatment effect are $F = 18.34$ and $P < 0.0001$, compared with $F = 1.25$ with the log transformation. Given the evidence of overdispersion, we can dismiss these test statistics as implausibly liberal. The reason for overdispersion is that in defining the model, we have neglected to account for variability attributable to experiment unit-level uniqueness. In the next three sections, we will explore options for doing so.

12.5.2 Poisson Mixed Model

At the beginning of the previous section, it was stated that the linear predictor of a Poisson GLMM for a blocked design may require a term to account for experimental unit uniqueness in addition to the block and treatment effects. We concluded the previous section by observing that to be true for the Data Set 12.5 example. A modified GLMM is the Poisson-normal model, described in Section 12.3.2. Its blocked design form is

$$\log\left(\lambda_{ij}\right) = \eta + \tau_i + b_j + u_{ij}$$

$$(12.6)$$

where u_{ij} denotes an experimental unit-level random effect, assumed to be distributed $\text{NI}(0, \sigma_u^2)$.

Program

You can implement this model using the PROC GLIMMIX statements in Program 12.8.

Program 12.8

```
proc glimmix data=bib_counts method=laplace;
 class block trt;
 model count=trt/d=poi;
 random intercept trt / subject=block;
 covtest 'eu-level variance=0'. 0;
run;
```

This program is the "naive" Poisson model with three changes. First, is the addition of the unit level effect, defined in the RANDOM statement by the combination of TRT and SUBJECT=BLOCK. In other words, the treatment and block uniquely identify the experimental unit. Second, a COVTEST statement is added to obtain a likelihood-ratio test of the unit-level variance component. Given that the unit-level effect can be understood as an overdispersion parameter, think of this as a formal test of overdispersion. The third change is replacing quadrature with METHOD=LAPLACE. You need integral approximation in order to obtain the Pearson χ^2/DF overdispersion diagnostic. Adding the unit-level random effect increases the computational load on the adaptive quadrature method. If you use METHOD=QUAD, you will get a warning:

```
ERROR: Insufficient resources to determine number of quadrature points adaptively.
```

You can use the QPOINTS option with METHOD=QUAD to override the adaptive search, or you can use the less computationally demanding METHOD=LAPLACE. With these data, METHOD=LAPLACE and METHOD=QUAD(FASTQUAD QPOINTS=3) yield identical Pearson Chi-Square values.

Results

Output 12.8 shows selected results obtained from the LAPLACE approximation.

Output 12.8: Overdispersion Diagnostic and Test of Unit-Level Variance for Poisson-normal GLMM

Fit Statistics for Conditional Distribution	
-2 log L(count | r. effects)	120.54
Pearson Chi-Square	4.53
Pearson Chi-Square / DF	0.16

Covariance Parameter Estimates			
Cov Parm	Subject	Estimate	Standard Error
Intercept	block	0.1857	0.2352
trt	block	0.6937	0.2685

Tests of Covariance Parameters Based on the Likelihood					
Label	DF	-2 Log Like	ChiSq	Pr > ChiSq	Note
eu-level variance=0	1	328.83	119.85	<.0001	MI

The overdispersion statistic, $\chi^2/DF = 0.16$, is a typical value for a Poisson-normal GLMM. Hence, there is no evidence of overdispersion with this model. The variance component estimates are $\hat{\sigma}_b^2 = 0.19$ for blocks and $\hat{\sigma}_u^2 = 0.69$ at the experimental unit level. These are estimates of variability on the link—i.e. $\log-$scale. The likelihood ratio statistics for the test of $H_0 : \sigma_u^2 = 0$ is 119.85 with $p < 0.0001$, strong evidence confirming the need for the unit-level effect in the model to account for overdispersion.

Analysis of Treatment Effects and Additional Post-Processing Using CONTRAST and LSMESTIMATE Statements

Having determined the terms needed in the linear predictor to fully account for overdispersion, continue with the analysis of treatment effects. As in the binomial example in Section 11.5, we switch from integral approximation, which is required for overdispersion diagnostics and covariance parameter testing, to pseudo-likelihood, which Stroup (2013), Couton and Stroup (2013) and Stroup and Claassen (2018) have shown to provide more accurate confidence interval coverage and more effective Type I error control for experiments with characteristics in common with this example. In particular, Stroup and Claassen show that if the mean counts are such that the normal approximation to the Poisson holds for the distribution of the observations given the random effects, the PROC GLIMMIX pseudo-likelihood default provides more accurate Type I error control and confidence interval coverage than the LAPLACE or QUADRATURE methods.

In addition to the basic analysis obtained from the MODEL and LSMEANS statements, you will probably want to ask more probing questions. As with other models discussed in this book, you can use statements such as CONTRAST and LSMESTIMATE to test more specific hypotheses or obtain more specific estimates. The following is an illustration.

Suppose that the treatments are divided into three groups. Treatments 1 and 2 form Group 1, treatments 3, 4 and 5 form Group 2, and treatments 6 and 7 form Group 3. The researchers want to know if there is a difference in the expected counts within each group, and, if not, they want to estimate the expected count for each group and the difference in expected counts between groups.

Program

The statements shown in Program 12.9 can be added to the PROC GLIMMIX program above to address these objectives.

Program 12.9

```
proc glimmix data=bib_counts;
 class trt block;
 model count = trt / dist=poisson ddfm=kr2;
 random intercept trt / subject=block;
 lsmeans trt / ilink cl;
 contrast 'within g1' trt 1 -1 0 0 0 0 0;
 contrast 'within g2' trt 0 0 1 -1 0 0 0, trt 0 0 1 0 -1 0 0;
 contrast 'within g3' trt 0 0 0 0 0 1 -1;
 lsmestimate trt 'g1 mean' 1 1 0 0 0 0 0,
                 'g2 mean' 0 0 1 1 1 0 0,
                 'g3 mean' 0 0 0 0 0 1 1,
                 'g1 v g2'  3 3 -2 -2 -2 0 0,
                 'g2 v g3'  0 0 2 2 2 -3 -3,
                 'g1 v g3'  1 1 0 0 0 -1 -1 / divisor=2,3,2,6,6,2 exp;
run;
```

The MODEL and LSMEANS statements cause the GLIMMIX procedure to compute an F value for the overall test of treatment effect, and model and data scale treatment mean estimates, standard errors and 95% confidence limits. The MODEL statement includes the DDFM=KR2 option. Although, strictly speaking, the supporting theory for the Kenward-Roger correction assumes a linear mixed model with all distributions Gaussian, KR2 has been found to be accurate when pseudo-likelihood is the recommended method, as is the case here. The CONTRAST statements obtain F values and associated p-values to test within group differences. Notice that Group 2 requires a 2 df test statistic because it has three treatments. The first three components of the LSMESTIMATE statement obtain means on the model scale for the three treatment groups. The next three elements define differences between each pair of groups. The divisors are required to fully specify the required coefficients for each estimate. For example, denote the model-scale least squares mean for the ith treatment as $\eta_i = \eta + \tau_i$. Then the Group 2 mean is $(1/3)(\eta_3 + \eta_4 + \eta_5)$. The EXP option converts the model scale estimates to data scale. For means, note that EXP is the inverse link function. For example, the data scale estimate for Group 2 is $\exp[(1/3)(\eta_3 + \eta_4 + \eta_5)]$. For differences, note that applying EXP converts differences to ratios. For example, let η_{G1} denote the model scale least squares mean for Group 1, i.e. $\eta_{G1} = (1/2)(\eta_1 + \eta_2)$, and η_{G2} denote the model scale least squares mean for Group 2 as defined above. Then $\exp(\eta_{G1} - \eta_{G2}) = \lambda_{G1}/\lambda_{G2}$, the ratio of the expected counts for the two groups.

Results

The results appear in Output 12.9.

Output 12.9: Selected Results for Analysis of Incomplete Block Design with Poisson-normal GLMM

	Type III Tests of Fixed Effects			
Effect	Num DF	Den DF	F Value	Pr > F
trt	6	16.63	1.24	0.3357

	Contrasts			
Label	Num DF	Den DF	F Value	Pr > F
within g1	1	14.68	0.00	0.9612
within g2	2	16.33	0.14	0.8674
within g3	1	18.71	0.05	0.8319

											Standard		
											Error	Lower	Upper
trt	Estimate	Standard Error	DF	t Value	Pr > |t|	Alpha	Lower	Upper	Mean		Mean	Mean	Mean
1	3.0398	0.5626	17.43	5.40	<.0001	0.05	1.8551	4.2245	20.9013		11.7585	6.3924	68.3412
2	3.0022	0.5636	17.47	5.33	<.0001	0.05	1.8155	4.1888	20.1292		11.3447	6.1442	65.9458
3	2.4246	0.5748	18.94	4.22	0.0005	0.05	1.2213	3.6279	11.2978		6.4937	3.3917	37.6334
4	2.2608	0.5806	19.54	3.89	0.0009	0.05	1.0480	3.4736	9.5907		5.5679	2.8518	32.2536
5	2.6739	0.5666	18.07	4.72	0.0002	0.05	1.4840	3.8638	14.4964		8.2130	4.4104	47.6481
6	1.6185	0.5885	20.82	2.75	0.0121	0.05	0.3940	2.8429	5.0453		2.9690	1.4830	17.1653
7	1.4443	0.6060	21	2.38	0.0267	0.05	0.1841	2.7045	4.2388		2.5686	1.2021	14.9462

trt Least Squares Means

Least Squares Means Estimates

Effect	Label	Estimate	Standard Error	DF	t Value	Pr > |t|	Exponentiated Estimate
trt	g1 mean	3.0210	0.4150	14.9	7.28	<.0001	20.5116
trt	g2 mean	2.4531	0.3550	12.2	6.91	<.0001	11.6243
trt	g3 mean	1.5314	0.4393	18.44	3.49	0.0026	4.6245
trt	g1 v g2	0.5679	0.5024	16.16	1.13	0.2748	1.7645
trt	g2 v g3	0.9217	0.5199	18.42	1.77	0.0928	2.5136
trt	g1 v g3	1.4896	0.5601	17.18	2.66	0.0164	4.4354

Interpretation

The *F* value for TRT in the table of "Type III Tests of Fixed Effects" is 1.24 with a *p*-value of 0.3357. However, this is a six degree-of-freedom test that can be partitioned into group and treatment within group components. Among group results are discussed below. Results for treatment within group appear in the table of "Contrasts." It shows all *F* values for tests of treatments within each group to be 0.14 or less. The table of "Least Squares Means" shows ESTIMATE, STANDARD ERROR, and confidence bounds on the treatment means on the model scale (that is, the log scale for this model). The estimate of expected count and standard error of expected count for each treatment and their upper and lower confidence bounds appear under MEAN, STANDARD ERROR MEAN, LOWER MEAN, and UPPER MEAN, respectively. The "Least Squares Mean Estimates" table, the column EXPONENTATED ESTIMATED shows data scale expected counts by group as 20.51, 11.62 and 4.62 for Group 1, 2 and 3, respectively. The estimated ratios of expected counts are 1.76 for Group 1 relative to Group 2, 2.51 for Group 2 relative to Group 3, and 4.44 for Group1 relative to Group 3. The *p*-values for the differences are 0.275, 0.093, and 0.016, respectively.

Alternative Post-Processing Recasting the MODEL as a Nested Design

Recall that treatments 1 and 2 form group 1; treatments 3, 4, and 5 form group 2; treatments 6 and 7 form group 3. Instead of using CONTRASTS and LSMEASTIMATE as above, you could define a new variable, GROUP, and analyze the data as a nested design with factors group and treatment within group.

Program

Use Program 12.10 to implement the analysis.

Program 12.10

```
data nested;
 set bib_counts;
  group=1+(trt>2)+(trt>5);
run;
proc glimmix data=nested;
 class block group trt;
 model count=group trt(group) / d=poi ddfm=kr2;
 random intercept trt(group) / subject=block;
```

```
lsmeans trt(group) / ilink slice=group slicediff=group;
lsmeans group / ilink diff;
run;
```

The DATA step uses indicator functions to create a new variable called GROUP. Treatments 1 and 2 are in group 1, treatments 3, 4, and 5 are in group 2, and treatments 6 and 7 are in group 3. The unit-level effect is now defined in the RANDOM statement by TRT(GROUP) in conjunction with SUBJECT=BLOCK.

Results

Output 12.10 shows selected results.

Output 12.10: Analysis of Incomplete Block Design, Poisson-normal GLMM with Nested Model Effects

	Type III Tests of Fixed Effects			
Effect	Num DF	Den DF	F Value	Pr > F
group	2	17.19	3.59	0.0499
trt(group)	4	16.4	0.08	0.9865

	Tests of Effect Slices for trt(group) Sliced By group			
group	Num DF	Den DF	F Value	Pr > F
1	1	14.68	0.00	0.9612
2	2	16.33	0.14	0.8674
3	1	18.71	0.05	0.8319

Simple Effect Comparisons of trt(group) Least Squares Means By group							
Simple Effect Level	trt	_trt	Estimate	Standard Error	DF	t Value	Pr > |t|
group 1	1	2	0.03764	0.7612	14.68	0.05	0.9612
group 2	3	4	0.1638	0.7901	17.01	0.21	0.8382
group 2	3	5	-0.2493	0.7751	15.88	-0.32	0.7519
group 2	4	5	-0.4131	0.7786	16.16	-0.53	0.6029
group 3	6	7	0.1742	0.8093	18.71	0.22	0.8319

group Least Squares Means							
group	Estimate	Standard Error	DF	t Value	Pr > |t|	Mean	Standard Error Mean
1	3.0210	0.4150	14.9	7.28	<.0001	20.5116	8.5119
2	2.4531	0.3550	12.2	6.91	<.0001	11.6243	4.1261
3	1.5314	0.4393	18.44	3.49	0.0026	4.6245	2.0317

	Differences of group Least Squares Means					
group	_group	Estimate	Standard Error	DF	t Value	Pr > |t|
1	2	0.5679	0.5024	16.16	1.13	0.2748
1	3	1.4896	0.5601	17.18	2.66	0.0164
2	3	0.9217	0.5199	18.42	1.77	0.0928

Interpretation

The "Type III Tests of Fixed Effects" partitions the overall treatment effects into GROUP and TRT within GROUP effects, providing no evidence of differences among treatment means within groups ($F = 0.08$) but evidence of a GROUP effect ($F = 3.59$, $p = 0.0499$). The "Test of Effect Slices" table duplicates the "within g1," "within g2" and "within g3" CONTRAST results in Output 12.9. The "Simple Effect Comparisons" table provides additional information about treatment differences within each group. The "group Least Squares Means" and "Differences" tables provide the same information as the "Least Squares Mean Estimates" table in Output 12.9. Notice that the table of differences only gives the model scale estimates. For example,

$$\hat{\alpha}_1 - \hat{\alpha}_2 + \overline{\tau(\alpha)}_{1\bullet} - \overline{\tau(\alpha)}_{2\bullet} = \hat{\eta}_{G1} - \hat{\eta}_{G2} = 0.57$$

for the group-1-versus-group-2 difference. If you want differences on the data scale, for example $\exp(\eta_{G1} - \eta_{G2}) = \lambda_{G1}/\lambda_{G2}$, you must use LSMESTIMATE or ESTIMATE statements with the EXP option.

12.5.3 Negative Binomial GLMM

An alternative model to account for experimental unit-level uniqueness and thus address the overdispersion of the "naive" Poisson model is to assume that the conditional distribution of the observations given the block effects is negative binomial. Fully specified, the required elements of the model are as follows:

- $y_{ij} \mid b_j \sim$ Negative Binomial$\left(\lambda_{ij}, \phi\right)$.

- $b_j \sim NI\left(0, \sigma_b^2\right)$.

- $\eta_{ij} = \log\left(\lambda_{ij}\right) = \eta + \tau_i + b_j$.

Using the group and treatment-within-group approach, you can rewrite the conditional distribution and linear predictor as follows:

- $y_{ijk} \mid b_j \sim$ Negative Binomial$\left(\lambda_{ijk}, \phi\right)$.

- $\eta_{ijk} = \log\left(\lambda_{ijk}\right) = \eta + \alpha_i + \tau(\alpha)_{ij} + b_k$.

Here, y_{ijk} denotes the observation in block k on the jth treatment within group i, α_i denotes the effect of group i, and $\tau(\alpha)_{ij}$ denotes the treatment within group effect.

As with the Poisson-normal model, implement the negative binomial analysis in two steps. First, compute overdispersion diagnostics using integral approximation. Then compute model and post-processing statistics using pseudo-likelihood.

Program

Use Program 12.11 for the first step.

Program 12.11

```
proc glimmix data=bib_counts method=quad;
 class block trt;
 model count=trt/d=negbin;
 random intercept / subject=block;
 covtest 'NB Scale=0?' . 0;
run;
```

The COVTEST statement is intended to test $H_0 : \phi = 0$, the motivation being that the negative binomial variance is $\lambda + \phi \lambda^2$ but if $\phi = 0$ then the variance reduces to λ, the variance of a Poisson random variable. Think of this as a test of "Poisson-ness." Unfortunately, as we see in the results, it is not a viable test.

Results

Results appear in Output 12.11.

Output 12.11: Overdispersion Diagnostics and COVTEST Result for Balanced Incomplete Block Negative Binomial GLMM

Fit Statistics for Conditional Distribution	
-2 log L(count | r. effects)	202.69
Pearson Chi-Square	19.80
Pearson Chi-Square / DF	0.71

Covariance Parameter Estimates			
Cov Parm	Subject	Estimate	Standard Error
Intercept	block	0.06125	0.1867
Scale		0.6330	0.2228

Tests of Covariance Parameters Based on the Likelihood					
Label	DF	-2 Log Like	ChiSq	Pr > ChiSq	Note
NB Scale=0	1	5.6E21	5.6E21	<.0001	MI

Interpretation

The overdispersion diagnostic, Pearson χ^2/DF =0.71, a value one would expect for a negative binomial GLMM with no evidence of overdispersion. The variance component estimates are $\hat{\sigma}_b^2 = 0.06$ and $\hat{\phi} = 0.63$. The block variance has the same interpretation as the block variance in the Poisson-normal GLMM, of the observations given blocks. The "Pr>ChiSq" in the "Tests of Covariance Parameters" table makes it appear that we can reject $H_0 : \phi = 0$, and conclude that $\phi > 0$. However, the likelihood ratio χ^2 and "–2 Log Like" are both 5.6E21. Interpret this as machine language for "cannot divide by zero." The problem is that the log likelihood for the negative binomial contains a term $1/\phi$, which is undefined if $\phi = 0$. Although a likelihood ratio test of ϕ is not possible, the fact that the Poisson model with the same linear predictor, the "naive" Poisson model in Program 12.7, showed strong evidence of overdispersion provides circumstantial evidence the ϕ must be >0. Either the Poisson-normal model with the unit-level effect or the negative binomial model with ϕ accounting for the unit-level effect, are logical candidates for an appropriate analysis of these data.

Program

Use Program 12.12 to complete the analysis.

Program 12.12

```
proc glimmix data=nested;
 class block group trt;
 model count=group trt(group) / d=negbin ddfm=kr2;
 random intercept / subject=block;
 lsmeans trt(group) / ilink slice=group slicediff=group;
 lsmeans group / ilink diff;
run;
```

Aside from specifying the negative binomial instead of the Poisson distribution and removing the unit-level random effect—TRT(GROUP)—from the RANDOM statement, this program's statements are identical to Program 12.10. When you run the program, the listing will say "did not converge." The iteration history shows why:

Iteration History					
Iteration	Restarts	Subiterations	Objective Function	Change	Max Gradient
0	0	7	76.395429955	0.99128279	7.609E-7
		...			
18	0	0	65.630732702	0.00000110	1.704E-6
19	0	0	65.630732791	0.00000041	2.078E-6

The column headed *Change* gives the progress of the convergence criterion. The default criterion for convergence is 10^{-8}. The default limit on the number of iterations is 20. On the last iteration, "Change" is close, but not quite there. You can also see from previous iteration that the procedure is making progress. Add the statement NLOPTIONS MAXITER=25 after the LSMEANS statement. This allows additional iterations. The procedure converges in 23 iterations. As a practical matter, there is no harm in setting MAXITER greater than 25. Regardless of whether you set MAXITER=25 or MAXITER=50 or MAXITER=1000, the procedure converges in 23 iterations.

Results

Results for the analysis appear in Output 12.12.

Output 12.12: Selected Results for Analysis of Balanced Incomplete Block Negative Binomial GLMM

Type III Tests of Fixed Effects				
Effect	Num DF	Den DF	F Value	Pr > F
group	2	18.58	6.39	0.0077
trt(group)	4	18.13	0.11	0.9765

trt(group) Least Squares Means								
group	trt	Estimate	Standard Error	DF	t Value	Pr > |t|	Mean	Standard Error Mean
1	1	3.3262	0.4603	19.08	7.23	<.0001	27.8312	12.8103
1	2	3.2931	0.4595	18.94	7.17	<.0001	26.9270	12.3726
2	3	2.6908	0.4704	20.9	5.72	<.0001	14.7434	6.9346
2	4	2.6190	0.4708	21	5.56	<.0001	13.7220	6.4606
2	5	2.9367	0.4653	19.97	6.31	<.0001	18.8542	8.7733
3	6	1.8205	0.4871	21	3.74	0.0012	6.1752	3.0079
3	7	1.5382	0.5076	21	3.03	0.0064	4.6563	2.3636

Tests of Effect Slices for trt(group) Sliced By group				
group	Num DF	Den DF	F Value	Pr > F
1	1	16.01	0.00	0.9584
2	2	17.51	0.14	0.8722
3	1	21	0.17	0.6810

Simple Effect Comparisons of trt(group) Least Squares Means By group							
Simple Effect Level	trt	_trt	Estimate	Standard Error	DF	t Value	Pr > |t|
group 1	1	2	0.03303	0.6238	16.01	0.05	0.9584
group 2	3	4	0.07180	0.6401	17.87	0.11	0.9119
group 2	3	5	-0.2459	0.6362	17.35	-0.39	0.7038
group 2	4	5	-0.3177	0.6359	17.33	-0.50	0.6236
group 3	6	7	0.2823	0.6771	21	0.42	0.6810

group Least Squares Means							
group	Estimate	Standard Error	DF	t Value	Pr > |t|	Mean	Standard Error Mean
1	3.3096	0.3379	15.87	9.79	<.0001	27.3754	9.2513
2	2.7488	0.2905	12.63	9.46	<.0001	15.6246	4.5390
3	1.6794	0.3645	21	4.61	0.0002	5.3622	1.9543

Differences of group Least Squares Means						
group	_group	Estimate	Standard Error	DF	t Value	Pr > |t|
1	2	0.5608	0.4061	16.54	1.38	0.1856
1	3	1.6303	0.4610	19.19	3.54	0.0022
2	3	1.0695	0.4287	20.79	2.49	0.0211

Interpretation

The *F* values for GROUP and TRT(GROUP) in the "Type III Tests of Fixed Effects" table are 6.39 and 0.11, respectively. For the Poisson-normal model these were 3.59 and 0.08. The data scale means for each treatment, which appear as TRT(GROUP) combinations in the "Least Squares Means" table, range from 4.7 to 27.8, compared with a range of 4.2 to 20.9 for the Poisson-normal model. This is typical. Recall from Figure 11.1 and the associated discussion in Section 11.4, that data arise from processes characterized by two distributions: $f(\mathbf{y} \mid \mathbf{u})$, the conditional distribution of the observations given the random effects, and $f(\mathbf{u})$ the distribution of the random effects. For count data, Poisson-normal models target the median of the marginal distribution $f(\mathbf{y}) = \int f(\mathbf{y} \mid \mathbf{u}) f(\mathbf{u}) d\mathbf{u}$, marginal models target the mean of the marginal distribution, and the negative binomial targets somewhere in between. If $f(\mathbf{y} \mid \mathbf{u}) \sim$ Negative Binomial(λ, ϕ) reasonable approximates the process giving rise to the data, the negative binomial model will target λ; the median of the marginal distribution will be less than λ and the marginal mean will be greater than λ. If the distribution giving rise to the data is approximately negative binomial, then the estimates in Output 12.12 are accurate estimates of the λ_{ij} for each treatment within group combination and the data scale values in Output 12.10 are underestimates of λ_{ij}. On the other hand, if the process giving rise to the data is better approximated by $f(\mathbf{y} \mid \mathbf{u}) \sim$ Poisson(λ) then the Poisson-normal model accurately estimates the λ_{ij} and the negative binomial model gives overestimates.

Because the underlying treatment effects, when they are different, are more spread out with the negative binomial model, the tests of treatment differences tend to have greater power, increasing their apparent significance. This is not in itself a justification for choosing the negative binomial model. It simply follows from the distribution characteristics discussed above.

Other results in Output 12.12, slices and simple effects, have similar interpretation to their analogs in Output 12.10.

12.5.4 Poisson or Negative Binomial GLMM: Model Selection

As you can see, depending on whether you use the Poisson-normal or negative binomial GLMM, results change. These changes have the potential to affect conclusions and alter decisions made based on the results of the analysis. Therefore, choosing between the Poisson-normal and the negative binomial GLMM is a consequential decision.

Unfortunately, this is an area of GLMM theory that is currently underdeveloped. What we do know is primarily what does *not* reliably distinguish between the two models. For example, a common strategy to assess competing Gaussian models is to plot predicted versus observed values. You can do this with either the Poisson-normal or negative binomial GLMM by adding the following statements after the post-processing statements, e.g. the CONTRAST and LSMESTIMATE statements in the examples above:

```
 output out=pred_values predicted(ilink)=count_hat;
run;
proc gplot data=pred_values;
 plot count_hat*count;
run;
```

The OUTPUT statement creates a new SAS data set with the original data—specifically the response variable COUNT—and creates a new variable whose name is whatever follows PREDICTED(ILINK)=`variable_name`. In this case the variable name is COUNT_HAT. By default, PROC GLIMMIX computes the predicted value on the model scale; use the option (ILINK) to compute it on the data scale to make the comparison with COUNT meaningful. Whatever follows OUT= is the name of the new data set. If you are creating data sets for the Poisson-normal and negative binomial, you could give the predicted values different names for each model. In the plots shown below, the predicted values are named PN_HAT and NB_HAT, respectively. Figure 12.2 shows the resulting plots.

Figure 12.2: Plots of Predicted versus Observed Counts for Two GLMMs

A. Poisson-normal GLMM

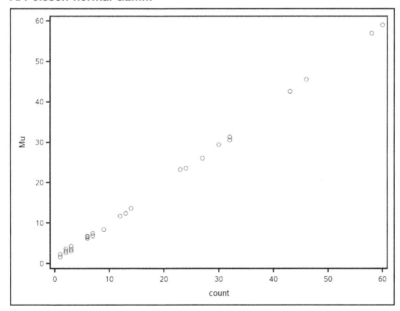

B. Negative Binomial GLMM

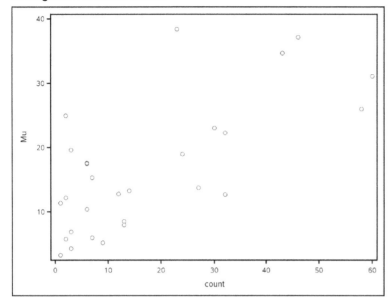

Inspecting the plots, the Poisson-normal GLMM shows an apparently better fit. In truth, the data for this example were simulated using a negative binomial GLMM. This is not a cherry-picked example: the plots above are typical for simulated negative binomial data from a blocked design. The plots are misleading because the predicted values for the Poisson-normal model are computed from a linear predictor that includes a unit-level effect, u_{ij} whereas the linear predictor for the negative binomial GLMM only has treatment and block effects. A tempting alternative is to compute predicted values for the Poisson-normal as $\hat{\eta} + \hat{\tau}_i + \hat{b}_j$, the same expression used to compute negative binomial predicted values. The authors have tried this and the results are, at best, ambiguous. Other common methods of model selection, e.g. fit statistics, produce similarly ambiguous results.

Given the above, we can summarize the state of the art as follows. First, we know that both the Poisson-normal and negative binomial GLMM provide results that are demonstrably more accurate that their pre-GLMM counterparts, the normal approximation to the Poisson and the variance stabilizing transformation. Second, we do not have reliable diagnostics to distinguish, based on the data, between the Poisson-normal and the negative binomial GLMM. Third, the Poisson-normal and negative binomial produce different results, so selecting which model to use is a consequential decision.

What is a data analyst to do? At this point, our advice is to choose between these two models using subject matter knowledge combined with an understanding of the assumptions underlying the Poisson and negative binomial processes giving rise to the data. The Poisson assumes completely random arrival, with new arrivals independent of the past. The negative binomial assumes aggregation, with the distribution of new arrivals conditional on past arrivals. If subject matter knowledge suggests complete independence, use the Poisson. If subject matter knowledge suggests aggregation—as is typical of *most* biological count data—use the negative binomial.

12.5.5 Marginal Model for Count Data in a Blocked Design

The Poisson-normal and negative binomial GLMMs discussed above are both conditional GLMMs. They are used for broad inference, i.e. inference that is applicable to the entire population of interest, when the focus is on expected counts for a *typical member of the population*. In some cases, interest is on the expected count averaged over all members of the population—that is, the mean of the marginal distribution of the observations. Often, inference focuses on the marginal mean because the primary objective is to estimate the total count in the population. Conditional broad inference targets a typical member; marginal inference targets the entire population. Put another way, a farmer may want to know, "how many damaged plants can I expect if I use this product?" A policy maker wants to know, "how many damaged plants statewide do we need to anticipate in our plans?" The farmer wants broad space conditional inference; the policy maker wants marginal broad inference.

We know that fitting the Gaussian linear mixed model to COUNT provides unbiased estimates of the marginal treatment mean counts, but it does not take into account the variance structure of counting distributions. If the primary objective of a study calls for marginal inference, use a marginal GLMM based on the Poisson distribution. Using the nested model with group and treatment within group introduced at the end of Section 12.5.2, the required elements of this model are as follows:

- Linear Predictor: $\log(\mu_{ij}) = \mu + \alpha_i + \tau(\alpha)_{ij}$.

- Quasi-distribution of the observations: $y_{ijk} \sim quasi - Poisson(\mu_{ij}, \varphi_W, \sigma_W)$, where μ_{ij} denotes the marginal mean count, φ_W denotes the working scale parameter, and σ_W denotes the working covariance.

- Working Covariance: let $\mathbf{y}_k$ denote the vector of observations in the kth block, then $E(y_{ij}) = \mu_{ij}$, where A is a diagonal matrix whose i^{th} diagonal component is the variance function μ_{ij}, and the definition is as follows:

$$
\mathbf{R} = \begin{bmatrix}
\varphi_W + \sigma_W & \sigma_W & \sigma_W & \sigma_W \\
\sigma_W & \varphi_W + \sigma_W & \sigma_W & \sigma_W \\
\sigma_W & \sigma_W & \varphi_W + \sigma_W & \sigma_W \\
\sigma_W & \sigma_W & \sigma_W & \varphi_W + \sigma_W
\end{bmatrix}
$$

Program

Implement this model by using Program 12.13.

Program 12.13

```
proc glimmix data=nested;
 class block group trt;
 model count=group trt(group) / d=poi ddfm=kr2;
 random trt / subject=block type=cs residual;
 lsmeans trt(group)/ilink slice=group slicediff=group;
 lsmeans group / ilink diff;
run;
```

Except for the RANDOM statement, this program is identical to the program used for the Poisson-normal GLMM. The RANDOM statement defines the compound symmetry—also called exchangeable—working covariance structure. Alternatively, you could write the RANDOM statement as RANDOM _RESIDUAL_ / SUBJECT=BLOCK TYPE=CS.

Results

Selected results appear in Output 12.13.

Output 12.13: Selected Results from Marginal GLMM for Count Data with Blocked Design

Fit Statistics	
-2 Res Log Pseudo-Likelihood	66.94
Generalized Chi-Square	239.23
Gener. Chi-Square / DF	11.39

Covariance Parameter Estimates			
Cov Parm	Subject	Estimate	Standard Error
CS	block	1.8803	3.1942
Residual		11.3920	4.1598

Type III Tests of Fixed Effects				
Effect	Num DF	Den DF	F Value	Pr > F
group	2	18.95	4.13	0.0324
trt(group)	4	17.62	0.15	0.9583

trt(group) Least Squares Means

group	trt	Estimate	Standard Error	DF	t Value	Pr > |t|	Mean	Standard Error Mean
1	1	3.3699	0.3445	20.99	9.78	<.0001	29.0756	10.0164
1	2	3.3837	0.3421	20.99	9.89	<.0001	29.4784	10.0856
2	3	2.7691	0.4652	20.99	5.95	<.0001	15.9450	7.4176
2	4	2.6300	0.4987	20.99	5.27	<.0001	13.8743	6.9192
2	5	3.0762	0.3990	20.99	7.71	<.0001	21.6753	8.6483
3	6	1.8548	0.7348	20.99	2.52	0.0197	6.3901	4.6957
3	7	1.6448	0.8162	20.99	2.02	0.0569	5.1800	4.2278

Tests of Effect Slices for trt(group) Sliced By group

group	Num DF	Den DF	F Value	Pr > F
1	1	17.57	0.00	0.9770
2	2	17.65	0.29	0.7521
3	1	17.6	0.04	0.8458

Simple Effect Comparisons of trt(group) Least Squares Means By group

Simple Effect Level	trt	_trt	Estimate	Standard Error	DF	t Value	Pr > |t|
group 1	1	2	-0.01376	0.4703	17.57	-0.03	0.9770
group 2	3	4	0.1391	0.6607	17.58	0.21	0.8357
group 2	3	5	-0.3070	0.5939	17.64	-0.52	0.6116
group 2	4	5	-0.4461	0.6191	17.72	-0.72	0.4806
group 3	6	7	0.2099	1.0640	17.6	0.20	0.8458

group Least Squares Means

group	Estimate	Standard Error	DF	t Value	Pr > |t|	Mean	Standard Error Mean
1	3.3768	0.2501	17.92	13.50	<.0001	29.2763	7.3232
2	2.8251	0.2790	13.44	10.13	<.0001	16.8630	4.7043
3	1.7498	0.5657	17.95	3.09	0.0063	5.7533	3.2548

Differences of group Least Squares Means

group	_group	Estimate	Standard Error	DF	t Value	Pr > |t|
1	2	0.5517	0.3481	18.17	1.58	0.1302
1	3	1.6270	0.5914	20.24	2.75	0.0122
2	3	1.0753	0.5953	19.2	1.81	0.0866

Interpretation

In the "Fit Statistics" table, notice that the results are based on a *pseudo-likelihood*, not a true likelihood. This means that statistics that require a true likelihood, e.g. likelihood ratio χ^2 statistics and information criteria, are undefined in the context of marginal models. Also notice that the generalized χ^2/DF equals 11.39. In the context of a conditional GLMM—i.e. one with no working covariance structure—this could suggest lack of fit of the model, possibly from overdispersion. This is *not* an appropriate interpretation in the context of a marginal model. In the context of the linear mixed pseudo-model, the generalized χ^2/DF is an estimate of the working scale parameter. Period. The "Covariance Parameter Estimates" table gives the estimates of working covariance and working scale. The working covariance estimate in the row labeled BLOCK is $\hat{\sigma}_W = 1.88$. The working scale parameter in the row labeled RESIDUAL is $\hat{\phi}_W = 11.39$. To repeat, the working scale parameter is estimated by generalized χ^2/DF.

Read and interpret the remaining results the same way that you read and interpret results for the previous models discussed in this section. Notice that the MEAN estimates range from 5.1 to 29.5. As expected, they are greater than the data scale estimates from the Poisson-normal and negative binomial models, because the marginal means are shifted to the right relative to the conditional λ_{ij}. Although not identical to the results for the Gaussian mixed model fit to COUNT, the $\hat{\mu}_{ij}$ are very close. They differ slightly because their estimates depend on the estimated working covariance matrix. However, their target is the same: the mean of the marginal distribution of y.

12.5.6 A Warning Regarding Blocks Effects Fixed or Random

Chapter 2 contains this book's first discussion of the characteristics and tradeoffs between fixed-block-effect and random-block-effect models. In a Gaussian mixed model for a blocked design, defining block effects fixed results in intra-block analysis, and defining block effects are random results in combined inter- and intra-block analysis. For testing treatment effects, while the combined analysis is somewhat more efficient, unless the blocked design is highly unbalanced, the results of the intra-block and combined analysis are usually similar.

> **Warning**: What happens with mixed models for Gaussian data does *not* happen with count data. The GLMM analog to intra-block analysis typically results in inflated F values and hence loss of Type I error control.

For example, you can obtain the intra-block analysis in this example using the following statements:

```
proc glimmix data=bib_counts method=quad;
 class block trt;
 model count=block trt/d=negbin;
run;
```

For testing treatment effects, this produces the result shown in Output 12.14.

Output 12.14: Test of Treatment Effect for Fixed Block Negative Binomial GLMM

	Type III Tests of Fixed Effects			
Effect	Num DF	Den DF	F Value	Pr > F
block	6	15	2.32	0.0873
trt	6	15	3.22	0.0308

The *p*-value for treatment with the combined inter- intra-block (random block effect) analysis shown in Section 12.5.4 was 0.0878. Here it is 0.0308. You would reject the hypothesis of equal treatment means under the intra-block analysis, whereas the combined analysis leads to a more guarded conclusion. This is a typical result. Early work on negative binomial GLMs, done with PROC GENMOD, which lacks a RANDOM effect capability, found that the negative binomial GLM for blocked data produced inflated Type I error rates. What they actually were observing was the tendency of intra-block analysis to inflate Type I error rates with non-Gaussian GLMMs. Type I error rate inflation disappears when you use the combined inter- and intra-block (random block effect) analysis.

12.6 Example 3: Linear Regression with a Discrete Count Dependent Variable

Section 12.2.3 describes a study to estimate the effect of varying amounts of a finishing treatment, denoted by X, ranging from X=0 to X=10. Data are obtained from a random sample of eight lots. Each lot is partitioned so that an observation at each level of X is obtained. The response, i.e. the dependent variable, is the number of aberrant micro-sites in the finished product. The researchers want to fit a regression model that enables them to predict the effect of finishing treatment on the number of aberrant micro-sites and, if possible, to determine what level of finishing treatment is required to ensure that the expected number of aberrant micro-sites is less than 10. This section presents the essential steps in addressing the researchers' objective. Section 12.6.1 shows the Poisson GLMM based on the standard random coefficient linear regression model. This model is often called the "naive" model because it is particularly vulnerable to overdispersion. Sections 12.6.2 and 12.6.3 present modified models to address overdispersion. Section 12.6.2 presents the standard conditional GLMM using the negative binomial. Section 12.6.3 presents the standard marginal model that accounts for overdispersion.

12.6.1 Naive GLMM with Overdispersion

As given in Section 12.2.2, given the study's design and its objectives, a random coefficient Poisson-based linear regression model seems an appropriate place to start. The required elements of the model are as follows:

- Linear predictor: $\eta_{ij} = \beta_0 + b_{0i} + (\beta_1 + b_{1i})X_j$, where the terms are defined as follows:

  - η_{ij} denotes $\log(\lambda_{ij})$ and λ_{ij} denotes the expected count of the ith lot at the jth finishing treatment level.

  - β_0 denotes the intercept.

  - β_{0i} denotes the effect of the ith lot on the intercept.

  - β_1 denotes the slope.

  - b_{1i} denotes the effect of the ith lot on the slope.

- Link function: $\eta_{ij} = \log(\lambda_{ij})$.

- Distributions, as follows:

  - $y_{ij} \mid b_{0i}, b_{1i} \sim \text{Poisson}(\lambda_{ij})$.

  - $b_{0i} \sim \text{NI}(0, \sigma_0^2)$.

  - $b_{1i} \sim \text{NI}(0, \sigma_1^2)$.

Notice that this model accounts for variability that is attributable to lots and to finishing treatment levels, but it does not account for variability that is attributable to uniqueness at the unit-of-observation level. Therefore, a reasonable first step is to fit this model, obtain the resulting Pearson χ^2/DF and see if it suggests overdispersion.

Program

Do so by using the PROC GLIMMIX statements in Program 12.14.

Program 12.14

```
proc glimmix data=rcr_counts method=quadrature;
  class lot;
  model count=x/solution d=poi;
  random intercept x / subject=lot;
run;
```

Notice that you must use either METHOD=QUADRATURE or LAPLACE to get the Pearson χ^2/DF overdispersion diagnostic.

Results

Relevant results are given in Output 12.15.

Output 12.15: Selected Results from Naive Poisson Random Coefficient Regression Model

Model Information	
Data Set	WORK.RCR_COUNTS
Response Variable	count
Response Distribution	Poisson
Link Function	Log
Variance Function	Default
Variance Matrix Blocked By	lot
Estimation Technique	Maximum Likelihood
Likelihood Approximation	Gauss-Hermite Quadrature
Degrees of Freedom Method	Containment

Optimization Information	
Optimization Technique	Dual Quasi-Newton
Parameters in Optimization	4
Lower Boundaries	2
Upper Boundaries	0
Fixed Effects	Not Profiled
Starting From	GLM estimates
Quadrature Points	1

Fit Statistics for Conditional Distribution	
-2 log L(count | r. effects)	464.56
Pearson Chi-Square	250.66
Pearson Chi-Square / DF	5.22

Interpretation

The "Model Information" table confirms that you are fitting a GLMM assuming the Poisson distribution and that the Gauss-Hermite estimation method is being used. The "Optimization Information" tells you how many quadrature points the Gauss-Hermite procedure used—in this case one. The Gauss-Hermite integral approximation with one quadrature point is equivalent to the LAPLACE approximation, which tells you that you could get identical results for this analysis using METHOD=LAPLACE. Finally, the crucial result from the "Fit Statistics for Conditional Distribution," the Pearson χ^2/DF is 5.22. This is strong evidence of overdispersion, confirming that this is a "naive" model: either the model fails to account for unit-of-observation level uniqueness or there is substantial departure from linear regression in the linear predictor.

Figure 12.3 shows a plot of the log mean counts by X, along with the 95% confidence bound.

Figure 12.3: Plot of Log Mean Counts by *X*, with Estimated Linear Regression and Confidence Bounds

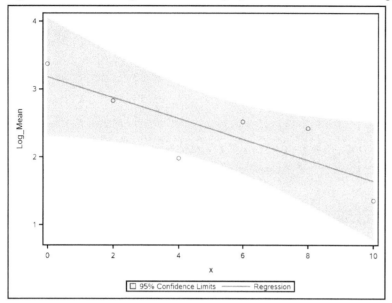

You can see that, with the exception of a possible outlying mean at $X = 4$, linear regression provides a visually reasonable fit. Therefore, we turn our attention to modifying the model to account for variation attributable to unit-level uniqueness.

12.6.2 Conditional GLMMs that Account for Overdispersion

The analysis in this section assumes that our target of inference is the broad inference space estimate of the expected count of the distribution of the observations for a typical lot. From Section 12.3.3, we know that there are two ways to do this that use distributions supported by the GLIMMIX procedure: the Poisson-normal model and the negative binomial, a.k.a. Poisson-gamma, model.

Program

Program 12.15 gives the PROC GLIMMIX statements for each model.

Program 12.15

```
/* GLIMMIX statements for Poisson-Normal GLMM */
proc glimmix data=rcr_counts method=quad(fastquad qpoints=5);
  class lot obs_id;
  model count=x/solution d=poi;
  random intercept x obs_id/ subject=lot;
  estimate 'x=0'  intercept 1 x 0  / exp cl;
  estimate 'x=5'  intercept 1 x 5  / exp cl;
  estimate 'x=10' intercept 1 x 10 / exp cl;
run;

/* GLIMMIX statements for negative binomial GLMM */
proc glimmix data=rcr_counts method=laplace;
  class lot obs_id;
  model count=x/solution d=negbin;
  random intercept x / subject=lot;
  estimate 'x=0'  intercept 1 x 0  / exp cl;
  estimate 'x=5'  intercept 1 x 5  / exp cl;
  estimate 'x=10' intercept 1 x 10 / exp cl;
run;
```

The key modification in the Poisson normal model is the addition of a unit-level random effect. The modified linear predictor is $\eta_{ij} = \beta_0 + b_{0i} + (\beta_1 + b_{1i})X_j + u_{ij}$ where $u_{ij} \sim N(0, \sigma_u^2)$. To define the u_{ij} term so that PROC GLIMMIX understands it, you create a variable that uniquely identifies each observation in the data set. Here, OBS_ID serves that purpose. Define OBS_ID as a CLASS variable and include it in the random statement as shown.

Important Note: including the unit-level term in the linear predictor is likely to overwhelm the default quadrature estimation method, even for small data sets. The quickest, least computationally demanding alternative is METHOD=LAPLACE. The 14.2 release of SAS 9.4 has a FASTQUAD option to speed up the run time for METHOD=QUADRATURE. You can also specify the number of quadrature points with the QPOINTS option, so the procedure does not have to search for the optimum number. In this example, running FASTQUAD with no QPOINTS option resulted in PROC GLIMMIX selecting 5 quadrature points as the optimum.

The key features of the negative binomial are (1) change D=POI to D=NEGBIN, and (2) retain the MODEL and RANDOM statements exactly as they were in the "naive" Poisson model. Recall that the unit-level effect is embedded in the scale parameter of the negative binomial, so an additional unit-level random term would be redundant, and thus define a nonsense model.

Finally, in both programs, ESTIMATE statements to obtain the predicted counts at various levels of X are included. These address the researchers' second objective, to determine what level of X is needed to provide reasonable assurance that the number of aberrant cells will be below the maximum acceptable value of 10.

Results

Results are shown in Output 12.16.

Output 12.16: Selected Results for the Poisson-Normal Model

Fit Statistics for Conditional Distribution	
-2 log L(count | r. effects)	194.30
Pearson Chi-Square	10.00
Pearson Chi-Square / DF	0.21

Covariance Parameter Estimates			
Cov Parm	Subject	Estimate	Standard Error
Intercept	lot	0.05079	0.2794
x	lot	0.008793	0.01428
obs_id	lot	0.7209	0.2227

Solutions for Fixed Effects					
Effect	Estimate	Standard Error	DF	t Value	Pr > |t|
Intercept	2.8876	0.2506	7	11.52	<.0001
x	-0.1777	0.05441	7	-3.27	0.0138

Estimates												
Label	Estimate	Standard Error	DF	t Value	Pr > |t|	Alpha	Lower	Upper	Mean	Standard Error Mean	Lower Mean	Upper Mean
x=0	2.8876	0.2506	7	11.52	<.0001	0.05	2.2950	3.4802	17.9509	4.4987	9.9248	32.4675
x=5	1.9992	0.2353	7	8.50	<.0001	0.05	1.4429	2.5556	7.3834	1.7372	4.2328	12.8791
x=10	1.1108	0.4427	7	2.51	0.0404	0.05	0.06408	2.1576	3.0369	1.3443	1.0662	8.6502

Interpretation

The Pearson χ^2/DF = 0.21 in the "Fit Statistics for Conditional Distribution" table. This provides evidence that the Poisson-normal model has accounted for overdispersion. Users often worry that because the Pearson χ^2/DF value is substantially less than one, is this an indication of *under*-dispersion? It is not: simulations repeatedly show that if you generate Poisson-normal data and then fit the same Poisson-normal model used to generate the data, Pearson χ^2/DF values typically average in the 0.20 to 0.25 range. The estimate of the unit-level variance, listed as OBS_ID in the "Covariance Parameter Estimates" table, is $\hat{\sigma}_u^2 = 0.72$. The "Solutions for Fixed Effects" table shows that the estimated fixed intercept and estimated fixed slope are 2.888 and −0.1777. The "Solutions for Fixed Effects" table gives the estimated regression equation:

$$\log\left(\hat{\lambda}\right) = 2.888 - 0.1777X$$

For a typical lot, $b_{i0} = b_{i1} = 0$, then

$$\log\left(\hat{\lambda}_{ij} \mid 0\right) = \log\left(\hat{\lambda}_{ij}\right) = 2.888 - 0.1777X_j$$

The "Estimates" table gives predicted counts on the link and data scale for selected values of X, in this case 0, 5 and 10. The columns labeled ESTIMATE, LOWER, and UPPER give the predicted value and 95% confidence bounds of the log counts. For example, for a typical lot with X=10, the predicted log count is $2.888 - 1.777 \times 10 = 1.1108$. Applying the inverse link, $\exp\left(2.888 - 0.1777X\right)$ gives the predicted count, shown in the column labeled MEAN. For $X = 10$, the predicted mean in 3.04 with confidence limits between 1.07 and 8.65. Given that the researchers want assurance that the counts will be less than 10, their focus is on the upper confidence bound. Here, the data suggest that counts decrease as the level of X increases. Values of X less than or equal to 5 clearly do not provide the needed assurance: the upper confidence limit UPPERMU is 12.88 at $X = 5$. It also appears that a value of X less than 10 would produce an acceptable result. You could add additional ESTIMATE statements to determine exactly what the cut-off value of X is. However, before we do this, we need to look at the results from the negative binomial model.

Results

Output 12.17 gives selected results from the negative binomial model.

Output 12.17: Selected Results from the Negative Binomial Random Coefficient Regression

Optimization Information	
Optimization Technique	Dual Quasi-Newton
Parameters in Optimization	5
Lower Boundaries	3
Upper Boundaries	0
Fixed Effects	Not Profiled
Starting From	GLM estimates
Quadrature Points	1

Fit Statistics for Conditional Distribution	
-2 log L(count | r. effects)	314.69
Pearson Chi-Square	32.34
Pearson Chi-Square / DF	0.67

Solutions for Fixed Effects					
Effect	Estimate	Standard Error	DF	t Value	Pr > |t|
Intercept	3.1650	0.2738	7	11.56	<.0001
x	-0.1686	0.04333	7	-3.89	0.0060

										Standard		
										Error	**Lower**	**Upper**
		Standard								**Mean**	**Mean**	**Mean**
Label	**Estimate**	**Error**	**DF**	**t Value**	**Pr > |t|**	**Alpha**	**Lower**	**Upper**	**Mean**			
x=0	3.1650	0.2738	7	11.56	<.0001	0.05	2.5175	3.8126	23.6897	6.4870	12.3979	45.2658
x=5	2.3221	0.2342	7	9.92	<.0001	0.05	1.7683	2.8758	10.1970	2.3880	5.8611	17.7404
x=10	1.4791	0.3586	7	4.12	0.0044	0.05	0.6312	2.3271	4.3892	1.5739	1.8799	10.2479

The "Optimization Information" table gives the number of required quadrature points as one, indicating that you could use either METHOD=QUAD or LAPLACE and obtain identical results. The "Fit Statistics for Conditional Distribution" gives Pearson χ^2/DF = 0.67, evidence that the negative binomial model addresses the issue of overdispersion. From the "Solutions of Fixed Effects" table, the estimated regression equation for a typical lot is

$$\log\left(\hat{\lambda}_{ij} \mid 0\right) = \log\left(\hat{\lambda}_{ij}\right) = 3.165 - 0.1686 X_j$$

or

$$\log\left(\hat{\lambda}\right) = 3.165 - 0.1686 X$$

The "Estimates" table gives the predicted values for the same three values of X used with the Poisson-normal model. The process used to obtain predictors and their confidence bounds is identical to that described above for the Poisson-normal model.

Notice that the upper confidence bound for the predicted count at $X = 10$ is now 10.25, greater than the acceptable maximum of 10. Using the negative binomial model suggests that a level of finishing treatment greater than 10 will be required to ensure that the aberrant cell count will be less than 10.

Why does the negative binomial model give predicted counts greater than the Poisson-normal model? Is this an artifact of this data set, or is there something more systematic? Stroup (2013) discusses this issue in detail. Recall that GLMM theory conceptualizes two distributions that contribute to the "how the data arose" process, the distribution of the observations given the random effects, and the distribution of the random model effects. However, neither is observable: we only see the marginal distribution of the observations. For count data, regardless of whether the observations given the random effects follow a Poisson or negative binomial distribution, the marginal distribution is strongly right-skewed. The estimates produced by the Poisson-normal GLMM target to median of this distribution, whereas the estimates from a mixed model using the normal approximation of the Poisson target the marginal mean. Estimates from the negative binomial fall somewhere between. Thus, if our goal is to make predictions at a given value of X for a *typical lot*, the normal approximation will always overestimate the predicted values in a regression model for counts. If the underlying distribution of the observations given the random effect is more closely modeled by the Poisson, the Poisson-normal model will produce accurate estimates and the negative binomial model will overestimate the predicted values. On the other hand, if the underlying distribution is closer to the negative binomial, the negative binomial model will yield accurate predictions and the Poisson-normal model will produce under-estimates.

All this said, how is a data analyst to know which result to report? Unfortunately, the current state of the art in GLMM diagnostics is such that there is no good, reliable way to choose between the two. In fact, in informal simulations conducted by the authors, conventional diagnostics, such as plotting predicted values against observed values, more often than not choose the wrong model. This is an active area of research, so reliable diagnostics will inevitably become available. In the meantime, users need to use judgment based on their knowledge of the processes giving rise to the data, such as the aggregation scenario described in Section 12.3.3 that motivates the negative binomial, or select the analysis given the context of a study's objectives. For example, in this example, if one is being conservative and wants to make sure that a given finishing treatment level will result in counts dependably less than 10, one should use the negative binomial analysis.

12.6.3 GLMM for Regression on Count Data When the Marginal Mean is the Intended Target

In the previous section, inference focused on, λ_{ij} interpreted as the predicted number of aberrant cells at a given level of X for a typical lot, that is, for $b_i = 0$. This is known as conditional broad inference. We know, however, that in some cases, the objective is not prediction for a typical lot, but prediction of the number of aberrant cells averaged over all lots, or, or, equivalently (and arguably more meaningfully), the total number of aberrant cells in the target population. If this is the objective, then you need to redirect the targeted inference space.

For this example, adding an overdispersion scale parameter to the "naive" Poisson model creates a quasi-marginal model that accounts for overdispersion. The model specification is identical to that given in Section 12.6.1, with two exceptions:

- Distribution of the observations given the random model effects is as follows:

$$y_{ij} \mid b_{0i}, b_{1i} \sim \text{quasi-Poisson}\left(\lambda_{ij}, \varphi\right)$$

- While the expected value, $E\left(y_{ij} \mid b_{0i} b_{1i}\right) = \lambda_{ij}$ remains the same, the variance now includes the scale parameter—that is,

$$\text{Var}\left(y_{ij} \mid b_{0i} b_{1i}\right) = \varphi \lambda_{ij}$$

As explained in Section 12.3.2, including the scale parameter in this way means that we no longer have a true probability distribution, and hence we no longer have a true likelihood. Instead, we have a quasi-likelihood. By modifying the model in this way, we redirect the target of inference from λ to the marginal population mean. Because this is still a random coefficient model, and hence still includes random intercept and slope effects, it is not a true marginal model, which would include only fixed effects and a working covariance structure. Hence, the term *quasi-marginal model*.

Program

To implement this model, use the PROC GLIMMIX statements in Program 12.16.

Program 12.16

```
proc glimmix data=rcr_counts;
  class lot;
  model count=x/solution d=poisson;
  random intercept x / subject=lot;
  random _residual_;
  estimate 'x=0'  intercept 1 x 0  / ilink cl;
  estimate 'x=5'  intercept 1 x 5  / ilink cl;
  estimate 'x=10' intercept 1 x 10 / ilink cl;
run;
```

These statements are identical to the "naive" Poisson model in Section 12.6.1, with the exception of the addition of a RANDOM _RESIDUAL_ statement. This creates the marginal quasi-likelihood by adding the overdispersion scale parameter.

RECALL: Because marginal GLMMs are by definition based on quasi-likelihoods, you cannot use integral approximation methods LAPLACE or QUAD, because they require a true likelihood. Whenever you include a RANDOM statement with the word RESIDUAL, you are specifying a quasi-likelihood. Therefore, you must use the pseudo-likelihood method if you want to use PROC GLIMMIX to implement the model.

Results

Results for the marginal GLMM appear in Output 12.18.

Output 12.18: Selected Results for Quasi-Marginal GLMM for Regression with Counts

Fit Statistics	
-2 Res Log Pseudo-Likelihood	131.50
Generalized Chi-Square	334.28
Gener. Chi-Square / DF	7.27

Covariance Parameter Estimates

Cov Parm	Subject	Estimate	Standard Error
Intercept	lot	0.2511	0.1895
x	lot	0	.
Residual (VC)		7.2670	1.6454

Solutions for Fixed Effects

Effect	Estimate	Standard Error	DF	t Value	Pr > |t|
Intercept	3.1595	0.2374	7	13.31	<.0001
x	-0.1550	0.03380	7	-4.58	0.0025

Estimates

Label	Estimate	Standard Error	DF	t Value	Pr > |t|	Alpha	Lower	Upper	Mean	Standard Error Mean	Lower Mean	Upper Mean
x=0	3.1595	0.2374	7	13.31	<.0001	0.05	2.5982	3.7208	23.5592	5.5923	13.4398	41.2979
x=5	2.3847	0.2175	7	10.96	<.0001	0.05	1.8704	2.8990	10.8556	2.3612	6.4906	18.1560
x=10	1.6098	0.3089	7	5.21	0.0012	0.05	0.8795	2.3402	5.0020	1.5449	2.4097	10.3830

Interpretation

The "Fit Statistics" table gives you the residual log pseudo-likelihood and the generalized chi-square statistic. Unlike the conditional GLMM, you do not interpret the chi-square as evidence of overdispersion. For marginal GLMMs estimated using pseudo-likelihood, generalized χ^2/DF estimates the working scale parameter φ. Notice that the generalized χ^2/DF and the estimate of the scale parameter, called RESIDUAL(VC) in the "Covariance Parameter Estimates" table, are identical. Both equal to 7.27. This is by definition, because the generalized χ^2/df is the estimate $\hat{\varphi}$.

Interpret the "Solution for Fixed Effects" and "Estimates" tables the same way that you did with the Poisson-normal and negative binomial GLMMs in Section 12.6.2. The estimated regression equation is

$$\log\left(\hat{\lambda}\right) = 3.1595 - 0.1550X$$

For a typical lot, $b_{0i} = b_{1i} = 0$; hence,

$$\log\left(\lambda_{ij} \mid 0\right) = \log\left(\hat{\lambda}_{ij}\right) = 3.1595 - 0.1550X_j$$

The predicted count at $X = 10$ is $\hat{\lambda} = 5.0$ with an upper 95% confidence bound of 10.38. Notice that the predicted count is greater than either the Poisson-normal model ($\hat{\lambda} = 3.04$) or the negative binomial model ($\hat{\lambda} = 4.39$). This is consistent with the discussion of targets of estimation for these three models given near the end of Section 12.6.2.

12.7 Blocked Design Revisited: What to Do When Block Variance Estimate is Negative

In Chapter 2 we saw that if the solution for block variance is negative, the MIXED and GLIMMIX procedures, by default, set the variance estimate to zero. We noted that this results in underestimated standard errors and inflated test statistics, and that one should, instead, either use a NOBOUND option to allow the variance estimate to become negative, or re-express the model using a compound symmetry covariance model, thereby changing the interpretation from block variance to within-block covariance among experimental units. We saw that if the block variance estimate is nonnegative, the random block variance component model and the compound symmetry covariance model are equivalent, but if the estimate is negative, the compound symmetry model does a better job with confidence interval coverage and Type I error control.

The same considerations apply when a GLMM produces a negative variance estimate. This example uses the same design as Section 12.5, but a different set of data.

The variance component estimates produced by the Poisson-normal and the negative binomial model are given in Output 12.19.

Output 12.19: Variance Estimates for Poisson-Normal and Negative Binomial with Alternative Data from BIB with Count Data

A. Poisson-normal

Covariance Parameter Estimates			
Cov Parm	Subject	Estimate	Standard Error
Intercept	block	0	.
trt	block	0.9070	0.4396

B. Negative Binomial

Covariance Parameter Estimates			
Cov Parm	Subject	Estimate	Standard Error
Intercept	block	0	.
Scale		0.5122	0.2356

Regardless of whether you decide that the process giving rise to these data are best explained by the Poisson-normal or negative binomial model, the fact that the block variance estimate has been set to zero indicates that reporting either analysis risks being compromised by confidence interval and Type I error issues described above. An adjustment for the negative block variance estimate is imperative.

If your objective calls for using the marginal model, the problem is self-correcting. Output 12.20 shows the working covariance parameter estimates.

Output 12.20: Working Covariance Estimate for Marginal Block Design GLMM

Covariance Parameter Estimates			
Cov Parm	Subject	Estimate	Standard Error
CS	block	-0.8925	2.2942
Residual		8.1227	4.0613

Notice that the estimate of the working covariance, $\hat{\sigma}_W = -0.89$. The marginal model has the working covariance structure parameterized in a form that allows a natural interpretation of the negative covariance estimate. This anticipates the required adjustments for the two conditional models.

12.7.1 Adjustment for Poisson-Normal GLMM

In Chapter 2 we saw that the negative variance problem can be addressed in two ways: the NOBOUND option or re-parameterizing the model. The latter was preferred with the Gaussian mixed model. With the GLMM, it is strongly preferred, because the NOBOUND option is prone to computational issues that experience suggests are even more prevalent with the GLMM than the Gaussian mixed model.

The Poisson-normal model was given in variance component mixed model form in Equation 12.6 of Section 12.5.2. We know that this model can be re-expressed in terms of compound symmetry as follows:

- Linear predictor: $\log(\lambda_{ij}) = \eta + \tau_i + w_{ij}$, where w_{ij} denotes the within-block unit level effect.

- Distributions: $y_{ij} \mid w_{ij} \sim \text{Poisson}(\lambda_{ij})$ and

$$\mathbf{w}_j \sim \text{MVN}\left(\begin{bmatrix} 0 \\ 0 \\ 0 \\ 0 \end{bmatrix}, \begin{bmatrix} \sigma^2 + \sigma_{CS} & \sigma_{CS} & \sigma_{CS} & \sigma_{CS} \\ \sigma_{CS} & \sigma^2 + \sigma_{CS} & \sigma_{CS} & \sigma_{CS} \\ \sigma_{CS} & \sigma_{CS} & \sigma^2 + \sigma_{CS} & \sigma_{CS} \\ \sigma_{CS} & \sigma_{CS} & \sigma_{CS} & \sigma^2 + \sigma_{CS} \end{bmatrix}\right)$$

where $\mathbf{w}_j$ is the vector of within-block unit effects for the four observations on the jth block, σ^2 denotes the unit-level variance on the model scale, and σ_{CS} denotes the covariance of the unit effects within block.

Program

Implement this model using Program 12.17.

Program 12.17

```
proc glimmix data=bib_counts2;
 class block trt;
 model count=trt/d=poi;
 random trt/ subject=block type=cs;
run;
```

Results

The resulting covariance estimates are shown in Output 12.21.

Output 12.21: Covariance Parameter Estimates for Poisson-normal CS GLMM

Covariance Parameter Estimates			
Cov Parm	Subject	Estimate	Standard Error
Variance	block	0.9614	0.5727
CS	block	-0.06013	0.3391

Interpretation

You can see that the parameter corresponding to the block effect, the CS term, is $\hat{\sigma}_{CS} = -0.06$. A negative covariance may indicate some form of competition among observations within the same block. To explore further, you can add LSMEANS and other post-processing statements (CONTRAST, LSMESTIMATE, etc.) as you did in Section 12.5. In the interest of space, they are not shown here, but program syntax, output and interpretation are identical to examples in Section 12.5.

12.7.2 Adjustment for Negative Binomial GLMM

The equivalence of the variance component and compound symmetry model holds for the Poisson-normal model but not the negative binomial. Why? If you use the compound symmetry linear predictor and associated random effect covariance structure as shown above for the Poisson-normal, the compound symmetry scale parameter, σ^2, is confounded with the negative binomial scale parameter, ϕ. Therefore, the NOBOUND option is the only alternative.

Program

Use the PROC GLIMMIX statements in Program 12.18.

Program 12.18

```
proc glimmix data=bib_count2 nobound;
 class block trt;
 model count=trt/d=negbin;
 random intercept / subject=block;
run;
```

The main difference between this and the statements for the negative binomial GLMM in Section 12.6.4 is the addition of the NOBOUND option in the PROC statement. In addition, you cannot use METHOD=QUAD with the NOBOUND option, so either LAPLACE or the default pseudo-likelihood methods must be used. Experience suggests negative binomial GLMMs are best implemented using integral approximation methods if possible. Hence, the LAPLACE option. However, you should always pay attention to the SASLOG and be alert for output in SAS results that raises a red flag. Technically, likelihood with a negative variance is undefined; the NOBOUND option can make the LAPLACE approximation unstable and unpredictable. In this example, it appears to work well, but there are no guarantees. The default pseudo-likelihood option is more forgiving. For many data sets, pseudo-likelihood with NOBOUND may be your only option if you need to use the negative binomial GLMM.

Results

Results are shown in Output 12.22.

Output 12.22: Covariance Parameter Estimates for Negative Binomial with NOBOUND Option

Covariance Parameter Estimates			
Cov Parm	Subject	Estimate	Standard Error
Intercept	block	-0.03594	0.1912
Scale		0.5189	0.3096

You can see that the variance estimate for block is $\hat{\sigma}_b^2 = -0.04$. This estimate is evidence against a standard variance component model with nonnegative variance. It is advised that you use a negative estimate in order to control Type I error for tests and guarantee accurate confidence interval coverage for estimable functions of interest. To fully assess impact on statistical conclusions, try simulating data under your design and compare performance of different models.

12.8 Summary

This chapter presents examples GLMMs intended for discrete count data. As with the binomial examples in Chapter 11, fitting models directly to count data, which implicitly assumes counts follow an approximate normal distribution, or using variance stabilizing transformations, is problematic in the context of mixed models. There are two potential targets for inference, the mean parameter, λ, of the conditional distribution of the counts given the random effects, and the mean of the marginal distribution. Because the marginal distribution is typically strongly right-skewed, λ and the marginal mean are not the same. Linear mixed models fitted directly to the count give estimates of the marginal mean, not λ.

This chapter focuses on two processes that plausibly give rise to count data: the Poisson-normal and the Poisson-gamma. The latter is equivalent to the negative binomial. Poisson-normal and negative binomial GLMMs both target λ, but the estimates they produce can be quite different. Model diagnostics can be misleading, so it is important to have an understanding of the process over and above what diagnostic statistics can provide.

Finally, inference focused on λ and inference focused on the marginal mean both have their place. One important feature of mixed models with non-Gaussian data that distinguishes them from Gaussian mixed models is the need to decide which inference target best addresses the objectives of the analysis. If λ is the target, a conditional GLMM should be used. If the marginal mean is the target, marginal GLMMs, of which GEE-type models are a special case, should be used. Including RESIDUAL in the PROC GLIMMIX RANDOM statement redirects inference from λ to the marginal mean. In some cases, including RESIDUAL specifies a true, GEE-type marginal model—Section 12.5.5 shows an example. In other cases, including RESIDUAL creates what we call a *quasi-marginal model*—Section 12.6.3 shows an example. If RESIDUAL does not appear in any RANDOM statement, the model is by definition a conditional GLMM. This chapter contains several examples of conditional GLMMs.

Chapter 13: Generalized Linear Mixed Models for Multilevel and Repeated Measures Experiments

13.1 Introduction 457
13.2 Two Examples Illustrating Generalized Linear Mixed Models with Complex Data............................457
    13.2.1 Split-Plot Experiment with Count Data.. 457
    13.2.2 Repeated Measures with Binomial Data 458
13.3 Example 1: Split-Plot Experiment with Count Data..458
    13.3.1 Overview of Modeling Considerations for Count Data.. 459
    13.3.2 Estimation Method Considerations for Complex Count Data 459
    13.3.3 Poisson GLMMs for Split Plot with Count Data 460
    13.3.4 Negative Binomial GLMM for Split Plot with Count Data.. 464
    13.3.5 Quasi-Marginal Model for Split Plot with Count Data 466
    13.3.6 What to Do If "Estimated G-matrix is Non-Singular"... 469
13.4 Example 2: Repeated Measures Experiment with Binomial Data..473
    13.4.1 Overview of Modeling Considerations for Non-Gaussian Repeated Measures Data................. 473
    13.4.2 Conditional (G-Side) GLMM for Repeated Measures 475
    13.4.3 Marginal (R-side) GLMM for Repeated Measures 481
    13.5 Summary 484

13.1 Introduction

The GLMM examples presented in Chapters 11 and 12 involve data from completely randomized designs or designs with a single blocking criterion, and from one-way or simple linear regression treatment designs. This chapter presents examples from commonly used but more complex design structures. The first example is from a split-plot experiment with count data, but the principles shown for constructing and implementing the model can be applied to any multilevel design with non-Gaussian data. The second example has a repeated measures (a.k.a. longitudinal) design structure with binomial data. Although principles underlying the construction of repeated measures GLMMs for non-Gaussian data are similar to those introduced for Gaussian mixed models in Chapter 8, there are crucial, and widely misunderstood, differences. Like the models introduced in Chapters 11 and 12, repeated measures GLMMs can be constructed as conditional or as marginal models. Each model targets a different inference space. You will see that if you "borrow" PROC GLIMMIX statements from the models presented in Chapter 8 and simply change the assumed distribution, you target the marginal inference space. However, recall from Chapters 11 and 12 that in many—perhaps most—cases you want to target the inference space associated with the conditional GLMM. This requires a different mindset.

The primary objective of this chapter is to introduce the changes in mindset required to work effectively with non-Gaussian multilevel and longitudinal data. Section 13.2 describes two data sets used as examples for this chapter. Section 13.3 presents the various modeling approaches for split-plot data, using count data to illustrate. Section 13.4 presents GLMM options for repeated measures using binomial data to illustrate.

13.2 Two Examples Illustrating Generalized Linear Mixed Models with Complex Data

This section presents two examples used to illustrate modeling strategies for multilevel and longitudinal data with non-Gaussian response variables.

13.2.1 Split-Plot Experiment with Count Data

Data set "Split-Plot with Count Data" contains data from a study to determine the effect of two environmental management methods and two mixes of varieties intended to reduce the incidence of harmful invasive species. The experiment was conducted on six randomly selected fields. Each field was divided into two sections. Each management method was randomly assigned to one of the sections. Each section was divided into two plots. Variety mix 1 was randomly assigned to one of the plots, and variety mix 2 to the other plot. Thus, the experiment is a split plot: section is the experimental unit with respect to management method, and plot is the experimental unit with respect to variety mix. Refer to Figure 5.6 in Chapter 5 to visualize this study.

The response variable is the number of invasive species counted on each plot. These counts were taken after the treatment combinations had sufficient time to become fully effective.

Discussion of this example begins with the standard linear predictor for a split plot experiment whose whole plot is a randomized block design. That is

$$\eta_{ijk} = \eta + \alpha_j + \beta_j + \alpha\beta_{ij} + r_k + w_{ik} \qquad (13.1)$$

where the terms are defined as follows:

- $\eta_{ijk} = \log(\lambda_{ijk})$ and λ_{ijk} denotes the expected count for the ith management method, j^{th} variety mix, and k^{th} field.

- η denotes the intercept.

- α_i denotes the main effect of the ith management method.

- β_j denotes main effect of the jth variety mix.

- $\alpha\beta_{ij}$ denotes the ij^{th} management method $\times$ variety mix interaction effect.

- r_k denotes the kth block effect, assumed $\sim \text{NI}\left(0, \sigma_r^2\right)$.

- w_{ik} denotes the ik^{th} whole plot effect, assumed $\sim \text{NI}\left(0, \sigma_w^2\right)$.

Section 13.3.1 presents additional considerations needed to complete the model and decide if the above linear predictor is adequate. Section 13.3.2 presents Poisson-based models. Section 13.3 presents negative-binomial based models. Section 13.3.4 presents a marginal model in case the marginal mean, rather than the expected count of a typical population member, is the target of inference.

13.2.2 Repeated Measures with Binomial Data

Data set "Repeated Measures with Binomial Data" contains data from a study comparing performance over time of two teaching methods. Twelve randomly sampled classrooms participate in the study. Six randomly assigned classrooms receive teaching method 1. The others receive teaching method 2. Fourteen students per classroom are followed throughout the class. At each of six pre-planned times, student proficiency was measured. Thus, at each time, for each classroom, the response variable is the number of proficient student out of fourteen.

As with the split plot with counts, we could adapt the linear predictor used in Chapter 8 for Gaussian repeated measures:

$$\eta_{ijk} = \eta + \alpha_i + \tau_j + \alpha\tau_{ij} + b_{ik} \qquad (13.2)$$

where terms are defined as follows:

- η denotes the intercept.

- α_i denotes the ith treatment main effect.

- τ_j denotes the jth time main effect.

- $\alpha\tau_{ij}$ denotes the ij^{th} treatment $\times$ time interaction effect.

- b_{ik} denotes the ik^{th} between subjects (a.k.a. between classrooms) effect, assumed $\sim \text{NI}\left(0, \sigma_b^2\right)$.

Section 13.4.1 presents modeling considerations for fully adapting the linear predictor to the analysis of these data. As with the split-plot for count data, these considerations entail a change in mind set from common practice for Gaussian mixed models. Section 13.4.2 presents the standard model when the target of inference is a typical student. Section 13.4.3 discusses strategies for selecting an appropriate covariance structure to account for serial correlation among repeated measurements on classrooms. Section 13.4.4 covers the marginal model for these data.

13.3 Example 1: Split-Plot Experiment with Count Data

This example is described in Section 13.2.1 and uses data set "Split-Plot with Count Data." Section 13.3.1 gives an overview of the considerations that you need to address for model construction. Section 13.3.2 presents split-plot models assuming that the data that are conditional on random model effects follow a Poisson distribution. Section 13.3.3 considers split-plot GLMMs based on the negative binomial distribution. The Poisson and negative binomial GLMMs in Sections 13.3.2 and 13.3.3 are conditional models. Section 13.3.4 presents a model that redirects inference to the marginal mean. We refer to this as a "quasi-marginal model" because it contains a residual covariance, meaning that variability among the observations is characterized by a quasi-likelihood rather than a true probability distribution, but the linear predictor also contains a random effect, so it is not a true marginal model. Although it is not a marginal model in the strict sense, the "quasi-marginal" model shares the inferential characteristics of a true marginal model. The final section, Section 13.3.5, covers analysis of conditional GLMMs if a variance component estimate is set to zero.

13.3.1 Overview of Modeling Considerations for Count Data

Model construction begins by visualizing the design structure and then listing sources of variation that 1) describe the processes in terms of model effects by which the data arose, and 2) provide a template for constructing a model for data analysis consistent with these processes. The process introduced in Chapter 5, Section 5.2 for Gaussian split-plot experiments is one way to proceed. Table 13.1 shows the process from design structure to combined table on which to base the model. Note the similarity to Figure 5.6 and its associated Table 5.5.

Table 13.1: Source of Variation for Which GLMM Must Account

Units and Blocks		Treatment Design		Combined	
Source	*df*	Source	*df*	Source	*df*
field	5			field	5
		management method	1	method	1
section(field)	6			section(field)|method	
				field × method[a]	6 − 1 = 5
		variety mix	1	mix	1
		method × mix	1	method × mix	1
plot(section)	12			plot(section)|mix, method	12 − 2 = 10
Total	**23**	**Total**	**23**	**Total**	**23**

[a] This term accounts for variation among whole plot experimental units (sections in this example). Technically it is defined as "section(field)\|method," which should be read "section within field after accounting for management method." This term is uniquely identified by field and method, i.e. if you know the field and the method, then you know exactly what section is referenced. Thus, in a SAS procedure, you identify section by field*method.

Notice that the linear predictor given in Equation 13.1 accounts for all sources of variation except the last line, read as "plot within section after accounting for mix and method." This source of variation corresponds to the unit of observation. To finalize the model you must resolve two issues. First, what is the conditional distribution of the observations given the random model effects (in this case, field and field × method)? Second, what term in the linear predictor or parameter in the distribution of the observations accounts for unit-of-observation level uniqueness? As with the blocked design with count data in Chapter 12, Section 12.5, there are three common ways to approach these issues. They are as follows:

1. Assume that the conditional distribution of the observations given the random model effects is Poisson.

2. Assume that the conditional distribution of the observations given the random model effects is negative binomial.

   Options (1) and (2) define a conditional model and assume that the target of inference is "as typical member of the population."

3. Account for variation at the whole plot experimental unit (section) and split plot experimental unit (plot) levels using working (a.k.a. residual or R-side) covariance structure.

   Option (3) redirects inference to the marginal mean, as illustrated in Figure 11.1, and discussed for count data in Section 12.5.5. Use this option when the intended target of inference is the marginal mean.

The following sections illustrate the implementation and interpretation of these models.

13.3.2 Estimation Method Considerations for Complex Count Data

PROC GLIMMIX has several options for estimation and inference, introduced in Chapter 6, and discussed in the context of GLMMs for simple designs with binomial data in Chapter 11 and count data in Chapter 12. For multilevel and repeated measures experiments, three methods are of particular relevance: the default RSPL (Residual Subject-specific Pseudo-Likelihood), and the two integral approximation methods, QUADRATURE and LAPLACE (METHOD=QUAD and METHOD=LAPLACE options in the PROC GLIMMIX statement).

RSPL creates a pseudo-variable defined by the response variable and the link function, and mimics the linear mixed model REML algorithm for estimation and inference. See Appendix B for details. RSPL implicitly assumes that the pseudo-variable, or equivalently, the observation conditional on the random model effects, follows a reasonably symmetric distribution. Or, to put in more accurately, it assumes that, for the distribution specified in the DIST= option in the PROC GLIMMIX MODEL statement, the normal approximation plausibly applies. For example, the Binomial(N, p) distribution is reasonably symmetric unless N is small and p is close to 0 or 1. The Poisson(λ) and Negative Binomial(λ, ϕ) distributions are reasonably symmetric except when λ is small or, the negative binomial ϕ is large. When the distribution specified in the DIST option is reasonably symmetric, RSPL performs well. However, when this distribution is highly skewed, RSPL has problems.

When PROC GLIMMIX was introduced in 2005, pseudo-likelihood was the only method available. QUADRATURE and LAPLACE options were added in the 2008 release. *Notes on the Bias of Estimators* was added to the SAS/STAT PROC GLIMMIX documentation in the 2008 release. This documentation focuses on cases in which pseudo-likelihood estimators show unacceptable bias and is a good summary of conventional wisdom circa 2008. This documentation, and the literature it cited, created the impression that, for most applications, one should use integral approximation for estimation and inference on treatment effects.

Since 2008, there has been a learning curve concerning the behavior of the various GLMM algorithms, similar to the learning curve for Gaussian mixed models that followed the initial release of PROC MIXED. A major issue not discussed in *Notes on the Bias of Estimators* concerns the fact that integral approximation methods have no REML analog—all variance component estimates are maximum likelihood, with the same issues with respect to Type I error control and confidence interval coverage discussion for Gaussian linear models in Chapters 2 and 6. Stroup (2013), Couton and Stroup (2013), Claassen (2014), Stroup and Claassen (2018) studied the small sample behavior of PROC GLIMMIX algorithms for proportion (binomial and beta) and count (Poisson and negative binomial) data in GLMMs for blocked and split-plot experiments. For relatively small experiments, or studies with relatively few observations, MLE bias in variance estimates, with its impact on standard error estimates and test statistics, can be severe. This bias is exacerbated by the fact that the Kenward-Roger adjustment is incompatible with integral approximation methods: standard error bias exists even with REML variance component estimates. On the other hand, the Kenward-Roger adjustment performs well in GLMMs for which RSPL performs well.

With the caveat that small sample behavior of the GLMM is an active area of research at the time of publication of this book, Table 13.2 summarizes our recommendations regarding the method of choice for model estimation and inference.

Table 13.2: Recommended Method for GLMM Estimation and Inference

Distribution of Observations given Random Effects	Small experiment (e.g. few replications per treatment)[a]	Large experiment
Symmetric	Use RSPL	Doesn't matter[b]
Asymmetric (e.g. skewed)	Quadrature least undesirable	Use quadrature or Laplace

[a]Small experiments are typical for research in academic institutions and many basic research and development settings.

[b]Estimators are equally accurate, but RSPL allows use of KR and is computationally less demanding.

Keep in mind that Table 13.2 applies to estimation and inferential statistics (e.g. mean comparisons, predicted response, tests of treatment effects and regression parameters, etc.). On the other hand, overdispersion diagnostics, e,g, Pearson χ^2/df, likelihood ratio tests of covariance parameters, comparison of completing covariance structures (shown in Section 13.4 for non-Gaussian repeated measures data) all require evaluation of a true likelihood. For these applications, you must use integral approximation methods, either QUADRATURE or LAPLACE.

Examples in the following sections use all of the above recommendations and requirements.

13.3.3 Poisson GLMMs for Split Plot with Count Data

Analysis of the Poisson GLMM consists of three steps. First, fit the model given in Equation 13.1 with the accompanying assumption that $y_{ijk} \mid r_k, w_{ik} \sim \text{Poisson}(\lambda_{ijk})$. This is the simplest Poisson GLMM for these data. Check this model for any problems. If there are problems, the second step is to modify the model to address these problems. Finally, the third step involves estimation and inference on treatment means and differences, thereby completing the analysis.

Program

Implement the first step using the PROC GLIMMIX statements in Program 13.1.

Program 13.1

```
proc glimmix data=count_splt_plt method=quad;
 class field method mix;
 model count=method|mix/d=poi;
 random intercept method / subject=field;
 lsmeans method*mix/ilink plot=meanplot(sliceby=method join ilink);
run;
```

You can anticipate that this model is vulnerable to overdispersion because there is no term in the linear predictor or parameter in the distribution at the unit-of-observation level that accounts for uniqueness among plots, over and above variation accounted for by the other effects in the model. The MEANPLOT option is included to enable you to visualize the consequences of overdispersion if the Pearson χ^2/DF statistic suggests that overdispersion is present.

Results

Output 13.1 shows relevant results.

Output 13.1: Results of Poisson GLMM for Split-Plot with Count Data

Fit Statistics for Conditional Distribution	
-2 log L(count | r. effects)	134.38
Pearson Chi-Square	42.30
Pearson Chi-Square / DF	1.76

Type III Tests of Fixed Effects				
Effect	Num DF	Den DF	F Value	Pr > F
method	1	5	3.35	0.1268
mix	1	10	53.22	<.0001
method*mix	1	10	15.34	0.0029

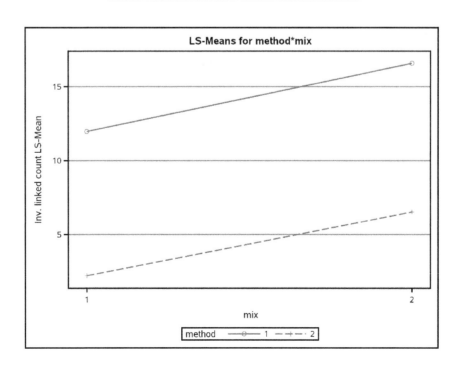

Interpretation

You can see from the MEANPLOT that there is no visual evidence of method × mix interaction, yet the test statistic for METHOD*MIX is $F = 15.34$ with $p = 0.0029$. The Pearson χ^2/DF suggests a possible reason for this apparent contradiction: $\chi^2/DF = 1.76$ may constitute evidence of overdispersion, and hence an inflated F value for METHOD*MIX interaction.

Overdispersion commonly results from omitting a unit-of-observation level term in the linear predictor. This is the split plot version of the "naive" Poisson model first discussed in Section 12.4. We can account for unit-of-observation, i.e. plot-level uniqueness, by adding a plot-level random effect to the linear predictor. The revised linear predictor is as follows:

$$\eta_{ijk} = \eta + \alpha_i + \beta_j + \alpha\beta_{ij} + r_k + w_{ik} + s_{ijk} \tag{13.3}$$

where s_{ijk} denotes the random effect, assumed $\sim NI(0, \sigma_S^2)$, corresponding to the last line, "plot(section)|method, mix" of the ANOVA sources of variation in Table 13.1. The linear predictor in Equation 13.3 is the Poisson-normal model for the split-plot experiment with the whole-plot set up in blocks.

Add the unit-level term to the model by modifying the RANDOM statement. You can also use the COVTEST statement to test $H_0 : \sigma_s^2 = 0$. Think of this as a formal test of overdispersion.

Program

Run Program 13.2 to implement this step of the analysis.

Program 13.2

```
proc glimmix data=sp_counts method=quad(qpoints=5);
 class field method mix;
 model count=method|mix / d=poisson;   * ddfm=kr;
 random intercept method method*mix / subject=field;
 covtest 'overdispersion?' . . 0;
run;
```

Note that you need to use an integral approximation method (QUAD or LAPLACE) to compute a valid likelihood ratio test of σ_s^2.

Results

The results that appear in Output 13.2 were obtained using 5-point quadrature. If you delete the (QPOINTS=5) option, PROC GLIMMIX will select five quadrature points as optimal.

Output 13.2: Variance Testing and Estimation Results for Poisson-normal Split-Plot GLMM

Fit Statistics for Conditional Distribution	
-2 log L(count | r. effects)	95.11
Pearson Chi-Square	4.63
Pearson Chi-Square / DF	0.19

Covariance Parameter Estimates			
Cov Parm	Subject	Estimate	Standard Error
Intercept	field	1.4755	1.3833
method	field	1.2804	0.9256
method*mix	field	0.1984	0.1300

Tests of Covariance Parameters Based on the Likelihood					
Label	DF	-2 Log Like	ChiSq	Pr > ChiSq	Note
overdispersion?	1	189.83	19.12	<.0001	MI

Interpretation

The Pearson χ^2/DF value of 0.19 in the "Fit Statistics for Conditional Distribution" table is evidence that the overdispersion problem has been addressed. Note that Pearson χ^2/DF values of approximate 0.20 are typical of Poisson-normal models, and are not cause for alarm (that is, they are not evidence of underdispersion). The estimated unit-level variance is $\hat{\sigma}_s^2 = 0.198$ and the likelihood ratio statistic that tests $H_0 : \sigma_s^2 = 0$ is 19.12 with a p-value less than 0.0001—strong evidence that accounting for unit-level effect is essential to address the overdispersion in the initial analysis of the "naive" Poisson model.

This completes the preliminary steps of the analysis. With an appropriate model selected, we now proceed with the analysis. In the initial steps we use integral approximation in order to compute valid overdispersion diagnostics and tests of relevant variance components. Following the guideline presented in Table 13.2, subsequent analysis should use the default RSPL method. Continuing to use quadrature risks inflating the likelihood of Type I error. To illustrate, compare the Type III tests of fixed effects and the data scale least square means obtained with integral approximation using METHOD=QUAD with analogous results obtained from the pseudo-likelihood default.

Program

First, the integral approximation is implemented with Program 13.3.

Program 13.3

```
proc glimmix data=sp_counts method=quad;
 class field method mix;
 model count=method|mix / d=poisson;
 random intercept method method*mix / subject=field;
 lsmeans method*mix / ilink cl;
run;
```

Results

Results appear in Output 13.3.

Output 13.3: Type III Tests of Fixed Effect and Data Scale Treatment Mean Estimates for Poisson Split-Plot GLMM Using Quadrature

Type III Tests of Fixed Effects				
Effect	Num DF	Den DF	F Value	Pr > F
method	1	5	3.30	0.1288
mix	1	10	10.83	0.0081
method*mix	1	10	2.95	0.1168

method*mix Least Squares Means					
method	mix	Mean	Standard Error Mean	Lower Mean	Upper Mean
1	1	10.8276	7.8061	2.1722	53.9717
1	2	16.1603	11.5656	3.2802	79.6143
2	1	1.8489	1.4459	0.3237	10.5599
2	2	6.5801	4.9174	1.2448	34.7844

Interpretation

The *F* value for METHOD*MIX is 2.95 with a *p*-value of 0.1168. The "method*mix Least Squares Means" table gives the estimated Poisson mean, $\hat{\lambda}_{ij}$ for each METHOD × MIX combination, computed as the inverse link of $\hat{\eta} + \hat{\alpha}_i + \hat{\beta}_i + \widehat{\alpha\beta}_{ij}$, along with the standard error and 95% confidence bounds. For example, for METHOD 1, MIX 1, $\hat{\lambda}_{11} = 10.83$ with SE = 7.81 and confidence bounds 2.17 and 53.97. In the interest of space, the model scale statistics are not shown in this, or subsequent tables of least squares means in this section.

Note that because this model adequately accounts for overdispersion, the discrepancy between the interaction plot and the test for METHOD*MIX is no longer present.

Program

Now, use Program 13.4 to obtain analogous results with pseudo-likelihood.

Program 13.4

```
proc glimmix data=sp_counts;
 class field method mix;
 model count=method|mix / d=poisson ddfm=kr2;
 random intercept method method*mix/ subject=field;
 lsmeans method*mix / ilink cl;
run;
```

Results

Results appear in Output 13.4.

Output 13.4: Type III Tests of Fixed Effect and Data Scale Treatment Mean Estimates for Poisson Split-Plot GLMM Using Pseudo-Likelihood

	Type III Tests of Fixed Effects			
Effect	Num DF	Den DF	F Value	Pr > F
method	1	5.008	2.72	0.1601
mix	1	8.381	8.30	0.0195
method*mix	1	8.388	2.19	0.1752

		method*mix Least Squares Means			
method	mix	Mean	Standard Error Mean	Lower Mean	Upper Mean
1	1	11.3075	8.5327	1.9816	64.5224
1	2	16.8509	12.6249	2.9680	95.6719
2	1	2.1008	1.7110	0.3432	12.8589
2	2	7.2808	5.6458	1.2473	42.4992

Interpretation

With pseudo-likelihood, the *F* value for METHOD*MIX is 2.19 with *p* = 0.1752, compared with *F* = 2.95 and *p* = 0.1168 obtained from quadrature. In this case, for commonly used α-levels your conclusions would not be affected, but they could be. Type I errors are more likely to occur using quadrature. Also, the 95% confidence interval for the METHOD 1 × MIX 1 mean is (1.98, 64.52) compared to (2.17, 53.97) if you use quadrature. This is consistent with Stroup (2013) finding that for Poisson GLMMs for split-plot experiments similar to the one in this example, quadrature-based confidence intervals are narrower that those obtained using pseudo-likelihood. With quadrature, coverage is consistently below 95%, whereas coverage with pseudo-likelihood is close to the nominal 95%.

13.3.4 Negative Binomial GLMM for Split Plot with Count Data

Instead of modeling the distribution of the observations conditional on the random effects as Poisson, you model them using the negative binomial. As we saw in Chapter 12, the assumptions underlying the negative binomial process often are more realistic, especially for biological count data where aggregation is expected. The negative binomial GLMM for the split plot structure in this example uses the linear predictor given in Equation 13.1 and assumes $y_{ijk} \mid r_k, w_{ik} \sim \text{NB}(\lambda_{ijk}, \phi)$. The scale parameter, ϕ, accounts for variability attributable to plot-level uniqueness. Hence, the model has a one-to-one correspondence with sources of variation, and you would not expect to see evidence of overdispersion.

Program

To confirm this, use Program 13.5 to obtain the Pearson χ^2 statistic.

Program 13.5

```
proc glimmix data=count_splt_plt method=quad;
 class field method mix;
 model count=method|mix/d=negbin;
 random intercept method / subject=field;
run;
```
Selected results appear in Output 13.5.

Results

Output 13.5: Overdispersion Diagnostic for Negative Binomial Split-Plot GLMM

Fit Statistics for Conditional Distribution	
-2 log L(count | r. effects)	130.73
Pearson Chi-Square	10.78
Pearson Chi-Square / DF	0.45

Interpretation

The "Pearson Chi-Square / DF" is 0.45. There is no evidence, based on this diagnostic, of overdispersion.

This completes the preliminary step; we now proceed with the analysis.

Program

Use Program 13.6 to obtain estimates of treatment means and tests of treatment effects.

Program 13.6

```
proc glimmix data=sp_counts;
 class field method mix;
 model count=method|mix / d=negbin;
 random intercept method / subject=field;
 lsmeans method*mix / cl ilink;
run;
```
As with the Poisson-normal GLMM, follow guidelines summarized in Table 13.2, and use the default pseudo-likelihood method. Note that this conflicts with conventional wisdom about negative binomial GLMMs that dates from before the 2008 release of PROC GLIMMIX, but is consistent with our understanding of best practices as of the time of publication, as discussed in Section 13.3.2.

Results

Results appear in Output 13.6.

Output 13.6: Covariance Parameter Estimates, Treat Effects Tests, and Estimates for Negative Binomial Split-Plot GLMM

Covariance Parameter Estimates			
Cov Parm	Subject	Estimate	Standard Error
Intercept	field	1.6394	1.6473
method	field	1.3825	1.0521
Scale		0.2291	0.1510

Type III Tests of Fixed Effects				
Effect	Num DF	Den DF	F Value	Pr > F
method	1	5.018	2.93	0.1473
mix	1	8.702	9.35	0.0141
method*mix	1	8.707	2.30	0.1647

method*mix Least Squares Means					
method	mix	Mean	Standard Error Mean	Lower Mean	Upper Mean
1	1	11.7558	8.8487	2.0629	66.9934
1	2	17.8282	13.3418	3.1405	101.21
2	1	2.1455	1.7348	0.3534	13.0262
2	2	7.3842	5.7027	1.2699	42.9377

Interpretation

From the "Covariance Parameter Estimates" table, estimates of the block (FIELD), whole-plot (METHOD×FIELD) variance and negative binomial scale parameter are $\hat{\sigma}_r^2 = 1.64$, $\hat{\sigma}_w^2 = 1.38$ and $\hat{\phi} = 0.23$, respectively. The "Type III Tests of Fixed Effects" table provides evidence of a main effect of MIX ($F = 9.85$, $p = 0.0105$), but no evidence of a METHOD×MIX interaction or a main effect of METHOD. The results are consistent with visual evidence in the interaction plot shown above. The table of "method*mix Least Squares Means" gives estimates of the expected count (λ_{ij}) for each treatment. These estimates are 11.76, 17.83, 2.14 and 7.38 for the four treatment combinations, versus 11.33, 16.85, 2.10 and 7.28 for the Poisson-normal GLMM. This is typical: Poisson-normal GLMMs tend to give estimates of λ_{ij} that are slightly lower than estimates from the corresponding negative binomial GLMM. Which do you report? See the discussion of this issue in Section 12.4. Here, the two models produce nearly identical results, but this is not always the case. Choosing between two sets of mutually contradictory results requires understanding the process by which data arise, the probability models implicit in the Poisson-normal GLMM and the negative binomial GLMM, and how these processes and probability models align—or fail to align.

13.3.5 Quasi-Marginal Model for Split Plot with Count Data

The Poisson-normal and negative binomial GLMMs discussed in Sections 13.3.2 and 13.3.3 are both conditional GLMMs. Their inference target is "a typical member of the population." If, instead, your inference target is "what is the total count in the population?" then the marginal mean is the target. If so, you should use a model that redirects the inference space to the marginal mean. Ideally, this means a marginal model. In practice—as in Section 12.6.3 and as is the case here—we use a model with both G-side and R-side covariance structures, what we call a *quasi-marginal model*. The presence of the residual covariance structure directs the inference space toward the marginal mean. Although quasi-marginal models do not perfectly target the marginal mean, in certain cases they are the best you can do. In this example, you must account for block effects. Recall from Section 12.5.6 the warning about modeling block effects as fixed; better to model block effects as random.

The required elements of the quasi-marginal model are as follows:

- Linear Predictor: $\eta_{ijk} = \eta + \alpha_i + \beta_j + \alpha\beta_{ij} + r_k$.

- Link function: $\eta_{ijk} = \log(\lambda_{ijk})$.

- Quasi-distribution of $y_{ijk} \mid r_k$: quasi-Poisson with $E(y_{ijk} \mid r_k) = \lambda_{ijk}$ and variance $Var(\mathbf{y}_{ik} \mid r_k) = \mathbf{A}^{\frac{1}{2}}\mathbf{R}\mathbf{A}^{\frac{1}{2}}$.

Where $\mathbf{A}$ is a diagonal matrix whose j^{th} diagonal element is λ_{ijk}, and $\mathbf{R}$ is assumed to have a compound symmetry structure, that is

$$\mathbf{R} = \begin{bmatrix} \varphi_W + \sigma_W & \sigma_W \\ \sigma_W & \varphi_W + \sigma_W \end{bmatrix}$$

The term "quasi-Poisson" refers to the quasi-likelihood, which has the structure of the Poisson log likelihood with the addition of the working covariance $\mathbf{R}$.

Program

Use the PROC GLIMMIX statements in Program 13.7 to implement the quasi-marginal model.

Program 13.7

```
proc glimmix data=count_splt_plt;
 class field method mix;
 model count=field method|method/d=poi ddfm=kr2;
 random intercept / subject=field;
 random mix / subject=field*method type=cs residual;
 lsmeans method*mix / ilink plot=meanplot(sliceby=method join ilink);
 nloptions maxiter=100;
run;
```

As with any multilevel experiment, use DDFM=KR2 as standard operating procedure. The only exceptions are when you use an integral approximation method (LAPLACE or QUAD) or when a sandwich estimator is a better choice (see below, this section and Section 13.4.3).

Results

Output 13.5 shows selected results.

Output 13.7: Working Covariance Estimates, Test Statistics, and Least Squares Means for Quasi-Marginal Model for Split Plot with Counts

Fit Statistics	
-2 Res Log Pseudo-Likelihood	61.76
Generalized Chi-Square	85.78
Gener. Chi-Square / DF	4.29

Covariance Parameter Estimates			
Cov Parm	Subject	Estimate	Standard Error
Intercept	field	0.5809	0.6775
CS	field*method	14.0988	9.1728
Residual		4.2891	1.9874

Type III Tests of Fixed Effects

Effect	Num DF	Den DF	F Value	Pr > F
method	1	6.303	0.46	0.5216
mix	1	13.48	9.68	0.0080
method*mix	1	13.48	2.79	0.1180

method*mix Least Squares Means

method	mix	Mean	Standard Error Mean	Lower Mean	Upper Mean
1	1	17.6235	9.1095	5.5158	56.3089
1	2	24.4129	11.5869	8.0140	74.3692
2	1	8.3784	5.5164	2.0142	34.8516
2	2	24.7019	11.6909	8.1170	75.1729

Interpretation

The table of "Fit Statistics" gives the pseudo-likelihood and the generalized chi-square statistics. Note that the "Gener. Ch-Square/DF" is merely the estimate of the residual covariance scale parameter. It is not a goodness-of-fit statistic and should not be interpreted as such. The table of "Covariance Parameter Estimates" gives the estimated residual scale, $\hat{\varphi} = 4.29$ and covariance, $\hat{\sigma}_{cs} = 14.10$, and the estimated block variance, $\hat{\sigma}_b^2 = 0.58$. The block variance can be interpreted as the variance among the log counts averaged over the whole-plots in each block. The residual scale and covariance are "working" rather than actual covariance parameters and therefore are not amenable to interpretation.

Interpret the F and p-values in the table of "Type III Tests of Fixed Effects" as you would any set of tests from a factorial treatment design. The table of "method*mix Least Squares Means" shows the data scale mean, standard error, and 95% confidence bounds. For example, for method 1, mix 1, the mean is 17.6 with a standard error of 9.1 and confidence interval (5.5, 56.3). Compare this to the negative binomial result for method 1, mix 1: mean 11.8, standard deviation 8.8, confidence interval (2.1, 67.0). The estimated mean for the quasi-marginal model is noticeably greater than the estimated mean for the negative binomial model. This is to be expected, because the marginal distribution of count data arising from a mixed model scenario is strongly right-skewed, and hence the marginal mean is always greater than the negative binomial or Poisson expected count. The inference target for the quasi-marginal model is between the Poisson expected count and the marginal mean. For practical purposes, interpret estimates from quasi-marginal models as you would estimates from a fully marginal model instead of interpretation you would give for a conditional model. The difference in standard error and confidence interval width reflects differences in the variance structure of the conditional model versus the working covariance structure of the quasi-marginal model.

The test statistics, standard errors and confidence bounds in Output 13.7 use *model-based* statistics. That is, they are computed using the estimated variance and working covariance parameters. By default, PROC GLIMMIX computes model-based statistics. Zeger (1994) describes an alternative method to compute standard errors and test statistics, called *robust* estimators in his paper. Also called *sandwich* or *empirical* estimators, these statistics are often used in conjunction with models with a working covariance structure. You can obtain sandwich estimators by adding the EMPIRICAL option to the PROC GLIMMIX statement. In addition, because this is a small experiment in terms of the number of replications, you should use the MBN option. For small sample sizes, the classical sandwich estimator produces upwardly biased tests statistics and standard errors that are biased downward. The MBN option corrects for this bias.

Program

Use Program 13.8 to obtain sandwich estimators.

Program 13.8

```
proc glimmix data=sp_counts empirical=mbn;
 class field method mix;
 model count=method|mix / d=poisson;
 random intercept  / subject=field;
 random mix / subject=field*method type=cs residual;
 lsmeans method*mix / cl ilink;
run;
```

Results

Results are shown in Output 13.8.

Output 13.8: Bias Corrected Empirical (Sandwich Estimator) Test Statistics for Poisson Quasi-Marginal Model

Type III Tests of Fixed Effects				
Effect	Num DF	Den DF	F Value	Pr > F
method	1	15	0.22	0.6484
mix	1	15	14.34	0.0018
method*mix	1	15	1.14	0.3034

method*mix Least Squares Means					
method	mix	Mean	Standard Error Mean	Lower Mean	Upper Mean
1	1	17.6235	10.3288	5.0533	61.4627
1	2	24.4129	12.6256	8.1076	73.5106
2	1	8.3784	7.7420	1.1690	60.0515
2	2	24.7019	17.7109	5.3583	113.88

Interpretation

These test statistics are more conservative than the model-based statistics. For example, for METHOD×MIX, $F = 1.14$ and $p = 0.3034$, versus $F = 2.79$ and $p = 0.1180$ for model-based statistics with the Kenward-Roger option. Similarly, the estimated data scale means are unchanged but the standard errors are greater and confidence intervals wider using the MBN corrected sandwich estimators. For example, for METHOD 1, MIX 1, the empirical standard error is 10.3 and the confidence interval is (5.1, 61.5) versus the model-based 9.1 and (5.5, 56.3).

Should you use the model-based or sandwich estimators? If the choice of working correlation structure is clear, as it is for the split plot, model-based statistics are more efficient, and they can be used in conjunction with the DDFM=KR2 option. On the other hand, there is evidence via simulation that bias-corrected sandwich estimators obtained with the EMPIRICAL=MBN option are more conservative when used with marginal or quasi-marginal models that are fit to small experiments. For marginal or quasi-marginal models that have competing covariance structures from which to select, as is the case with repeated measures data, the choice between model-based and sandwich estimators is more consequential. This will be illustrated in the repeated measures binomial example, specifically in Section 13.4.3.

13.3.6 What to Do If "Estimated G-matrix Is Not Positive Definite"

In the Poisson-normal and negative binomial examples in Sections 13.3.3 and 13.3.4, all variance component estimates are positive. This does not always happen. We know from discussions in Chapter 2 and 5 that estimating equations for variance components can produce negative solutions, and that the PROC GLIMMIX default is to set such estimates to zero. This produces the warning "Estimated G-matrix is not positive definite." The set-to-zero default has an adverse impact on Type I error control and confidence interval coverage. With Gaussian mixed models, you have two choices: use the NOBOUND option or use the compound symmetry reparameterization of the covariance structure.

For GLMMs, the situation is more complicated. You still need to address the problem, because the set-to-zero default inflates Type I error rate for non-Gaussian data just as it does for Gaussian data. However, what works for Gaussian mixed models does not necessarily work for GLMMs. This section illustrates strategies and things that can go wrong with PROC GLIMMIX.

Output 13.9 is the "Covariance Parameter Estimates" table applying Program 13.2 to count data from a design with the same structure as the data set "Split-Plot with Count Data", but different counts. Recall that Program 13.2 applies the Poisson-normal model with the unit-level term to account for overdispersion.

Output 13.9: Covariance Parameter Estimates for Poisson-Normal Model

Covariance Parameter Estimates			
Cov Parm	Subject	Estimate	Standard Error
Intercept	field	0.1385	0.1574
method	field	0	.
method*mix	field	1.1681	0.1110

However, the "Covariance Parameter Estimates" table reveals that the estimate of the whole plot (method × field) variance, $\hat{\sigma}_W^2$ has been set to zero, raising issues similar to those discussed in Section 12.6. Following the strategy recommended in Section 12.6, reparameterize the linear predictor from variance component form to compound symmetry form, as follows:

- Linear Predictor: $\eta_{ijk} = \eta + \alpha_i + \beta_j + \alpha\beta_{ij} + r_k + p_{ijk}$, where p_{ijk} denotes the plot within section effect.

- Distribution of plot within section effect: let $\mathbf{p}_{ik}$ denote the vector of plot effects within the ith section of the kth field.

$$\mathbf{p}_{ik} \sim MVN\left(\begin{bmatrix} 0 \\ 0 \end{bmatrix}, \begin{bmatrix} \sigma_P^2 + \sigma_{CS} & \sigma_{CS} \\ \sigma_{CS} & \sigma_P^2 + \sigma_{CS} \end{bmatrix}\right)$$

Here σ_{CS} denotes the covariance between plot effects within a section and σ_P^2 denotes the variance of the plot effect.

Program

Implement this model using Program 13.9. Output 13.9 shows selected results. Note that in order to get a valid overdispersion statistic you need integral approximation, which means using either METHOD=LAPLACE or METHOD=QUAD. Program 13.9 and results shown in Output 13.9 use METHOD=LAPLACE because METHOD=QUAD yielded nonsense F values in the "Type III Tests of Fixed Effects" table (with METHOD=QUAD, F for METHOD was 26968.3 and the other two F values were "Infinity").

Program 13.9

```
proc glimmix data=count_splt_plt method=laplace;
 class field method mix;
 model count=method|mix/d=poi;
 random intercept / subject=field;
 random mix / subject=method*field type=cs;
run;
```

Note the use of two RANDOM statements. The first RANDOM statement accounts for the block (FIELD) effects. The syntax follows from the assumption $r_k \sim NI(0, \sigma_r^2)$. The second RANDOM statement defines the compound symmetry structure of the $\mathbf{p}_{ik}$ effects as defined above, that is the SUBJECT identifies the ik^{th} METHOD × FIELD combination and within each SUBJECT are levels of MIX.

Results

Output 13.10 shows the results.

Output 13.10: Selected Results for Compound Symmetry Poisson-normal GLMM for Split Plot

Fit Statistics for Conditional Distribution	
-2 log L(count | r. effects)	91.60
Pearson Chi-Square	3.68
Pearson Chi-Square / DF	0.15

Covariance Parameter Estimates			
Cov Parm	Subject	Estimate	Standard Error
Intercept	field	0.4203	0.3247
Variance	field*method	1.7474	0.8371
CS	field*method	-0.7692	0.4362

Type III Tests of Fixed Effects				
Effect	Num DF	Den DF	F Value	Pr > F
method	1	15	14.99	0.0015
mix	1	15	1.43	0.2509
method*mix	1	15	0.41	0.5321

The change from variance component to compound symmetry has little impact on the Pearson χ^2/DF overdispersion diagnostic: it was 0.13; it is now 0.15. The estimated compound symmetry covariance, $\hat{\sigma}_{CS} = -0.77$. This could be interpreted as absence of detectable variation among whole plot experimental units (plots) or as evidence of within section competition effects between plots. Deciding which interpretation best fits is a subject matter, not a statistical, decision.

Program

You could then proceed with the analysis using the pseudo-likelihood default, using Program 13.10.

Program 13.10

```
proc glimmix data=count_splt_plt;
 class field method mix;
 model count=method|mix/d=poi ddfm=kr2;
 random intercept / subject=field;
 random mix / subject=method*field type=cs;
 lsmeans method*mix/ilink cl;
run;
```

Note that this program is the same as Program 13.4 shown earlier in this chapter.

Results

Output 13.11 shows selected results.

Output 13.11: Analysis of Split-Plot with Counts using CS to Allow Negative Covariance Estimate

Covariance Parameter Estimates			
Cov Parm	Subject	Estimate	Standard Error
Intercept	field	0.4555	0.3865
Variance	field*method	1.9803	1.0120
CS	field*method	-0.8544	0.5330

Type III Tests of Fixed Effects				
Effect	Num DF	Den DF	F Value	Pr > F
method	1	5.287	11.47	0.0179
mix	1	9.63	1.12	0.3152
method*mix	1	9.527	0.30	0.5994

method*mix Least Squares Means					
method	mix	Mean	Standard Error Mean	Lower Mean	Upper Mean
1	1	2.4036	1.4215	0.7000	8.2530
1	2	6.4114	3.5058	2.0063	20.4883
2	1	9.2118	5.0380	2.8760	29.5052
2	2	12.6457	6.7464	4.0369	39.6131

The estimates shown in the "Covariance Parameter Estimates" table are REML-like estimates, whereas those in Output 13.10 are ML estimates. As mentioned in discussions in the previous sections, the REML-like estimates computed using pseudo-likelihood allow better Type I error control and more accurate confidence interval estimation. Also note that the KR2 option produces Satterthwaite approximations of the denominator degrees of freedom. You can continue with additional post-processing statistics. These are not shown here in the interest of space and because they are the same as the inferential statistics that you would use for any 2 × 2 factorial treatment design, as introduced in Chapter 3, and discussed in the context of split-plot experiments in Chapter 5.

Instead of using the Poisson-normal GLMM, what if you use the negative binomial model. Implementing Program 13.5 for this data set produces the table of "Covariance Parameter Estimates" shown as Output 13.12.

Output 13.12: Covariance Parameter Estimates for Negative Binomial Model

Covariance Parameter Estimates			
Cov Parm	Subject	Estimate	Standard Error
Intercept	field	0.1291	0.4756
method	field	6.19E-12	.
Scale		0.9969	0.4144

The whole-plot (field × method) variance estimate is essentially zero. Although the standard error of a variance component estimate is not generally considered useful for relatively small samples, the dot (" . ") by the field×method variance estimate is not a good sign. This suggests that one should consider modifying the analysis to accommodate what appears to be a negative solution for σ^2_{FM}.

The compound symmetry reparameterization used for the Poisson-normal GLMM cannot be used with the negative binomial, because σ^2_S, the compound symmetry variance parameter, and ϕ, the negative binomial scale parameter, are confounded. The only option is to use NOBOUND.

Program

Program 13.11 shows a modified PROC GLIMMIX program to implement NOBOUND for the negative binomial GLMM using the integral approximation method.

Program 13.11

```
proc glimmix data=count_splt_plt method=laplace nobound;
 class field method mix;
 model count=method|mix/d=negbin;
 random intercept method / subject=field;
 parms (0.1)(0.1)(1);
run;
```

You must use METHOD=LAPLACE because quadrature will not work with NOBOUND. If you run the program without the PARMS statement, you get an error message: "The initial estimates did not yield a valid objective function." This tells you that PROC GLIMMIX's default algorithm to determine starting values failed with these data. The PARMS statement substitutes starting values that you provide, and turns off the PROC GLIMMIX starting value algorithm. Running the program with the PARMS statement yields a different problem: "The gradient of the objective function cannot be computed during the optimization process." In Section 12.6, the NOBOUND option worked well with the negative binomial GLMM using METHOD=LAPLACE, but be warned: because LAPLACE is an integral approximation method, negative variance implies an undefined likelihood function and hence may cause trouble. That is exactly what is happening in this example.

As an alternative, you can use the default pseudo-likelihood algorithm. To do so, delete METHOD=LAPLACE from the PROC statement. Running pseudo-likelihood, iteration fails after 83 iterations and the SAS log will give you a warning whose wording depends on the version of SAS you are running.

```
"ERROR: Invalid Operation.
ERROR: Termination due to Floating Point Exception"
```

The bottom line is that for these data and the negative binomial GLMM, NOBOUND will not provide any results, much less useable results. If the justification for using the negative binomial model is compelling—as it often is for biological count data—you must use the results of the program without NOBOUND and accept the set-to-zero default for variance estimates when it occurs or adjust the model further.

13.4 Example 2: Repeated Measures Experiment with Binomial Data

This section covers GLMMs for repeated measures data—also known as longitudinal data—that follow a non-Gaussian distribution. Although the example in this section has binomial data, the modeling approach can be applied to other non-Gaussian distributions. Section 13.4.1 provides an overview. Section 13.4.2 focuses on conditional GLMMs for repeated measures. Section 13.4.3 presents models appropriate for the marginal inference space. Section 13.4.3 includes discussion on model-based versus empirical estimators, a particularly relevant issue in the context of marginal models for longitudinal data.

13.4.1 Overview of Modeling Considerations for Non-Gaussian Repeated Measures Data

With the split-plot experiment in Section 13.3, the primary modeling issue involved constructing a linear predictor that accounted for the sources of variation that plausibly described how the data arose. In addition, modeling repeated measures data requires accounting for serial correlation between observations over time on the same experimental unit, and selecting among competing serial correlation models. Chapter 8 presented methods for Gaussian data. Modeling non-Gaussian repeated measures data, while superficially similar to the approaches shown in Chapter 8, entails additional considerations. This section presents an example with binomial data to highlight the issues. The methods shown here can be adapted to Poisson-distributed count data. Methods for other non-Gaussian distributions comprise an active area of GLMM research and are beyond the scope of this book.

As with the split-plot example is Section 13.3, model construction for the repeated measures begins by listing sources of variation to formulate a linear predictor, e.g. via the process demonstrated in Section 5.2. You can apply the same process to the longitudinal study described in Section 13.2.2. Table 13.3 shows the result.

Table 13.3: Sources of Variation for Repeated Measures Data

Units and Blocks		Treatment Design		Combined	
Source	*df*	**Source**	*df*	**Source**	*df*
		Treatment	1	Treatment	1
Classroom	11			Cclassroom(treatment)	11 − 1=10
		Time	5	Time	5
		Treatment × time	5	Treatment × time	5
Occasion(classroom)	12 × (6 − 1) = 60			Occasion(classroom) | treatment, time	60 − 10 = 50
Total	**71**	**Total**	**71**	**Total**	**71**

The linear predictor given in Equation 13.2 accounts for the sources of variation up to, but not including, the last line of the combined table. Note that the last line corresponds to the unit of observation, and, for each treatment × classroom combination, these units form a sequence of observations over the six times of measurement. As a result, these observations are potentially correlated, and a completely specified model must accurately account for this correlation. As we saw with Gaussian repeated measures in Chapter 8, inadequately accounting for correlation is a form of overdispersion, whereas an over specified correlation model adversely affects power.

With Gaussian linear models, the mean and residual variance structures are specified separately. Denote the mean structure as $\mu = \mathbf{X}\boldsymbol{\beta} + \mathbf{Z}\mathbf{u}$ and the residual covariance structure by the covariance matrix $\boldsymbol{\Sigma}$. For Gaussian data, we write the distribution of the random model effects as $\mathbf{u} \sim \mathrm{N}(\mathbf{0}, \mathbf{G})$ and the covariance matrix as $\boldsymbol{\Sigma} = \mathrm{Var}(\mathbf{y} \mid \mathbf{u}) = \mathbf{R}$. In SAS vocabulary, variance among the random model effects, $\mathrm{Var}(\mathbf{u})$, is often referred to as *G-side* variance and the covariance structure $\mathrm{Var}(\mathbf{y} \mid \mathbf{u})$ as *R-side* covariance. In PROC GLIMMIX terms, you specify the mean structure with MODEL statement for fixed components and RANDOM statement(s) for the random components, and you specify the covariance structure with a RANDOM...RESIDUAL statement. The mean and variance structures are completely distinct.

However, for the binomial and Poisson distributions, the variance is a function of the mean. There are no additional covariance parameters. You cannot specify mean and covariance structure separately as you do with Gaussian data. You must use a different strategy to account for correlation among repeated measures. There are two alternatives:

- conditional (a.k.a. *G-side*) model: this is an elaboration of the logit-normal and Poisson-normal approaches to accounting for overdispersion. Add a random unit-level effect, usually called the within-subjects random effect, to the linear predictor. Denote it w_{ijk}. Let $\mathbf{w}_{ik}$ denote the vector of within-subject effects, i.e. $\mathbf{w}'_{ik} = \begin{bmatrix} w_{i1k} & w_{i2k} & \dots & w_{i6k} \end{bmatrix}$, and let $\mathbf{w}_{ik} \sim \mathrm{N}(\mathbf{0}, \boldsymbol{\Sigma})$, where the covariance matrix $\boldsymbol{\Sigma}$ specifies the serial correlation structure.

- marginal (a.k.a. *R-side*) model: this is an elaboration of the working covariance approach for binomial and Poisson examples shown in Chapters 11, 12, and earlier in this chapter. Whereas previous examples use the compound symmetry structure, models for longitudinal data often have working covariance structures that are analogous to those typically used with repeated measures, e.g. AR(1), ANTE(1), etc. Note that in some cases, "quasi-marginal" models that include both R-side and G-side covariance structures may be needed. The presence of R-side covariance redirects inference toward the marginal mean.

Note that the approach you use depends on your target of inference. If your objectives call for inference on "a typical member of the population," you should use the conditional model. If you need to focus on the marginal mean to address your objectives, you should use the marginal—or quasi-marginal—model. This is a decision that you make *before* you begin model-fitting and data analysis.

If you use the conditional model, you can use either the integral approximation or pseudo-likelihood methods. Integral approximation methods compute a true likelihood, allowing you to use information criteria and likelihood ratio statistics to compare different covariance structures, and select among competing covariance structures just as you would with Gaussian repeated measures models. For most of the covariance structures discussed below, you will find that METHOD=LAPLACE is a better option than QUADRATURE. The complexity of repeated measures structures often overwhelms the QUADRATURE method.

Once you select the best-fitting covariance model, follow the guideline in Table 13.2 in selecting the estimation method to complete the analysis. When the number of Bernoulli observations at given times on each subject is very small ($n_{ijk} < 5$) or π_{ijk} is very close to 0 or 1, integral approximation—LAPLACE is best because of the complexity of the covariance structure. Otherwise, proceed using PROC GLIMMX's pseudo-likelihood default.

If your objectives call for inference from the marginal model, you can use the GLIMMIX procedure with the pseudo-likelihood method. You can also implement marginal repeated measures models with the GENMOD procedure's REPEATED statement, which uses a generalized estimating equation (GEE) algorithm. The GENMOD and GLIMMIX procedures produce similar, but not identical results. From an accuracy point of view, there is no compelling reason to choose one over the other for the example discussed in this section. However, if your data set calls for random model effects in addition to a working covariance structure, that is, if you need to use a quasi-marginal model to target the marginal inference space and at the same time fully account for all relevant sources of variation, PROC GLIMMIX is the only choice. In this sense, PROC GLIMMIX is more versatile. For this reason, the example below shows PROC GLIMMIX programs and results only.

13.4.2 Conditional (G-Side) GLMM for Repeated Measures

Following the discussion in the previous section, the fully specified GLMM for binomial repeated measures for this example is as follows:

- Linear predictor: $\eta_{ijk} = \eta + \alpha_i + \beta_j + \alpha\beta_{ij} + b_{ik} + w_{ijk}$.

- Distributions:

  - $b_{ik} \sim \text{NI}\left(0, \sigma_b^2\right)$.

  - $\mathbf{w}_{ik} \sim \text{MVN}\left(\mathbf{0}, \boldsymbol{\Sigma}\right)$, where $\mathbf{w}_{ik} = \begin{bmatrix} w_{i1k} & w_{i2k} & w_{i3k} & w_{i4k} & w_{i5k} & w_{i6k} \end{bmatrix}$.

  - $y_{ijk} \mid b_{ik}, w_{ijk} \sim \text{Binomial}\left(N_{ijk}, \pi_{ijk}\right)$.

- Link function: $\eta_{ijk} = \text{logit}\left(\pi_{ijk}\right)$.

Alternatively, you could use the probit link function, or the complementary log-log link. As with previous examples with binomial data, the logit and probit link produce essentially interchangeable results; which link you use depends more on the culture of the discipline that produced the data, than on any statistically based considerations. The complementary log-log should be considered if the observed proportions are predominantly close zero or predominantly close to one. The covariance, $\boldsymbol{\Sigma}$, of the unit-level effects may be as simple as compound symmetry or as complex as unstructured. You select the covariance structure much as you do for the Gaussian repeated measures models in Chapter 8. As with Gaussian repeated measures, you implement the model in two steps: first, select the covariance model, i.e. $\boldsymbol{\Sigma}$; then complete the analysis using the covariance model you select.

Selecting the Covariance Model

For step one, selection of the covariance model, suppose the alternatives are compound symmetry (CS), first-order auto regression [AR(1)], or first-order antedependence [ANTE(1)].

Program

Program 13.12 shows the sets of PROC GLIMMIX statements to enable covariance model selection.

Program 13.12

```
proc glimmix data=binomial_rptm method=laplace;
 class id trt time;
 model y/n = trt|time;
 random time / subject=id(trt) type=cs;
run;

proc glimmix data=binomial_rptm method=laplace;
 class id trt time;
 model y/n = trt|time;
 random intercept / subject=id(trt);
 random time / subject=id(trt) type=ar(1);
run;

proc glimmix data=binomial_rptm method=laplace;
 class id trt time;
 model y/n = trt|time;
 random time / subject=id(trt) type=ante(1);
run;
```

Use METHOD=LAPLACE to get valid information criteria for each competing covariance model. Notice that the betweensubjects random effect, ID(TRT), is confounded with the compound symmetry covariance parameter, so `random intercept / subject=id(trt)` does not appear in the PROC GLIMMIX statements for the compound symmetry model. The ID(TRT) random effect also does not appear in the statements for the ANTE(1) model. Technically, the between-subjects and ANTE(1) covariance structures are identifiable, but in practice, especially in relatively small data sets, including both often results in convergence failures or nonsense estimates. For this reason, we recommend against including `random intercept / subject=id(trt)` in the ANTE(1) model.

Results

Output 13.13 shows information criteria results for the three covariance models under consideration.

Output 13.13: Fit Statistics to Compare Three G-side Covariance Models

CS

Fit Statistics	
-2 Log Likelihood	346.61
AIC (smaller is better)	374.61
AICC (smaller is better)	381.98
BIC (smaller is better)	381.40
CAIC (smaller is better)	395.40
HQIC (smaller is better)	372.10

AR(1)

Fit Statistics	
-2 Log Likelihood	341.92
AIC (smaller is better)	371.92
AICC (smaller is better)	380.50
BIC (smaller is better)	379.20
CAIC (smaller is better)	394.20
HQIC (smaller is better)	369.23

ANTE(1)

Fit Statistics	
-2 Log Likelihood	331.53
AIC (smaller is better)	375.53
AICC (smaller is better)	396.19
BIC (smaller is better)	386.20
CAIC (smaller is better)	408.20
HQIC (smaller is better)	371.58

Interpretation

You can see that the AR(1) covariance model has the smallest value for all information criteria. For example, the AICC for the CS model is 381.98; for AR(1) it is 380.50; for ANTE(1) it is 396.19. Based on the information criteria, the AR(1) model is the best model among these three covariance models. While not shown here, you could modify the TYPE= option in the PROC GLIMMIX programs shown above to obtain information criteria for other covariance models if they are deemed plausible candidates.

As a final step in selecting the covariance structure, you can use the COVTEST statement to test the between-subject effect, that is, test $H_0 : \sigma_b^2 = 0$. The resulting likelihood ratio statistic is $\chi^2 = 0.03$. Dropping the between-subjects effect improves the AICC from 380.50 to 377.33. Based on this evidence, analysis proceeds without the between subject effect.

Proceeding with the Analysis

Once you select the covariance structure, you can analyze the data using essentially the same approach used for Gaussian data shown in Chapter 8. There are two primary differences. First, with a GLMM, estimates computed on the link scale must be translated to the data scale. Second, with Gaussian models, inferential statistics computed from REML covariance parameter estimates are well-established as the method of choice. With non-Gaussian repeated measures, REML is undefined. As discussed in Section 13.3.2, although integral approximation methods (LAPLACE and QUAD) are useful for selecting an appropriate covariance structure, they also yield maximum likelihood covariance parameter estimates, which have the same issues of bias as ML covariance estimates for Gaussian data. On the other hand, the default pseudo-likelihood method yields REML-like covariance parameter estimates. Noting that there are N=14 Bernoulli observations at all times for all subjects, and most of the sample proportions are not close to zero or one, following the Table 13.2 guideline we use pseudo-likelihood to complete the analysis.

Program

We begin by obtaining an interaction plot to visualize changes in response over time and the treatments' impact on those changes. Use Program 13.13.

Program 13.13

```
proc glimmix data=RptM_Binomial;
 class id trt time;
 model fav/N=trt|time;
 random time / subject=id(trt) type=ar(1);
 lsmeans trt*time / plot=meanplot(sliceby=trt join ilink) ilink;
run;
```

Eliminating METHOD=LAPLACE causes PROC GLIMMIX to use the default pseudo-likelihood option. The ILINK option in the MEANPLOT options causes the plot to use the data scale, i.e. the estimated probability of a favorable outcome for a given time and treatment. The ILINK option outside the MEANPLOT option list causes the LSMEANS table to include the data scale estimates, but it has no effect on the MEANPLOT statement. In other words, if you include the ILINK option outside the parentheses, but do not include an ILINK option within the parentheses, the MEANPLOT will use the link scale (in this case, the logit).

Results

Figure 13.1 shows the plot.

Figure 13.1: Interaction Plot for Repeated Measures Data

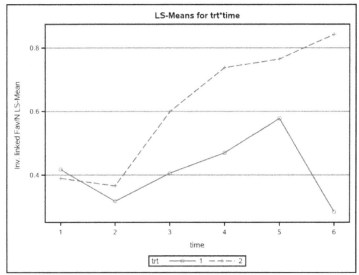

The plot suggests that students under treatment 2 consistently improve after time 2, whereas students under treatment 1 also improve, although more slowly, until time 5, but then their probabilities decrease dramatically from time 5 to time 6.

In addition to plots that allow you to visualize the data, formal inferential statistics will generally be required. There are several ways one could proceed. Shown below are selected estimates and tests of possible interest. These are merely examples—different or additional estimates and tests using post-processing statements such as CONTRAST, ESTIMATE, and LSMESTIMATE, might be more appropriate, depending on specific objectives. Obviously, selection of formal statistics must be guided by the objectives of a given study. We leave this to reader.

Program

Use Program 13.14 to obtain the overall tests and estimates described above.

Program 13.14

```
proc glimmix data=RptM_Binomial;
 class id trt time;
 model fav/N=trt|time;
 random time / subject=id(trt) type=ar(1);
 lsmeans trt*time / slice=time slicediff=time cl oddsratio ilink;
 lsmestimate trt*time
```

```
            'time 5 vs 6, treatment 1' 0 0 0 0 1 -1  0 0 0 0 0 0,
            'time 5 vs 6, treatment 2' 0 0 0 0 0 0   0 0 0 0 1 -1/cl exp;
 contrast 'trt x linear until time 5'
    trt*time 2 1 0 -1 -2 0  -2 -1 0 1 2 0;
 contrast 'trt non-linear until time 5'
    trt*time 2 -1 -2 -1 2 0   -2 1 2  1 -2 0,
    trt*time 1 -2 0 2 -1 0  -1 2 0 -2 1 0,
    trt*time 1 -4 6 -4 1 0  -1 4 -6 4 -1 0;
 contrast 'trt x time 5 vs time 6' trt*time 0 0 0 0 1 -1  0 0 0 0 -1 1;
 run;
```

The SLICE and SLICEDIFF options obtain tests and estimates of the simple effects of treatment at each time. The ODDSRATIO option converts difference estimates on the logit scale to estimates of odds ratios on the data scale. The LSMESTIMATE statement obtains an estimate of the change in proportion from time 5 to time 6 for treatment 1, the change that appears visually as an abrupt drop. The CONTRAST statements partition the treatment × time interaction into a comparison of linear trends for the two treatments through time 5, a departure from linear trend for the two treatments through time 5, and a comparison of the two treatments' change from time 5 to time 6.

Results

Output 13.14 shows selected results.

Output 13.14: Selected Estimates and Test Statistics for G-side Repeated Measures Analysis

Fit Statistics	
-2 Res Log Pseudo-Likelihood	212.39
Generalized Chi-Square	61.48
Gener. Chi-Square / DF	1.02

Covariance Parameter Estimates			
Cov Parm	Subject	Estimate	Standard Error
Variance	id(trt)	1.2914	0.3909
AR(1)	id(trt)	0.6315	0.1263

Type III Tests of Fixed Effects				
Effect	Num DF	Den DF	F Value	Pr > F
trt	1	60	3.55	0.0643
time	5	60	1.89	0.1094
trt*time	5	60	1.74	0.1389

Contrasts				
Label	Num DF	Den DF	F Value	Pr > F
trt x linear until time 5	1	60	1.39	0.2428
trt non-linear until time 5	3	60	0.22	0.8795
trt x time 5 vs time 6	1	60	4.75	0.0333

											Standard		
trt	time	Estimate	Standard Error	DF	t Value	Pr > |t|	Alpha	Lower	Upper	Mean	Error Mean	Lower Mean	Upper Mean
1	1	-0.3335	0.5192	60	-0.64	0.5231	0.05	-1.3720	0.7051	0.4174	0.1263	0.2023	0.6693
1	2	-0.7640	0.5293	60	-1.44	0.1541	0.05	-1.8227	0.2946	0.3178	0.1147	0.1391	0.5731
1	3	-0.3806	0.5285	60	-0.72	0.4742	0.05	-1.4379	0.6766	0.4060	0.1275	0.1919	0.6630
1	4	-0.1209	0.5294	60	-0.23	0.8201	0.05	-1.1799	0.9380	0.4698	0.1319	0.2351	0.7187
1	5	0.3160	0.5400	60	0.59	0.5607	0.05	-0.7643	1.3962	0.5783	0.1317	0.3177	0.8016
1	6	-0.9243	0.5387	60	-1.72	0.0914	0.05	-2.0020	0.1533	0.2841	0.1096	0.1190	0.5383
2	1	-0.4487	0.5224	60	-0.86	0.3937	0.05	-1.4936	0.5961	0.3897	0.1242	0.1834	0.6448
2	2	-0.5498	0.5262	60	-1.04	0.3003	0.05	-1.6024	0.5028	0.3659	0.1221	0.1676	0.6231
2	3	0.4041	0.5265	60	0.77	0.4458	0.05	-0.6491	1.4573	0.5997	0.1264	0.3432	0.8111
2	4	1.0324	0.5398	60	1.91	0.0606	0.05	-0.04741	2.1122	0.7374	0.1045	0.4882	0.8921
2	5	1.1824	0.5387	60	2.20	0.0320	0.05	0.1049	2.2599	0.7654	0.09673	0.5262	0.9055
2	6	1.6756	0.5552	60	3.02	0.0037	0.05	0.5650	2.7863	0.8423	0.07374	0.6376	0.9419

trt*time Least Squares Means

Tests of Effect Slices for trt*time Sliced By time

time	Num DF	Den DF	F Value	Pr > F
1	1	60	0.02	0.8762
2	1	60	0.08	0.7751
3	1	60	1.11	0.2971
4	1	60	2.33	0.1324
5	1	60	1.29	0.2605
6	1	60	11.29	0.0014

Simple Effect Comparisons of trt*time Least Squares Means By time

Simple Effect Level	trt	_trt	Estimate	Standard Error	DF	t Value	Pr > |t|	Alpha	Lower	Upper	Odds Ratio
time 1	1	2	0.1153	0.7365	60	0.16	0.8762	0.05	-1.3580	1.5885	1.122
time 2	1	2	-0.2142	0.7463	60	-0.29	0.7751	0.05	-1.7071	1.2787	0.807
time 3	1	2	-0.7847	0.7460	60	-1.05	0.2971	0.05	-2.2770	0.7076	0.456
time 4	1	2	-1.1533	0.7561	60	-1.53	0.1324	0.05	-2.6658	0.3591	0.316
time 5	1	2	-0.8664	0.7627	60	-1.14	0.2605	0.05	-2.3921	0.6593	0.420
time 6	1	2	-2.6000	0.7737	60	-3.36	0.0014	0.05	-4.1475	-1.0524	0.074

Simple Effect Comparisons of trt*time Least Squares Means By time

Simple Effect Level	trt	_trt	Lower Odds Ratio	Upper Odds Ratio
time 1	1	2	0.257	4.896
time 2	1	2	0.181	3.592
time 3	1	2	0.103	2.029
time 4	1	2	0.070	1.432

Simple Effect Comparisons of trt*time Least Squares Means By time				
Simple Effect Level	trt	_trt	Lower Odds Ratio	Upper Odds Ratio
time 5	1	2	0.091	1.933
time 6	1	2	0.016	0.349

Least Squares Means Estimates										
Effect	Label	Estimate	Standard Error	DF	t Value	Pr > |t|	Alpha	Lower	Upper	Exponentiated Estimate
trt*time	time 5 vs 6, treatment 1	1.2403	0.5561	60	2.23	0.0295	0.05	0.1278	2.3528	3.4566
trt*time	time 5 vs 6, treatment 2	-0.4933	0.5690	60	-0.87	0.3895	0.05	-1.6315	0.6450	0.6106

Least Squares Means Estimates			
Effect	Label	Exponentiated Lower	Exponentiated Upper
trt*time	time 5 vs 6, treatment 1	1.1364	10.5145
trt*time	time 5 vs 6, treatment 2	0.1956	1.9060

Interpretation

The Generalized χ^2/DF in the "Fit Statistics" table is not a recommended diagnostic. If you want a diagnostic statistic for overdispersion, you need to compute the Pearson χ^2/DF statistic using METHOD=LAPLACE. Although not shown here, the Pearson χ^2/DF is 0.39.

The "Covariance Parameter Estimates" table gives the estimated variance among logits between subjects with treatments at each time period (VARIANCE = $\hat{\sigma}_W^2 = 1.29$) and the correlation between adjacent measurements in time (AR(1) = $\hat{\rho} = 0.63$) , again on the logit scale.

The "Type III Tests of Fixed Effects" table gives F values and associated p-values for overall tests of treatment $\times$ time interaction and the main effects of treatment and time. The "Contrasts" table shows a decomposition of the five degrees of freedom treatment $\times$ time interaction through time 5. The two elements of the decomposition are linear and non-linear (lack of fit from linear) polynomial regression components. The p-value for the trt $\times$ non-linear contrast is close to 0.88 and for the trt $\times$ linear contrast is just less than 0.25. The visual evidence that the proportion of favorable outcomes increases more for treatment 2 than for treatment 1 through time 5 is not strongly supported by formal test statistics. On the other hand, for the treatment difference in proportions from time 5 to time 6 ("trt x time 5 vs time 6"), the p-value is 0.03, indicating that the change in proportion from time 5 to time 6 differs between treatment 1 and treatment 2

The table "trt*time Least Squares Means" give the model scale estimated logits (ESTIMATE) and the data scale estimated proportions (MEAN) for each treatment $\times$ time combination. Note that the table includes standard errors and 95% confidence bounds.

The table "Tests of Effect Slices for trt*time Sliced By time," gives F values and associated p-values for test of no treatment difference at each time. If $\alpha = 0.05$ is the criterion, only at time 6 is there statistically significant evidence of a treatment difference. The table "Simple Effect Comparisons of trt*time Least Squares Means By time," gives the results from the SLICEDIFF option. This table also includes p-values identical to those in the SLICES table. They are not shown here in the interest of space and because they already appeared above in SLICES. The SLICEDIFF gives estimates, standard errors, and confidence bounds as well as p-values. In most cases, if you obtain SLICEDIFF results, there is no need to also compute SLICE. As with previous binomial examples, the data scale statistic for treatment difference with the logit link is the odds ratio. You can see that the 95% confidence intervals for the odds ratio at times 1 through 5 all include 1; only for time 6 is the odds ratio confidence interval (0.016, 0.35) entirely below 1.

Finally, the table "Least Squares Means Estimates" gives the estimate difference between times 5 and 6 for each treatment on the logit scale (ESTIMATE) and the data scale odds ratio, the (EXPONENTATED ESTIMATE). For treatment 1, the data scale estimate is 1.24 and the estimated odds ratio is 3.46. For treatment 2, the data scale difference is -0.49 and the estimated odds ratio is 0.61. For treatment 1, the 95% confidence interval for the odds ratio extends from

1.13 to 10.51; for treatment 2, the 95% confidence interval extends from 0.20 to 1.91. The visual evidence of a decrease in the probability of favorable outcome from time 5 to time 6 for treatment 1 is consistent the formal evidence provided by the confidence interval on the odds ratio.

13.4.3 Marginal (R-side) GLMM for Repeated Measures

Recalling the discussion in Section 13.4.1, if the marginal means are the appropriate target of inference, then you must use a marginal model that accounts for correlation between repeated measurements within subjects using a working covariance structure. The fully specified marginal model for binomial repeated measures for this example is as follows:

- Linear predictor: $\eta_{ijk} = \eta + \alpha_i + \tau_j + \alpha\tau_{ij}$.

- Distributions: $y_{ijk} \sim quasi - \text{Binomial}(N_{ijk}, \pi_{ijk})$ $\text{Var}(\mathbf{y}_{ik}) = \mathbf{A}^{\frac{1}{2}}\mathbf{R}\mathbf{A}^{\frac{1}{2}}$ where the vector $\mathbf{y}_{ik}$ denotes the six observations on the kth class assigned to method i; that is, the following:

  ○ $\mathbf{y}_{ik} = \begin{bmatrix} y_{i1k} & y_{i2k} & y_{i3k} & y_{i4k} & y_{i5k} & y_{i6k} \end{bmatrix}$.

  ○ $\mathbf{A}$ contains the binomial variance function for each observation, i.e. a diagonal matrix with elements $N_{ijk}\pi_{ijk}(1 - \pi_{ijk})$.

  ○ $\mathbf{R}$ is the residual covariance, also called the R-side covariance or the working covariance. The generic form of the residual covariance is as follows, where $\sigma_{W,jj}$ denotes the working "variance" at time j, and $\sigma_{W,jj'}$ denotes the working covariance between observations on the same class at time j and time j', where $j \neq j'$ (note that the generic form as given here is the unstructured (UN) residual covariance. See comments below regarding simplification):

$$\mathbf{R} = \begin{bmatrix} \sigma_{W,11} & \sigma_{W,12} & \cdots & \sigma_{W,16} \\ & \sigma_{W,22} & \cdots & \sigma_{W,26} \\ & & \cdots & \cdots \\ & & & \sigma_{W,66} \end{bmatrix}$$

- Link function: $\eta_{ijk} = \text{logit}(\pi_{ijk})$.

As with the conditional GLMM, you could use the probit link function, or the complementary log-log link, instead of the logit link.

The residual covariance as specified above is intended as a generic description. If you define it literally as given above, it is an unstructured (UN) working covariance. Usually, more parsimonious forms are used. For example, for the AR(1) working covariance, all $\sigma_{W,jj} = \varphi$, where φ denotes a working scale parameter, and $\sigma_{W,jj'} = \varphi\rho_W^{|j-j'|}$, where ρ_W denotes working autocorrelation parameter. In theory, the covariance models used for the conditional GLMM—and for Gaussian repeated measures models—all have working covariance analogs.

Program

Program 13.15 shows the PROC GLIMMIX statements that specify a marginal repeated measures GLMM, using AR(1) residual covariance structure. This program includes the same mean comparison LSMEANS, LSMESTIMATE, and CONTRAST statements as the conditional GLMM Program 13.14. The syntax for these statements does not change.

Program 13.15

```
proc glimmix data=RptM_Binomial empirical=mbn ic=pq;
 class id trt time;
 model fav/N=trt|time;
 random time / subject=id(trt) type=ar(1) residual;
 lsmeans trt*time / slice=time slicediff=time cl oddsratio ilink;
 lsmestimate trt*time
   'time 5 vs 6, treatment 1' 0 0 0 0 1 -1  0 0 0 0 0 0,
   'time 5 vs 6, treatment 2' 0 0 0 0 0 0  0 0 0 0 1 -1/cl exp;
 contrast 'trt x linear until time 5'
   trt*time 2 1 0 -1 -2 0  -2 -1 0 1 2 0;
 contrast 'trt non-linear until time 5'
   trt*time 2 -1 -2 -1 2 0  -2 1 2  1 -2 0,
   trt*time 1 -2 0 2 -1 0  -1 2 0 -2  1 0,
   trt*time 1 -4 6 -4 1 0  -1 4 -6 4 -1 0;
```

```
contrast 'trt x time 5 vs time 6'
  trt*time 0 0 0 0 1 -1  0 0 0 0 -1 1;
title 'Marginal (GEE-type) model';
run;
```

Unlike the conditional GLMM, you cannot use integral approximation methods for GLMMs that have an R-side covariance structure. In SAS syntax terms, you cannot use LAPLACE or QUAD if you have a RANDOM statement containing the word RESIDUAL. The IC=PQ option allows you to compute pseudo-likelihood analogs of information criteria as described by Vonesh and Chinchilli (1997) and Verbeke and Molenberghs (2000). Because the pseudo-likelihood arising from different residual covariance structures are not comparable, you cannot use the pseudo information criteria to select among competing working covariance models. The problem of selecting among competing working covariance models is an active area of research. As of this printing, no method for doing so has gained acceptance, and there is no procedure in SAS for choosing between working covariance models. Because model-based standard errors and test statistics depend on which working covariance you use, the standard approach to interval estimation and testing is to use the EMPIRICAL procedure, also known as the sandwich estimator or the robust estimate. This procedure is called "robust" because it is less vulnerable to model misspecification than model-based procedures. As we have seen in previous examples in Chapters 11 and 12, with small samples, the classical EMPIRICAL procedure produces inflated test statistics and downward biased standard errors. The bias correction developed by Morel, et al. (2002) and the MBN option in PROC GLIMMIX is recommended in these cases.

Results

Output 13.15 shows selected results.

Output 13.15: Estimates and Inferential Statistics for Marginal Repeated Measures GLMM

Fit Statistics	
-2 Res Log Pseudo-Likelihood	190.53
Pseudo-AIC	218.53
Pseudo-AICC	227.86
Pseudo-BIC	247.85
Pseudo-CAIC	261.85
Pseudo-HQIC	230.00
Generalized Chi-Square	228.38
Gener. Chi-Square / DF	3.81

REML information criteria are adjusted for fixed effects and covariance parameters. Fit statistics based on pseudo-likelihoods are not useful for comparing models that differ in their pseudo-data.

Covariance Parameter Estimates			
Cov Parm	Subject	Estimate	Standard Error
AR(1)	id(trt)	0.4857	0.1086
Residual		3.8063	0.8214

Type III Tests of Fixed Effects				
Effect	Num DF	Den DF	F Value	Pr > F
trt	1	10	2.22	0.1670
time	5	50	1.24	0.3054
trt*time	5	50	2.06	0.0862

Contrasts				
Label	Num DF	Den DF	F Value	Pr > F
trt x linear until time 5	1	50	0.96	0.3322
trt non-linear until time 5	3	50	0.10	0.9612
trt x time 5 vs time 6	1	50	4.04	0.0497

trt*time Least Squares Means														
trt	time	Estimate	Standard Error	DF	t Value	Pr > |t|	Alpha	Lower	Upper	Mean	Standard Error Mean	Lower Mean	Upper Mean
1	1	-0.2877	0.4565	50	-0.63	0.5315	0.05	-1.2047	0.6293	0.4286	0.1118	0.2306	0.6523
1	2	-0.6400	0.5765	50	-1.11	0.2722	0.05	-1.7980	0.5179	0.3452	0.1303	0.1421	0.6267
1	3	-0.2877	0.6401	50	-0.45	0.6551	0.05	-1.5734	0.9981	0.4286	0.1568	0.1717	0.7307
1	4	-0.09531	0.6044	50	-0.16	0.8753	0.05	-1.3093	1.1186	0.4762	0.1508	0.2126	0.7537
1	5	0.2392	0.7100	50	0.34	0.7376	0.05	-1.1868	1.6653	0.5595	0.1750	0.2338	0.8409
1	6	-0.7472	0.5900	50	-1.27	0.2112	0.05	-1.9322	0.4378	0.3214	0.1287	0.1265	0.6077
2	1	-0.3857	0.4867	50	-0.79	0.4319	0.05	-1.3633	0.5920	0.4048	0.1173	0.2037	0.6438
2	2	-0.4855	0.5397	50	-0.90	0.3726	0.05	-1.5695	0.5985	0.3810	0.1273	0.1723	0.6453
2	3	0.2877	0.5307	50	0.54	0.5902	0.05	-0.7783	1.3536	0.5714	0.1300	0.3147	0.7947
2	4	0.8587	0.6429	50	1.34	0.1877	0.05	-0.4326	2.1500	0.7024	0.1344	0.3935	0.8957
2	5	1.0361	0.5107	50	2.03	0.0478	0.05	0.01032	2.0619	0.7381	0.09872	0.5026	0.8871
2	6	1.6094	0.4623	50	3.48	0.0010	0.05	0.6809	2.5380	0.8333	0.06421	0.6639	0.9268

Tests of Effect Slices for trt*time Sliced By time				
time	Num DF	Den DF	F Value	Pr > F
1	1	50	0.02	0.8839
2	1	50	0.04	0.8457
3	1	50	0.48	0.4922
4	1	50	1.17	0.2848
5	1	50	0.83	0.3666
6	1	50	9.89	0.0028

Simple Effect Comparisons of trt*time Least Squares Means By time											
Simple Effect Level	trt	_trt	Estimate	Standard Error	DF	t Value	Pr > |t|	Alpha	Lower	Upper	Odds Ratio
time 1	1	2	0.09798	0.6673	50	0.15	0.8839	0.05	-1.2424	1.4384	1.103
time 2	1	2	-0.1545	0.7897	50	-0.20	0.8457	0.05	-1.7407	1.4316	0.857
time 3	1	2	-0.5754	0.8315	50	-0.69	0.4922	0.05	-2.2455	1.0948	0.562
time 4	1	2	-0.9540	0.8824	50	-1.08	0.2848	0.05	-2.7263	0.8183	0.385
time 5	1	2	-0.7969	0.8746	50	-0.91	0.3666	0.05	-2.5535	0.9598	0.451
time 6	1	2	-2.3567	0.7495	50	-3.14	0.0028	0.05	-3.8621	-0.8512	0.095

Simple Effect Comparisons of trt*time Least Squares Means By time				
Simple Effect Level	trt	_trt	Lower Odds Ratio	Upper Odds Ratio
time 1	1	2	0.289	4.214
time 2	1	2	0.175	4.185
time 3	1	2	0.106	2.988
time 4	1	2	0.065	2.267
time 5	1	2	0.078	2.611
time 6	1	2	0.021	0.427

Least Squares Means Estimates										
Effect	Label	Estimate	Standard Error	DF	t Value	Pr > |t|	Alpha	Lower	Upper	Exponentiated Estimate
trt*time	time 5 vs 6, treatment 1	0.9864	0.5935	50	1.66	0.1027	0.05	-0.2056	2.1785	2.6817
trt*time	time 5 vs 6, treatment 2	-0.5733	0.4993	50	-1.15	0.2563	0.05	-1.5763	0.4296	0.5636

Least Squares Means Estimates			
Effect	Label	Exponentiated Lower	Exponentiated Upper
trt*time	time 5 vs 6, treatment 1	0.8142	8.8328
trt*time	time 5 vs 6, treatment 2	0.2067	1.5367

Interpretation

Most of the listing for the marginal model is similar in interpretation to analogous statistics computed for the conditional GLMM (see Output 13.14 and its interpretation). The major difference is that the estimated probabilities for each treatment at various times and the mean comparison statistics that follow from these means all focus on the mean of the marginal distribution rather than the probability of the outcome of interest for a typical member of the population. Recall that the former is the target of the inference space in a marginal model, whereas the latter is the broad inference target in a conditional model.

Important note: In the "Fit Statistics" table, the "Gener. Chi-Sq / DF" statistic, equal to 3.81 in this example, should not be interpreted as an overdispersion diagnostic. In the context of a marginal model, the generalized chi-square statistic is simply the estimate of the scale parameter (or residual variance) of the residual covariance model. The estimate of the latter, also 3.81, appears in the "Covariance Parameter Estimates" table. The AR(1) correlation, although a "working" correlation rather than a true auto-correlation, can be interpreted similarly to the interpretation you give the AR(1) correlation in the conditional GLMM.

13.5 Summary

This chapter introduces the analysis of non-Gaussian data from multilevel experiments. Examples focus on binomial data and discrete count data from studies with split-plot and repeated measures structures. Analysis draws on linear mixed model concepts and methods for split-plot and repeated measures introduced in Chapters 5 and 8, and on GLMM concepts and methods introduced in Chapter 11 for binomial data and Chapter 12 for count data.

Four important ideas from this chapter are as follows:

- How to construct a plausible model from a description of study design and response variable
- How to deal with overdispersion in the context of multilevel experiments
- The interplay between conditional and marginal broad inference, and how within-subject covariance is modeled
- Best practices with regard to when to use integral approximation (QUADRATURE or LAPLACE) or pseudo-likelihood methods to implement analysis

Model construction draws on and extends techniques used in Chapters 5, 8, 11, and 12.

Gaussian LMMs account for within-subject correlation through the residual covariance matrix, defined in PROC GLMMIX by a RANDOM statement containing the word RESIDUAL (referred to in this text by the shorthand "RANDOM...RESIDUAL"). In spilt-plot experiments, the residual covariance matrix typically reduces to split-plot error. On the other hand, binomial and Poisson distributions do not have a scale parameter, and the negative binomial scale parameter is not readily amenable to being expanded into a correlated error structure. As a result, GLMMs must use different strategies. GLMMs can account for overdispersion and within-subject correlation either by including random model effects in the linear predictor with suitably defined covariance structures, or they can use residual covariance models—often referred to as working covariance structures. Including random effects in the linear predictor results in conditional models, suitable for inference that targets a "typical member of the population." Using a working covariance structure results in marginal (or quasi-marginal) models that target (or approximately target) the marginal mean. PROC GLIMMIX RANDOM...RESIDUAL statements define marginal GLMMs, and closely resemble syntax used with Gaussian LMMs. On the other hand, PROC GLIMMIX statements for conditional GLMMs define within-subject covariance via RANDOM statements that define the assumed covariance structure of the random model effects.

Integral approximation methods must be used to compute overdispersion diagnostic statistics and information criteria to assess competing potential covariance structures. However, pseudo-likelihood or integral approximation may be preferred for estimation and computing inferential statistics, depending on the size and structure of the design, and the characteristics of the distribution of the observations conditional on the random model effects. Section 13.3.2 presents current-at-the-time-of-publication guidelines. The remainder of Section 13.3 presents a split-plot analysis. Section 13.4 presents a repeated measures analysis.

Chapter 14: Power, Precision, and Sample Size II: General Approaches

14.1 Introduction 487
14.2 Split Plot Example Suggesting the Need for a Follow-Up Study 487
14.3 Precision and Power Analysis for Planning a Split-Plot Experiment 489
14.4 Use of Mixed Model Methods to Compare Two Proposed Designs 492
14.5 Precision and Power Analysis: A Repeated Measures Example 495
    14.5.1 Using Pilot Data to Inform Precision and Power Analysis 495
    14.5.2 Repeated Measures Precision and Power Analysis 498
    14.5.3 Final Thoughts on Repeated Measures Power Analysis 501
14.6 Precision and Power Analysis for Non-Gaussian Data: A Binomial Example 501
    14.6.1 A Simplistic Approach 501
    14.6.2 Precision and Power: Blocked Design, Binomial Response 502
14.7 Precision and Power: Example with Incomplete Blocks and Count Data 505
14.8 Summary 508

14.1 Introduction

In Chapter 4, mixed-model-based procedures for precision and power analysis were introduced, focusing on studies with simple blocking structure and a single size experimental unit. However, as seen in Chapters 5 and 8, many studies have a more complex design structure with more than one size experimental units, giving rise to models with multiple sources of error, or repeated measures that require accounting for within-subject correlation. In addition, Chapters 11, 12, and 13 present mixed models with non-Gaussian response variables.

Greater model complexity increases the need for well-planned and well-designed studies. Most of the problems associated with complex mixed models and generalized linear mixed models occur in the context of inadequately designed or underpowered studies. To alleviate these problems, we need GLMM-based methods to anticipate the precision and power of proposed designs. These methods build on approaches introduced in Chapter 4.

In this chapter, we begin in Section 14.2 with a scenario involving a split-plot experiment that suggests the need for a follow-up study. Section 14.3 shows how to implement precision and power analysis for such a follow-up study. Section 14.4 demonstrates how to compare competing proposed designs using mixed model methods. Section 14.5 presents precision and power analyses of a proposed repeated measures experiment. Finally, Section 14.6 introduces GLMM-based analysis of precision and power for non-Gaussian data, using a multilocation example with binomial data to illustrate.

As with Chapter 4, the main purpose of this chapter is to show planning methods that take advantage of mixed model methodology. Unlike the examples in Chapter 4, for which conventional, non-mixed model methods can provide approximate power and sample size calculations, you will see that the examples in this chapter *require* mixed model thinking, and that power and sample size determinations done without mixed model methodology can produce inaccurate—possibly catastrophically inaccurate—recommendations.

A final comment. One of the take-home messages of this chapter should be that using mixed model thinking in the planning of statistical studies is a *process*, often involving the comparison of competing plausible designs, and not merely a final power calculation once a design has been chosen. Done properly, the stages that precede final design selection are the most important. Many require good communication between statistician and subject matter specialist. A few terms used in the chapter are not precise technical terms but are essential nonetheless. For example, in planning a study, researchers must decide how large a difference they consider to be "consequential." Another way of putting this would be, "what is the minimum difference considered 'scientifically relevant'?" or "Is a difference of X units large enough to matter if it is a real difference?" This is not a technical statistical quantity. It is a judgment—possibly subjective to some extent—that someone with expertise and experience in the subject matter being studied must make.

14.2 Split Plot Example Suggesting the Need for a Follow-Up Study

This example involves a 2×2 factorial experiment conducted as a split plot. Factor A is the whole plot factor. The whole plot was implemented in complete blocks. Data set "Split Plot Pilot" contains the data for this example. This section shows the analysis leading up to the main point: certain estimated treatment differences were not statistically significant, but the research team considered those differences to be consequential (i.e. "scientifically relevant" in the judgment of the principal investigator), if they could be demonstrated to be reproducible. To do this, our task is to use the information from this experiment to design a follow-up study with sufficient precision and power.

Consistent with the design, the model for the data is $y_{ijk} \mid r_k, w_{ik} \sim N\left(\mu_{ijk}, \sigma^2\right)$, $\mu_{ijk} = \mu + \alpha_i + \beta_j + \alpha\beta_{ij} + r_k + w_{ik}$, and

$$\begin{bmatrix} r_k \\ w_{ik} \end{bmatrix} \sim N\left(\begin{bmatrix} 0 \\ 0 \end{bmatrix}, \begin{bmatrix} \sigma_r^2 & 0 \\ 0 & \sigma_w^2 \end{bmatrix} \right)$$

where r_k denotes the block effect, with variance σ_r^2, w_{ik} denotes the whole plot error with variance σ_w^2, and α and β refer to A and B effects. Program 14.1 shows the statements for this analysis.

Program 14.1

```
proc glimmix;
   class block a b;
   model y=a|b;
   random intercept a / subject=block;
   lsmeans a*b / slicediff=(a b);
run;
```

Output 14.1shows the results that motivate the precision and power analysis in Section 14.3.

Output 14.1: Type III Tests of Fixed Effects, Means, and Differences from Split Plot Data

Covariance Parameter Estimates

Cov Parm	Subject	Estimate	Standard Error
Intercept	block	20.5121	35.2531
a	block	21.3339	38.3592
Residual		68.5338	30.6493

Type III Tests of Fixed Effects

Effect	Num DF	Den DF	F Value	Pr > F
a	1	5	1.36	0.2965
b	1	10	3.81	0.0794
a*b	1	10	1.15	0.3097

a*b Least Squares Means

a	b	Estimate	Standard Error	DF	t Value	Pr > |t|
1	1	40.5000	4.2891	10	9.44	<.0001
1	2	43.4833	4.2891	10	10.14	<.0001
2	1	41.9000	4.2891	10	9.77	<.0001
2	2	52.1167	4.2891	10	12.15	<.0001

Simple Effect Comparisons of a*b Least Squares Means By a

Simple Effect Level	b	_b	Estimate	Standard Error	DF	t Value	Pr > |t|
a 1	1	2	-2.9833	4.7796	10	-0.62	0.5465
a 2	1	2	-10.2167	4.7796	10	-2.14	0.0583

Simple Effect Comparisons of a*b Least Squares Means By b							
Simple Effect Level	a	_a	Estimate	Standard Error	DF	t Value	Pr > |t|
b 1	1	2	-1.4000	5.4732	10	-0.26	0.8033
b 2	1	2	-8.6333	5.4732	10	-1.58	0.1458

The *p*-value exceeds 0.10 for all tests of model effects and treatment differences, except for the main effect of B and the simple effect of B given A2, whose *p*-values are between 0.05 and 0.10. At $\alpha = 0.05$, nothing is statistically significant (based on alpha = 0.05). The variance components estimates, the least squares means, and the simple effects, particularly the effects of B given A2 and A given B2, will be of interest in the next section.

The research team is especially concerned about the estimated simple effect of B given A2, i.e. $\hat{\mu}_{21} - \hat{\mu}_{22}$ where μ_{ij} denotes the mean of the $A_i \times B_j$ treatment combination. The estimated difference is 10.22. In addition, they are concerned about the simple effect of A given B2, i.e. $\hat{\mu}_{12} - \hat{\mu}_{22}$, whose estimated difference is 8.63. They are concerned about the difference between these simple effects and those given A1 and B1. They are concerned that reporting only a main effect of B, ignoring the discrepancy between the simple effects of B given A1 and A2, might constitute misinformation. The research team considers 5 to be the minimum consequential (i.e. scientifically relevant) difference; if the estimated simple effects of A given B2 and B given A2 can be shown to be reproducible, and different from the simple effects of A given B1 and B given A1, this would be important.

If the observed differences are consequential and yet not statistically significant, it is reasonable to suggest that this study was underpowered. In the next section, we use the approach introduced in Chapter 4 with the information and model from this analysis to plan a follow-up study.

14.3 Precision and Power Analysis for Planning a Split-Plot Experiment

Recalling Chapter 4, there are three steps in mixed-model-based power analysis:

1. Exemplary DATA step. Create a data set with the same structure as the data to be collected in the study.
2. PROC GLIMMIX (or PROC MIXED) step. Use the MODEL and RANDOM statements when the data are collected. Hold the variance components constant at values that are consistent with one's best knowledge about them at the time the study is planned.
3. Power step. Use the *F* value and degrees of freedom from Step 2 to compute the non-centrality parameter and the critical value. Use those to determine power.

Here, assume that we want to use the same design as the study in Section 14.2, but increase replication sufficiently for adequate precision and power. Thus, the exemplary data set will have the same structure as the pilot study. For this design, increase replication by increasing the number of blocks.

Programs

Program 14.2 shows example statements to create the exemplary data set.

Program 14.2

```
data exemplary;
n_blocks=24;
 input a b mu;
  do block=1 to n_blocks;
   output;
  end;
datalines;
1 1 40
1 2 44
2 1 42
2 2 52
;
run;
```

The data give the anticipated means for the four treatment combinations. In this case, they are simply the estimated means from the analysis in Section 14.2 rounded to the nearest integer. The simple effect of A given B2 to be evaluated in this power analysis would thus be 8, and the simple effect of B given A2 to be evaluated would be 10. The variable N_BLOCKS specifies the number of blocks—hence the amount of replication—to be assessed. Just as we did in Chapter 4, you vary the number of replicates, in this case by changing N_BLOCKS, if the 24 blocks specified here do not provide the desired precision or power.

Note that, although the means of the first study are used in the power analysis presented in this section, you are not compelled to use those means. If those planning the study have additional information, you could certainly use that information and modify the expected means accordingly.

Once you create the exemplary data set, the PROC GLIMMIX step is next shown in Program 14.3.

Program 14.3

```
proc glimmix data=exemplary;
   class block a b;
   model mu=a|b;
   random intercept a / subject=block;
   parms (20)(21.3)(68.5)/hold=1,2,3;
   lsmeans a*b/slicediff=(a b) cl;
   contrast 'a|b=1' a 1 -1 a*b 1 0 -1 0;
   contrast 'a|b=2' a 1 -1 a*b 0 1 0 -1;
   contrast 'b|a=1' b 1 -1 a*b 1 -1 0 0;
   contrast 'b|a=2' b 1 -1 a*b 0 0 1 -1;
   ods output tests3=overall_F contrasts=simple_effects;
run;
```

The variance components given in the PARMS statement come from the estimates shown in Output 14.1. As with all precision and power programs, you must use the HOLD option to make sure that PROC GLIMMIX uses the variance components given and does not attempt to re-estimate them using the exemplary data. The LSMEANS statement provides the precision analysis. In this case, we focus on simple effects using the SLICEDIFF option. The CL option enables you to see the expected width of the confidence intervals. While you could use the information from SLICEDIFF to compute power for the simple effect tests, using CONTRAST statements is easier. The CONTRAST information can be merged with the Type III tests of the main effects and interaction and a single set of program statements can be used to obtain power.

Note that you get the correct coefficients by converting the definition of simple effect in terms of the μ_{ij} into an expression in terms of model effects. For example, the first contrast, "A|B = 1" the main effect of A given B1, is defined as $\mu_{11} - \mu_{21} = (\mu + \alpha_1 + \beta_1 + \alpha\beta_{11}) - (\mu + \alpha_2 + \beta_1 + \alpha\beta_{21}) = \alpha_1 - \alpha_2 + \alpha\beta_{11} - \alpha\beta_{21}$, and hence the following statement:

```
contrast 'a|b=1' a 1 -1 a*b 1 0 -1 0;
```

Results

Output 14.2 shows the results of the precision analysis for 24 blocks.

Output 14.2 Precision Analysis: Simple Effects from Split Plot with 24 blocks

Simple Effect Comparisons of a*b Least Squares Means By a										
Simple Effect Level	b	_b	Estimate	Standard Error	DF	t Value	Pr > |t|	Alpha	Lower	Upper
a 1	1	2	-4.0000	2.3892	46	-1.67	0.1009	0.05	-8.8092	0.8092
a 2	1	2	-10.0000	2.3892	46	-4.19	0.0001	0.05	-14.8092	-5.1908

			Simple Effect Comparisons of a*b Least Squares Means By b							
Simple Effect Level	a	_a	Estimate	Standard Error	DF	t Value	Pr > |t|	Alpha	Lower	Upper
b 1	1	2	-2.0000	2.7356	46	-0.73	0.4684	0.05	-7.5064	3.5064
b 2	1	2	-8.0000	2.7356	46	-2.92	0.0053	0.05	-13.5064	-2.4936

Interpretation

The key pieces of information here are the anticipated standard errors of the simple effect differences, and the anticipated width of their confidence intervals. For the simple effect of B given A, the expected standard error is 2.39 and the confidence interval width is 9.6 units. For the simple effect of A given B, the expected standard error is 2.74, and the anticipated confidence interval width is approximately 11 units. The discrepancy stems from the fact that B given A is a within-whole-plot comparison, whereas A given B is an across-whole-plot comparison.

This could stimulate a discussion when planning the study. Using this particular split plot structure implicitly defines differences between levels of factor B as more important comparisons than differences between levels of factor A. If this is not what the research team intends, this is a good time to rethink the design of the study.

Program

The final step in planning the follow-up study is to determine the power of the various tests of interest. Program 14.4 shows the required statements.

Program 14.4

```
data power;
 set overall_F simple_effects;
 ncp=numdf*Fvalue;
 alpha=0.05;
 Fcrit=finv(1-alpha,numdf,dendf,0);
 Power=1-ProbF(Fcrit,numdf,dendf,ncp);
run;
proc print data=power;
run;
```

Results

Output 14.3 shows the result.

Output 14.3: Power for Split Plot Experiment with 24 Blocks

Obs	Effect	NumDF	DenDF	FValue	ProbF	Label	ncp	alpha	Fcrit	Power
1	a	1	23	5.40	0.0293		5.4005	0.05	4.27934	0.60498
2	b	1	46	17.17	0.0001		17.1679	0.05	4.05175	0.98194
3	a*b	1	46	3.15	0.0824		3.1533	0.05	4.05175	0.41254
4		1	46	0.53	0.4684	a|b=1	0.5345	0.05	4.05175	0.11047
5		1	46	8.55	0.0053	a|b=2	8.5523	0.05	4.05175	0.81672
6		1	46	2.80	0.1009	b|a=1	2.8029	0.05	4.05175	0.37438
7		1	46	17.52	0.0001	b|a=2	17.5182	0.05	4.05175	0.98369

Interpretation

You can see that with 24 blocks the power exceeds 0.80 for detecting an 8-unit difference for the simple effect of A given B2 and greatly exceeds 0.8 for detecting a 10-unit difference for the simple effect of B given A2. However, the power of the test for the A × B interaction is less than 0.5. This may be a problem, because a significant A × B interaction is often a pre-condition for being able to report simple effects. Increasing N_BLOCKS from 24 to 62 in Program 14.3 leads to the following power calculation.

Results

Output 14.4 shows the result.

Output 14.4 Power for Split Plot with 62 Blocks

Obs	Effect	NumDF	DenDF	FValue	ProbF	Label	ncp	alpha	Fcrit	Power
1	a	1	61	13.95	0.0004		13.9514	0.05	3.99849	0.95690
2	b	1	122	44.35	<.0001		44.3504	0.05	3.91882	1.00000
3	a*b	1	122	8.15	0.0051		8.1460	0.05	3.91882	0.80829
4		1	122	1.38	0.2422	a|b=1	1.3808	0.05	3.91882	0.21445
5		1	122	22.09	<.0001	a|b=2	22.0935	0.05	3.91882	0.99657
6		1	122	7.24	0.0081	b|a=1	7.2409	0.05	3.91882	0.76105
7		1	122	45.26	<.0001	b|a=2	45.2555	0.05	3.91882	1.00000

Interpretation

With 62 blocks, the power of the test for A × B interaction is just above 0.80. This is the minimum number of blocks required to achieve 80% power for the test of interaction.

Output 14.3 and 14.4 provide those planning the study the information needed to proceed. If the only requirement is showing 8- and 10-unit differences to be statistically significant, if in fact they exist, then doing the study with 24 blocks should suffice. However, if showing the A × B interaction to be significant is a priority, then the study obviously becomes much more expensive.

Notice that mixed model-based power analysis is required to plan this study. Any power and sample size approach that lacks the ability to use the variance component information for multiple error terms is incapable of providing accurate information about the precision and power characteristics of a split-plot experiment. Also notice that these calculations depend on the values of the variance components that you specify. It is often good practice to decide on a range of variance components values that are reasonable and that use upper limits of what is reasonable to obtain "worst-case" precision and power requirements. If you have pilot data, you can use upper confidence bounds, rather than the point estimates of the variance components.

14.4 Use of Mixed Model Methods to Compare Two Proposed Designs

In this example, suppose that you want to compare four treatments. The resources available to the study are matched pairs, or, in design terms, blocks with two experimental units each. There are several ways to design such a study, but in this example, consider the two we present.

Programs for Two Designs

Design Table 14.1 is a balanced incomplete block design. Design Table 14.2 at first glance appears to be a disconnected design with discrete subsets of treatments, but as Milliken and Johnson (2009) point out, it is better understood as a member of the split plot family. That is, think of treatments 1 and 2 as two levels of factor B applied in conjunction with A1 and treatments 3 and 4 two levels of factor B applied in conjunction with A2.

You can use precision analysis—e.g. based on expected confidence bounds—to assess the relative merits of these two designs (you could also use power analysis, but precision analysis is easier and more informative). First, create an exemplary data set for each design. You can use the statements in Programs 14.5 and 14.6.

Table 14.1 BIB Design

Block	Treatments	
1	1	2
2	1	3
3	1	4
4	2	3
5	2	4
6	3	4

Table 14.2 Disconnected/Split plot Design

Block	Treatments	
1	1	2
2	3	4
3	1	2
4	3	4
5	1	2
6	3	4

Program 14.5

```
data exmp_bib;
n_sets=2;
 input block @@;
  do eu=1 to 2;
   input trt @@;
    do set=1 to n_sets;
    mu=0;
    output;
   end;
  end;
datalines;
1  1 2
2  1 3
3  1 4
4  2 3
5  2 4
6  3 4
;
run;
```

Program 14.6

```
data exmp_sp;
n_sets=2;
 input block @@;
  do eu=1 to 2;
   input trt @@;
    do set=1 to n_sets;
    mu=0;
    output;
   end;
  end;
datalines;
1  1 2
2  3 4
3  1 2
4  3 4
5  1 2
6  3 4
;
run;
```

The lines following DATALINES give the treatment assignments to the minimum number of blocks possible for Design 14.1, the balanced incomplete block. The N_SETS variable and the DO SET=1 TO N_SETS statement enable you to increase replication while maintaining the balanced incomplete design structure, and explore the impact of doing so on precision. Set MU=0 so that the confidence intervals for treatment differences produced by the PROC GLIMMIX DIFF option (see below) will be symmetric about zero, making it easy for you to tell how wide they will be.

Program 14.7 provides PROC GLIMMIX statements that you can use with either exemplary data set.

Program 14.7

```
proc glimmix data=exmp_<bib or sp>;
   class set block trt;
   model mu=trt;
   random intercept / subject=block*set;
   parms (0.5)(1)/hold=1,2;
   lsmeans trt/diff cl;
   lsmestimate trt 'a'   1 1 -1 -1,
                   'b'   1 -1 1 -1,
                   'a*b' 1 -1 -1 1 / cl divisor=2;
run;
```

You can use Program 14.7 with either the EXMP_BIB or EXMP_SP exemplary data set. Modify the DATA= option accordingly. Note that BLOCK*SET uniquely defines each block created in the exemplary DATA step. The DIFF CL option in the LSMEANS statement enables you to compare the expected width of the treatment mean difference confidence intervals for the two designs. If you set the residual variance equal to one, as is done in this program, all standard errors will actually be the coefficient by which σ, the residual standard deviation, is multiplied. To compare designs with the same block size, you only need the relative values of this coefficient and the relative widths of the confidence intervals. The exact values will be multiples of σ. The value 0.5 corresponding to block variance actually specifies the ratio σ_b^2/σ^2 where σ_b^2 denotes the block variance. The value 0.5 represents the authors' experience with typical ratios. You can change it given your knowledge of the setting in which you are doing design comparison.

The LSMESTIMATE statements are included to illustrate a way to assess to relative precision of the two designs if the treatment design was, in fact, a 2 × 2 factorial. If your treatment design is something else, modify these statements accordingly.

Results

Output 14.5 and 14.6 give selected results for the two designs, assuming N_SETS=2, i.e. assuming we plan to use 12 blocks in the study.

Output 14.5: Precision Analysis of Design 14.4.1 – Balanced Incomplete Block

			Differences of trt Least Squares Means							
trt	_trt	Estimate	Standard Error	DF	t Value	Pr > |t|	Alpha	Lower	Upper
1	2	0	0.6325	9	0.00	1.0000	0.05	-1.4307	1.4307
1	3	0	0.6325	9	0.00	1.0000	0.05	-1.4307	1.4307
1	4	0	0.6325	9	0.00	1.0000	0.05	-1.4307	1.4307
2	3	0	0.6325	9	0.00	1.0000	0.05	-1.4307	1.4307
2	4	0	0.6325	9	0.00	1.0000	0.05	-1.4307	1.4307
3	4	0	0.6325	9	0.00	1.0000	0.05	-1.4307	1.4307

			Least Squares Means Estimates						
Effect	Label	Estimate	Standard Error	DF	t Value	Pr > |t|	Alpha	Lower	Upper
trt	a	0	0.4472	9	0.00	1.0000	0.05	-1.0117	1.0117
trt	b	0	0.4472	9	0.00	1.0000	0.05	-1.0117	1.0117
trt	a*b	0	0.4472	9	0.00	1.0000	0.05	-1.0117	1.0117

Output 14.6: Precision Analysis for Design 14.4.2—Split Plot

			Differences of trt Least Squares Means						
trt	_trt	Estimate	Standard Error	DF	t Value	Pr > |t|	Alpha	Lower	Upper
1	2	0	0.5774	10	0.00	1.0000	0.05	-1.2864	1.2864
1	3	0	0.7071	10	0.00	1.0000	0.05	-1.5755	1.5755
1	4	0	0.7071	10	0.00	1.0000	0.05	-1.5755	1.5755
2	3	0	0.7071	10	0.00	1.0000	0.05	-1.5755	1.5755
2	4	0	0.7071	10	0.00	1.0000	0.05	-1.5755	1.5755
3	4	0	0.5774	10	0.00	1.0000	0.05	-1.2864	1.2864

			Least Squares Means Estimates						
Effect	Label	Estimate	Standard Error	DF	t Value	Pr > |t|	Alpha	Lower	Upper
trt	a	0	0.5774	10	0.00	1.0000	0.05	-1.2864	1.2864
trt	b	0	0.4082	10	0.00	1.0000	0.05	-0.9096	0.9096
trt	a*b	0	0.4082	10	0.00	1.0000	0.05	-0.9096	0.9096

Interpretation

The standard error for all treatment difference estimates with the BIB is 0.63. For the split plot, within-whole-plot comparisons have a standard error of 0.58, but across-whole-plot comparisons have a standard error of 0.71. If the researchers' priority is estimating or testing the simple effect of B given A, the split plot will provide greater precision. Otherwise, the BIB is a better all-around design.

For the factorial effects, the BIB gives a standard error of 0.45 for both main effects and for the A × B interaction. The split plot gives a standard error of 0.41 for the A × B interaction. If the researchers' priority is being able to detect, estimate, or test the A × B interaction, the split plot provides greater precision and power.

This illustrates how mixed-model-based power and precision methods can be used to realistically portray to pros and cons of two plausible designs. To repeat the concluding remark from Section 14.3, this type of comparison is possible only if you use mixed-model-based precision analysis. Conventional power and sample size software procedures—including PROC POWER and PROC GLMPOWER in SAS—were not designed to provide, and cannot provide, the precision analysis shown here.

14.5 Precision and Power Analysis: A Repeated Measures Example

In this section, our task is to design a study to compare a placebo with an experimental decongestant intended to improve breathing comfort during allergy season. Specifically, subjects are to be measured at 5 times after exposure to the treatment. Researchers are interested in the initial effect of the decongestant and how long the benefit persists, or, put another way, how quickly the benefit dissipates. The response variable is a measure of breathing comfort: ≥ 60 is considered "comfortable;" between 50 and 60 is "moderately comfortable;" 40–50 is "moderately uncomfortable" and $<$ 40 is "uncomfortable."

By definition, this study will be a repeated measures experiment. You can adapt the precision and power methodology from previous sections for repeated measures. The additional piece of information that you need is the anticipated covariance structure among observations at different times on the same subject and the anticipated variance and covariance or correlation components (or correlation coefficients).

Before implementing the exemplary DATA step, we should describe how the study will be conducted and the model we intend to use. In this example, suppose that we plan to randomly assign n patients to the placebo and n patients to the experimental decongestant. Breathing comfort will then be measured on each patient at pre-determined times 1, 2, 3, 4 and 5. Assume that the times are equally spaced. An appropriate model is thus:

- $\mathbf{y}_{ik} \mid b_{ik} \sim N(\boldsymbol{\mu}_{ik}, \boldsymbol{\Sigma})$.

- $\mathbf{y}'_{ik} = \begin{bmatrix} y_{i1k} & y_{i2k} & y_{i3k} & y_{i4k} & y_{i5k} \end{bmatrix}$.

- $\boldsymbol{\mu}'_{ik} = \begin{bmatrix} \mu_{i1k} & \mu_{i2k} & \mu_{i3k} & \mu_{i4k} & \mu_{i5k} \end{bmatrix}$.

- $\mu_{ijk} = \mu + \alpha_i + \tau_j + \alpha\tau_{ij} + b_{ik}$.

- $b_{ik} \sim N(0, \sigma_b^2)$.

Where α and τ denote treatment and time effects, respectively, b_{ik} denotes the between-subjects effect, and $\boldsymbol{\Sigma}$ denotes the within-subjects covariance matrix.

You can see that we need to specify how we think the placebo and experimental decongestant will respond over time. We also need to make sure differences considered clinically relevant are reflected in the exemplary data. In addition, we need to specify the structure of $\boldsymbol{\Sigma}$ and we need to be able to specify σ_b^2 and the components of $\boldsymbol{\Sigma}$. As with any precision and power analysis, we do this either based on our best current understanding of the problem, for example, from the literature or previous experience, or we can use pilot data if available.

14.5.1 Using Pilot Data to Inform Precision and Power Analysis

Suppose in this case we do have pilot data. You can access these data from data set "Repeated Measures Pilot." The pilot study consists of data observed on the placebo at 5 times on 10 subjects.

Program

Program 14.8 illustrates PROC GLIMMIX statements that you can use to give you an idea of how to obtain the needed information for the precision and power analysis we have been assigned to do.

Program 14.8

```
ods results off;
ods html exclude all;
proc glimmix data=rpt_pilot ;
   class t id;
   model y=t;
   *random intercept/subject= id;
   random t /residual subject= id type=cs;
```

```
      ods output fitstatistics=cs;
run;
proc glimmix data=rpt_pilot ;
   class t id;
   model y=t;
   *random intercept/subject= id;
   random t /residual subject= id type=ar(1);
   ods output fitstatistics=ar1;
run;
proc glimmix data=rpt_pilot ;
   class t id;
   model y=t;
   random intercept/subject= id;
   random t /residual subject= id type=ar(1);
   ods output fitstatistics=ar1_subj;
run;
proc glimmix data=rpt_pilot ;
   class t id;
   model y=t;
   *random intercept/subject= id;
   random t /residual subject= id type=ante(1);
   ods output fitstatistics=ante;
run;
proc glimmix data=rpt_pilot ;
   class t id;
   model y=t;
   random intercept/subject= id;
   random t /residual subject= id type=ante(1);
   ods output fitstatistics=ante_subj;
run;
ods results on;
ods html select all;
proc print data=cs;
run;
data csa;
 set cs;
   if descr='AICC (smaller is better)';
   cs_aicc=value;
   drop value;
run;
data ar1a;
 set ar1;
   if descr='AICC (smaller is better)';
   ar1_aicc=value;
   drop value;
run;
data ar1sa;
 set ar1_subj;
   if descr='AICC (smaller is better)';
   ar1_sbj_aicc=value;
   drop value;
run;
data ante1a;
 set ante;
   if descr='AICC (smaller is better)';
   ante1_aicc=value;
   drop value;
run;
data ante1sa;
 set ante_subj;
   if descr='AICC (smaller is better)';
   ante1_sbj_aicc=value;
   drop value;
run;
data summary1;
 merge csa ar1a ar1sa ante1a ante1sa;
run;
proc print data=summary1;
run;
```

These programs obtain the information criteria—specifically the AICC—for the compound symmetry, AR(1) and ANTE(1), and AR(1) and ANTE(1) with a random subject effect subject covariance models. The ODS OUTPUT statement in each PROC GLIMMIX program creates a data set with the information criteria. Each data set is then reduced so that it contains only the AICC. Then the data sets are merged so that the AICC for each competing covariance model can be printed in a common PROC PRINT. The ODS RESULTS and ODS HTML statements cause the listing to be suppressed while the PROC GLIMMIX programs are running, then resumed for the final PROC PRINT. The five covariance models shown are for illustration purposes only. In practice, you could add additional covariance models deemed to be plausible candidates to complete the comparison.

Results

Output 14.7 shows the AICC for the five covariance models considered in this example.

Output 14.7 Information Criteria for Three Covariance Models from Pilot Repeated Measures

Obs	Descr	cs_aicc	ar1_aicc	ar1_sbj_aicc	ante1_aicc	ante1_sbj_aicc
1	AICC (smaller is better)	385.421	377.736	379.941	385.495	385.544

Interpretation

The AICC for the AR(1) covariance structure, 377.7, is the smallest. The obvious next step is to use TYPE=AR(1) for subsequent planning purposes. In addition, one could proceed with precision and power calculations for each candidate covariance structure. The risk is, because the CS model tends to inflate type I error rate in the presence of serial correlation, precision and power analysis using CS will tend to give overly optimistic assessments of required replication. ANTE(1), on the other hand, will tend to give more conservative, worst-case assessments. If you decide to do precision and power assessments with all three covariance structures, keep these risks in mind. We now proceed with the example using AR(1).

The next step is to estimate the covariance components of the AR(1) model from the pilot data, and to use the breathing comfort mean estimates to get a picture of how the placebo behaves over time.

Program

Use the PROC GLIMMIX statements in Program 14.9. Output 14.8 shows the relevant listing.

Program 14.9

```
proc glimmix data=rpt_pilot ;
   class t id;
   model y=t;
   random t /residual subject= id type=ar(1);
   lsmeans t;
   ods html covparms lsmeans;
run;
```

Results

Results appear in Output 14.8.

Output 14.8: Covariance and Mean Estimates for Repeated Measures Pilot Data

Covariance Parameter Estimates			
Cov Parm	Subject	Estimate	Standard Error
AR(1)	id	0.6793	0.1004
Residual		298.98	87.4271

t Least Squares Means					
t	Estimate	Standard Error	DF	t Value	Pr > |t|
1	50.0800	5.4679	36	9.16	<.0001
2	51.0800	5.4679	36	9.34	<.0001
3	42.8600	5.4679	36	7.84	<.0001

	t Least Squares Means				
t	Estimate	Standard Error	DF	t Value	Pr > |t|
4	45.3400	5.4679	36	8.29	<.0001
5	42.6700	5.4679	36	7.80	<.0001

Interpretation

The relevant covariance components to be used in the precision and power analysis are the AR(1) correlation, $\hat{\rho} = 0.68$ and the residual variance, $\hat{\sigma}^2 = 299$. The means appear to be at the low end of "moderately comfortable," i.e. just above 50, for times 1 and 2, then drop to "moderately uncomfortable" after time 2. One can assume that the fluctuation between 42.7 and 45.3 at times 3 and 5 is random noise.

14.5.2 Repeated Measures Precision and Power Analysis

The pilot data provides information about covariance parameters and time 1 through 5 means for the PLACEBO treatment to be included in the exemplary data set. It remains to specify expected means at time 1 through 5 for the experimental decongestant. In practice, this requires a conversation with the subject matter specialists. Suppose that the result of this conversation is as follows: the research team believes that the experimental decongestant can maintain "comfortable" breathing, i.e. a breathing comfort response of at least 60, through time 4, and drop to "moderately comfortable" at time 5. In addition, the researchers consider a 5-unit difference in breathing comfort to be the minimum clinically relevant difference. In other words, they think a difference of less than 5 would be imperceptible to the vast majority of patients.

Programs

Accordingly, the DATA step shown in Program 14.10 creates a plausible exemplary data set consistent with the above.

Program 14.10

```
data exemplary;
 input trt$ @@;
  do time=1 to 5;
   input mu @@;
   do id=1 to <number of subjects>;
    output;
   end;
  end;
datalines;
placebo 50 50 45 42 42
x_decon 60 60 60 60 55
;
run;
```

As in previous examples, you can vary to number of subjects per treatment (left generically as <number of subjects> in Program 14.10; users need to replace this with a proposed number) to assess the impact on precision and power with regard to various objectives of interest.

Next is the PROC GLIMMIX step. Program 14.11 includes examples of mean comparisons and overall tests that might be of interest.

Program 14.11

```
proc glimmix data=exemplary noprofile;
   class trt id time;
   model mu=trt*time;
   random time/type=ar(1) subject=id(trt) residual;
   parms (299)(0.68)/hold=1,2;
   lsmeans trt*time / slicediff=time cl;
   contrast 'time x trt' trt*time 1 0 0 0 -1  -1 0 0 0 1,
                         trt*time 0 1 0 0 -1  0 -1 0 0 1,
                         trt*time 0 0 1 0 -1  0 0 -1 0 1,
                         trt*time 0 0 0 1 -1  0 0 0 -1 1;
   contrast 'time lin x trt' trt*time -2 -1 0 1 2 2 1 0 -1 -2;
   contrast 'time quad x trt' trt*time 2 -1 -2 -1 2 -2 1 2 1 -2;
   contrast 'time cubic x trt' trt*time -1 2 0 -2 1 1 -2 0 2 -1;
```

```
   contrast '5 unit diff' trt*time 1 0 -1 0 0 0 0 0 0 0;
   contrast '10 unit diff' trt*time 1 0 0 0 0 -1 0 0 0 0;
   ods output contrasts=F;
run;
```

When you use the NOPROFILE option, the order in which PROC GLIMMIX processes the AR(1) correlation and the residual variance is reversed, so notice the order of the parameters in the PARMS statement. If you have any doubt, run the program and make sure the order of the variance components in the listing and the starting values you specify are consistent.

If you try to run this program without the NOPROFILE option in the PROC statement, it may not run. This is a frequent occurrence when using PROC GLIMMIX for precision and power analysis with repeated measures covariance structures. When you run the above program, you may get the following warning in the SAS Log:

```
ERROR: Values given in PARMS statement are not feasible.
```

The GLIMMIX procedure can be fussy (for want of a better word) about values given in the PARMS statement. Often, you can get around this problem by changing the PARMS values slightly. In this case, simply taking them out to more decimal places works, i.e. change the PARMS statement to the following:

```
parms (298.98)(0.679)/hold=1,2;
```

These are the values given in Output 14.8.

The LSMEANS statement focuses on a precision analysis giving you the anticipated width of confidence intervals for the simple effect of treatment at each time. The contrast statements are written to address the overall test of treatment × time interaction, a polynomial regression decomposition of the interaction up to a 3rd order (cubic) polynomial, and specific 5- and 10-unit differences in breathing comfort. Note that this is one case in which orthogonal polynomial contrasts are extremely useful. These are just examples of contrasts that might be of interest.

Results

Output 14.9 gives the result for 48 subjects per treatment, obtained by writing the following statement when you are creating the exemplary data set:

```
do id=1 to 48;
```

We start with 48 because, after some trial and error, it is the minimum number of subjects required to show a 10-unit difference to be significant at α = 0.05 with 80% power.

Output 14.9: Precision and Power Results for Study with 48 Subjects per Treatment

Simple Effect Level	trt	_trt	Estimate	Standard Error	DF	t Value	Pr > |t|	Alpha	Lower	Upper
time 1	placebo	x_decon	-10.0000	3.5296	375	-2.83	0.0049	0.05	-16.9404	-3.0596
time 2	placebo	x_decon	-10.0000	3.5296	375	-2.83	0.0049	0.05	-16.9404	-3.0596
time 3	placebo	x_decon	-15.0000	3.5296	375	-4.25	<.0001	0.05	-21.9404	-8.0596
time 4	placebo	x_decon	-18.0000	3.5296	375	-5.10	<.0001	0.05	-24.9404	-11.0596
time 5	placebo	x_decon	-13.0000	3.5296	375	-3.68	0.0003	0.05	-19.9404	-6.0596

Obs	Label	NumDF	DenDF	FValue	ProbF	ncp	alpha	crit	power
1	time x trt	4	375	1.74	0.1408	6.95344	0.05	2.39574	0.53095
2	time lin x trt	1	375	1.53	0.2170	1.52902	0.05	3.86638	0.23444
3	time quad x trt	1	375	1.72	0.1905	1.71965	0.05	3.86638	0.25775
4	time cubic x trt	1	375	4.60	0.0326	4.60052	0.05	3.86638	0.57122
5	5 unit diff	1	375	3.73	0.0541	3.73268	0.05	3.86638	0.48693
6	10 unit diff	1	375	8.03	0.0049	8.02676	0.05	3.86638	0.80674

Interpretation

You can see that if this study is done with 48 subjects per treatment, 95% confidence intervals for the simple effect of TREATMENT at a given TIME can be expected to be approximately 13.9 units wide. The power to declare a 10 unit simple effect of TREATMENT given TIME significant at $\alpha = 0.05$ would be just over 0.80, but the power to show a 5-unit difference is just under 0.50, and the power to detect the TREATMENT × TIME interaction would be just over 0.50, respectively.

If you increase the number of subjects per treatment to 84, i.e. change the statement when creating the exemplary data set to `do id=1 to 84;` then the power for the test of interaction exceeds 80%. Unless you do a lot of trial-and-error modifying with PROC GLIMMIX, you will probably get the following message:

`ERROR: Values given in PARMS statement are not feasible.`

Program

So long as you can assume that the data follow a Gaussian distribution, rather than spending time trying to find PARMS values that work in PROC GLIMMIX, you can switch to PROC MIXED. Use the statements in Program 14.12.

Program 14.12

```
proc mixed data=exemplary noprofile;
   class trt id time;
   model mu=trt*time;
   repeated time/type=ar(1) subject=id(trt);
   parms (298.98)(0.679)/hold=1,2;
   lsmeans trt*time / diff cl;
   contrast 'time  x trt' trt*time 1 0 0 0 -1  -1 0 0 0 1,
                          trt*time 0 1 0 0 -1   0 -1 0 0 1,
                          trt*time 0 0 1 0 -1   0 0 -1 0 1,
                          trt*time 0 0 0 1 -1   0 0 0 -1 1;
   contrast 'time lin x trt' trt*time -2 -1 0 1 2 2 1 0 -1 -2;
   contrast 'time quad x trt' trt*time 2 -1 -2 -1 2 -2 1 2 1 -2;
   contrast 'time cubic x trt' trt*time -1 2 0 -2 1 1 -2 0 2 -1;
   contrast '5 unit diff' trt*time 1 0 -1 0 0 0 0 0 0 0;
   contrast '10 unit diff' trt*time 1 0 0 0 0 -1 0 0 0 0;
   ods output contrasts=F;
run;
```

These statements are mostly identical to the PROC GLIMMIX statements. The primary differences are 1) the absence of a SLICEDIFF option in PROC MIXED, and 2) in PROC MIXED, the REPEATED statement specifies residual covariance structure. The PROC MIXED LSMEANS statement does not have a SLICEDIFF option, so you need to use the DIFF option instead. This gives you a more cumbersome listing, but it still enables you to focus on the simple effects of interest. In addition, remember that you must replace the PROC GLIMMIX RANDOM...RESIDUAL statement with the PROC MIXED REPEATED statement.

Results

Output 14.10 shows the result of the power analysis for 84 subjects per treatment.

Output 14.10 Power Analysis: Repeated Measures Experiment with 84 Subjects per Treatment

Obs	Label	NumDF	DenDF	FValue	ProbF	ncp	alpha	crit	power
1	time x trt	4	663	3.03	0.0171	12.1322	0.05	2.38537	0.80413
2	time lin x trt	1	663	2.67	0.1026	2.6719	0.05	3.85552	0.37171
3	time quad x trt	1	663	3.00	0.0837	3.0006	0.05	3.85552	0.40906
4	time cubic x trt	1	663	8.02	0.0048	8.0234	0.05	3.85552	0.80744
5	5 unit diff	1	663	6.52	0.0109	6.5162	0.05	3.85552	0.72208
6	10 unit diff	1	663	14.05	0.0002	14.0478	0.05	3.85552	0.96268

Interpretation

You can see that for the means specified in the exemplary data set for this example the power results associated with the TIME CUBIC × TRT and overall TIME × TRT interaction are similar. The minimum required replication for this study to obtain 80% power for the test of interaction is 84 subjects per treatment. Although the test for a 5-unit difference still shows power of only about 72%, 84 subjects per treatment may be approaching the upper limit of the study size, depending on funding and other necessary resources. If 80% power to detect a 5-unit difference is an absolute requirement, 102 subjects per treatment is the minimum study size.

14.5.3 Final Thoughts on Repeated Measures Power Analysis

You can see that the steps required to implement precision and power analysis for repeated measures are identical to those for completely randomized designs, blocked designs, and experiments with split plot features. If you can write the model, and if you have at least a plausible idea of the anticipated means, covariance structure and covariance parameters, you can implement the precision and power analysis. Note also that these analyses absolutely require mixed model methodology. To repeat a familiar mantra, conventional power and sample size software is not designed to provide accurate power analysis of complex experiments. Mixed model methodology provides the appropriate tools for the job.

What to Do If You Have No Pilot Data

In this example, we were able to select the AR(1) covariance model by computing information criteria from candidate covariance structures using pilot data. Often, perhaps in most cases, pilot data will not be available. What then? We suggest, absent of knowledge to the contrary, using the AR(1) covariance model. As a general principle, most of the benefit of the mixed model approach to repeated measures analysis come from *some* attempt to account for within-subject correlation as a function of distance apart in time versus *no* such attempt. The simplest case is AR(1) (*some* attempt) versus compound symmetry (*no* attempt). Choosing among AR(1), Toeplitz, ANTE(1), unstructured, etc. is, to borrow a phrase from a recent Biometric Society session, "Tweaking with the last 10%." If non-negligible distance-dependent within-subject correlation exists, switching from CS to AR(1) accomplishes the first 90%.

An alternative repeated measures school of thought recommends, "When in doubt, use the unstructured model." While this may be, at least arguably, sound advice for data analysis, it is impractical for precision and power analysis. Using the AR(1) model requires you to specify a single within-subject correlation parameter, ρ, whereas UN requires you to specify all $\sigma_{jj'}$. If you use AR(1) to implement precision and power analysis as shown above, a good rule of thumb is to set $\rho = 0.6$ in the PARMS statement. If you use UN, and you lack detailed knowledge about the individual $\sigma_{jj'}$, you will probably specify a covariance based on ρ along the first diagonal of the covariance matrix, ρ^2 along the second diagonal, and so on. In other words, absent of better knowledge, you will probably use the AR(1) covariance structure even if you do your precision and power analysis with UN. The risk of encountering problems getting the PROC GLIMMIX step (or PROC MIXED step) to run increases when you use a more complex covariance model. In other words, keep the covariance structure you use to do precision and power analysis as simple as possible, while still accounting for serial correlation.

A Caveat

In Chapter 8, we stressed the need to use the Kenward Roger standard error and degree of freedom correction with repeated measures analysis. If you have any non-negligible distance-apart-in-time-dependent within-subject correlation, the Kenward-Roger option should be considered a mandatory feature of the analysis. That said, the exemplary data methods shown in this section do not account for the Kenward Roger correction. Therefore, the results obtained with the exemplary data method should be considered approximate, as well as generally somewhat optimistic. Stroup (2002) showed how to include a Kenward Roger adjustment in the exemplary data method but doing so is tedious and frankly not worth the effort. A better approach is to use the exemplary data method shown above to get you close to the required replication, then use simulation to fine-tune your required replication estimates.

14.6 Precision and Power Analysis for Non-Gaussian Data: A Binomial Example

Suppose that we want to plan a study to compare two treatments and the response variable is binomial. For example, we may have a standard treatment known to have a success rate of 15%, and an experimental treatment believed to have the potential to have a success rate of 25% or more. The study will require N subjects per treatment. Each subject responds either favorably to the treatment (a "success") or unfavorably. If we denote Y_i as the number of successes for treatment i, then $\hat{p}_i = Y_i/N$ is the observed sample proportion, it is reasonable to assume that $Y_i \sim \text{Binomial}(N, p_i)$, where p_i denotes the probability of a favorable response given treatment i.

Our task is to determine the number of subjects per treatment required for adequate power and precision.

14.6.1 A Simplistic Approach

The standard power analysis for this problem would define $p_1 = 0.15$, and ask what N is required to show a statistically significant difference with a specified power if $p_2 = 0.25$? Many textbooks, e.g. Cochran and Cox (1957), have tables you can use to look up the answer. Or there is software you can use. In SAS, PROC POWER, using the statements in Program 14.13 will compute the required N:

Program 14.13

```
proc power;
   twosamplefreq test=lrchi
   alpha=0.05  power=0.80
   refproportion=0.15
   proportiondiff=0.10
   npergroup=.;
run;
```

The option TWOSAMPLEFREQ specifies a comparison between two binomial probabilities assuming a completely randomized design. The TEST=LRCHI requests a power analysis assuming the data will be analyzed using a likelihood ratio test, which is equivalent to the test PROC GLIMMIX implements for binomial data from a completely randomized design. The statement REFPROPORTION defines the lower of the two probabilities involved in the hypothesis, in this case $p_1 = 0.15$; PROPORTIONDIFF defines $p_2 - p_1$, which in this case is $0.25 - 0.15 = 0.10$. Setting NPERGROUP equal to a period instructs the procedure to determine the number of observations per treatment required for the ALPHA level and POWER given in the program. Output 14.11 shows the result.

Output 14.11: PROC POWER Listing: (Naive) Required Sample Size for Binomial Example

Computed N per Group	
Actual Power	N per Group
0.802	250

The required N is 250 subjects per treatment. The heading for Output 14.11 labels this as a "naive" assessment of required sample size. In fact, $N = 250$ is a valid recommendation if the study is truly conducted as a completely randomized design, that is, if there is a single clinic with 500 patients, 250 of whom are assigned at random to the standard treatment and the other 250 to the experimental treatment. In many studies, this is a big if. Suppose instead, the study is to be conducted at multiple clinics representing a sample of the population.

14.6.2 Precision and Power: Blocked Design, Binomial Response

A question that often arises in conjunction with the PROC POWER result in Output 14.11 is, "If we plan to do this study at L locations, should we divide the 250 subjects among those locations, e.g. observe $250/L$ subjects per treatment per location?" Answering this question accurately requires mixed model thinking, or more precisely, GLMM thinking.

Because locations are blocking criteria, we can adapt models for binomial data from blocked designs developed in Chapter 11. Specifically, a model for a multilocation study with binomial data, is as follows:

- Linear Predictor: $\eta_{ij} = \eta + \tau_i + r_j + rt_{ij}$.

- Link function: $\eta_{ij} = g(p_{ij})$; typically, $p_{ij} = \text{logit}(p_{ij})$.

- Distribution of observations: $y_{ij} \mid r_j, rt_{ij} \sim \text{Binomial}(N_{ij}, p_{ij})$.

- Random effect distribution:

$$\begin{bmatrix} r_j \\ rt_{ij} \end{bmatrix} \sim N\left(\begin{bmatrix} 0 \\ 0 \end{bmatrix}, \begin{bmatrix} \sigma_r^2 & 0 \\ 0 & \sigma_{rt}^2 \end{bmatrix} \right) \tag{14.1}$$

Where τ denotes treatment effects and r denotes block (in this case, location) effects. Use this model in the PROC GLIMMIX step when planning this study.

The steps of the GLMM-based precision and power analysis are identical to those previously discussed. Specifically,

1. Create exemplary data. In this case, the expected response must be in terms of the binomial response variable
2. PROC GLIMMIX step. For GLMMs, unlike mixed models with Gaussian data, PROC MIXED is not an option. PROC GLIMMIX is uniquely capable of implementing linear mixed models with non-Gaussian data for the purpose of precision and power analysis.
3. Power step. This uses the approximate F statistic and is identical to previous examples.

The main issue that is unique to planning with non-Gaussian data involves what to specify for covariance parameters in the PARMS statement of the PROC GLIMMIX step. To do this, we must understand what the variance components, σ_r^2 and σ_n^2, measure. If you use the logit link, keep in mind that the *odds* are defined as $p/(1-p)$. Hence, the logit is the log of the odds. It follows that the block (in this case, location) variance, σ_r^2, is the variance of $\log[\overline{p}_{\bullet j}/(1-\overline{p}_{\bullet j})]$, where $\overline{p}_{\bullet j}$ denotes the probability of a favorable response averaged over both treatments at location *j*. In other words, σ_r^2 measures variance of the log odds over locations. Similarly, σ_n^2 measures the variance of the log *odds ratio* over locations. It is reasonable to assume that both variances are nonzero. Given that the locations are a sample of a target population, it is reasonable to assume that the probability of a favorable response varies at least somewhat over locations.

In the GLMM as specified in Equation 14.1, the location log odds and log odds ratios are assumed to have a distribution symmetric about zero. This gives us a way to engage the researcher in a conversation that leads to reasonable values of the variance components to use for precision and power analysis. Specifically, you can ask the researcher what the probability of a favorable response would be expected to be at the worst-case and best-case locations. For example, if the researcher believes that success rates for the standard treatment vary between 10% and 20% over locations, this tells you that the log odds vary between -2.2 and -1.39. The range is thus $-1.39-(-2.2)=0.81$. Once you have the range, use the "6σ rule." That is, assuming normality, 99% of the probability mass of a random variable lies within $\pm 3\sigma$ of its mean. Hence, dividing the anticipated range by six gives you a good approximation of the anticipated standard deviation. Using the "6σ" rule, the approximate standard deviation is $\sigma \cong 0.81/6 = 0.135$. The approximate variance is thus $\sigma^2 = 0.0182$. Use this for σ_r^2. Suppose the researcher expects, by analogy, for the success rate for the experimental treatment to vary between 20% to 30% over locations. As a result, the odds ratio could vary between 0.25 and 1, and hence the log odds ratio between -1.35 and 0, over locations. The approximate variance is thus $\sigma^2 = (1.35/6)^2 \cong 0.05$. Use this value for σ_n^2.

Programs

As this point, we are ready to implement a multilocation precision and power analysis. Suppose the initial plan is to do the study at 5 locations and distribute the 250 subjects per treatment equally over the locations. The statements in Program 14.14 create the exemplary data set.

Program 14.14

```
data exemplary;
 N_Loc=5
 input trt p;
 do location=1 to N_Loc;
  n_per_trt=250/N_Loc;
  mu=p*50;
  output;
 end;
datalines;
1 0.15
2 0.25
;
run;
```

N_LOC specifies the number of locations and N_PER_TRT is the number of subjects per treatment at each location. MU specifies the expected number of favorable outcomes for a given treatment at a given location. Notice that MU does not need to be an integer.

Program 14.15 shows the PROC GLIMMIX step.

Program 14.15

```
proc glimmix data=exemplary initglm;
   class trt location;
   model mu/n_per_trt = trt / oddsratio;
   random intercept trt / subject=location;
```

```
    parms (0.018) (0.05) / hold=1,2;
    ods output tests3=pwr;
run;
```

The PARMS statement specifies the location and treatment × location, whose approximate values were determined above using the "6σ" rule. Use the same statements for the power step as in previous examples (for example, see Program 14.4).

Results

Output 14.12 shows the results of the power analysis.

Output 14.12: Power for Test to Compare Binomial Probabilities, 5 Locations, 250 Subjects

Obs	Effect	NumDF	DenDF	FValue	ProbF	alpha	ncparm	crit	power
1	trt	1	4	5.56	0.0778	0.10	5.56326	4.5448	0.61789
2	trt	1	4	5.56	0.0778	0.05	5.56326	7.7086	0.43643
3	trt	1	4	5.56	0.0778	0.01	5.56326	21.1977	0.14432

Interpretation

You can see that the power for the treatment effect test (i.e. $H_0 : \tau_1 = \tau_2$) at $\alpha = 0.05$ is only 0.436. Even with $\alpha = 0.10$, the power is just under 62%. Both results are very far from the power of 80% originally obtained for 250 subjects per treatment. Why the discrepancy? The result obtained with PROC POWER does not account for variation among locations. As mentioned earlier, when you use PROC POWER you implicitly assume that the study will occur at a single location (or block). If you implement this study at multiple locations, you must adjust the sample size to account for variation among locations. You can see that doing so requires GLMM methodology.

Program

You can increase the number of locations to determine its effect on power. For example, Program 14.16 creates an exemplary data set with 16 locations.

Program 14.16

```
data exemplary;
 N_Loc=16;
 input trt p;
 do location=1 to N_Loc;
  n_per_trt=250/N_Loc; *560/N_Loc;
  mu=p*N_per_trt;
  output;
 end;
datalines;
1 0.15
2 0.25
;
run;
```

Notice that neither MU nor N_PER TRT need to be integers. Once you create the exemplary data set, run the same PROC GLIMMIX and DATA POWER statements as above.

Results

Output 14.13 shows the result.

Output 14.13: Power for Test to Compare Binomial Probabilities, 16 Locations, 250 Subjects

Obs	Effect	NumDF	DenDF	FValue	ProbF	alpha	ncparm	crit	power
1	trt	1	15	6.86	0.0193	0.10	6.86075	3.07319	0.80333
2	trt	1	15	6.86	0.0193	0.05	6.86075	4.54308	0.68763
3	trt	1	15	6.86	0.0193	0.01	6.86075	8.68312	0.40407

Increasing to 16 locations increases the power for a test at $\alpha = 0.10$ to just over 0.80. Because $250/16 = 15.625$, you would actually need 16 subjects at each location for each treatment, or a total of 296 subjects.

Table 14.1 summarized the tradeoff between number of locations and number of subjects per location required to achieve 80% power for an $\alpha = 0.05$ test.

Table 14.1 Tradeoff between Number of Subjects, Number of Locations and Available Power

Subjects per Location	Locations	Power for $\alpha = 0.05$ test	Total Subjects per Treatment
50	5	0.43	250
15–16	16	0.69	250
1	250	0.78	250
50	9	0.79	450
50	10	>0.80	500
112	5	0.80[a]	560

[a] only if $\alpha = 0.10$.

First, even if you can increase the number of locations to 250 with 1 subject per treatment at each location, the maximum power that you can achieve with 250 subjects per treatment is 0.78. If you increase the number of subjects per treatment from 250 to 560, and stick with 5 locations, the power is just over 0.80 for a test at $\alpha = 0.10$. Obviously, you would need considerably more subjects per treatment if you want 80% power with $\alpha = 0.05$. If you stick with 50 subjects per treatment at each location and increase the number of locations to 9, the power is 0.79 for an $\alpha = 0.05$ test. Ten locations will guarantee 80% power. Nine locations translate to 450 subjects per treatment, versus 560 subjects at five locations for an $\alpha = 0.10$ test. GLMM methodology enables you to see clearly the tradeoffs between increasing locations versus increasing subjects, and in the process to see how to achieve adequate power most efficiently, within the constraints of what is possible in terms of conducting the study.

As an aside, it is fair to say that many of the problems conventional wisdom attributes to limitations in GLMM methodology have their roots in attempts to analyze studies designed using conventional power and sample size methodology—in other words, studies that are inappropriately designed and underpowered.

14.7 Precision and Power: Example with Incomplete Blocks and Count Data

In this example, the objectives resemble the example in Section 14.4—design an experiment with 4 treatments and a block size of 2—but here the response variable is a discrete count. Suppose we have chosen the balanced incomplete block structure, and we need to determine how many blocks we need for adequate precision and power. In this section, a GLMM-based method for doing so is presented. As with the previous example, this illustration uses the three steps of the exemplary data method.

For precision and power analysis with count data, we recommend using the negative binomial distribution in the PROC GLIMMIX step. First, as discussed in Chapter 12, the theory underlying the negative binomial is more consistent with the way we think count data, especially biological count data, arises. Second, precision and power analysis for count data is less prone to overly optimistic assessment of required sample size if you use the negative binomial rather than the Poisson distribution.

In the exemplary data, we need to specify the mean counts, so that they anticipate the expected counts and the minimum scientifically relevant differences among treatment mean counts. In the PROC GLIMMIX step, we need to state the anticipated variance components, including the negative binomial scale parameter. As with the binomial example, the variance components reflect variation on the model scale—in this case, the log count. To do this, we use a similar thought process to what we used for binomial data in the previous section. For example, suppose that for the reference treatment, it is known that for typical experimental units, the average count is 20. Suppose, in addition, that researchers expect these average counts to vary over blocks, from as low as 10 to as high as 50. Applying the "6σ" rule we used for binomial data in Section 14.6, we approximate the block variance as $\sigma_b^2 \cong \{[\log(50) - \log(10)] / 6\}^2 = 0.072$. To anticipate the negative binomial scale parameter, use the fact that the variance of a negative binomial random variable is $\lambda + \phi\lambda^2$, where λ is the expected count and ϕ denotes the scale parameter. Suppose the researchers believe that when the expected count is 10, a standard deviation between 5 and 6 is plausible (and hence a variance between 25 and 36 would be plausible); and for expected counts of 50, a standard deviation in the 20 to 25 range, and hence a variance between 400 and 625, would be plausible. Solving for the scale parameter gives $\phi \cong 0.25$. Note that the negative binomial is a right-skewed distribution. These standard deviation values imply that if $\lambda = 10$, observed counts are likely to vary between 0 and 30, and if $\lambda = 50$, observed counts are likely to vary between 10 and 125.

Programs

The final information we need is some idea of the minimum mean count difference between treatments considered to be consequential. Suppose a difference in treatment mean count of 10 is considered the minimum consequential difference, and 30 units is considered the largest plausible difference. A possible exemplary data could be created by the DATA step given in Program 14.17.

Program 14.17

```
data bib_xmpl;
 n_sets=3; /* change this to increase replication */
 mu1=20; mu2=30; mu3=40; mu4=50;
 input block @@;
  do eu=1 to 2;
    input trt @@;
     mu=(trt=1)*mu1+(trt=2)*mu2+(trt=3)*mu3+(trt=4)*mu4;
    do set=1 to n_sets;
     output;
    end;
  end;
datalines;
1  1 2
2  1 3
3  1 4
4  2 3
5  2 4
6  3 4
;
run;
```

The reference treatment, TRT=1, has an expected mean count (MU1) of $\lambda = 20$. The other three treatment means (MU2, MU3, and MU4) are set to 10, 20 and 30 units greater than MU1, respectively. The variable N_SETS defines how many sets of 6 blocks are to be evaluated, anticipating the likelihood that an experiment with only 6 blocks may not provide adequate power. Indeed, the power for detecting a 30-unit difference using an $\alpha = 0.05$ test is just over 0.28.

Use Program 14.18 for the PROC GLIMMIX step.

Program 14.18

```
proc glimmix data=bib_xmpl;
   class set block trt;
   model mu=trt / d=negbin;
   random intercept / subject=block*set;
   lsmeans trt / ilink cl;
   lsmestimate trt '1 v 2' 1 -1 0 0,
                   '1 v 3' 1 0 -1 0,
                   '1 v 4' 1 0 0 -1,
                   '2 v 3' 0 1 -1 0,
                   '2 v 4' 0 1 0 -1,
                   '3 v 4' 0 0 1 -1 / exp cl;
   contrast '1 v 2: 10 unit diff' trt 1 -1 0 0;
   contrast '1 v 3: 20 unit diff' trt 1 0 -1 0;
   contrast '1 v 4: 30 unit diff' trt 1 0 0 -1;
   parms (0.072)(0.25)/hold=1,2;
   ods output contrasts=ftests;
run;
```

If you have more than one set of blocks, SET*BLOCK uniquely defines each block and must be used to define SUBJECT in the random statement. Alternatively, you could use the statement RANDOM SET*BLOCK; or RANDOM SET / SUBJECT=BLOCK; These RANDOM statements are equivalent. The CL option in conjunction with ILINK enables you to see the anticipated widths of the confidence intervals for the estimated treatment mean counts. The EXP and CL options in the LSMESTIMATE statement enables you to see the anticipated widths of the estimated ratios of expected means counts for all possible pairs to treatments. That is, on the model scale, $\hat{\tau}_i - \hat{\tau}_{i'} = \log(\hat{\lambda}_i) - \log(\hat{\lambda}_{i'}) = \log(\hat{\lambda}_i / \hat{\lambda}_{i'})$; thus $\exp(\hat{\tau}_i - \hat{\tau}_{i'}) = \hat{\lambda}_i / \hat{\lambda}_{i'}$. The CONTRAST statements generate the information needed for the power step. Use Program 14.19 to complete the power analysis.

Program 14.19

```
data power;
 set ftests;
 ncp=fvalue*numdf;
 alpha=0.05;
 FCrit=finv(1-alpha,numdf,dendf,0);
 power=1-ProbF(FCrit,numdf,dendf,ncp);
run;
proc print data=power;
run;
```

Results

Output 14.14 shows selected results for 3 sets of blocks, i.e. 18 blocks and hence 36 observations total, 9 replications per treatment. This is the minimum sample size for this experiment capable of at least 80% power for the 30-unit difference.

Output 14.14: Precision and Power Analysis for Incomplete Block Design with Count Data

trt Least Squares Means											
trt	Estimate	Standard Error	DF	t Value	Pr > |t|	Alpha	Lower	Upper	Mean	Standard Error Mean	Lower Mean	Upper Mean
1	2.9957	0.2008	15	14.92	<.0001	0.05	2.5678	3.4236	20.0000	4.0150	13.0376	30.6804
2	3.4012	0.1961	15	17.34	<.0001	0.05	2.9832	3.8192	30.0000	5.8836	19.7504	45.5686
3	3.6889	0.1938	15	19.04	<.0001	0.05	3.2759	4.1019	40.0000	7.7506	26.4665	60.4539
4	3.9120	0.1923	15	20.34	<.0001	0.05	3.5021	4.3220	50.0000	9.6169	33.1838	75.3379

Least Squares Means Estimates										
Effect	Label	Estimate	Standard Error	DF	t Value	Pr > |t|	Alpha	Lower	Upper	Exponentiated Estimate
trt	1 v 2	-0.4055	0.2697	15	-1.50	0.1535	0.05	-0.9803	0.1694	0.6667
trt	1 v 3	-0.6931	0.2680	15	-2.59	0.0207	0.05	-1.2644	-0.1219	0.5000
trt	1 v 4	-0.9163	0.2670	15	-3.43	0.0037	0.05	-1.4854	-0.3472	0.4000
trt	2 v 3	-0.2877	0.2646	15	-1.09	0.2941	0.05	-0.8516	0.2763	0.7500
trt	2 v 4	-0.5108	0.2635	15	-1.94	0.0716	0.05	-1.0726	0.05091	0.6000
trt	3 v 4	-0.2231	0.2618	15	-0.85	0.4074	0.05	-0.7812	0.3349	0.8000

Least Squares Means Estimates			
Effect	Label	Exponentiated Lower	Exponentiated Upper
trt	1 v 2	0.3752	1.1846
trt	1 v 3	0.2824	0.8852
trt	1 v 4	0.2264	0.7066
trt	2 v 3	0.4267	1.3182
trt	2 v 4	0.3421	1.0522
trt	3 v 4	0.4579	1.3978

Obs	Label	NumDF	DenDF	FValue	ProbF	ncp	alpha	FCrit	power
1	1 v 2: 10 unit diff	1	15	2.26	0.1535	2.2603	0.05	4.54308	0.29082
2	1 v 3: 20 unit diff	1	15	6.69	0.0207	6.6892	0.05	4.54308	0.67668
3	1 v 4: 30 unit diff	1	15	11.78	0.0037	11.7788	0.05	4.54308	0.89351

Interpretation

The first table in the output, the PROC PRINT of the POWER data set, shows that power to detect a 30-unit difference using an $\alpha = 0.05$ test is just above 0.89, but the power to show 20- and 10-unit differences is well below 80%. More sets of blocks would be required if detecting these differences is a priority.

The second table, the Least Squares Means, shows the anticipated widths of 95% confidence intervals to estimate treatment mean counts. Use the data scale estimates, i.e. the four right-hand columns of the table. For example, the expected confidence interval for treatment 1 is approximately (13.0, 30.7), or just over 17 units wide. Notice that because this is count data, the standard error of the estimate and the confidence interval widths increase as the expected mean count increases. This is because the variance increases with expected mean count.

The table of "Least Squares Means Estimates" gives the width of confidence intervals for estimated ratios of pairs of treatment means. For example, for treatments 1 and 2, the mean ratio is $20/30 = 0.667$, and the expected interval width (two right-hand columns of the table) is approximately (0.38, 1.18).

You can change N_SETS in the exemplary DATA step to determine how many blocks are needed to detect a 20- and 10-unit difference. Four sets, i.e. 24 blocks and hence 48 observations and 12 replications per treatment are needed to detect a 20-unit difference. Eleven sets, i.e. 66 blocks, are required to detect a 10-unit difference. When you attempt to run the PROC GLIMMIX step with 11 sets, you may get the SAS Log message

```
ERROR: Values given in PARMS statement are not feasible.
```

This means you need to modify the values in the PARMS statement. The following statement worked for this example:

```
parms (0.07195)(0.2501)/hold=1,2;
```

With a bit of trial and error, you can get the PROC GLIMMIX step to compute the needed precision and power information.

14.8 Summary

The chapter builds on the mixed-model-based precision and power methods introduced in Chapter 4. GLMM-based methods can, in principle, be used for designs and covariance structure of arbitrary complexity, as well as with non-Gaussian response variables whose distributions are available with PROC GLIMMIX.

This chapter presents split-plot and repeated measures examples with Gaussian data, and block design examples with binomial and count data were presented. Though not shown here, you can adapt the split-plot and repeated measures examples to binomial and count data using the models shown in Chapter 13.

You can show that the exemplary data methods shown here are very accurate for split-plot Gaussian data, and reasonably accurate for Gaussian repeated measures and for models with binomial data. The method is close, but more of an approximation with count data. Our suggestion for repeated measures and for non-Gaussian data is that the methods shown in this chapter be used to get you close to the required sample size. You can then use simulation if you need to refine your recommendations. However, even without a simulation step, the recommended sample size using these methods is close and quite useful. The most likely source of inaccuracy comes from the possible use of underestimated variance components. This is especially true if you use pilot data, or data from previous, similar studies, to anticipate variance components. We suggest that, in such cases, you use an upper confidence bound of the variance component estimates to obtain "worst case" assessments of design structure and sample size requirements.

Finally, note that when you plan designs with blocking, hierarchical structure, or repeated measures, accounting for random effects (i.e., GLMM-thinking and methodology) are crucial. Conventional approaches to power analysis that do not account for the impact of random effects can result in sample size recommendations that are not merely wrong, but catastrophically wrong.

Chapter 15: Mixed Model Troubleshooting and Diagnostics

15.1 Introduction 509
15.2 Troubleshooting 510
    15.2.1 Best Practices When Fitting Mixed Models...510
    15.2.2 Search Strategy and Two Good References 512
    15.2.3 Frequently Asked Questions...512
15.3 Residuals 514
    15.3.1 Residuals in the Linear Model 514
    15.3.2 Marginal and Conditional Residuals 516
    15.3.3 Split-Plot Design: An Example..517
15.4 Influence Diagnostics...520
    15.4.1 Influence Measures in the Linear Model..521
    15.4.2 Generalized Least Squares and Influence 521
    15.4.3 Types of Mixed Model Influence...522
    15.4.4 Iterative and Non-Iterative Analyses..523
    15.4.5 Unequally Spaced Repeated Measures: An Example................................524
    15.4.6 Insect Count Data: An Example..531
15.5 Two Diagnostic Plots Useful for Non-Gaussian Data 538
15.5 Summary..541

15.1 Introduction

A statistical model is a mathematical and probabilistic representation of a data-generating mechanism. A model that fits the data well represents a mechanism that could have produced the observed data to a reasonable degree of approximation. Naturally, we raise questions as to what extent the model and data agree, whether the model needs to be adjusted, whether the data need to be adjusted (e.g., outlier removal), or both. We take a fairly broad view of linear modeling in this book and focus out a little further in this concluding chapter to provide a higher-level mindset toward mixed modeling and handling difficulties when they arise. Your ability to do this will increase directly with your proficiency with these models.

Difficulties with mixed modeling fall into two main categories: those encountered during model fitting and those encountered while interpreting results. Within this chapter, troubleshooting largely focuses on the former category, whereas diagnostics deal with the latter. For troubleshooting, you will encounter a fair number of SAS notes, warnings, and errors while fitting mixed models. The next section covers these in some detail along with several frequently asked questions (FAQs) and a general search-based approach to handling them.

The specification of a mixed model includes the choice of response, transformations, or link functions, fixed effects, random effects, distributional assumptions, covariance structure, as well as all of the targeted inferential and predictive statistics discussed in previous chapters. Fitting the model generally entails solving a nonlinear optimization problem corresponding to maximization of a statistical likelihood function. Numerical methods are generally required to perform this optimization, and these methods can fail for various reasons. The next section covers the most common problems and provides you with general guidance on dealing with them.

Once you have succeeded in implementing your mixed model, you will want to check the model's fit using diagnostics. For these we build upon the rich set of developments for the classical linear model providing information about modeling assumptions and breakdowns. For example, you can use the graphical examination of fitted residuals to assess distributional assumptions such as variance homogeneity and lack of serial correlation, and to examine the need to add or transform fixed model effects. Summary measures and statistics based on residuals are used to test the goodness of fit of a model. You can use collinearity diagnostics to study the interrelationship between fixed effects and their impact on the analysis. Influence diagnostics measure the importance and weight of individual and clusters of observations on the analysis.

It is often helpful to think of these diagnostic techniques as perturbation analysis. You are interested in gauging the stability of the model output under perturbations of its inputs, which is the classic way to assess causality. For example, influence analysis perturbs the data by removing observations from the analysis; residual plots are often compared after adding or removing explanatory variables, a perturbation of the fixed effects structure. The challenge is to determine when changes in model output justify reformulation of the model or data, while at the same time not developing a model that is overly rigid or crafted too closely to the data at hand.

Comparatively little work in this area has been done for mixed models. The reasons for this are explored in detail in Section 15.2. Briefly, mixed models have these characteristics:

- They are considerably more difficult to fit than linear models, typically requiring iterative numerical optimization.

- They have more model components.

- They can have different kinds and levels of residuals.

- They have conditional and marginal distributions.

- They are usually applied to data with clustered structure (dependent observations, e.g. from repeated measures in time or space), and this structure is critical in verifying modeling assumptions and assessing degrees of departure from them.

This chapter presents residual and influence diagnostics for mixed models and some of their connections to similar or identical measures for the linear model. Special emphasis is placed on understanding the connection to the linear model, as well as the important differences in residual and influence analysis. Throughout, it is important to remember that the results of diagnostic analysis depend fundamentally on the model. For example, an observation can be highly influential and/or it can be an outlier because the model is not correct. The appropriate action may be to change the model, not to remove the data point. Outliers can be the most important and noteworthy data points, because they can point to a model breakdown. The task is typically to develop models that fit the data (assuming that all data points are trustworthy), not to coerce a set of data to fit a particular model.

Section 15.2 provides some guidelines for handling troubles and difficulties while fitting mixed models. Section 15.3 explores residuals in the linear and the linear mixed model after a successful fit. Sections 15.4 examines influence diagnostics and associated statistics.

15.2 Troubleshooting

Given the complex nature and intricacies of mixed modeling, you will inevitably face difficulties and even unexpected results. This section provides you with guidance on dealing with these issues, so you can quickly and effectively produce a well-fitted mixed model; and move confidently to the important statistical inferences and predictions.

15.2.1 Best Practices When Fitting Mixed Models

As in most of life, the best way to deal with troubles is to adopt good practices that minimize their chances of ever occurring in the first place. That is, being preventative rather than reactive. In addition, the general problem-solving strategies of simplify-until-understood and divide-and-conquer work well while mixed modeling. The three main hurdles you will face initially when fitting mixed models are making sure that

1. Your input data are properly formatted, well-conditioned, and correctly coded.
2. Your mixed model syntax is correct and aligned with the study design and data coding.
3. The optimization algorithm finds a good solution, producing a fitted mixed model from which you can reliably draw statistical inferences.

For (1), the primary input data set almost always needs to be in stacked form (one row per observation, also called long format), and you should verify that its dimensions and its numeric and character variable codings are correct and as expected. Because nearly all mixed model inferential methods are translation-scale invariant, it is good practice to standardize and scale all numeric X covariates to have a mean around or near 0 and a standard deviation at or near 1. For linear mixed models, normalizing and/or transforming the response variable Y can also be helpful, especially if its initial scale is extreme (very small or very large). While standardization is the ideal, it competes with the need to have quantitative measures on an interpretable scale with understandable units, so you may need to compromise here a bit. The main rationale for rescaling is that the optimization problem required to fit the mixed model computes first and second derivatives of the residual likelihood function, which involves third and fourth moments of the data, and these can push the limits of machine precision and the effectiveness of the steps made during each iteration if the original data are badly scaled (for example, with range 1e-8 or 1e+8). For character variables, verify that the levels are as intended and pay attention if some are set up to be nested or crossed within others. You should do some initial plots and crosstabulations of your data to verify that the distributions are within reasonable bounds and to screen for any severe outliers or data coding mistakes.

For (2), it is usually good practice to begin from a known and trusted example similar to the ones provided in this book. Probably one of the most valuable aspects of this book is its rich collection of examples, and one recommended approach is to find an example that most closely matches your case and compare results side-by-side. Make sure that you understand your design and associated covariance structure thoroughly, as well as all forms of experimental units, then set up appropriate statements to specify them. Chapters 2 and 5 provided guidelines for translating study design to plausible model. If followed, these guidelines will help you avoid trying to fit a misspecified model. Note also that the order of PROC GLIMMIX and PROC MIXED statements is important, and you should mimic examples in this book and the SAS/STAT documentation as much as possible. Probably the most difficult part of this is setting up your RANDOM and/or REPEATED statements correctly. If you are not sure, start with a simple model and take small steps toward the complex one you think is most appropriate, and try to understand the corresponding covariance structures of, and differences between, each model you fit. This can be an interesting iterative process and can sometimes reveal hidden patterns or unexpected aspects of the design or inferential results.

For (3), after specifying your model and running a block of SAS code, *always* check the SAS log for all instances of NOTE, WARNING, and ERROR and make sure you understand them. These three keywords are in order of increasing severity, and the latter two should certainly draw your attention. The messages themselves will sometimes be self-explanatory and provide guidance on what to do next, but at other times they can be confusing or perplexing. The subsequent two subsections will help you find ways to properly interpret them and provide both strategy and tactics for dealing with the troubles you will most likely encounter.

Always check the first part of PROC GLIMMIX or PROC MIXED output to verify that the printed information aligns with what you expect. These include the dimensions of the data and class effect levels. Staying in a "cross-check" mindset throughout your analysis will provide you with confidence at each step of the process and help you catch and fix any errors as soon as they happen.

The next critical table to check is the iteration history. Ideally, you will see the objective criterion decline at approximately a quadratic rate to full convergence, indicating the algorithm has found an optimal solution. If the algorithm does not converge, but the objective function is decreasing toward the convergence criterion, you may simply need to override the default limit on the number of iterations allowed. If the objective function does not appear to be steadily decreasing, this is a typical symptom of some type of problem, either with the data or with the specified model. You must then address this before you continue with the analysis.

Keep in mind that the optimization algorithm (for example, Gauss-Newton or quasi-Newton) begins by finding starting values, then uses computed first and second derivatives to make adjustments to all unknown parameters (those in the mixed model variance covariance structure), taking steps toward a presumably global optimum set of values that maximize the residual maximum likelihood. While PROC GLIMMIX and PROC MIXED typically have very good automatic generation of starting values, no default algorithm can cover every conceivable scenario. Hence, there are occasions when the default starting values are not good and the algorithm gets stuck far from the desired optimal point. In this case, you can try using the SCORING= option in the PROC statement to take a few Fisher scoring steps. Fisher scoring can often be robust to poor starting values.

Alternatively, you can provide your own starting values with the PARMS statement. These can be chosen in several ways. One easy thing to try in PROC MIXED is

```
parms / ols;
```

which just uses simple ordinary least squares estimates. Beyond this, a good way to find starting values is to use results from previous successful runs of simpler models and/or good guesses based on your domain knowledge. Refer to Chapter 8 for one example of using the PARMS statement to sidestep default starting values. Furthermore, you can specify a grid of starting values and let the PROC choose the best point from the grid.

If the algorithm starts well—meaning that the objective function appears to decrease as it should—but does not converge because the objective function never quite reaches the default convergence criterion, you can override the default tolerances with the NLOPTIONS statement in PROC GLIMMIX or the CONVF, CONVG, or CONVH options in the PROC MIXED statement. While this is usually not necessary, it can be sensible for data with unusual noise patterns and/or complex covariance structures.

15.2.2 Search Strategy and Two Good References

Since the writing of the Second Edition of this book, web search engines such as Google have improved at a tremendous rate in terms of both coverage and speed. They provide rapid access to valuable content both from the main SAS technical support page at support.sas.com, as well as a large number of publications, discussion forums, and communities with varying degrees of activity. We can now access a richly indexed and instantly searchable live and growing repository of information about mixed modeling. As a general approach for understanding a specific WARNING, ERROR, or mixed model catch-phrase, we recommend copying and pasting the phrase you encounter into your favorite browser and perusing the results for answers or asking a well-formed question on a community forum. Given the tens of thousands of users of this methodology worldwide, the chance of finding an informative answer is quite high and continues to increase. There are also many experts frequently online who are kindly willing to spend time helping you. If you go this route, etiquette calls for you to put in time and effort first to find a solution on your own. If you cannot, then raise the question. When you have arrived at a solution, document it in a way that makes your question and its solution easily accessible and helps the community at large in the future. As with any web search, exercise some caution while reading and dialoguing, and be sure to verify the source and credentials behind an answer before trusting it.

Two reliable references for troubleshooting mixed models that you can find online are Kiernan, Tao, and Gibbs (2012) and Tao, Kiernan, and Gibbs (2015). These authors have a high level of expertise and have been faithfully supporting SAS mixed models and other related procedures in SAS Technical Support for over twenty years. The two papers are filled with great information, including details about mixed model checking and problem solving. In effect, these two papers can be considered supplemental chapters to this book. The 2012 paper has three sections. The first provides tips on how to make programs more efficient by reducing memory and execution time. The second provides suggestions for troubleshooting convergence problems. The third includes a brief discussion of some of the commonly reported notes, warnings, and errors that are reported in the SAS log for a mixed model analysis using PROC GLIMMIX, PROC MIXED, or PROC NLMIXED. The 2015 paper first discusses a complex mixed model example with multiple subject effects and how to correctly specify them. It also helps you clearly understand when a REPEATED (PROC MIXED) or RESIDUAL (PROC GLIMMIX) effect is necessary. It then explains how you can use PROC PLM to post-process a mixed model via a SAS item store. This enables you to perform additional statistical inference without rerunning PROC GLIMMIX or PROC MIXED.

15.2.3 Frequently Asked Questions

Here you will find, by category, questions commonly arising when fitting mixed models, each followed by a brief answer and then a link to a more detailed one from SAS technical support.

Warning and Error Messages

What does PROC MIXED's "Estimated G matrix not positive definite" message mean? This typically occurs when one or more variance components are estimated to be zero. It is usually not of serious concern, especially if it is plausible that one or more sources of variability modeled by the associated variance components are small or have few degrees of freedom in design to estimate them. Certainly, pay close attention to which variance components are estimated to be zero, or, more generally, any causes of singularity, and be aware of potential implications for fixed effects tests. If you are in a situation where negative covariances make sense (for example, competition for resources within a block), consider using the NOBOUND option or a more general covariance structure. http://support.sas.com/kb/22614

How do I fix the error "Final Hessian Nonpositive Definite"? This usually means that the covariance structure model is overspecified. That is, some of it can likely be eliminated without changing the final model. Check your model carefully and try simpler versions to track down the source of the redundancy. http://support.sas.com/kb/23237

How should I deal with the warning "Stopped Because of Infinite Likelihood"? This usually occurs when there are duplicate measurements within a subject or when starting values are not good. Check different parts of the specified model and try fitting simpler versions and comparing results to track what is happening. It may also help to provide known, good starting values with the PARMS statement. https://groups.google.com/forum/#!topic/comp.soft-sys.sas/23FAeV042lU

Model Specification

When can I omit the repeated effect (preceding the slash) in the REPEATED statement in PROC MIXED? You can omit this when you have either no missing data or the missing data pattern is identical across subjects and the measurements are sorted the same within subject. In general, it is safer to include this effect. http://support.sas.com/kb/23757

When is it appropriate to list random effects in the MODEL statement? For PROC MIXED and PROC GLIMMIX, never! But when you have a SUBJECT= effect in the RANDOM statement, it can appear as if the same effects are specified in both the MODEL and RANDOM statements. In actuality, the effects in the RANDOM statement can be viewed as being nested within the SUBJECT= effect so that they are not the same as the fixed effects in the MODEL statement. http://support.sas.com/kb/23693

How do I set the reference levels for the CLASS predictor variables? Use the "(REF=<level>)" specification after the variable in the CLASS statement. http://support.sas.com/kb/37108

When should I use PROC MIXED or PROC GLIMMIX instead of PROC GLM? Typically, always whenever you have random effects, repeated measures, or any type of covariance structure or data whose observations are not independent. http://support.sas.com/kb/22584

How do I write a CONTRAST or ESTIMATE statement to test a particular hypothesis or estimate a particular quantity? This book has a large number of examples. Check the table of contents to find a situation closest to yours and look for examples that are similar. http://support.sas.com/kb/23000

Can PROC MIXED or PROC GLIMMIX be used to fit Hierarchical Linear Models (HLMs)? Yes. The HLM terminology is popular in the social sciences and education research. HLMs are typically the same as random coefficient models as described in this book. http://support.sas.com/kb/22882

How do I obtain subject-specific parameter estimates and tests for a random coefficients model or hierarchical linear model (HLM) with PROC MIXED or PROC GLIMMIX? See Chapter 10 for several examples. http://support.sas.com/kb/37109

Performance

How large of a hierarchical linear model (HLM) can PROC MIXED fit? This depends on the structure of the model and the capabilities of your computer. Typically, design matrices with dimensions in the hundreds can be handled quickly but begin to slow when moving into the thousands. Computations are typically of order n^3, although sometimes much larger data sets can be handled by using the SUBJECT= effect to factorize the likelihood into small blocks. You can also consider using PROC HPMIXED and PROC HPLMIXED for large Gaussian-response problems (see http://support.sas.com/kb/37057).

How do I fix an Out of Memory condition or reduce execution time in PROC MIXED or PROC GLIMMIX? It might be possible to use a different syntax to fit the same model with less memory. For example, factor out common effects into the SUBJECT= option. You may alternatively want to switch to PROC HPMIXED or PROC HPLMIXED if the response is Gaussian or approximately so (see http://support.sas.com/kb/37047).

Interpretation of Unusual or Unexpected Results

Why do the results of the Type 3 *F* tests differ from the *t* tests that are produced by the SOLUTION option in the MODEL statement? This can happen when you specify an interaction between a covariate and a class variable. It is good to make such comparisons in general to ensure that all of the modeling results make sense. http://support.sas.com/kb/23695

How do I compare covariance structures and test covariance parameters using the COVTEST statement in PROC GLIMMIX? The basic approach is to fit several models and compare various output statistics of interest, for example, information criteria like AICC or BIC. See Chapter 6, and the following link also provides some good examples. For comparing covariance structures for repeated measures, see Chapter 8 and http://support.sas.com/kb/40724.

Why am I getting zero denominator degrees of freedom for classification fixed effects when using DDFM=BW in mixed models? This results from the way the between-within method works. You may want to try a more sophisticated method like DDFM=KR2 (see http://support.sas.com/kb/41688).

Why are the degrees of freedom for some of my model effects less than I expect or, in some cases, zero? This depends on what method you are using to compute these degrees of freedom and possible lack of balance or confounding in your experimental design. Usually, DDFM=KR2 provides very sensible estimates that are typically near optimal in terms of small sample performance. The values of the degrees of freedom can themselves be revealing about the structure of your design and (perhaps unexpected) missing value patterns (see http://support.sas.com/kb/23131).

Why are the degrees of freedom for some of my model effects larger than I expected? This depends on the method you are using and is typically related to imbalance patterns in the data. See the preceding answer. http://support.sas.com/kb/23130

Why are my results from the CONTRAST, ESTIMATE, or LSMEANS statements missing/nonestimable? One of the most common causes is a failure to specify all effects required to make the contrast estimable, so double-check to make sure all relevant effects are specified and coefficients are ordered properly. Beyond these reasons, there can be subtle aliasing between interaction effects in unbalanced designs, making some linear combinations nonestimable. This can sometimes be a difficult and frustrating problem. One strategy is to first simplify and use a completely balanced subset of data and make sure all output statistics are as expected. Then carefully add more data and see exactly when the problems begin happening. An alternative, and often easier approach, is to switch and use LSMESTIMATE statements (see http://support.sas.com/kb/22582).

How can I obtain multiple comparison tests in a repeated measures analysis? Use options in the LSMEANS statement like ADJUST= and ADJDFE=. http://support.sas.com/kb/22905

If you remain completely stuck with unanswered questions or have a possible bug or concern to report, please contact SAS technical support at support.sas.com (web) or support@sas.com (email) at any time.

15.3 Residuals

From henceforth in this chapter we assume you have successfully fit your mixed model and are now seeking to verify underlying assumptions and explore how each data point affects the model fit. Two types of statistics are very useful here: residuals and influence diagnostics. The former are simply observed minus predicted values, possibly standardized or normalized in some fashion. The latter are statistics to measure how much a single point affects aspects of the model fit. This section discusses residuals and the next covers influence diagnostics.

Examining residuals is a great place to begin assessing how well a mixed model is fitting your data. Residuals also provide an excellent way of verifying distributional assumptions and detecting outliers. We first review residual computation in the standard linear model then move on to how you can compute and interpret them in a mixed model. As expected, things become more complicated when making this move, but the complexity is manageable with proper understanding of concepts from previous chapters as well as some patience while applying them.

One key point to keep in mind throughout the remainder of this chapter is that mixed models fit by restricted maximum likelihood are effectively minimizing a weighted form of squared loss (also known as L2-norm loss). As such, they can be vulnerable to measurements lying outside the standard distributional assumptions. We note in passing that it is possible to perform more robust fits using absolute loss (e.g. assuming a Laplace distribution instead of Gaussian in the linear case and L1-norm loss) or by transforming the Y variables to ranks. We consider these methods beyond the scope of this book and instead focus on how to most effectively use standard theory and understand its pitfalls and benefits. By doing so you will likely achieve models with the best possible statistical properties (error control and power).

15.3.1 Residuals in the Linear Model

In the standard linear model with uncorrelated errors of the form

$$\mathbf{Y} = \mathbf{X}\boldsymbol{\beta} + \mathbf{e}, \quad \mathbf{e} \sim \left(\mathbf{0}, \sigma^2 \mathbf{I}\right)$$

residual analysis starts with the basic residuals (also known as raw residuals)

$$\hat{\mathbf{e}} = \mathbf{y} - \mathbf{X}\hat{\boldsymbol{\beta}}$$

where $\hat{\boldsymbol{\beta}}$ is the ordinary least squares (OLS) estimate

$$\hat{\boldsymbol{\beta}} = \left(\mathbf{X}'\mathbf{X}\right)^{-}\mathbf{X}'\mathbf{y}$$

The properties of the OLS estimated residuals have been extensively studied for decades in the statistical and related literature. One key basic property is that $\hat{\mathbf{e}}$ has zero mean and, if the model contains an intercept, the OLS residuals sum to zero. It is thus customary to examine the distribution of residuals to verify it is centered at zero and to begin making inferences about the unobservable model errors **e**. Note that $\hat{\mathbf{e}}$ does not share many properties with **e** beyond a zero mean. For example, the OLS residuals are neither homoscedastic nor uncorrelated; their variance is

$$\mathrm{Var}\left(\hat{\mathbf{e}}\right) = \sigma^2 \mathbf{M} = \sigma^2 \left(\mathbf{I} - \mathbf{H}\right) = \sigma^2 \left(\mathbf{I} - \mathbf{X}\left(\mathbf{X}'\mathbf{X}\right)^{-} \mathbf{X}'\right)$$

which is a non-diagonal matrix with possibly heterogeneous values on the diagonal. Furthermore, the fitted residuals are rank-deficient; if X has rank k, then there can be only $n–k$ linearly independent fitted residuals. To modify these characteristics of the raw residuals, manipulations and transformations of the vector of fitted residuals are common.

Standardization and Studentization

Raw residuals are on the scale of the original data, and it can often be helpful to divide them by some measure of variability in order to normalize them into a signal-to-noise ratio. One direct way is to simply divide by the estimated standard deviation of the residual error for the corresponding row:

$$\frac{\hat{e}_i}{\sqrt{\hat{\sigma}^2}}$$

This is known as Pearson standardization. One drawback of this approach is that the denominator used here is not the standard error of the residual, and therefore Pearson residuals still have heterogeneous variances. To address this, you can instead divide by h_{ii}, which is the ith diagonal element of the leverage ("hat") matrix $\mathbf{H} = \mathbf{X}\left(\mathbf{X}'\mathbf{X}\right)^{-} \mathbf{X}'$. The ith studentized residual is obtained by dividing it by its estimated standard deviation,

$$r_i = \frac{\hat{e}_i}{\sqrt{\hat{\mathrm{Var}}\left(\hat{e}_i\right)}} = \frac{\hat{e}_i}{\sqrt{\hat{\sigma}^2 (1 - h_{ii})}}$$

Studentized residuals have equal variances to a high degree of approximation, remedying a subtle problem of the raw residual, variance heterogeneity. If the estimate of the variance is replaced with an estimate that does not use the ith observation, a leave-one-out estimate of σ^2, the externally studentized residual t_i is as follows:

$$t_i = \frac{\hat{e}_i}{\sqrt{\hat{\sigma}^2_{-i} (1 - h_{ii})}}$$

The subscript notation $-i$ is intended to signify that the estimate is obtained without the participation of the ith observation. External studentization also stabilizes the variance of the residual. In addition, if the data are normally distributed, the t_i follow a t distribution—a fact sometimes used to compare t_i's to cutoffs from Student's t distributions. These types of residuals can offer less biased assessments of the effect of a single observation because that observation is not used in the estimates of the variance used to studentize it.

Error Recovery

Studentized residuals combat a single shortcoming of the raw residuals, variance heterogeneity. A different route is taken by methods that simultaneously rectify more than one issue. Schabenberger and Gotway (2005, Ch. 6.1.2) collect these issues under the term error recovery. An error recovery method generates $n–k$ variance-covariance stabilized residuals that have zero mean and constant variance, and are uncorrelated. Residuals in this class are the recursive or sequential residuals (Brown, Durbin, and Evans 1975, Kianifard and Swallow 1996) and the linearly unbiased scaled (LUS) estimates of Theil (1971). Residual recursion is the process of fitting the model initially to k data points and then adding the remaining data points in turn. The jth recursive residual is the scaled difference between y_j and $\hat{y}_{-j}$, the predicted values based on previous observations. Recursive residuals are useful to detect outliers, serial correlation, and departures from the constant variance assumptions. A drawback is their dependence on the initial choice of k observations used to fit the model.

LUS estimates apply error recovery based on projections. We are seeking an $(n \times n)$ matrix Q such that the first $n–k$ elements of $\mathbf{Q}'\hat{\mathbf{e}}$ have unit variance and are uncorrelated. This process is also known as whitening the residuals. The matrix Q can be constructed from a spectral decomposition of the variance matrix $\sigma^2 \mathbf{M}$ of $\hat{\mathbf{e}}$. You can obtain recursive residuals and LUS estimates in fixed effects models with the AUTOREG procedure in SAS/ETS.

In general, if the random vector **u** has variance **A**, and **A** is positive-definite, then you can use the lower triangular Cholesky root **C** of **A** to construct a vector of uncorrelated random variables. Because $\mathbf{CC'} = \mathbf{A}$, $\text{Var}(\mathbf{C}^{-1}\mathbf{u}) = \mathbf{I}$. This idea cannot readily be applied to a vector of fitted residuals, because **M** is a rank-deficient matrix. But you can compute the Cholesky root of the estimate of $\text{Var}(\mathbf{Y})$. In the linear model this leads to the simple matrix $\sigma\mathbf{I}$. Applying the inverse Cholesky root of the variance of the data to the fitted residuals leads to the scaled or Cholesky residuals

$$\mathbf{C}^{-1}\hat{\mathbf{e}}$$

Like the LUS estimates, Cholesky residuals depend on the data order, and it is not possible to associate the jth recovered error with a single observation (let alone the jth observation). These residuals are linear combinations of one or more residuals and cannot be used to identify outliers. LUS estimates produce uncorrelated residuals, but Cholesky residuals are not uncorrelated, because they are scaled not by the inverse Cholesky root of *their* variance, but by the inverse root of the variance of the data. LUS and Cholesky residuals are well suited to diagnose deviations from the normality assumption (see, e.g., Houseman, Ryan, and Coull 2004 and Fitzmaurice, Laird, and Ware 2004, Ch. 9). In the linear model with uncorrelated errors, for example, the ith Cholesky residual is identical to the Pearson residual.

15.3.2 Marginal and Conditional Residuals

Mixed models contain random effects with variances modeled in the **G** matrix or may have an **R** matrix with a structure more complicated than $\sigma^2\mathbf{I}$. These introduce complications when computing residuals. In the presence of random effects, there are now two sets of residuals. In the mixed model $\mathbf{Y} = \mathbf{X}\boldsymbol{\beta} + \mathbf{Zu} + \mathbf{e}$, with normal random effects and errors, the conditional distribution of $\mathbf{Y} \mid \mathbf{u}$ has mean $\mathbf{X}\boldsymbol{\beta} + \mathbf{Zu}$ and variance **R**. The marginal distribution of **Y** has mean $\mathbf{X}\boldsymbol{\beta}$ and variance $\mathbf{ZGZ'} + \mathbf{R}$. Consequently, we can define the conditional residuals

$$\mathbf{r}_c = \mathbf{Y} - \mathbf{X}\hat{\boldsymbol{\beta}} - \mathbf{Z}\hat{\mathbf{u}}$$

that measure deviations from the conditional mean, and marginal residuals

$$\mathbf{r}_m = \mathbf{Y} - \mathbf{X}\hat{\boldsymbol{\beta}} = \mathbf{r}_c + \mathbf{Z}\hat{\mathbf{u}}$$

that measure deviations from the overall mean. Marginal and conditional residuals have different standardization and studentization, because the variances of $\mathbf{r}_c$ and $\mathbf{r}_m$ differ. Consequently, there are two versions of each of the basic residuals from the linear model—studentized marginal, studentized conditional, externally studentized marginal, externally studentized conditional residuals, and so on, for error recovery.

More importantly, the properties of the marginal and conditional residuals can differ greatly, and the marginal residuals in the mixed model can behave differently from the residuals in the standard linear model. The latter is a consequence of a non-diagonal variance matrix $\mathbf{V} = \mathbf{ZGZ'} + \mathbf{R}$. The fixed effects solution in the linear mixed model is

$$\hat{\boldsymbol{\beta}} = \left(\mathbf{X'}\hat{\mathbf{V}}^{-1}\mathbf{X}\right)^{-}\mathbf{X'}\hat{\mathbf{V}}^{-1}\mathbf{y}$$

Because **V** is estimated, this is an estimated generalized least squares (EGLS) estimator. Thus, the structure and estimates of **G** and **R** have a direct impact on the conditional and marginal residuals. When **G** and **R** are known, the marginal residuals have zero mean in the mixed model, as they do in the standard linear model,

$$\text{E}\left(\mathbf{r}_m\right) = \text{E}\left(\mathbf{Y} - \mathbf{X}\hat{\boldsymbol{\beta}}\right) = \mathbf{X}\boldsymbol{\beta} - \mathbf{X}\boldsymbol{\beta} = \mathbf{0}$$

When they are unknown and estimates are plugged in, the expectation calculation is much more difficult and is in general no longer exactly zero, but should be very close in nearly all practical applications. Moreover, the residuals will sum to zero as long as there is an overall intercept or a linear combination of independent variables that equal an intercept. That is, whenever the vector of 1s is in the column space of **X**.

Note that BLUPs

$$\hat{\mathbf{u}} = \hat{\mathbf{G}}\mathbf{Z'}\hat{\mathbf{V}}^{-1}\left(\mathbf{y} - \mathbf{X}\hat{\boldsymbol{\beta}}\right)$$

transform marginal residuals in the observation space to the dimension and scaling of the random effects space. You can therefore view BLUPs both as residuals and as estimates of realized values of the random effects. They will also sum to zero if you include an overall intercept in your model, which occurs by default in SAS mixed modeling procedures.

15.3.3 Split-Plot Design: An Example

To highlight the difference between conditional and marginal residuals in the mixed model and the corresponding quantities in a fixed effects model, we consider a split-plot experiment discussed by Littell, Freund, and Spector (1991). The experiment is conducted using four blocks. Each block is divided into halves, and cultivar (CULT, 2 levels) A or B is randomly assigned to each half (or whole-plot unit). Each whole-plot unit consists of three-plot, or split-plot, units. Three inoculation treatments (INOC) are randomly assigned to subplot units within each whole plot. Hence, the block halves represent the whole-plot experimental units and the CULT factor is the whole plot factor. The inoculation treatments compose the subplot factor. The data for this experiment are given as Data Set, "Cultivar-Inoculation Trial".

We fit this model with the GLIMMIX procedure (Program 15.1) because of the ease with which you can produce residual graphics and various types of residuals in the OUTPUT statement. The same CLASS, MODEL, and RANDOM statements can be used to fit the model with PROC MIXED.

Program 15.1

```
ods html;
ods graphics on;
proc glimmix data=cultspd
     plots=(studentpanel(type=noblup)
            studentpanel(type=blup));
  class block cult inoc;
  model drywt = cult inoc cult*inoc / ddfm=satterth;
  random block block*cult;
  output out=resid
     residual
     residual(noblup)
     residual(ilink)
     residual(noblup ilink)
     pearson
     pearson(noblup)
     pearson(noblup ilink)
     student
     student(noblup);
run;
ods graphics off;
ods html close;
```

The ODS GRAPHICS statement requests that statistical graphics be produced by the following procedure invocations. The ODS HTML statement selects a destination for the display of the listing and graphical output.

The PLOTS= option in the PROC GLIMMIX statement requests two panel plots of studentized residuals. You can use the TYPE= option of the STUDENTPANEL plot to determine what type of residual to construct. The NOBLUP type results in the marginal residuals r_m. The BLUP type produces the conditional residuals r_c.

The OUTPUT statement produces a new SAS data set named RESID containing a complete set of different types of residuals. The default residuals are conditional, and as in the PLOTS= option, the NOBLUP keyword makes them marginal. The ILINK keyword transforms the results using the inverse link function. For this example, this is the identity function and so results are the same as when not specifying ILINK, but they will be different when using a non-identity link function. The PEARSON and STUDENT options request standardized and studentized residuals, respectively. The SAS variables in the output data set have matching names as the options, except marginal residuals have suffix "PA", an abbreviation for "Population Averaged." You can rename any of these variables in the OUTPUT statement by specifying "=" then the new name you desire after each option.

Results

Output 15.1 displays partial output from the GLIMMIX procedure for the split-plot analysis (these results agree with those from PROC MIXED). The panel of graphics of the studentized residuals appear in Figures 15.1 and 15.2.

Output 15.1: Results for Split-Plot Analysis

Fit Statistics	
-2 Res Log Likelihood	65.06
AIC (smaller is better)	71.06
AICC (smaller is better)	72.78
BIC (smaller is better)	69.22
CAIC (smaller is better)	72.22
HQIC (smaller is better)	67.02
Generalized Chi-Square	12.70
Gener. Chi-Square / DF	0.71

Covariance Parameter Estimates		
Cov Parm	Estimate	Standard Error
block	0.8800	1.2264
block*cult	0.8182	0.8654
Residual	0.7054	0.2880

Type III Tests of Fixed Effects				
Effect	Num DF	Den DF	F Value	Pr > F
cult	1	3	0.76	0.4471
inoc	2	12	83.76	<.0001
cult*inoc	2	12	1.29	0.3098

Figure 15.1: Marginal Studentized Residuals in Split-Plot Analysis

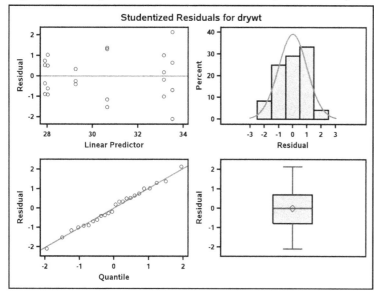

Figure 15.2: Conditional Studentized Residuals in Split-Plot Analysis

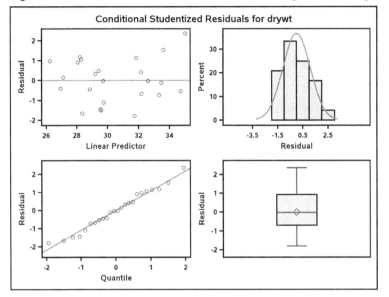

Interpretation

In the upper-left-hand corner of the panel display, you can see a scatter plot of the residual versus the linear predictor. The linear predictor is simply $\mathbf{x}'\hat{\boldsymbol{\beta}}$ for a marginal residual (Figure 15.1) and $\mathbf{x}'\hat{\boldsymbol{\beta}} + \mathbf{z}'\hat{\mathbf{u}}$ for a conditional residual (Figure 15.2). Because the BLOCK and BLOCK × CULT effects are random effects, there are only six distinct values for the linear predictor in Figure 15.1, corresponding to the six combinations of the INOC and CULT factors. The marginal residuals do not contain direct information about the BLOCK and BLOCK × CULT effects in this model. Their influence on the marginal predicted values is indirect, through the variance component estimates that determine the $\mathbf{V}$ matrix. In Figure 15.2, the BLOCK and BLOCK × CULT effects affect the predicted values directly, through the BLUPs of the random effects.

The histograms in the upper right corner appear to show some asymmetry, although the normal quantile-quantile plots in the lower left corner show no serious departures from a Gaussian distribution.

The box plots in the lower right corner of Figures 15.1 and 15.2 show that there are no outlying marginal or conditional residuals and that the residuals have a mean of zero. You can readily verify that the residuals in this model have a mean of zero with the statements in Program 15.2

Program 15.2

```
proc glimmix data=cultspd;
   class block cult inoc;
   model drywt = cult inoc cult*inoc / ddfm=satterth;
   random block block*cult;
   output out=gmxout student(blup)  = resid_cond
                     student(noblup)= resid_marg;
run;
proc means data=gmxout min max mean;
   var resid_cond resid_marg;
run;
```

The OUTPUT statement saves the conditional and marginal residuals to a data set, and PROC MEANS computes the sample statistics (Output 15.2). The residuals do not sum to exactly 0.0 because of the limits of finite precision computing.

Output 15.2: Sample Statistics for Studentized Residuals

Variable	Minimum	Maximum	Mean
resid_cond	-1.6812934	2.2118656	6.032212E-15
resid_marg	-2.1040484	2.1412882	3.362125E-14

If you ignore the split-plot nature of the experiment for the moment and resort to a fixed effects model, you can fit the model as a two-way factorial. Use the statements in Program 15.3.

Program 15.3

```
ods html;
ods graphics on;
proc glimmix data=cultspd plots=studentpanel(type=noblup);
   class block cult inoc;
   model drywt = block cult block*cult
                 inoc cult*inoc / ddfm=satterth;
run;
ods graphics off;
ods html close;
```

Results and Interpretation

The marginal studentized residuals—the only studentized residuals in this case—are shown in Figure 15.3.

Figure 15.3: Studentized Residuals in Factorial Analysis

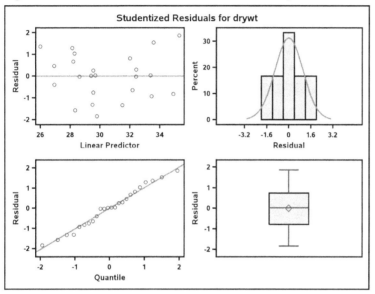

The scatter plot and the residual histogram are a bit different from the marginal mixed model residuals in Figure 15.1. The linear predictor is now more sensitive to the levels of the BLOCK effect because it is considered to be a fixed effect. Otherwise, there are no dramatic differences between the residuals from the two specifications.

15.4 Influence Diagnostics

In addition to looking at deviations from observed and fitted values (residuals), you can also assess to what degree individual observations or clusters of them affect aspects of the mixed model fit. Such statistics are called influence diagnostics and come in a few different forms in a mixed model setting.

The procedure we recommend for assessing influence in mixed models has a "drill-down" character. Because influence can manifest itself in various ways, it is best to start with a summary measure of the overall influence for an observation or sets of observations of interest and then take various directions from there depending on what you discover. This starting point usually flags observations that are particularly influential on *some* aspect of the analysis. If no observations are identified that would warrant further investigation at this stage, the process stops. Otherwise, we ask more specific questions about the nature of the influence. This can be done by quantifying impact on vectors of parameter estimates and impact on the precision of those vectors. For example, we can inquire about the overall change in the vector of fixed effects or in the vector of covariance parameters and their precision. Finally, a plot of the parameter estimates after deletion compared to the full-data estimates is often insightful.

Before discussing various kinds and levels of influence in a mixed model, we review some foundational concepts from the standard linear model as well as how to generalize them with a nontrivial covariance structure.

15.4.1 Influence Measures in the Linear Model

The goal of influence analysis is to determine how observations impact the analysis. Of course, all observations are influential, in the sense that their removal changes the numerical results of the analysis. The goal is to identify those observations that are *so* influential that their presence or absence from the data changes an important aspect of the analysis, yields qualitatively different inferences, or violates assumptions of the model. The goal is *not* to determine observations for removal from the analysis, but to determine which cases exert undue influence on the analysis and in what form. You thus need to decide prior to influence analysis exactly what types of inference matter the most to guide the decision about what to do with influential data points. For example, if the primary goal of the analysis is prediction, and if removing a data point changes the estimate of the residual variance, but not the fixed effect solutions, the data point does not present a problem. If, however, the goal is confidence intervals for predicted values, the influence on the residual variance estimate matters.

Influence is measured through perturbation analysis. The basic idea of perturbation analysis is simple: Remove one or more observations, recompute the important model output quantities, and quantify the change. In the linear model without random effects this process is made simple by the following three facts:

1. The fixed effects solution does not depend on covariance parameters; $\hat{\boldsymbol{\beta}} = (\mathbf{X'X})^{-} \mathbf{X'y}$ does not depend on σ^2.

2. The change in $\hat{\boldsymbol{\beta}}$ after removing the ith observation can be computed without refitting the model. It is available based on quantities from the overall fit: $\hat{\boldsymbol{\beta}}_{-i} = \hat{\boldsymbol{\beta}} - (\mathbf{X'X})^{-} \mathbf{x}_i \, \hat{e}_i / (1 - h_{ii})$.

3. Many important influence diagnostics are closely related; they can be derived from the same basic quantities: the raw residual $\hat{e}_i$ and the leverage h_{ii}.

For example, Cook's *D* statistic (Cook 1977, 1979), which measures the scaled change in the fixed effects solutions following removal of observation *i*, can be written in terms of the studentized residual and the leverage,

$$D = \frac{r_i^2 h_{ii}}{\text{rank}(\mathbf{X})(1 - h_{ii})}$$

The DFFITS statistic, which measures the change in fit in terms of standard error units (Belsley, Kuh, and Welsch 1980), can be written in terms of the externally studentized residual and the leverage

$$\text{DFFITS}_i = t_i \sqrt{\frac{h_{ii}}{1 - h_{ii}}}$$

15.4.2 Generalized Least Squares and Influence

The modifications brought about by estimated generalized least squares (EGLS) estimation are much more severe for influence diagnostics than for residual diagnostics. When your model contains random effects, or the **R** matrix is not just $\sigma^2\mathbf{I}$, the estimate of $\boldsymbol{\beta}$ depends critically on the estimates of the covariance parameters. A direct update formula to compute $\hat{\boldsymbol{\beta}}_{-i}$ from $\hat{\boldsymbol{\beta}}$ is then only available if the covariance parameters are known (Cook and Weisberg 1982). In that case, they would not change with the removal or addition of points. The practical consequence is that you can avoid refitting the model following the removal of observations only if you are willing to assume that the removal of an observation does not alter the covariance parameters.

A further complication of the linkage between fixed effects solutions and covariance parameter estimates is that it takes considerably more work to determine how the influence of an observation manifests itself. For example, consider a repeated measures study in which the correlations over time are modeled with a first-order autoregressive structure (AR(1)). An observation that has small leverage in the regressor space would not exert much influence on the fixed effects in a standard model for independent data. But in the repeated measures model the observation can have considerable indirect influence. If it affects the AR(1) correlation parameter, then it can affect $\hat{\boldsymbol{\beta}}$ because it alters $\hat{\mathbf{V}}$. But the reverse is also possible. Even if an observation affects the correlation parameter considerably, it may exert little influence on the fixed effects. For the purpose of prediction this influence is inconsequential, but for the accuracy of prediction intervals the influence can be critical.

Finally, an important difference between influence diagnostics in classical linear models and in mixed models is the clustered nature of the data. In many applications, notably longitudinal data and repeated measures, the data consist of independent groups or clusters corresponding to the subjects in your analysis. You are then more interested in assessing the influence of entire subjects than the influence of individual observations. The questions of how a particular patient affects the results in a clinical trial or the impact of a center in a multicenter study arise naturally. This calls for set-deletion diagnostics, the removal of more than one observation at a time.

15.4.3 Types of Mixed Model Influence

We now discuss three types of influence statistics. We recommend beginning with overall influence and then drilling down to mean and variance parameters depending on what you observe. Refer to Schabenberger (2004), Zhu *et al* (2012), and Schneider and Tobias (2014) for additional discussion and details.

Overall Influence

An overall influence statistic measures the global impact on the model by quantifying a change in the objective function. In linear mixed models the objective function is tied to the maximum likelihood and the residual maximum likelihood in ML and REML estimation, respectively. An overall influence measure is thus the likelihood distance of Cook and Weisberg (1982), also termed the likelihood displacement by Beckman, Nachtsheim, and Cook (1987). The basic concept is to do the following:

1. Remove an observation or group of observations.
2. Refit the model and recompute the parameter estimates for the reduced data set.
3. Assess the height of the original (restricted) likelihood surface at the deleted-data parameter estimates and compare it to the original height.

Notice that distance or displacement measure is not the difference of the log likelihoods or restricted log likelihoods in two models, one with n, the other with n–d data points (where d denotes the number of observations deleted). The displacement is instead the distance between the (restricted) log likelihoods based on all n observations, computed at two points in the parameter space. To reiterate, you cannot calculate this measure by running PROC MIXED twice, once with the full data and once with the reduced data set, and then just taking differences of the log likelihoods. Some more complex calculations are required, as detailed below.

Influence on the Parameter Estimates

A common way to measure the impact on a vector of parameter estimates is to compute a quadratic form in the difference between the full-data and reduced-data estimates. Cook's D statistic is of this nature. In general, it can be expressed as

$$D(\boldsymbol{\beta}) = \left(\hat{\boldsymbol{\beta}} - \hat{\boldsymbol{\beta}}_U\right)' \operatorname{Var}\left(\hat{\boldsymbol{\beta}}\right)^{-} \left(\hat{\boldsymbol{\beta}} - \hat{\boldsymbol{\beta}}_U\right) \Big/ \operatorname{rank}(\mathbf{X})$$

where the subscript U denotes the estimates after deleting observations in the set U (to allow for multiple point deletion). A closely related statistic is the multivariate DFFITS statistic of Belsley, Kuh, and Welsch (1980, p. 32):

$$\operatorname{MDFFITS}(\boldsymbol{\beta}) = \left(\hat{\boldsymbol{\beta}} - \hat{\boldsymbol{\beta}}_U\right)' \operatorname{Var}\left(\hat{\boldsymbol{\beta}}_U\right)^{-} \left(\hat{\boldsymbol{\beta}} - \hat{\boldsymbol{\beta}}_U\right) \Big/ \operatorname{rank}(\mathbf{X})$$

The primary difference between the two statistics is that the variance matrix of the fixed effects is based on an externalized estimate that does not involve the observations in the set U.

The idea of D and MDFFITS can be applied to the covariance parameters as well. For either statistic, influence increases with the magnitude of the statistics.

Influence on the Precision of Estimates

D and *MDFFITS* are quadratic forms in the difference of the full-data and reduced-data parameter estimates. To contrast the change in the precision, we need to engage not the vectors themselves, but their covariance matrices. The two common ways to do this are through trace and determinant operations. This leads to the COVTRACE and COVRATIO statistics:

$$\text{COVTRACE}(\boldsymbol{\beta}) = \left| \text{trace}\left(\hat{\text{Var}}\left(\hat{\boldsymbol{\beta}}\right)^{-} \hat{\text{Var}}\left(\hat{\boldsymbol{\beta}}_U\right) \right) - \text{rank}\left(\mathbf{X}\right) \right|$$

$$\text{COVRATIO}(\boldsymbol{\beta}) = \frac{\left| \hat{\text{Var}}\left(\hat{\boldsymbol{\beta}}_U\right) \right|}{\left| \hat{\text{Var}}\left(\hat{\boldsymbol{\beta}}\right) \right|}$$

The reasoning behind the COVTRACE statistic is as follows. If **A** is a positive semi-definite matrix, then trace($\mathbf{A}^-\mathbf{A}$) equals the rank of **A**. If the variance of parameter estimates is not affected by the removal of observations, then the trace in the COVTRACE statistic should equal the rank of **X**. The benchmark for lack of influence is thus a value of 0. As the value of the COVTRACE statistic increases, so does the influence on the precision of the parameter estimates and linear functions thereof, such as tests of fixed effects.

The COVRATIO statistic relates the determinants of the covariance matrices of the full-data and reduced-data estimates. The benchmark of no influence is a value of 1.0. Values larger than 1.0 indicate increased precision in the full-data case, and values smaller than 1.0 indicate higher precision for the reduced-data estimates. Such an interpretation in terms of increase or decrease in precision is not possible with the COVTRACE statistic. The disadvantage of the COVRATIO statistic is primarily computational. When the **X** matrix is of less than full rank, special manipulations are required to compute the determinants of the non-singular components of the variance matrices.

As with the Cook's *D* and *MDFFITS* statistics, the covariance trace and ratios can be computed for the fixed effects or the covariance parameters. Obtaining deletion statistics for the covariance parameters is not possible, however, unless the covariance parameters are updated as well. This requires refitting the linear mixed model, also known as iterative influence analysis.

15.4.4 Iterative and Non-Iterative Analyses

A non-iterative influence analysis relies on the full-data estimates and update formulas to compute estimates for the model in the reduced data set and to compute influence statistics from the delete-data estimates. As mentioned earlier, this is possible in the linear mixed model only if the covariance parameters are known. In practice, this implies holding the covariance parameters fixed at the full-data estimates, unless a closed-form update is possible. You can obtain such a closed-form update of the profiled residual variance, but not of other covariance parameters. This has an effect on the values of the influence statistics. A likelihood distance in non-iterative analysis, for example, reflects only changes in the estimates of $\boldsymbol{\beta}$ and σ^2. By holding other covariance parameters fixed, the estimate $\hat{\boldsymbol{\beta}}_U$ tends not to move as far from the full-data estimate compared to an analysis in which all parameters are allowed to vary. If the likelihood surface is unimodal, the resultant likelihood distance is smaller. In other words, by not allowing all covariance parameters to be updated, one tends to underestimate the full importance of an observation for the analysis. On the other hand, a non-iterative analysis is fairly easy to obtain and consumes relatively low computing resources.

If computing time permits, an iterative influence analysis, which involves refitting of the model for the reduced data set, is recommended. It provides influence statistics for the covariance parameters and measures the full importance of observations on all aspects of the analysis. It can be computationally expensive, however. Consider, for example, a longitudinal study with *N* subjects where deletion sets correspond to the observations for a particular subject. An iterative influence analysis involves the fitting of *N*+1 mixed models, each an iterative process. The initial model is fit to the full data, followed by *N* fits, each of which burdens the observations with the corresponding subject removed. Fortunately, the computational burden can be reduced in some ways:

- You can limit the number of iterations for each deletion set. Allowing for only a single iteration leads to so-called one-step updates, which are arguably better than updating only the fixed effects. Limiting the number of iterations has the further advantage of yielding additional qualitative information about the deletion points or sets. If, for example, you allow for up to five additional iterations, and some sets do not converge within that limit, the influence measures calculated from the delete estimates at the fifth iteration are probably underestimates. The parameter estimates are still changing and the model fitting trajectory itself is sensitive to the presence or absence of the deletion set.

- In contrast to the initial fit of the model, you have good starting values for fitting the model to the deleted-data: the full-data parameter estimates. If the observations removed are *not* influential, then convergence will be obtained quickly, typically in one or two steps. This is true for most of the observations.

Influence statistics and plots are available in PROC MIXED and in the %SCDMixed macro from Schneider and Tobias (2014). You can perform both iterative and non-iterative influence analyses, with the latter being the default. The following section presents an example.

15.4.5 Unequally Spaced Repeated Measures: An Example

We return in this example to the data set "Heart Rates" introduced in Chapter 5. Repeated measurements on the heart rates of patients are taken at five unequally spaced repeated time intervals: 1 minute, 5 minutes, 15 minutes, 30 minutes, and 1 hour. Each patient is subjected to one of three possible drug treatment levels, *a*, *b*, and *p*. The treatment level *p* represents a placebo.

No Temporal Effects in Mean Structure

We first fit these data with a repeated measures model that adjusts the mean for treatment and baseline effects. Use Program 15.4 to fit this model. A model that includes temporal effects in the mean structure is considered later in Section 15.4.2.

Program 15.4

```
proc mixed data=hr order=data;
   class drug hours patient;
   model hr = drug basehr / noint s residual
              influence(iter 5 effect=patient est);
   repeated hours / type=sp(exp)(hours) sub=patient;
run;
```

The RESIDUAL option produces statistical graphics of various mixed model residuals, and the INFLUENCE option in the MODEL statement requests influence diagnostics. When ODS GRAPHICS are ON, this produces graphical displays of influence diagnostics in addition to the tabular output in the listing. The ITER=5 suboption of the INFLUENCE option specifies that the influence analysis is iterative with a maximum of five iterations per observation or deletion set. The EFFECT=PATIENT suboption specifies that observations that share the same level of the PATIENT variable comprise a deletion set. PROC MIXED computes influence diagnostics at the level of the patient, rather than for the individual observation. The EST suboption requests that graphics of the delete estimates are produced in addition to the graphics of the influence diagnostics.

Results

The results of the influence analysis are reported in a table with one row per deletion set. The table is reproduced in Output 15.3.

Output 15.3: Influence Diagnostics for Repeated Measures Model

								Influence Diagnostics for Levels of patient

patient	Number of Observations in Level	Iterations	PRESS Statistic	Cook's D	MDFFITS	COVRATIO	COVTRACE	Cook's D CovParms
201	5	2	280.23	0.00692	0.00578	1.3067	0.2860	0.01886
202	5	2	408.45	0.15659	0.09979	1.5690	0.5691	0.07213
203	5	1	263.81	0.03905	0.03374	1.2008	0.1944	0.04527
204	5	2	67.20	0.00058	0.00047	1.4555	0.4041	0.05584
205	5	2	477.33	0.00380	0.00328	1.1951	0.1898	0.01437
206	5	1	103.38	0.01702	0.01317	1.4143	0.3840	0.05781
207	5	2	854.76	0.00037	0.00032	0.9498	0.0253	0.12247
208	5	3	775.13	0.21872	0.17803	0.9822	0.0129	0.11759
209	5	3	790.12	0.08113	0.06889	1.2268	0.2189	0.84822
210	5	2	350.21	0.05812	0.04994	1.1412	0.1443	0.04671
211	5	1	170.31	0.03380	0.02885	1.2350	0.2248	0.04838
212	5	2	77.05	0.00004	0.00004	1.6180	0.5352	0.05521

								Cook's D
patient	Number of Observations in Level	Iterations	PRESS Statistic	Cook's D	MDFFITS	COVRATIO	COVTRACE	CovParms
214	5	1	989.60	0.07652	0.06918	0.9926	0.0002	0.04301
215	5	1	201.56	0.02360	0.01747	1.4343	0.4113	0.01272
216	5	3	1421.35	0.25594	0.26536	0.5132	0.6045	0.49491
217	5	2	119.56	0.00902	0.00732	1.4729	0.4162	0.04807
218	5	2	459.17	0.07585	0.06576	1.1018	0.1080	0.02239
219	5	2	1335.53	0.19162	0.17917	0.7750	0.2359	0.16452
220	5	1	88.39	0.01266	0.01059	1.3395	0.3114	0.09604
221	5	2	45.21	0.00323	0.00252	1.5581	0.4840	0.05713
222	5	1	558.05	0.04327	0.03735	1.1806	0.1774	0.00701
223	5	2	174.31	0.00049	0.00040	1.4622	0.4069	0.05379
224	5	1	821.01	0.11293	0.10519	0.8810	0.1178	0.23626
232	5	2	105.62	0.00571	0.00477	1.3598	0.3271	0.04977

Influence Diagnostics for Levels of patient

patient	MDFFITS CovParms	COVRATIO CovParms	COVTRACE CovParms	RMSE without deleted level	Restricted Likelihood Distance
201	0.01660	1.2220	0.2118	9.13972	0.0437
202	0.07021	1.0627	0.0648	9.14579	0.6946
203	0.04256	1.0997	0.0995	9.16496	0.1999
204	0.04822	1.2697	0.2545	9.26450	0.0548
205	0.01316	1.1696	0.1643	9.07817	0.0283
206	0.05212	1.1600	0.1562	9.21659	0.1216
207	0.13595	0.8630	0.1406	8.80300	0.1359
208	0.13323	0.8638	0.1386	8.92787	1.0894
209	0.74545	1.2360	0.2571	8.89571	1.1744
210	0.04592	1.0621	0.0628	9.11372	0.2751
211	0.04486	1.1255	0.1238	9.18051	0.1785
212	0.04715	1.3121	0.2915	9.26857	0.0514
214	0.04412	1.0313	0.0329	8.93370	0.3615
215	0.01169	1.1481	0.1434	9.15591	0.1055
216	0.66349	0.6157	0.4287	8.49945	1.9113
217	0.04119	1.3065	0.2866	9.24438	0.0766
218	0.02256	1.0251	0.0260	9.06948	0.3275
219	0.19196	0.7866	0.2248	8.73670	1.0575
220	0.08523	1.1778	0.1741	9.25525	0.1401
221	0.04866	1.3203	0.2987	9.26869	0.0657
222	0.00650	1.1533	0.1487	9.07493	0.1766
223	0.04539	1.3248	0.3030	9.23268	0.0509
224	0.25793	0.9762	0.0145	8.78276	0.7404
232	0.04378	1.2153	0.2061	9.23950	0.0686

Interpretation

The listing results of the influence analysis are presented here in two tables. The first contains information about the number of iterations, and statistics related to the fixed effects. The second table contains information about the covariance parameters and the overall influence (residual likelihood ratio distance).

The first key result is that the number of iterations required to obtain convergence in the reduced data models is less than five in all cases. For most patients, convergence was achieved in a single step or with only two updates.

The last column in Output 15.3 suggests that the overall influence of patients 202, 208, 209, 216, 219, and 224 stands out compared to that of the rest of the patients. In order to determine what model components these study subjects influence, we examine the individual statistics. For example, the covariance parameter deletion diagnostics for patient 202 do not appear large compared to other patients. The Cook's *D* statistic is larger than that of most patients, however. If patient 202 is eliminated from the study, the primary change in model output is in the fixed effects estimates.

Patient 209, on the other hand, exhibits a small Cook's *D* and *MDFFITS* statistic, and their influence is primarily on the point estimates of the covariance parameters, as seen from a large statistic for "Cook's D CovParms" (0.84822). Finally, some patients exert influence throughout the model (for example, patient 216). Removing the data from this individual changes greatly the fixed effects solutions as well as the covariance parameter estimates (Cook's *D* is large in both cases). Furthermore, the data from this individual exert considerable influence on the precision of estimates. The COVRATIO statistic is considerably less than 1.0 for the fixed effects and the covariance parameters (0.5132, 0.6157). The presence of this individual's data reduces the precision of the estimates. Removal increases precision.

It can be tedious to go through a large table of influence diagnostics to examine in detail which observation or set of observations is influential and how. Graphical displays are better suited for this task. Figures 15.4 through 15.7 display the deletion statistics for each patient. We now consider each in turn.

Figure 15.4: Overall Influence of Each Patient

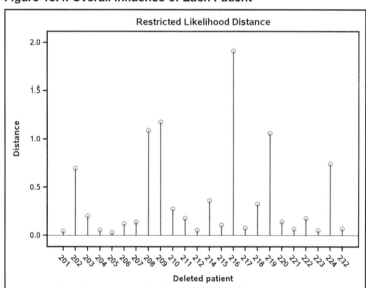

Figure 15.4 shows a needle plot of the REML likelihood distance, which is the difference in REML values with and without the patient included. The six patients identified in Output 15.3 clearly stand out here with large needles: 202, 208, 209, 216, 219, and 224. A reasonable next step would be to examine the raw data for each of these patients, but for sake of time and space we move forward to consider other influence statistics.

Figure 15.5: Patient Influence on Fixed Effects and Covariance Parameter Estimates

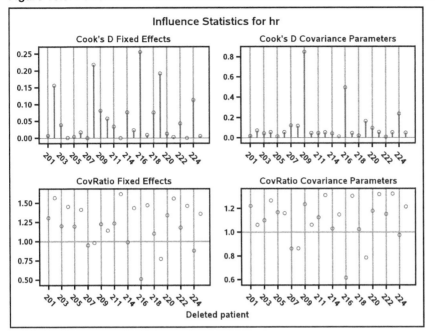

The top half of Figure 15.5 graphs Cook's *D* for both the fixed effects and covariance parameter estimates. Note how patient 209 stands out as being influential on the covariance parameter estimates, but the impact of this patient's data on the fixed effects is moderate at best. If the goal of the analysis is to predict the heart rate of patients, the data from patient 209 is relatively inconsequential. However, if the analytic goal depends on quantities involving the covariance parameter estimates, the five data points associated with patient 209 are important. Their presence in the data reduces the estimate of the SP(EXP) parameter (Figure 15.7), essentially reducing the degree of correlation among data points from any patient. Observations from patient 216, on the other hand, have the opposite effect. The temporal correlation drops when the data points are removed.

The bottom half of Figure 15.5 graphs the CovRatio statistic for both the fixed effects and covariance parameter estimates. These statistics measure influence on the precision of the estimates. Here patient 216 stands out as reducing precision for the whole analysis.

Figure 15.6: Comparison of Full-Data and Delete-Data Fixed Effect Estimates

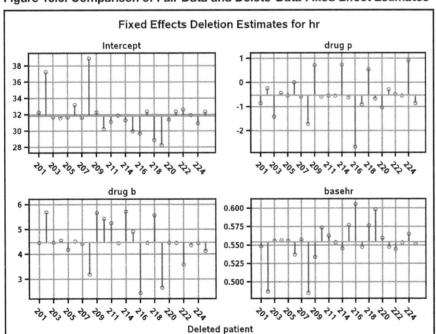

Figure 15.7: Comparison of Full-Data and Delete-Data Covariance Parameter Estimates

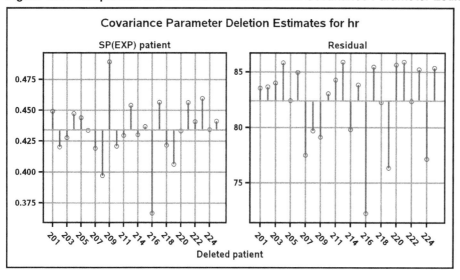

Figures 15.6 and 15.7 drill down further on influence and examine impact on each mean and covariance parameter estimate. Results here are concordant and provide some explanation behind the Cook's *D* statistics in Figure 15.5.

To examine Cook's *D* even further, Zhu *et al.* (2012) describe how, in a repeated measures model, larger subjects can appear to be overly influential mostly because of their size. They advocate scaling the Cook's distance values for subjects by the so-called degree of perturbation to account for this. The %SCDMixed macro by Schneider and Tobias (2014) implements the approach, and it is especially recommended when subjects have varying sample sizes. Schneider and Tobias coincidentally analyze the same heart rate data in their Example 2. Here subjects are balanced with five observations each, but the degrees of perturbation are not exactly equal and are worth examining. The macro also provides a nice facility for labeling influential subjects in plots as shown in Figure 15.8, which reveals a few more influential subjects. Refer to Schneider and Tobias for details about how to obtain and run the macro and reproduce this analysis.

Figure 15.8: Plot from %SCDMixed Macro of Schneider and Tobias (2014)

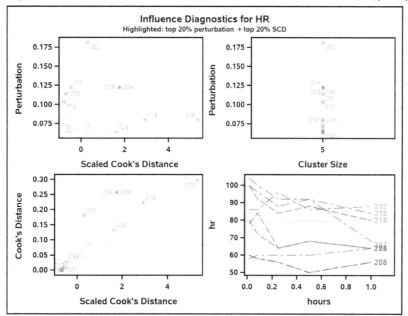

Based on this influence analysis, you can reconsider the model and/or data. For example, consider the situation in which you have one noticeable outlying and influential subject. What should you do? This is a critical juncture in your mixed modeling of these data and it is important to make a good decision. The recommended next step is to reassess the data quality of this observation and double check all data values for that subject are legitimate and delve deeper into why they are unusual. Next, review your objectives for the study and how they would best be served by deleting or including this subject. Here it may make a difference, say if you are a bench scientist performing an exploratory experiment or a clinical trial analyst under regulatory review. In the end it can be a difficult and subjective decision, and you might want to consult with other experts before making a final call. In general, your tendency should be to retain all data that are reasonably measured, understanding that mixed models are never perfect representations of reality, and in fact, a poor model can even provide a distorted perception.

As mentioned earlier, the results of a perturbation analysis should always be seen in light of the model you work with. Observations may appear as unusual because the model is wrong. For example, there is a noticeable trend in the plot of studentized residuals for smaller values of the predicted mean, as shown in the upper left corner of Figure 15.9. An important effect may be missing from the model.

Another fairly common occurrence is when a small number of points stand out as clear outliers. This is an important moment in your analysis as these points are also likely highly influential on the results. A typically good strategy is to look carefully at each point in turn and first verify all accompanying data in their corresponding rows are correct. When anomalies are found, try to determine root causes and check original data sources for potential recording errors, correcting them when possible. There is typically no harm in rerunning an analysis with outliers removed just to see what happens, but when reporting results officially it is naturally important to make sure all input data are correct and your mixed model is well-fit. Using some type of data transformation might make better sense for modeling, for example, transforming your Y variable to log scale. You can also specify alternative data distributions in PROC GLIMMIX. All that said, sometimes outliers are legitimate and represent something unusual that happened in the experiment that may be valuable.

Figure 15.9: Studentized Residuals

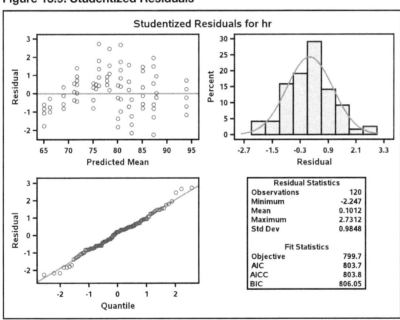

With Temporal Effects in Mean Structure

The shortcoming of the previous model is that it does not include systematic effects of time. Program 15.5 allows for HOURS effects and their interaction with the treatments. Graphical results are presented in Figures 15.10 through 15.12 for comparison with those in the previous section.

Program 15.5

```
ods html;
ods graphics on;
proc mixed data=hr order=data;
   class drug hours patient;
   model hr = drug hours drug*hours basehr / s
              residual
              influence(iter=5 effect=patient);
   repeated hours / type=sp(exp)(hours) sub=patient;
run;
ods graphics off;
ods html close;
```

Figure 15.10: Studentized Residuals After Including Temporal Fixed Effects

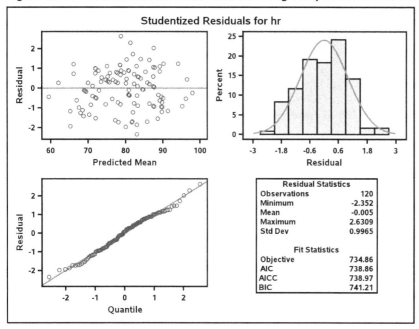

Figure 15.11: Overall Influence After Including Temporal Fixed Effects

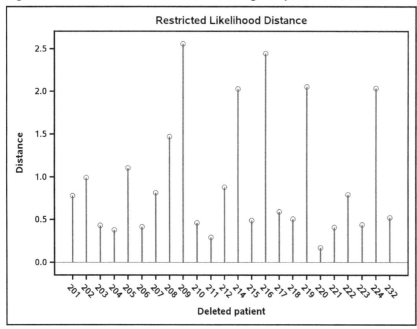

Figure 15.12: Influence on Mean and Covariance Parameters After Including Temporal Fixed Effects

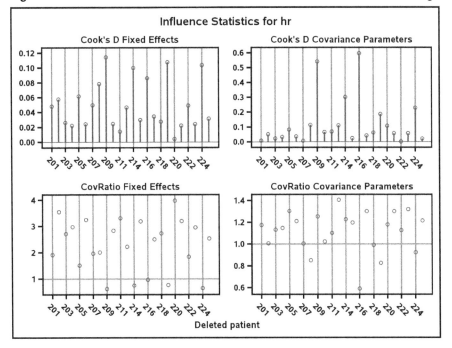

The studentized residuals show much less trend than before (Figure 15.10); also notice that their mean is now much closer to zero. The likelihood distance and Cook's *D* statistics for the fixed effects are much more evenly distributed compared to the analysis without temporal adjustment in the previous section. The "sore thumbs" that continue to stick out are patients 209 and 216. Although not shown here, the residuals for patient 209 have a "zigzag" appearance over time, which runs counter to the notion of positive serial correlation. The residuals for patient 216 are most extreme in negative value (see PRESS :Statistic in Figure 15.11). With all of this noted, deletion of these patients does not appear warranted.

15.4.6 Insect Count Data: An Example

While PROC GLIMMIX does not currently provide the same detailed influence diagnostic computations as PROC MIXED, it is fairly straightforward to perform your own influence computations using SAS code. This offers the advantage of letting you control exactly what is going on and also aids in understanding.

For example, consider the data set "Insect Count Data." These data are from McCullagh and Nelder (1989) and analyzed in detail from a fixed-effects perspective in Section 10.4 of Littell, Stroup, and Freund (2002). The treatment design consists of an untreated control and a 3 × 3 factorial for a total of 10 treatment combinations. The experiment is conducted as a randomized complete block design with 4 blocks and the response variable is insect count. The two treatment factors, A and B, have 3 levels each (1, 2, and 3) and are both coded 0 for the control.

Initial Analysis

We first fit these data with a GLMM with random block effect using Program 15.6, and deal with one resulting problem. Then we show how to compute influence diagnostics on a per-block basis.

Program 15.6

```
proc glimmix data=counts nobound;
   class block a b;
   model count = a b a*b / dist=negbin;
   random block;
run;
```

This is the standard GLMM specification for this type of design as discussed in Chapter 2, except we specify the NOBOUND option to allow for the possibility of a negative estimate of the block effect, which can indicate a competitive scenario within each block. The NOBOUND option also avoids concerns of bias in the fixed effect estimates that may be incurred by enforcing the default nonnegative constraint on the block variance component estimate. Both the negative binomial distribution and random block effect handle potential overdispersion in the data.

Results

The results of the initial analysis are listed in Output 15.4.

Output 15.4: Initial Analysis of Insect Count Data

Model Information	
Data Set	WORK.COUNTS
Response Variable	count
Response Distribution	Negative Binomial
Link Function	Log
Variance Function	Default
Variance Matrix	Not blocked
Estimation Technique	Residual PL
Degrees of Freedom Method	Containment

Class Level Information		
Class	Levels	Values
block	4	1 2 3 4
a	4	0 1 2 3
b	4	0 1 2 3

Number of Observations Read	40
Number of Observations Used	40

Dimensions	
G-side Cov. Parameters	1
R-side Cov. Parameters	1
Columns in X	19
Columns in Z	4
Subjects (Blocks in V)	1
Max Obs per Subject	40

Optimization Information	
Optimization Technique	Dual Quasi-Newton
Parameters in Optimization	2
Lower Boundaries	0
Upper Boundaries	0
Fixed Effects	Profiled
Starting From	Data

Iteration History					
Iteration	Restarts	Subiterations	Objective Function	Change	Max Gradient
0	0	8	93.890582647	2.00000000	0.000082
1	0	8	83.927756449	0.38969913	0.000086
2	0	5	85.48208447	0.06843558	0.00026
3	0	4	85.312176407	0.00845234	0.00007
4	0	3	85.332657175	0.00596711	0.000019
5	0	2	85.329137814	0.00291721	0.02382
6	0	3	85.329231964	0.00247954	1.415E-8
7	0	3	85.325005604	0.00095704	1.613E-8
8	0	2	85.325253145	0.00075824	2.892E-6
9	0	1	85.324773797	0.00042869	3.697E-6
10	0	2	85.324564448	0.00026562	5.489E-7
11	0	2	85.324434897	0.00017013	2.518E-7
12	0	2	85.324348797	0.00010691	1.071E-7
13	0	2	85.324296198	0.00006692	3.495E-8
14	0	2	85.324262948	0.00004184	2.236E-7
15	0	1	85.324242103	0.00002611	9.116E-6
16	0	2	85.324227611	0.00001612	1.716E-7
17	0	1	85.324221545	0.00001052	5.946E-6
18	0	1	85.324214823	0.00000622	6.191E-6
19	0	1	85.324212002	0.00000396	0.00012

Did not converge.

Covariance Parameter Estimates		
Cov Parm	Estimate	Standard Error
block	-0.03069	.
Scale	0.4645	.

Interpretation

The initial results tables appear correct but the residual pseudo-likelihood optimization algorithm does not converge. Inspecting the values in the Iteration History table reveals that convergence looks like it was nearly achieved, as the objective function stabilizes and the maximum gradients become small in later iterations. This appears to be a case where raising the convergence threshold slightly is reasonable. We also note in passing that the estimate of the block variance component at the final iteration is negative.

Modified Initial Analysis

Let's see what happens when we raise the convergence threshold to 1e-5. Use Program 15.7 to implement this change.

Program 15.7

```
proc glimmix data=counts nobound pconv=1e-5;
   class block a b;
   model count = a b a*b / dist=negbin;
   random block;
run;
```

This is the same specification as before but we have added the PCONV = 1e-5 option to the PROC GLIMMIX statement. This loosens the overall parameter-based convergence tolerance. We do not use the NLOPTIONS statement here, as it controls tolerances for the inner linear mixed model fits, which appear to be okay based on the original iteration history.

Results

The results of the modified initial analysis are listed in Output 15.5.

Output 15.5: Modified Initial Analysis of Insect Count Data

Model Information	
Data Set	WORK.COUNTS
Response Variable	count
Response Distribution	Negative Binomial
Link Function	Log
Variance Function	Default
Variance Matrix	Not blocked
Estimation Technique	Residual PL
Degrees of Freedom Method	Containment

Class Level Information		
Class	Levels	Values
block	4	1 2 3 4
a	4	0 1 2 3
b	4	0 1 2 3

Number of Observations Read	40
Number of Observations Used	40

Dimensions	
G-side Cov. Parameters	1
R-side Cov. Parameters	1
Columns in X	19
Columns in Z	4
Subjects (Blocks in V)	1
Max Obs per Subject	40

Optimization Information	
Optimization Technique	Dual Quasi-Newton
Parameters in Optimization	2
Lower Boundaries	0
Upper Boundaries	0
Fixed Effects	Profiled
Starting From	Data

			Iteration History		
Iteration	Restarts	Subiterations	Objective Function	Change	Max Gradient
0	0	8	93.890582647	2.00000000	0.000082
1	0	8	83.927756449	0.38969913	0.000086
2	0	5	85.48208447	0.06843558	0.00026
3	0	4	85.312176407	0.00845234	0.00007
4	0	3	85.332657175	0.00596711	0.000019
5	0	2	85.329137814	0.00291721	0.02382
6	0	3	85.32923197	0.00247954	1.415E-8
7	0	3	85.325005602	0.00095704	1.612E-8
8	0	2	85.325253145	0.00075824	2.888E-6
9	0	1	85.324773798	0.00042869	3.696E-6
10	0	2	85.324564447	0.00026562	5.518E-7
11	0	2	85.324434896	0.00017013	1.834E-7
12	0	2	85.324348804	0.00010691	4.917E-8
13	0	2	85.324296198	0.00006692	4.854E-9
14	0	2	85.32426295	0.00004184	4.202E-8
15	0	1	85.324242128	0.00002611	9.16E-6
16	0	2	85.324227594	0.00001611	2.11E-7
17	0	1	85.324221561	0.00001053	5.865E-6
18	0	1	85.32421475	0.00000620	6.124E-6

Convergence criterion (PCONV=0.00001) satisfied.

Estimated G matrix is not positive definite.

Fit Statistics	
-2 Res Log Pseudo-Likelihood	85.32
Generalized Chi-Square	28.95
Gener. Chi-Square / DF	0.96

Covariance Parameter Estimates		
Cov Parm	Estimate	Standard Error
block	-0.03069	0.03468
Scale	0.4645	0.1764

Type III Tests of Fixed Effects				
Effect	Num DF	Den DF	F Value	Pr > F
a	2	27	3.35	0.0501
b	2	27	0.05	0.9554
a*b	4	27	1.06	0.3945

Interpretation

The model now converges under the larger and more lenient PCONV tolerance. The generalized chi-square statistic divided by model degrees of freedom equals 0.96, which indicates that we are nicely controlling for overdispersion. (This value will typically be larger than 1 when the model does not adequately account for overdispersion.)   The estimate of the block variance component is negative, indicating a possible competitive effect within each block. For the fixed effects, all of the action appears to be in the A main effect, with a *p*-value coincidentally almost identical to the classic 0.05 threshold.

Influence Analysis

We now proceed with an influence analysis. We would like to perform an iterative influence analysis and determine the influence of each block in turn. We accomplish this with a SAS macro shown in Program 15.8

Program 15.8

```
%macro block_influence;
   ods exclude all;
   ods noresults;
   %do b = 1 %to 4;
         data cb;
            set counts;
            if block = &b then count = .;
         run;
         title "Dropping Block &b";
         proc glimmix data=cb nobound pconv=1e-3;
               class block a b;
               model count = a b a*b / dist=negbin;
               random block;
               parms -0.03 0.4645 / lowerb=-0.04;
               ods output fitstatistics=fsb covparms=cpb
                  tests3=t3b;
         run;
         data fsb; retain drop_block &b; set fsb; _i = _n_; run;
         data cpb; retain drop_block &b; set cpb; _i = _n_; run;
         data t3b; retain drop_block &b; set t3b; _i = _n_; run;
         %if &b = 1 %then %do;
               data fs; set fsb; run;
               data cp; set cpb; run;
               data t3; set t3b; run;
         %end;
         %else %do;
               data fs; set fs fsb; run;
               data cp; set cp cpb; run;
               data t3; set t3 t3b; run;
         %end;
   %end;
   title;
   ods exclude none;
   ods results;
%mend;

%block_influence;

proc sort data=fs; by _i drop_block; run;
proc sort data=cp; by _i drop_block; run;
proc sort data=t3; by _i drop_block; run;

proc print data=fs(drop=_i);
proc print data=cp(drop=_i);
proc print data=t3(drop=_i);
run;
```

The code creates a SAS macro named BLOCK_INFLUENCE to run PROC GLIMMIX four times in a loop, setting the response values to be missing for each block in turn and collecting results from each run. We increase the PCONV tolerance even further to 1e-3 to accommodate instabilities in the data subsets. We also specify a PARMS statement to give good starting values based on the modified initial analysis and place a lower bound on the block variance of -0.04 to provide stability in the estimates and limit the amount of competition modeled in each block.

The code assesses influence on three sets of statistics in the Fit Statistics, Covariance Parameters, and Type 3 Tests tables, respectively. It collects the results into three overall tables for each set of statistics and includes a column indexing the block that is dropped.

Results

The results of the influence analysis are reported in Output 15.6 in three tables, each showing the effects of dropping one block at a time.

Output 15.6: Influence Diagnostics for Insect Count Data

Obs	drop_block	Descr	Value
1	1	-2 Res Log Pseudo-Likelihood	55.58
2	2	-2 Res Log Pseudo-Likelihood	59.14
3	3	-2 Res Log Pseudo-Likelihood	52.74
4	4	-2 Res Log Pseudo-Likelihood	52.55
5	1	Generalized Chi-Square	20.84
6	2	Generalized Chi-Square	18.83
7	3	Generalized Chi-Square	19.50
8	4	Generalized Chi-Square	17.10
9	1	Gener. Chi-Square / DF	1.04
10	2	Gener. Chi-Square / DF	0.94
11	3	Gener. Chi-Square / DF	0.97
12	4	Gener. Chi-Square / DF	0.85

Obs	drop_block	CovParm	Estimate	StdErr
1	1	block	-0.04000	.
2	2	block	-0.04000	.
3	3	block	0.000903	0.04937
4	4	block	-0.01512	0.04057
5	1	Scale	0.3707	0.1612
6	2	Scale	0.5243	0.1881
7	3	Scale	0.2212	0.1426
8	4	Scale	0.2815	0.1461

Obs	drop_block	Effect	NumDF	DenDF	FValue	ProbF
1	1	a	2	18	3.01	0.0747
2	2	a	2	18	2.04	0.1584
3	3	a	2	18	3.32	0.0593
4	4	a	2	18	5.23	0.0162
5	1	b	2	18	0.18	0.8337
6	2	b	2	18	0.16	0.8552
7	3	b	2	18	0.48	0.6238
8	4	b	2	18	0.55	0.5856
9	1	a*b	4	18	1.47	0.2538
10	2	a*b	4	18	0.83	0.5215
11	3	a*b	4	18	1.42	0.2685
12	4	a*b	4	18	1.05	0.4098

Interpretation

In the first table, focusing on the last four rows, we see that dropping the fourth block leads to a standardized generalized chi-square of 0.85, which may indicate a bit of overfitting, but is not a large cause for concern.

In the second table, dropping the first and second blocks both result in the block variance component estimate hitting the specified lower bound of -0.04. Dropping the third block results in a positive estimate, suggesting that the most competitive effects are in that third block. It may be worth looking at data sources for that block in more detail to see why.

In the third table, we see a range of effects on the *F* test for the A effect. Dropping the first and second blocks make it less significant in terms of its *p*-value and dropping the fourth block makes it more significant.

All of these results provide deeper insight into the influence of each block on the overall analysis. A key is to distinguish between normally expected variability and something really happening in the data. One way to make this distinction more definitive is to set up one or more simulation studies to generate data in which you know the ground truth values for all parameters. You can readily modify, customize, and loop over the preceding macro to match most common designs, and it should run relatively quickly except for very large data sets. With the same simulations you can also assess size and power of relevant test statistics. In general, we recommend performing influence analyses like these to really make sure you have a mixed model that will produce reliable inferences in the future, leaving no "data stone" unturned.

15.5 Two Diagnostic Plots Useful for Non-Gaussian Data

When you fit a mixed model with non-Gaussian data, there are model-checking issues that do not arise with Gaussian mixed models. Because you often have a choice of distributions that could plausibly describe the process giving rise to the data, and because you fit the linear predictor to a link function rather than directly to the mean of the response variable, you should ask the following questions. First, does the model use a distribution that adequately describes the data? Second, does the model's link function provide an adequate fit?

McCullagh and Nelder (1989) suggest a number of plots that are useful for model checking with generalized linear models. This section continues the count data example begun in the previous section (Section 15.4) by presenting the PROC GLIMMIX compatible version of two plots from McCullagh and Nelder that are particularly useful for addressing these questions regarding the choice of distribution and link function. These are as follows:

- Plot the absolute values of standardized residuals against the predicted values. McCullach and Nelder suggest using either deviance residuals or Pearson residuals—the two types of residuals typically provide similar information. You can compute the latter using PROC GLIMMIX. (PROC GENMOD allows you to compute deviance residuals, but PROC GENMOD only fits fixed-effects-only GLMs—if you have a mixed model you should use PROC GLIMMIX.)

- McCullach and Nelder suggest adjusting predicted values to a constant information scale, e.g.,

$$2 \times \sqrt{\hat{\lambda}_{ij}}$$

for the log link function, where $\hat{\lambda}_{ij}$ denotes the predicted value for the observation on the ij^{th} treatment × block combination. This plot is particularly useful for revealing an inappropriate or poorly fitting variance function, and hence a poor choice of distribution used to model the response variable.

- Plot the linear predictor against the pseudo-variable $\hat{y}^* = \hat{\eta} + D(y - \hat{\lambda})$, where $D = [\partial\hat{\eta}/\partial\lambda]$, which is an adjusted version of the original Y variable that is well-approximated with a Gaussian mixed model. Use this plot to visualize "goodness of link function." The plot should be approximately linear. Deviation from linear constitutes visual evidence of an inappropriate or poorly fitting link function.

You can obtain the values needed for these plots with PROC GLIMMIX's OUPUT statement. Program 15.9 shows the needed PROC GLIMMIX statements.

Program 15.9

```
proc glimmix data=counts nobound pconv=1e-05;
 class BLOCK CTL_TRT a b;
/* model count=CTL_TRT a b a*b/dist=poisson;*/
 model count=CTL_TRT a b a*b/dist=negbin;
 random intercept / subject=block;
```

```
 OUTPUT out=glmxcheck pred(blup noilink)=linear_predictor
    pred(blup ilink)=lambda pearson=pearson_residual;
 title 'compute model checking statistics';
run;
```

The PROC statement uses the same NOBOUND and PCONV options found to be necessary in the previous section. The OUTPUT statement creates a SAS data set called GLMXCHECK. The new variables in this data set are called LINEAR_PREDICTOR (created by the PRED option), LAMBDA (also created by the PRED option, but with the inverse link applied) and PEARSON_RESIDUAL (created by the PEARSON option). The PRED option with the BLUP and NOILINK options creates a variable defined in the model-scale linear predictor,

$$\hat{\boldsymbol{\eta}} = \mathbf{X}\hat{\boldsymbol{\beta}} + \mathbf{Z}\hat{\mathbf{u}}$$

For a given observation, the element corresponding to the ith treatment and j^{th} block, η_{ij} is the value of LINEAR_PREDICTOR. Its inverse link, $\lambda_{ij} = \exp(\eta_{ij})$ is the value of LAMBDA for treatment $i \times$ block j. As the name implies, PEARSON_RESIDUAL is the Pearson residual for the ij^{th} observation.

Notice that there are two MODEL statements. The active statement uses the D=NEGBIN option to fit the negative binomial. The statement commented out would fit the Poisson model. You could use it to create plots for the Poisson model and compare them to the negative binomial model.

Program 15.10 shows the DATA step that is required to create the additional variables, adjusted

$$\left(\hat{\lambda}_{ij}\right) = 2\sqrt{\hat{\lambda}_{ij}}$$

and the pseudo variable $\hat{\mathbf{y}}^* = \hat{\boldsymbol{\eta}} + \mathbf{D}(\mathbf{y} - \hat{\boldsymbol{\lambda}})$, where $\mathbf{D} = [\partial\hat{\boldsymbol{\eta}}/\partial\lambda]$.

Program 15.10 also shows the PROC SGPLOT statements to create the plots.

Program 15.10

```
data glmxplot;
 set glmxcheck;
 adjlamda=2*sqrt(lambda);
 ystar=xbeta+(count-lambda)/lambda;
 absres_p=abs(Peason_residual);
run;

proc sgplot data=glmxplot;
 scatter x=adjlamda y=absres_p;
 title 'Absolute Value of Pearson Residual vs. Adjusted Predicted Value';
run;

proc sgplot data=glmxplot;
 reg x=linear_predictor y=ystar / cli;
 title1 'Goodness of Link';
 title2 'Pseudo Variable (Y*) vs. Linear Predictor';
run;
```

Results

Figures 15.13 and 15.14 show the plots of the absolute Pearson residual versus adjusted $\hat{\lambda}_{ij}$ and $\hat{y}_{ij}^*$ versus $\hat{\eta}_{ij}$, respectively.

Figure 15.13: Plot of Absolute Pearson Residual versus Adjusted Predicted Value (λ_{ij})

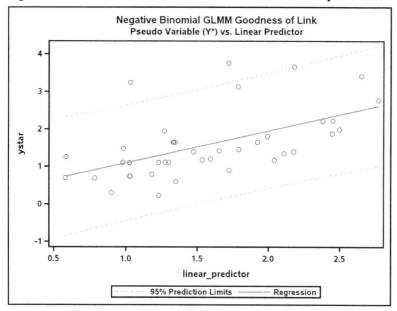

Figure 15.14: Plot of Absolute Pearson Residual versus Adjusted Predicted Value (λ_{ij})

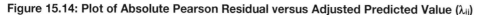

Interpretation

Figure 15.13 shows no obvious discernable pattern, characteristic of an appropriate variance function and typical of a distribution with adequate fit. Figure 15.14 shows the signature linear relationship between linear predictor and pseudo-variable characteristic of a link function with adequate fit. Figure 15.14 includes 95% confidence bands, indicated by the dashed lines. Two observations have values outside the confidence bands and one other has values right on the upper confidence limit. Those outside the confidence bands are observations 27 (block 3, treatment 6) and 40 (block 4, treatment 4). These happen to be the two observations with the greatest absolute Pearson residuals plotted in Figure 15.12. The observation on the confidence bound is block 2, treatment 0. Its absolute Pearson residual is an unremarkable 1.04, versus 2.55 and 2.44 for observations 27 and 40.

You can use the information provided by these plots in two ways. First, and most importantly, they provide visual evidence of an appropriately chosen distribution and link function. Second, they raise questions about observations 27 and 40 as possible outliers.

If you change MODEL statements in Program 15.9 to fit the Poisson, model, you can plot Poisson versions of Figures 15.13 and 15.14. Figure 15.15 shows the plot of absolute Pearson residuals for the Poisson model.

Figure 15.15: Plot of absolute Pearson residuals versus Predicted Values from Poisson Model

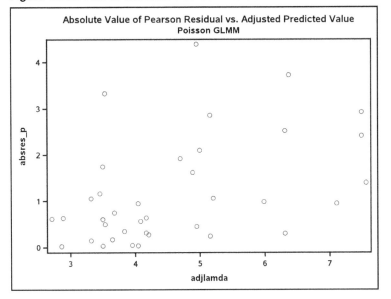

You can see that Figure 15.15 provides visual evidence, although admittedly subtle, of unequal spread—specifically, somewhat greater variance associated with larger values of ADJLAMDA, the adjusted predicted value. This could be taken as a mild visual symptom of overdispersion resulting from an inappropriate choice of distribution. It is consistent with the decision to replace a Poisson model (whose Pearson χ^2/DF showed evidence of overdispersion attributable to an inadequate variance function) with a negative binomial model. To summarize, if you compare Figures 15.13 and 15.15, the latter (Poisson) shows visual evidence of a distribution providing a poor fit, whereas the former (negative binomial) does not. In other words, Figure 15.13 and 15.15, taken together, provide visual evidence that the negative binomial is the distribution of choice. You can complement this visual approach with statistical comparisons of likelihood or information criteria, as well as with comparisons of residual and influence diagnostics as described in previous sections.

15.5 Summary

This chapter discusses three topics associated with handling problems and verifying assumptions while mixed modeling. Section 15.2 provides an overall guide to troubleshooting, including a search strategy and pointers to some helpful references from SAS Technical Support. Section 15.3 discusses residuals in a mixed model setting and their usefulness for visually assessing goodness of fit and finding outliers. Section 15.4 covers various levels of influence diagnostics in mixed models and illustrates them with a repeated measures example using PROC MIXED and a count data example using PROC GLIMMIX. Section 15.5 illustrates plots useful for checking distribution and link function choices for mixed models with non-Gaussian data.

Appendix A: Linear Mixed Model Theory

A.1 Introduction 543
A.2 Matrix Notation 543
A.3 Formulation of the Mixed Model...544
    A.3.1 The General Linear Mixed Model...544
    A.3.2 Conditional and Marginal Distributions..545
    A.3.3 Example: Growth Curve with Compound Symmetry..545
    A.3.4 Example: Split-Plot Design...547
A.4 Estimating Parameters, Predicting Random Effects...549
    A.4.1 Estimating β and Predicting u: The Mixed Model Equations...550
    A.4.2 Random Effects, Ridging, and Shrinking 551
    A.4.3 Use of the Sweep Operation for Solutions..551
    A.4.4 Maximum Likelihood and Restricted Maximum Likelihood for Covariance Parameters...........553
A.5 Statistical Properties 557
A.6 Model Selection 558
    A.6.1 Model Comparisons via Likelihood Ratio Tests...558
    A.6.2 Model Comparisons via Information Criteria..558
A.7 Inference and Test Statistics 559
    A.7.1 Inference about the Covariance Parameters..559
    A.7.2 Inference about Fixed and Random Effects 560

A.1 Introduction

This appendix provides an overview of a modern approach to linear mixed models. This approach simplifies and unifies many common statistical analyses, including those involving repeated measures, random effects, random coefficients, spatial smoothing, and Gaussian regularization methods. The main focus of this appendix is the linear mixed model (LMM) for normally distributed data with normally distributed random effects. Appendix B focuses on the generalized linear mixed model (GLMM), which extends the mixed model for non-Gaussian data.

The primary aim of this appendix is to provide you with additional mathematical and statistical background regarding fitting linear mixed models, beyond the material covered in the main chapters of this book. Also, we hope to give you a better understanding of statistical inference using linear mixed models, including prediction and hypothesis testing.

A.2 Matrix Notation

Suppose you observe n data points $y_1,\ldots, y_n$ and you want to explain them using n values for each of p explanatory variables $x_{11},\ldots, x_{1p}, x_{21},\ldots, x_{2p}, \ldots, x_{n1},\ldots, x_{np}$. The x_{ij} values may be either regression-type continuous variables or dummy variables indicating class membership. The standard linear model for this setup is

$$Y_i = \sum_{j=1}^{p} x_{ij}\beta_j + e_i$$
$$i = 1,\ldots, n$$

(A.1)

where $\beta_1,\ldots,\beta_p$ are unknown fixed effects parameters to be estimated and the errors $e_1,\ldots,e_n$ are unknown independent and identically distributed normal (Gaussian) random variables with mean 0 and variance σ^2.

Model (A.1) can be written using vectors and a matrix as follows:

$$\begin{bmatrix} Y_1 \\ Y_2 \\ \vdots \\ Y_n \end{bmatrix} = \begin{bmatrix} x_{11} & x_{12} & \cdots & x_{1p} \\ x_{21} & x_{22} & \cdots & x_{2p} \\ \vdots & \vdots & \ddots & \vdots \\ x_{n1} & x_{n2} & \cdots & x_{np} \end{bmatrix} \begin{bmatrix} \beta_1 \\ \beta_2 \\ \vdots \\ \beta_n \end{bmatrix} + \begin{bmatrix} e_1 \\ e_2 \\ \vdots \\ e_n \end{bmatrix}$$

For convenience and simplicity, we write this entire system as

$$\mathbf{Y} = \mathbf{X}\boldsymbol{\beta} + \mathbf{e} \tag{A.2}$$

where $\mathbf{Y}$ denotes the vector of responses, $\mathbf{X}$ is the known matrix of x_{ij}'s, $\boldsymbol{\beta}$ is the unknown fixed effects parameter vector, and $\mathbf{e}$ is the unobserved vector of independent and identically distributed Gaussian random errors. When we refer to the responses as random variables, we use uppercase notation, $\mathbf{Y}$. When we refer to the observed values, lowercase notation is used, $\mathbf{y} = [y_1, y_2, \ldots, y_n]'$. The fact that a random vector $\mathbf{U}$ is normally distributed with mean $\boldsymbol{\mu}$ and variance $\mathbf{V}$ is denoted $\mathbf{U} \sim N(\boldsymbol{\mu}, \mathbf{V})$. So, in the model in Equation A.2 we write $\mathbf{e} \sim N(\mathbf{0}, \sigma^2\mathbf{I})$.

Equation A.2 can be written in probability distribution form as $\mathbf{y} \sim N\left(\mathbf{X}\boldsymbol{\beta}, \sigma^2\mathbf{I}\right)$. This model is historically referred to as the "general" linear model and is the model on which PROC GLM is based. From a contemporary linear model perspective, you can see that Equation A.2 is a special case of more general linear models. Hence this model is now referred to by the acronym LM (linear model). See Searle (1971) for an extensive development of the LM.

In addition to denoting data, random variables, and explanatory variables in the preceding fashion, the subsequent development makes use of basic matrix operators such as transpose ('), inverse ($^{-1}$), generalized inverse ($^-$), determinant ($|\mathbf{V}|$), and matrix multiplication. Refer to Searle (1982) and Harville (1997) for details on these and other matrix techniques.

A.3 Formulation of the Mixed Model

The LM is certainly a useful model in an extensive variety of applications. However, many times the independence assumption about $\mathbf{Y}$ is too restrictive. The mixed model extends the LM by allowing elements of $\mathbf{Y}$ to be correlated.

A.3.1 The General Linear Mixed Model

You can motivate the extension of the LM to the LMM by allowing a more flexible specification of the covariance matrix of $\mathbf{e}$—say, $\mathbf{e} \sim N(\mathbf{0}, \mathbf{R})$. This is the approach taken in some models for repeated measures data, temporal data, or spatial data. Or you can motivate the extension as one that permits random effects and random coefficients in the analysis, giving rise to the $\mathbf{Zu}$ terms in the model, where $\mathbf{u}$ is normal with mean $\mathbf{0}$ and variance $\mathbf{G}$. The two approaches are sometimes used interchangeably, but there are important differences. We refer to a model using random effects and a $\mathbf{Z}$ matrix as a conditional model, whereas models without a $\mathbf{Z}$ matrix that capture complex covariance structure directly through the variance matrix of the errors $\mathbf{e}$ are called marginal models. Because the variance matrix of the random effects $\mathbf{u}$ is typically denoted $\mathbf{G}$ and the variance matrix of $\mathbf{e}$ is typically denoted $\mathbf{R}$, we also refer to $\mathbf{G}$-side and $\mathbf{R}$-side modeling of the variation in the data.

The linear mixed model (hereafter referred to be the acronym LMM) can be written as follows:

$$\begin{aligned}
\mathbf{Y} &= \mathbf{X}\boldsymbol{\beta} + \mathbf{Zu} + \mathbf{e} \\
\mathbf{u} &\sim N(\mathbf{0}, \mathbf{G}) \\
\mathbf{e} &\sim N(\mathbf{0}, \mathbf{R}) \\
\mathrm{Cov}\left[\mathbf{u}, \mathbf{e}\right] &= \mathbf{0}
\end{aligned} \tag{A.3}$$

In the LM A.1, it is possible to relax the normality assumption on the errors and to assume that they just have mean zero and variance σ^2, leading often to methods that are robust to specific distributional assumptions. We do not pursue this kind of modeling here but rather make an explicit normality assumption accompanying the specification of $\mathbf{u}$ and $\mathbf{e}$. This assumption is often verified informally in practice via various plots. Also, the assumption that $\mathbf{u}$ and $\mathbf{e}$ are uncorrelated (because of the normality, this implies independence) is a key aspect of the model that avoids parameter confounding.

Parameters of a statistical model are fixed unknown constants to be estimated from the data. The parameters in Equation A.3 are thus the fixed effects vector $\boldsymbol{\beta}$ and all unknowns in the covariance matrices $\mathbf{G}$ and $\mathbf{R}$. The random effects $\mathbf{u}$ are *not* parameters, because they are not fixed. Although $\mathbf{Z}$, like $\mathbf{X}$, can contain either continuous or dummy variables, the vector $\mathbf{u}$ contains random variables. It is the presence of fixed effects parameters $\boldsymbol{\beta}$ and of $\mathbf{G}$-side random effects $\mathbf{u}$ from which the class of mixed models derives its classical name, although we use "mixed models" in a much broader sense to include general covariance modeling in $\mathbf{G}$ and $\mathbf{R}$. All unknowns in the $\mathbf{G}$ and $\mathbf{R}$ matrices are collectively referred to as the covariance parameters and denoted as $\boldsymbol{\theta}$.

Refer to Henderson (1990) and Searle, Casella, and McCulloch (1992) for historical developments of the mixed model.

A.3.2 Conditional and Marginal Distributions

Because the right-hand side of the LMM contains two random vectors, **u** and **e**, we can consider different distributions. The conditional distribution of **Y**|**u** and the marginal distribution of **Y** are as follows:

$$\mathbf{Y} \mid \mathbf{u} \sim \mathrm{N}\left(\mathbf{X}\boldsymbol{\beta} + \mathbf{Z}\mathbf{u}, \mathbf{R}\right)$$

$$\mathbf{Y} \sim \mathrm{N}\left(\mathbf{X}\boldsymbol{\beta}, \mathbf{V}\right)$$

$$\mathbf{V} = \mathrm{Var}\left[\mathbf{Y}\right] = \mathbf{Z}\mathbf{G}\mathbf{Z}' + \mathbf{R}$$

Notice that the variance of the conditional distribution is simply Var[**e**] = **R**. If a model does not have **G**-side random effects (**u** = **0**, **G** = **0**), the two conditional and marginal distributions are the same and **R** is also the marginal variance. This is the approach taken in, for example, Chapter 8, where repeated measures are modeled in PROC GLIMMIX by including the word RESIDUAL in the RANDOM statement, and in PROC MIXED using the REPEATED statement. Such a model is not a mixed model in the classical sense of fixed and random effects. Similarly, the heterogeneous variance models and some of the spatial models in Volume 2 are not mixed models in the classical sense, because variation is not modeled through random effects, but directly through the **R** matrix. However, mixed model software such as PROC MIXED can often be used to fit marginal models because the procedure accommodates complex variation in the conditional variance matrix **R**.

Details about the process of fitting a mixed model by (restricted) maximum likelihood are given below. Suffice it to say at this point that the fitting process relies on maximizing the marginal log likelihood of the data. Two models that differ in their specification for **G**, **R**, and **u** can lead to the same marginal log likelihood. A common example is a conditional model with a single variance component and a marginal model with compound-symmetric covariance structure, introduced in Chapter 2 and developed further in Chapters 5 and 8. This model equivalency can be exploited to fit a model in the most computationally efficient manner. For example, in models without **G**-side random effects the **Z** matrix does not have to be formed and stored. However, the equivalency is one with respect to the marginal distribution alone. You may need random effects in the model to obtain certain inferential quantities such as predicted values using empirical BLUPs or prediction standard errors. Also, the equivalency of the models may hold only under certain additional restriction. For example, the marginal compound-symmetry model and the variance component model are equivalent only if the intra-class correlation is nonnegative, because the variance component must be nonnegative.

A.3.3 Example: Growth Curve with Compound Symmetry

Suppose you have three growth curve measurements for *s* individuals, and you want to fit an overall linear trend in time. Your **X** matrix is as follows:

$$\mathbf{X} = \begin{bmatrix} 1 & 1 \\ 1 & 2 \\ 1 & 3 \\ \vdots & \vdots \\ 1 & 1 \\ 1 & 2 \\ 1 & 3 \end{bmatrix}$$

The first column (coded entirely with 1s) fits an intercept, and the second column (coded with times of 1,2,3) fits a slope. Here $n = 3s$ and $p = 2$.

Suppose further that you want to introduce a common correlation among the observations from a single individual, and that correlation is the same for all individuals. One way of setting this up in the general mixed model is to eliminate the **Z** and **G** matrices and let the **R** matrix be block diagonal with blocks corresponding to the individuals, each block having the *compound-symmetry* structure. This structure has two unknown parameters, one modeling a common covariance and the other modeling a residual variance. The form for $\mathbf{R}$ is then as follows:

$$
\mathbf{R} = \begin{bmatrix}
\sigma_1^2 + \sigma^2 & \sigma_1^2 & \sigma_1^2 & & & & \\
\sigma_1^2 & \sigma_1^2 + \sigma^2 & \sigma_1^2 & & & & \\
\sigma_1^2 & \sigma_1^2 & \sigma_1^2 + \sigma^2 & & & & \\
& & & \ddots & & & \\
& & & & \sigma_1^2 + \sigma^2 & \sigma_1^2 & \sigma_1^2 \\
& & & & \sigma_1^2 & \sigma_1^2 + \sigma^2 & \sigma_1^2 \\
& & & & \sigma_1^2 & \sigma_1^2 & \sigma_1^2 + \sigma^2
\end{bmatrix}
$$

The PROC GLIMMIX program to fit this model is the following:

```
proc glimmix;
   class indiv;
   model y = time;
   random _residual_ / type=cs subject=indiv;
run;
```

You can fit this model using PROC MIXED by replacing RANDOM _RESIDUAL_ by REPEATED. Here INDIV is a classification variable indexing individuals. The MODEL statement fits a straight line for TIME; the intercept is fit by default. The RANDOM _RESIDUAL_ statement models the $\mathbf{R}$ matrix: TYPE=CS specifies the compound symmetry structure and SUBJECT=INDIV specifies the blocks of $\mathbf{R}$.

An alternative way of specifying the common intra-individual correlation is to let

$$
\mathbf{Z} = \begin{bmatrix}
1 & & & \\
1 & & & \\
1 & & & \\
& 1 & & \\
& 1 & & \\
& 1 & & \\
& & \ddots & \\
& & & 1 \\
& & & 1 \\
& & & 1
\end{bmatrix}
\qquad
\mathbf{G} = \begin{bmatrix}
\sigma_1^2 & & & \\
& \sigma_1^2 & & \\
& & \ddots & \\
& & & \sigma_1^2
\end{bmatrix}
$$

and $\mathbf{R} = \sigma^2 \mathbf{I}_n$. $\mathbf{Z}$ has $3s$ rows and s columns, and $\mathbf{G}$ is $s \times s$.

You can set up this model in PROC GLIMMIX in two different but equivalent ways:

```
proc glimmix;
   class indiv;
   model y = time;
   random indiv;
run;
```

```
proc glimmix;
   class indiv;
   model y = time;
   random intercept / subject=indiv;
run;
```

Both specifications fit models that are equivalent as long as the INDIV variance component is non-negative. However, the RANDOM specifications constrain the correlation to be nonnegative, whereas the RANDOM _RESIDUAL_ (or REPEATED) specification leaves the correlation unconstrained.

A.3.4 Example: Split-Plot Design

The split-plot design involves two experimental treatment factors, A and B, and two different sizes of experimental units to which they are applied (see Winer 1971, Snedecor and Cochran 1989, Milliken and Johnson 2009). The levels of A are randomly assigned to the larger size of experimental unit, called whole plots, whereas the levels of B are assigned to the smaller size of experimental unit, the sub-plots. The sub-plots are assumed to be nested within the whole plots so that a whole plot consists of a cluster of sub-plots and a level of A is applied to the entire cluster.

Such an arrangement is often necessary by the nature of the experiment, the classical example being the application of fertilizer to large plots of land, and different crop varieties planted in subdivisions of the large plots. For this example, fertilizer is the whole-plot factor A and variety the sub-plot factor B. In addition, we assume the whole plots are arranged in a randomized block design. The appropriate PROC GLIMMIX program for this model is as follows:

```
proc glimmix;
   class a b block;
   model y = a|b;
   random block a*block;
run;
```

Here, $\mathbf{R} = \sigma^2 \mathbf{I}_{24}$ and $\mathbf{X}$, $\mathbf{G}$, and $\mathbf{Z}$ have the following form (vertical lines delineate columns associated with individual effects):

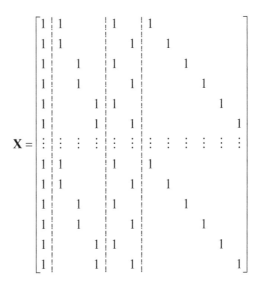

$$
\mathbf{Z} = \begin{bmatrix}
1 & & & & 1 & & & & & & & & & & & \\
1 & & & & 1 & & & & & & & & & & & \\
1 & & & & & 1 & & & & & & & & & & \\
1 & & & & & 1 & & & & & & & & & & \\
1 & & & & & & 1 & & & & & & & & & \\
1 & & & & & & 1 & & & & & & & & & \\
& 1 & & & & & & 1 & & & & & & & & \\
& 1 & & & & & & 1 & & & & & & & & \\
& 1 & & & & & & & 1 & & & & & & & \\
& 1 & & & & & & & 1 & & & & & & & \\
& 1 & & & & & & & & 1 & & & & & & \\
& 1 & & & & & & & & 1 & & & & & & \\
& & 1 & & & & & & & & 1 & & & & & \\
& & 1 & & & & & & & & 1 & & & & & \\
& & 1 & & & & & & & & & 1 & & & & \\
& & 1 & & & & & & & & & 1 & & & & \\
& & 1 & & & & & & & & & & 1 & & & \\
& & 1 & & & & & & & & & & 1 & & & \\
& & & 1 & & & & & & & & & & 1 & & \\
& & & 1 & & & & & & & & & & 1 & & \\
& & & 1 & & & & & & & & & & & 1 & \\
& & & 1 & & & & & & & & & & & 1 & \\
& & & 1 & & & & & & & & & & & & 1 \\
& & & 1 & & & & & & & & & & & & 1 \\
\end{bmatrix}
$$

where σ^2_B is the variance component for BLOCK, and σ^2_{AB} is the variance component for A × BLOCK. Changing the RANDOM statement to

```
random intercept a / subject=block;
```

fits the same model, but with **Z** and **G** sorted differently:

$$\mathbf{Z} = \begin{bmatrix}
1 & 1 & & & & & & & & & & & & \\
1 & 1 & & & & & & & & & & & & \\
1 & & 1 & & & & & & & & & & & \\
1 & & 1 & & & & & & & & & & & \\
1 & & & 1 & & & & & & & & & & \\
1 & & & 1 & & & & & & & & & & \\
 & & & & 1 & 1 & & & & & & & & \\
 & & & & 1 & 1 & & & & & & & & \\
 & & & & 1 & & 1 & & & & & & & \\
 & & & & 1 & & 1 & & & & & & & \\
 & & & & 1 & & & 1 & & & & & & \\
 & & & & 1 & & & 1 & & & & & & \\
 & & & & & & & & 1 & 1 & & & & \\
 & & & & & & & & 1 & 1 & & & & \\
 & & & & & & & & 1 & & 1 & & & \\
 & & & & & & & & 1 & & 1 & & & \\
 & & & & & & & & 1 & & & 1 & & \\
 & & & & & & & & 1 & & & 1 & & \\
 & & & & & & & & & & & & 1 & 1 \\
 & & & & & & & & & & & & 1 & 1 \\
 & & & & & & & & & & & & 1 & 1 \\
 & & & & & & & & & & & & 1 & 1 \\
 & & & & & & & & & & & & 1 & 1 \\
 & & & & & & & & & & & & 1 & 1 \\
\end{bmatrix}$$

$$\mathbf{G} = \begin{bmatrix}
\sigma_B^2 & & & & & & & \\
 & \sigma_{AB}^2 & & & & & & \\
 & & \sigma_{AB}^2 & & & & & \\
 & & & \sigma_{AB}^2 & & & & \\
 & & & & \ddots & & & \\
 & & & & & \sigma_B^2 & & \\
 & & & & & & \sigma_{AB}^2 & \\
 & & & & & & & \sigma_{AB}^2 & \\
 & & & & & & & & \sigma_{AB}^2 \\
\end{bmatrix}$$

A.4 Estimating Parameters, Predicting Random Effects

To proceed with statistical inference in a mixed model we need to estimate the unknowns $\boldsymbol{\beta}$, **G**, and **R** and predict the random variables **u**. The special structure of the normal distribution for **u** and **e** allows us to divide the theoretical development into two steps. First, we consider **G** and **R** to be known and show how to obtain solutions for $\boldsymbol{\beta}$ and **u**. Second, we inquire how to estimate the unknowns in **G** and **R**. (Note that in actual computations, the second step is performed first.) In a subsequent section we address the consequences of working with estimates of **G** and **R** rather than known matrices. As demonstrated throughout this book, the fact that statistical inference in mixed models relies on estimated covariance parameters has implications for the quality of standard errors, p-values, and Type I errors.

A.4.1 Estimating β and Predicting u: The Mixed Model Equations

If θ, the vector of covariance parameters, is known, we can construct the $\mathbf{G}$ and $\mathbf{R}$ matrices. Let g denote the number of elements in $\mathbf{u}$, and let n be the total sample size (the dimension of $\mathbf{y}$). Henderson (1950, 1984) motivated estimation of β and prediction of $\mathbf{u}$ through a set of least-squares-type estimating equations. Although initially referred to as joint maximum likelihood estimation, the function being maximized is not a true likelihood. This part of mixed model estimation must not be confused with (restricted) maximum likelihood estimation of the covariance parameters θ. It is simply a method to motivate estimating equations for β and $\mathbf{u}$. Commence by formulating the joint distribution of $\mathbf{u}$ and $\mathbf{e}$,

$$f(\mathbf{u},\mathbf{e}) = \frac{1}{(2\pi)^{(n+g)/2}} \begin{vmatrix} \mathbf{G} & \mathbf{0} \\ \mathbf{0} & \mathbf{R} \end{vmatrix}^{-1/2} \exp\left\{ -\frac{1}{2} \begin{bmatrix} \mathbf{u} \\ \mathbf{y}-\mathbf{X}\beta-\mathbf{Z}\mathbf{u} \end{bmatrix}' \begin{bmatrix} \mathbf{G}^{-1} & \mathbf{0} \\ \mathbf{0} & \mathbf{R}^{-1} \end{bmatrix} \begin{bmatrix} \mathbf{u} \\ \mathbf{y}-\mathbf{X}\beta-\mathbf{Z}\mathbf{u} \end{bmatrix} \right\}$$

Maximization of $f(\mathbf{u},\mathbf{e})$ with respect to β and $\mathbf{u}$ requires minimization of

$$\mathbf{Q} = \begin{bmatrix} \mathbf{u} \\ \mathbf{y}-\mathbf{X}\beta-\mathbf{Z}\mathbf{u} \end{bmatrix}' \begin{bmatrix} \mathbf{G}^{-1} & \mathbf{0} \\ \mathbf{0} & \mathbf{R}^{-1} \end{bmatrix} \begin{bmatrix} \mathbf{u} \\ \mathbf{y}-\mathbf{X}\beta-\mathbf{Z}\mathbf{u} \end{bmatrix}$$

$$= \mathbf{u}'\mathbf{G}^{-1}\mathbf{u} + (\mathbf{y}-\mathbf{X}\beta-\mathbf{Z}\mathbf{u})' \mathbf{R}^{-1} (\mathbf{y}-\mathbf{X}\beta-\mathbf{Z}\mathbf{u})$$

where we have taken advantage of the independence of $\mathbf{u}$ and $\mathbf{e}$. This leads to the equations

$$\partial \mathbf{Q}/\partial\beta = 0 \Leftrightarrow \mathbf{X}'\mathbf{R}^{-1}\mathbf{X}\tilde{\beta} + \mathbf{X}'\mathbf{R}^{-1}\mathbf{Z}\tilde{\mathbf{u}} = \mathbf{X}'\mathbf{R}^{-1}\mathbf{y}$$

$$\partial \mathbf{Q}/\partial\mathbf{u} = 0 \Leftrightarrow \left(\mathbf{Z}'\mathbf{R}^{-1}\mathbf{Z} + \mathbf{G}^{-1}\right)\tilde{\mathbf{u}} + \mathbf{Z}'\mathbf{R}^{-1}\mathbf{X}\tilde{\beta} = \mathbf{Z}'\mathbf{R}^{-1}\mathbf{y}$$

After some rearranging, these can be written as

$$\begin{bmatrix} \mathbf{X}'\mathbf{R}^{-1}\mathbf{X} & \mathbf{X}'\mathbf{R}^{-1}\mathbf{Z} \\ \mathbf{Z}'\mathbf{R}^{-1}\mathbf{X} & \mathbf{Z}'\mathbf{R}^{-1}\mathbf{Z}+\mathbf{G}^{-1} \end{bmatrix} \begin{bmatrix} \tilde{\beta} \\ \tilde{\mathbf{u}} \end{bmatrix} = \begin{bmatrix} \mathbf{X}'\mathbf{R}^{-1}\mathbf{y} \\ \mathbf{Z}'\mathbf{R}^{-1}\mathbf{y} \end{bmatrix} \tag{A.4}$$

The equations in A.4 are known as Henderson's mixed model equations, or simply as the mixed model equations. The solutions are

$$\begin{bmatrix} \tilde{\beta} \\ \tilde{\mathbf{u}} \end{bmatrix} = \begin{bmatrix} \mathbf{X}'\mathbf{R}^{-1}\mathbf{X} & \mathbf{X}'\mathbf{R}^{-1}\mathbf{Z} \\ \mathbf{Z}'\mathbf{R}^{-1}\mathbf{X} & \mathbf{Z}'\mathbf{R}^{-1}\mathbf{Z}+\mathbf{G}^{-1} \end{bmatrix}^{-} \begin{bmatrix} \mathbf{X}'\mathbf{R}^{-1}\mathbf{y} \\ \mathbf{Z}'\mathbf{R}^{-1}\mathbf{y} \end{bmatrix}$$

$$= \begin{bmatrix} \left(\mathbf{X}'\mathbf{V}^{-1}\mathbf{X}\right)^{-1}\mathbf{X}'\mathbf{V}^{-1}\mathbf{y} \\ \mathbf{G}\mathbf{Z}'\mathbf{V}^{-1}\left(\mathbf{y}-\mathbf{X}\left(\mathbf{X}'\mathbf{V}^{-1}\mathbf{X}\right)^{-1}\mathbf{X}'\mathbf{V}^{-1}\mathbf{y}\right) \end{bmatrix} \tag{A.5}$$

Because the right-most term in the parentheses for the random effects solution is the fixed effects estimate, we can also write

$$\tilde{\mathbf{u}} = \mathbf{G}\mathbf{Z}'\mathbf{V}^{-1}\left(\mathbf{y}-\mathbf{X}\tilde{\beta}\right)$$

A.4.2 Random Effects, Ridging, and Shrinking

Before going into further details about clever ways of solving this system of equations, it is helpful to ponder the mixed model equations for a moment. The equations in A.4 have an almost familiar form, resembling estimating equations in the linear model. Suppose that the model of interest is $\mathbf{Y} = \mathbf{X}\boldsymbol{\beta}_1 + \mathbf{Z}\boldsymbol{\beta}_2 + \mathbf{e}$, where both $\boldsymbol{\beta}_1$ and $\boldsymbol{\beta}_2$ are fixed effects, and $\mathbf{e}$ has mean $\mathbf{0}$ and variance $\mathbf{R}$. Then the generalized least-squares equations would be

$$\begin{bmatrix} \tilde{\boldsymbol{\beta}}_1 \\ \tilde{\boldsymbol{\beta}}_2 \end{bmatrix} = \begin{bmatrix} \mathbf{X}'\mathbf{R}^{-1}\mathbf{X} & \mathbf{X}'\mathbf{R}^{-1}\mathbf{Z} \\ \mathbf{Z}'\mathbf{R}^{-1}\mathbf{X} & \mathbf{Z}'\mathbf{R}^{-1}\mathbf{Z} \end{bmatrix}^{-} \begin{bmatrix} \mathbf{X}'\mathbf{R}^{-1}\mathbf{y} \\ \mathbf{Z}'\mathbf{R}^{-1}\mathbf{y} \end{bmatrix}$$

The matrix in the lower-right corner of the coefficient matrix changes from $\mathbf{Z}'\mathbf{R}^{-1}\mathbf{Z}$ in the all-fixed-effects model to $\mathbf{Z}'\mathbf{R}^{-1}\mathbf{Z} + \mathbf{G}^{-1}$ in the mixed model. When you move an effect from the fixed effects part to the random effects part of the model, you do not achieve the same predictions, because the random effects solutions are not identical to the solutions you would obtain had the same effect been fixed. An interesting way of looking at this comparison is to think of the $\mathbf{G}^{-1}$ matrix as a ridge factor applied to the random effects regression component. Ridge factors are used in standard regression to combat multicollinearity; the ridging has the effect of shrinking the parameter estimates. In the mixed model equations, the "ridge factor" $\mathbf{G}^{-1}$ also creates shrinkage in the random effects solutions—a regression toward the mean. The mixed model equations are sometimes referred to as extended normal equations because of the involvement of $\mathbf{G}^{-1}$.

It can be helpful to consider extremes. First assume that $\mathbf{G}$ is non-singular and that its eigenvalues are very large. In the case of a diagonal $\mathbf{G}$ matrix means that the diagonal elements are large, and the random effects have large variance. In this case, $\mathbf{G}^{-1}$ contributes very little to the equations, and $\tilde{\mathbf{u}}$ is very close to what it would be if $\mathbf{u}$ actually contained fixed effects parameters. On the other hand, when the eigenvalues of $\mathbf{G}$ are very small, $\mathbf{G}^{-1}$ dominates the equations and $\tilde{\mathbf{u}}$ is close to $\mathbf{0}$. If $\mathbf{G}$ is singular, the equations must be modified (Henderson 1984), and the elements of $\tilde{\mathbf{u}}$ corresponding to the singular portion of $\mathbf{G}$ equal $\mathbf{0}$. An example of this situation is when a variance component estimate falls on the boundary constraint of $\mathbf{0}$. For intermediate cases, $\mathbf{G}^{-1}$ shrinks the fixed effects estimates of $\mathbf{u}$ toward $\mathbf{0}$ (Robinson 1991).

In nonparametric regression, splines are often fit by adding a penalty criterion to control the magnitude of the spline coefficients and the degree of smoothing. If $\mathbf{B}$ is some matrix formed from a spline basis, and $\boldsymbol{\alpha}$ are the spline coefficients, then a solution can be obtained by, for example,

$$\hat{\boldsymbol{\alpha}} = \left(\mathbf{B}'\mathbf{B} + \lambda\mathbf{D}\right)^{-1}\mathbf{B}'\mathbf{y}$$

where $\mathbf{D}$ is a symmetric matrix and λ is the smoothing parameter (see, for example, Eilers and Marx 1996). If you put $\lambda\mathbf{D} = \mathbf{G}^{-1}$, the estimation criterion for penalized splines can be cast in terms of mixed model equations (Ruppert, Wand, and Carroll 2003).

A.4.3 Use of the Sweep Operation for Solutions

It is typically very inefficient to compute the solutions for $\boldsymbol{\beta}$ and $\mathbf{u}$ directly according to the last expression in equation A.5, because it involves the inverse of the marginal variance matrix. For example, in a variance component model, $\mathbf{R}$ and $\mathbf{G}$ are diagonal matrices, but $\mathbf{V} = \mathbf{Z}\mathbf{G}\mathbf{Z}' + \mathbf{R}$ is not diagonal. The formation and inversion of $\mathbf{V}$ is a computationally costly proposition. A much more elegant way to obtain solutions is by way of a sweep (Goodnight 1979), an operation related to Gauss-Jordan elimination and the Forward Doolittle procedure (Doolittle 1878). To fix ideas, consider the nonnegative definite, symmetric matrix

$$\mathbf{A} = \begin{bmatrix} \mathbf{A}_{11} & \mathbf{A}_{12} \\ \mathbf{A}_{12}' & \mathbf{A}_{22} \end{bmatrix}$$

and apply the sweep operator to its leading partition ($\mathbf{A}_{11}$). This operation, denoted SWEEP($\mathbf{A}, \mathbf{A}_{11}$), yields

$$\mathrm{SWEEP}(\mathbf{A}, \mathbf{A}_{11}) = \begin{bmatrix} \mathbf{A}_{11}^{-} & \mathbf{A}_{11}^{-}\mathbf{A}_{12} \\ -\mathbf{A}_{12}'\mathbf{A}_{11}^{-} & \mathbf{A}_{22} - \mathbf{A}_{12}'\mathbf{A}_{11}^{-}\mathbf{A}_{12} \end{bmatrix}$$

where $\mathbf{A}^-$ is a generalized inverse (a g2-generalized inverse). You can apply sweep operations in the mixed model problem as follows. First, augment the coefficient matrix on the left-hand side of the mixed model equations in A.4 with a "**y** border."

$$\mathbf{C}^- = \begin{bmatrix} \mathbf{X'R^{-1}X} & \mathbf{X'R^{-1}Z} \\ \mathbf{Z'R^{-1}X} & \mathbf{Z'R^{-1}Z + G^{-1}} \end{bmatrix}$$

$$\mathbf{M} = \left[\begin{array}{cc|c} \mathbf{X'R^{-1}X} & \mathbf{X'R^{-1}Z} & \mathbf{X'R^{-1}y} \\ \mathbf{Z'R^{-1}X} & \mathbf{Z'R^{-1}Z + G^{-1}} & \mathbf{Z'R^{-1}y} \\ \hline \mathbf{y'R^{-1}X} & \mathbf{y'R^{-1}Z} & \mathbf{y'R^{-1}y} \end{array} \right] = \begin{bmatrix} \mathbf{C}^- & \begin{bmatrix} \mathbf{X'} \\ \mathbf{Z'} \end{bmatrix}\mathbf{R^{-1}y} \\ \mathbf{y'R^{-1}}\begin{bmatrix} \mathbf{X} & \mathbf{Z} \end{bmatrix} & \mathbf{y'R^{-1}y} \end{bmatrix}$$

The operation SWEEP(**M**,**C**$^-$) yields a number of important quantities that are also needed later in computing the (restricted) log likelihood of the data. First, the matrix **M** is transformed into

$$\text{SWEEP}(\mathbf{M},\mathbf{C}^-) = \begin{bmatrix} \mathbf{C} & \begin{bmatrix} \tilde{\boldsymbol{\beta}} \\ \tilde{\mathbf{u}} \end{bmatrix} \\ -\begin{bmatrix} \tilde{\boldsymbol{\beta}} & \tilde{\mathbf{u}} \end{bmatrix}' & \mathbf{r'V^{-1}r} \end{bmatrix}$$

where

$$\mathbf{r} = \mathbf{y} \quad \mathbf{X}\tilde{\boldsymbol{\beta}}$$
$$\mathbf{C} = \begin{bmatrix} \boldsymbol{\Omega} & -\boldsymbol{\Omega}\mathbf{X'V^{-1}ZG} \\ -\mathbf{GZ'V^{-1}X}\boldsymbol{\Omega} & \mathbf{Q} + \mathbf{GZ'V^{-1}X}\boldsymbol{\Omega}\mathbf{X'V^{-1}ZG} \end{bmatrix}$$
$$\boldsymbol{\Omega} = \left(\mathbf{X'V^{-1}X} \right)^-$$
$$\mathbf{Q} = \left(\mathbf{Z'R^{-1}Z + G^{-1}} \right)^{-1}$$

(A.6)

The "**y** border" of **M** has been transformed into the solutions for the fixed effects parameter estimates and the solutions for the random effects. In the lower-right corner of the swept matrix we find the weighted residual sum of squares, **r'V**$^{-1}$**r**.

The matrix **C**, which occupies the swept partition, is the estimated covariance matrix of $[\tilde{\boldsymbol{\beta}} \quad \tilde{\mathbf{u}} - \mathbf{u}]$. Its leading term, $\boldsymbol{\Omega}$, is the variance-covariance matrix of the fixed effects parameter estimates. The term in the lower-right corner of **C** is the prediction variance matrix of the random effects. Because the **u** are random, it is often not appropriate to simply consider Var[$\tilde{\mathbf{u}}$] in statistical inference. This would not take into account that the **u** are unobservable quantities. Instead, we need to consider the variance of the difference between the solutions and the unknown random effects. Here we end up with the variance of a difference—rather than Var[$\tilde{\mathbf{u}}$].

The fact that the same rationale seemingly does not apply to the fixed effects is easily explained. Both variances are in fact mean-squared prediction errors. Suppose we want to predict the quantity U based on some function $f(\mathbf{Y})$, and suppose that U is unbiased in the sense that E[U] = E[$f(\mathbf{Y})$]. The mean-squared prediction error for U based on $f(\mathbf{Y})$ is

$$\text{MSE}[U; f(\mathbf{Y})] = \text{E}[(U - f(\mathbf{Y}))^2] = \text{Var}[U - f(\mathbf{Y})] = \text{Var}[U] + \text{Var}[f(\mathbf{Y})] - 2\text{Cov}[U, f(\mathbf{Y})]$$

If the target U is fixed, not random, then the mean-squared prediction error reduces to Var[$f(\mathbf{Y})$]. This is the case for the fixed effects. For the random effects, the target is **u** and we are predicting it with $f(\mathbf{Y}) = \tilde{\mathbf{u}}$. Because $\tilde{\mathbf{u}}$ is unbiased for **u** in the sense that both have expectation zero—which relied on the fact that $\tilde{\boldsymbol{\beta}}$ is unbiased for $\boldsymbol{\beta}$—the mean-squared prediction error for the random effects has the form of a variance of a difference.

We can also view the LMM setup from a Bayesian perspective, where a prior distribution is assumed for $\boldsymbol{\beta}$ and **u**. The prior for the fixed effects parameters is flat, whereas the prior for **u** is assumed to be normal with mean **0** and variance **G**. With **G** and **R** known, the posterior distribution for $[\boldsymbol{\beta} \quad \mathbf{u}]$ is normal, and the variance and mean correspond to the partitions in the first row of SWEEP(**M**,**C**$^-$).

A side product of sweeping, albeit a very important one, is the log determinant of the swept matrix. It is obtained by summing the log pivots (the log of the diagonal element prior to sweeping the row) of the rows that are swept. You can show that $\log |\mathbf{C}^-|$ equals

$$\log | \mathbf{X}'\mathbf{V}^{-1}\mathbf{X} | + \log | \mathbf{V} | - \log | \mathbf{R} | - \log | \mathbf{G} |$$
$$= \log | \mathbf{X}'\mathbf{V}^{-1}\mathbf{X} | + \log | \mathbf{Z}'\mathbf{R}\mathbf{Z} + \mathbf{G}^{-1} |$$

These log determinants are components of the (restricted) log likelihood of the mixed model (see below). It really is "all in the sweep."

The previous expressions and derivations tacitly assumed that $\boldsymbol{\theta}$ is known and hence $\mathbf{G}$ and $\mathbf{R}$ can be formed as needed. We also tacitly assumed that $\mathbf{G}$ and $\mathbf{R}$ are positive definite. Although we are not going to address in this appendix how to handle the case of non-positive definite variance matrices, the issue of not knowing the covariance parameters needs to be addressed. Otherwise, none of the mentioned results are operational. An obvious amendment of the derivations is to use "plug-in estimates"—that is, replace the unknown quantities in the equations with estimates. For example, $\mathbf{R}$ and $\mathbf{G}$ are replaced with $\hat{\mathbf{R}}$ and $\hat{\mathbf{G}}$, which are formed by evaluating their elements based on the estimate $\hat{\boldsymbol{\theta}}$ of $\boldsymbol{\theta}$. The estimator of $\boldsymbol{\beta}$ and the predictor of $\mathbf{u}$ given above are a generalized least squares estimator (GLSE) and a best linear unbiased predictor (BLUP), respectively. When these are computed based on estimated covariance parameters, we refer to them as estimated GLS estimator (EGLSE) and as estimated (or empirical) BLUP (EBLUP).

A.4.4 Maximum Likelihood and Restricted Maximum Likelihood for Covariance Parameters

Throughout this text we have invoked various methods for estimating covariance parameters: method of moments (Type 1, 2, 3), minimum variance quadratic unbiased estimation (MIVQUE0), maximum likelihood (ML), restricted maximum likelihood (REML), and pseudo-likelihood (PL). Arguably the most important method of estimating covariance parameters is restricted maximum likelihood estimation, and it is the default of PROC MIXED. (It is also the default of PROC GLIMMIX for mixed models with normally distributed data.) The details on likelihood estimation in LMMs that apply to PROC MIXED are given in Wolfinger, Tobias, and Sall (1994). Further details can be found in, e.g., Hartley and Rao (1967), Patterson and Thompson (1971), Harville (1977), Laird and Ware (1982), and Jennrich and Schluchter (1986). We report here the necessary details to tie the optimization of a likelihood function to the solution of the mixed model equations in the previous sections and to exemplify the differences between maximum likelihood and restricted maximum likelihood estimation. For models for normally distributed data, details for PROC MIXED apply to PROC GLIMMIX as well. Subsequent discussion in this chapter, while framed in terms of PROC MIXED, is equally applicable to PROC GLIMMIX with regard to LMMs. Appendix B provides additional detail about PROC GLIMMIX.

PROC MIXED minimizes twice the negative of the (restricted) log likelihood. Following Wolfinger, Tobias, and Sall (1994), the subscript R is used in the following expressions to distinguish REML estimation from ML estimation.

Maximum Likelihood (ML)

The –2 log likelihood for Equation A.3 is

$$-2l\left(\boldsymbol{\theta}, \boldsymbol{\beta}; \mathbf{y}\right) = \log | \mathbf{V} | + \left(\mathbf{y} - \mathbf{X}\boldsymbol{\beta}\right)' \mathbf{V}^{-1} \left(\mathbf{y} - \mathbf{X}\boldsymbol{\beta}\right) + c \qquad (A.7)$$

where c is the constant $n \log(2\pi)$. In Section A.4.1 we have seen that, given the covariance parameter $\boldsymbol{\theta}$, a solution for $\boldsymbol{\beta}$ can be obtained in closed form as

$$\tilde{\boldsymbol{\beta}}(\boldsymbol{\theta}) = \left(\mathbf{X}'\mathbf{V}(\boldsymbol{\theta})^{-1} \mathbf{X}\right)^{-1} \mathbf{X}\mathbf{V}(\boldsymbol{\theta})^{-1} \mathbf{y}$$

We have written this solution here as an explicit function of the covariance parameters, to make the dependency apparent. You can substitute $\tilde{\boldsymbol{\beta}}(\boldsymbol{\theta})$ for $\boldsymbol{\beta}$ in equation A.7 to obtain a likelihood from which the fixed effects have been profiled. This process reduces the number of parameters for which the optimization needs to be carried out. The only unknowns in the resulting –2 log likelihood,

$$-2l(\mathbf{\theta};\mathbf{y}) = \log |\mathbf{V}(\mathbf{\theta})| + \left(\mathbf{y} - \mathbf{X}\tilde{\mathbf{\beta}}(\mathbf{\theta})\right)' \mathbf{V}(\mathbf{\theta})^{-1} \left(\mathbf{y} - \mathbf{X}\tilde{\mathbf{\beta}}(\mathbf{\theta})\right) + c \tag{A.8}$$

are the covariance parameters.

The minimum of this objective function, $\hat{\mathbf{\theta}}$, is the maximum likelihood estimator of $\mathbf{\theta}$, provided the elements of $\hat{\mathbf{\theta}}$ are in the parameter space. The ML estimator of the fixed effects parameters is then obtained by evaluating $\tilde{\mathbf{\beta}}(\mathbf{\theta})$ at the ML estimate of $\mathbf{\theta}$.

$$\hat{\mathbf{\beta}} = \left(\mathbf{X}'\mathbf{V}\left(\hat{\mathbf{\theta}}\right)^{-1}\mathbf{X}\right)^{-1} \mathbf{X}'\mathbf{V}\left(\hat{\mathbf{\theta}}\right)^{-1}\mathbf{y}$$

Restricted Maximum Likelihood (REML)

REML estimation is arguably the most important technique for estimating covariance parameters in mixed models. It is a likelihood-based technique that aims to remedy some of the shortcomings of regular maximum likelihood estimation; it traces back to Thompson (1962) and Patterson and Thompson (1971). ML estimates are very desirable statistically—for example, they tend to be asymptotically efficient estimates and follow asymptotic normal distributions under some mild regularity conditions. However, most of the desirable properties are asymptotic, and require an increasing sample size. For example, many MLEs are asymptotically unbiased but biased for any fixed sample size. The small-sample bias can be easily illustrated with the following simple example.

Suppose that $Y_1, \ldots, Y_n$ is a random sample from a $N(\mu, \sigma^2)$ distribution, and suppose that μ and σ^2 are unknown. Twice the negative of the log likelihood of the sample is

$$-2l(\mu,\sigma^2;\mathbf{y}) = n\ln(2\pi) + n\ln(\sigma^2) + \frac{1}{\sigma^2}\sum_{i=1}^{n}(y_i - \mu)^2$$

It is easy to show that this function is minimized by

$$\hat{\mu} = n^{-1}\sum_{i=1}^{n} y_i = \bar{y}$$

$$\hat{\sigma}^2 = n^{-1}\sum_{i=1}^{n}(y_i - \hat{\mu})^2$$

the maximum likelihood estimators of the mean and the variance. Whereas the MLE of μ is an unbiased estimator, the MLE of σ^2 is biased,

$$E\left[\hat{\sigma}^2 - \sigma^2\right] = -\frac{1}{n}\sigma^2$$

This bias shrinks with the sample size, and it is negative. The MLE of σ^2 underestimates the variance on average. Notice that if we had known the mean μ, then our MLE for the variance would have been

$$\hat{\sigma}^2 = n^{-1}\sum_{i=1}^{n}(y_i - \mu)^2 \tag{A.9}$$

which is an unbiased estimator of σ^2. So the finite-sample-size "problem" of MLEs for variance or covariance parameters appears to be linked to "not knowing the mean." More precisely, it is linked to not accounting for the unknown mean in the estimation. In the terminology of mixed models, the issue is the accounting of the fixed effects parameters in estimating the covariance parameters. That is the motivation of Patterson and Thompson (1971).

REML estimation can be cast as likelihood estimation for transformed data. Instead of the log likelihood of **Y**, we consider the log likelihood of **KY**, where the matrix **K** is chosen so that E[**KY**] = **0**. **K** is also called a matrix of error contrasts; hence the alternate name of residual log likelihood. If we consider the –2 log likelihood of **KY**, then

$$-2l_R(\theta; \mathbf{Ky}) = \log |\mathbf{KV}(\theta)\mathbf{K}'| + \mathbf{y}'\mathbf{K}'\mathbf{V}(\theta)^{-1}\mathbf{Ky} + c_R$$

and the fixed effects β have seemingly dropped from estimation. The process is not quite identical to profiling β, because the REML objective function by definition is an objective function for the covariance parameters only. For the linear model with E[**Y**] = **Xβ**, Harville (1977) points out that the $(n-p) \times n$ matrix (where p is the rank of **X**) constructed from linearly independent rows of **M** = **I** – **X**(**X**'**X**)$^{-1}$**X**' leads to the same objective function, which differs by only a constant amount that does not depend on the parameters.

We can use this result to find the REML estimator of σ^2 in the random sample example above. First, we can express the random sampling situation with a simple model,

$$\mathbf{Y} = \mathbf{1}\mu + \mathbf{e} \qquad \mathbf{e} \sim \mathrm{N}(\mathbf{0}, \sigma^2\mathbf{I})$$

so that $p = 1$, **X** = **1**, and **M** = **I** – **J**$/n$, where **J** is an $(n \times n)$ matrix of ones. So we choose as the matrix **K** of error contrasts the first n–1 rows of **M**:

$$\mathbf{K}_{(n-1)\times n} = \begin{bmatrix} 1-\dfrac{1}{n} & -\dfrac{1}{n} & \cdots & \dfrac{1}{n} \\ -\dfrac{1}{n} & 1-\dfrac{1}{n} & \cdots & -\dfrac{1}{n} \\ \vdots & & \ddots & \vdots \\ -\dfrac{1}{n} & -\dfrac{1}{n} & \cdots & 1-\dfrac{1}{n} \end{bmatrix} \Rightarrow \mathbf{KY} = \begin{bmatrix} Y_1 - \bar{Y} \\ Y_2 - \bar{Y} \\ \vdots \\ Y_{n-1} - \bar{Y} \end{bmatrix}$$

The new "data" vector **KY** now consists of the deviations of the first n–1 observations from the sample mean. We have seemingly reduced the size of the data from n to n–1, but we have not lost any information. If we know the sample mean and n–1 observations, the full data set of n observations can be constructed. Also, it does not matter which of the observations is dropped (which row of **M** is eliminated); all vectors in the vector **KY** are sufficient for σ^2. Or, in the words of Harville (1977): "the REML estimator does not ignore any information that is actually *used* by the full approach" (ML). To construct the REML log likelihood for this problem, we now follow Schabenberger and Pierce (2002, Ch. 7.4.1) and the details provided therein. First, denote **KY** = **U** and note that Var[**U**] = σ^2**KK**' = σ^2**P**. The matrix **P** has some remarkable properties—for example, $|\mathbf{P}| = 1/n$, $\mathbf{P}^{-1} = \mathbf{I}_{n-1} + \mathbf{J}_{n-1}$. The –2 log likelihood for **U** is

$$-2l_R(\sigma^2; \mathbf{u}) = (n-1)\ln(\sigma^2) + \frac{1}{\sigma^2}\sum_{i=1}^{n}(y_i - \bar{y})^2 + c_R$$

and the solution is the REML estimate

$$\hat{\sigma}_R^2 = (n-1)^{-1}\sum_{i=1}^{n}(y_i - \bar{y})^2 \tag{A.10}$$

The REML estimate equals the sample variance and is an unbiased estimator of σ^2. If you compare $\hat{\sigma}^2$ in equation A.9 and $\hat{\sigma}_R^2$ in equation A.10, both estimators involve a sum-of-squares term with deviations from the sample mean. The presence of $\bar{y}$ in the formula for the estimators has a different origin, however. In ML estimation, we substitute the MLE for μ, and that happens to be $\bar{y}$. In REML estimation we have eliminated the unknown mean from the estimation altogether. $\bar{y}$ appears in the formula for $\hat{\sigma}_R^2$ because the quadratic form $\mathbf{u}'\mathbf{P}^{-1}\mathbf{u}$ equals the corrected sum of squares. This underscores the point that—by itself—REML estimation does not provide estimates of the fixed effect parameters. It yields only estimates of the covariance parameters.

For the general linear mean function $E[\mathbf{Y}] = \mathbf{X}\boldsymbol{\beta}$, the process works in the same way, by forming a matrix of error contrast based on the independent rows of the projection matrix $\mathbf{M} = \mathbf{I} - \mathbf{X}(\mathbf{X'X})^{-1}\mathbf{X'}$. Because any set of rows will do, the following objective function is common for REML estimation:

$$-2l_R(\boldsymbol{\theta};\mathbf{y}) = \log|\mathbf{V}(\boldsymbol{\theta})| + \log|\mathbf{X'V}(\boldsymbol{\theta})^{-1}\mathbf{X}| + \left(\mathbf{y} - \mathbf{X}\tilde{\boldsymbol{\beta}}(\boldsymbol{\theta})\right)' \mathbf{V}(\boldsymbol{\theta})^{-1} \left(\mathbf{y} - \mathbf{X}\tilde{\boldsymbol{\beta}}(\boldsymbol{\theta})\right) + c_R$$

Dropping the notational dependence on the covariance parameters and replacing the residual vector with $\mathbf{r}$, we can write

$$-2l_R(\boldsymbol{\theta};\mathbf{y}) = \log|\mathbf{V}| + \log|\mathbf{X'V}^{-1}\mathbf{X}| + \mathbf{r'V}^{-1}\mathbf{r} + c_R \tag{A.11}$$

The REML estimate of $\boldsymbol{\theta}$ is the vector $\hat{\boldsymbol{\theta}}_R$ that minimizes equation A.11 and whose elements are in the parameter space of $\boldsymbol{\theta}$. The fixed effects estimates are obtained as estimated generalized least squares estimates evaluated at the REML estimate of the covariance parameters

$$\hat{\boldsymbol{\beta}}_R = \left(\mathbf{X'V}\left(\hat{\boldsymbol{\theta}}_R\right)^{-1}\mathbf{X}\right)^{-1} \mathbf{X'V}\left(\hat{\boldsymbol{\theta}}_R\right)^{-1}\mathbf{y}$$

Final Connections

The interplay of minimizing equation A.11 for REML estimation or equation A.8 for ML estimation and the mixed model equations is now becoming apparent. The likelihood optimization yields values for the covariance parameters. Given these values we can set up and solve the mixed model equations by sweeping, thereby acquiring the necessary pieces to compute the objective function. The kernel of the -2 restricted log likelihood can be computed from elements of the sweep alone.

Because $\boldsymbol{\theta}$ is involved nonlinearly in equation A.11 or A.8, the process of estimating the covariance parameters relies on numerical methods. Starting from initial values of the covariance parameters $\boldsymbol{\theta}^0$, subsequent updates are obtained by an optimization algorithm until a convergence criterion is achieved. The MIXED procedure determines initial covariance parameters as MIVQUE0 estimates unless you provide starting values with the PARMS statement. The optimization method implemented in PROC MIXED is a ridge-stabilized Newton-Raphson algorithm with analytic derivatives. Lindstrom and Bates (1988) provide reasons for preferring Newton-Raphson to the Expectation-Maximization (EM) algorithm described in Dempster, Laird, and Rubin (1977) and Laird, Lange, and Stram (1987), as well as analytical details for implementing a QR-decomposition approach to the problem. Wolfinger, Tobias, and Sall (1994) present the sweep-based algorithms that are implemented in PROC MIXED.

One advantage of using the Newton-Raphson algorithm is that the second derivative matrix of the objective function evaluated at the optima is available upon completion. Denoting this matrix $\mathbf{H}$, the asymptotic theory of maximum likelihood (refer to Serfling 1980) shows that the matrix $2\mathbf{H}^{-1}$ is an asymptotic variance-covariance matrix of the estimated parameters of $\mathbf{G}$ and $\mathbf{R}$. Thus, tests and confidence intervals based on asymptotic normality can be obtained. However, these can be unreliable in small samples, especially for parameters such as variance components whose small-sample sampling distributions tend to be skewed to the right.

Instead of ML or REML, you can use the noniterative MIVQUE0 method to estimate $\mathbf{G}$ and $\mathbf{R}$ (Rao 1972, LaMotte 1973, Goodnight 1978, Wolfinger, Tobias, and Sall 1994). However, Swallow and Monahan (1984) present simulation evidence favoring REML and ML over MIVQUE0. MIVQUE0 is recommended primarily for large data sets or for situations where the iterative REML and ML procedures fail to converge.

A.5 Statistical Properties

If **G** and **R** are known, $\tilde{\beta}$ is the best linear unbiased estimator (BLUE) of β and $\tilde{u}$ is the best linear unbiased predictor (BLUP) of **u** (Searle 1971, Harville 1988, 1990, Robinson 1991, McLean, Sanders, and Stroup 1991). Here *best* means minimum mean squared error. We established earlier that the covariance matrix of $[\tilde{\beta}, \tilde{u} - u]$ is

$$C = \begin{bmatrix} X'R^{-1}X & X'R^{-1}Z \\ Z'R^{-1}X & Z'R^{-1}Z + G^{-1} \end{bmatrix}^{-}$$

where the minus sign ($^-$) is used to denote a generalized inverse (refer to Searle 1971).

However, **G** and **R** are usually unknown and are estimated using one of the aforementioned methods. To be more precise, we could write these matrices as functions of the covariance parameters, $G(\theta)$ and $R(\theta)$. Estimates of the covariance parameters θ are substituted to obtain estimates of the covariance matrices, $\hat{G} = G(\hat{\theta})$ and $\hat{R} = R(\hat{\theta})$. These, in turn, are substituted into the preceding expressions to obtain the "plug-in" mixed model equations:

$$\begin{bmatrix} X'\hat{R}^{-1}X & X'\hat{R}^{-1}Z \\ Z'\hat{R}^{-1}X & Z'\hat{R}^{-1}Z + \hat{G}^{-1} \end{bmatrix} \begin{bmatrix} \hat{\beta} \\ \hat{u} \end{bmatrix} = \begin{bmatrix} X'\hat{R}^{-1}y \\ Z'\hat{R}^{-1}y \end{bmatrix}$$

Notice that we now use caret notation ($^\wedge$) instead of tildes ($\sim$) to denote an estimator or predictor that depends on the estimated covariance parameters.

The BLUE and BLUP acronyms no longer apply in all respects to the solutions to the mixed model equations,

$$\hat{\beta} = \left(X'\hat{V}^{-1}X \right)^{-1} X'\hat{V}^{-1}y$$

$$\hat{u} = \hat{G}Z'\hat{V}^{-1}\left(y - X\hat{\beta} \right)$$

For example, $\hat{\beta}$ is no longer a linear function of the data. The word empirical (or estimated) is often added to indicate such a plug-in estimator. The appropriate acronyms thus become EBLUE and EBLUP. Because plug-in estimates are used to form the mixed model equations, the first partition of the mixed model solution now also depends on the covariance parameter estimates:

$$\hat{C} = \begin{bmatrix} X'\hat{R}^{-1}X & X'\hat{R}^{-1}Z \\ Z'\hat{R}^{-1}X & Z'\hat{R}^{-1}Z + \hat{G}^{-1} \end{bmatrix}^{-}$$

is a model-based variance-covariance matrix of $[\hat{\beta}, \hat{u} - u]$. This covariance matrix can be exact or approximate, depending on the structure of the model and the data. For example, in many balanced variance component models, it is *the* covariance matrix of $[\hat{\beta}, \hat{u} - u]$. Expression A.6 provides formulas for the specific blocks of $\hat{C}$. See also Henderson (1984) and McLean and Sanders (1988).

As a cautionary note, when $\hat{C}$ is not exact, it tends to underestimate the true sampling variability of $\hat{\beta}$ and $\hat{u}$ because no account is made for the uncertainty in estimating **G** and **R**. Several inflation factors have been proposed to the variance of linear functions (Kackar and Harville 1984, Kass and Steffey 1989, Prasad and Rao 1990, Harville and Jeske 1992) or covariance matrices (Kenward and Roger 1997, 2009). These factors tend to be small for data sets that are fairly well balanced but can be substantial for small unbalanced designs, or in cases with many covariance parameters. The DDFM=KR2 option in the MODEL statement of PROC MIXED (and PROC GLIMMIX) applies the standard error correction for fixed effects according to Kenward and Roger (2009). There is an older option, DDFM=KR, based on their 1997 paper. The 2009 version (KR2) corrects a minor error in the original 1997 version. The prediction standard errors for random effects are adjusted according to what Harville and Jeske (1992) term the Prasad-Rao estimator. In their notation, this adjustment is $\tilde{m}^@(\hat{\theta})$. Note that the Prasad-Rao-Jeske-Kackar-Harville adjustment for a linear function of the fixed effects is identical to the Kenward and Roger adjustment if the covariance matrix does not have second derivatives (with respect to the covariance parameters). The Kenward-Roger method, however, also provides adjustments to *t*- and *F*-statistics and their degrees of freedom for testing hypotheses and constructing confidence intervals (see Section A.7).

A.6 Model Selection

The previous sections on estimation and statistical properties of the estimators assume the specification of a mixed model in terms of **X**, **Z**, **G**, and **R**. Even though **X** and **Z** have known elements, their specific form and construction is flexible, and several possibilities may present themselves for a particular data set. Likewise, several different covariance structures for **G** and **R** might be reasonable.

Space does not permit a thorough discussion of mixed model selection, but a few brief comments and references are in order. First, subject-matter considerations and objectives should certainly be foremost in your mind when selecting models. A few of the numerous useful references include Jennrich and Schluchter (1986), Diggle (1988), Lindsey (1993), Brown and Prescott (1999), and Verbeke and Molenberghs (1997, 2000).

Second, when the data themselves are looked to for guidance, many of the graphical methods and diagnostics appropriate for the general linear model extend to the mixed model setting as well (Christensen, Pearson, and Johnson 1992, Muller and Fetterman 2002).

A.6.1 Model Comparisons via Likelihood Ratio Tests

Many analysts prefer a statistical test for model comparisons. When models are fit by maximum or restricted maximum likelihood, you can form a likelihood ratio test statistic by comparing –2 (Res) Log Likelihood between the full and a reduced model. The important aspect here is that the "reduced" model is in fact nested in the full model. This means that you can attain the reduced model by imposing constraints on the full model, such as by setting covariance parameters to zero. When models are fit by restricted maximum likelihood (REML), the comparisons of models via restricted likelihood ratio tests must be confined to models that are nested with respect to the covariance parameters alone. Two models that have different **X** matrices, whether nested or not, cannot be compared based on –2 Res Log Likelihood. As shown in Section A.4.4, REML estimation can be viewed as maximum likelihood estimation for transformed data, **KY**, where $E[\mathbf{KY}] = \mathbf{0}$. Changing the fixed effects part of the model changes **K**, so that the two models are performing maximum likelihood estimation for two different sets of data.

Recently, increased attention has been given to the problem of likelihood ratio testing under nonstandard conditions. Typically, the nonstandard condition stems from boundary constraints on the parameters, such as when a variance component is tested against zero. These tests are normally carried out as one-sided tests, with hypotheses

$$H_0 : \sigma^2 = 0 \qquad H_a : \sigma^2 > 0$$

Under the null hypothesis the parameter falls on the boundary of the parameter space, unless you consider unbounded estimation (NOBOUND option in PROC MIXED) and a two-sided test. The usual asymptotic theory for the likelihood-ratio χ^2 statistic would suggest that the difference of the –2 log likelihoods is distributed as a χ^2 variable with a single degree of freedom. When tested parameters or nuisance parameters (the parameters not specified in the hypothesis) fall on the boundary of the parameter space, the standard theory does not apply (see, for example, Self and Liang 1987 and Shapiro 1988). In this case, however, the null sampling distribution of the test statistic is a 50:50 mixture of a χ_0^2 and a χ_1^2 variable. As a consequence, you can perform the likelihood ratio test as if the standard conditions apply, and divide the resulting *p*-value by two. In more complex cases, such as when multiple parameters are tested, or when nuisance parameters fall on the boundary, the correction for the likelihood ratio test is not as straightforward. A number of cases have been explored in Self and Liang (1987) and specifically for variance component models in Stram and Lee (1994, 1995). Silvapulle and Silvapulle (1995) and Verbeke and Molenberghs (2003) consider similar problems with the score test.

A.6.2 Model Comparisons via Information Criteria

As an alternative to likelihood ratio testing, one can take an information-theoretical perspective and compute a variety of information-based measures. These are usually computed as a penalty term applied to the likelihood function. The most common of these are the likelihood ratio test and Akaike's and Schwarz's criteria (Bozdogan 1987, Wolfinger 1993a). A small sample corrected version of Akaike's criterion, known as AICC, has received considerable attention (Hurvich and Tsai, 1989, Burnham and Anderson 2002). Despite their varied philosophical origins, the information criteria tend to have penalty terms that are a function of the number of parameters (*d*) and some measure of sample size (*n*). In some instances, such as REML estimation in the mixed model, it is not entirely clear how to best determine *d* and *n*, because the fixed effects are removed from the estimation. One approach considers the number of covariance parameters and the number of subjects in the analysis (PROC MIXED, PROC GLIMMIX default). Verbeke and Molenberghs (2000, Table 6.7, p. 74) and Vonesh and Chinchilli (1997, p. 263) count the rank of **X** in *d* and determine *n* as the total sample size minus the rank of **X**. You can obtain information criteria computed according to these definitions for REML estimation with the IC option in the GLIMMIX procedure. The most appropriate term for *n* is probably linked to the effective sample size, taking into account the covariance structure in the data. For example, if the data consist of *s* subjects whose observations are perfectly correlated, then *n* = *s*. If the observations among subjects were independent, then

$$n = \sum_{i=1}^{s} n_i$$

Covariance structures in mixed models yield effective sample sizes between these extremes.

The use of information criteria with REML estimation has the same caveats as likelihood ratio testing based on the –2 Res Log Likelihood. If two models have different fixed effects—whether they are nested or not—the –2 Res Log Likelihoods are not comparable. Consequently, the information criteria based on these –2 Res Log Likelihoods are also not comparable. Adding $2 \times p$ to numbers that are not comparable does not create a basis for comparison. This difficulty does not arise with ML estimation.

The lack of comparability in REML estimation has to do with the fact that the underlying data sets are not comparable. The same issue surfaces, but more severely, in generalized linear mixed models and nonlinear mixed models based on pseudo-data (PROC GLIMMIX, %NLINMIX). Because the fitting process consists of repeatedly fitting a linear mixed model constructed from pseudo-data, the likelihoods are not comparable in the models encountered during the model-fitting process. In addition, likelihoods based on pseudo-data from different models are not directly comparable, whether estimation of the linear mixed models relies on a maximum likelihood or restricted maximum likelihood principle. The NLMIXED procedure produces log likelihoods and information criteria for nonlinear or generalized linear mixed models that can be used for model comparisons.

In contrast to standard linear models, especially regression models, the graphical analysis of residuals is not used as frequently in mixed models. Chapter 15 discusses mixed model diagnostics and the various forms of residuals that arise in mixed models (for example, marginal and conditional residuals). You cannot distill the complexity of model–data interaction, and the adequacy of a model in a single summary measure such as the log likelihood or an information criterion. Residual graphics inform you about aspects of the model fit that summary measures cannot address—for example, the presence of outliers, heterogeneity of variance, the need for transformation, and so on.

A.7 Inference and Test Statistics

Parameter estimation is rarely the end of the process. You typically want to make some sort of inference about the parameters that were estimated. Depending on the situation, inference about the covariance parameters or the fixed and random effects may be of interest.

A.7.1 Inference about the Covariance Parameters

For inferences concerning the covariance parameters in your model, you can use likelihood-based statistics. One common such statistic is the Wald *Z*, which is computed as the parameter estimate divided by its estimated asymptotic standard error. The asymptotic standard errors are computed from the inverse of the second derivative matrix of the log likelihood with respect to the covariance parameters. The Wald *Z* test is valid for large samples, but it can be unreliable for small data sets and for parameters such as variance components that are known to have a skewed or bounded sampling distribution.

A better alternative is the likelihood ratio χ^2. This test compares two models that are nested with respect to the covariance parameters. The two models are often referred to as the full model and the reduced model. The reduced model is obtained from the full model by imposing one or more constraints on the covariance parameters—a process known as nesting models. The test statistic is the difference of the –2 log likelihoods between the reduced and the full model. Issues surrounding likelihood ratio testing in mixed models were addressed in A.6.1—for example, the need for models to have the same **X** matrix when –2 Res Log Likelihoods are used to form test statistics and the nonstandard distribution theory when parameters are on the boundary of the parameter space. In order to perform likelihood ratio tests for covariance parameters, you need to run PROC MIXED twice to obtain the –2 (Res) Log Likelihoods under the full and reduced model. The COVTEST statement in PROC GLIMMIX allows you to specify likelihood ratio tests of interest for variance and covariance components and eliminates the need for two runs. The COVTEST statement also has options that allow you to compute profile likelihood confidence intervals for the parameters of the covariance model.

For variance component models, the null hypothesis of no effect can be tested using the fixed effects *F*-tests (Morgan and Gumpertz 1996, Pantula 1996, Khuri, Mathew, and Sinha 1998). Confidence intervals on variance components can be constructed in a variety of ways (Burdick and Graybill 1992, Burdick, Borror, and Montgomery 2005). Bayesian inference on variance components can be conducted by generating a sample from their posterior distribution as described in Chapter 13.

A.7.2 Inference about Fixed and Random Effects

For inferences concerning the fixed and random effects parameters in the mixed model, consider estimable linear combinations of the following form:

$$\omega = \mathbf{L}\begin{bmatrix} \boldsymbol{\beta} \\ \mathbf{u} \end{bmatrix}$$

Functions of this form are called predictable functions if the $\boldsymbol{\beta}$ portion of $\mathbf{L}$ satisfies the estimability requirement (Searle 1971). Chapter 6 gives examples of the logic underlying the construction of predictable functions. Such a formulation in terms of a general $\mathbf{L}$ matrix encompasses a wide variety of common inferential procedures such as those employed with Type I and III tests and least-squares means. The CONTRAST and ESTIMATE statements in PROC MIXED and PROC GLIMMIX allow you to specify your own $\mathbf{L}$ matrices. Typically, inference on fixed effects is the focus, and in this case the $\mathbf{u}$ portion of $\mathbf{L}$ is assumed to contain all 0s.

Statistical inferences can be obtained by testing the null hypothesis

$$H_0 : \mathbf{L}\begin{bmatrix} \boldsymbol{\beta} \\ \mathbf{u} \end{bmatrix} = \mathbf{0}$$

or by constructing point and/or interval estimates.

When $\mathbf{L}$ consists of a single row, a general t-statistic can be constructed as follows:

$$t = \frac{\mathbf{L}\begin{bmatrix} \hat{\boldsymbol{\beta}} \\ \hat{\mathbf{u}} \end{bmatrix}}{\sqrt{\mathbf{L}\hat{\mathbf{C}}\mathbf{L}'}} \tag{A.12}$$

See McLean and Sanders (1988) and Stroup (1989) for details. Under the assumed normality of $\mathbf{u}$ and $\mathbf{e}$, t has an exact t-distribution only for data exhibiting certain types of balance and for some special unbalanced cases. In general, t is only approximately t-distributed, and its degrees of freedom must be estimated. See the DDFM= option in the MODEL statement for a description of the various degrees of freedom methods available in PROC MIXED.

If ν denotes the degrees of freedom associated with ω, the associated confidence interval for ω is

$$\mathbf{L}\begin{bmatrix} \hat{\boldsymbol{\beta}} \\ \hat{\mathbf{u}} \end{bmatrix} \pm t_{\nu, \alpha/2} \sqrt{\mathbf{L}\hat{\mathbf{C}}\mathbf{L}'}$$

where $t_{\nu, \alpha/2}$ is the $(1-\alpha/2)100^{\text{th}}$ percentile of the t_ν-distribution.

When the rank of $\mathbf{L}$ is greater than 1, the following general F-statistic can be considered:

$$F = \frac{\begin{bmatrix} \hat{\boldsymbol{\beta}} \\ \hat{\mathbf{u}} \end{bmatrix} \mathbf{L}'\left(\mathbf{L}\hat{\mathbf{C}}\mathbf{L}'\right)^{-1}\mathbf{L}\begin{bmatrix} \hat{\boldsymbol{\beta}} \\ \hat{\mathbf{u}} \end{bmatrix}}{\text{rank}(\mathbf{L})} \tag{A.13}$$

Analogous to t, F in general has an approximate F-distribution, with rank($\mathbf{L}$) numerator degrees of freedom and $\hat{\nu}$ denominator degrees of freedom.

As sample sizes grow large, equation A.12 has a normal distribution and equation A.13 has a chi-square distribution. You can base statistical inference in PROC MIXED on these asymptotic distributions with the CHISQ option in the MODEL and CONTRAST statements. In the GLIMMIX procedure you can choose DDFM=NONE in the MODEL statement to compute p-values according to the asymptotic distributions (or use the CHISQ options).

The t- and F-statistics allow you to make inferences about fixed effects that account for the variance-covariance model you select. An alternative for large samples is the χ^2-statistic associated with the likelihood ratio test. This statistic compares two fixed effects models, one a special case of the other. It is computed just as when comparing different covariance models. However, you should not compare likelihoods of models that differ in their fixed effects when the covariance parameters are estimated by REML (see Section A.6.1); use ML estimation instead. You can also use information-theoretical criteria to compare fixed effects using ML (see Section A.6.2).

Appendix B: Generalized Linear Mixed Model Theory

B.1 Introduction 563
B.2 Formulation of the Generalized Linear Model...563
    B.2.1 Essential Background..563
    B.2.2 Required Elements of the Generalized Linear Model 564
    B.2.3 Estimating Equations for the Generalized Linear Model 565
    B.2.4 Quasi-Likelihood 566
B.3 Formulation of the Generalized Linear Mixed Model 566
    B.3.1 Pseudo-Likelihood Estimating Equations...566
    B.3.2 Inference about Fixed and Random Effects 567
B.4 Conditional versus Marginal Models and Inference Space 569
B.5 Integral Approximation..572
    B.5.1 Adaptive Quadrature..573
    B.5.2 Laplace Approximation..573
    B.5.3 Integral Approximation or Pseudo-Likelihood: Pros and Cons...574

B.1 Introduction

Appendix A gave on overview of the linear mixed models; in the SAS system, models for normally distributed data that require a RANDOM statement. This appendix presents the extension of LM and LMM theory and methodology to non-Gaussian data.

The goal of this appendix is to provide you with additional mathematical and statistical background regarding the distribution theory underlying generalized linear models, details of the estimation and inference theory implemented in SAS GLMM software, and important subtleties in GLMM thought processes that can be overlooked with Gaussian linear models, but are crucially important when working with non-Gaussian data. The most important of these is the distinction between inference for conditional GLMMs and inference for marginal GLMMs. With Gaussian data, when your interest is limited to fixed effects, the two are equivalent. This is not the case for mixed models with non-Gaussian data.

B.2 Formulation of the Generalized Linear Model

In this section we present the background, model specification and estimating approach for the generalized linear model. These are essential pre-requisites for formulating and working with the generalized linear mixed model.

B.2.1 Essential Background

The probability distribution form of the LM is $\mathbf{y} \sim \mathrm{N}\left(\mathbf{X}\boldsymbol{\beta}, \sigma^2\mathbf{I}\right)$, or $\mathbf{y} \sim \mathrm{N}\left(\mathbf{X}\boldsymbol{\beta}, \mathbf{R}\right)$ if the model does not call for random effects, but the assumption of independent, identically distributed residuals is inappropriate. The fundamental idea motivating the generalized linear model is to retain the usefulness of the linear predictor, $\mathbf{X}\boldsymbol{\beta}$, but allow the observation vector $\mathbf{y}$ to be modeled by a more realistic distribution. Nelder and Wedderburn (1972) published the first GLM paper. They began with the log likelihood of members of the exponential family. Three common examples are the Gaussian, binomial and Poisson distribution. Their log likelihoods are as follows. In the case of the binomial, it is standard practice to work with the sample proportion, y/N where y denotes the number of successes in N independent Bernoulli trials. Accordingly, the log likelihood is given for $\mathrm{Binomial}\left(y; N, p\right)/N$ rather than just for $\mathrm{Binomial}\left(y; N, p\right)$.

- Gaussian: $\ell\left(\mu, \sigma^2; y\right) = -\left(1/2\right)\log\left(2\pi\sigma^2\right) - \left\{\left(y-\mu\right)^2/2\sigma^2\right\} =$

$$\left(y\mu - \mu^2/2\right)/\sigma^2 - \left(y^2/2\sigma^2\right) - \left(1/2\right)\log\left(2\pi\sigma^2\right)$$

- Binomial/N: $\ell\left(p; N, y\right)/N = \log\binom{N}{Ny} + Ny\log\left(p\right) + \left(N - Ny\right)\log\left(1-p\right) =$

$$\left[y\log\left[p/\left(1-p\right)\right] + \log\left(1-p\right)\right]/\left(1/N\right) + \log\binom{N}{Ny}$$

- Poisson: $\ell\left(\lambda; y\right) = y\log\left(\lambda\right) - \lambda - \log\left(y!\right)$

Each of these log-likelihood functions, suitably arranged, has a common structure: y is multiplied by a function of $\mathrm{E}\left(y\right)$ (μ, p and λ respectively), a function of $\mathrm{E}\left(y\right)$ is subtracted from this product, the difference is divided by a scale parameter, and a function involving y and the scale parameter but not $E(y)$ is subtracted from this ratio. More formally, you can write this as follows:

$$\left[y\theta - b(\theta) \right] / \phi + c(y, \phi)$$

(B.1)

where θ, or more precisely $\theta(\mu)$, is the natural, or canonical parameter, μ generically denotes $E(y)$, $b(\theta)$ is a function of θ, and ϕ is a scale parameter. Table B.1 summarizes these terms for the Gaussian, binomial and Poisson distributions.

Table B.1: Log-likelihood Parameters of Gaussian, Binomial and Poisson

Distribution	$E(y)$	θ	$b(\theta)$	ϕ	$c(y, \phi)$
Gaussian	μ	μ	$\mu^2/2$	σ^2	$-\left(y^2/2\sigma^2\right) - (1/2)\log\left(2\pi\sigma^2\right)$
Binomial	p	$\log\left[p/(1-p) \right]$	$1/\left[1 + \exp(-\theta)\right]$	$1/N$	$\log\binom{N}{Ny}$
Poisson	λ	$\log(\lambda)$	$\exp(\theta)$	1	$\log(y!)$

You can express Equation B.1 in matrix form as follows:

$$\mathbf{y}'\mathbf{A}^{-1}\theta - \mathbf{b}'\mathbf{A}^{-1} + \mathbf{c}$$

(B.2)

where $\mathbf{A}^{-1} = diag\left[1/\phi\right]$, θ is an n vector whose elements are θ_i corresponding to the ith observation, $\mathbf{b}$ denotes a n vector whose elements are the $b(\theta_i)$, and $\mathbf{c}$ is an n vector whose i^{th} element is $c(y_i, \phi)$.

The generalized linear model fits a linear predictor $\mathbf{X}\boldsymbol{\beta}$ to a function of the expected value of y. Nelder and Wedderburn called this function, denoted $\boldsymbol{\eta} = g(\boldsymbol{\mu})$ the link function. Often, the canonical parameter serves as the link function: all Gaussian linear models use the linear predictor to model μ; logistic models are Binomial GLMs using the binomial θ, referred to as the "logit," as the link function; log-linear models are Poisson GLMs using $\log(\lambda)$ as the link function.

The following results are important for model specification and development of the GLM estimating equations.

- $E(y) = \mu = \partial b(\theta)/\partial\theta$.

- $\text{Var}(y) = \phi\left[\partial^2 b(\theta)/\partial\theta^2\right]$.

- The second derivative $\partial^2 b(\theta)/\partial\theta^2$ is called the variance function, and denoted $v(\mu)$. For random variables with non-Gaussian distributions, the variance typically depends of the mean. The function $v(\mu)$ expresses this dependence. In matrix notation, $\mathbf{V}_\mu$ denotes $diag\left[v(\mu_i)\right]$.

B.2.2 Required Elements of the Generalized Linear Model

The following items fully specify a GLM.

- The response variable and its distribution. Generically denote this as $\mathbf{y} \sim \mathcal{D}(\boldsymbol{\mu}, \phi)$.

- The link function: $\boldsymbol{\eta} = g(\boldsymbol{\mu})$.

- The linear predictor: $\boldsymbol{\eta} = \mathbf{X}\boldsymbol{\beta}$.

Notice that the LM is a special case of the GLM:

- Distribution: $\mathbf{y} \sim N\left(\boldsymbol{\mu}, \sigma^2 \mathbf{I}\right)$.

- Link: $\boldsymbol{\eta} = \boldsymbol{\mu}$, called the *identity link.*

- Linear predictor: $\boldsymbol{\eta} = \mathbf{X}\boldsymbol{\beta}\ (=\boldsymbol{\mu})$.

Also notice that with many GLMs, the model equation $\mathbf{Y} = \mathbf{X}\boldsymbol{\beta} + \mathbf{e}$ is nonsense. The LM model equation implies $E(\mathbf{y}) = \mathbf{X}\boldsymbol{\beta}$ and $Var(\mathbf{y}) = \sigma^2 \mathbf{I}$. On the other hand, consider the log-linear model, a Poisson GLM with link function $\log(\lambda)$. The estimate of $E(\mathbf{y}) = \lambda$ is thus $\exp(\mathbf{X}\boldsymbol{\beta})$, as is $Var(\mathbf{y})$. Once you know the mean, you know the variance; no separate estimate of a scale parameter is required. In this type of model, a residual term has no meaning. This is why we state that the model equation form impedes extension of the linear model from Gaussian to non-Gaussian data, whereas the probability distribution form corresponds exactly to the required elements of the GLM given above.

With the model specified, we turn our attention to estimating the parameter vector $\boldsymbol{\beta}$.

B.2.3 Estimating Equations for the Generalized Linear Model

As with the LMM, we estimate the parameter vector in the GLM using maximum likelihood. Specifically, we maximize expression (B.2), $\mathbf{y}'\mathbf{A}^{-1}\boldsymbol{\theta} - \mathbf{b}'\mathbf{A}^{-1} + \mathbf{c}$, the exponential family log likelihood, with respect to $\boldsymbol{\beta}$. Recognize that $\boldsymbol{\theta}$ is a function of $\boldsymbol{\mu}$ which in turn is a function of $\boldsymbol{\eta}$ which is equal to the linear predictor $\mathbf{X}\boldsymbol{\beta}$. Thus, we use the chain rule:
$\partial \ell(\boldsymbol{\theta}; \mathbf{y}, \phi)/\partial \boldsymbol{\beta} = (\partial \ell/\partial \boldsymbol{\theta})(\partial \boldsymbol{\theta}/\partial \boldsymbol{\mu})(\partial \boldsymbol{\mu}/\partial \boldsymbol{\eta})(\partial \boldsymbol{\eta}/\partial \boldsymbol{\beta})$.

Taking each element in turn,

- $\partial \boldsymbol{\eta}/\partial \boldsymbol{\beta} = \partial \mathbf{X}\boldsymbol{\beta}/\partial \boldsymbol{\beta} = \mathbf{X}'$

- $\partial \boldsymbol{\mu}/\partial \boldsymbol{\eta} = (\partial \boldsymbol{\eta}/\partial \boldsymbol{\mu})^{-1} = (\partial g(\boldsymbol{\mu})/\partial \boldsymbol{\mu})^{-1}$

- $\partial \boldsymbol{\theta}/\partial \boldsymbol{\mu} = (\partial \boldsymbol{\mu}/\partial \boldsymbol{\theta})^{-1} = \left[\partial(\partial b(\boldsymbol{\theta})/\partial \boldsymbol{\theta})/\partial \boldsymbol{\theta}\right]^{-1} = \mathbf{V}_{\mu}^{-1}$

- $\partial \ell/\partial \boldsymbol{\theta} = \partial\left(\mathbf{y}'\mathbf{A}^{-1}\boldsymbol{\theta} - \mathbf{b}'\mathbf{A}^{-1}\right)/\partial \boldsymbol{\theta} = \mathbf{A}^{-1}\mathbf{y} - \mathbf{A}^{-1}(\partial \mathbf{b}/\partial \boldsymbol{\theta}) = \mathbf{A}^{-1}(\mathbf{y} - \boldsymbol{\mu})$

Applying the entire chain rule gives the result $\mathbf{X}'\mathbf{D}^{-1}\mathbf{V}_{\mu}^{-1}\mathbf{A}^{-1}(\mathbf{y} - \boldsymbol{\mu})$, where $\mathbf{D}^{-1} = \partial \boldsymbol{\mu}/\partial \boldsymbol{\eta} = (\partial g(\boldsymbol{\mu})/\partial \boldsymbol{\mu})^{-1}$. Note that $\mathbf{V}_{\mu}^{-1}\mathbf{A}^{-1} = \left[Var(\mathbf{y})\right]^{-1}$, which we denote by $\mathbf{V}^{-1}$. Hence, we write the chain rule result as

$$\partial \ell/\partial \boldsymbol{\beta} = \mathbf{X}'\mathbf{D}^{-1}\mathbf{V}^{-1}(\mathbf{y} - \boldsymbol{\mu}) = \mathbf{X}'\mathbf{D}^{-1}\mathbf{V}^{-1}\mathbf{D}^{-1}\mathbf{D}(\mathbf{y} - \boldsymbol{\mu}) = \mathbf{X}'\mathbf{W}\mathbf{D}(\mathbf{y} - \boldsymbol{\mu})$$

where $\mathbf{W} = (\mathbf{D}\mathbf{V}\mathbf{D})^{-1}$.

Now use the Fisher scoring result: $\hat{\boldsymbol{\beta}} = \tilde{\boldsymbol{\beta}} + \left[Var(\partial \ell/\partial \boldsymbol{\beta})\right]^{-1}(\partial \ell/\partial \boldsymbol{\beta})$, noting that

$$Var(\partial \ell/\partial \boldsymbol{\beta}) = Var\left(\mathbf{X}'\mathbf{W}\mathbf{D}(\mathbf{y} - \boldsymbol{\mu})\right) = \mathbf{X}'\mathbf{W}\mathbf{D}\mathbf{V}\mathbf{D}\mathbf{W}\mathbf{X} = \mathbf{X}'\mathbf{W}\mathbf{X}$$

The Fisher scoring ML estimate is

$$\hat{\boldsymbol{\beta}} = \tilde{\boldsymbol{\beta}} + (\mathbf{X}'\mathbf{W}\mathbf{X})^{-1}\mathbf{X}'\mathbf{W}\mathbf{D}(\mathbf{y} - \boldsymbol{\mu})$$

With some algebra, this can be re-expressed as

$$\mathbf{X}'\mathbf{W}\mathbf{X}\boldsymbol{\beta} = \mathbf{X}'\mathbf{W}\mathbf{y}^{*} \tag{B.3}$$

where $\mathbf{y}^* = \mathbf{X}\tilde{\boldsymbol{\beta}} + \mathbf{D}(\mathbf{y} - \boldsymbol{\mu})$. The vector $\mathbf{y}^*$ is called a pseudo-variable. Although the estimating equations in Equation B.3 are derived by maximum likelihood, they can be given a generalized least square interpretation. Specifically,

- $E(\mathbf{y}^*) = \mathbf{X}\boldsymbol{\beta}$

- $\text{Var}(\mathbf{y}^*) = \text{Var}\left[\mathbf{X}\tilde{\boldsymbol{\beta}} + \mathbf{D}(\mathbf{y} - \boldsymbol{\mu})\right] = \mathbf{DVD} = \mathbf{W}^{-1}$

Therefore, a GLS estimator of $\boldsymbol{\beta}$ can be written $\mathbf{X}'\mathbf{W}\mathbf{X}\boldsymbol{\beta} = \mathbf{X}'\mathbf{W}\mathbf{y}^*$. This insight is important as we extend the mixed model equations to the GLMM case.

B.2.4 Quasi-Likelihood

Expression B.2 gives the exponential family log-likelihood, $\mathbf{y}'\mathbf{A}^{-1}\boldsymbol{\theta} - \mathbf{b}'\mathbf{A}^{-1} + \mathbf{c}$. However, the vector $\mathbf{c}$ plays no role in deriving the maximum likelihood estimate of $\boldsymbol{\beta}$. This insight motivated Wedderburn (1974) to develop theory for quasi-likelihood. In scalar terms, quasi-likelihood is defined as $\int^{\mu}(y - t)/\phi v(t)$. In matrix terms, you can think of the quasi-likelihood as $\mathbf{y}'\mathbf{A}^{-1}\boldsymbol{\theta} - \mathbf{b}'\mathbf{A}^{-1}$. The practical importance of quasi-likelihood is that you can define a GLM, estimate it parameter vector, and perform inference, provided you can specify its mean, scale parameter and variance function. All true likelihoods contain a quasi-likelihood component, but you can specify characteristics of a GLM for which a well-defined probability distribution does not exist. Chapters 11, 12 and 13 have quasi-likelihood examples: the marginal GLMMs and so-called "GEE-type" models use working covariance or working correlation matrices to define $\mathbf{A}$. They are well defined GLMs, but instead of specifying a distribution for the observation vector, these models specify a quasi-likelihood. Section B.4 below provides additional discussion of marginal GLMMs defined by quasi-likelihoods.

B.3 Formulation of the Generalized Linear Mixed Model

Building on the required elements of the GLM, the GLMM adds random effects to the linear predictor. The GLMM is thus defined by the following:

- Distribution of the observations: $\mathbf{y} \mid \mathbf{u} \sim \mathscr{D}\left(\boldsymbol{\mu}, \mathbf{V}_{\mu}^{1/2}\mathbf{A}\mathbf{V}_{\mu}^{1/2}\right)$
- Distribution of the random effects: $\mathbf{u} \sim \text{N}(\mathbf{0}, \mathbf{G})$
- Link function: $\boldsymbol{\eta} = g(\boldsymbol{\mu})$
- Linear Predictor: $\boldsymbol{\eta} = \mathbf{X}\boldsymbol{\beta} + \mathbf{Z}\mathbf{u}$

where $\mathscr{D}$ can denote either a probability distribution or a well-defined quasi-likelihood,

$$\mathbf{V}_{\mu}^{1/2} = diag\left[\sqrt{v(\mu_i)}\right]$$

and $\mathbf{A}$ is either the scale matrix from a probability distribution or a working covariance or correlation matrix. In GLMM, we assume that random effects have a Gaussian distribution. In some advanced applications in Volume 2, we relax this assumption. Technically, $E(\mathbf{y} \mid \mathbf{u})$ should be denoted $\boldsymbol{\mu} \mid \mathbf{u}$, but for convenience and because doing so causes no ambiguity, refer to $E(\mathbf{y} \mid \mathbf{u})$ as $\boldsymbol{\mu}$.

As with the LMM, maximum likelihood estimation requires the marginal distribution, whose general form for the GLMM is written

$$\log\left[f(\boldsymbol{\beta}; \mathbf{y})\right] = \log\left\{\int\left[f(\boldsymbol{\beta}; \mathbf{y} \mid \mathbf{u}) \times f(\mathbf{u})\right]d\mathbf{u}\right\}$$

With rare exceptions, for the distributions modeled the GLMM, this integral is intractable. One of three strategies is typically used to circumvent this problem: linearization, integral approximation, or Bayesian methods such as Monte Carlo Markov Chain used in PROC MCMC. PROC GLIMMIX implements linearization by default and has options for integral approximation.

B.3.1 Pseudo-Likelihood Estimating Equations

By default, PROC GLIMMIX computes solutions for the model effects $\boldsymbol{\beta}$ and $\mathbf{u}$ using a pseudo-likelihood algorithm due to Wolfinger and O'Connell (1993). A similar algorithm is presented by Breslow and Clayton (1993). The Breslow-

Clayton algorithm is referred to as "penalized quasi-likelihood." In this section, we present the essential overview of the pseudo-likelihood procedure. You can find additional detail in Wolfinger and O'Connell.

The essence of the pseudo-likelihood procedure begins with the pseudo-variable defined by the GLM estimation equations, $\tilde{\eta} + \mathbf{D}(\mathbf{y} - \boldsymbol{\mu})$. Extending this to the GLMM, $\boldsymbol{\eta}$ is defined by $\mathbf{X}\boldsymbol{\beta} + \mathbf{Z}\mathbf{u}$. Hence, we have the following:

- $E(\mathbf{y}^* \mid \mathbf{u}) = \mathbf{X}\boldsymbol{\beta} + \mathbf{Z}\mathbf{u}$.

- $\mathrm{Var}(\mathbf{y}^* \mid \mathbf{u}) = \mathbf{D}\mathbf{V}_\mu^{1/2}\mathbf{A}\mathbf{V}_\mu^{1/2}\mathbf{D}$, which we can denote as $\mathbf{W}^{-1}$.

Using an argument based on a Laplace approximation, you can show that an approximate maximum likelihood solution can be obtained from the equations

$$\begin{bmatrix} \mathbf{X'WX} & \mathbf{X'WZ} \\ \mathbf{Z'WX} & \mathbf{Z'WZ} + \mathbf{G}^{-1} \end{bmatrix} \begin{bmatrix} \boldsymbol{\beta} \\ \mathbf{u} \end{bmatrix} = \begin{bmatrix} \mathbf{X'Wy}^* \\ \mathbf{Z'Wy}^* \end{bmatrix} \tag{B.4}$$

These are the pseudo-likelihood estimating equations. You can see that they are simply the mixed model equations with $\mathbf{W}$ replacing $\mathbf{R}^{-1}$. You can also see that for Gaussian data, $\mathbf{y}^* = \mathbf{y}$ and $\mathbf{W}^{-1} = \mathbf{A}$, but in the Gaussian case, $\mathbf{A}$ is the covariance matrix $\mathbf{R}$, hence $\mathbf{W}^{-1} = \mathbf{R}$. In the Gaussian case, Equation B.4 shows true maximum likelihood estimating equations. In fact, the estimating equations for the LM, GLM and LMM are all special cases of Equation B.4, which explains why you can use PROC GLIMMIX for any linear model.

The only potentially unknown parameters in the $\mathbf{W}$ matrix are scale or covariance parameters contained in the $\mathbf{G}$ and $\mathbf{A}$ matrices. These are estimated using pseudo-likelihood functions, written as follows:

- log pseudo-likelihood: $l(\boldsymbol{\sigma}; \mathbf{y}) = -(1/2)\left\{ \log |\mathbf{V}^*(\boldsymbol{\sigma})| + (\mathbf{y} - \mathbf{X}\tilde{\boldsymbol{\beta}})' \mathbf{V}^*(\boldsymbol{\sigma})^{-1}(\mathbf{y} - \mathbf{X}\tilde{\boldsymbol{\beta}}) + c \right\}$

- log restricted pseudo-likelihood:

$$l_R(\boldsymbol{\sigma}; \mathbf{y}) = -(1/2)\left\{ \log |\mathbf{V}^*(\boldsymbol{\sigma})| + \log |\mathbf{X}'\mathbf{V}^*(\boldsymbol{\sigma})^{-1}\mathbf{X}| + (\mathbf{y} - \mathbf{X}\tilde{\boldsymbol{\beta}})' \mathbf{V}^*(\boldsymbol{\sigma})^{-1}(\mathbf{y} - \mathbf{X}\tilde{\boldsymbol{\beta}}) + c_R \right\}$$

where $\boldsymbol{\sigma}$ denotes the vector of covariance or scale parameters contained in $\mathbf{G}$ and $\mathbf{A}$, and $\mathbf{V}^*(\boldsymbol{\sigma}) = \mathbf{Z}\mathbf{G}\mathbf{Z}' + \mathbf{D}\mathbf{V}_\mu^{1/2}\mathbf{A}\mathbf{V}_\mu^{1/2}\mathbf{D}$. Note that these are the likelihood equations used for ML and REML covariance component estimation, with $\mathbf{V}^*$ replacing $\mathbf{V} = \mathbf{Z}\mathbf{G}\mathbf{Z}' + \mathbf{R}$.

By default, PROC GLIMMIX maximizes the log restricted pseudo-likelihood to obtain a solution vector $\hat{\boldsymbol{\sigma}}$. For Gaussian models, these are REML estimates; for non-Gaussian GLMMs, these are REML-like estimates. You can obtain ML or ML-like estimates, depending on whether your data are Gaussian or not, using the option METHOD=MSPL in the PROC GLIMMIX statement.

The pseudo-likelihood algorithm is sometimes incorrectly referred to as a penalized quasi-likelihood algorithm. This is misleading and wrong for a couple of reasons. First, GLMMs such as the logit-normal model for the multi-clinic example in Chapter 11 or the split-plot with negative binomial data in Chapter 13 are defined by true probability distributions, not quasi-likelihoods. Second, there is no quasi-likelihood involved at any point in the estimation process—only estimating equations and pseudo-likelihoods that are consequences of a pseudo-variable.

B.3.2 Inference about Fixed and Random Effects

As with Gaussian mixed models, estimable and predictable functions are the fundamental building blocks of inference with the GLMM. Following the notation from Appendix A, these functions can generically be written as follows:

$$\omega = \begin{bmatrix} \mathbf{K} & \mathbf{M} \end{bmatrix} \begin{bmatrix} \boldsymbol{\beta} \\ \mathbf{u} \end{bmatrix} = \mathbf{L} \begin{bmatrix} \boldsymbol{\beta} \\ \mathbf{u} \end{bmatrix}$$

Similar results hold relevant to inference on ω. When $\mathbf{L}$ is a vector, you can test

$$H : \mathbf{L}\begin{bmatrix} \boldsymbol{\beta} \\ \mathbf{u} \end{bmatrix} = \mathbf{0}$$

using an approximate t-statistic,

$$t = \frac{\mathbf{L}\begin{bmatrix} \hat{\boldsymbol{\beta}} \\ \hat{\mathbf{u}} \end{bmatrix}}{\sqrt{\mathbf{L}\hat{\mathbf{C}}\mathbf{L}'}}$$

and construct a confidence interval as

$$\mathbf{L}\begin{bmatrix} \hat{\boldsymbol{\beta}} \\ \hat{\mathbf{u}} \end{bmatrix} \pm t_{v,\alpha/2}\sqrt{\mathbf{L}\hat{\mathbf{C}}\mathbf{L}'}$$

where $t_{v,\alpha/2}$ is the $(1 - \alpha/2)100^{\text{th}}$ percentile of the t_v-distribution. With the GLMM, $\mathbf{C}$ is defined in terms of the pseudo-likelihood equations—that is,

$$\mathbf{C} = \begin{bmatrix} \mathbf{X}'\mathbf{W}\mathbf{X} & \mathbf{X}'\mathbf{W}\mathbf{Z} \\ \mathbf{Z}'\mathbf{W}\mathbf{X} & \mathbf{Z}'\mathbf{W}\mathbf{Z} + \mathbf{G}^{-1} \end{bmatrix}^{-}$$

the generalized inverse of the left-hand side of the pseudo-likelihood estimating Equation B.4. Substituting estimated covariance and scale parameters where needed in $\mathbf{W}$ and $\mathbf{G}$ gives you $\hat{\mathbf{C}}$.

If $\mathbf{L}$ is a matrix, the approximate F-statistic, then

$$F = \frac{\begin{bmatrix} \hat{\boldsymbol{\beta}} \\ \hat{\mathbf{u}} \end{bmatrix}\mathbf{L}'\left(\mathbf{L}\hat{\mathbf{C}}\mathbf{L}'\right)^{-1}\mathbf{L}\begin{bmatrix} \hat{\boldsymbol{\beta}} \\ \hat{\mathbf{u}} \end{bmatrix}}{\text{rank}(\mathbf{L})} \tag{B.5}$$

has the same form as the approximate F for Gaussian linear models, the only difference being that $\hat{\mathbf{C}}$ comes from the left-hand side of the pseudo-likelihood equations, not the mixed model equations. For generalized linear models with no random effects and no covariance or scale parameter to be estimated, Equation B.5 reduces to the Wald Statistic $\chi^2_{rank(L)} = \boldsymbol{\beta}'\mathbf{L}'\left(\mathbf{L}'\mathbf{C}\mathbf{L}\right)^{-}\mathbf{L}\boldsymbol{\beta}$, where $\mathbf{C}$ has the reduced form $\left(\mathbf{X}'\mathbf{W}\mathbf{X}\right)^{-}$. In this case, you should evaluate the test statistic using the χ^2 and not the F distribution. Because PROC GLIMMIX evaluates all tests statistics of the form Equation B.5 as F values, if you are testing a hypothesis from a GLM for which no scale parameter estimation occurs, you need to override the default using the DDFM=NONE option in the model statement.

As is the case for standard errors and test statistics with the LMM,

$$E\left[\left(\mathbf{L}'\hat{\mathbf{C}}\mathbf{L}\right)^{-}\right] \le \left(\mathbf{L}'\mathbf{C}\mathbf{L}\right)^{-}$$

with strict inequality for unbalanced designs and models with non-trivial covariance structure such as those for repeated measures. PROC GLIMMIX computes the Kenward-Roger correction using the DDFM=KR2 option for GLMMs provided you use the pseudo-likelihood algorithm. For GLMMs, GLIMMIX computes the standard error correction from the log-pseudo-likelihood functions shown in the previous section. Although there is no formal theory justifying the Kenward-Roger correction in conjunction with pseudo-likelihood and the GLMM, the correction is both needed and accurate, in the authors' experience, for the examples presented in Chapters 11, 12 and 13. For novel applications, you should use simulation to decide if the correction is appropriate before proceeding.

The estimates

$$\mathbf{L}\begin{bmatrix} \hat{\boldsymbol{\beta}} \\ \hat{\mathbf{u}} \end{bmatrix}$$

are said to be on the "model scale," also called the "link scale." That is, for logistic model, estimates are on the logit scale, for models that use the log link estimates are on the log scale, and so forth. Usually, these estimates need to be converted to the "data scale" to make them understandable. For example, if you have binomial data, the ESTIMATE produced by the LSMEAN statement is the logit of the probability. You use the ILINK option to obtain the MEAN, that is, an estimate of the probability for each treatment level. Formally, the LSMEAN is computed as $\mathbf{K}\hat{\boldsymbol{\beta}}$ and ILINK causes GLIMMIX to compute $g^{-1}(\mathbf{K}\hat{\boldsymbol{\beta}})$, where $g^{-1}(\bullet)$ denotes the inverse link function.

When you ask for a "data scale" estimate, the ILINK option also causes GLIMMIX to compute a standard error. The standard error is computed using the Delta Rule, specifically,

$$s.e.\left[g^{-1}(\mathbf{K}\boldsymbol{\beta})\right] = \left[\partial g^{-1}(\eta)/\partial \eta\right]\Big|_{\eta = \mathbf{K}\boldsymbol{\beta}} \times s.e.\left(\mathbf{K}\hat{\boldsymbol{\beta}}\right) \tag{B.6}$$

Often, GLMs and GLMMs use the canonical link, that is, the natural parameter of the distribution of $\mathbf{y} \mid \mathbf{u}$ is used as the link function. Examples include the logit for binomial data and the log for Poisson data. For models using the canonical link, the inverse link is $b(\boldsymbol{\theta})$ from Equation B.1. In such cases, the derivative term on the right-hand side of Equation B.6 is simply the inverse-linked, data scale LSMEAN.

The standard error obtained from the Delta Rule should *not* be used to construct confidence intervals. That is,

$$g^{-1}(\mathbf{K}\hat{\boldsymbol{\beta}}) \pm t \times s.e.(\mathbf{K}\hat{\boldsymbol{\beta}})$$

does not give you appropriate confidence intervals. You can easily verify this using examples from binomial and Poisson data, for which the confidence bounds can often be outside the parameter space (try explaining to a client what a confidence interval of (-0.2, 0.3) for a binomial probability means). The appropriate way to obtain confidence intervals for GLMs and GLMMs is the apply the inverse link to the lower and upper model-scale confidence bounds, i.e.

- Lower bound: $\mathbf{g}^{-1}\left\{ \mathbf{L}\begin{bmatrix} \hat{\boldsymbol{\beta}} \\ \hat{\mathbf{u}} \end{bmatrix} - t_{v,\alpha/2} \sqrt{\mathbf{L}\hat{\mathbf{C}}\mathbf{L}'} \right\}$

- Upper bound: $\mathbf{g}^{-1}\left\{ \mathbf{L}\begin{bmatrix} \hat{\boldsymbol{\beta}} \\ \hat{\mathbf{u}} \end{bmatrix} + t_{v,\alpha/2} \sqrt{\mathbf{L}\hat{\mathbf{C}}\mathbf{L}'} \right\}$

B.4 Conditional versus Marginal Models and Inference Space

Recall from the examples in Chapters 11, 12 and 13, if you assume normality and use a traditional linear model (LM) as defined by Equation A.1 in Appendix A, you get estimates that differ from the estimates produced by GLMMs. Yet ordinary least squares (OLS) estimators associated with the LM are known to be best linear unbiased estimators (BLUE). Also, when $\mathrm{Var}(\mathbf{y}) = \sigma^2\boldsymbol{\Sigma}$ and $\boldsymbol{\Sigma}$ is known but not equal to $\mathbf{I}$, generalized least squares (GLS) estimators are BLUE as well. If these estimators are BLUE, does this mean that the estimates produced by GLMMs are biased and hence less desirable? The answers lies in the fact that, yes, OLS and GLS estimators are unbiased—but unbiased estimators of what? The key to addressing this question is to understand the probability distributions that give rise to non-Gaussian data. This is the conditional versus marginal issue, and its G-side versus R-side modeling analog.

Under normality, the mixed model is defined by two distributions, $\mathbf{y} \mid \mathbf{u} \sim \mathrm{N}(\mathbf{X}\boldsymbol{\beta} + \mathbf{Z}\mathbf{u}, \mathbf{R})$ and $\mathbf{u} \sim \mathrm{N}(\mathbf{0}, \mathbf{G})$. The marginal distribution of $\mathbf{y}$ is thus $\mathbf{y} \sim \mathrm{N}(\mathbf{X}\boldsymbol{\beta}, \mathbf{V})$ where $\mathbf{V} = \mathbf{Z}\mathbf{G}\mathbf{Z}' + \mathbf{R}$. If your objectives call for inference exclusively using estimable functions, $\mathbf{K}'\boldsymbol{\beta}$, you can use either a conditional model with linear predictor $\mathbf{X}\boldsymbol{\beta} + \mathbf{Z}\mathbf{u}$ and define both the $\mathbf{G}$ and $\mathbf{R}$ matrices, or use the marginal model with linear predictor $\mathbf{X}\boldsymbol{\beta}$ and define $\mathbf{V}$ using the RANDOM statement with the RESIDUAL option in PROC GLMMIX or the REPEATED statement in PROC MIXED.

With non-normal data,

$$\mathbf{y} \mid \mathbf{u} \sim \mathcal{D}\left(g^{-1}\left(\mathbf{X}\boldsymbol{\beta} + \mathbf{Zu}\right), \mathbf{V}_{\mu}^{\frac{1}{2}} \mathbf{A} \mathbf{V}_{\mu}^{\frac{1}{2}} \right)$$

replaces $\mathbf{y} \mid \mathbf{u} \sim N\left(\mathbf{X}\boldsymbol{\beta} + \mathbf{Zu}, \mathbf{R}\right)$. The p.d.f. of the marginal distribution is now

$$f(\mathbf{y}) = \int_{\mathbf{u}} f(\mathbf{y} \mid \mathbf{u}) f(\mathbf{u}) d\mathbf{u} \tag{B.7}$$

where $f(\mathbf{y} \mid \mathbf{u})$ and $f(\mathbf{u})$ denote the p.d.f. of the observations given the random model effects and the p.d.f. of the random model effects respectively. For most GLMMs, the distributions involved preclude writing $f(\mathbf{y})$ is closed form. The best way to visualize $f(\mathbf{y})$ is to simulate it. As an example, consider a GLMM for a blocked design and count data. The possible model would be the Poisson-normal with linear predictor $\eta_{ij} = \eta + \tau_i + u_j$ where τ denotes treatment effects and u denotes block effects, assumed $u_j \sim \text{NI}\left(0, \sigma_u^2\right)$; $y_{ij} \mid u_j \sim \text{Poisson}\left(\lambda_{ij}\right)$ and link function $\eta_{ij} = \log\left(\lambda_{ij}\right)$. Suppose the true mean for treatment 1 is $\lambda_1 = 10$. Figures B.1, B.2 and B.3 depict the p.d.f. of u_j, $y_{1j} \mid u_j$ and y_{1j} respectively, assuming that $\sigma_u = 0.8$ or $\sigma_u^2 = 0.64$.

Figure B.1: Plot of Block Effect Density Function

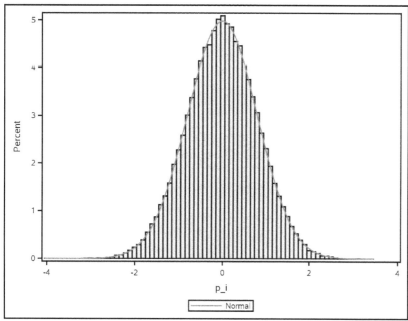

Figure B.2: Conditional Density Function of Observations, Given Block Effect

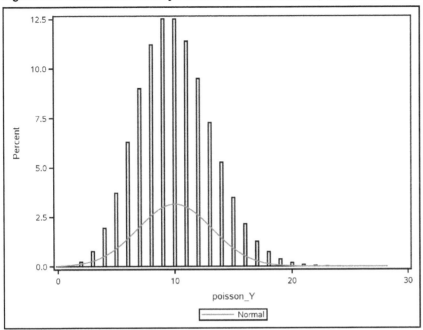

Figure B.3: Marginal Density Function of Observations

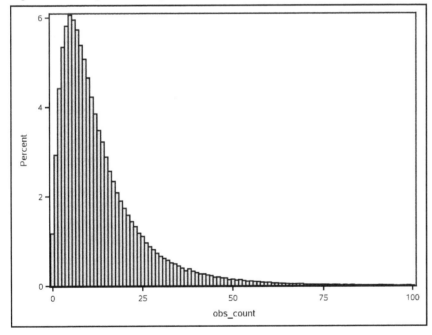

Interpretation

You can see that at $\lambda = 10$ the Poisson distribution, the distribution of $y_{ij} \mid u_j$, is symmetric and closely approximates a Gaussian distribution. The block effect distribution is Gaussian by assumption. These distributions describe the two processes that give rise to the data. Neither can be observed directly. You can only see the observations and their associated density. Yet despite the symmetry of the two distributions that give rise to the data, the marginal distribution—the one we can actually observe—is strongly right skewed. You can approximate the mean of the marginal distribution by Gauss-Hermite quadrature. With 9 quadrature points $E\left(y_{1j}\right) \cong 13.77$. The median of the marginal distribution is 10, equal to the Poisson $E\left(y_{1j} \mid u_j\right) = \lambda = 10$.

While this example uses the Poisson, the discrepancy between the marginal mean and the expected value of $y_{ij} \mid u_j$, the conditional mean, is a feature common to all mixed models with non-Gaussian data. Unlike models with Gaussian data, when you work with GLMMs, you need to decide whether your objectives are best addressed by the conditional mean—in this case the Poisson λ—or the marginal mean. They are not the same.

Returning to the question, "What the OLS estimate a best linear unbiased estimator of?" the answer is that when you fit the model $y_{ij} = \mu + \tau_i + u_j + e_{ij}$ assuming the distribution of the counts approximates a normal approximation, you obtain a BLUE of the marginal mean—in this case 13.77.

This raises the real question: which measure of central tendency is the appropriate target of inference when modeling non-Gaussian data? One way to think about this is the way students are taught to think about central tendency in introductory statistics classes. When a distribution is strongly skewed, the median is the measure of choice. Another way to think about this dilemma is the way economists report income. If they want to characterize income (notoriously right skewed) for a typical household, they report median income. On the other hand, if they want to know how much money is in the economy, they use the marginal mean multiplied by the population size. Finally, if we want to know something about the number of cases of flu to expect, we would focus on λ, the conditional mean, if we wanted to know how many cases to expect in a typical community (if community is our blocking factor) but we would want to use the marginal mean if we wanted to know how many cases nationwide we should be prepared to treat. You can see that there is no single "correct" inference target for GLMMs. You need to select the target most appropriate for your objective. Again, this is an aspect of inference with GLMMs that does not arise with Gaussian data.

As we see in Chapters 11, 12, and 13, conditional GLMMs, those that are defined by a true likelihood and typically include random effects in the linear predictor, target the conditional mean—in this example, λ. Marginal GLMMs are defined by quasi-likelihoods and working correlation structures. In GLIMMIX, you target the marginal mean by including a RANDOM ... RESIDUAL statement. The GEE-type models of Liang and Zeger (1986) are perhaps the most familiar and widely used marginal models.

A Final Word about a Pervasive Misconception

The words *conditional* and *marginal* are frequently misconstrued. This is exacerbated by the fact that Liang and Zeger appropriated the term "population-averaged" to characterize the inference target of GEE-type models. Out of this terminology arose the myth that the inference space is somehow narrower for conditional models. *This is, in no uncertain terms, not true.*

Conditional inference implicitly targets $E(\mathbf{y} \mid \mathbf{u} = \mathbf{0})$; $\mathbf{u} = \mathbf{0}$ is what defines a "typical member of the population." The fact of implicit conditioning on $\mathbf{u} = \mathbf{0}$, however, does not translate to narrow inference. You estimate $E(\mathbf{y} \mid \mathbf{u} = \mathbf{0})$, or linear combinations of $E(\mathbf{y} \mid \mathbf{u} = \mathbf{0})$, using estimable functions $\mathbf{K'\beta}$. These are, by definition, *broad* inference space estimators. They differ from marginal means not because their inference space differs but because assumptions about their variance structure differ: marginal means are estimated using working covariance structures and hence quasi-likelihoods; conditional means require models with well-defined true likelihoods. Denote $\hat{\boldsymbol{\beta}}_C$ as the estimate of the fixed effects from the conditional model and $\hat{\boldsymbol{\beta}}_M$ as the estimate from the marginal model. $\mathbf{K'}\hat{\boldsymbol{\beta}}_C$ and $\mathbf{K'}\hat{\boldsymbol{\beta}}_M$ are both well-defined broad inference space estimators. They simply use parameter vector estimates obtained with different central tendency targets in mind.

B.5 Integral Approximation

GLMM estimation requires maximizing the marginal log-likelihood, denoted here as $\ell(\boldsymbol{\beta}; \mathbf{y}, \boldsymbol{\sigma}) = \log(f(\boldsymbol{\beta}; \mathbf{y}, \boldsymbol{\sigma}))$, where $\boldsymbol{\sigma}$ denotes the vector of covariance parameters and $f(\boldsymbol{\beta}; \mathbf{y}, \boldsymbol{\sigma})$ had the same functional form as Equation B.7.

Section B.3 shows one approach to maximizing $\ell(\boldsymbol{\beta}; \mathbf{y}, \boldsymbol{\sigma})$: a linearization that results in a pseudo-variate and estimating equations that are generalizations of the mixed model equations.

An alternative approach uses numerical approximations of the integral

$$\int_{\mathbf{u}} f(\mathbf{y} \mid \mathbf{u}, \boldsymbol{\beta}, \boldsymbol{\sigma}) f(\mathbf{u}; \boldsymbol{\sigma}) d\mathbf{u} \tag{B.8}$$

To see how this works, begin with this integral is scalar form. From equation B.1, we know that $f(y \mid u, \beta, \sigma)$ has the form

$$\exp\left\{\left[y\theta - b(\theta)\right]/\phi + c(y, \phi)\right\}$$

Noting that θ is a function of μ, rewrite the natural parameter as the function $\theta(\mu)$. Also, μ is modeled by the inverse link of $X\beta + Zu$, i.e. $\mu = h(\eta) = h(X\beta + Zu)$. We can write the natural parameter as $\theta\big[h(X\beta + Zu)\big]$. For convenience, refer to $\theta\big[h(X\beta + Zu)\big]$ by the shorthand $\theta(\beta, u, \sigma)$. We can rewrite Equation B.8 as

$$\int_u \exp\Big[\big\{y\theta(\beta, u, \sigma) - b\big[\theta(\beta, u, \sigma)\big]\big\}\Big/\phi\Big] \times \Big(1\big/\sqrt{2\pi\sigma^2}\Big)\exp\big(-u^2\big/2\sigma^2\big)\,du \qquad (B.9)$$

Note that as a consequence of the model assumptions, the link function $\eta \sim N\big(X\beta, \sigma^2\big)$. Let $z = (\eta - X\beta)\big/\sigma$ and hence $\eta = z\sigma + X\beta$. Now let $x^2 = z^2\big/2$ and hence

$$z = \sqrt{2}x$$

Substituting into (.7), we have

$$\int_u \exp\Big[\big\{y\theta\big[h\big(\sigma x\sqrt{2} + X\beta\big)\big] - b\big[\theta\big[h\big(\sigma x\sqrt{2} + X\beta\big)\big]\big]\big\}\Big/\phi\Big] \times \big(1\big/\sqrt{\pi}\big)\exp\big(-x^2\big)\,dx$$

B.5.1 Adaptive Quadrature

Gauss-Hermite quadrature allows us to approximate an integral whose form is

$$\int f(x) \times \exp\big(-x^2\big)$$

by

$$\sum_i w_i f(x_i)$$

where w_i are quadrature weights and x_i quadrature abscissas. In this case the function $f(x)$ is as follows:

$$f(x_i) = \exp\Big[\big\{y\theta\big[h\big(\sigma x_i \sqrt{2} + X\beta\big)\big] - b\big[\theta\big[\sigma x_i \sqrt{2} + X\beta\big]\big]\big\}\Big/\phi\Big] \times \big(1\big/\sqrt{\pi}\big)$$

PROC GLIMMIX uses an adaptive quadrature procedure (Pinhiero and Bates, 2006) in which the abscissas are scaled as $a_i = \hat{u} + \sqrt{2} \times f''\big(y, \beta, \hat{u}, \sigma\big)x_i$ once the random effect solution $\hat{u}$ is computed. See SAS/STAT documentation for PROC GLIMMIX for further details.

If you do not specify the number of quadrature points (abscissas) using the QPOINTS= option, PROC GLIMMIX does an initial step to determine the optimal number of points given the data. The log-likelihood is evaluated at the starting values for increasing numbers of points until a tolerance is met. The greater the number of abscissas, the closer the approximation is to the true integral. However, there is a point of diminishing returns where the increase of the number of points does not change the evaluation sufficiently to merit the complexity and increased computation required.

B.5.2 Laplace Approximation

A simpler form of integral approximation is the Laplace approximation. Write Equation B.8 as follows:

$$\int_u f(\mathbf{y} \mid \boldsymbol{\beta}, \mathbf{u}, \boldsymbol{\sigma}) f(\mathbf{u}; \boldsymbol{\sigma})\,d\mathbf{u} = \int_u \exp\big[c_i \ell(\mathbf{y}, \boldsymbol{\beta}, \mathbf{u}, \boldsymbol{\sigma})\big]\,d\mathbf{u}$$

The Laplace approximation is

$$\big(2\pi\big/c_i\big)^{n_i/2}\big|\ell''(\mathbf{y}, \boldsymbol{\beta}, \mathbf{u}, \boldsymbol{\sigma})\big|^{-1/2}\exp\big[c_i \ell(\mathbf{y}, \boldsymbol{\beta}, \mathbf{u}, \boldsymbol{\sigma})\big]$$

You can write $c_i \ell(\mathbf{y}, \boldsymbol{\beta}, \mathbf{u}, \boldsymbol{\sigma})$ in scalar form as Equation B.1 or in matrix form as B.2. The Laplace approximation is equivalent to quadrature with a single quadrature point, but implementation in PROC GLIMMIX is more versatile than one-point quadrature. Among other things, this allows Laplace to be used with complex covariance structures in the **G** matrix, including AR(1) and ANTE(1). You can see the advantage in doing so in the repeated measures examples in Chapter 13.

B.5.3 Integral Approximation or Pseudo-Likelihood: Pros and Cons

How do the integral approximation procedures compare to the pseudo-likelihood default? Each approach has its advantages and disadvantages.

Integral Approximation

The *advantages* of integral approximation are as follows:

- You evaluate a true likelihood.
- You can compute well-defined likelihood ratio statistics (for example, to test covariance parameters).
- You can compute well defined information criteria (for example, to select covariance structure for repeated measures).
- You obtain more accurate estimates for certain GLMMs (for example, binomial data with many subjects but few observations per subject; two-parameter non-Gaussian distributions such as the negative binomial).
- You can compute well-defined likelihood ratio statistics (for example, to test covariance parameters).
- You can compute well defined information criteria (for example, to select covariance structure for repeated measures).

By contrast, the *disadvantages* are as follows:

- Covariance parameter estimates are strictly ML estimators.
- ML variance estimators are downward biased, just as they are for the LMM.
- Standard errors are downward biased; test statistics are biased upward.
- The KR biased adjustment is undefined and therefore unavailable.
- ML covariance bias and lack of KR combine to adversely affect confidence interval coverage and type I error control.
- Quadrature and Laplace require that the specified distribution and the data be compatible. Neither method is robust to misspecified distribution.

Pseudo-Likelihood

For pseudo-likelihood, the *advantages* are as follows:

- Covariance parameters use a REML-like algorithm, alleviating the bias issue.
- You can use KR bias correction with pseudo-likelihood.
- Confidence interval coverage and type I error control tend to be better than integral approximation for most commonly used GLMMs.
- PL is more robust to misspecified models and misspecified distributions.
- PL can be used with a much wider variety of models.

By contrast, the disadvantages are as follows:

- Pseudo-likelihood is not true likelihood, meaning you cannot compute legitimate likelihood ratio statistics or information criteria
- This limits your ability to do model-checking, e.g. with repeated measures
- Parameter and covariance estimates can be very inaccurate for certain GLMMs, e.g. underpowered study designs, large number of subjects but few observations per subject with binomial
- Convergence failure is more likely than with integral approximation

Despite considerable mythology, there are no one-size-fits-all rules for using pseudo-likelihood or quadrature. Chapters 11, 12 and 13 give guidelines applicable to the examples presented in those chapters. You can see that in some cases, pseudo-likelihood is clearly the method of choice; in others, quadrature is better; in still others, Laplace is the only viable alternative.

If you are working with marginal GLMMs including GEE-type models, you cannot use integral approximation. Marginal GLMMs by definition use quasi-likelihood in place of the log p.d.f. of a well-defined probability distribution. With PROC GLIMMIX, you must use pseudo-likelihood anytime you work with a marginal GLMM. Put another way, anytime you have a RANDOM statement with the RESIDUAL option, you cannot use quadrature or Laplace.

Finally, because accessible GLMM software is relatively new—PROC GLIMMIX with all the options discussed in this book was released in 2008—we are still in a learning period with regard to the small sample behavior of the various methods for GLMM estimation and inference. The best advice the authors can give at this point is that if you are working with a model that differs from the examples given in Chapters 11, 12 and 13, do a simulation study to see how PL, quadrature and Laplace methods compare before you commit to a particular method.

References

Abrams, D. I., A. I. Goldman, C. Launer, J. A. Korvick, J. D. Neaton, L. R. Crane, M. Grodesky, S. Wakefield, K. Muth, S. Kornegay, D. L. Cohn, A. Harris, R. Luskin-Hawk, N. Markowitz, J. H. Sampson, M. Thompson, L. Deyton, and the Terry Beirn Community Programs for Clinical Research on AIDS. 1994. "Comparative Trial of Didanosine and Zalcitabine in Patients with Human Immunodeficiency Virus Infection Who Are Intolerant of or Have Failed Zidovudine Therapy." *New England Journal of Medicine* 330:657–662.

Aitkin, M. 1987. "Modeling Variance Heterogeneity in Normal Regressing Using GLIM." *Applied Statistics* 36:332–339.

Akaike, H. 1974. "A New Look at the Statistical Model Identification." *IEEE Transactions on Automatic Control* AIC-19:716–723.

Allard, R. W. 1966. *Principles of Plant Breeding.* New York: Wiley.

Allison, D. B., G. P. Page, T. M. Beasley, and J. W. Edwards. 2006. *DNA Microarrays and Related Genomics Techniques: Design, Analysis, and Interpretation of Experiments.* New York: Chapman and Hall.

Azevedo, C. F., M. D. Vilela de Resende, F. Fonseca e Silva, J. M. S. Viana, M. S. F. Valente, M. F. R. Resende Jr., and P. Muñoz. 2015. "Ridge, Lasso and Bayesian additive-dominance genomic models. *BMC* Genetics 16:105.

Bates, D., and D. Watts. 1988. *Nonlinear Regression Analysis and Its Applications.* New York: Wiley.

Bayarri, M. J., and J. O. Berger. 2000. "*P* Values for Composite Null Models." *Journal of the American Statistical Association* 95:1127–1142.

Beal, S. L., and L. B. Sheiner, eds. 1992. *NONMEM User's Guide.* San Francisco: University of California–San Francisco, NONMEM Project Group.

Beal, S. L., and L. B. Sheiner. 1982. "Estimating Population Kinetics." *CRC Crit. Rev. Biomed. Eng.* 8:195–222.

Beal, S. L., and L. B. Sheiner. 1988. "Heteroskedastic Nonlinear Regression." *Technometrics* 30:327–338.

Beckman, R. J., C. J. Nachtsheim, and D. R. Cook. 1987. "Diagnostics for Mixed-Model Analysis of Variance." *Technometrics* 29:413–426.

Beitler, P. J., and J. R. Landis. 1985. "A Mixed-Effects Model for Categorical Data." *Biometrics* 41:991–1000.

Bello, N. M., J. P. Steibel, and J. R. Pursley. 2006. "Optimizing Ovulation to First GnRH Improved Outcomes to each Hormonal Injection of Ovsynch in Lactating Dairy Cows. *Journal of Dairy Science* 89(9):3413–3424.

Belsley, D. A., E. Kuh, and R. E. Welsch. 1980. *Regression Diagnostics: Identifying Influential Data and Sources of Collinearity.* New York: Wiley.

Berger, J. O. 2003. "Could Fisher, Jeffreys, and Neyman Have Agreed on Testing?" (with comments). *Statistical Science* 18:1–32.

Berger, J. O., and M. Delampady. 1987. "Testing Precise Hypotheses" (with comments). *Statistical Science* 2:317–352.

Berger, J. O., and T. Sellke. 1987. "Testing a Point Null Hypothesis: The Irreconcilability of P Values and Evidence (with comments)." *Journal of the American Statistical Association* 82:112–139.

Bishop, Y. M. M., S. E. Fienberg, and P. W. Holland. 1975. *Discrete Multivariate Analysis.* Cambridge, MA: MIT Press.

Bjerke, F., A. H. Aastviet, W. W. Stroup, B. Kirkhus, and T. Næs. 2004. "Design and Analysis of Storing Experiments: A Case Study." *Journal of Quality Engineering* 16(4):591–611.

Bohning, D., E. Dietz, P. Schlattman, L. Mendonca, and U. Kirchner. 1999. "The Zero-Inflated Poisson Model and the Decayed, Missing and Filled Teeth Index in Dental Epidemiology." *Journal of the Royal Statistical Society, Series A,* 162:195–209.

Box, G. E. P. 1950. "Problems in the Analysis of Growth and Wear Curves." *Biometrics* 6:362–389.

Box, G. E. P., and D. R. Cox. 1964. "An Analysis of Transformations." *Journal of the Royal Statistical Society, Series B,* 26:211–252.

Box, G. E. P., and G. C. Tiao. 1973. *Bayesian Inference in Statistical Analysis.* Wiley Classics Library Edition, published 1992. New York: Wiley.

Box, G. E. P., W. G. Hunter, and J. S. Hunter. 1978. *Statistics for Experimenters.* New York: Wiley.

Bozdogan, H. 1987. "Model Selection and Akaike's Information Criterion (AIC): The General Theory and Its Analytical Extensions." *Psychometrika* 52:345–370.

Breslow, N. R., and D. G. Clayton. 1993. "Approximate Inference in Generalized Linear Mixed Models." *Journal of the American Statistical Association* 88:9–25.

Brown, H., and R. Prescott. 1999. *Applied Mixed Models in Medicine.* New York: Wiley.

Brown, R. L., J. Durbin, and J. M. Evans. 1975. "Techniques for Testing the Constancy of Regression Relationships over Time." *Journal of the Royal Statistical Society, Series B,* 37:149–192.

Brownie, C., and M. L. Gumpertz. 1997. "Validity of Spatial Analyses of Large Field Trials." *Journal of Agricultural, Biological, and Environmental Statistics* 2(1):1–23.

Brownie, C., D. T. Bowman, and J. W. Burton. 1993. "Estimating Spatial Variation in Analysis of Data from Yield Trials: A Comparison of Methods." *Agronomy Journal* 85:1244–1253.

Bryk, A. S., and S. W. Raudenbush. 1992. *Hierarchical Linear Models: Applications and Data Analysis Methods.* Newbury Park, CA: Sage Publications.

Burdick, R. K., and F. A. Graybill. 1992. *Confidence Intervals on Variance Components.* New York: Marcel Dekker.

Burdick, R. K., and F. A. Graybill. 1992. *Confidence Intervals on Variance Components.* New York: Marcel Dekker.

Burdick, R. K., C. M. Borror, and D. C. Montgomery. 2005. *Design and Analysis of Gauge R & R Studies: Making Decisions with Confidence Intervals in Random and Mixed ANOVA Models.* ASA-SIAM Series on Statistics and Applied Probability. Philadelphia: SIAM; Alexandria, VA: ASA.

Burnham, K. P., and D. R. Anderson. 1998. *Model Selection and Inference: A Practical Information-Theoretic Approach.* New York: Springer-Verlag.

Burnham, K. P., and D. R. Anderson. 2002. *Model Selection and Multimodel Inference: A Practical Information-Theoretic Approach.* New York: Springer-Verlag.

Cameron, A. C., and P. K. Trivedi. 1998. *Regression Analysis for Count Data.* Cambridge, UK: Cambridge University Press.

Carlin, B. P., and T. A. Louis. 1996. *Bayes and Empirical Bayes Methods for Data Analysis.* Boca Raton, FL: Chapman & Hall/CRC Press.

Carroll, R. J., and D. Ruppert. 1988. *Transformation and Weighting in Regression.* London: Chapman & Hall.

Casella, G., and R. L. Berger. 1987. "Reconciling Bayesian and Frequentist Evidence in the One-Sided Testing Problem." *Journal of the American Statistical Association* 82:106–111.

Castelloe, J. M., and R. G. O'Brien. 2000. "Power and Sample Size Determination for Linear Models." *Proceedings of the Twenty-Sixth Annual SAS Users Group International Conference.* Cary, NC: SAS Institute.

Chilès, J.-P., and P. Delfiner. 1999. *Geostatistics: Modeling Spatial Uncertainty.* New York: Wiley.

Christensen, R., L. M. Pearson, and W. Johnson. 1992. "Case-Deletion Diagnostics for Mixed Models." *Technometrics* 34:38–45.

Chu, T.-M., B. Weir, and R. D. Wolfinger. 2004. "Comparison of Li-Wong and Mixed Model Approaches to Oligonucleotide Array Data Analysis." *Bioinformatics* 20(4):500–506.

Claassen, E. A. 2014. *A Reduced Bias Method of Estimating Variance Components in Generalized Linear Mixed Models.* PhD Dissertation. Lincoln, NE: University of Nebraska-Lincoln.

Cochran, W. G., and G. M. Cox. 1957. *Experimental Designs.* 2d ed. New York: Wiley.

Cook, R. D. 1977. "Detection of Influential Observations in Linear Regression." *Technometrics* 19:15–18.

Cook, R. D. 1979. "Influential Observations in Linear Regression." *Journal of the American Statistical Association* 74:169–174.

Cook, R. D., and S. Weisberg. 1982. *Residuals and Influence in Regression.* New York: Chapman & Hall.

Couton, J., and W. Stroup. 2013. "On the Small Sample Behavior of Generalized Linear Mixed Models with Complex Experiments." *Proceedings of the 25th Annual Conference on Applied Statistics in Agriculture.* Manhattan, KS: Kansas State University.

Craig, B. A., O. Vitek, M. A. Black, M. Tanurdzic, and R. W. Doerge. 2001. "Designing Microarrays." In *Proceedings of the Thirteenth Annual Conference on Applied Statistics in Agriculture*, 159–182. Manhattan: Kansas State University.

Cressie, N. A. C. 1993. *Statistics for Spatial Data.* Rev. ed. New York: Wiley.

D'Agostini, G. 1998. "Bayesian Reasoning versus Conventional Statistics in High Energy Physics." Invited talk at the XVIII International Workshop on Maximum Entropy and Bayesian Methods, Garching/München (Germany).

Daniels, M. J., and R. E. Kass. 2001. "Shrinkage Estimators for Covariance Matrices." *Biometrics* 57:1173–1184.

Davidian, M., and D. Giltinan. 1993. "Some General Estimation Methods for Nonlinear Mixed Effects Models." *Journal of Biopharmaceutical Statistics* 3:23–55.

Davidian, M., and D. M. Giltinan. 1995. *Nonlinear Models for Repeated Measurement Data.* New York: Chapman & Hall.

Davidian, M., and R. A. Gallant. 1993. "The Nonlinear Mixed Effects Model with a Smooth Random Effects Density." *Biometrika* 80:475–488.

Dempster, A. P., N. M. Laird, and D. B. Rubin. 1977. "Maximum Likelihood from Incomplete Data via the EM Algorithm." *Journal of the Royal Statistical Society, Series B*, 39:1–38.

Diggle, P. J. 1988. "An Approach to the Analysis of Repeated Measures." *Biometrics* 44:959–971.

Draper, N. R., and H. Smith. 1981. *Applied Regression Analysis.* 2d ed. New York: Wiley.

Eilers, P. H. C., and B. D. Marx. 1996. "Flexible Smoothing with *B*-Splines and Penalties." *Statistical Science* 11(2):89–121.

Falconer, D. S., and T. F. C. Mackay. 1996. *Introduction to Quantitative Genetics.* Essex, UK: Longman Group Ltd.

Feng, S., W. D. Wolfinger, T.-M. Chu, G. C. Gibson, and L. A. McGraw. 2006. "Empirical Bayesian Analysis of Variance Component Models for Microarray Data." *Journal of Agricultural, Biological, and Environmental Statistics.*

Fisher, R. A. 1925. *Statistical Methods for Research Workers.* Edinburgh: Oliver and Boyd.

Fitzmaurice, G. M., N. L. Laird, and J. H. Ware. 2004. *Applied Longitudinal Analysis.* New York: Wiley.

Fleming, T. R., J. D. Neaton, A. Goldman, D. L. DeMets, C. Launer, J. Korvick, and D. Abrams. 1995. "Insights from Monitoring the CPCRA Didanosine/Zalcitabine Trial. Terry Beirn Community Programs for Clinical Research on AIDS." *Journal of Acquired Immune Deficiency Syndromes and Human Retrovirology* 10(supp. 2):S9–18.

Fry, J. D. 2004. "Estimation of Genetic Variances and Covariances by Restricted Maximum Likelihood Using PROC MIXED." *Genetic Analysis of Complex Traits Using SAS*, ed. A. Saxton. Cary, NC: SAS Institute Inc.

Fuller, W. A., and G. E. Battese. 1974. "Estimation of Linear Models with Crossed-Error Structure." *Journal of Econometrics* 2:67–78.

Galecki, A. T. 1994. "General Class of Covariance Structures for Two or More Repeated Factors in Longitudinal Data Analysis." *Communications in Statistics: Theory and Methods* 23(11):3105–3119.

Galecki, A. T., R. D. Wolfinger, O. A. Linares, M. J. Smith, and J. B. Halter. 2004. "Ordinary Differential Equation PK/PD Models Using the SAS Macro NLINMIX." *Journal of Biopharmaceutical Statistics* 14:483–504.

Gallant, A. R. 1987. *Nonlinear Statistical Models.* New York: Wiley.

Gelfand, A. E., S. E. Hills, A. Racine-Poon, and A. F. M. Smith. 1990. "Illustration of Bayesian Inference in Normal Data Models Using Gibbs Sampling." *Journal of the American Statistical Association* 85:972–985.

Gennings, C., V. M. Chinchilli, and W. H. Carter. 1989. "Response Surface Analysis with Correlated Data: A Nonlinear Model Approach." *Journal of the American Statistical Association* 84:805–809.

Ghosh, M. 1992. Discussion of M. Schervish, *Bayesian Analysis of Linear Models.* In *Bayesian Statistics 4*, ed. J. M. Bernardo, J. O. Berger, A. P. Dawid, and A. F. M. Smith, 432–433. Oxford: Oxford University Press.

Giesbrecht, F. G., and J. C. Burns. 1985. "Two-Stage Analysis Based on a Mixed Model: Large-Sample Asymptotic Theory and Small-Sample Simulation Results." *Biometrics* 41:477–486.

Gigerenzer, G. 2004. "Mindless Statistics." *Journal of Socio-Economics* 33:587–606.

Gill, J. 2002. *Bayesian Methods for the Social and Behavioral Sciences.* New York: Chapman & Hall.

Goldstein, H. 1987. *Multilevel Models in Educational and Social Research.* New York: Oxford University Press.

Good, I. J. 1988. "Statistical Evidence." In volume 8 of *Encyclopedia of Statistical Sciences,* ed. N. L. Johnson and S. Kotz. New York: Wiley.

Good, I. J. 1992. "The Bayes/Non-Bayes Compromise: A Brief Review." *Journal of the American Statistical Association* 87:597–606.

Goodman, S. N. 1999a. "Toward Evidence-Based Medical Statistics. 1: The *P* Value Fallacy." *Ann. Intern. Med.* 130:995–1004.

Goodman, S. N. 1999b. "Toward Evidence-Based Medical Statistics. 2: The Bayes Factor." *Ann. Intern. Med.* 130:1005–1013.

Goodnight, J. H. 1978. SAS Technical Report R-105: *Computing MIVQUE0 Estimates of Variance Components.* Cary, NC: SAS Institute Inc.

Goodnight, J. H. 1979. "A Tutorial on the Sweep Operator." *The American Statistician* 33:149–158.

Grasela, T. H., Jr., and S. M. Donn. 1985. "Neonatal Population Pharmacokinetics for Phenobarbital Derived from Routine Clinical Data." *Dev. Pharmacol. Ther.* 8:374–383.

Guerin, L., and W. Stroup. 2000. "A Simulation Study to Evaluate PROC MIXED Analysis of Repeated Measures Data." *Proceedings of the Twelfth Annual Conference on Applied Statistics in Agriculture.* Manhattan: Kansas State University.

Gumpertz, M. L., and S. G. Pantula. 1992. "Nonlinear Regression with Variance Components." *Journal of the American Statistical Association* 87:201–209.

Guo, X., and B. P. Carlin. 2003. "Separate and Joint Modeling of Longitudinal and Event Time Data Using Standard Computer Packages." *The American Statistician* 58(1):16–24.

Hain, M. 2004. "Influence of Laundering and Drying Parameters on PLA Fabrics." Unpublished M.S. thesis (Yiqi Yang, advisor), University of Nebraska.

Hartley, A. 2004. "The Philosophy of the Law Idea and the Role of the Prescientific in Statistical Inference." *Journal of the ACMS 1,* 1. http://www.acmsonline.org/Hartley-04.pdf.

Hartley, H. O., and J. N. K. Rao. 1967. "Maximum-Likelihood Estimation for the Mixed Analysis of Variance Model." *Biometrika* 54:93–108.

Harvey, A. C. 1976. "Estimating Regression Models with Multiplicative Heteroscedasticity." *Econometrica* 44:461–465.

Harville, D. A. 1976. "Extension of the Gauss-Markov Theorem to Include the Estimation of Random Effects." *Annals of Statistics* 2:384–395.

Harville, D. A. 1977. "Maximum Likelihood Approaches to Variance Component Estimation and to Related Problems." *Journal of the American Statistical Association* 72:320–338.

Harville, D. A. 1988. "Mixed-Model Methodology: Theoretical Justifications and Future Directions." *Proceedings of the Statistical Computing Section,* 41–49. New Orleans: American Statistical Association.

Harville, D. A. 1990. "BLUP (Best Linear Unbiased Prediction), and Beyond." *Advances in Statistical Methods for Genetic Improvement of Livestock,* 239–276. New York: Springer-Verlag.

Harville, D. A. 1997. *Matrix Algebra from a Statistician's Perspective.* New York: Springer-Verlag.

Harville, D. A., and D. R. Jeske. 1992. "Mean Squared Error of Estimation or Prediction under a General Linear Model. *Journal of the American Statistical Association* 87:724–731.

Helms, R. W. 1992. "Intentionally Incomplete Longitudinal Designs: I. Methodology and Comparison of Some Full Span Designs." *Statistics in Medicine* 11(14–15):1889–1913.

Henderson, C. R. 1950. "The Estimation of Genetic Parameters." *The Annals of Mathematical Statistics* 21:309–310.

Henderson, C. R. 1963. "Selection Index and Expected Genetic Advance." In *Statistical Genetics and Plant Breeding,* ed. W. D. Hanson and H. F. Robinson, 141–163. Washington, DC: National Academy of Sciences and National Research Council, Publication No. 982.

Henderson, C. R. 1984. *Applications of Linear Models in Animal Breeding.* University of Guelph.

Henderson, C. R. 1990. "Statistical Method in Animal Improvement: Historical Overview." In *Advances in Statistical Methods for Genetic Improvement of Livestock,* 1–14. New York: Springer-Verlag.

Hirst, K., G. O. Zerbe, D. W. Boyle, and R. B. Wilkening. 1991. "On Nonlinear Random Effects Models for Repeated Measurements." *Communications in Statistics: Simulation and Computation* 20:463–478.

Hively, W. 1996. "The Mathematics of Making Up Your Mind." *Discover* 17(5).

Hoenig, J. M., and D. M. Heisey. 2001. "The Abuse of Power: The Pervasive Fallacy of Power Calculations for Data Analysis." *The American Statistician* 55:19–24.

Houseman, E. A., L. M. Ryan, and B. A. Coull. 2004. "Cholesky Residuals for Assessing Normal Errors in a Linear Model with Correlated Outcomes." *Journal of the American Statistical Association* 99:383–394.

Hsu, J. C. 1996. *Multiple Comparisons: Theory and Methods.* London: Chapman & Hall.

Hsu, J. C., and B. Nelson. 1998. "Multiple Comparisons in the General Linear Model." *Journal of Computational and Graphical Statistics* 7:23–41.

Hsu, J. C., and M. Peruggia. 1994. "Graphical Representation of Tukey's Multiple Comparison Method." *Journal of Computational and Graphical Statistics* 3:143–161.

Huber, W. A. 2013. What is the intuition behind conditional Gaussian distributions? Stack Exchange. https://stats.stackexchange.com/questions/71260/what-is-the-intuition-behind-conditional-gaussian-distributions.

Hurvich, C. M., and C.-L. Tsai. 1989. "Regression and Time Series Model Selection in Small Samples." *Biometrika* 76:297–307.

Huynh, H., and L. S. Feldt. 1970. "Conditions Under Which Mean Square Ratios in Repeated Measurements Designs Have Exact *F*-Distributions." *Journal of the American Statistical Association* 65:1582–1589.

International Conference on Harmonisation. 2003. *ICH Harmonised Tripartite Guideline: Stability Testing of New Drug Substances and Products Q1A(R2).*

International Conference on Harmonisation. 2003. *ICH Harmonised Tripartite Guideline: Evaluation for Stability Data Q1E.*

Isaaks, E. H., and R. M. Srivastava. 1989. *An Introduction to Applied Geostatistics.* Oxford: Oxford University Press.

Jeffreys, H. 1961. *Theory of Probability.* 3d ed. Oxford: Oxford University Press.

Jennrich, R. I., and M. D. Schluchter. 1986. "Unbalanced Repeated-Measures Models with Structured Covariance Matrices." *Biometrics* 42:805–820.

Jin, W., R. Riley, R. D. Wolfinger, K. P. White, G. Passador-Gurgel, and G. Gibson. 2001. "Contributions of Sex, Genotype, and Age to Transcriptional Variance in *Drosophila melanogaster.*" *Nature Genetics* 29:389–395. http://statgen.ncsu.edu/ggibson/ gibson_website/publications.html.

Johnson, D. E., U. N. Chaudhuri, and E. T. Kanemasu. 1983. "Statistical Analysis of Line-Source Sprinkler Experiments and Other Nonrandomized Experiments Using Multivariate Methods." *Journal of the American Soil Science Society* 47(2):309–312.

Johnson, D. H. 1999. "The Insignificance of Statistical Significance Testing." *Journal of Wildlife Management* 63(3):763–772.

Johnson, V. 2004. "Bayes Factors Based on Test Statistics." The University of Michigan Department of Biostatistics Working Paper Series, No. 1029. Berkeley, CA: Berkeley Electronic Press.

Journal of Educational and Behavioral Statistics. 1995. Special Issue: Hierarchical Linear Models: Problems and Prospects. Summer (20:2):109–240.

Journel, A. G., and C. J. Huijbregts. 1978. *Mining Geostatistics.* London: Academic Press.

Kackar, R. N., and D. A. Harville. 1984. "Approximations for Standard Errors of Estimators of Fixed and Random Effects in Mixed Linear Models." *Journal of the American Statistical Association* 79:853–862.

Kass, R. E., and A. Raftery. 1995. "Bayes Factors." *Journal of the American Statistical Association* 90:773–795.

Kass, R. E., and D. Steffey. 1989. "Approximate Bayesian Inference in Conditionally Independent Hierarchical Models (Parametric Empirical Bayes Models)." *Journal of the American Statistical Association* 84:717–726.

Kenward, M. G., and J. H. Roger. 1997. "Small Sample Inference for Fixed Effects from Restricted Maximum Likelihood." *Biometrics* 53:983–997.

Keselman, H. J., J. Algina, R. K. Kowalchuk, and R. D. Wolfinger. 1998. "A Comparison of Two Approaches for Selecting Covariance Structures in the Analysis of Repeated Measures." *Communications in Statistics: Simulation and Computation* 27(3):591–604.

Keselman, H. J., J. Algina, R. K. Kowalchuk, and R. D. Wolfinger. 1999a. "A Comparison of Recent Approaches to the Analysis of Repeated Measurements." *British Journal of Mathematical and Statistical Psychology* 52:63–78.

Keselman, H. J., J. Algina, R. K. Kowalchuk, and R. D. Wolfinger. 1999b. "Analysis of Repeated Measurements: A Comparison of Mixed-Model Satterthwaite F Tests and a Nonpooled Adjusted Degrees of Freedom Multivariate Test." *Communications in Statistics: Theory and Methods* 28(12): 2967–2999.

Khuri, A. I., and J. A. Cornell. 1996. *Response Surfaces.* 2d ed. New York: Dekker.

Khuri, A. I., T. Mathew, and B. K. Sinha. 1998. *Statistical Tests for Mixed Linear Models.* New York: Wiley.

Kianifard, F., and W. H. Swallow. 1996. "A Review of the Development and Application of Recursive Residuals in Linear Models." *Journal of the American Statistical Association* 91:391–400.

Kiernan, K., J. Tao, and P. Gibbs. 2012. "Tips and Strategies for Mixed Modeling with SAS/STAT Procedures." *Proceedings of the SAS Global Forum 2012 Conference.* Paper 332-2012. Cary, NC: SAS Institute Inc.

Kowalchuk, R. K., H. J. Keselman, J. Algina, and R. D. Wolfinger. 2004. "The Analysis of Repeated Measurements with Mixed-Model Adjusted *F*-tests." *Educational and Psychological Measurement* 64(2): 224–242.

Kramer, M. 2005. "R^2 Statistics for Mixed Models." In *Proceedings of the Kansas State Conference on Applied Statistics in Agriculture*, 2005. Manhattan: Kansas State University.

Kreft, I. G. G., J. De Leeuw, and R. Van Der Leeden. 1994. "Review of Five Multilevel Analysis Programs: BMDP-5V, GENMOD, HLM, ML3, VARCL." *The American Statistician* 48:324–335.

Krige, D. G. 1951. "A Statistical Approach to Some Basic Mine Valuation Problems on the Witswaterrand." *Journal of the Chemical, Metallurgical, and Mining Society of South Africa* 52:119–139.

Lahiri, P., ed. 2001. *Model Selection.* Institute of Mathematical Statistics, Lecture Notes—Monograph Series, Volume 38.

Laird, N. M., and J. H. Ware. 1982. "Random-Effects Models for Longitudinal Data." *Biometrics* 38:963–974.

Laird, N. M., N. Lange, and D. Stram. 1987. "Maximum Likelihood Computations with Repeated Measures: Application of the EM Algorithm." *Journal of the American Statistical Association* 82:97–105.

Lambert, D. 1992. "Zero-Inflated Poisson Regression, with an Application to Defects in Manufacturing." *Technometrics* 34(1):1–14.

LaMotte, L. R. 1973. "Quadratic Estimation of Variance Components." *Biometrics* 29:311–330.

Lange, N., B. P. Carlin, and A. E. Gelfand. 1992. "Hierarchical Bayes Models for the Progression of HIV Infection Using Longitudinal CD4 T-cell Numbers" (with discussion). *Journal of the American Statistical Association* 87:615–632.

Lavine, M., and M. J. Schervish. 1999. "Bayes Factors: What They Are and What They Are Not." *The American Statistician* 53:119–122.

Lenth, R. V. 2001. "Some Practical Guidelines for Effective Sample Size Determination." *The American Statistician* 55:187–193. http://www.stat.uiowa.edu/~rlenth/Power/.

Liang, K. Y., and S. L. Zeger. 1986. "Longitudinal Data Analysis Using Generalized Linear Models." *Biometrika* 73:13–22.

Lindsey, J. K. 1993. *Models for Repeated Measurements.* Oxford: Clarendon Press.

Lindstrom, M. J., and D. M. Bates. 1988. "Newton-Raphson and EM Algorithms for Linear Mixed-Effects Models for Repeated-Measures Data." *Journal of the American Statistical Association* 83:1014–1022.

Lindstrom, M. J., and D. M. Bates. 1990. "Nonlinear Mixed Effects Models for Repeated Measures Data." *Biometrics* 46:673–687.

Littell, R. C., J. Pendergast, and R. Natarajan. 2000. "Modelling Covariance Structure in the Analysis of Repeated Measures Data." *Statistics in Medicine* 19:1793–1819.

Littell, R. C., R. J. Freund, and P. C. Spector. 1991. *SAS System for Linear Models.* 3d ed. Cary, NC: SAS Institute Inc.

Littell, R. C., W. W. Stroup, and R. J. Freund. 2002. *SAS for Linear Models.* 4th ed. Cary, NC: SAS Institute Inc.

Louis, T. A. 1988. "General Methods for Analysing Repeated Measures." *Statistics in Medicine* 7:29–45.

Matheron, G. 1963. "Principles of Geostatistics." *Economic Geology* 58:1246–1266.

McCullagh, P., and J. A. Nelder. 1989. *Generalized Linear Models.* 2d ed. New York: Chapman & Hall.

McLean, R. A., and W. L. Sanders. 1988. "Approximating Degrees of Freedom for Standard Errors in Mixed Linear Models." In *Proceedings of the Statistical Computing Section*, 50–59. New Orleans: American Statistical Association.

McLean, R. A., W. L. Sanders, and W. W. Stroup. 1991. "A Unified Approach to Mixed Linear Models." *The American Statistician* 45:54–64.

Mead, R. 1988. *The Design of Experiments.* New York: Cambridge University Press.

Mendenhall, W., D. D. Wackerly, and R. L. Scheaffer. 1990. *Mathematical Statistics with Applications.* 4th ed. Belmont, CA: Duxbury Press.

Messina, F. J., and J. D. Fry. 2003. "Environment-Dependent Reversal of a Life History Trade-off in the Seed Beetle *Callosobruchus maculatus.*" *Journal of Evolutionary Biology.* 16:501–509.

Milliken, G. A., and D. E. Johnson. 1989. *Analysis of Messy Data.* Volume 2: *Nonreplicated Experiments.* New York: Chapman & Hall.

Milliken, G. A., and D. E. Johnson. 1992. *Analysis of Messy Data.* Volume 1: *Designed Experiments.* London: Chapman & Hall.

Milliken, G. A., and D. E. Johnson. 2002. *Analysis of Messy Data.* Volume 3: *Analysis of Covariance.* London: Chapman & Hall.

Molenberghs, G., and G. Verbeke. 2005. *Models for Discrete Longitudinal Data.* New York: Springer-Verlag.

Mood, A. M. 1950. *Introduction to the Theory of Statistics.* New York: McGraw-Hill.

Morgan, J. E., and M. L. Gumpertz. 1996. "Random Effects Models: Testing Whether Variance Components Are Zero." In *Proceedings of the Joint Statistical Meetings*, 118–126. Alexandria, VA: American Statistical Association.

Muller, K. E., and B. A. Fetterman. 2002. *Regression and ANOVA: An Integrated Approach Using SAS Software.* Cary, NC: SAS Institute.

Murray, D. M., and R. D. Wolfinger. 1994. "Analysis Issues in the Evaluation of Community Trials: Progress toward Solutions in SAS/STAT MIXED." *Journal of Community Psychology,* CSAP Special Issue:140–154.

Murray, D. M., P. J. Hannan, R. D. Wolfinger, W. L. Baker, and J. H. Dwyer. 1998. "Analysis of Data from Group-Randomized Trials with Repeat Observations on the Same Groups." *Statistics in Medicine* 17(14): 1581–1600.

Myers, R. H., and D. C. Montgomery. 2002. *Response Surface Methodology: Process and Product Optimization Using Designed Experiments.* 2d ed. New York: Wiley.

Nelder, J. A., and R. W. M. Wedderburn. 1972. "Generalised Linear Models." *Journal of the Royal Statistical Society, Series* A, 135:370–384.

Nelson, P. R. 1982. "Exact Critical Points for the Analysis of Means." *Communications in Statistics* 11:699–709.

Nelson, P. R. 1991. "Numerical Evaluation of Multivariate Normal Integrals with Correlations $\rho_{ij} = -\alpha_i \alpha_j$." *The Frontiers of Statistical Scientific Theory & Industrial Applications*, 97–114.

Nelson, P. R. 1993. "Additional Uses for the Analysis of Means and Extended Tables of Critical Values." *Technometrics* 35:61–71.

Ott, E. R. 1967. "Analysis of Means—A Graphical Procedure." *Industrial Quality Control*, 101–109. Reprinted in *Journal of Quality Technology* 15 (1983):10–18.

Pantula, S. G. 1996. Discussion of "Likelihood Ratio Tests for Variance Components." In *Proceedings of the Joint Statistical Meetings,* 127–129. Alexandria, VA: American Statistical Association.

Patel, H. I. 1991. "Analysis of Incomplete Data from a Clinical Trial with Repeated Measurements." *Biometrika* 78:609–619.

Patterson, H. D., and R. Thompson. 1971. "Recovery of Inter-block Information When Block Sizes Are Unequal." *Biometrika* 58:545–554.

Pauler, D. K., J. C. Wakefield, and R. E. Kass. 1999. "Bayes Factors for Variance Component Models." *Journal of the American Statistical Association* 94:1242–1253.

Perkins, J., and D. Wang. 2004. "A Comparison of Bayesian and Frequentist Statistics as Applied in a Simple Repeated Measures Example." *Journal of Modern Applied Statistical Methods* 3(1): 227–233.

Phadke, M. S., R. N. Kackar, D. V. Speeney, and M. J. Grieco. 1983. "Off-line Quality Control for Integrated Circuit Fabrication Using Experimental Design." *Bell System Technical Journal* 62:1273–1309.

Pinheiro, J. C., and D. M. Bates. 1995. "Approximations to the Log-Likelihood Function in the Nonlinear Mixed-Effects Model." *Journal of Computational and Graphical Statistics* 4:12–35.

Prasad, N. G. N., and J. N. K. Rao. 1990. "The Estimation of Mean Squared Error of Small-Area Estimators." *Journal of the American Statistical Association* 85:163–171.

Prentice, R. L., and L. P. Zhao. 1991. "Estimating Equations for Parameters in Means and Covariances of Multivariate Discrete and Continuous Responses." *Biometrics* 47:825–839.

Rao, C. R. 1972. "Estimation of Variance and Covariance Components in Linear Models." *Journal of the American Statistical Association* 67:112–115.

Remmenga, M., G. A. Milliken, D. D. Kratzer, J. W. Schwenke, and H. R. Rolka. 1997. "Estimating the Maximum Effective Dose in a Quantitative Dose-Response Experiment." *Journal of Animal Sciences* 75:2174–2183.

Robert, C. P. 1994. *The Bayesian Choice: A Decision-Theoretic Motivation.* New York: Springer-Verlag.

Robinson, G. K. 1991. "That BLUP Is a Good Thing: The Estimation of Random Effects." *Statistical Science* 6:15–51.

Roe, D. J. 1997. "Comparison of Population Pharmacokinetic Modeling Methods Using Simulated Data: Results from the Population Modeling Workgroup." *Statistics in Medicine* 16:1241–1262.

Rosa, G. J. M., and R. J. Tempelman. 2004. "Bayesian Mapping Methodology." In *Genetic Analysis of Complex Traits Using SAS,* ed. A. Saxton. Cary, NC: SAS Institute Inc.

Rosa, G. J. M., J. P. Steibel, and R. J. Tempelman. 2005. "Reassessing Design and Analysis of Two-Colour Microarray Experiments Using Mixed Effects Models." *Comp. Funct. Genom.* 6:123–131.

Royall, R. M. 1986. "The Effect of Sample Size on the Meaning of Significance Tests." *The American Statistician* 40(4): 313–315. Also: Bailey, K. R. 1987. "Comment on Royall (1986)." *The American Statistician* 41(3): 245–246.

Rubin, D. B. 1976. "Inference and Missing Data." *Biometrika* 63:581–592.

Ruppert, D., M. P. Wand, and R. J. Carroll. 2003. *Semiparametric Regression.* Cambridge, UK: Cambridge University Press.

Rutter, C. M., and R. M. Elashoff. 1994. "Analysis of Longitudinal Data: Random Coefficient Regression Modelling." *Statistics in Medicine* 13:1211–1231.

SAS Institute Inc. 1990. *SAS/STAT User's Guide, Version 6, Fourth Edition.* Vol. 2. Cary, NC: SAS Institute Inc.

SAS Institute Inc. 1993. *SAS/ETS User's Guide, Version 6, Second Edition.* Cary, NC: SAS Institute Inc.

SAS Institute Inc. 1996. SAS/STAT Software: Changes and Enhancements through Release 6.11. Cary, NC: SAS Institute Inc.

SAS Institute Inc. 2004. *Getting Started with the SAS Power and Sample Size Application.* Cary, NC: SAS Press.

Satterthwaite, F. E. 1946. "An Approximate Distribution of Estimates of Variance Components." *Biometrics Bulletin* 2:110–114.

Schabenberger, O. 2004. "Mixed Model Influence Diagnostics." *Proceedings of the Twenty-ninth Annual SAS Users Group International Conference.* Cary, NC: SAS Institute Inc. Available in electronic form at http://www2.sas.com/proceedings/sugi29/toc.html.

Schabenberger, O. 2004. "Mixed Model Influence Diagnostics." *Proceedings of the Twenty-Ninth Annual SAS Users Group International Conference.* Paper 189-29. Cary, NC: SAS Institute Inc.

Schabenberger, O., and C. A. Gotway. 2005. *Statistical Methods for Spatial Data Analysis.* Boca Raton, FL: CRC Press/Chapman & Hall.

Schabenberger, O., and F. J. Pierce. 2002. *Contemporary Statistical Models for the Plant and Soil Sciences.* Boca Raton, FL: CRC Press.

Schervish, M. J. 1992. "Bayesian Analysis of Linear Models." In *Bayesian Statistics 4*, ed. J. M. Bernardo, J. O. Berger, A. P. Dawid, and A. F. M. Smith, 419–434 (with discussion). Oxford: Oxford University Press.

Schervish, M. J. 1996. "P Values: What They Are and What They Are Not." *The American Statistician* 50:203–206.

Schield, M. 1997. "Interpreting Statistical Confidence." In *Proceedings of the ASA Joint Statistical Meetings Section on Statistical Education.* http://web.augsburg.edu/~schield/ MiloPapers/97ASA.pdf.

Schneider, G. W., and R. D. Tobias. 2014. "A SAS Macro to Diagnose Influential Subjects in Longitudinal Studies." *Proceedings of the SAS Global Forum 2014 Conference.* Paper 1461-2014. Cary, NC: SAS Institute Inc. http://support.sas.com/resources/papers/proceedings14/1461-2014.pdf.

Schwarz, G. 1978. "Estimating the Dimension of a Model." *Annals of Statistics* 6:461–464.

Searle, S. R. 1971. *Linear Models.* New York: Wiley.

Searle, S. R. 1982. *Matrix Algebra Useful for Statisticians.* New York: Wiley.

Searle, S. R., G. Casella, and C. E. McCulloch. 1992. *Variance Components.* New York: Wiley.

Seber, G. A. F., and C. J. Wild. 2003. *Nonlinear Regression.* New York: Wiley.

Self, S. G., and K. Y. Liang. 1987. "Asymptotic Properties of Maximum Likelihood Estimators and Likelihood Ratio Tests under Nonstandard Conditions." *Journal of the American Statistical Association* 82:605–610.

Sellke, T., M. J. Bayarri, and J. O. Berger. 2001. "Calibration of p Values for Testing Precise Null Hypotheses." *The American Statistician* 55:62–71.

Serfling, R. J. 1980. *Approximation Theorems of Mathematical Statistics.* New York: Wiley.

Shapiro, A. 1988. "Towards a Unified Theory of Inequality Constrained Testing in Multivariate Analysis." *International Statistical Review* 56(1):49–62.

Sheiner, L. B., and S. L. Beal. 1985. "Pharmacokinetic Parameter Estimates from Several Least Squares Procedures: Superiority of Extended Least Squares." *Journal of Pharmacokinetics and Biopharmaceutics* 13:185–201.

Shmueli, G. 2010. "To Explain or to Predict?" *Statistical Science* 25(3):289–310.

Silvapulle, M. J., and P. Silvapulle. 1995. "A Score Test against One-Sided Alternatives." *Journal of the American Statistical Association* 90:342–349.

Snedecor, G. W., and W. G. Cochran. 1989. *Statistical Methods.* 8th ed. Ames: Iowa State University Press.

Sokal, R. R., and F. J. Rohlf. 1981. *Biometry.* New York: W. H. Freeman.

Steel, R. D. G., and J. H. Torrie. 1980. *Principles and Procedures of Statistics.* 2d ed. New York: McGraw-Hill.

Stoup, W., and R. C. Littell. 2002. "Impact of Variance Component Estimates on Fixed Effect Inference in Unbalanced Mixed Models." In *Proceedings of the Fourteenth Annual Kansas State University Conference in Applied Statistics in Agriculture*, 32–48.

Stram, D. O., and J. W. Lee. 1994. "Variance Components in the Longitudinal Mixed Effects Model." *Biometrics* 50:1171–1177.

Stram, D. O., and J. W. Lee. 1995. Correction to "Variance Components in the Longitudinal Mixed Effects Model." *Biometrics* 51:1196.

Strenio, J. F., H. I. Weisberg, and A. S. Bryk. 1983. "Empirical Bayes Estimation of Individual Growth-Curve Parameters and Their Relationship to Covariates." *Biometrics* 39:71–86.

Stroup, W. W. 1989. "Predictable Functions and Prediction Space in the Mixed Model Procedure." In *Applications of Mixed Models in Agriculture and Related Disciplines*, 39–48. Southern Cooperative Series Bulletin No. 343. Baton Rouge: Louisiana Agricultural Experiment Station.

Stroup, W. W. 2002. "Power Analysis Based on Spatial Effects Mixed Models: A Tool for Comparing Design and Analysis Strategies in the Presence of Spatial Variability." *Journal of Agricultural, Biological, and Environmental Statistics* 7:491–511.

Stroup, W. W. 2013a. *Generalized Linear Mixed Models: Modern Concepts, Methods and Applications.* Boca Raton, FL: CRC Press.

Stroup, W. W. 2013b. "Non-normal Data in Agricultural Experiments." *Proceedings of the 25th Annual Conference on Applied Statistics in Agriculture.* Manhattan, KS: Kansas State University.

Stroup, W. W. and E. A. Claassen. 2018. "Pseudo-likelihood or Quadrature? What We Thought We Knew, What We Think We Know, and What We Are Still Trying to Figure Out." *Proceedings of the 30th Annual Conference on Applied Statistics in Agriculture.* Manhattan, KS: Kansas State University.

Stroup, W. W. and M. Quinlan. 2016. "Statistical Considerations for Stability and the Estimation of Shelf Life." *Nonclinical Statistics for Pharmaceutical and Biotechnology Industries.* Zhang, L., editor. New York: Springer.

Stroup, W. W., P. S. Baenziger, and D. K. Mulitze. 1994. "Removing Spatial Variation from Wheat Yield Trials: A Comparison of Methods." *Crop Science* 34:62–66.

Swallow, W. H., and J. F. Monahan. 1984. "Monte Carlo Comparison of ANOVA, MIVQUE, REML, and ML Estimators of Variance Components." *Technometrics* 28:47–57.

Swinburne, R., ed. 2002. *Bayes Theorem.* Oxford: Oxford University Press.

Tao, J., K. Kiernan, and P. Gibbs. 2015. "Advanced Techniques for Fitting Mixed Models Using SAS/STAT Software." *Proceedings of the SAS Global Forum 2015 Conference.* Paper SAS1919-2915. Cary, NC: SAS Institute Inc.

Tempelman, R. J. 2006. "Assessing Statistical Precision, Power, and Robustness of Alternative Experimental Designs for Two Colour Microarray Platforms Based on Mixed Effects Models." *Vet. Immunol. Immunopathol.* In press.

Theil, H. 1971. *Principles of Econometrics.* New York: Wiley.

Thompson, B. 2001. 402 Citations Questioning the Indiscriminate Use of Null Hypothesis Significance Tests in Observational Studies. http://biology.uark.edu/Coop/Courses/ thompson5.html.

Thompson, W. A. 1962. "The Problem of Negative Estimates of Variance Components." *Annals of Mathematical Statistics* 33:273–289.

Tierney, L. 1994. "Markov Chains for Exploring Posterior Distributions" (with discussion). *Annals of Statistics* 22:1701–1762.

Verbeke, G., and G. Molenberghs. 1997. *Linear Mixed Models in Practice: A SAS Oriented Approach.* Lecture Notes in Statistics, Vol. 126. New York: Springer.

Verbeke, G., and G. Molenberghs. 2000. *Linear Mixed Models for Longitudinal Data.* New York: Springer-Verlag.

Verbeke, G., and G. Molenberghs. 2003. "The Use of Score Tests for Inference on Variance Components." *Biometrics* 59:254–262.

Vitezica, Z. G., L. Varona, and A. Legarra. 2013. "On the Additive and Dominant Variance and Covariance of Individuals within the Genomic Selection Scope." *Genetics* 195(4):1223-1230

Vonesh, E. F. 1992. "Nonlinear Models for the Analysis of Longitudinal Data." *Statistics in Medicine* 11:1929–1954.

Vonesh, E. F. 1996. "A Note on Laplace's Approximation in Nonlinear Mixed Effects Models." *Biometrika* 83:447–452.

Vonesh, E. F., and R. L. Carter. 1992. "Mixed-Effects Nonlinear Regression for Unbalanced Repeated Measures." *Biometrics* 48:1–17.

Vonesh, E. F., and V. M. Chinchilli. 1997. *Linear and Nonlinear Models for the Analysis of Repeated Measurements.* New York: Marcel Dekker.

Wedderburn, R. W. M. 1974. "Quasilikelihood Methods, Generalised Linear Models, and the Gauss-Newton Method." *Biometrika* 61:439–447.

Westfall, P. H. 1997. "Multiple Testing of General Contrasts Using Logical Constraints and Correlations." *Journal of the American Statistical Association* 92:299–306.

Wicklin, R. 2013. *Simulating Data with SAS.* Cary, NC: SAS Institute Inc.

Zhang, L., M. Kuhn, I. Peers, and S. Altan (Ed.). 2016. *Nonclinical Statistics for Pharmaceutical and Biotechnology Industries.* New York: Springer.

Zhu, H., J. G. Ibrahim, and H. Cho. 2012. "Perturbation and Scaled Cook's Distance," *Annals of Statistics* 40(2):785–811. https://projecteuclid.org/euclid.aos/1337268212.

Index

A

A x B effect 88–89
ADJUST option 58
adjusted means 220
ALPHA option 71
alternative distributions 423–424
analysis of covariance
    about 13, 171, 217–218
    multilevel design with covariate measured on large-size experimental
        unit or whole plot 256–267
    one-way fixed effects treatment structure with simple linear
        regression models 218–223
    one-way treatment structure in BIB design structure 246–253
    one-way treatment structure in incomplete block design structure
        237–246
    one-way treatment structure in RCB design structure 223–237
    one-way treatment structure in unbalanced incomplete block design
        structure 254–256
    split-plot design with covariate measured on large-size experimental
        unit or whole plot 256–267
analysis of variance (ANOVA) 7, 21, 52–58, 149, 214–216, 429–432
angular transformation 395–398
ANOVA (analysis of variance) 7, 21, 52–58, 149, 214–216, 429–432
ASYCOV option 211–212

B

balanced designs 149
balanced incomplete block designs (BIBD) 32
best linear unbiased predictor (BLUP)
    about 188
    broad inference space 320
    empirical 315
    estimation using 367–371
    examples motivating 308–311
    inference on random effects and 307–336
    intermediate inference spaced 319–320
    machine-operator two-factor mixed model 316–322
    matrix notation for 334–336
    multilocation example 322–334
    obtainment of, in breeding random effects model 311–316
    of regression coefficients 369–371
between-subjects factor 269, 271
BIB design structure, one-way treatment structure in 246–253
BIBD (balanced incomplete block designs) 32
Binary Data from a Dairy Cattle Breeding Trial example 379–380, 412–417
binomial data
    generalized linear mixed models (GLMMs) for 377–417
    repeated measures with 458
Binomial Data in a Multicenter Clinical Trial example 379, 394–412
Binomial O-Ring Data example 378, 380–383
block effects 19
block size 33
blocked design
    about 453–456
    count data from 420–421
    marginal model for count data in 442–445
    one-way treatment structure in incomplete 237–246
    precision and power analysis for 502–505
blocking 9, 19, 108–109
blocks 19
BLUP. see best linear unbiased predictor (BLUP)
breeding random effects model 308, 311–316
broad inference space BLUP 320
BY EXPT statement 118
BY statement 106
BYLEVEL option 35, 37

C

canonical link function 387
canonical parameter 381
center-specific inference 329–334
characterization of the mean 15
characterization of the probability distribution 15
CHISQ option 425–427
CLASS statement
    analysis with fixed effects and random coefficients 349
    Binomial Data in a Multicenter Clinical Trial example 402, 410
    Completely Random Design with Count Data example 428
    data set creation 105
    fit with unequal slopes for each level of GRP 249
    layouts and 145–146
    MIXED procedure analysis based on likelihood 26
    orthogonal polynomial contrasts 66
    simple effect comparisons 78
    Split-Plot Design example 517
    testing for lack of fit 363
    two-way factorial experiments 73
    Type x Dose response example 168
column designs 134–135
combined estimator 232–237
common slope model 255–256
comparisons
    competing designs 108–112, 112–117
    of levels of factors 82–84
    models at preselected value of covariate 243–246
    multiple 57–58
    with operator effects fixed model 320–322
    planned 57–58
    of quantitative factors 58–66
    regression models 220–222
    of results from two covariance structures 280–283
    of several means 52–58
    simple effect 78–79
    of two treatments 50–52
comparisonwise error rate 58
complete block designs, compared with incomplete block designs 112–117
Completely Random Design with Count Data example 424–429
completely randomized design (CRD)
    about 133
    whole plot as 135–137
compound symmetry 43–44, 175, 272, 280
conditional (G-side) GLMM, for repeated measures 475–481
conditional GLMMs 448–451
conditional hierarchical linear model 196–202
conditional hierarchical mixed model 205–206
conditional mean 15
conditional models 388–390
conditional residuals 516–517
confidence interval estimation 149–150
confidence intervals
    about 391
    using GLIMMIX procedure for 201–202
    for variance components 29–31
CONTRAST statement
    analysis of semiconductor data 160–161
    analysis with fixed center effects 325
    comparing models at preselected value of covariate 243
    comparisons within subgroups 82–83
    Completely Random Design with Count Data example 426
    completing standard error 149
    data set creation 106, 107
    FEV1 data analysis 295, 297–298, 300
    negative binomial GLMM 441
    orthogonal polynomial contrasts 66
    Poisson mixed model 433, 434, 435
    Poisson-normal GLMM 455
    precision and power analysis for planning split-plot experiments 490

relationship between LSMEANS and fixed effects solution 52–54
Repeated Measures Experiment with Binomial Data example 477–478, 481–482
simple effect comparisons 79
simultaneous contrasts 81
standard errors for mean comparisons 55
in two-way factorial experiments 77–78
Type x Dose response example 165–167, 170
Cook's D statistic 521, 523, 526, 527, 528
correlated errors 175
correlation 174–177
count data
from blocked design 420–421
estimation methods for complex 459–460
generalized linear mixed models (GLMM) for 419–456
generalized linear mixed models (GLMM) for regression on 451–453
modeling considerations for 459
negative binomial GLMM for split plot with 464–466
quasi-marginal model for split plot design with 466–469
split plot with 460–464
split-plot experiment with 457–458
Count Data from an Incomplete Block Design example 429–445
covariance structure 270, 283–293, 371–374
covariate, comparing models at preselected value of 243–246
COVRATIO statistic 523, 526
COVTEST statement
analysis of regression experiment 60
analysis with fixed effects and random coefficients 349
Binomial Data in a Multicenter Clinical Trial example 411
comparing competing designs 109
Completely Random Design with Count Data example 428
confidence intervals for variance components 31
estimating heritability 211–212
fitting model to data 206–207
GLIMMIX procedure 190–192, 293–294, 394
MIXED procedure 189
one-way random effects treatment structure 343
Poisson mixed model 432
Repeated Measures Experiment with Binomial Data example 476
repeated measures growth study example 359
Split-Plot Experiment with Count Data example 462
testing for noncorrelation of intercept and slope coefficients 368–369
unequal variance model 209
unequally spaced repeated measures example 304
COVTRACE statistic 523
CRD. see completely randomized design (CRD)
critical value 103

D

DATA= option 349
DATALINES statement 120
DDFM=NONE option 425–427, 426
degrees of freedom 149–150, 158–159
Delta method 398
design structure
for 2 x 2 factorial treatment design 132–143
about 131, 143
components of 132
determination of appropriate mixed model for given layouts 143–146
experiment structure and associated models 132–146
models with multiple random effects 131–179
three-level nested 202–210
treatment structure and associated models 132–146
designed experiments 1
DFFITS statistic 521
diagnostic plots 538–541
diagnostics. see troubleshooting and diagnostics
DIFF option 37, 52, 56, 124, 160–161, 493
difference estimates, variance of 147–149
DIFFS option 105
direct fit, of polynomials 62–65
direct regression 88–89

distribution of the observations 388
distribution of the random effects 388
DISTRIBUTION option 93, 423–424
DIVISOR option 160–161
DO loop 107
dose-response random coefficient regression model 310–311
dot-notation 69
dot-notation with a bar 69

E

EBLUE (estimate of the best linear unbiased estimate) 38
effect 2
effects model 7
efficiency factors 116–117
EGLS (estimated generalized least squares) estimator 516, 521–522
ELR confidence intervals, providing using GLIMMIX procedure 204–205
empirical Bayes models 339
empirical BLUP 315
empirical estimators 468
EMPIRICAL procedure 468, 482
equal slopes hypothesis 223–237, 238–239, 247–248, 254–255
error messages 512
error recovery 515–516
estimable functions 316
estimate of the best linear unbiased estimate (EBLUE) 38
ESTIMATE statement
ADJUST option 58
analysis of semiconductor data 160–161
analysis with fixed center effects 325
analyzing data using MIXED procedure 198
Binary Data from a Dairy Cattle Breeding Trial example 414–417
Binomial Data in a Multicenter Clinical Trial example 397–398, 403, 409
Binomial O-Ring Data example 380–381, 382–383
BLUPs of regression coefficients 370
breeding random effects model 311–312
center-specific inference 331
compared with LSMESTIMATE statement 79–81
comparisons with operator effects fixed model 322
Completely Random Design with Count Data example 426
Count Data from an Incomplete Block Design example 431
estimation using "naive" mixed model approach 375
FEV1 data analysis 297
fit with unequal slopes for each level of GRP 253
fitting common slope model 230
GLIMMIX procedure 149
for linear combinations of model effects 55–56
Linear Regression with a Discrete Count Dependent Variable example 449, 450, 452
MIXED procedure 149
obtaining estimates 317–319
one-way random effects treatment structure 188–190, 191
Poisson mixed model 437
random center effects 328
relationship between LSMEANS and fixed effects solution 52–54
Repeated Measures Experiment with Binomial Data example 477
standard errors for mean comparisons 55
testing equal slopes hypothesis 248
in two-way factorial experiments 77–78
Type x Dose response example 170
unequal slopes model 263–267
estimated generalized least squares (EGLS) estimator 516, 521–522
"Estimated G-Matrix is Non-Singular" message 469–473
estimation
about 317–319, 391
methods for complex count data 459–460
methods in GLIMMIX procedure 392–394
using best linear unbiased prediction (BLUP) 367–371
using fixed effects analysis of covariance 371–374
using "naive" mixed model approach 375–376
expected mean squares 21–22
experiment design 67, 131, 132–146

experimental units 3, 4–5
experimentwise error rate 58
exponential family 385

F

factor 2
factorial designs
    about 131
    inference with 146–150
    mean comparisons in 67–98
    with two continuous factors 92–98
factorial effects model 258–259
factorial experiments 67–72, 74
FAQ 512–514
FASTQUAD option 449
FEV1 data, analysis of 293–301
FINV function 120
first-order autoregressive 284
fit model
    with slopes expressed as main effects of two factors 259–260
    with unequal slopes for each 260–267
fit the model
    common slope model 227–232, 255–256
    to test equal slopes hypothesis 238–239
    to test slopes-equal-to-zero hypothesis 224–226
    with unequal slopes for each level of GRP 248–253
    unequal slopes model 239–242, 246–247, 257–258
fixed center effects 324–327
fixed effects models
    about 8–9
    analysis with random coefficients and 348–350
    estimation of covariance using 371–374
    mean comparisons for 49–99
    relationships between LSMEANS and 52–54
    simple linear regression models with additional 348
fixed treatment 13
F-tests 152–154

G

G option 343
Gaussian distribution 141
GCORR option 343, 358, 368, 370
"general" linear model 2
generalized estimating equations 387
generalized inverse model 7
generalized least squares (GLS) 38, 521–522
generalized linear mixed models (GLMMs)
    about 15–16
    adjustment for Poisson-normal 454–455
    analysis using Logit (canonical) link function 398–406
    for binomial data 377–417
    conditional 448–451, 475–481
    for count data 419–456
    examples of 378–380, 420–421
    margin analysis using logit link 409–412
    marginal 481–484
    for multilevel and repeated measures experiments 457–508
    negative 437–440
    negative binomial 441–442, 455–456
    with overdispersion 429–432
    Poisson 460–464
    for regression on count data 451–453
generalized linear model (GLM) 8, 377–378, 383–394, 386–387
GENMOD procedure
    Binomial Data in a Multicenter Clinical Trial example 399
    diagnostic plots 538
    marginal model for count data in blocked design 445
    Repeated Measures Experiment with Binomial Data example 474

GLIMMIX procedure
    about 12, 15, 16
    analysis of FEV1 data 293–301
    analysis of semiconductor data 154–161
    analysis using 51–52
    analysis with a negative block variance estimate 41–44
    analysis with fixed center effects 324
    analysis with fixed effects and random coefficients 350–351
    to analyze RCBD data 23
    based on likelihood 26–27
    basic analysis 28
    Binary Data from a Dairy Cattle Breeding Trial example 413
    Binomial Data in a Multicenter Clinical Trial example 395–398, 399, 402, 403, 406
    Binomial O-Ring Data example 382, 390, 391, 392
    blocked design 453
    broad inference space BLUP 320
    center-specific inference 330–331
    combined intra- and inter-block PBIB data analysis with 37–41
    compared to GLM procedure 177–179
    compared with GLM procedure 161–162
    comparing models at preselected value of covariate 245
    comparisons of results from two covariance structures 280–283
    comparisons with operator effects fixed model 320–322
    Completely Random Design with Count Data example 425–427
    Completely Random Design with Count Data example procedure 428
    confidence intervals for variance components 29–31
    Count Data from an Incomplete Block Design example 430
    covariance structures and 283–293
    COVTEST statement 394
    creating exemplary data sets using 104–105
    defaults in 61
    diagnostic plots 538
    DISTRIBUTION options 423–424
    ESTIMATE statement 58, 149
    estimating heritability 211–212
    estimating variance components using 184–185, 204–205
    estimation methods available in 194–196
    estimation methods in 392–394
    factorial experiments 71
    factorial with two continuous factors 92
    fit the unequal slopes model 239
    fit with unequal slopes for each level of GRP 250
    fitting mixed models 511
    fitting model to data using 206–208
    for fitting separate regression equations for each level of factor A 92
    generalized linear mixed models (GLMM) 420
    generalized linear mixed models (GLMM) for regression on count data 452
    generalized linear model (GLM) 387
    incomplete block designs compared with complete block designs 113, 115
    influencers 529
    influent example 182–184
    Insect Count Data example 531–538
    intermediate inference spaced BLUP 320
    intra-block analysis of PBIB data 35–36
    Linear Regression with a Discrete Count Dependent Variable example 446, 448
    linear regression with discrete counts 421
    LMESTIMATE statement 58
    LSMEANS statement 58, 74–76
    LSMESTIMATE statement 79
    mean comparisons for fixed effects 53
    METHOD= option 393
    mixed model estimator 232–233, 236–237
    mixed models for comparing two proposed designs 493
    MODEL statement 62–63
    multiple comparisons 57–58
    negative binomial generalized linear mixed models (GLMM) 455–456
    negative binomial GLMM 441
    negative variance 175
    NOINT option 225
    obtaining estimated and predictors 317–318

one-way random effects treatment structure 190–194, 342
overriding defaults 425–427
overriding set-to-zero default 173–174
pilot data to anticipate components for analysis of power and
        precision 109–110
planned comparisons 57–58
PLOT option 72
Poisson mixed model 434
power and precision analysis for non-Gaussian data 502
power calculations 102–104
precision and power analysis for blocked design 502
Precision and Power Example with Incomplete Blocks and Count
        Data 505–508
precision and power for changing sample size with blocked design
        111–112
precision calculations 102–104
providing ELR confidence intervals using 204–205
random center effects 328
RANDOM statement 270–271
repeated measures example 495–501, 498–501
Repeated Measures Experiment with Binomial Data example 474,
        475–481, 481–482
repeated measures growth study example 353–354, 359
repeated measures syntax in 275–280
revision of power calculation steps 108
search strategy 512
simulation as an alternative way to compute precision or power 120–
        124
simulation to approximate change in variance components 124–129
simulation to characterize possible outcomes 117–120
Split-Plot Design example 517
Split-Plot Experiment with Count Data example 459–460, 461, 465,
        467, 468, 469, 472–473
standard errors and 312
standard errors for mean comparisons 54–57
testing for noncorrelation of intercept and slope coefficients 368–369
Type III Tests of Fixed Effects in 61
Type x Dose response example 162–164, 165, 170
unbalanced two-way mixed model 32
unequal variance model 208–210
unequally spaced repeated measures example 302–304
using for analysis and confidence intervals 201–202
using NOBOUND option to avoid loss of type I error control 42–43
variance component estimates equal to zero example 172–173
GLM (generalized linear model) 8, 377–378, 383–394, 386–387
GLM procedure
    about 131–132, 161–162
    compared to GLIMMIX procedure and MIXED procedure 177–179
    comparisons with operator effects fixed model 320, 322
    NOUNI option 274
    REPEATED statement 270
    TEST option 322
    unbalanced two-way mixed model 32
    using for analysis of mixed models 31–32
GLMM. see generalized linear mixed models (GLMMs)
GLMPOWER procedure 102, 112–117
GLS (generalized least squares) 38, 521–522
Gompertz model 14
goodness of fit 391–392
GRAPHICS statement 517

H

heritability, estimating 210–214
hierarchical linear models 339
HOLD option 490
HTML statement
    repeated measures example 497
    Split-Plot Design example 517
hypothesis testing 149–150, 392

I

ILINK option
    GLIMMIX procedure 391
    Repeated Measures Experiment with Binomial Data example 477
IML procedure 165
incomplete block designs, compared with complete block designs 112–117
inference
    with factorial treatment designs 146–150
    on random effects 307–336
    for randomized block mixed model 46–47
inference space 12
influence diagnostics 520–538
INFLUENCE option 524
information criteria 289–290
Insect Count Data example 531–538
interaction contrast 68
interaction plot 164–165
interactions 67, 68–69
inter-block PBIB data analysis 37–41
intercept coefficients, noncorrelation of slope coefficients and 368–369
intercepts
    calculating values of 346
    fitting factorial effects model for 258–259
intermediate inference space BLUP 319–320
interpretation of results 513–514
intra-block analysis, of PBIB data 33–41
intraclass correlation 175
inverse link 8
inverse link function 386–387
iterative analyses 523–524

J

Journal of Educational and Behavioral Statistics 339

K

Kenward-Roger bias adjustment 283, 293

L

lack of fit analysis
    of qualitative by quantitative factorial 89–90
    testing for 363–364
    testing of simple linear regression model 242–243
LAPLACE method 185, 393, 394, 460, 473
Latin square 134–135, 141–143
least significant difference (LSD) 57–58
least squares means (LSM) 79, 220
level 2
LIFEREG procedure 16
likelihood, MIXED procedure based on 26–27
likelihood ratio tests 392
linear mixed model (LMM) 3, 16, 377
linear model
    influence measures in 521
    residuals in 514–516
linear predictors 6–8, 386, 388
linear regression model
    defined 7
    with discrete counts 421
    one-way fixed effects treatment structure with simple 218–223
Linear Regression with a Discrete Count Dependent Variable example
    445–453
linear statistical model 2
linear transformations 270
link function 8, 382, 386–387, 388
LMM (linear mixed model) 3, 16, 377
log likelihoods, probability distributions and 384–386
LOG(COUNT) statement 431

logistic ANOVA 387
logistic model 387
LOGISTIC procedure 16, 399
logistic regression 381–383
logit (canonical) link function
    GLMM analysis using 398–406
    margin GLMM analysis using 409–412
LSD (least significant difference) 57–58
LSM (least squares means) 79, 220
LSMEANS statement
    ADJUST option 58
    analysis of semiconductor data 158
    analysis with fixed center effects 325
    analyzing data using MIXED procedure 199
    Binomial Data in a Multicenter Clinical Trial example 397–398, 402, 410
    comparing regression models 220–221
    comparisons with operator effects fixed model 321–322
    Completely Random Design with Count Data example 426
    Count Data from an Incomplete Block Design example 431
    data set creation 105
    DIFF option 56, 160–161
    estimation of covariance using fixed effects analysis 373–374
    factorial experiments 71, 72
    fit with unequal slopes for each level of GRP 253
    fitting common slope model 230
    fitting model to data 206–207
    GLIMMIX procedure 74–76
    GLM procedure and 178
    intra-block analysis of PBIB data 34–35, 37
    mixed models for comparing two proposed designs 493
    multiple comparisons for factorial experiments 74
    one-way treatment structure in unbalanced incomplete block design structure 254, 255–256
    Poisson mixed model 433, 434
    Poisson-normal GLMM 455
    precision and power analysis for planning split-plot experiments 490
    relationship between fixed effects solution and 52–54
    repeated measures example 499–501, 500–501
    Repeated Measures Experiment with Binomial Data example 477, 481–482
    repeated measures growth study example 361
    unequal slopes model 262–267
LSMESTIMATE statement
    ADJUST option 58
    compared with ESTIMATE statement 79–81
    Completely Random Design with Count Data example 426
    factorial experiments 71
    FEV1 data analysis 297
    GLIMMIX procedure 79
    mixed models for comparing two proposed designs 494
    negative binomial GLMM 441
    Poisson mixed model 433, 434, 435, 437
    Poisson-normal GLMM 455
    Precision and Power Example with Incomplete Blocks and Count Data 506–508
    Repeated Measures Experiment with Binomial Data example 477–478, 481–482
    simple effect comparisons using 78–79
    in two-way factorial experiments 77–78

M

machine-operator two-factor mixed model 316–322
machine-operator two-way mixed model 308–309
main effects 67, 69–70
MANOVA approach 274–275
marginal (R-side) GLMM, for repeated measures 481–484
marginal models 44, 388–390, 442–445
marginal quasi-likelihood (MQL) approach 393
marginal residuals 516–517
matrix generalization, of mixed model F tests 152–154

matrix notation
    for BLUP 334–336
    RCBD model in 45–46
    regression model in 44–45
MBN option 482
MDFFITS statistic 523, 526
mean comparisons
    in factorial designs 67–98
    for fixed effects 49–99
    standard errors for 54–57
MEANPLOT option 72, 293–294, 295, 461–462, 477
MEANPLOT option, GLIMMIX procedure 164–165
mean(s)
    comparison of several 52–58
    conditional 15
    differences among 160
    for randomized block design 21
    unconditional 15
means model 7, 15
MEANS procedure 121, 233–234, 519
METHOD= option, GLIMMIX procedure 393
METHOD-REML 203
METHOD-TYPE1 204
METHOD=TYPE3 option 173–174, 212–214
mixed model estimator 232–237
mixed model methods 270
mixed models 9–10
    analysis of data from basic repeated measures design 272–283
    for comparing two proposed designs 492–495
    conditional hierarchical 205–206
    determining appropriate model for given layouts 143–146
    equations 185–186
    fitting 510–511
    F-tests 152–154
    machine-operator two-factor 316–322
    Poisson 432–437
    power 102–104
    precision 102–104
    for randomized block design 20–23
    running 16–18
    theory of 44–47
    types of influencers 522–523
    typology for 15–16
    unbalanced two-way 32–41
    using GLM procedure for analysis of 31–32
MIXED procedure
    analysis of semiconductor data 155, 158–159
    analysis with a negative block variance estimate 41–44
    analysis with fixed center effects 324
    analysis with fixed effects and random coefficients 348–350
    to analyze RCBD data 23
    analyzing data using 197–201
    based on likelihood 26–27
    based on sums of squares 23–25
    blocked design 453
    compared to GLM procedure 177–179
    compared with GLM procedure 161–162
    comparisons with operator effects fixed model 320–322
    covariance structures and 283–293
    data analysis using 203
    DATA= option 349
    ESTIMATE statement 149
    estimating variance components using 184, 204
    estimation methods available in 194–196
    fitting mixed models 511
    fitting model to data using 206–208
    influencers 522, 524
    influent example 182–184
    Insect Count Data example 531–538
    method of moments estimators using 186–188
    METHOD-REML 203
    METHOD=TYPE1 204
    METHOD=TYPE3 212–214
    mixed models 15, 16
    MODEL statement 524

negative variance 175
one-way random effects treatment structure 188–190
overriding set-to-zero default 173–174
power calculations 102–104
precision and power analysis for blocked design 503
precision and power for changing sample size with blocked design 111–112
precision calculations 102–104
random effects model 11
repeated measures 12
repeated measures example 500–501
repeated measures growth study example 353–354, 359
repeated measures syntax in 275–280
REPEATED statement 270–271
with Satterthwaite approximation 352–353
search strategy 512
simulation as an alternative way to compute precision or power 120–124
simulation to characterize possible outcomes 117–120
Split-Plot Design example 517
Type III Tests of Fixed Effects in 61
unbalanced two-way mixed model 32–33
unequally spaced repeated measures example 304
using NOBOUND option to avoid loss of type I error control 42–43
variance component estimates equal to zero example 172–173
model equation approach 2, 383
MODEL statement
    analysis with fixed effects and random coefficients 348, 349
    analyzing data using MIXED procedure 197
    Binary Data from a Dairy Cattle Breeding Trial example 413
    Binomial Data in a Multicenter Clinical Trial example 399, 402, 406, 410
    Binomial O-Ring Data example 380–381, 382
    BLUPs of regression coefficients 370
    breeding random effects model 311
    comparisons of results from two covariance structures 282
    Completely Random Design with Count Data example 426
    Count Data from an Incomplete Block Design example 431
    data set creation 105
    diagnostic plots 539, 540
    estimating heritability 211–212
    estimation of covariance using fixed effects analysis 373–374
    factorial experiments 71
    fit with unequal slopes for each level of GRP 249
    GLIMMIX procedure 62–63
    influent example 182
    intra-block analysis of PBIB data 37
    layouts and 145–146
    MIXED procedure analysis based on likelihood 26
    MIXED procedure analysis based on sums of squares 24
    NOINT option 225, 239, 247, 255
    one-way random effects treatment structure 343
    orthogonal polynomial contrasts 66
    Poisson mixed model 433, 434
    quantitative by qualitative factorial 89
    relationship between LSMEANS and fixed effects solution 54
    repeated measures growth study example 358
    SOLUTION option 53, 186, 189, 255
    Split-Plot Design example 517
    Split-Plot Experiment with Count Data example 460
    two-way factorial experiments 73
    unequal variance model 208
    Unequally Spaced Repeated Measures example 524
model-based statistics 468
models
    for fitting separate regression equations for each level of factor A 90–92
    with multiple random effects 131–179
    simple effect comparisons using parameters 79–81
    specifying 512–513
MQL (marginal quasi-likelihood) approach 393
multicenter trial 323–324
multilevel design 3, 256–267, 457–508
multilevel linear models 339
multilocation example 11–12, 322–334

multilocation model, with multiple error terms 309–310
multiple comparisons 57–58, 74–76
multiplicity 57, 58
multivariate analysis 270
multivariate format 272

N

naive analyses 429–432
naive GLMM, with overdispersion 446–448
naive method 314
"naive" mixed model approach, estimation using 375–376
narrow inference predictable functions 316
natural parameter 381, 387
negative binomial GLMM 437–440, 441–442, 455–456, 464–466
negative binomial models 423
negative block variance estimate, analysis with a 41–44
negative variance 174–177
%NLINMIX macros 16
NLMIXED procedure 16, 512
NLMM (nonlinear mixed model) 16
NLOPTIONS statement
    fitting mixed models 511
    GLIMMIX procedure 294
    negative generalized linear mixed models (GLMM) 439
    unequally spaced repeated measures example 303
NOBOUND option
    blocked design 453
    Insect Count Data example 531
    negative binomial generalized linear mixed models (GLMM) 455–456
    negative variance or correlation 177
    overriding set-to-zero default using 173–174
    Poisson-normal GLMM 454–455
    quantitative by qualitative factorial 86
    Split-Plot Experiment with Count Data example 469, 472, 473
    using to avoid loss of type I error control 42–43
NOINT option
    factorial experiments 71
    GLIMMIX procedure 225
    influent example 182
    MODEL statement 225, 239, 247, 255, 373–374
non-Gaussian data
    diagnostic plots useful for 538–541
    power and precision analysis for 501–505
non-Gaussian repeated measures data, modeling considerations for 473–474
non-iterative analyses 523–524
nonlinear effects, repeated measures and split plots with 13–14
nonlinear mixed model (NLMM) 16
nonlinear models 8
nonlinear regression 171
non-normal (binomial) 13
non-normal (count) data, repeated measures with 13
NOPROFILE option
    GLIMMIX procedure 205
    PROC statement 192–193, 299
    repeated measures example 499–501
normal approximation 395–398
NOUNI option 274

O

observational studies 1
ODDSRATIO option 402, 478
OLS (ordinary least squares) 38
one-parameter distribution 385
one-way fixed effects treatment structure, with simple linear regression models 218–223
one-way random effects treatment structure
    in completely randomized design structure 342–348
    example of 188–196

one-way treatment structure
 in BIB design structure 246–253
 in incomplete block design structure 237–246
 in RCB design structure 223–237
 in unbalanced incomplete block design structure 254–256
OPTEX procedure 32
ORDER statement 303
ordinary least squares (OLS) 38
ORPOL function 165
orthogonal polynomial contrasts 65–66
OUTPUT statement
 Binomial Data in a Multicenter Clinical Trial example 397–398
 breeding random effects model 311
 Count Data from an Incomplete Block Design example 431
 data set creation 105
 diagnostic plots 538, 539
 intra-block analysis of PBIB data 38
 MIXED procedure 190
 modern ANOVA with variance components 215
 negative binomial GLMM 441
 one-way random effects treatment structure 343, 346
 repeated measures example 497
 simulation to characterize possible outcomes 117–120
 Split-Plot Design example 517, 519
overdispersion 391–392, 422–423, 429–432, 446–448
over-parameterized model 7

P

PARMS statement
 comparing estimation methods 195
 fitting mixed models 511
 Insect Count Data example 536
 mixed model estimator 236
 precision and power analysis for blocked design 504
 precision and power analysis for planning split-plot experiments 490
 Precision and Power Example with Incomplete Blocks and Count Data 508
 repeated measures example 499–501
 simulation to approximate change in variance components 124
 Split-Plot Experiment with Count Data example 473
partially balanced incomplete block design (PBIBD) 32
PBIB data, intra-block analysis of 33–37
PBIBD (partially balanced incomplete block design) 32
PCONV option 539
PDF (probability density function) 381
performance 513
PL (pseudolikelihood) 387
planned comparisons 57–58, 77–78
PLM procedure 512
PLOT option, GLIMMIX procedure 72
PLOTS= option 517
PLOTS=MEANPLOT option 71
PLR (profile likelihood ratio) 31
Poisson distribution 419, 421–422
Poisson GLMMs 441–442, 460–464
Poisson mixed model 432–437
Poisson-normal GLMM, adjustment for 454–455
polynomial regression 58–66
polynomials, direct fit of 62–65
population-wide inference 336
positive definite 348
power
 analysis for 495–501, 498–501
 analysis for non-Gaussian data 501–505
 analysis for planning a split-plot experiment 489–492
 for changing sample size with blocked design 111–112
 computing for CRD 104–107
 defined 101
 mixed model 102–104
 pilot data to anticipate components for analysis of 109–110
 revision of calculation of 108
 using simulation for 117–129

POWER procedure
 about 102
 complete versus incomplete block designs 112–117
 power and precision analysis for non-Gaussian data 502
 precision and power analysis for blocked design 502, 504
Prasad-Rao-Harville-Jeske standard error adjustment 314
precision
 analysis for 495–501, 498–501
 analysis for non-Gaussian data 501–505
 analysis for planning a split-plot experiment 489–492
 for changing sample size with blocked design 111–112
 computing for CRD 104–107
 defined 101
 mixed model 102–104
 pilot data to anticipate components for analysis of 109–110
 of treatment differences with blocking 108–109
 using simulation for 117–129
Precision and Power Example with Incomplete Blocks and Count Data 505–508
PRED option 539
predictors
 program to obtain 317–319
 of shelf life of a product 364–376
PRINT procedure
 Precision and Power Example with Incomplete Blocks and Count Data 507–508
 repeated measures example 497
probability density function (PDF) 381
probability distribution 3, 15, 383, 384–386
PROBF function 120
PROC statement
 diagnostic plots 539
 negative binomial generalized linear mixed models (GLMM) 456
 NOPROFILE option 299
 repeated measures example 499–501
PROC statement, NOPROFILE option 192–193
process 487
profile likelihood ratio (PLR) 31
pseudolikelihood (PL) 387
pseudolikelihood equations 185

Q

QPOINTS option
 Linear Regression with a Discrete Count Dependent Variable example 449
 Poisson mixed model 433
QUADRATURE method 394, 474
qualitative by quantitative factorial, lack of fit analysis of 89–90
quantitative by qualitative factorial 84–92
quantitative factors, comparisons of 58–66
quasi-likelihood methods 378, 390, 410
quasi-marginal model, for split plot with count data 466–469

R

random block 13
random center effects 327–329
random coefficient models
 about 339–341
 one-way random effects treatment structure in completely randomized design structure 342–348
 prediction of shelf life of a product 364–376
 random student effects example 348–353
 repeated measures growth study example 353–364
 simple linear regression model and 342
random effects models
 about 8–9, 10–11, 181
 best linear unbiased predictor (BLUP) and inference on 307–336
 estimating variance components using GLIMMIX procedure 184–185
 estimating variance components using MIXED procedure 184

influent example 182–184
    method of moments estimators using MIXED procedure 186–188
    mixed model equations 185–186
    modern ANOVA with variance components 214–216
    multiple 131–179
    one-way treatment structure 188–196
    simple conditional hierarchical linear model example 196–202
    three-level nested design structure example 202–210
    two-way treatment structure to estimate heritability example 210–214
RANDOM statement
    analysis of semiconductor data 154–155, 158
    analysis with fixed effects and random coefficients 348, 349
    analyzing data using MIXED procedure 197
    Binary Data from a Dairy Cattle Breeding Trial example 413
    Binomial Data in a Multicenter Clinical Trial example 399, 401, 402, 404, 406, 410
    Binomial O-Ring Data example 384, 390
    BLUPs of regression coefficients 370
    CBD model in matrix notation 45
    comparing competing designs 108, 109
    comparisons with operator effects fixed model 322
    Completely Random Design with Count Data example 425–426, 428
    confidence intervals for variance components 31
    covariance structures and 285, 290, 291
    data analysis using MIXED procedure 203
    estimating heritability 211–212
    estimating variance components using GLIMMIX procedure 185
    factorial with two continuous factors 93
    generalized linear mixed models (GLMM) for regression on count data 452
    generalized linear model (GLM) 387–388
    GLIMMIX procedure 270–271
    intra-block analysis of PBIB data 37
    layouts and 145–146
    marginal model for count data in blocked design 443
    mixed model estimator 232
    MIXED procedure analysis based on likelihood 26
    MIXED procedure analysis based on sums of squares 24–25
    negative generalized linear mixed models (GLMM) 439
    negative variance 175–177
    obtaining estimated and predictors 317
    one-way random effects treatment structure 189, 191, 344–346
    Poisson mixed model 432, 436
    Precision and Power Example with Incomplete Blocks and Count Data 506–508
    re-parameterization of models as compound symmetry 43
    repeated measures and 276–277
    Repeated Measures Experiment with Binomial Data example 474, 482
    repeated measures growth study example 356, 358
    Split-Plot Design example 517
    Split-Plot Experiment with Count Data example 462, 470
    SUBJECT=VARIETY option 342
    Type x Dose response example 167
    unequal variance model 208
random student effects example 348–353
randomized block design 19, 20–23, 21
randomized block mixed model 46–47
randomized complete block 133–134
randomized complete design (RCBD)
    about 9
    GLIMMIX procedure to analyze 23
    in matrix notation 45–46
    MIXED procedure to analyze 23
    one-way treatment structure in 223–237
    whole plot conducted as 137–139
RANDOM-RESIDUAL statement 175
RANNOR function 118
RCBD. see randomized complete design (RCBD)
regression analysis
    constructing data for regression lines 347
    Type x Dose response example 165–171
regression coefficients, batch-specific BLUPs of 369–371

regression models
    comparing 220–222
    dose-response random coefficient 310–311
    extensions to complex 223
    in matrix notation 44–45
REML (residual/restricted maximum likelihood) 26, 149
re-parameterization, of models as compound symmetry 43–44
repeated measures
    about 12, 175, 269
    analysis of 355–356
    basic concepts of 269–270
    with binomial data 458
    comparing results from two covariance structures 280–283
    conditional (G-side) GLMM for 475–481
    covariance structures 283–293
    example of 495–501
    generalized linear mixed models (GLMM) for 457–508
    GLIMMIX procedure analysis of FEV1 data 293–301
    MANOVA 274–275
    marginal (R-side) GLMM for 481–484
    mixed model analysis of data from 272–283
    with non-normal (count) data 13
    precision and power analysis 498–501
    reassessing with means model accounting for baseline measurement 292–293
    selecting models 285–292
    split plot in time 274–275
    and split plots with nonlinear effects 13–14
    statistical model for 271–272
    syntax in GLIMMIX procedure and MIXED procedure 273–280
    types of analyses of 270–271
    unequally spaced 301–305
Repeated Measures Experiment with Binomial Data example 473–484
repeated measures growth study example 353–364
REPEATED statement
    Binomial O-Ring Data example 384
    covariance structures and 285, 290, 291
    generalized linear model (GLM) 387–388
    GLM procedure 270
    MIXED procedure 270–271
    negative variance 176–177
    repeated measures and 276–277
    repeated measures example 500–501
    Repeated Measures Experiment with Binomial Data example 474
research hypothesis 101
residual covariance structure 388
residual maximum likelihood (REML) 149
RESIDUAL option 524
residual term 7–8
residuals
    about 514
    conditional 516–517
    in linear model 514–516
    marginal 516–517
restricted maximum likelihood (REML) 149
robust estimators 468
row designs 134–135
RSREG procedure 92

S

sample size
    defined 101
    precision and power for changing 111–112
sample surveys 1
sampling unit 3
sandwich estimators 468
SAS for Linear Models, 4th Edition 65
SAS software, selecting 16–18
SAS System for Linear Models, Fourth Edition 11–12
Satterthwaite approximation 29–30, 150, 152, 159, 352–353
%SCDMixed macro 524, 528
search strategy 512

Second International Mathematics Study (SIMS) 348
sensitivity 101
serial correlation 275
set-to-zero default, overriding 173–174
SGPLOT procedure 250, 286, 539
SGRENDER procedure 97
shrinkage estimation 314
simple conditional hierarchical linear model 196–202
simple effect comparisons 78–79, 79–81
simple effects 67
simple linear regression model
    with additional fixed effects 348
    with random coefficients 342
    testing lack of fit of 242–243
SIMS (Second International Mathematics Study) 348
SIMULATE option 58
simulation
    to approximate change in variance components 124–129
    using for precision and power 117–129
simultaneous contrasts, in two-way classifications 81–82
single random effect
    about 19–20
    mixed model for randomized block design 20–23
SLICE option 52, 74–76, 293–294, 295–296, 478
SLICEBY option 71
SLICEDIFF option
    GLIMMIX procedure 293–294, 295–296
    multiple comparisons of METHOD means 74–76
    precision and power analysis for planning split-plot experiments 490
    repeated measures example 500–501
    Repeated Measures Experiment with Binomial Data example 478, 480
slopes
    calculating values of 346
    fitting factorial effects model for 258–259
    noncorrelation of intercepts coefficients and coefficients of 368–369
slopes-equal-to-zero hypothesis 224–226, 257–258
SOLUTION statement 53, 186, 189, 255, 311, 343, 344, 380–381
SORT procedure 121
special parametric structure on the covariance matrices 270
Split Plot example 487–489
split plot in time 270, 274–275
split-plot design
    about 135–139
    with count data 460–464
    with covariate measured on large-size experimental unit/whole plot 256–267
    defined 3
    example of 517–520
    negative binomial GLMM for 464–466
    quasi-marginal model 466–469
    repeated measures and 13–14
    semiconductor experiment 150–161
    with whole plot conducted as replicated 2 x 2 Latin square 141–143
Split-Plot Experiment with Count Data example 458–473
split-plot experimental units 136
split-plot experiments 12, 457–458
standard errors 54–57, 146–147, 149–150, 312, 391
standard normal distribution 8
standardization 515
statistical models
    about 2
    experimental units 4–5
    model characteristics 2–3
    simple example of 2
    simple hierarchical design 5–6
    subsampling 3–4
strip-split plot 139–141
studentization 515
study 2
SUBJECT option 276

subjects 269
subject-specific inference 336
subject-specific predictable functions 317
subject-specific terms 310
SUBJECT=VARIETY option, RANDOM statement 342
subsampling 3–4
sums of squares
    MIXED procedure based on 23–25
    Type I versus Type III 61–62
sum-to-zero constraint 7

T

TEMPLATE procedure 94, 97
TEST option, GLM procedure 322
testing
    equal slopes hypothesis 247–248, 254–255
    slopes-equal-to-zero hypothesis 257–258
three-dimensional plot 97–98
three-level nested design structure 202–210
tilde (~) 335
time main effect 269–270
Toeplitz model 284
treatment design
    about 131, 132–146
    components of 132
    factorial 146–150
    two-way random effects treatment structure 210–214
treatment main effect 269–270
treatment mean
    variance of 147–149
    visualization of 156
treatment-by-time interaction 269–270
treatments 19
troubleshooting and diagnostics
    about 509–510
    best practices for fitting mixed models 510–511
    FAQ 512–514
    influence diagnostics 520–538
true positive rate 101
TTEST procedure 50–51
2 x 2 factorial treatment design, design structure for 132–143
two-parameter distribution 385
two-way factorial experiments 72–74, 77–78, 81–82
two-way random effects treatment structure 210–214
TYPE= option 276, 517
Type x Dose response example 162–171

U

unbalanced incomplete block design structure, one-way treatment structure in 254–256
unconditional expectation 334
unconditional hierarchical nested linear model 202–203
unconditional mean 15
unequal slopes model 239–242, 246–247, 257–258, 260–267
unequal variance model 208–210
Unequally Spaced Repeated Measures example 301–305, 524–531
unit of observation 3
unit of randomization 4
univariate analysis 270
univariate analysis of variance 270
UNIVARIATE procedure 120, 121
unstructured covariance model 271

V

variance
    confidence intervals for components of 29–31
    degrees of freedom 149–150
    of difference estimates 147–149
    estimating components 149–150
    estimating components equal to zero 171–177
    estimating components using GLIMMIX procedure 184–185
    estimating components using MIXED procedure 184
    negative 174–177
    for randomized block design 21
    of treatment mean 147–149
variance function 385
VCORR option 279
vertical bar (|) 71, 189

W

Wald statistic 392
warning messages 512
What Would Fisher Do? (WWFD) 4
whole-plot experimental units 136
within-subjects factor 271
working covariance models (GEE-type model) 387
WWFD (*What Would Fisher Do?*) 4

Z

ZEROG option 293–294, 428

Ready to take your SAS® and JMP® skills up a notch?

Be among the first to know about new books,
special events, and exclusive discounts.
support.sas.com/newbooks

Share your expertise. Write a book with SAS.
support.sas.com/publish

 sas.com/books
for additional books and resources.

 **§sas**

THE POWER TO KNOW®

CPSIA information can be obtained
at www.ICGtesting.com
Printed in the USA
BVHW072124071219
565748BV00011BA/423/P